D1125952

THE MODERN LIBRARY
of the World's Best Books

>>

BULFINCH'S
MYTHOLOGY

>>>>>>>>>>>>>>>>>>>>>>>

THE AGE OF FABLE

THE AGE OF CHIVALRY

LEGENDS OF CHARLEMAGNE

The publishers will be pleased to send, upon request, an illustrated folder setting forth the purpose and scope of THE MODERN LIBRARY, *and listing each volume in the series. Every reader of books will find titles he has been looking for, handsomely printed, in unabridged editions, and at an unusually low price.*

BULFINCH'S
MYTHOLOGY

>>>

THE AGE OF FABLE

THE AGE OF CHIVALRY

LEGENDS OF CHARLEMAGNE

>>>

>>>

THE MODERN LIBRARY
NEW YORK

*Distributed in Canada
by Random House of Canada Limited, Toronto*

THE MODERN LIBRARY
is published by RANDOM HOUSE, INC.
BENNETT CERF · DONALD S. KLOPFER
Manufactured in the United States of America by H. Wolff

THOMAS BULFINCH

(1796-1867)

A NOTE ON THE AUTHOR OF "MYTHOLOGY"

His course at Harvard College and his years devoted to teaching in his native Boston made Thomas Bulfinch feel the need of something more than a classical dictionary and less than a formal and faithful translation of the enormous literature on the origins of the myths and legends surviving from the remote past. Accordingly, he gave himself the task of crystallizing and popularizing classical literature for the joy and benefit of those who could not seek out original sources. Continuing his work on the golden age of fable—the pagan era of Greek and Roman gods, of Egyptian and Oriental deities and the sagas of the North—while employed as an accountant in the Boston Merchants' Bank, he re-created the second age of fable—the Middle Ages—and then concluded the series with a similar treatment of the Legends of Charlemagne. So completely has his work entered the consciousness of present-day readers that the mere mention of the word "mythology" evokes the immediate response, by association, of the name "Bulfinch."

BIBLIOGRAPHY

Hebrew Lyrical History (1853)
The Age of Fable (1855)
The Age of Chivalry (1858)
The Boy Inventor (1860)
Legends of Charlemagne. or
    Romance of the Middle Ages (1863)
Poetry of the Age of Fable (1863)
Oregon and Eldorado, or
    Romance of the Rivers (1866)

CONTENTS

THE AGE OF FABLE

CHAPTER		PAGE
I.	INTRODUCTION	7
II.	PROMETHEUS AND PANDORA	15
III.	APOLLO AND DAPHNE—PYRAMUS AND THISBE—CEPHALUS AND PROCRIS	21
IV.	JUNO AND HER RIVALS, IO AND CALLISTO—DIANA AND ACTÆON—LATONA AND THE RUSTICS	28
V.	PHAËTON	36
VI.	MIDAS—BAUCIS AND PHILEMON	42
VII.	PROSERPINE—GLAUCUS AND SCYLLA	47
VIII.	PYGMALION—DRYOPE—VENUS AND ADONIS—APOLLO AND HYACINTHUS	55
IX.	CEYX AND HALCYONE	60
X.	VERTUMNUS AND POMONA	65
XI.	CUPID AND PSYCHE	68
XII.	CADMUS—THE MYRMIDONS	77
XIII.	NISUS AND SCYLLA—ECHO AND NARCISSUS—CLYTIE—HERO AND LEANDER	83
XIV.	MINERVA—NIOBE	89
XV.	THE GRÆÆ AND GORGONS—PERSEUS AND MEDUSA	96
XVI.	MONSTERS: GIANTS—SPHINX—PEGASUS AND CHIMÆRA—CENTAURS—GRIFFIN—PYGMIES	101
XVII.	THE GOLDEN FLEECE—MEDEA	107
XVIII.	MELEAGER AND ATALANTA	114
XIX.	HERCULES—HEBE AND GANYMEDE	118
XX.	THESEUS AND DÆDALUS—CASTOR AND POLLUX	124
XXI.	BACCHUS AND ARIADNE	131
XXII.	THE RURAL DEITIES—ERISICHTHON—RHŒCUS—THE WATER DEITIES — THE CAMENÆ —- THE WINDS	136
XXIII.	ACHELOUS AND HERCULES—ADMETUS AND ALCESTIS—ANTIGONE—PENELOPE	144
XXIV.	ORPHEUS AND EURYDICE—ARISTÆUS—AMPHION—LINUS — THAMYRIS — MARSYAS — MELAMPUS — MUSÆUS	150
XXV.	ARION—IBYCUS—SIMONIDES—SAPPHO	158

CHAPTER   PAGE

XXVI. Endymion—Orion—Aurora and Tithonus—Acis and Galatea 165
XXVII. The Trojan War 171
XXVIII. The Fall of Troy—Return of the Greeks—Agamemnon, Orestes and Electra 183
XXIX. Adventures of Ulysses—The Lotus-Eaters—The Cyclopses—Circe—Sirens—Scylla and Charybdis—Calypso 190
XXX. The Phæacians—Fate of the Suitors 198
XXXI. Adventures of Æneas—The Harpies—Dido—Palinurus 207
XXXII. The Infernal Regions—The Sibyl 213
XXXIII. Æneas in Italy—Camilla—Evander—Nisus and Euryalus—Mezentius—Turnus 221
XXXIV. Pythagoras—Egyptian Deities—Oracles . . . 230
XXXV. Origin of Mythology—Statues of Gods and Goddesses—Poets of Mythology 240
XXXVI. Monsters (Modern)—The Phœnix—Basilisk—Unicorn—Salamander 248
XXXVII. Eastern Mythology—Zoroaster—Hindu Mythology—Castes—Buddha—The Grand Lama—Prester John 254
XXXVIII. Northern Mythology—Valhalla—The Valkyrior 262
XXXIX. Thor's Visit to Jotunheim 269
XL. The Death of Baldur—The Elves—Runic Letters—Skalds—Iceland 274
XLI. The Druids—Iona 280
XLII. Beowulf 287
Proverbial Expressions 289
Index 291

THE AGE OF CHIVALRY

Part I

King Arthur and His Knights

I. Introduction 303
II. The Mythical History of England 314
III. Arthur 322
IV. Caradoc Briefbras 342
V. Sir Gawain 346
VI. Launcelot of the Lake 350

CHAPTER   PAGE

VII. THE STORY OF LAUNCELOT: THE ADVENTURE OF THE
        CART 358
VIII. THE STORY OF LAUNCELOT: THE LADY OF SHALOTT   365
IX. THE STORY OF LAUNCELOT: QUEEN GUENEVER'S
        PERIL 369
X. THE STORY OF TRISTRAM OF LYONESSE 372
XI. TRISTRAM AND ISOUDE 378
XII. THE STORY OF SIR TRISTRAM 383
XIII. THE END OF THE STORY OF SIR TRISTRAM . . . 389
XIV. THE STORY OF PERCEVAL 395
XV. THE QUEST OF THE SANGREAL 401
XVI. THE END OF THE QUEST 410
XVII. SIR AGRIVAIN'S TREASON 421
XVIII. MORTE D'ARTHUR 427

PART II

THE MABINOGEON

XIX. THE BRITONS 439
XX. THE LADY OF THE FOUNTAIN 442
XXI. THE LADY OF THE FOUNTAIN (continued) . . . 447
XXII. THE LADY OF THE FOUNTAIN (continued) . . . 453
XXIII. GERAINT, THE SON OF ERBIN 458
XXIV. GERAINT, THE SON OF ERBIN (continued) . . . 466
XXV. GERAINT, THE SON OF ERBIN (continued) . . . 472
XXVI. PWYLL, PRINCE OF DYVED 480
XXVII. BRANWEN, THE DAUGHTER OF LLYR, ... 484
XXVIII. MANAWYDDAN 491
XXIX. KILWICH AND OLWEN 499
XXX. KILWICH AND OLWEN (continued) 508
XXXI. PEREDUR, THE SON OF EVRAWC 513
XXXII. TALIESIN 520

PART III

THE KNIGHTS OF ENGLISH HISTORY

XXXIII. KING RICHARD AND THE THIRD CRUSADE 529
XXXIV. ROBIN HOOD OF SHERWOOD FOREST 547
XXXV. ROBIN HOOD AND HIS ADVENTURES 554
XXXVI. CHEVY CHASE 561
XXXVII. THE BATTLE OF OTTERBOURNE 567
XXXVIII. EDWARD THE BLACK PRINCE 574
        INDEX 591

LEGENDS OF CHARLEMAGNE

CHAPTER		PAGE
I.	INTRODUCTION	599
II.	THE PEERS, OR PALADINS	606
III.	THE TOURNAMENT	612
IV.	THE SIEGE OF ALBRACCA	618
V.	ADVENTURES OF RINALDO AND ORLANDO	627
VI.	THE INVASION OF FRANCE	634
VII.	THE INVASION OF FRANCE (continued)	641
VIII.	BRADAMANTE AND ROGERO	649
IX.	ASTOLPHO AND THE ENCHANTRESS	656
X.	THE ORC	664
XI.	ASTOLPHO'S ADVENTURES CONTINUED, AND ISABELLA'S BEGUN	670
XII.	MEDORO	675
XIII.	ORLANDO MAD	681
XIV.	ZERBINO AND ISABELLA	687
XV.	ASTOLPHO IN ABYSSINIA	694
XVI.	THE WAR IN AFRICA	699
XVII.	ROGERO AND BRADAMANTE	708
XVIII.	THE BATTLE OF RONCESVALLES	718
XIX.	RINALDO AND BAYARD	728
XX.	DEATH OF RINALDO	732
XXI.	HUON OF BORDEAUX	737
XXII.	HUON OF BORDEAUX (continued)	742
XXIII.	HUON OF BORDEAUX (continued)	750
XXIV.	OGIER, THE DANE	755
XXV.	OGIER, THE DANE (continued)	761
XXVI.	OGIER, THE DANE (continued)	767
	INDEX	775

ILLUSTRATIONS

The illustrations listed below are to be found facing Page 372

PLATE

Zeus I

Venus, Ceres and Juno—RAPHAEL II

Saturn—VERONESE III

Pallas Subduing a Centaur—BOTTICELLI IV

Leda and the Swan—MICHELANGELO V

Laocoön VI

The Education of Achilles—DELACROIX VII

The Wine of Circe—BURNE-JONES VIII

The Return of Ulysses—PINTURICCHIO IX

Æneas Carrying Anchises from Troy—RAPHAEL X

Æneas in the Underworld—BREUGHEL XI

The Oath of Knighthood—ABBEY XII

Galahad the Deliverer—ABBEY XIII

Charlemagne—DÜRER XIV

Charlemagne Crowned Emperor at Rome—RETHEL XV

The Battle of Cordova—RETHEL XVI

THE AGE OF FABLE

OR

STORIES OF GODS AND HEROES

PREFACE

IF no other knowledge deserves to be called useful but that which helps to enlarge our possessions or to raise our station in society, then mythology has no claim to the appellation. But if that which tends to make us happier and better can be called useful then we claim that epithet for our subject. For mythology is the handmaid of literature; and literature is one of the best allies of virtue and promoters of happiness.

Without a knowledge of mythology much of the elegant literature of our own language cannot be understood and appreciated. When Byron calls Rome "the Niobe of nations," or says of Venice, "She looks a Sea-Cybele fresh from ocean," he calls up to the mind of one familiar with our subject, illustrations more vivid and striking than the pencil could furnish, but which are lost to the reader ignorant of mythology. Milton abounds in similar allusions. The short poem "Comus" contains more than thirty such, and the ode "On the Morning of the Nativity" half as many. Through "Paradise Lost" they are scattered profusely. This is one reason why we often hear persons by no means illiterate say that they cannot enjoy Milton. But were these persons to add to their more solid acquirements the easy learning of this little volume, much of the poetry of Milton which has appeared to them "harsh and crabbed" would be found "musical as is Apollo's lute." Our citations, taken from more than twenty-five poets, from Spenser to Longfellow, will show how general has been the practice of borrowing illustrations from mythology.

The prose writers also avail themselves of the same source of elegant and suggestive illustration. One can hardly take up a number of the "Edinburgh" or "Quarterly Review" without meeting with instances. In Macaulay's article on Milton there are twenty such.

But how is mythology to be taught to one who does not learn it through the medium of the languages of Greece and Rome? To devote study to a species of learning which relates wholly to false marvels and obsolete faiths is not to be expected of the general reader in a practical age like this. The time even of the young is claimed by so many sciences of facts and things that little can be spared for set treatises on a science of mere fancy.

But may not the requisite knowledge of the subject be acquired

3

by reading the ancient poets in translations? We reply, the field is too extensive for a preparatory course; and these very translations require some previous knowledge of the subject to make them intelligible. Let any one who doubts it read the first page of the "Æneid," and see what he can make of "the hatred of Juno," the "decree of the Parcæ," the "judgment of Paris," and the "honours of Ganymede," without this knowledge.

Shall we be told that answers to such queries may be found in notes, or by a reference to the Classical Dictionary? We reply, the interruption of one's reading by either process is so annoying that most readers prefer to let an allusion pass unapprehended rather than submit to it. Moreover, such sources give us only the dry facts without any of the charm of the original narrative; and what is a poetical myth when stripped of its poetry? The story of Ceyx and Halcyone, which fills a chapter in our book, occupies but eight lines in the best (Smith's) Classical Dictionary; and so of others.

Our book is an attempt to solve this problem, by telling the stories of mythology in such a manner as to make them a source of amusement. We have endeavoured to tell them correctly, according to the ancient authorities, so that when the reader finds them referred to he may not be at a loss to recognize the reference. Thus we hope to teach mythology not as a study, but as a relaxation from study; to give our work the charm of a story-book, yet by means of it to impart a knowledge of an important branch of education. The index at the end will adapt it to the purposes of reference, and make it a Classical Dictionary for the parlour.

Most of the classical legends in this book are derived from Ovid and Virgil. They are not literally translated, for, in the author's opinion, poetry translated into literal prose is very unattractive reading. Neither are they in verse, as well for other reasons as from a conviction that to translate faithfully under all the embarrassments of rhyme and measure is impossible. The attempt has been made to tell the stories in prose, preserving so much of the poetry as resides in the thoughts and is separable from the language itself, and omitting those amplifications which are not suited to the altered form.

The Northern mythological stories are copied with some abridgement from Mallet's "Northern Antiquities." These chapters, with those on Oriental and Egyptian mythology, seemed necessary to complete the subject, though it is believed these topics have not usually been presented in the same volume with the classical fables.[1]

---

[1] Previous editions of *The Age of Fable* have lacked the story of Beowulf. It is accordingly added to these Stories of Gods and Heroes.

The poetical citations so freely introduced are expected to answer several valuable purposes. They will tend to fix in memory the leading fact of each story, they will help to the attainment of a correct pronunciation of the proper names, and they will enrich the memory with many gems of poetry, some of them such as are most frequently quoted or alluded to in reading and conversation.

Having chosen *mythology as connected with literature* for our province, we have endeavoured to omit nothing which the reader of elegant literature is likely to find occasion for. Such stories and parts of stories as are offensive to pure taste and good morals are not given. But such stories are not often referred to, and if they occasionally should be, the English reader need feel no mortification in confessing his ignorance of them.

Our book is not for the learned, nor for the theologian, nor for the philosopher, but for the reader of English literature, of either sex, who wishes to comprehend the allusions so frequently made by public speakers, lecturers, essayists, and poets, and those which occur in polite conversation.

We trust our young readers will find it a source of entertainment; those more advanced a useful companion in their reading; those who travel, and visit museums and galleries of art, an interpreter of paintings and sculptures; those who mingle in cultivated society a key to allusions which are occasionally made; and last of all, those in advanced life pleasure in retracing a path of literature which leads them back to the days of their childhood, and revives at every step the associations of the morning of life.

The permanency of those associations is beautifully expressed in the well-known lines of Coleridge, in "The Piccolomini," Act ii. Scene 4:

> "The intelligible forms of ancient poets,
> The fair humanities of old religion,
> The Power, the Beauty, and the Majesty
> That had their haunts in dale or piny mountain,
> Or forest, by slow stream, or pebbly spring,
> Or chasms and watery depths; all these have vanished;
> They live no longer in the faith of reason;
> But still the heart doth need a language; still
> Doth the old instinct bring back the old names;
> Spirits or gods that used to share this earth
> With man as with their friend; and at this day
> 'Tis Jupiter who brings whate'er is great,
> And Venus who brings every thing that's fair."

CHAPTER I

THE religions of ancient Greece and Rome are extinct. The s. called divinities of Olympus have not a single worshipper among living men. They belong now not to the department of theology, but to those of literature and taste. There they still hold their place, and will continue to hold it, for they are too closely connected with the finest productions of poetry and art, both ancient and modern, to pass into oblivion.

We propose to tell the stories relating to them which have come down to us from the ancients, and which are alluded to by modern poets, essayists, and orators. Our readers may thus at the same time be entertained by the most charming fictions which fancy has ever created, and put in possession of information indispensable to every one who would read with intelligence the elegant literature of his own day.

In order to understand these stories, it will be necessary to acquaint ourselves with the ideas of the structure of the universe which prevailed among the Greeks—the people from whom the Romans, and other nations through them, received their science and religion.

The Greeks believed the earth to be flat and circular, their own country occupying the middle of it, the central point being either Mount Olympus, the abode of the gods, or Delphi, so famous for its oracle.

The circular disk of the earth was crossed from west to east and divided into two equal parts by the *Sea,* as they called the Mediterranean, and its continuation the Euxine, the only seas with which they were acquainted.

Around the earth flowed the *River Ocean,* its course being from south to north on the western side of the earth, and in a contrary direction on the eastern side. It flowed in a steady, equable current, unvexed by storm or tempest. The sea, and all the rivers on earth, received their waters from it.

The northern portion of the earth was supposed to be inhabited by a happy race named the Hyperboreans, dwelling in everlasting bliss and spring beyond the lofty mountains whose caverns were

supposed to send forth the piercing blasts of the north wind, which
chilled the people of Helias (Greece). Their country was inaccessible
by land or sea. They lived exempt from disease or old age, from
toils and warfare. Moore has given us the "Song of a Hyperborean,"
beginning

> "I come from a land in the sun-bright deep,
>   Where golden gardens glow,
> Where the winds of the north, becalmed in sleep,
>   Their conch shells never blow."

On the south side of the earth, close to the stream of Ocean,
dwelt a people happy and virtuous as the Hyperboreans. They were
named the Æthiopians. The gods favoured them so highly that they
were wont to leave at times their Olympian abodes and go to share
their sacrifices and banquets.

On the western margin of the earth, by the stream of Ocean, lay
a happy place named the Elysian Plain, whither mortals favoured
by the gods were transported without tasting of death, to enjoy
an immortality of bliss. This happy region was also called the
"Fortunate Fields," and the "Isles of the Blessed."

We thus see that the Greeks of the early ages knew little of any
real people except those to the east and south of their own country,
or near the coast of the Mediterranean. Their imagination meantime
peopled the western portion of this sea with giants, monsters, and
enchantresses; while they placed around the disk of the earth,
which they probably regarded as of no great width, nations enjoying
the peculiar favour of the gods, and blessed with happiness and
longevity.

The Dawn, the Sun, and the Moon were supposed to rise out
of the Ocean, on the eastern side, and to drive through the air,
giving light to gods and men. The stars, also, except those forming
the Wain or Bear, and others near them, rose out of and sank into
the stream of Ocean. There the sun-god embarked in a winged
boat, which conveyed him round by the northern part of the earth,
back to his place of rising in the east. Milton alludes to this in his
"Comus":

> "Now the gilded car of day
> His golden axle doth allay
> In the steep Atlantic stream,
> And the slope Sun his upward beam
> Shoots against the dusky pole,
> Facing towards the other goal
> Of his chamber in the east."

The abode of the gods was on the summit of Mount Olympus,
in Thessaly. A gate of clouds, kept by the goddesses named the

Seasons, opened to permit the passage of the Celestials to earth, and to receive them on their return. The gods had their separate dwellings; but all, when summoned, repaired to the palace of Jupiter, as did also those deities whose usual abode was the earth, the waters, or the under-world. It was also in the great hall of the palace of the Olympian king that the gods feasted each day on ambrosia and nectar, their food and drink, the latter being handed round by the lovely goddess Hebe. Here they conversed of the affairs of heaven and earth; and as they quaffed their nectar, Apollo, the god of music, delighted them with the tones of his lyre, to which the Muses sang in responsive strains. When the sun was set, the gods retired to sleep in their respective dwellings.

The following lines from the "Odyssey" will show how Homer conceived of Olympus:

"So saying, Minerva, goddess azure-eyed,
Rose to Olympus, the reputed seat
Eternal of the gods, which never storms
Disturb, rains drench, or snow invades, but calm
The expanse and cloudless shines with purest day.
There the inhabitants divine rejoice
For ever."   *Cowper.*

The robes and other parts of the dress of the goddesses were woven by Minerva and the Graces, and everything of a more solid nature was formed of the various metals. Vulcan was architect, smith, armourer, chariot builder, and artist of all work in Olympus. He built of brass the houses of the gods; he made for them the golden shoes with which they trod the air or the water, and moved from place to place with the speed of the wind, or even of thought. He also shod with brass the celestial steeds, which whirled the chariots of the gods through the air, or along the surface of the sea. He was able to bestow on his workmanship self-motion, so that the tripods (chairs and tables) could move of themselves in and out of the celestial hall. He even endowed with intelligence the golden handmaidens whom he made to wait on himself.

Jupiter, or Jove (Zeus [1]), though called the father of gods and men, had himself a beginning. Saturn (Cronos) was his father, and Rhea (Ops) his mother. Saturn and Rhea were of the race of Titans, who were the children of Earth and Heaven, which sprang from Chaos, of which we shall give a further account in our next chapter.

There is another cosmogony, or account of the creation, according to which Earth, Erebus, and Love were the first of beings. Love (Eros) issued from the egg of Night, which floated on Chaos. By

[1] The names included in parentheses are the Greek, the others being the Roman or Latin names.

his arrows and torch he pierced and vivified all things, producing life and joy.

Saturn and Rhea were not the only Titans. There were others, whose names were Oceanus, Hyperion, Iapetus, and Ophion, males; and Themis, Mnemosyne, Eurynome, females. They are spoken of as the elder gods, whose dominion was afterwards transferred to others. Saturn yielded to Jupiter, Oceanus to Neptune, Hyperion to Apollo. Hyperion was the father of the Sun, Moon, and Dawn. He is therefore the original sun-god, and is painted with the splendour and beauty which were afterwards bestowed on Apollo.

> "Hyperion's curls, the front of Jove himself."
> *Shakespeare.*

Ophion and Eurynome ruled over Olympus till they were dethroned by Saturn and Rhea. Milton alludes to them in "Paradise Lost." He says the heathens seem to have had some knowledge of the temptation and fall of man.

> "And fabled how the serpent, whom they called
> Ophion, with Eurynome, (the wide-
> Encroaching Eve perhaps,) had first the rule
> Of high Olympus, thence by Saturn driven."

The representations given of Saturn are not very consistent; for on the one hand his reign is said to have been the golden age of innocence and purity, and on the other he is described as a monster who devoured his children.[1] Jupiter, however, escaped this fate, and when grown up espoused Metis (Prudence), who administered a draught to Saturn which caused him to disgorge his children. Jupiter, with his brothers and sisters, now rebelled against their father Saturn and his brothers the Titans; vanquished them, and imprisoned some of them in Tartarus, inflicting other penalties on others. Atlas was condemned to bear up the heavens on his shoulders.

On the dethronement of Saturn, Jupiter with his brothers Neptune (Poseidon) and Pluto (Dis) divided his dominions. Jupiter's portion was the heavens, Neptune's the ocean, and Pluto's the realms of the dead. Earth and Olympus were common property. Jupiter was king of gods and men. The thunder was his weapon, and he bore a shield called Ægis, made for him by Vulcan. The eagle was his favourite bird, and bore his thunderbolts.

Juno (Hera) was the wife of Jupiter, and queen of the gods. Iris, the goddess of the rainbow, was her attendant and messenger. The peacock was her favourite bird.

Vulcan (Hephæstos), the celestial artist, was the son of Jupiter

---

[1] This inconsistency arises from considering the Saturn of the Romans the same with the Grecian deity Cronos (Time), which, as it brings an end to all things which have had a beginning, may be said to devour its own offspring.

and Juno. He was born lame, and his mother was so displeased
at the sight of him that she flung him out of heaven. Other accounts
say that Jupiter kicked him out for taking part with his mother in
a quarrel which occurred between them. Vulcan's lameness, according to this account, was the consequence of his fall. He was a whole
day falling, and at last alighted in the Island of Lemnos, which was
thenceforth sacred to him. Milton alludes to this story in "Paradise
Lost," Book I.:

> "... From morn
> To noon he fell, from noon to dewy eve,
> A summer's day; and with the setting sun
> Dropped from the zenith, like a falling star,
> On Lemnos, the Ægean isle."

Mars (Ares), the god of war, was the son of Jupiter and Juno.
Phœbus Apollo, the god of archery, prophecy, and music, was
the son of Jupiter and Latona, and brother of Diana (Artemis). He
was god of the sun, as Diana, his sister, was the goddess of the
moon.

Venus (Aphrodite), the goddess of love and beauty, was the
daughter of Jupiter and Dione. Others say that Venus sprang from
the foam of the sea. The zephyr wafted her along the waves to the
Isle of Cyprus, where she was received and attired by the Seasons,
and then led to the assembly of the gods. All were charmed with
her beauty, and each one demanded her for his wife. Jupiter gave
her to Vulcan, in gratitude for the service he had rendered in forging
thunderbolts. So the most beautiful of the goddesses became the
wife of the most ill-favoured of gods. Venus possessed an embroidered girdle called Cestus, which had the power of inspiring
love. Her favourite birds were swans and doves, and the plants
sacred to her were the rose and the myrtle.

Cupid (Eros), the god of love, was the son of Venus. He was
her constant companion; and, armed with bow and arrows, he shot
the darts of desire into the bosoms of both gods and men. There
was a deity named Anteros, who was sometimes represented as the
avenger of slighted love, and sometimes as the symbol of reciprocal
affection. The following legend is told of him:

Venus, complaining to Themis that her son Eros continued always
a child, was told by her that it was because he was solitary, and
that if he had a brother he would grow apace. Anteros was soon
afterwards born, and Eros immediately was seen to increase rapidly
in size and strength.

Minerva (Pallas, Athene, the goddess of wisdom,) was the offspring of Jupiter, without a mother. She sprang forth from his head

completely armed. Her favourite bird was the owl, and the plant sacred to her the olive.

Byron, in "Childe Harold," alludes to the birth of Minerva thus:

"Can tyrants but by tyrants conquered be,
And Freedom find no champion and no child,
Such as Columbia saw arise, when she
Sprang forth a Pallas, armed and undefiled?
Or must such minds be nourished in the wild,
Deep in the unpruned forest, 'midst the roar
Of cataracts, where nursing Nature smiled
On infant Washington? Has earth no more
Such seeds within her breast, or Europe no such shore?"

Mercury (Hermes) was the son of Jupiter and Maia. He presided over commerce, wrestling, and other gymnastic exercises, even over thieving, and everything, in short, which required skill and dexterity. He was the messenger of Jupiter, and wore a winged cap and winged shoes. He bore in his hand a rod entwined with two serpents, called the caduceus.

Mercury is said to have invented the lyre. He found, one day, a tortoise, of which he took the shell, made holes in the opposite edges of it, and drew cords of linen through them, and the instrument was complete. The cords were nine, in honour of the nine Muses. Mercury gave the lyre to Apollo, and received from him in exchange the caduceus.[1]

Ceres (Demeter) was the daughter of Saturn and Rhea. She had a daughter named Proserpine (Persephone), who became the wife of Pluto, and queen of the realms of the dead. Ceres presided over agriculture.

Bacchus (Dionysus), the god of wine, was the son of Jupiter and Semele. He represents not only the intoxicating power of wine, but its social and beneficent influences likewise, so that he is viewed as the promoter of civilization, and a lawgiver and lover of peace.

The Muses were the daughters of Jupiter and Mnemosyne (Memory). They presided over song, and prompted the memory. They were nine in number, to each of whom was assigned the presidence over some particular department of literature, art, or science. Calliope was the muse of epic poetry, Clio of history, Euterpe of lyric poetry, Melpomene of tragedy, Terpsichore of

[1] From this origin of the instrument, the word "shell" is often used as synonymous with "lyre," and figuratively for music and poetry. Thus Gray, in his ode on the "Progress of Poesy," says:

"O Sovereign of the willing Soul,
Parent of sweet and solemn-breathing airs,
Enchanting shell! the sullen Cares
And frantic Passions hear thy soft control."

choral dance and song, Erato of love poetry, Polyhymnia of sacred poetry, Urania of astronomy, Thalia of comedy.

The Graces were goddesses presiding over the banquet, the dance, and all social enjoyments and elegant arts. They were three in number. Their names were Euphrosyne, Aglaia, and Thalia.

Spenser describes the office of the Graces thus:

"These three on men all gracious gifts bestow
Which deck the body or adorn the mind,
To make them lovely or well-favoured show;
As comely carriage, entertainment kind,
Sweet semblance, friendly offices that bind,
And all the complements of courtesy;
They teach us how to each degree and kind
We should ourselves demean, to low, to high,
To friends, to foes; which skill men call Civility."

The Fates were also three—Clotho, Lachesis, and Atropos. Their office was to spin the thread of human destiny, and they were armed with shears, with which they cut it off when they pleased. They were the daughters of Themis (Law), who sits by Jove on his throne to give him counsel.

The Erinnyes, or Furies, were three goddesses who punished by their secret stings the crimes of those who escaped or defied public justice. The heads of the Furies were wreathed with serpents, and their whole appearance was terrific and appalling. Their names were Alecto, Tisiphone, and Megæra. They were also called Eumenides.

Nemesis was also an avenging goddess. She represents the righteous anger of the gods, particularly towards the proud and insolent.

Pan was the god of flocks and shepherds. His favourite residence was in Arcadia.

The Satyrs were deities of the woods and fields. They were conceived to be covered with bristly hair, their heads decorated with short, sprouting horns, and their feet like goats' feet.

Momus was the god of laughter, and Plutus the god of wealth.

ROMAN DIVINITIES

The preceding are Grecian divinities, though received also by the Romans. Those which follow are peculiar to Roman mythology:

Saturn was an ancient Italian deity. It was attempted to identify him with the Grecian god Cronos, and fabled that after his dethronement by Jupiter he fled to Italy, where he reigned during what was called the Golden Age. In memory of his beneficent dominion, the feast of Saturnalia was held every year in the winter season. Then all public business was suspended, declarations of war and criminal executions were postponed, friends made presents to one another, and the slaves were indulged with great liberties. A feast was given them at which they sat at table, while their masters served them, to show the natural equality of men, and that all things belonged equally to all, in the reign of Saturn.

Faunus,[1] the grandson of Saturn, was worshipped as the god of fields and shepherds, and also as a prophetic god. His name in the plural, Fauns, expressed a class of gamesome deities, like the Satyrs of the Greeks.

Quirinus was a war god, said to be no other than Romulus, the founder of Rome, exalted after his death to a place among the gods.

Bellona, a war goddess.

Terminus, the god of landmarks. His statue was a rude stone or post, set in the ground to mark the boundaries of fields.

Pales, the goddess presiding over cattle and pastures.

Pomona presided over fruit trees.

Flora, the goddess of flowers.

Lucina, the goddess of childbirth.

Vesta (the Hestia of the Greeks) was a deity presiding over the public and private hearth. A sacred fire, tended by six virgin priestesses called Vestals, flamed in her temple. As the safety of the city was held to be connected with its conservation, the neglect of the virgins, if they let it go out, was severely punished, and the fire was rekindled from the rays of the sun.

Liber is the Latin name of Bacchus; and Mulciber of Vulcan.

Janus was the porter of heaven. He opens the year, the first month being named after him. He is the guardian deity of gates, on which account he is commonly represented with two heads, because every door looks two ways. His temples at Rome were numerous. In war time the gates of the principal one were always open. In peace they were closed; but they were shut only once between the reign of Numa and that of Augustus.

The Penates were the gods who were supposed to attend to the welfare and prosperity of the family. Their name is derived from Penus, the pantry, which was sacred to them. Every master of a family was the priest of the Penates of his own house.

The Lares, or Lars, were also household gods, but differed from the Penates in being regarded as the deified spirits of mortals. The family Lars were held to be the souls of the ancestors, who watched over and protected their descendants. The words Lemur and Larva more nearly correspond to our word Ghost.

The Romans believed that every man had his Genius, and every woman her Juno: that is, a spirit who had given them being, and

[1] There was also a goddess called Fauna, or Bona Dea.

was regarded as their protector through life. On their birthdays men made offerings to their Genius, women to their Juno.

A modern poet thus alludes to some of the Roman gods:

"Pomona loves the orchard,
And Liber loves the vine,
And Pales loves the straw-built shed;
Warm with the breath of kine;
And Venus loves the whisper
Of plighted youth and maid,
In April's ivory moonlight,
Beneath the chestnut shade."

Macaulay, "Prophecy of Capys."

N.B.—It is to be observed that in proper names the final *e* and *es* are to be sounded. Thus Cybele and Penates are words of three syllables. But Proserpine and Thebes are exceptions, and to be pronounced as English words. In the Index at the close of the volume we shall mark the accented syllable in all words which appear to require it.

CHAPTER II

PROMETHEUS AND PANDORA

THE creation of the world is a problem naturally fitted to excite the liveliest interest of man, its inhabitant. The ancient pagans, not having the information on the subject which we derive from the pages of Scripture, had their own way of telling the story, which is as follows:

Before earth and sea and heaven were created, all things wore one aspect, to which we give the name of Chaos—a confused and shapeless mass, nothing but dead weight, in which, however, slumbered the seeds of things. Earth, sea, and air were all mixed up together; so the earth was not solid, the sea was not fluid, and the air was not transparent. God and Nature at last interposed, and put an end to this discord, separating earth from sea, and heaven from both. The fiery part, being the lightest, sprang up, and formed the skies; the air was next in weight and place. The earth, being heavier, sank below; and the water took the lowest place, and buoyed up the earth.

Here some god—it is not known which—gave his good offices in arranging and disposing the earth. He appointed rivers and bays their places, raised mountains, scooped out valleys, distributed woods, fountains, fertile fields, and stony plains. The air being cleared, the stars began to appear, fishes took possession of the sea, birds of the air, and four-footed beasts of the land.

But a nobler animal was wanted, and Man was made. It is not known whether the creator made him of divine materials, or whether in the earth, so lately separated from heaven, there lurked still some heavenly seeds. Prometheus took some of this earth, and kneading it up with water, made man in the image of the gods. He gave him an upright stature, so that while all other animals turn their faces downward, and look to the earth, he raises his to heaven, and gazes on the stars.

Prometheus was one of the Titans, a gigantic race, who inhabited the earth before the creation of man. To him and his brother Epimetheus was committed the office of making man, and providing him and all other animals with the faculties necessary for their preservation. Epimetheus undertook to do this, and Prometheus was to overlook his work, when it was done. Epimetheus accordingly proceeded to bestow upon the different animals the various gifts of courage, strength, swiftness, sagacity; wings to one, claws to another, a shelly covering to a third, etc. But when man came to be provided for, who was to be superior to all other animals, Epimetheus had been so prodigal of his resources that he had nothing left to bestow upon him. In his perplexity he resorted to his brother Prometheus, who, with the aid of Minerva, went up to heaven, and lighted his torch at the chariot of the sun. and brought down fire to man. With this gift man was more than a match for all other animals. It enabled him to make weapons wherewith to subdue them; tools with which to cultivate the earth; to warm his dwelling, so as to be comparatively independent of climate; and finally to introduce the arts and to coin money, the means of trade and commerce.

Woman was not yet made. The story (absurd enough!) is that Jupiter made her, and sent her to Prometheus and his brother, to punish them for their presumption in stealing fire from heaven; and man, for accepting the gift. The first woman was named Pandora. She was made in heaven, every god contributing something to perfect her. Venus gave her beauty, Mercury persuasion, Apollo music, etc. Thus equipped, she was conveyed to earth, and presented to Epimetheus, who gladly accepted her, though cautioned by his brother to beware of Jupiter and his gifts. Epimetheus had in his house a jar, in which were kept certain noxious articles for which, in fitting man for his new abode, he had had no occasion. Pandora was seized with an eager curiosity to know what this jar contained; and one day she slipped off the cover and looked in. Forthwith there escaped a multitude of plagues for hapless man,—

such as gout, rheumatism, and colic for his body, and envy, spite, and revenge for his mind,—and scattered themselves far and wide. Pandora hastened to replace the lid! but, alas! the whole contents of the jar had escaped, one thing only excepted, which lay at the bottom, and that was *hope*. So we see at this day, whatever evils are abroad, hope never entirely leaves us; and while we have *that,* no amount of other ills can make us completely wretched.

Another story is that Pandora was sent in good faith, by Jupiter, to bless man; that she was furnished with a box containing her marriage presents, into which every god had put some blessing. She opened the box incautiously, and the blessings all escaped, *hope* only excepted. This story seems more probable than the former; for how could *hope*, so precious a jewel as it is, have been kept in a jar full of all manner of evils, as in the former statement?

The world being thus furnished with inhabitants, the first age was an age of innocence and happiness, called the *Golden Age*. Truth and right prevailed, though not enforced by law, nor was there any magistrate to threaten or punish. The forest had not yet been robbed of its trees to furnish timbers for vessels, nor had men built fortifications round their towns. There were no such things as swords, spears, or helmets. The earth brought forth all things necessary for man, without his labour in ploughing or sowing. Perpetual spring reigned, flowers sprang up without seed, the rivers flowed with milk and wine, and yellow honey distilled from the oaks.

Then succeeded the *Silver Age*, inferior to the golden, but better than that of brass. Jupiter shortened the spring, and divided the year into seasons. Then, first, men had to endure the extremes of heat and cold, and houses became necessary. Caves were the first dwellings, and leafy coverts of the woods, and huts woven of twigs. Crops would no longer grow without planting. The farmer was obliged to sow the seed, and the toiling ox to draw the plough.

Next came the *Brazen Age*, more savage of temper, and readier to the strife of arms, yet not altogether wicked. The hardest and worst was the *Iron Age*. Crime burst in like a flood; modesty, truth, and honour fled. In their places came fraud and cunning, violence, and the wicked love of gain. Then seamen spread sails to the wind, and the trees were torn from the mountains to serve for keels to ships, and vex the face of the ocean. The earth, which till now had been cultivated in common, began to be divided off into possessions. Men were not satisfied with what the surface produced, but must dig into its bowels, and draw forth from thence the ores of metals. Mischievous *iron,* and more mischievous *gold,* were produced. War sprang up, using both as weapons; the guest was not safe in his friend's house; and sons-in-law and fathers-in-law, brothers and sisters, husbands and wives, could not trust one another. Sons wished their fathers dead, that they might come to the inheritance; family love lay prostrate. The earth was wet with slaughter, and the gods abandoned it, one by one, till Astræa [1] alone was left, and finally she also took her departure.

Jupiter, seeing this state of things, burned with anger. He summoned the gods to council. They obeyed the call, and took the road to the palace of heaven. The road, which any one may see in a clear night, stretches across the face of the sky, and is called the Milky Way. Along the road stand the palaces of the illustrious gods; the common people of the skies live apart, on either side. Jupiter addressed the assembly. He set forth the frightful condition of things on the earth, and closed by announcing his intention to destroy the whole of its inhabitants, and provide a new race, unlike the first, who would be more worthy of life, and much better worshippers of the gods. So saying he took a thunderbolt, and was about to launch it at the world, and destroy it by burning; but recollecting the danger that such a conflagration might set heaven itself on fire, he changed his plan, and resolved to drown it. The north wind, which scatters the clouds, was chained up; the south was sent out, and soon covered all the face of heaven with a cloak of pitchy darkness. The clouds, driven together, resound with a crash; torrents of rain fall; the crops are laid low; the year's labour of the husbandman perishes in an hour. Jupiter, not satisfied with his own waters, calls on his brother Neptune to aid him with his. He lets loose the rivers, and pours them over the land. At the same time, he heaves the land with an earthquake, and brings in the reflux of the ocean over the shores. Flocks, herds, men, and houses are swept away, and temples, with their sacred enclosures, profaned. If any edifice remained standing, it was overwhelmed, and its turrets lay hid beneath the waves. Now all was sea, sea without

[1] The goddess of innocence and purity. After leaving earth, she was placed among the stars, where she became the constellation Virgo—the Virgin. Themis (Justice) was the mother of Astræa. She is represented as holding aloft a pair of scales, in which she weighs the claims of opposing parties.

It was a favourite idea of the old poets that these goddesses would one day return, and bring back the Golden Age. Even in a Christian hymn, the "Messiah" of Pope, this idea occurs:

> "All crimes shall cease, and ancient fraud shall fail,
> Returning Justice lift aloft her scale,
> Peace o'er the world her olive wand extend,
> And white-robed Innocence from heaven descend."

See, also, Milton's "Hymn on the Nativity," stanzas xiv. and xv.

shore. Here and there an individual remained on a projecting hill-top, and a few, in boats, pulled the oar where they had lately driven the plough. The fishes swim among the tree-tops; the anchor is let down into a garden. Where the graceful lambs played but now, unwieldy sea calves gambol. The wolf swims among the sheep, the yellow lions and tigers struggle in the water. The strength of the wild boar serves him not, nor his swiftness the stag. The birds fall with weary wing into the water, having found no land for a resting-place. Those living beings whom the water spared fell a prey to hunger.

Parnassus alone, of all the mountains, overtopped the waves; and there Deucalion, and his wife Pyrrha, of the race of Prometheus, found refuge—he a just man, and she a faithful worshipper of the gods. Jupiter, when he saw none left alive but this pair, and remembered their harmless lives and pious demeanour, ordered the north winds to drive away the clouds, and disclose the skies to earth, and earth to the skies. Neptune also directed Triton to blow on his shell, and sound a retreat to the waters. The waters obeyed, and the sea returned to its shores, and the rivers to their channels. Then Deucalion thus addressed Pyrrha: "O wife, only surviving woman, joined to me first by the ties of kindred and marriage, and now by a common danger, would that we possessed the power of our ancestor Prometheus, and could renew the race as he at first made it! But as we cannot, let us seek yonder temple, and inquire of the gods what remains for us to do." They entered the temple, deformed as it was with slime, and approached the altar, where no fire burned. There they fell prostrate on the earth, and prayed the goddess to inform them how they might retrieve their miserable affairs. The oracle answered, "Depart from the temple with head veiled and garments unbound, and cast behind you the bones of your mother." They heard the words with astonishment. Pyrrha first broke silence: "We cannot obey; we dare not profane the remains of our parents." They sought the thickest shades of the wood, and revolved the oracle in their minds. At length Deucalion spoke: "Either my sagacity deceives me, or the command is one we may obey without impiety. The earth is the great parent of all; the stones are her bones; these we may cast behind us; and I think this is what the oracle means. At least, it will do no harm to try." They veiled their faces, unbound their garments, and picked up stones, and cast them behind them. The stones (wonderful to relate) began to grow soft, and assume shape. By degrees, they put on a rude resemblance to the human form, like a block half finished in the hands of the sculptor. The moisture and slime that were about them became flesh; the stony part became bones; the veins remained veins, retaining their name, only changing their use. Those thrown by the hand of the man became men, and those by the woman became women. It was a hard race, and well adapted to labour, as we find ourselves to be at this day, giving plain indications of our origin.

The comparison of Eve to Pandora is too obvious to have escaped Milton, who introduces it in Book IV. of "Paradise Lost":

> "More lovely than Pandora, whom the gods
> Endowed with all their gifts; and O, too like
> In sad event, when to the unwiser son
> Of Japhet brought by Hermes, she insnared
> Mankind with her fair looks, to be avenged
> On him who had stole Jove's authentic fire."

Prometheus and Epimetheus were sons of Iapetus, which Milton changes to Japhet.

Prometheus has been a favourite subject with the poets. He is represented as the friend of mankind, who interposed in their behalf when Jove was incensed against them, and who taught them civilization and the arts. But as, in so doing, he transgressed the will of Jupiter, he drew down on himself the anger of the ruler of gods and men. Jupiter had him chained to a rock on Mount Caucasus, where a vulture preyed on his liver, which was renewed as fast as devoured. This state of torment might have been brought to an end at any time by Prometheus, if he had been willing to submit to his oppressor; for he possessed a secret which involved the stability of Jove's throne, and if he would have revealed it, he might have been at once taken into favour. But that he disdained to do. He has therefore become the symbol of magnanimous endurance of unmerited suffering, and strength of will resisting oppression.

Byron and Shelley have both treated this theme. The following are Byron's lines:

> "Titan! to whose immortal eyes
> The sufferings of mortality,
> Seen in their sad reality,
> Were not as things that gods despise;
> What was thy pity's recompense?
> A silent suffering, and intense;
> The rock, the vulture, and the chain;
> All that the proud can feel of pain;
> The agony they do not show;
> The suffocating sense of woe.
>
> "Thy godlike crime was to be kind;
> To render with thy precepts less
> The sum of human wretchedness,

And strengthen man with his own mind.
  And, baffled as thou wert from high,
    Still, in thy patient energy
In the endurance and repulse
  Of thine impenetrable spirit,
Which earth and heaven could not convulse,
  A mighty lesson we inherit."

Byron also employs the same allusion, in his "Ode to Napoleon Bonaparte":

"Or, like the thief of fire from heaven,
  Wilt thou withstand the shock?
And share with him—the unforgiven—
  His vulture and his rock?"

CHAPTER III

APOLLO AND DAPHNE—PYRAMUS AND THISBE—CEPHALUS AND PROCRIS

THE slime with which the earth was covered by the waters of the flood produced an excessive fertility, which called forth every variety of production, both bad and good. Among the rest, Python, an enormous serpent, crept forth, the terror of the people, and lurked in the caves of Mount Parnassus. Apollo slew him with his arrows—weapons which he had not before used against any but feeble animals, hares, wild goats, and such game. In commemoration of this illustrious conquest he instituted the Pythian games, in which the victor in feats of strength, swiftness of foot, or in the chariot race was crowned with a wreath of beech leaves; for the laurel was not yet adopted by Apollo as his own tree.

The famous statue of Apollo called the Belvedere represents the god after this victory over the serpent Python. To this Byron alludes in his "Childe Harold," iv. 161:

"... The lord of the unerring bow,
The god of life, and poetry, and light,
The Sun, in human limbs arrayed, and brow
All radiant from his triumph in the fight.
The shaft has just been shot; the arrow bright
With an immortal's vengeance; in his eye
And nostril, beautiful disdain, and might
And majesty flash their full lightnings by,
Developing in that one glance the Deity."

APOLLO AND DAPHNE

Daphne was Apollo's first love. It was not brought about by accident, but by the malice of Cupid. Apollo saw the boy playing with his bow and arrows; and being himself elated with his recent victory over Python, he said to him, "What have you to do with warlike weapons, saucy boy? Leave them for hands worthy of them. Behold the conquest I have won by means of them over the vast serpent who stretched his poisonous body over acres of the plain! Be content with your torch, child, and kindle up your flames, as you call them, where you will, but presume not to meddle with my weapons." Venus's boy heard these words, and rejoined, "Your arrows may strike all things else, Apollo, but mine shall strike you." So saying, he took his stand on a rock of Parnassus, and drew from his quiver two arrows of different workmanship, one to excite love, the other to repel it. The former was of gold and sharp pointed, the latter blunt and tipped with lead. With the leaden shaft he struck the nymph Daphne, the daughter of the river god Peneus, and with the golden one Apollo, through the heart. Forthwith the god was seized with love for the maiden, and she abhorred the thought of loving. Her delight was in woodland sports and in the spoils of the chase. Many lovers sought her, but she spurned them all, ranging the woods, and taking no thought of Cupid nor of Hymen. Her father often said to her, "Daughter, you owe me a son-in-law; you owe me grandchildren." She, hating the thought of marriage as a crime, with her beautiful face tinged all over with blushes, threw her arms around her father's neck, and said, "Dearest father, grant me this favour, that I may always remain unmarried, like Diana." He consented, but at the same time said, "Your own face will forbid it."

Apollo loved her, and longed to obtain her; and he who gives oracles to all the world was not wise enough to look into his own fortunes. He saw her hair flung loose over her shoulders, and said, "If so charming in disorder, what would it be if arranged?" He saw her eyes bright as stars; he saw her lips, and was not satisfied with only seeing them. He admired her hands and arms, naked to the shoulder, and whatever was hidden from view he imagined more beautiful still. He followed her; she fled, swifter than the wind, and delayed not a moment at his entreaties. "Stay," said he, "daughter of Peneus; I am not a foe. Do not fly me as a lamb flies the wolf, or a dove the hawk. It is for love I pursue you. You make me miserable, for fear you should fall and hurt yourself on these stones, and I should be the cause. Pray run slower, and I will follow slower. I am no clown, no rude peasant. Jupiter is my father, and I am lord of Delphos and Tenedos, and know all things, present and future. I am the god of song and the lyre. My arrows fly true to the mark; but, alas! an arrow more fatal than mine has pierced my heart! I am the god of medicine, and know the virtues of all healing plants. Alas! I suffer a malady that no balm can cure!"

The nymph continued her flight, and left his plea half uttered. And even as she fled she charmed him. The wind blew her garments, and her unbound hair streamed loose behind her. The god grew impatient to find his wooings thrown away, and, sped by Cupid, gained upon her in the race. It was like a hound pursuing a hare, with open jaws ready to seize, while the feebler animal darts forward, slipping from the very grasp. So flew the god and the virgin—he on the wings of love, and she on those of fear. The pursuer is the more rapid, however, and gains upon her, and his panting breath blows upon her hair. Her strength begins to fail, and, ready to sink, she calls upon her father, the river god: "Help me, Peneus! open the earth to enclose me, or change my form, which has brought me into this danger!" Scarcely had she spoken, when a stiffness seized all her limbs; her bosom began to be enclosed in a tender bark; her hair became leaves; her arms became branches; her foot stuck fast in the ground, as a root; her face became a tree-top, retaining nothing of its former self but its beauty. Apollo stood amazed. He touched the stem, and felt the flesh tremble under the new bark. He embraced the branches, and lavished kisses on the wood. The branches shrank from his lips. "Since you cannot be my wife," said he, "you shall assuredly be my tree. I will wear you for my crown; I will decorate with you my harp and my quiver; and when the great Roman conquerors lead up the triumphal pomp to the Capitol, you shall be woven into wreaths for their brows. And, as eternal youth is mine, you also shall be always green, and your leaf know no decay." The nymph, now changed into a Laurel tree, bowed its head in grateful acknowledgment.

That Apollo should be the god both of music and poetry will not appear strange, but that medicine should also be assigned to his province, may. The poet Armstrong, himself a physician, thus accounts for it:

> "Music exalts each joy, allays each grief,
> Expels diseases, softens every pain;
> And hence the wise of ancient days adored
> One power of physic, melody, and song."

The story of Apollo and Daphne is often alluded to by the poets. Waller applies it to the case of one whose amatory verses, though they did not soften the heart of his mistress, yet won for the poet wide-spread fame:

"Yet what he sung in his immortal strain,
Though unsuccessful, was not sung in vain.
All but the nymph that should redress his wrong,
Attend his passion and approve his song.
Like Phœbus thus, acquiring unsought praise,
He caught at love and filled his arms with bays."

The following stanza from Shelley's "Adonais" alludes to Byron's early quarrel with the reviewers:

"The herded wolves, bold only to pursue;
The obscene ravens, clamorous o'er the dead;
The vultures, to the conqueror's banner true,
Who feed where Desolation first has fed,
And whose wings rain contagion: how they fled,
When like Apollo, from his golden bow,
The Pythian of the age one arrow sped
And smiled! The spoilers tempt no second blow;
They fawn on the proud feet that spurn them as they go."

PYRAMUS AND THISBE

Pyramus was the handsomest youth, and Thisbe the fairest maiden, in all Babylonia, where Semiramis reigned. Their parents occupied adjoining houses; and neighbourhood brought the young people together, and acquaintance ripened into love. They would gladly have married, but their parents forbade. One thing, however, they could not forbid—that love should glow with equal ardour in the bosoms of both. They conversed by signs and glances, and the fire burned more intensely for being covered up. In the wall that parted the two houses there was a crack, caused by some fault in the structure. No one had remarked it before, but the lovers discovered it. What will not love discover! It afforded a passage to the voice; and tender messages used to pass backward and forward through the gap. As they stood, Pyramus on this side, Thisbe on that, their breaths would mingle. "Cruel wall," they said, "why do you keep two lovers apart? But we will not be ungrateful. We owe you, we confess, the privilege of transmitting loving words to willing ears." Such words they uttered on different sides of the wall; and when night came and they must say farewell, they pressed their lips upon the wall, she on her side, he on his, as they could come no nearer.

Next morning, when Aurora had put out the stars, and the sun had melted the frost from the grass, they met at the accustomed spot. Then, after lamenting their hard fate, they agreed that next night, when all was still, they would slip away from the watchful eyes, leave their dwellings and walk out into the fields; and to insure a meeting, repair to a well-known edifice standing without the city's bounds, called the Tomb of Ninus, and that the one who came first should await the other at the foot of a certain tree. It was a white mulberry tree, and stood near a cool spring. All was agreed on, and they waited impatiently for the sun to go down beneath the waters and night to rise up from them. Then cautiously Thisbe stole forth, unobserved by the family, her head covered with a veil, made her way to the monument and sat down under the tree. As she sat alone in the dim light of the evening she descried a lioness, her jaws reeking with recent slaughter, approaching the fountain to slake her thirst. Thisbe fled at the sight, and sought refuge in the hollow of a rock. As she fled she dropped her veil. The lioness after drinking at the spring turned to retreat to the woods, and seeing the veil on the ground, tossed and rent it with her bloody mouth.

Pyramus, having been delayed, now approached the place of meeting. He saw in the sand the footsteps of the lion, and the colour fled from his cheeks at the sight. Presently he found the veil all rent and bloody. "O hapless girl," said he, "I have been the cause of thy death! Thou, more worthy of life than I, hast fallen the first victim. I will follow. I am the guilty cause, in tempting thee forth to a place of such peril, and not being myself on the spot to guard thee. Come forth, ye lions, from the rocks, and tear this guilty body with your teeth." He took up the veil, carried it with him to the appointed tree, and covered it with kisses and with tears. "*My* blood also shall stain your texture," said he, and drawing his sword plunged it into his heart. The blood spurted from the wound, and tinged the white mulberries of the tree all red; and sinking into the earth reached the roots, so that the red colour mounted through the trunk to the fruit.

By this time Thisbe, still trembling with fear, yet wishing not to disappoint her lover, stepped cautiously forth, looking anxiously for the youth, eager to tell him the danger she had escaped. When she came to the spot and saw the changed colour of the mulberries she doubted whether it was the same place. While she hesitated she saw the form of one struggling in the agonies of death. She started back, a shudder ran through her frame as a ripple on the face of the still water when a sudden breeze sweeps over it. But as soon as she recognized her lover, she screamed and beat her breast, embracing the lifeless body, pouring tears into its wounds, and imprinting kisses on the cold lips. "O Pyramus," she cried, "what has done this? Answer me, Pyramus; it is your own Thisbe that speaks. Hear me, dearest, and lift that drooping head!" At the name of Thisbe Pyramus opened his eyes, then closed them again. She saw her veil stained blood and the scabbard empty of its sword. "Thy own hand has slain thee, and for my sake," she said. "I too can be brave for once, and my love is as strong as thine. I will follow thee in death, for I have been the cause; and death which alone could part us shall not prevent my joining thee. And ye, unhappy parents of us both, deny us not our united request. As love and death have joined us, let one tomb contain us. And thou, tree, retain the marks of slaughter. Let thy berries still serve for memorials of our blood." So saying she plunged the sword into her breast. Her parents ratified her wish, the gods also ratified it. The two bodies were buried in one sepulchre, and the tree ever after brought forth purple berries, as it does to this day.

Moore, in the "Sylph's Ball," speaking of Davy's Safety Lamp, is reminded of the wall that separated Thisbe and her lover:

> "O for that Lamp's metallic gauze,
>   That curtain of protecting wire,
> Which Davy delicately draws
>   Around illicit, dangerous fire!
>
> The wall he sets 'twixt Flame and Air,
>   (Like that which barred young Thisbe's bliss,)
> Through whose small holes this dangerous pair
>   May see each other, but not kiss."

In Mickle's translation of the "Lusiad" occurs the following allusion to the story of Pyramus and Thisbe, and the metamorphosis of the mulberries. The poet is describing the Island of Love:

> "...here each gift of Pomona's hand bestows
> In cultured garden, free uncultured flows,
> The flavour sweeter and the hue more fair
> Than e'er was fostered by the hand of care.
> The cherry here in shining crimson glows,
> And stained with lovers' blood, in pendent rows,
> The mulberries o'erload the bending boughs."

If any of our young readers can be so hard-hearted as to enjoy a laugh at the expense of poor Pyramus and Thisbe, they may find an opportunity by turning to Shakespeare's play of the "Midsummer Night's Dream," where it is most amusingly burlesqued.

CEPHALUS AND PROCRIS

Cephalus was a beautiful youth and fond of manly sports. He would rise before the dawn to pursue the chase. Aurora saw him when she first looked forth, fell in love with him, and stole him away. But Cephalus was just married to a charming wife whom he devotedly loved. Her name was Procris. She was a favourite of Diana, the goddess of hunting, who had given her a dog which could outrun every rival, and a javelin which would never fail of its mark; and Procris gave these presents to her husband. Cephalus was so happy in his wife that he resisted all the entreaties of Aurora, and she finally dismissed him in displeasure, saying, "Go, ungrateful mortal, keep your wife, whom, if I am not much mistaken, you will one day be very sorry you ever saw again."

Cephalus returned, and was as happy as ever in his wife and his woodland sports. Now it happened some angry deity had sent a ravenous fox to annoy the country; and the hunters turned out in great strength to capture it. Their efforts were all in vain; no dog could run it down; and at last they came to Cephalus to borrow his famous dog, whose name was Lelaps. No sooner was the dog let loose than he darted off, quicker than their eye could allow him. If they had not seen his footprints in the sand they would have thought he flew. Cephalus and others stood on a hill and saw the race. The fox tried every art; he ran in a circle and turned on his track, the dog close upon him, with open jaws, snapping at his heels, but biting only the air. Cephalus was about to use his javelin, when suddenly he saw both dog and game stop instantly. The heavenly powers who had given both were not willing that either should conquer. In the very attitude of life and action they were turned into stone. So lifelike and natural did they look, you would have thought, as you looked at them, that one was going to bark, the other to leap forward.

Cephalus, though he had lost his dog, still continued to take delight in the chase. He would go out at early morning, ranging the woods and hills unaccompanied by any one, needing no help, for his javelin was a sure weapon in all cases. Fatigued with hunting, when the sun got high he would seek a shady nook where a cool stream flowed, and, stretched on the grass, with his garments thrown aside, would enjoy the breeze. Sometimes he would say aloud, "Come, sweet breeze, come and fan my breast, come and allay the heat that burns me." Some one passing by one day heard him talking in this way to the air, and, foolishly believing that he was talking to some maiden, went and told the secret to Procris, Cephalus's wife. Love is credulous. Procris, at the sudden shock, fainted away. Presently recovering, she said, "It cannot be true; I will not believe it unless I myself am a witness to it." So she waited, with anxious heart, till the next morning, when Cephalus went to hunt as usual. Then she stole out after him, and concealed herself in the place where the informer directed her. Cephalus came as he was wont when tired with sport, and stretched himself on the green bank, saying, "Come, sweet breeze, come and fan me;

you know how I love you! you make the groves and my solitary rambles delightful." He was running on in this way when he heard, or thought he heard, a sound as of a sob in the bushes. Supposing it some wild animal, he threw his javelin at the spot. A cry from his beloved Procris told him that the weapon had too surely met its mark. He rushed to the place, and found her bleeding, and with sinking strength endeavouring to draw forth from the wound the javelin, her own gift. Cephalus raised her from the earth, strove to stanch the blood, and called her to revive and not to leave him miserable, to reproach himself with her death. She opened her feeble eyes, and forced herself to utter these few words: "I implore you, if you have ever loved me, if I have ever deserved kindness at your hands, my husband, grant me this last request; do not marry that odious Breeze!" This disclosed the whole mystery: but alas! what advantage to disclose it now? She died; but her face wore a calm expression, and she looked pityingly and forgivingly on her husband when he made her understand the truth.

Moore, in his "Legendary Ballads," has one on Cephalus and Procris, beginning thus:

"A hunter once in a grove reclined,
    To shun the noon's bright eye,
And oft he wooed the wandering wind
    To cool his brow with its sigh.
While mute lay even the wild bee's hum,
    Nor breath could stir the aspen's hair,
His song was still, 'Sweet Air, O come!'
    While Echo answered, 'Come, sweet Air!'"

CHAPTER IV

JUNO AND HER RIVALS, IO AND CALLISTO—DIANA AND ACTÆON—
LATONA AND THE RUSTICS

JUNO one day perceived it suddenly grow dark, and immediately suspected that her husband had raised a cloud to hide some of his doings that would not bear the light. She brushed away the cloud, and saw her husband on the banks of a glassy river, with a beautiful heifer standing near him. Juno suspected the heifer's form concealed some fair nymph of mortal mould—as was, indeed, the case; for it was Io, the daughter of the river god Inachus, whom Jupiter had been flirting with, and, when he became aware of the approach of his wife, had changed into that form.

Juno joined her husband, and noticing the heifer praised its beauty, and asked whose it was, and of what herd. Jupiter, to stop questions, replied that it was a fresh creation from the earth. Juno asked to have it as a gift. What could Jupiter do? He was loath to give his mistress to his wife; yet how refuse so trifling a present as a simple heifer? He could not, without exciting suspicion; so he consented. The goddess was not yet relieved of her suspicions; so she delivered the heifer to Argus, to be strictly watched.

Now Argus had a hundred eyes in his head, and never went to sleep with more than two at a time, so that he kept watch of Io constantly. He suffered her to feed through the day, and at night tied her up with a vile rope round her neck. She would have stretched out her arms to implore freedom of Argus, but she had no arms to stretch out, and her voice was a bellow that frightened even herself. She saw her father and her sisters, went near them, and suffered them to pat her back, and heard them admire her beauty. Her father reached her a tuft of grass, and she licked the outstretched hand. She longed to make herself known to him, and would have uttered her wish; but, alas! words were wanting. At length she bethought herself of writing, and inscribed her name—it was a short one—with her hoof on the sand. Inachus recognized it, and discovering that his daughter, whom he had long sought in vain, was hidden under this disguise, mourned over her, and, embracing her white neck, exclaimed, "Alas! my daughter, it would have been a less grief to have lost you altogether!" While he thus lamented, Argus, observing, came and drove her away, and took his seat on a high bank, from whence he could see all round in every direction.

Jupiter was troubled at beholding the sufferings of his mistress, and calling Mercury told him to go and despatch Argus. Mercury made haste, put his winged slippers on his feet, and cap on his head, took his sleep-producing wand, and leaped down from the heavenly towers to the earth. There he laid aside his wings, and kept only his wand, with which he presented himself as a shepherd driving his flock. As he strolled on he blew upon his pipes. These were what are called the Syrinx or Pandean pipes. Argus listened with delight, for he had never seen the instrument before. "Young man," said he, "come and take a seat by me on this stone. There is no better place for your flocks to graze in than hereabouts, and here is a pleasant shade such as shepherds love." Mercury sat down, talked, and told stories till it grew late, and played upon his pipes his most soothing strains, hoping to lull the watchful eyes to sleep, but all in vain; for Argus still contrived to keep some of his eyes open though he shut the rest.

Among other stories, Mercury told him how the instrument on which he played was invented. "There was a certain nymph, whose name was Syrinx, who was much beloved by the satyrs and spirits of the wood; but she would have none of them, but was a faithful worshipper of Diana, and followed the chase. You would have thought it was Diana herself, had you seen her in her hunting dress, only that her bow was of horn and Diana's of silver. One day, as she was returning from the chase, Pan met her, told her just this, and added more of the same sort. She ran away, without stopping to hear his compliments, and he pursued till she came to the bank of the river, where he overtook her, and she had only time to call for help on her friends the water nymphs. They heard and consented. Pan threw his arms around what he supposed to be the form of the nymph, and found he embraced only a tuft of reeds! As he breathed a sigh, the air sounded through the reeds, and produced a plaintive melody. The god, charmed with the novelty and with the sweetness of the music, said, 'Thus, then, at least, you shall be mine.' And he took some of the reeds, and placing them together, of unequal lengths, side by side, made an instrument which he called Syrinx, in honour of the nymph." Before Mercury had finished his story he saw Argus's eyes all asleep. As his head nodded forward on his breast, Mercury with one stroke cut his neck through, and tumbled his head down the rocks. O hapless Argus! the light of your hundred eyes is quenched at once! Juno took them and put them as ornaments on the tail of her peacock, where they remain to this day.

But the vengeance of Juno was not yet satiated. She sent a gadfly to torment Io, who fled over the whole world from its pursuit. She swam through the Ionian sea, which derived its name from her, then roamed over the plains of Illyria, ascended Mount Hæmus, and crossed the Thracian strait, thence named the Bosphorus (cowford), rambled on through Scythia, and the country of the Cimmerians, and arrived at last on the banks of the Nile. At length Jupiter interceded for her, and upon his promising not to pay her any more attentions Juno consented to restore her to her form. It was curious to see her gradually recover her former self. The coarse hairs fell from her body, her horns shrank up, her eyes grew narrower, her mouth shorter; hands and fingers came instead of hoofs to her forefeet; in fine there was nothing left of the heifer, except her beauty. At first she was afraid to speak, for fear she should low, but gradually she recovered her confidence and was restored to her father and sisters.

In a poem dedicated to Leigh Hunt, by Keats, the following allusion to the story of Pan and Syrinx occurs:

> "So did he feel who pulled the bough aside,
> That we might look into a forest wide,

. . . .

Telling us how fair trembling Syrinx ued
Arcadian Pan, with such a fearful dread.
Poor nymph—poor Pan—how he did weep to find
Nought but a lovely sighing of the wind
Along the reedy stream; a half-heard strain,
Full of sweet desolation, balmy pain."

CALLISTO

Callisto was another maiden who excited the jealousy of Juno, and the goddess changed her into a bear. "I will take away," said she, "that beauty with which you have captivated my husband." Down fell Callisto on her hands and knees; she tried to stretch out her arms in supplication—they were already beginning to be covered with black hair. Her hands grew rounded, became armed with crooked claws, and served for feet; her mouth, which Jove used to praise for its beauty, became a horrid pair of jaws; her voice, which if unchanged would have moved the heart to pity, became a growl, more ft to inspire terror. Yet her former disposition remained, and with continual groaning, she bemoaned her fate, and stood upright as well as she could, lifting up her paws to beg for mercy, and felt that Jove was unkind, though she could not tell him so. Ah, how often, afraid to stay in the woods all night alone, she wandered about the neighbourhood of her former haunts; how often, frightened by the dogs, did she, so lately a huntress, fly in terror from the hunters! Often she fled from the wild beasts, forgetting that she was now a wild beast herself; and, bear as she was, was afraid of the bears.

One day a youth espied her as he was hunting. She saw him and recognized him as her own son, now grown a young man. She stopped and felt inclined to embrace him. As she was about to approach, he, alarmed, raised his hunting spear, and was on the point of transfixing her, when Jupiter, beholding, arrested the crime, and snatching away both of them, placed them in the heavens as the Great and Little Bear.

Juno was in a rage to see her rival so set in honour, and hastened to ancient Tethys and Oceanus, the powers of ocean, and in answer to their inquiries thus told the cause of her coming: "Do you ask why I, the queen of the gods, have left the heavenly plains and sought your depths? Learn that I am supplanted in heaven—my place is given to another. You will hardly believe me; but look when night darkens the world, and you shall see the two of whom I have so much reason to complain exalted to the heavens, in that part where the circle is the smallest, in the neighborhood of the pole. Why should any one hereafter tremble at the thought of offending Juno when such rewards are the consequence of my displeasure? See what I have been able to effect! I forbade her to wear the human form—she is placed among the stars! So do my punishments result—such is the extent of my power! Better that she should have resumed her former shape, as I permitted Io to do. Perhaps he means to marry her, and put me away! But you, my foster-parents, if you feel for me, and see with displeasure this unworthy treatment of me, show it, I beseech you, by forbidding this couple from coming into your waters." The powers of the ocean assented, and consequently the two constellations of the Great and Little Bear move round and round in heaven, but never sink, as the other stars do, beneath the ocean.

Milton alludes to the fact that the constellation of the Bear never sets, when he says:

"Let my lamp at midnight hour
Be seen in some high lonely tower,
Where I may oft outwatch the Bear," etc.

And Prometheus, in J. R. Lowell's poem, says:

"One after one the stars have risen and set,
Sparkling upon the hoar frost of my chain;
The Bear that prowled all night about the fold
Of the North-star, hath shrunk into his den,
Scared by the blithesome footsteps of the Dawn."

The last star in the tail of the Little Bear is the Polestar, called also the Cynosure. Milton says:

"Straight mine eye hath caught new pleasures
While the landscape round it measures.

. . . . . .

Towers and battlements it sees
Bosomed high in tufted trees,
Where perhaps some beauty lies
The Cynosure of neighbouring eyes."

The reference here is both to the Polestar as the guide of mariners, and to the magnetic attraction of the North. He calls it also the "Star of Arcady," because Callisto's boy was named Arcas, and they lived in Arcadia. In "Comus," the brother, benighted in the woods, says:

"...Some gentle taper!
Though a rush candle, from the wicker hole
Of some clay habitation, visit us
With thy long levelled rule of streaming light,
And thou shalt be our star of Arcady.
Or Tyrian Cynosure."

DIANA AND ACTÆON

Thus in two instances we have seen Juno's severity to her rivals; now let us learn how a virgin goddess punished an invader of her privacy.

It was midday, and the sun stood equally distant from either goal, when young Actæon, son of King Cadmus, thus addressed the youths who with him were hunting the stag in the mountains: "Friends, our nets and our weapons are wet with the blood of our victims; we have had sport enough for one day, and to-morrow we can renew our labours. Now, while Phœbus parches the earth, let us put by our implements and indulge ourselves with rest."

There was a valley thick enclosed with cypresses and pines, sacred to the huntress queen, Diana. In the extremity of the valley was a cave, not adorned with art, but nature had counterfeited art in its construction, for she had turned the arch of its roof with stones, as delicately fitted as if by the hand of man. A fountain burst out from one side, whose open basin was bounded by a grassy rim. Here the goddess of the woods used to come when weary with hunting and lave her virgin limbs in the sparkling water.

One day, having repaired thither with her nymphs, she handed her javelin, her quiver, and her bow to one, her robe to another, while a third unbound the sandals from her feet. Then Crocale, the most skilful of them, arranged her hair, and Nephele, Hyale, and the rest drew water in capacious urns. While the goddess was thus employed in the labours of the toilet, behold Actæon, having quitted his companions, and rambling without any especial object, came to the place, led thither by his destiny. As he presented himself at the entrance of the cave, the nymphs, seeing a man, screamed and rushed towards the goddess to hide her with their bodies. But she was taller than the rest and overtopped them all by a head. Such a colour as tinges the clouds at sunset or at dawn came over the countenance of Diana thus taken by surprise. Surrounded as she was by her nymphs, she yet turned half away, and sought with a sudden impulse for her arrows. As they were not at hand, she dashed the water into the face of the intruder, adding these words: "Now go and tell, if you can, that you have seen Dianna unapparelled." Immediately a pair of branching stag's horns grew out of his head, his neck gained in length, his ears grew sharp-pointed, his hands became feet, his arms long legs, his body was covered with a hairy spotted hide. Fear took the place of his former boldness, and the hero fled. He could not but admire his own speed; but when he saw his horns in the water, "Ah, wretched me!" he would have said, but no sound followed the effort. He groaned, and tears flowed down the face which had taken the place of his own. Yet his consciousness remained. What shall he do?—go home to seek the palace, or lie hid in the woods? The latter he was afraid, the former he was ashamed, to do. While he hesitated the dogs saw him. First Melampus, a Spartan dog, gave the signal with his bark, then Pamphagus, Dorceus, Lelaps, Theron, Nape, Tigris, and all the rest, rushed after him swifter than the wind. Over rocks and cliffs, through mountain gorges that seemed impracticable, he fled and they followed. Where he had often chased the stag and cheered on his pack, his pack now chased him, cheered on by his huntsmen. He longed to cry out, "I am Actæon; recognize your master!" but the words came not at his will. The air resounded with the bark of the dogs. Presently one fastened on his back, another seized his shoulder. While they held their master, the rest of the pack came up and buried their teeth in his flesh. He groaned,—not in a human voice, yet certainly not in a stag's,—and falling on his knees, raised his eyes, and would have raised his arms in supplication, if he had had them. His friends and fellow-huntsmen cheered on the dogs, and looked everywhere for Actæon, calling on him to join the sport. At the sound of his name he turned his head, and heard them regret that he should be away. He earnestly wished he was. He would have been well pleased to see the exploits of his dogs, but to feel them was too much. They were all around him, rending and tearing; and it was not till they had torn his life out that the anger of Diana was satisfied.

In Shelley's poem "Adonais" is the following allusion to the story of Actæon:

> " 'Midst others of less note came one frail form,
> A phantom among men: companionless
> As the last cloud of an expiring storm,
> Whose thunder is its knell; he, as I guess,
> Had gazed on Nature's naked loveliness,
> Actæon-like, and now he fled astray
> With feeble steps o'er the world's wilderness;
> And his own Thoughts, along that rugged way,
> Pursued like raging hounds their father and their prey."
>
> Stanza 31.

The allusion is probably to Shelley himself.

LATONA AND THE RUSTICS

Some thought the goddess in this instance more severe than was just, while others praised her conduct as strictly consistent with her virgin dignity. As usual, the recent event brought older ones to mind, and one of the bystanders told this story: "Some country-men of Lycia once insulted the goddess Latona, but not with impunity. When I was young, my father, who had grown too old for active labours, sent me to Lycia to drive thence some choice oxen, and there I saw the very pond and marsh where the wonder happened. Near by stood an ancient altar, black with the smoke of sacrifice and almost buried among the reeds. I inquired whose altar it might be, whether of Faunus or the Naiads, or some god of the neighbouring mountain, and one of the country people re-plied, 'No mountain or river god possesses this altar, but she whom royal Juno in her jealousy drove from land to land, denying her any spot of earth whereon to rear her twins. Bearing in her arms the infant deities, Latona reached this land, weary with her burden and parched with thirst. By chance she espied in the bottom of the valley this pond of clear water, where the country people were at work gathering willows and osiers. The goddess approached, and kneeling on the bank would have slaked her thirst in the cool stream, but the rustics forbade her. "Why do you refuse me water?" said she; "water is free to all. Nature allows no one to claim as property the sunshine, the air, or the water. I come to take my share of the common blessing. Yet I ask it of you as a favour. I have no intention of washing my limbs in it, weary though they be, but only to quench my thirst. My mouth is so dry that I can hardly speak. A draught of water would be nectar to me; it would revive me, and I would own myself indebted to you for life itself. Let these infants move your pity, who stretch out their little arms as if to plead for me;" and the children, as it happened, were stretching out their arms.

" 'Who would not have been moved with these gentle words of the goddess? But these clowns persisted in their rudeness; they even added jeers and threats of violence if she did not leave the place. Nor was this all. They waded into the pond and stirred up the mud with their feet, so as to make the water unfit to drink. Latona was so angry that she ceased to mind her thirst. She no longer supplicated the clowns, but lifting her hands to heaven ex-claimed, "May they never quit that pool, but pass their lives there!" And it came to pass accordingly. They now live in the water, sometimes totally submerged, then raising their heads above the surface or swimming upon it. Sometimes they come out upon the bank, but soon leap back again into the water. They still use their base voices in railing, and though they have the water all to them-selves, are not ashamed to croak in the midst of it. Their voices are harsh, their throats bloated, their mouths have become stretched by constant railing, their necks have shrunk up and disappeared, and their heads are joined to their bodies. Their backs are green, their disproportioned bellies white, and in short they are now frogs, and dwell in the slimy pool.' "

This story explains the allusion in one of Milton's sonnets, "On the detraction which followed upon his writing certain treatises."

> "I did but prompt the age to quit their clogs
> By the known laws of ancient liberty,
> When straight a barbarous noise environs me
> Of owls and cuckoos, asses, apes and dogs.
> As when those hinds that were transformed to frogs
> Railed at Latona's twin-born progeny,
> Which after held the sun and moon in fee."

The persecution which Latona experienced from Juno is alluded to in the story. The tradition was that the future mother of Apollo and Diana, flying from the wrath of Juno, besought all the islands of the Ægean to afford her a place of rest, but all feared too much the potent queen of heaven to assist her rival. Delos alone consented to become the birthplace of the future deities. Delos was then a floating island; but when Latona arrived there, Jupiter fastened it with adamantine chains to the bottom of the sea, that it might be a secure resting-place for his beloved. Byron alludes to Delos in his "Don Juan":

> "The isles of Greece! the isles of Greece!
> Where burning Sappho loved and sung,
> Where grew the arts of war and peace,
> Where Delos rose and Phœbus sprung!"

CHAPTER V

PHAËTON

PHAËTON was the son of Apollo and the nymph Clymene. One day a schoolfellow laughed at the idea of his being the son of the god, and Phaëton went in rage and shame and reported it to his mother. "If," said he, "I am indeed of heavenly birth, give me, mother, some proof of it, and establish my claim to the honour." Clymene stretched forth her hands towards the skies, and said, "I call to witness the Sun which looks down upon us, that I have told you the truth. If I speak falsely, let this be the last time I behold his light. But it needs not much labour to go and inquire for yourself; the land whence the Sun rises lies next to ours. Go and demand of him whether he will own you as a son." Phaëton heard with delight. He travelled to India, which lies directly in the regions of sunrise; and, full of hope and pride, approached the goal whence his parent begins his course.

The palace of the Sun stood reared aloft on columns, glittering with gold and precious stones, while polished ivory formed the ceilings, and silver the doors. The workmanship surpassed the material; [1] for upon the walls Vulcan had represented earth, sea, and skies, with their inhabitants. In the sea were the nymphs, some sporting in the waves, some riding on the backs of fishes, while others sat upon the rocks and dried their sea-green hair. Their faces were not all alike, nor yet unlike,—but such as sisters' ought to be.[1] The earth had its towns and forests and rivers and rustic divinities. Over all was carved the likeness of the glorious heaven; and on the silver doors the twelve signs of the zodiac, six on each side.

Clymene's son advanced up the steep ascent, and entered the halls of his disputed father. He approached the paternal presence, but stopped at a distance, for the light was more than he could bear. Phœbus, arrayed in a purple vesture, sat on a throne, which glittered as with diamonds. On his right hand and his left stood the Day, the Month, and the Year, and, at regular intervals, the Hours. Spring stood with her head crowned with flowers, and Summer, with garment cast aside, and a garland formed of spears of ripened grain, and Autumn, with his feet stained with grape-juice, and icy Winter, with his hair stiffened with hoar frost. Surrounded by these attendants, the Sun, with the eye that sees everything, beheld the youth dazzled with the novelty and splendour of the scene, and inquired the purpose of his errand. The youth replied, "O light of the boundless world, Phœbus, my father,—if you permit me to use that name,—give me some proof, I beseech you, by which I may be known as yours." He ceased; and his father, laying aside the beams that shone all around his head, bade him approach, and embracing him, said, "My son, you deserve not to be disowned, and I confirm what your mother has told you. To put an end to your doubts, ask what you will, the gift shall be yours. I call to witness that dreadful lake, which I never saw, but which we gods swear by in our most solemn engagements." Phaëton immediately asked to be permitted for one day to drive the chariot of the sun. The father repented of his promise; thrice and four times he shook his radiant head in warning. "I have spoken rashly," said he; "this only request I would fain deny. I beg you to withdraw it. It is not a safe boon, nor one, my Phaëton, suited to your youth and strength. Your lot is mortal, and you ask what is beyond a mortal's power. In your ignorance you aspire to do that which not even the gods themselves may do. None but myself may drive the flaming car of

[1] See Proverbial Expressions, page 289.

day. Not even Jupiter, whose terrible right arm hurls the thunder-bolts. The first part of the way is steep, and such as the horses when fresh in the morning can hardly climb; the middle is high up in the heavens, whence I myself can scarcely, without alarm, look down and behold the earth and sea stretched beneath me. The last part of the road descends rapidly, and requires most careful driving. Tethys, who is waiting to receive me, often trembles for me lest I should fall headlong. Add to all this, the heaven is all the time turning round and carrying the stars with it. I have to be per-petually on my guard lest that movement, which sweeps everything else along, should hurry me also away. Suppose I should lend you the chariot, what would you do? Could you keep your course while the sphere was revolving under you? Perhaps you think that there are forests and cities, the abodes of gods, and palaces and temples on the way. On the contrary, the road is through the midst of fright-ful monsters. You pass by the horns of the Bull, in front of the Archer, and near the Lion's jaws, and where the Scorpion stretches its arms in one direction and the Crab in another. Nor will you find it easy to guide those horses, with their breasts full of fire that they breathe forth from their mouths and nostrils. I can scarcely govern them myself, when they are unruly and resist the reins. Beware, my son, lest I be the donor of a fatal gift; recall your request while yet you may. Do you ask me for a proof that you are sprung from my blood? I give you a proof in my fears for you. Look at my face— I would that you could look into my breast, you would there see all a father's anxiety. Finally," he continued, "look round the world and choose whatever you will of what earth or sea contains most precious—ask it and fear no refusal. This only I pray you not to urge. It is not honour, but destruction you seek. Why do you hang round my neck and still entreat me? You shall have it if you persist, —the oath is sworn and must be kept,—but I beg you to choose more wisely."

He ended; but the youth rejected all admonition and held to his demand. So, having resisted as long as he could, Phœbus at last led the way to where stood the lofty chariot.

It was of gold, the gift of Vulcan; the axle was of gold, the pole and wheels of gold, the spokes of silver. Along the seat were rows of chrysolites and diamonds which reflected all around the bright-ness of the sun. While the daring youth gazed in admiration, the early Dawn threw open the purple doors of the east, and showed the pathway strewn with roses. The stars withdrew, marshalled by the Day-star, which last of all retired also. The father, when he saw the earth beginning to glow, and the Moon preparing to retire, ordered the Hours to harness up the horses. They obeyed, and led

forth from the lofty stalls the steeds full fed with ambrosia, and
attached the reins. Then the father bathed the face of his son with
a powerful unguent, and made him capable of enduring the brightness of the flame. He set the rays on his head, and, with a foreboding sigh, said, "If, my son, you will in this at least heed my advice,
spare the whip and hold tight the reins. They go fast enough of their
own accord; the labour is to hold them in. You are not to take the
straight road directly between the five circles, but turn off to the
left. Keep within the limit of the middle zone, and avoid the northern
and the southern alike. You will see the marks of the wheels, and
they will serve to guide you. And, that the skies and the earth may
each receive their due share of heat, go not too high, or you will
burn the heavenly dwellings, nor too low, or you will set the earth
on fire; the middle course is safest and best.[1] And now I leave you
to your chance, which I hope will plan better for you than you have
done for yourself. Night is passing out of the western gates and we
can delay no longer. Take the reins; but if at last your heart fails
you, and you will benefit by my advice, stay where you are in
safety, and suffer me to light and warm the earth." The agile youth
sprang into the chariot, stood erect, and grasped the reins with
delight, pouring out thanks to his reluctant parent.

Meanwhile the horses fill the air with their snortings and fiery
breath, and stamp the ground impatient. Now the bars are let down,
and the boundless plain of the universe lies open before them. They
dart forward and cleave the opposing clouds, and outrun the morning breezes which started from the same eastern goal. The steeds
soon perceived that the load they drew was lighter than usual;
and as a ship without ballast is tossed hither and thither on the sea,
so the chariot, without its accustomed weight, was dashed about as
if empty. They rush headlong and leave the travelled road. He is
alarmed, and knows not how to guide them; nor, if he knew, has
he the power. Then, for the first time, the Great and Little Bear were
scorched with heat, and would fain, if it were possible, have plunged
into the water; and the Serpent which lies coiled up round the north
pole, torpid and harmless, grew warm, and with warmth felt its rage
revive. Boötes, they say, fled away, though encumbered with his
plough, and all unused to rapid motion.

When hapless Phaëton looked down upon the earth, now spreading in vast extent beneath him, he grew pale and his knees shook
with terror. In spite of the glare all around him, the sight of his
eyes grew dim. He wished he had never touched his father's horses,
never learned his parentage, never prevailed in his request. He is
borne along like a vessel that flies before a tempest, when the

[1] See Proverbial Expressions, page 280

pilot can do no more and betakes himself to his prayers. What shall he do? Much of the heavenly road is left behind, but more remains before. He turns his eyes from one direction to the other; now to the goal whence he began his course, now to the realms of sunset which he is not destined to reach. He loses his self-command, and knows not what to do,—whether to draw tight the reins or throw them loose; he forgets the names of the horses. He sees with terror the monstrous forms scattered over the surface of heaven. Here the Scorpion extended his two great arms, with his tail and crooked claws stretching over two signs of the zodiac. When the boy beheld him, reeking with poison and menacing with his fangs, his courage failed, and the reins fell from his hands. The horses, when they felt them loose on their backs, dashed headlong, and unrestrained went off into unknown regions of the sky, in among the stars, hurling the chariot over pathless places, now up in high heaven, now down almost to the earth. The moon saw with astonishment her brother's chariot running beneath her own. The clouds begin to smoke, and the mountain tops take fire; the fields are parched with heat, the plants wither, the trees with their leafy branches burn, the harvest is ablaze! But these are small things. Great cities perished, with their walls and towers; whole nations with their people were consumed to ashes! The forest-clad mountains burned, Athos and Taurus and Tmolus and Œte; Ida, once celebrated for fountains, but now all dry; the Muses' mountain Helicon, and Hæmus; Ætna, with fires within and without, and Parnassus, with his two peaks, and Rhodope, forced at last to part with his snowy crown. Her cold climate was no protection to Scythia, Caucasus burned, and Ossa and Pindus, and, greater than both, Olympus; the Alps high in air, and the Apennines crowned with clouds.

Then Phaëton beheld the world on fire, and felt the heat intolerable. The air he breathed was like the air of a furnace and full of burning ashes, and the smoke was of a pitchy darkness. He dashed forward he knew not whither. Then, it is believed, the people of Æthiopia became black by the blood being forced so suddenly to the surface, and the Libyan desert was dried up to the condition in which it remains to this day. The Nymphs of the fountains, with dishevelled hair, mourned their waters, nor were the rivers safe beneath their banks: Tanais smoked, and Caicus, Xanthus, and Meander; Babylonian Euphrates and Ganges, Tagus with golden sands, and Cayster where the swans resort. Nile fled away and hid his head in the desert, and there it still remains concealed. Where he used to discharge his waters through seven mouths into the sea, there seven dry channels alone remained. The earth cracked open, and through the chinks light broke into Tartarus, and frightened the king of shadows and his queen. The sea shrank up. Where before was water, it became a dry plain; and the mountains that lie beneath the waves lifted up their heads and became islands. The fishes sought the lowest depths, and the dolphins no longer ventured as usual to sport on the surface. Even Nereus, and his wife Doris, with the Nereids, their daughters, sought the deepest caves for refuge. Thrice Neptune essayed to raise his head above the surface, and thrice was driven back by the heat. Earth, surrounded as she was by waters, yet with head and shoulders bare, screening her face with her hand, looked up to heaven, and with a husky voice called on Jupiter:

"O ruler of the gods, if I have deserved this treatment, and it is your will that I perish with fire, why withhold your thunderbolts? Let me at least fall by your hand. Is this the reward of my fertility, of my obedient service? Is it for this that I have supplied herbage for cattle, and fruits for men, and frankincense for your altars? But if I am unworthy of regard, what has my brother Ocean done to deserve such a fate? If neither of us can excite your pity, think, I pray you, of your own heaven, and behold how both the poles are smoking which sustain your palace, which must fall if they be destroyed. Atlas faints, and scarce holds up his burden. If sea, earth, and heaven perish, we fall into ancient Chaos. Save what yet remains to us from the devouring flame. O, take thought for our deliverance in this awful moment!"

Thus spoke Earth, and overcome with heat and thirst, could say no more. Then Jupiter omnipotent, calling to witness all the gods, including him who had lent the chariot, and showing them that all was lost unless some speedy remedy were applied, mounted the lofty tower from whence he diffuses clouds over the earth, and hurls the forked lightnings. But at that time not a cloud was to be found to interpose for a screen to earth, nor was a shower remaining unexhausted. He thundered, and brandishing a lightning bolt in his right hand launched it against the charioteer, and struck him at the same moment from his seat and from existence! Phaëton, with his hair on fire, fell headlong, like a shooting star which marks the heavens with its brightness as it falls, and Eridanus, the great river, received him and cooled his burning frame.[1] The Italian Naiads reared a tomb for him, and inscribed these words upon the stone:

> "Driver of Phœbus' chariot, Phaëton,
> Struck by Jove's thunder, rests beneath this stone.
> He could not rule his father's car of fire,
> Yet was it much so nobly to aspire."

[1] See Proverbial Expressions, page 289.

His sisters, the Heliades, as they lamented his fate, were turned into poplar trees, on the banks of the river, and their tears, which continued to flow, became amber as they dropped into the stream.

Milman, in his poem of "Samor," makes the following allusion to Phaëton's story:

"As when the palsied universe aghast
Lay ... mute and still,
When drove, so poets sing, the Sun-born youth
Devious through Heaven's affrighted signs his sire's
Ill-granted chariot. Him the Thunderer hurled
From th' empyrean headlong to the gulf
Of the half-parched Eridanus, where weep
Even now the sister trees their amber tears
O'er Phaëton untimely dead."

In the beautiful lines of Walter Savage Landor, descriptive of the Sea-shell, there is an allusion to the Sun's palace and chariot. The water-nymph says:

"...I have sinuous shells of pearly hue
Within, and things that lustre have imbibed
In the sun's palace porch, where when unyoked
His chariot wheel stands midway on the wave.
Shake one and it awakens; then apply
Its polished lip to your attentive ear,
And it remembers its august abodes,
And murmurs as the ocean murmurs there."

Gebir, Book I.

CHAPTER VI

MIDAS—BAUCIS AND PHILEMON

BACCHUS, on a certain occasion, found his old schoolmaster and foster-father, Silenus, missing. The old man had been drinking, and in that state wandered away, and was found by some peasants, who carried him to their king, Midas. Midas recognized him, and treated him hospitably, entertaining him for ten days and nights with an unceasing round of jollity. On the eleventh day he brought Silenus back, and restored him in safety to his pupil. Whereupon Bacchus offered Midas his choice of a reward, whatever he might wish. He asked that whatever he might touch should be changed into *gold*. Bacchus consented, though sorry that he had not made a better choice. Midas went his way, rejoicing in his new-acquired power, which he hastened to put to the test. He could scarce believe his eyes when he found a twig of an oak, which he plucked from the branch, become gold in his hand. He took up a stone; it changed to gold. He touched a sod; it did the same. He took an apple from the tree; you would have thought he had robbed

the garden of the Hesperides. His joy knew no bounds, and as soon
as he got home, he ordered the servants to set a splendid repast
on the table. Then he found to his dismay that whether he touched
bread, it hardened in his hand; or put a morsel to his lip, it defied
his teeth. He took a glass of wine, but it flowed down his throat
like melted gold.

In consternation at the unprecedented affliction, he strove to divest
himself of his power; he hated the gift he had lately coveted. But
all in vain; starvation seemed to await him. He raised his arms,
all shining with gold, in prayer to Bacchus, begging to be delivered
from his glittering destruction. Bacchus, merciful deity, heard and
consented. "Go," said he, "to the River Pactolus, trace the stream
to its fountain-head, there plunge your head and body in, and wash
away your fault and its punishment." He did so, and scarce had
he touched the waters before the gold-creating power passed into
them, and the river sands became changed into *gold*, as they remain to this day.

Thenceforth Midas, hating wealth and splendour, dwelt in the
country, and became a worshipper of Pan, the god of the fields. On
a certain occasion Pan had the temerity to compare his music with
that of Apollo, and to challenge the god of the lyre to a trial of
skill. The challenge was accepted, and Tmolus, the mountain god,
was chosen umpire. The senior took his seat, and cleared away the
trees from his ears to listen. At a given signal Pan blew on his pipes,
and with his rustic melody gave great satisfaction to himself and
his faithful follower Midas, who happened to be present. Then
Tmolus turned his head toward the Sun-god, and all his trees
turned with him. Apollo rose, his brow wreathed with Parnassian
laurel, while his robe of Tyrian purple swept the ground. In his
left hand he held the lyre, and with his right hand struck the strings.
Ravished with the harmony, Tmolus at once awarded the victory
to the god of the lyre, and all but Midas acquiesced in the judgment.
He dissented, and questioned the justice of the award. Apollo
would not suffer such a depraved pair of ears any longer to wear
the human form, but caused them to increase in length, grow hairy,
within and without, and movable on their roots; in short, to be on
the perfect pattern of those of an ass.

Mortified enough was King Midas at this mishap; but he consoled himself with the thought that it was possible to hide his
misfortune, which he attempted to do by means of an ample turban
or head-dress. But his hair-dresser of course knew the secret. He
was charged not to mention it, and threatened with dire punishment if he presumed to disobey. But he found it too much for his
discretion to keep such a secret; so he went out into the meadow,

dug a hole in the ground, and stooping down, whispered the story, and covered it up. Before long a thick bed of reeds sprang up in the meadow and as soon as it had gained its growth, began whispering the story, and has continued to do so, from that day to this, every time a breeze passes over the place.

The story of King Midas has been told by others with some variations. Dryden, in the "Wife of Bath's Tale," makes Midas's queen the betrayer of the secret:

> "This Midas knew, and durst communicate
> To none but to his wife his ears of state."

Midas was king of Phrygia. He was the son of Gordius, a poor countryman, who was taken by the people and made king, in obedience to the command of the oracle, which had said that their future king should come in a wagon. While the people were deliberating, Gordius with his wife and son came driving his wagon into the public square.

Gordius, being made king, dedicated his wagon to the deity of the oracle, and tied it up in its place with a fast knot. This was the celebrated *Gordian knot*, which, in after times it was said, whoever should untie should become lord of all Asia. Many tried to untie it, but none succeeded, till Alexander the Great, in his career of conquest, came to Phrygia. He tried his skill with as ill success as others, till growing impatient he drew his sword and cut the knot. When he afterwards succeeded in subjecting all Asia to his sway, people began to think that he had complied with the terms of the oracle according to its true meaning.

BAUCIS AND PHILEMON

On a certain hill in Phrygia stands a linden tree and an oak, enclosed by a low wall. Not far from the spot is a marsh, formerly good habitable land, but now indented with pools, the resort of fen-birds and cormorants. Once on a time Jupiter, in human shape, visited this country, and with him his son Mercury (he of the caduceus), without his wings. They presented themselves, as weary travellers, at many a door, seeking rest and shelter, but found all closed, for it was late, and the inhospitable inhabitants would not rouse themselves to open for their reception. At last a humble mansion received them, a small thatched cottage, where Baucis, a pious old dame, and her husband Philemon, united when young, had grown old together. Not ashamed of their poverty, they made it endurable by moderate desires and kind dispositions. One need not look there for master or for servant; they two were the whole household, master and servant alike. When the two heavenly guests crossed the humble threshold, and bowed their heads to pass under the low door, the old man placed a seat, on which Baucis, bustling and attentive, spread a cloth, and begged them to sit down. Then she raked out the coals from the ashes, and kindled up a fire, fed it with leaves and dry bark, and with her scanty breath blew it into a flame. She brought out of a corner split sticks and dry branches, broke them up, and placed them under the small kettle. Her husband collected some pot-herbs in the garden, and she shred them from the stalks, and prepared them for the pot. He reached down with a forked stick a flitch of bacon hanging in the chimney, cut a small piece, and put it in the pot to boil with the herbs, setting away the rest for another time. A beechen bowl was filled with warm water, that their guests might wash. While all was doing, they beguiled the time with conversation.

On the bench designed for the guests was laid a cushion stuffed with sea-weed; and a cloth, only produced on great occasions, but ancient and coarse enough, was spread over that. The old lady, with her apron on, with trembling hand set the table. One leg was shorter than the rest, but a piece of slate put under restored the level. When fixed, she rubbed the table down with some sweet-smelling herbs. Upon it she set some of chaste Minerva's olives, some cornel berries preserved in vinegar, and added radishes and cheese, with eggs lightly cooked in the ashes. All were served in earthen dishes, and an earthenware pitcher, with wooden cups, stood beside them. When all was ready, the stew, smoking hot, was set on the table. Some wine, not of the oldest, was added; and for dessert, apples and wild honey; and over and above all, friendly faces, and simple but hearty welcome.

Now while the repast proceeded, the old folks were astonished to see that the wine, as fast as it was poured out, renewed itself in the pitcher, of its own accord. Struck with terror, Baucis and Philemon recognized their heavenly guests, fell on their knees, and with clasped hands implored forgiveness for their poor entertainment. There was an old goose, which they kept as the guardian of their humble cottage; and they bethought them to make this a sacrifice in honour of their guests. But the goose, too nimble, with the aid of feet and wings, for the old folks, eluded their pursuit, and at last took shelter between the gods themselves. They forbade it to be slain; and spoke in these words: "We are gods. This inhospitable village shall pay the penalty of its impiety; you alone shall go free from the chastisement. Quit your house, and come with us to the top of yonder hill." They hastened to obey, and, staff in hand, laboured up the steep ascent. They had reached to within an arrow's flight of the top, when, turning their eyes below, they beheld all the country sunk in a lake, only their own house left standing. While they gazed with wonder at the sight, and lamented the fate of their neighbours, that old house of theirs was changed into a *temple*. Columns took the place of the corner posts, the thatch grew yellow and appeared a gilded roof, the floors became marble, the doors were enriched with carving and ornaments of gold. Then spoke Jupiter in benignant accents: "Excellent old man, and woman worthy of such a husband, speak, tell us your wishes; what favour have you to ask of us?" Philemon took counsel with Baucis a few moments; then declared to the gods their united wish. "We ask to be priests and guardians of this your temple; and since here we have passed our lives in love and concord, we wish that one and the same hour may take us both from life, that I may not live to see her grave, nor be laid in my own by her." Their prayer was granted. They were the keepers of the temple as long as they lived. When grown very old, as they stood one day before the steps of the sacred edifice, and were telling the story of the place, Baucis saw Philemon begin to put forth leaves, and old Philemon saw Baucis changing in like manner. And now a leafy crown had grown over their heads, while exchanging parting words, as long as they could speak. "Farewell, dear spouse," they said, together, and at the same moment the bark closed over their mouths. The Tyanean shepherd still shows the two trees, standing side by side, made out of the two good old people.

The story of Baucis and Philemon has been imitated by Swift, in a burlesque style, the actors in the change being two wandering saints, and the house being changed into a church, of which Philemon is made the parson. The following may serve as a specimen:

> "They scarce had spoke, when, fair and soft,
> The root began to mount aloft;
> Aloft rose every beam and rafter;
> The heavy wall climbed slowly after.
> The chimney widened and grew higher,
> Became a steeple with a spire.
> The kettle to the top was hoist,
> And there stood fastened to a joist,
> But with the upside down, to show
> Its inclination for below;
> In vain, for a superior force,
> Applied at bottom, stops its course;
> Doomed ever in suspense to dwell,
> 'Tis now no kettle, but a bell.
> A wooden jack, which had almost
> Lost by disuse the art to roast,
> A sudden alteration feels.
> Increased by new intestine wheels:

And, what exalts the wonder more,
The number made the motion slower;
The flier, though 't had leaden feet,
Turned round so quick you scarce could see 't;
But slackened by some secret power,
Now hardly moves an inch an hour.
The jack and chimney, near allied,
Had never left each other's side:
The chimney to a steeple grown,
The jack would not be left alone;
But up against the steeple reared,
Became a clock, and still adhered;
And still its love to household cares
By a shrill voice at noon declares,
Warning the cook-maid not to burn
That roast meat which it cannot turn.
The groaning chair began to crawl,
Like a huge snail, along the wall;
There stuck aloft in public view,
And with small change, a pulpit grew.
A bedstead of the antique mode,
Compact of timber many a load,
Such as our ancestors did use,
Was metamorphosed into pews,
Which still their ancient nature keep
By lodging folks disposed to sleep."

CHAPTER VII

PROSERPINE—GLAUCUS AND SCYLLA

WHEN Jupiter and his brothers had defeated the Titans and banished them to Tartarus, a new enemy rose up against the gods. They were the giants Typhon, Briareus, Enceladus, and others. Some of them had a hundred arms, others breathed out fire. They were finally subdued and buried alive under Mount Ætna, where they still sometimes struggle to get loose, and shake the whole island with earthquakes. Their breath comes up through the mountain, and is what men call the eruption of the volcano.

The fall of these monsters shook the earth, so that Pluto was alarmed, and feared that his kingdom would be laid open to the light of day. Under this apprehension, he mounted his chariot. drawn by black horses, and took a circuit of inspection to satisfy himself of the extent of the damage. While he was thus engaged, Venus, who was sitting on Mount Eryx playing with her boy Cupid, espied him, and said, "My son, take your darts with which you conquer all, even Jove himself, and send one into the breast of yonder dark monarch, who rules the realm of Tartarus. Why should he alone escape? Seize the opportunity to extend your empire and mine. Do you not see that even in heaven some despise our power? Minerva the wise, and Diana the huntress, defy us; and there is that daughter of Ceres, who threatens to follow their example. Now do you, if you have any regard for your own interest or mine, join these two in one." The boy unbound his quiver, and selected his sharpest and truest arrow; then straining the bow against his knee, he attached the string, and, having made ready, shot the arrow with its barbed point right into the heart of Pluto.

In the vale of Enna there is a lake embowered in woods, which screen it from the fervid rays of the sun, while the moist ground is covered with flowers, and Spring reigns perpetual. Here Proserpine was playing with her companions, gathering lilies and violets, and filling her basket and her apron with them, when Pluto saw her, loved her, and carried her off. She screamed for help to her mother and companions; and when in her fright she dropped the corners of her apron and let the flowers fall, childlike she felt the loss of them as an addition to her grief. The ravisher urged on his steeds, calling them each by name, and throwing loose over their heads and necks his iron-coloured reins. When he reached the River Cyane, and it opposed his passage, he struck the river-bank with his trident, and the earth opened and gave him a passage to Tartarus.

Ceres sought her daughter all the world over. Bright-haired Aurora, when she came forth in the morning, and Hesperus when he led out the stars in the evening, found her still busy in the search. But it was all unavailing. At length, weary and sad, she sat down upon a stone, and continued sitting nine days and nights, in the open air, under the sunlight and moonlight and falling showers. It was where now stands the city of Eleusis, then the home of an old man named Celeus. He was out on the field, gathering acorns and blackberries, and sticks for his fire. His little girl was driving home their two goats, and as she passed the goddess, who appeared in the guise of an old woman, she said to her, "Mother,"—and the name was sweet to the ears of Ceres,—"why do you sit here alone upon the rocks?" The old man also stopped, though his load was heavy, and begged her to come into his cottage, such as it was. She declined, and he urged her. "Go in peace," she replied, "and be happy in your daughter; I have lost mine." As she spoke, tears —or something like tears, for the gods never weep—fell down her cheeks upon her bosom. The compassionate old man and his child wept with her. Then said he, "Come with us, and despise not our humble roof; so may your daughter be restored to you in safety." "Lead on," said she, "I cannot resist that appeal!" So she rose from the stone and went with them. As they walked he told her that his only son, a little boy, lay very sick, feverish, and sleepless. She stooped and gathered some poppies. As they entered the cottage, they found all in great distress, for the boy seemed past hope of recovery. Metanira, his mother, received her kindly, and the goddess stooped and kissed the lips of the sick child. Instantly the paleness left his face, and healthy vigour returned to his body. The whole family were delighted—that is, the father, mother, and little girl, for they were all; they had no servants. They spread the table, and put upon it curds and cream, apples, and honey in the comb. While they ate, Ceres mingled poppy juice in the milk of the boy. When night came and all was still, she arose, and taking the sleeping boy, moulded his limbs with her hands, and uttered over him three times a solemn charm, then went and laid him in the ashes. His mother, who had been watching what her guest was doing, sprang forward with a cry and snatched the child from the fire. Then Ceres assumed her own form, and a divine splendour shone all around. While they were overcome with astonishment, she said, "Mother, you have been cruel in your fondness to your son. I would have made him immortal, but you have frustrated my attempt. Nevertheless, he shall be great and useful. He shall teach men the use of the plough, and the rewards which labour can win from the cultivated soil." So saying, she wrapped a cloud about her, and mounting her chariot rode away.

Ceres continued her search for her daughter, passing from land to land, and across seas and rivers, till at length she returned to Sicily, whence she at first set out, and stood by the banks of the River Cyane, where Pluto made himself a passage with his prize to his own dominions. The river nymph would have told the goddess all she had witnessed, but dared not, for fear of Pluto; so she only ventured to take up the girdle which Proserpine had dropped in her flight, and waft it to the feet of the mother. Ceres, seeing this, was no longer in doubt of her loss, but she did not yet know the cause, and laid the blame on the innocent land. "Ungrateful soil," said she, "which I have endowed with fertility and clothed with herbage and nourishing grain, no more shall you enjoy my favours." Then the cattle died, the plough broke in the furrow, the seed failed to come up; there was too much sun, there was too much rain; the birds stole the seeds—thistles and brambles were the only growth. Seeing this, the fountain Arethusa interceded for the land. "Goddess," said she, "blame not the land; it opened unwillingly to yield a passage to your daughter. I can tell you of her fate, for I have seen her. This is not my native country; I came hither from Elis. I was a woodland nymph, and delighted in the chase. They praised my beauty, but I cared nothing for it, and rather boasted of my hunting exploits. One day I was returning from the wood, heated with exercise, when I came to a stream silently flowing, so clear that you might count the pebbles on the bottom. The willows shaded it, and the grassy bank sloped down to the water's edge. I approached, I touched the water with my foot. I stepped in knee-deep, and not content with that, I laid my garments on the willows and went in. While I sported in the water, I heard an indistinct murmur coming up as out of the depths of the stream; and made haste to escape to the nearest bank. The voice said, 'Why do you fly, Arethusa? I am Alpheus, the god of this stream.' I ran, he pursued; he was not more swift than I, but he was stronger, and gained upon me, as my strength failed. At last, exhausted, I cried for help to Diana. 'Help me, goddess! help your votary!' The goddess heard, and wrapped me suddenly in a thick cloud. The river god looked now this way and now that, and twice came close to me, but could not find me. 'Arethusa! Arethusa!' he cried. Oh, how I trembled,—like a lamb that hears the wolf growling outside the fold. A cold sweat came over me, my hair flowed down in streams; where my foot stood there was a pool. In short, in less time than it takes to tell it, I became a fountain. But in this form Alpheus knew me and attempted to mingle his stream with mine. Diana cleft the ground, and I, endeavouring to escape him, plunged into the cavern, and through the bowels of the earth came out here in Sicily. While I passed through the lower parts of the earth, I saw your Proserpine. She was sad, but no longer showing alarm in her countenance. Her look was such as became a queen—the queen of Erebus; the powerful bride of the monarch of the realms of the dead."

When Ceres heard this, she stood for a while like one stupefied; then turned her chariot towards heaven, and hastened to present herself before the throne of Jove. She told the story of her bereavement, and implored Jupiter to interfere to procure the restitution of her daughter. Jupiter consented on one condition, namely, that Proserpine should not during her stay in the lower world have taken any food; otherwise, the Fates forbade her release. Accordingly, Mercury was sent, accompanied by Spring, to demand Proserpine of Pluto. The wily monarch consented; but, alas! the maiden had taken a pomegranate which Pluto offered her, and had sucked the sweet pulp from a few of the seeds. This was enough to prevent her complete release; but a compromise was made, by which she was to pass half the time with her mother, and the rest with her husband Pluto.

Ceres allowed herself to be pacified with this arrangement, and restored the earth to her favour. Now she remembered Celeus and his family, and her promise to his infant son Triptolemus. When the boy grew up, she taught him the use of the plough, and how to sow the seed. She took him in her chariot, drawn by winged dragons, through all the countries of the earth, imparting to mankind valuable grains, and the knowledge of agriculture. After his return, Triptolemus built a magnificent temple to Ceres in Eleusis, and established the worship of the goddess, under the name of the Eleusinian mysteries, which, in the splendour and solemnity of their observance, surpassed all other religious celebrations among the Greeks.

There can be little doubt of this story of Ceres and Proserpine being an allegory. Proserpine signifies the seed-corn which when cast into the ground lies there concealed—that is, she is carried off by the god of the underworld. It reappears—that is, Proserpine is restored to her mother. Spring leads her back to the light of day.

Milton alludes to the story of Proserpine in "Paradise Lost," Book IV.:

> "...Not that fair field
> Of Enna where Proserpine gathering flowers,
> Herself a fairer flower, by gloomy Dis
> Was gathered, which cost Ceres all that pain
> To seek her through the world,—
> ...might with this Paradise
> Of Eden strive."

Hood, in his "Ode to Melancholy," uses the same allusion very beautifully:

> "Forgive, if somewhile I forget,
> In woe to come the present bliss;
> As frighted Proserpine let fall
> Her flowers at the sight of Dis."

The River Alpheus does in fact disappear underground, in part of its course, finding its way through subterranean channels till it again appears on the surface. It was said that the Sicilian fountain Arethusa was the same stream, which, after passing under the sea, came up again in Sicily. Hence the story ran that a cup thrown into the Alpheus appeared again in Arethusa. It is this fable of the underground course of Alpheus that Coleridge alludes to in his poem of "Kubla Khan":

> "In Xanadu did Kubla Khan
> A stately pleasure-dome decree,
> Where Alph, the sacred river, ran
> Through caverns measureless to man,
> Down to a sunless sea."

In one of Moore's juvenile poems he thus alludes to the same story, and to the practice of throwing garlands or other light objects on his stream to be carried downward by it, and afterwards reproduced at its emerging:

"O my beloved, how divinely sweet
Is the pure joy when kindred spirits meet!
Like him the river god, whose waters flow,
With love their only light, through caves below,
Wafting in triumph all the flowery braids
And festal rings, with which Olympic maids
Have decked his current, as an offering meet
To lay at Arethusa's shining feet.
Think, when he meets at last his fountain bride,
What perfect love must thrill the blended tide!
Each lost in each, till mingling into one,
Their lot the same for shadow or for sun,
A type of true love, to the deep they run."

The following extract from Moore's "Rhymes on the Road" gives an account of a celebrated picture by Albano, at Milan, called a Dance of Loves:

" 'Tis for the theft of Enna's flower from earth
These urchins celebrate their dance of mirth,
    Round the green tree, like fays upon a heath;—
    Those that are nearest linked in order bright,
Cheek after cheek, like rosebuds in a wreath;
And those more distant showing from beneath
    The others' wings their little eyes of light.
While see! among the clouds, their eldest brother,
    But just flown up, tells with a smile of bliss,
This prank of Pluto to his charmed mother,
    Who turns to greet the tidings with a kiss."

GLAUCUS AND SCYLLA

Glaucus was a fisherman. One day he had drawn his nets to land, and had taken a great many fishes of various kinds. So he emptied his net, and proceeded to sort the fishes on the grass. The place where he stood was a beautiful island in the river, a solitary spot, uninhabited, and not used for pasturage of cattle, not ever visited by any but himself. On a sudden, the fishes, which had been laid on the grass, began to revive and move their fins as if they were in the water; and while he looked on astonished, they one and all moved off to the water, plunged in, and swam away. He did not know what to make of this, whether some god had done it or some secret power in the herbage. "What herb has such a power?" he exclaimed; and gathering some of it, he tasted it. Scarce had the juices of the plant reached his palate when he found himself agitated with a longing desire for the water. He could no longer restrain himself, but bidding farewell to earth, he plunged into the stream. The gods of the water received him graciously, and admitted him to the honour of their society. They obtained the consent of Oceanus and Tethys, the sovereigns of the sea, that all that was

mortal in him should be washed away. A hundred rivers poured
their waters over him. Then he lost all sense of his former nature
and all consciousness. When he recovered, he found himself changed
in form and mind. His hair was sea-green, and trailed behind him
on the water; his shoulders grew broad, and what had been thighs
and legs assumed the form of a fish's tail. The sea-gods compli-
mented him on the change of his appearance, and he fancied himself
rather a good-looking personage.

One day Glaucus saw the beautiful maiden Scylla, the favourite
of the water-nymphs, rambling on the shore, and when she had
found a sheltered nook, laving her limbs in the clear water. He
fell in love with her, and showing himself on the surface, spoke to
her, saying such things as he thought most likely to win her to stay;
for she turned to run immediately on the sight of him, and ran till
she had gained a cliff overlooking the sea. Here she stopped and
turned round to see whether it was a god or a sea animal, and
observed with wonder his shape and colour. Glaucus partly emerging from the water, and supporting himself against a rock, said,
"Maiden, I am no monster, nor a sea animal, but a god; and neither
Proteus nor Triton ranks higher than I. Once I was a mortal, and
followed the sea for a living; but now I belong wholly to it." Then
he told the story of his metamorphosis, and how he had been promoted to his present dignity, and added, "But what avails all this
if it fails to move your heart?" He was going on in this strain, but
Scylla turned and hastened away.

Glaucus was in despair, but it occurred to him to consult the enchantress Circe. Accordingly he repaired to her island—the same
where afterwards Ulysses landed, as we shall see in one of our
later stories. After mutual salutations, he said, "Goddess, I entreat
your pity; you alone can relieve the pain I suffer. The power of
herbs I know as well as any one, for it is to them I owe my change
of form. I love Scylla. I am ashamed to tell you how I have sued
and promised to her, and how scornfully she has treated me. I beseech you to use your incantations, or potent herbs, if they are
more prevailing, not to cure me of my love,—for that I do not
wish,—but to make her share it and yield me a like return." To
which Circe replied, for she was not insensible to the attractions of
the sea-green deity, "You had better pursue a willing object; you
are worthy to be sought, instead of having to seek in vain. Be not
diffident, know your own worth. I protest to you that even I, goddess though I be, and learned in the virtues of plants and spells,
should not know how to refuse you. If she scorns you scorn her;
meet one who is ready to meet you half way, and thus make a due
return to both at once." To these words Glaucus replied, "Sooner

shall trees grow at the bottom of the ocean, and sea-weed on the top of the mountains, than I will cease to love Scylla, and her alone."

The goddess was indignant, but she could not punish him, neither did she wish to do so, for she liked him too well; so she turned all her wrath against her rival, poor Scylla. She took plants of poisonous powers and mixed them together, with incantations and charms. Then she passed through the crowd of gambolling beasts, the victims of her art, and proceeded to the coast of Sicily, where Scylla lived. There was a little bay on the shore to which Scylla used to resort, in the heat of the day, to breathe the air of the sea, and to bathe in its waters. Here the goddess poured her poisonous mixture, and muttered over it incantations of mighty power. Scylla came as usual and plunged into the water up to her waist. What was her horror to perceive a brood of serpents and barking monsters surrounding her! At first she could not imagine they were a part of herself, and tried to run from them, and to drive them away; but as she ran she carried them with her, and when she tried to touch her limbs, she found her hands touch only the yawning jaws of monsters. Scylla remained rooted to the spot. Her temper grew as ugly as her form, and she took pleasure in devouring hapless mariners who came within her grasp. Thus she destroyed six of the companions of Ulysses, and tried to wreck the ships of Æneas, till at last she was turned into a rock, and as such still continues to be a terror to mariners.

Keats, in his "Endymion," has given a new version of the ending of "Glaucus and Scylla." Glaucus consents to Circe's blandishments, till he by chance is witness to her transactions with her beasts.[1] Disgusted with her treachery and cruelty, he tries to escape from her, but is taken and brought back, when with reproaches she banishes him, sentencing him to pass a thousand years in decrepitude and pain. He returns to the sea, and there finds the body of Scylla, whom the goddess has not transformed but drowned. Glaucus learns that his destiny is that, if he passes his thousand years in collecting all the bodies of drowned lovers, a youth beloved of the gods will appear and help him. Endymion fulfils this prophecy, and aids in restoring Glaucus to youth, and Scylla and all the drowned lovers to life.

The following is Glaucus's account of his feelings after his "sea-change":

> "I plunged for life or death. To interknit
> One's senses with so dense a breathing stuff
> Might seem a work of pain; so not enough
> Can I admire how crystal-smooth it felt,

[1] See page 209.

And buoyant round my limbs. At first I dwelt
Whole days and days in sheer astonishment;
Forgetful utterly of self-intent,
Moving but with the mighty ebb and flow.
Then like a new-fledged bird that first doth show
His spreaded feathers to the morrow chill,
I tried in fear the pinions of my will.
'Twas freedom! and at once I visited
The ceaseless wonders of this ocean-bed," etc.—*Keats*.

CHAPTER VIII

PYGMALION—DRYOPE—VENUS AND ADONIS—APOLLO AND HYACINTHUS

PYGMALION saw so much to blame in women that he came at last to abhor the sex, and resolved to live unmarried. He was a sculptor, and had made with wonderful skill a statue of ivory, so beautiful that no living woman came anywhere near it. It was indeed the perfect semblance of a maiden that seemed to be alive, and only prevented from moving by modesty. His art was so perfect that it concealed itself and its product looked like the workmanship of nature. Pygmalion admired his own work, and at last fell in love with the counterfeit creation. Oftentimes he laid his hand upon it as if to assure himself whether it were living or not, and could not even then believe that it was only ivory. He caressed it, and gave it presents such as young girls love,—bright shells and polished stones, little birds and flowers of various hues, beads and amber. He put raiment on its limbs, and jewels on its fingers, and a necklace about its neck. To the ears he hung earrings, and strings of pearls upon the breast. Her dress became her, and she looked not less charming than when unattired. He laid her on a couch spread with cloths of Tyrian dye, and called her his wife, and put her head upon a pillow of the softest feathers, as if she could enjoy their softness.

The festival of Venus was at hand—a festival celebrated with great pomp at Cyprus. Victims were offered, the altars smoked, and the odour of incense filled the air. When Pygmalion had performed his part in the solemnities, he stood before the altar and timidly said, "Ye gods, who can do all things, give me, I pray you, for my wife"—he dared not say "my ivory virgin," but said instead—"one like my ivory virgin." Venus, who was present at the festival, heard him and knew the thought he would have uttered; and as an omen of her favour, caused the flame on the altar to shoot up thrice in a fiery point into the air. When he returned home, he went to see his statue, and leaning over the couch, gave a kiss to the mouth. It seemed to be warm. He pressed its lips again, he laid his hand upon the limbs; the ivory felt soft to his touch and yielded to his fingers like the wax of Hymettus. While he stands astonished and glad, though doubting, and fears he may be mistaken, again and again with a lover's ardour he touches the object of his hopes. It was indeed alive! The veins when pressed yielded to the finger and again resumed their roundness. Then at last the votary of Venus found words to thank the goddess, and pressed his lips upon lips as real as his own. The virgin felt the kisses and blushed, and opening her timid eyes to the light, fixed them at the same moment on her lover. Venus blessed the nuptials she had formed, and from this union Paphos was born, from whom the city, sacred to Venus, received its name.

Schiller, in his poem the "Ideals," applies this tale of Pygmalion to the love of nature in a youthful heart. The following translation is furnished by a friend:

"As once with prayers in passion flowing,
　　Pygmalion embraced the stone,
Till from the frozen marble glowing,
　　The light of feeling o'er him shone,
So did I clasp with young devotion
　　Bright nature to a poet's heart;
Till breath and warmth and vital motion
　　Seemed through the statue form to dart.

"And then, in all my ardour sharing,
　　The silent form expression found;
Returned my kiss of youth daring,
　　And understood my heart's quick sound.
Then lived for me the bright creation,
　　The silver rill with song was rife;
The trees, the roses shared sensation,
　　An echo of my boundless life."—*S. G. B.*

DRYOPE

Dryope and Iole were sisters. The former was the wife of Andræmon, beloved by her husband, and happy in the birth of her first child. One day the sisters strolled to the bank of a stream that sloped gradually down to the water's edge, while the upland was overgrown with myrtles. They were intending to gather flowers for forming garlands for the altars of the nymphs, and Dryope carried her child at her bosom, precious burden, and nursed him as she walked. Near the water grew a lotus plant, full of purple flowers. Dryope gathered some and offered them to the baby, and Iole was about to do the same, when she perceived blood dropping from the places where her sister had broken them off the stem. The plant

was no other than the nymph Lotis, who, running from a base
pursuer, had been changed into this form. This they learned from
the country people when it was too late.

Dryope, horror-struck when she perceived what she had done,
would gladly have hastened from the spot, but found her feet
rooted to the ground. She tried to pull them away, but moved
nothing but her upper limbs. The woodiness crept upward and by
degrees invested her body. In anguish she attempted to tear her
hair, but found her hands filled with leaves. The infant felt his
mother's bosom begin to harden, and the milk cease to flow. Iole
looked on at the sad fate of her sister, and could render no assistance. She embraced the growing trunk, as if she would hold
back the advancing wood, and would gladly have been enveloped
in the same bark. At this moment Andræmon, the husband of
Dryope, with her father, approached; and when they asked for
Dryope, Iole pointed them to the new-formed lotus. They embraced
the trunk of the yet warm tree, and showered their kisses on its
leaves.

Now there was nothing left of Dryope but her face. Her tears
still flowed and fell on her leaves, and while she could she spoke.
"I am not guilty. I deserve not this fate. I have injured no one. If
I speak falsely, may my foliage perish with drought and my trunk
be cut down and burned. Take this infant and give it to a nurse.
Let it often be brought and nursed under my branches, and play
in my shade; and when he is old enough to talk, let him be taught
to call me mother, and to say with sadness, 'My mother lies hid
under this bark.' But bid him be careful of river banks, and beware
how he plucks flowers, remembering that every bush he sees may
be a goddess in disguise. Farewell, dear husband, and sister, and
father. If you retain any love for me, let not the axe wound me,
nor the flocks bite and tear my branches. Since I cannot stoop to
you, climb up hither and kiss me; and while my lips continue to
feel, lift up my child that I may kiss him. I can speak no more, for
already the bark advances up my neck, and will soon shoot over
me. You need not close my eyes, the bark will close them without
your aid." Then the lips ceased to move, and life was extinct;
but the branches retained for some time longer the vital heat.

Keats, in "Endymion," alludes to Dryope thus:

> "She took a lute from which there pulsing came
> A lively prelude, fashioning the way
> In which her voice should wander. 'Twas a lay
> More subtle-cadenced, more forest-wild
> Than Dryope's lone lulling of her child;" etc.

VENUS AND ADONIS

Venus, playing one day with her boy Cupid, wounded her bosom with one of his arrows. She pushed him away, but the wound was deeper than she thought. Before it healed she beheld Adonis, and was captivated with him. She no longer took any interest in her favourite resorts—Paphos, and Cnidos, and Amathos, rich in metals. She absented herself even from heaven, for Adonis was dearer to her than heaven. Him she followed and bore him company. She who used to love to recline in the shade, with no care but to cultivate her charms, now rambles through the woods and over the hills, dressed like the huntress Diana; and calls her dogs, and chases hares and stags, or other game that it is safe to hunt, but keeps clear of the wolves and bears, reeking with the slaughter of the herd. She charged Adonis, too, to beware of such dangerous animals. "Be brave towards the timid," said she; "courage against the courageous is not safe. Beware how you expose yourself to danger and put my happiness to risk. Attack not the beasts that Nature has armed with weapons. I do not value your glory so high as to consent to purchase it by such exposure. Your youth, and the beauty that charms Venus, will not touch the hearts of lions and bristly boars. Think of their terrible claws and prodigious strength! I hate the whole race of them. Do you ask me why?" Then she told him the story of Atalanta and Hippomenes, who were changed into lions for their ingratitude to her.

Having given him this warning, she mounted her chariot drawn by swans, and drove away through the air. But Adonis was too noble to heed such counsels. The dogs had roused a wild boar from his lair, and the youth threw his spear and wounded the animal with a sidelong stroke. The beast drew out the weapon with his jaws, and rushed after Adonis, who turned and ran; but the boar overtook him, and buried his tusks in his side, and stretched him dying upon the plain.

Venus, in her swan-drawn chariot, had not yet reached Cyprus, when she heard coming up through mid-air the groans of her beloved, and turned her white-winged coursers back to earth. As she drew near and saw from on high his lifeless body bathed in blood, she alighted and, bending over it, beat her breast and tore her hair. Reproaching the Fates, she said, "Yet theirs shall be but a partial triumph; memorials of my grief shall endure, and the spectacle of your death, my Adonis, and of my lamentation shall be annually renewed. Your blood shall be changed into a flower; that consolation none can envy me." Thus speaking, she sprinkled nectar on the blood: and as they mingled, bubbles rose as in a pool on which raindrops fall, and in an hour's time there sprang up a flower of bloody hue like that of the pomegranate. But it is short-lived. It is said the wind blows the blossoms open, and afterwards blows the petals away; so it is called Anemone, or Wind Flower, from the cause which assists equally in its production and its decay.

Milton alludes to the story of Venus and Adonis in his "Comus":

"Beds of hyacinth and roses
Where young Adonis oft reposes,
Waxing well of his deep wound
In slumber soft, and on the ground
Sadly sits th' Assyrian queen;" etc.

APOLLO AND HYACINTHUS

Apollo was passionately fond of a youth named Hyacinthus. He accompanied him in his sports, carried the nets when he went fishing, led the dogs when he went to hunt, followed him in his excursions in the mountains, and neglected for him his lyre and his arrows. One day they played a game of quoits together, and Apollo, heaving aloft the discus, with strength mingled with skill, sent it high and far. Hyacinthus watched it as it flew, and excited with the sport ran forward to seize it, eager to make his throw, when the quoit bounded from the earth and struck him in the forehead. He fainted and fell. The god, as pale as himself, raised him and tried all his art to stanch the wound and retain the flitting life, but all in vain; the hurt was past the power of medicine. As when one has broken the stem of a lily in the garden it hangs its head and turns its flowers to the earth, so the head of the dying boy, as if too heavy for his neck, fell over on his shoulder. "Thou diest, Hyacinth," so spoke Phœbus, "robbed of thy youth by me. Thine is the suffering, mine the crime. Would that I could die for thee! But since that may not be, thou shalt live with me in memory and in song. My lyre shall celebrate thee, my song shall tell thy fate, and thou shalt become a flower inscribed with my regrets." While Apollo spoke, behold the blood which had flowed on the ground and stained the herbage ceased to be blood; but a flower of hue more beautiful than the Tyrian sprang up, resembling the lily, if it were not that this is purple and that silvery white.[1] And this was not enough for Phœbus; but to confer still greater honour, he marked the petals with his sorrow, and inscribed "Ah! ah!" upon them, as we see to this day. The flower bears the name of Hyacinthus, and with every returning spring revives the memory of his fate.

[1] It is evidently not our modern hyacinth that is here described. It is perhaps some species of iris, or perhaps of larkspur or of pansy.

It was said that Zephyrus (the West wind), who was also fond of Hyacinthus and jealous of his preference of Apollo, blew the quoit out of its course to make it strike Hyacinthus. Keats alludes to this in his "Endymion," where he describes the lookers-on at the game of quoits:

> "Or they might watch the quoit-pitchers, intent
> On either side, pitying the sad death
> Of Hyacinthus, when the cruel breath
> Of Zephyr slew him; Zephyr penitent,
> Who now ere Phœbus mounts the firmament,
> Fondles the flower amid the sobbing rain."

An allusion to Hyacinthus will also be recognized in Milton's "Lycidas":

> "Like to that sanguine flower inscribed with woe."

CHAPTER IX

CEYX AND HALCYONE: OR, THE HALCYON BIRDS

CEYX was king of Thessaly, where he reigned in peace, without violence or wrong. He was son of Hesperus, the Day-star, and the glow of his beauty reminded one of his father. Halcyone, the daughter of Æolus, was his wife, and devotedly attached to him. Now Ceyx was in deep affliction for the loss of his brother, and direful prodigies following his brother's death made him feel as if the gods were hostile to him. He thought best, therefore, to make a voyage to Carlos in Ionia, to consult the oracle of Apollo. But as soon as he disclosed his intention to his wife Halcyone, a shudder ran through her frame, and her face grew deadly pale. "What fault of mine, dearest husband, has turned your affection from me? Where is that love of me that used to be uppermost in your thoughts? Have you learned to feel easy in the absence of Halcyone? Would you rather have me away?" She also endeavoured to discourage him, by describing the violence of the winds, which she had known familiarly when she lived at home in her father's house,—Æolus being the god of the winds, and having as much as he could do to restrain them. "They rush together," said she, "with such fury that fire flashes from the conflict. But if you must go," she added, "dear husband, let me go with you, otherwise I shall suffer not only the real evils which you must encounter, but those also which my fears suggest."

These words weighed heavily on the mind of King Ceyx, and it was no less his own wish than hers to take her with him, but he could not bear to expose her to the dangers of the sea. He answered, therefore, consoling her as well as he could, and finished with these

words: "I promise, by the rays of my father the Day-star, that if
fate permits I will return before the moon shall have twice rounded
her orb." When he had thus spoken, he ordered the vessel to be
drawn out of the shiphouse, and the oars and sails to be put aboard
When Halcyone saw these preparations she shuddered, as if with
a presentiment of evil. With tears and sobs she said farewell, and
then fell senseless to the ground.

Ceyx would still have lingered, but now the young men grasped
their oars and pulled vigorously through the waves, with long and
measured strokes. Halcyone raised her streaming eyes, and saw her
husband standing on the deck, waving his hand to her. She answered his signal till the vessel had receded so far that she could
no longer distinguish his form from the rest. When the vessel itself
could no more be seen, she strained her eyes to catch the last
glimmer of the sail, till that too disappeared. Then, retiring to her
chamber, she threw herself on her solitary couch.

Meanwhile they glide out of the harbour, and the breeze plays
among the ropes. The seamen draw in their oars, and hoist their
sails. When half or less of their course was passed, as night drew
on, the sea began to whiten with swelling waves, and the east wind
to blow a gale. The master gave the word to take in sail, but the
storm forbade obedience, for such is the roar of the winds and
waves his orders are unheard. The men, of their own accord, busy
themselves to secure the oars, to strengthen the ship, to reef the
sail. While they thus do what to each one seems best, the storm
increases. The shouting of the men, the rattling of the shrouds,
and the dashing of the waves, mingle with the roar of the thunder.
The swelling sea seems lifted up to the heavens, to scatter its foam
among the clouds; then sinking away to the bottom assumes the
colour of the shoal—a Stygian blackness.

The vessel shares all these changes. It seems like a wild beast
that rushes on the spears of the hunters. Rain falls in torrents,
as if the skies were coming down to unite with the sea. When the
lightning ceases for a moment, the night seems to add its own darkness to that of the storm; then comes the flash, rending the darkness
asunder, and lighting up all with a glare. Skill fails, courage sinks,
and death seems to come on every wave. The men are stupefied
with terror. The thought of parents, and kindred, and pledges left
at home, comes over their minds. Ceyx thinks of Halcyone. No
name but hers is on his lips, and while he yearns for her, he yet
rejoices in her absence. Presently the mast is shattered by a stroke
of lightning, the rudder broken, and the triumphant surge curling
over looks down upon the wreck, then falls, and crushes it to fragments. Some of the seamen, stunned by the stroke, sink, and rise

no more; others cling to fragments of the wreck. Ceyx, with the hand that used to grasp the sceptre, holds fast to a plank, calling for help,—alas, in vain,—upon his father and his father-in-law. But oftenest on his lips was the name of Halcyone. To her his thoughts cling. He prays that the waves may bear his body to her sight, and that it may receive burial at her hands. At length the waters overwhelm him, and he sinks. The Day-star looked dim that night. Since it could not leave the heavens, it shrouded its face with clouds.

In the meanwhile Halcyone, ignorant of all these horrors, counted the days till her husband's promised return. Now she gets ready the garments which he shall put on, and now what she shall wear when he arrives. To all the gods she offers frequent incense, but more than all to Juno. For her husband, who was no more, she prayed incessantly: that he might be safe; that he might come home; that he might not, in his absence, see any one that he would love better than her. But of all these prayers, the last was the only one destined to be granted. The goddess, at length, could not bear any longer to be pleaded with for one already dead, and to have hands raised to her altars that ought rather to be offering funeral rites. So, calling Iris, she said, "Iris, my faithful messenger, go to the drowsy dwelling of Somnus, and tell him to send a vision to Halcyone in the form of Ceyx, to make known to her the event."

Iris puts on her robe of many colours, and tinging the sky with her bow, seeks the palace of the King of Sleep. Near the Cimmerian country, a mountain cave is the abode of the dull god Somnus. Here Phœbus dares not come, either rising, at midday, or setting. Clouds and shadows are exhaled from the ground, and the light glimmers faintly. The bird of dawning, with crested head, never there calls aloud to Aurora, nor watchful dog, nor more sagacious goose disturbs the silence. No wild beast, nor cattle, nor branch moved with the wind, nor sound of human conversation, breaks the stillness. Silence reigns there; but from the bottom of the rock the River Lethe flows, and by its murmur invites to sleep. Poppies grow abundantly before the door of the cave, and other herbs, from whose juices Night collects slumbers, which she scatters over the darkened earth. There is no gate to the mansion, to creak on its hinges, nor any watchman; but in the midst a couch of black ebony, adorned with black plumes and black curtains. There the god reclines, his limbs relaxed with sleep. Around him lie dreams, resembling all various forms, as many as the harvest bears stalks, or the forest leaves, or the seashore sand grains.

As soon as the goddess entered and brushed away the dreams that hovered around her, her brightness lit up all the cave. The god, scarce opening his eyes, and ever and anon dropping his beard upon his breast, at last shook himself free from himself, and leaning on his arm, inquired her errand,—for he knew who she was. She answered, "Somnus, gentlest of the gods, tranquillizer of minds and soother of care-worn hearts, Juno sends you her commands that yor despatch a dream to Halcyone, in the city of Trachine, representing her lost husband and all the events of the wreck."

Having delivered her message, Iris hasted away, for she could not longer endure the stagnant air, and as she felt drowsiness creeping over her, she made her escape, and returned by her bow the way she came. Then Somnus called one of his numerous sons,—Morpheus,—the most expert in counterfeiting forms, and in imitating the walk, the countenance, and mode of speaking, even the clothes and attitudes most characteristic of each. But he only imitates men, leaving it to another to personate birds, beasts, and serpents. Him they call Icelos; and Phantasos is a third, who turns himself into rocks, waters, woods, and other things without life. These wait upon kings and great personages in their sleeping hours, while others move among the common people. Somnus chose, from all the brothers, Morpheus, to perform the command of Iris; then laid his head on his pillow and yielded himself to grateful repose.

Morpheus flew, making no noise with his wings, and soon came to the Hæmonian city, where, laying aside his wings, he assumed the form of Ceyx. Under that form, but pale like a dead man, naked, he stood before the couch of the wretched wife. His beard seemed soaked with water, and water trickled from his drowned locks. Leaning over the bed, tears streaming from his eyes, he said, "Do you recognize your Ceyx, unhappy wife, or has death too much changed my visage? Behold me, know me, your husband's shade, instead of himself. Your prayers, Halcyone, availed me nothing. I am dead. No more deceive yourself with vain hopes of my return. The stormy winds sunk my ship in the Ægean Sea, waves filled my mouth while it called aloud on you. No uncertain messenger tells you this, no vague rumour brings it to your ears. I come in person, a shipwrecked man, to tell you my fate. Arise! give me tears, give me lamentations, let me not go down to Tartarus unwept." To these words Morpheus added the voice, which seemed to be that of her husband; he seemed to pour forth genuine tears; his hands had the gestures of Ceyx.

Halcyone, weeping, groaned, and stretched out her arms in her sleep, striving to embrace his body, but grasping only the air. "Stay!" she cried; "whither do you fly? let us go together." Her own voice awakened her. Starting up, she gazed eagerly around, to see if he was still present, for the servants, alarmed by her cries, had brought a light. When she found him not, she smote her breast and rent her garments. She cares not to unbind her hair, but tears it wildly. Her nurse asks what is the cause of her grief. "Halcyone is no more," she answers, "she perished with her Ceyx. Utter not words of comfort, he is shipwrecked and dead. I have seen him, I have recognized him. I stretched out my hands to seize him and detain him. His shade vanished, but it was the true shade of my husband. Not with the accustomed features, not with the beauty that was his, but pale, naked, and with his hair wet with sea water, he appeared to wretched me. Here, in this very spot, the sad vision stood,"—and she looked to find the mark of his footsteps. "This it was, this that my presaging mind foreboded, when I implored him not to leave me, to trust himself to the waves. Oh, how I wish, since thou wouldst go, thou hadst taken me with thee! It would have been far better. Then I should have had no remnant of life to spend without thee, nor a separate death to die. If I could bear to live and struggle to endure, I should be more cruel to myself than the sea has been to me. But I will not struggle, I will not be separated from thee, unhappy husband. This time, at least, I will keep thee company. In death, if one tomb may not include us, one epitaph shall; if I may not lay my ashes with thine, my name, at least, shall not be separated." Her grief forbade more words, and these were broken with tears and sobs.

It was now morning. She went to the seashore, and sought the spot where she last saw him, on his departure. "While he lingered here, and cast off his tacklings, he gave me his last kiss." While she reviews every object, and strives to recall every incident, looking out over the sea, she descries an indistinct object floating in the water. At first she was in doubt what it was, but by degrees the waves bore it nearer, and it was plainly the body of a man. Though unknowing of whom, yet, as it was of some shipwrecked one, she was deeply moved, and gave it her tears, saying, "Alas! unhappy one, and unhappy, if such there be, thy wife!" Borne by the waves, it came nearer. As she more and more nearly views it, she trembles more and more. Now, now it approaches the shore. Now marks that she recognizes appear. It is her husband! Stretching out her trembling hands towards it, she exclaims, "O dearest husband, is it thus you return to me?"

There was built out from the shore a mole, constructed to break the assaults of the sea, and stem its violent ingress. She leaped upon this barrier and (it was wonderful she could do so) she flew, and striking the air with wings produced on the instant, skimmed along the surface of the water, an unhappy bird. As she flew, her throat poured forth sounds full of grief, and like the voice of one lamenting. When she touched the mute and bloodless body, she enfolded its beloved limbs with her new-formed wings, and tried to give kisses with her horny beak. Whether Ceyx felt it, or whether it was only the action of the waves, those who looked on doubted, but the body seemed to raise its head. But indeed he did feel it, and by the pitying gods both of them were changed into birds. They mate and have their young ones. For seven placid days, in winter time, Halcyone broods over her nest, which floats upon the sea. Then the way is safe to seamen. Æolus guards the winds and keeps them from disturbing the deep. The sea is given up, for the time, to his grandchildren.

The following lines from Byron's "Bride of Abydos" might seem borrowed from the concluding part of this description, if it were not stated that the author derived the suggestion from observing the motion of a floating corpse:

> "As shaken on his restless pillow,
> His head heaves with the heaving billow;
> That hand, whose motion is not life,
> Yet feebly seems to menace strife,
> Flung by the tossing tide on high,
> Then levelled with the wave ..."

Milton, in his "Hymn on the Nativity," thus alludes to the fable of the Halcyon:

> "But peaceful was the night
> Wherein the Prince of light
>   His reign of peace upon the earth began;
> The winds with wonder whist
> Smoothly the waters kist
>   Whispering new joys to the mild ocean,
> Who now hath quite forgot to rave
> While birds of calm sit brooding on the charmed wave."

Keats also, in "Endymion," says:

> "O magic sleep! O comfortable bird
> That broodest o'er the troubled sea of the mind
> Till it is hushed and smooth."

CHAPTER X

VERTUMNUS AND POMONA

THE Hamadryads were Wood-nymphs. Pomona was of this class, and no one excelled her in love of the garden and the culture of fruit. She cared not for forests and rivers, but loved the cultivated country, and trees that bear delicious apples. Her right hand bore for its weapon not a javelin, but a pruning-knife. Armed with this, she busied herself at one time to repress the too luxuriant growths, and curtail the branches that straggled out of place; at another, to split the twig and insert therein a graft, making the branch adopt a nursling not its own. She took care, too, that her favourites should not suffer from drought, and led streams of water by them, that the thirsty roots might drink. This occupation was her pursuit, her passion; and she was free from that which Venus inspires. She was not without fear of the country people, and kept her orchard locked, and allowed not men to enter. The Fauns and Satyrs would have given all they possessed to win her, and so would old Sylvanus, who looks young for his years, and Pan, who wears a garland of pine leaves around his head. But Vertumnus loved her best of all; yet he sped no better than the rest. O how often, in the disguise of a reaper, did he bring her corn in a basket, and looked the very image of a reaper! With a hay band tied round him, one would think he had just come from turning over the grass. Sometimes he would have an ox-goad in his hand, and you would have said he had just unyoked his weary oxen. Now he bore a pruning-hook, and personated a vine-dresser; and again, with a ladder on his shoulder, he seemed as if he was going to gather apples. Sometimes he trudged along as a dis-charged soldier, and again he bore a fishing-rod, as if going to fish. In this way he gained admission to her again and again, and fed his passion with the sight of her.

One day he came in the guise of an old woman, her grey hair surmounted with a cap, and a staff in her hand. She entered the garden and admired the fruit. "It does you credit, my dear," she said, and kissed her, not exactly with an old woman's kiss. She sat down on a bank, and looked up at the branches laden with fruit which hung over her. Opposite was an elm entwined with a vine loaded with swelling grapes. She praised the tree and its associated vine, equally. "But," said she, "if the tree stood alone, and had no vine clinging to it, it would have nothing to attract or offer us but its useless leaves. And equally the vine, if it were not twined round the elm, would lie prostrate on the ground. Why will you not take a lesson from the tree and the vine, and consent to unite yourself with some one? I wish you would. Helen herself had not more numerous suitors, nor Penelope, the wife of shrewd Ulysses. Even while you spurn them, they court you,—rural deities and others of every kind that frequent these mountains. But if you are prudent and want to make a good alliance, and will let an old woman advise you,—who loves you better than you have any idea of,—dismiss all the rest and accept Vertumnus, on my recommendation. I know him as well as he knows himself. He is not a wandering deity, but belongs to these mountains. Nor is he like too many of the lovers nowadays, who love any one they happen to see; he loves you, and you only. Add to this, he is young and handsome, and has the art of assuming any shape he pleases, and can make himself just what you command him. More-over, he loves the same things that you do, delights in gardening, and handles your apples with admiration. But *now* he cares nothing for fruits nor flowers, nor anything else, but only yourself. Take pity on him, and fancy him speaking now with my mouth. Remember that the gods punish cruelty, and that Venus hates a hard heart, and will visit such offences sooner or later. To prove this, let me tell you a story, which is well known in Cyprus to be a fact; and I hope it will have the effect to make you more merciful.

"Iphis was a young man of humble parentage, who saw and loved Anaxarete, a noble lady of the ancient family of Teucer. He struggled long with his passion, but when he found he could not subdue it, he came a suppliant to her mansion. First he told his passion to her nurse, and begged her as she loved her foster-child to favour his suit. And then he tried to win her domestics to his side. Sometimes he committed his vows to written tablets, and often hung at her door garlands which he had moistened with his tears. He stretched himself on her threshold, and uttered his complaints to the cruel bolts and bars. She was deafer than the surges which rise in the November gale; harder than steel from the German forges, or a rock that still clings to its native cliff. She mocked and laughed at him, adding cruel words to her ungentle treatment, and gave not the slightest gleam of hope.

"Iphis could not any longer endure the torments of hopeless love, and, standing before her doors, he spake these last words: 'Anaxarete, you have conquered, and shall no longer have to bear my importunities. Enjoy your triumph! Sing songs of joy, and bind your forehead with laurel,—you have conquered! I die; stony heart, rejoice! This at least I can do to gratify you, and force you to praise me; and thus shall I prove that the love of you left me but with life, Nor will I leave it to rumour to tell you of my death. I will come myself, and you shall see me die, and feast your eyes on the spectacle, Yet, O ye Gods, who look down on mortal woes, observe my fate! I ask but this: let me be remembered in coming ages, and add those years to my fame which you have reft from my life.' Thus he said, and, turning his pale face and weeping eyes towards her mansion, he fastened a rope to the gate-post, on which he had often hung garlands, and putting his head into the noose, he murmured, 'This garland at least will please you, cruel girl!' and falling hung suspended with his neck broken. As he fell he struck against the gate, and the sound was as the sound of a groan. The servants opened the door and found him dead, and with exclamations of pity raised him and carried him home to his mother, for his father was not living. She received the dead body of her son, and folded the cold form to her bosom, while she poured forth the sad words which bereaved mothers utter. The mournful funeral passed through the town, and the pale corpse was borne on a bier to the place of the funeral pile.

By chance the home of Anaxarete was on the street where the procession passed, and the lamentations of the mourners met the ears of her whom the avenging deity had already marked for punishment.

"'Let us see this sad procession,' said she, and mounted to a turret, whence through an open window she looked upon the funeral. Scarce had her eyes rested upon the form of Iphis stretched on the bier, when they began to stiffen, and the warm blood in her body to become cold. Endeavouring to step back, she found she could not move her feet; trying to turn away her face, she tried in vain; and by degrees all her limbs became stony like her heart. That you may not doubt the fact, the statue still remains, and stands in the temple of Venus at Salamis, in the exact form of the lady. Now think of these things, my dear, and lay aside your scorn and your delays, and accept a lover. So may neither the vernal frosts blight your young fruits, nor furious winds scatter your blossoms!"

When Vertumnus had spoken thus, he dropped the disguise of an old woman, and stood before her in his proper person, as a comely youth. It appeared to her like the sun bursting through a cloud. He would have renewed his entreaties, but there was no need; his arguments and the sight of his true form prevailed, and the Nymph no longer resisted, but owned a mutual flame.

Pomona was the especial patroness of the Apple-orchard, and as such she was invoked by Phillips, the author of a poem on Cider, in blank verse. Thomson in the "Seasons" alludes to him:

> "Phillips, Pomona's bard, the second thou
> Who nobly durst, in rhyme-unfettered verse,
> With British freedom, sing the British song."

But Pomona was also regarded as presiding over other fruits, and as such is invoked by Thomson:

> "Bear me, Pomona, to thy citron groves,
> To where the lemon and the piercing lime,
> With the deep orange, glowing through the green,
> Their lighter glories blend. Lay me reclined
> Beneath the spreading tamarind, that shakes,
> Fanned by the breeze, its fever-cooling fruit."

CHAPTER XI

CUPID AND PSYCHE

A CERTAIN king and queen had three daughters. The charms of the two elder were more than common, but the beauty of the youngest was so wonderful that the poverty of language is unable to express its due praise. The fame of her beauty was so great that strangers from neighbouring countries came in crowds to enjoy the sight, and looked on her with amazement, paying her that homage which is due only to Venus herself. In fact Venus found her altars deserted, while men turned their devotion to this young virgin. As she passed along, the people sang her praises, and strewed her way with chaplets and flowers.

This perversion of homage due only to the immortal powers to the exaltation of a mortal gave great offence to the real Venus. Shaking her ambrosial locks with indignation, she exclaimed, "Am I then to be eclipsed in my honours by a mortal girl? In vain then did that royal shepherd, whose judgment was approved by Jove himself, give me the palm of beauty over my illustrious rivals, Pallas and Juno. But she shall not so quietly usurp my honours. I will give her cause to repent of so unlawful a beauty."

Thereupon she calls her winged son Cupid, mischievous enough in his own nature, and rouses and provokes him yet more by her complaints. She points out Psyche to him and says, "My dear son, punish that contumacious beauty; give thy mother a revenge as sweet as her injuries are great; infuse into the bosom of that haughty girl a passion for some low, mean, unworthy being, so that she may reap a mortification as great as her present exultation and triumph."

Cupid prepared to obey the commands of his mother. There are two fountains in Venus's garden, one of sweet waters, the other of bitter. Cupid filled two amber vases, one from each fountain, and suspending them from the top of his quiver, hastened to the chamber of Psyche, whom he found asleep. He shed a few drops from the bitter fountain over her lips, though the sight of her almost moved him to pity; then touched her side with the point of his arrow. At the touch she awoke, and opened eyes upon Cupid (himself invisible), which so startled him that in his confusion he wounded himself with his own arrow. Heedless of his wound, his whole thought now was to repair the mischief he had done, and he poured the balmy drops of joy over all her silken ringlets.

Psyche, henceforth frowned upon by Venus, derived no benefit from all her charms. True, all eyes were cast eagerly upon her, and every mouth spoke her praises; but neither king, royal youth, nor plebeian presented himself to demand her in marriage. Her two elder sisters of moderate charms had now long been married to two royal princes; but Psyche, in her lonely apartment, deplored her solitude, sick of that beauty which, while it procured abundance of flattery, had failed to awaken love.

Her parents, afraid that they had unwittingly incurred the anger of the gods, consulted the oracle of Apollo, and received this answer: "The virgin is destined for the bride of no mortal lover. Her future husband awaits her on the top of the mountain. He is a monster whom neither gods nor men can resist."

This dreadful decree of the oracle filled all the people with dismay, and her parents abandoned themselves to grief. But Psyche said, "Why, my dear parents, do you now lament me? You should rather have grieved when the people showered upon me undeserved honours, and with one voice called me a Venus. I now perceive that I am a victim to that name. I submit. Lead me to that rock to which my unhappy fate has destined me." Accordingly, all things being prepared, the royal maid took her place in the procession, which more resembled a funeral than a nuptial pomp, and with her parents, amid the lamentations of the people, ascended the mountain, on the summit of which they left her alone, and with sorrowful hearts returned home.

While Psyche stood on the ridge of the mountain, panting with fear and with eyes full of tears, the gentle Zephyr raised her from the earth and bore her with an easy motion into a flowery dale. By degrees her mind became composed, and she laid herself down on the grassy bank to sleep. When she awoke refreshed with sleep, she looked round and beheld near by a pleasant grove of tall and stately trees. She entered it, and in the midst discovered a fountain, sending forth clear and crystal waters, and fast by, a magnificent palace whose august front impressed the spectator that it was not the work of mortal hands, but the happy retreat of some god. Drawn by admiration and wonder, she approached the building and ventured to enter. Every object she met filled her with pleasure and amazement. Golden pillars supported the vaulted roof, and the walls were enriched with carvings and paintings representing beasts of the chase and rural scenes, adapted to delight the eye of the beholder. Proceeding onward, she perceived that besides the apartments of state there were others filled with all manner of treasures, and beautiful and precious productions of nature and art.

While her eyes were thus occupied, a voice addressed her, though she saw no one, uttering these words: "Sovereign lady, all that you see is yours. We whose voices you hear are your servants and shall obey all your commands with our utmost care and diligence. Retire, therefore, to your chamber and repose on your bed of down, and when you see fit repair to the bath. Supper awaits you in the adjoining alcove when it pleases you to take your seat there."

Psyche gave ear to the admonitions of her vocal attendants, and after repose and the refreshment of the bath, seated herself in the alcove, where a table immediately presented itself, without any visible aid from waiters or servants, and covered with the greatest delicacies of food and the most nectareous wines. Her ears too were feasted with music from invisible performers; of whom one sang, another played on the lute, and all closed in the wonderful harmony of a full chorus.

She had not yet seen her destined husband. He came only in the hours of darkness and fled before the dawn of morning, but his accents were full of love, and inspired a like passion in her. She often begged him to stay and let her behold him, but he would not consent. On the contrary he charged her to make no attempt to see him, for it was his pleasure, for the best of reasons, to keep concealed. "Why should you wish to behold me?" he said; "have you any doubt of my love? have you any wish ungratified? If you saw me, perhaps you would fear me, perhaps adore me, but all I ask of you is to love me. I would rather you would love me as an equal than adore me as a god."

This reasoning somewhat quieted Psyche for a time, and while the novelty lasted she felt quite happy. But at length the thought of her parents, left in ignorance of her fate, and of her sisters, precluded from sharing with her the delights of her situation, preyed on her mind and made her begin to feel her palace as but a splendid prison. When her husband came one night, she told him her distress, and at last drew from him an unwilling consent that her sisters should be brought to see her.

So, calling Zephyr, she acquainted him with her husband's commands, and he, promptly obedient, soon brought them across the mountain down to their sister's valley. They embraced her and she returned their caresses. "Come," said Psyche, "enter with me my house and refresh yourselves with whatever your sister has to offer." Then taking their hands she led them into her golden palace, and committed them to the care of her numerous train of attendant voices, to refresh them in her baths and at her table, and to show them all her treasures. The view of these celestial delights caused envy to enter their bosoms, at seeing their young sister possessed of such state and splendour, so much exceeding their own.

They asked her numberless questions, among others what sort of a person her husband was. Psyche replied that he was a beautiful youth, who generally spent the daytime in hunting upon the mountains. The sisters, not satisfied with this reply, soon made her confess that she had never seen him. Then they proceeded to fill her bosom with dark suspicions. "Call to mind," they said, "the Pythian oracle that declared you destined to marry a direful and tremendous monster. The inhabitants of this valley say that your husband is a terrible and monstrous serpent, who nourishes you for a while with dainties that he may by and by devour you. Take our advice. Provide yourself with a lamp and a sharp knife; put them in concealment that your husband may not discover them, and when he is sound asleep, slip out of bed, bring forth your lamp, and see for yourself whether what they say is true or not. If it is, hesitate not to cut off the monster's head, and thereby recover your liberty."

Psyche resisted these persuasions as well as she could, but they did not fail to have their effect on her mind, and when her sisters were gone, their words and her own curiosity were too strong for her to resist. So she prepared her lamp and a sharp knife, and hid them out of sight of her husband. When he had fallen into his first sleep, she silently rose and uncovering her lamp beheld not a hideous monster, but the most beautiful and charming of the gods, with his golden ringlets wandering over his snowy neck and crimson cheek, with two dewy wings on his shoulders, whiter than snow, and with shining feathers like the tender blossoms of spring. As she leaned the lamp over to have a nearer view of his face a drop of burning oil fell on the shoulder of the god, startled with which he opened his eyes and fixed them full upon her; then, without saying one word, he spread his white wings and flew out of the window. Psyche, in vain endeavouring to follow him, fell from the window to the ground. Cupid, beholding her as she lay in the dust, stopped his flight for an instant and said, "O foolish Psyche, is it thus you repay my love? After having disobeyed my mother's commands and made you my wife, will you think me a monster and cut off my head? But go; return to your sisters, whose advice you seem to think preferable to mine. I inflict no other punishment on you than to leave you for ever. Love cannot dwell with suspicion." So saying, he fled away, leaving poor Psyche prostrate on the ground, filling the place with mournful lamentations.

When she had recovered some degree of composure she looked around her, but the palace and gardens had vanished, and she found herself in the open field not far from the city where her sisters dwelt. She repaired thither and told them the whole story of her misfortunes, at which, pretending to grieve, those spiteful creatures inwardly rejoiced. "For now," said they, "he will perhaps choose one of us." With this idea, without saying a word of her intentions, each of them rose early the next morning and ascended the mountain, and having reached the top, called upon Zephyr to receive her and bear her to his lord; then leaping up, and not being sustained by Zephyr, fell down the precipice and was dashed to pieces.

Psyche meanwhile wandered day and night, without food or repose, in search of her husband. Casting her eyes on a lofty mountain having on its brow a magnificent temple, she sighed and said to herself, "Perhaps my love, my lord, inhabits there," and directed her steps thither.

She had no sooner entered than she saw heaps of corn, some in loose ears and some in sheaves, with mingled ears of barley. Scattered about, lay sickles and rakes, and all the instruments of harvest, without order, as if thrown carelessly out of the weary reapers' hands in the sultry hours of the day.

This unseemly confusion the pious Psyche put an end to, by separating and sorting everything to its proper place and kind, believing that she ought to neglect none of the gods, but endeavour by her piety to engage them all in her behalf. The holy Ceres, whose temple it was, finding her so religiously employed, thus spoke to her: "O Psyche, truly worthy of our pity, though I cannot shield you from the frowns of Venus, yet I can teach you how best to allay her displeasure. Go, then, and voluntarily surrender yourself to your lady and sovereign, and try by modesty and submission to win her forgiveness, and perhaps her favour will restore you the husband you have lost."

Psyche obeyed the commands of Ceres and took her way to the temple of Venus, endeavouring to fortify her mind and ruminating on what she should say and how best propitiate the angry goddess, feeling that the issue was doubtful and perhaps fatal.

Venus received her with angry countenance. "Most undutiful and faithless of servants," said she, "do you at last remember that you really have a mistress? Or have you rather come to see your sick husband, yet laid up of the wound given him by his loving wife? You are so ill-favoured and disagreeable that the only way you can merit your lover must be by dint of industry and diligence. I will make trial of your housewifery." Then she ordered Psyche to be led to the storehouse of her temple, where was laid up a great quantity of wheat, barley, millet, vetches, beans, and lentils prepared for food for her pigeons, and said, "Take and separate all these grains, putting all of the same kind in a parcel by themselves, and see that you get it done before evening." Then Venus departed and left her to her task.

But Psyche, in a perfect consternation at the enormous work, sat stupid and silent, without moving a finger to the inextricable heap.

While she sat despairing, Cupid stirred up the little ant, a native of the fields, to take compassion on her. The leader of the ant-hill, followed by whole hosts of his six-legged subjects, approached the heap, and with the utmost diligence taking grain by grain, they separated the pile, sorting each kind to its parcel; and when it was all done, they vanished out of sight in a moment.

Venus at the approach of twilight returned from the banquet of the gods, breathing odours and crowned with roses. Seeing the task done, she exclaimed, "This is no work of yours, wicked one, but his, whom to your own and his misfortune you have enticed." So saying, she threw her a piece of black bread for her supper and went away.

Next morning Venus ordered Psyche to be called and said to her, "Behold yonder grove which stretches along the margin of the water. There you will find sheep feeding without a shepherd, with golden-shining fleeces on their backs. Go, fetch me a sample of that precious wool gathered from every one of their fleeces."

Psyche obediently went to the riverside, prepared to do her best to execute the command. But the river god inspired the reeds with harmonious murmurs, which seemed to say, "O maiden, severely tried, tempt not the dangerous flood, nor venture among the formidable rams on the other side, for as long as they are under the influence of the rising sun, they burn with a cruel rage to destroy mortals with their sharp horns or rude teeth. But when the noontide sun has driven the cattle to the shade, and the serene spirit of the flood has lulled them to rest, you may then cross in safety, and you will find the woolly gold sticking to the bushes and the trunks of the trees."

Thus the compassionate river god gave Psyche instructions how to accomplish her task, and by observing his directions she soon returned to Venus with her arms full of the golden fleece; but she received not the approbation of her implacable mistress, who said, "I know very well it is by none of your own doings that you have succeeded in this task, and I am not satisfied yet that you have any capacity to make yourself useful. But I have another task for you. Here, take this box and go your way to the infernal shades, and give this box to Proserpine and say, 'My mistress Venus desires you to send her a little of your beauty, for in tending her sick son she has lost some of her own.' Be not too long on your errand, for I must paint myself with it to appear at the circle of the gods and goddesses this evening."

Psyche was now satisfied that her destruction was at hand, being obliged to go with her own feet directly down to Erebus. Wherefore, to make no delay of what was not to be avoided, she goes to the top of a high tower to precipitate herself headlong, thus to descend the shortest way to the shades below. But a voice from the tower said to her, "Why, poor unlucky girl, dost thou design to put an end to thy days in so dreadful a manner? And what cowardice makes thee sink under this last danger who hast been so miraculously supported in all thy former?" Then the voice told her how by a certain cave she might reach the realms of Pluto, and how to avoid all the dangers of the road, to pass by Cerberus, the three-headed dog, and prevail on Charon, the ferryman, to take her across the black river and bring her back again. But the voice added, "When Proserpine has given you the box filled with her beauty, of all things this is chiefly to be observed by you, that you never once open or look into the box nor allow your curiosity to pry into the treasure of the beauty of the goddesses."

Psyche, encouraged by this advice, obeyed it in all things, and taking heed to her ways travelled safely to the kingdom of Pluto. She was admitted to the palace of Proserpine, and without accepting the delicate seat or delicious banquet that was offered her, but contented with coarse bread for her food, she delivered her message from Venus. Presently the box was returned to her, shut and filled with the precious commodity. Then she returned the way she came, and glad was she to come out once more into the light of day.

But having got so far successfully through her dangerous task, a longing desire seized her to examine the contents of the box. "What," said she, "shall I, the carrier of this divine beauty, not take the least bit to put on my cheeks to appear to more advantage in the eyes of my beloved husband!" So she carefully opened the box, but found nothing there of any beauty at all, but an infernal and truly Stygian sleep, which being thus set free from its prison, took possession of her, and she fell down in the midst of the road, a sleepy corpse without sense or motion.

But Cupid, being now recovered from his wound, and not able longer to bear the absence of his beloved Psyche, slipping through the smallest crack of the window of his chamber which happened to be left open, flew to the spot where Psyche lay, and gathering up the sleep from her body closed it again in the box, and waked Psyche with a light touch of one of his arrows. "Again," said he, "hast thou almost perished by the same curiosity. But now perform exactly the task imposed on you by my mother, and I will take care of the rest."

Then Cupid, as swift as lightning penetrating the heights of heaven, presented himself before Jupiter with his supplication. Jupiter lent a favouring ear, and pleaded the cause of the lovers so earnestly with Venus that he won her consent. On this he sent Mercury to bring Psyche up to the heavenly assembly, and when she arrived, handing her a cup of ambrosia, he said, "Drink this, Psyche, and be immortal; nor shall Cupid ever break away from the knot in which he is tied, but these nuptials shall be perpetual."

Thus Psyche became at last united to Cupid, and in due time they had a daughter born to them whose name was Pleasure.

The fable of Cupid and Psyche is usually considered allegorical. The Greek name for a *butterfly* is Psyche, and the same word means the *soul*. There is no illustration of the immortality of the soul so striking and beautiful as the butterfly, bursting on brilliant wings from the tomb in which it has lain, after a dull, grovelling, caterpillar existence, to flutter in the blaze of day and feed on the most fragrant and delicate productions of the spring. Psyche, then, is the human soul, which is purified by sufferings and misfortunes, and is thus prepared for the enjoyment of true and pure happiness.

In works of art Psyche is represented as a maiden with the wings of a butterfly, along with Cupid, in the different situations described in the allegory.

Milton alludes to the story of Cupid and Psyche in the conclusion of his "Comus":

> "Celestial Cupid, her famed son, advanced,
> Holds his dear Psyche sweet entranced,
> After her wandering labours long,
> Till free consent the gods among
> Make her his eternal bride;
> And from her fair unspotted side
> Two blissful twins are to be born,
> Youth and Joy; so Jove hath sworn."

The allegory of the story of Cupid and Psyche is well presented in the beautiful lines of T. K. Harvey:

> "They wove bright fables in the days of old,
>   When reason borrowed fancy's painted wings;
> When truth's clear river flowed o'er sands of gold,
>   And told in song its high and mystic things!
> And such the sweet and solemn tale of her
>   The pilgrim heart, to whom a dream was given,
> That led her through the world,—Love's worshipper,—
>   To seek on earth for him whose home was heaven!
>
> "In the full city,—by the haunted fount,—
>   Through the dim grotto's tracery of spars,—
> 'Mid the pine temples, on the moonlit mount,
>   Where silence sits to listen to the stars;
> In the deep glade where dwells the brooding dove,
>   The painted valley, and the scented air,
> She heard far echoes of the voice of Love,
>   And found his footsteps' traces everywhere.
>
> "But nevermore they met! since doubts and fears,
>   Those phantom shapes that haunt and blight the
>   earth,
> Had come 'twixt her, a child of sin and tears,
>   And that bright spirit of immortal birth;
> Until her pining soul and weeping eyes
> Had learned to seek him only in the skies;
> Till wings unto the weary heart were given,
> And she became Love's angel bride in heaven!"

The story of Cupid and Psyche first appears in the works of Apuleius, a writer of the second century of our era. It is therefore of much more recent date than most of the legends of the Age of Fable. It is this that Keats alludes to in his "Ode to Psyche":

> "O latest born and loveliest vision far
>   Of all Olympus' faded hierarchy!
> Fairer than Phœbe's sapphire-regioned star
>   Or Vesper, amorous glow-worm of the sky;
> Fairer than these, though temple thou hast none,
>   Nor altar heaped with flowers;
> Nor virgin choir to make delicious moan
>   Upon the midnight hours;
> No voice, no lute, no pipe, no incense sweet,
>   From chain-swung censer teeming;
> No shrine, no grove, no oracle, no heat
>   Of pale-mouthed prophet dreaming."

In Moore's "Summer Fête" a fancy ball is described, in which one of the characters personated is Psyche—

> "...not in dark disguise to-night
> Hath our young heroine veiled her light;—
> For see, she walks the earth, Love's own.
>   His wedded bride, by holiest vow
> Pledged in Olympus, and made known
>   To mortals by the type which now
>   Hangs glittering on her snowy brow,
> That butterfly, mysterious trinket,
> Which means the soul, (though few would think it,)
> And sparkling thus on brow so white
> Tells us we've Psyche here to-night."

CHAPTER XII

CADMUS—THE MYRMIDONS

JUPITER, under the disguise of a bull, had carried away Europa, the daughter of Agenor, king of Phœnicia. Agenor commanded his son Cadmus to go in search of his sister, and not to return without her. Cadmus went and sought long and far for his sister, but could not find her, and not daring to return unsuccessful, consulted the oracle of Apollo to know what country he should settle in. The oracle informed him that he should find a cow in the field, and should follow her wherever she might wander, and where she stopped, should build a city and call it Thebes. Cadmus had hardly left the Castalian cave, from which the oracle was delivered, when he saw a young cow slowly walking before him. He followed her close, offering at the same time his prayers to Phœbus. The cow went on till she passed the shallow channel of Cephisus and came out into the plain of

Panope. There she stood still, raising her broad forehead to the sky, filled the air with her lowings. Cadmus gave thanks, and stooping down kissed the foreign soil, then lifting his eyes, greeted the surrounding mountains. Wishing to offer a sacrifice to Jupiter, he sent his servants to seek pure water for a libation. Near by there stood an ancient grove which had never been profaned by the axe, in the midst of which was a cave, thick covered with the growth of bushes, its roof forming a low arch, from beneath which burst forth a fountain of purest water. In the cave lurked a horrid serpent with a crested head and scales glittering like gold. His eyes shone like fire, his body was swollen with venom, he vibrated a triple tongue, and showed a triple row of teeth. No sooner had the Tyrians dipped their pitchers in the fountain, and the in-gushing waters made a sound, than the glittering serpent raised his head out of the cave and uttered a fearful hiss. The vessels fell from their hands, the blood left their cheeks, they trembled in every limb. The serpent, twisting his scaly body in a huge coil, raised his head so as to overtop the tallest trees, and while the Tyrians from terror could neither fight nor fly, slew some with his fangs, others in his folds, and others with his poisonous breath.

Cadmus, having waited for the return of his men till midday, went in search of them. His covering was a lion's hide, and besides his javelin he carried in his hand a lance, and in his breast a bold heart, a surer reliance than either. When he entered the wood, and saw the lifeless bodies of his men, and the monster with his bloody jaws, he exclaimed, "O faithful friends, I will avenge you, or share your death." So saying he lifted a huge stone and threw it with all his force at the serpent. Such a block would have shaken the wall of a fortress, but it made no impression on the monster. Cadmus next threw his javelin, which met with better success, for it penetrated the serpent's scales, and pierced through to his entrails. Fierce with pain, the monster turned back his head to view the wound, and attempted to draw out the weapon with his mouth, but broke it off, leaving the iron point rankling in his flesh. His neck swelled with rage, bloody foam covered his jaws, and the breath of his nostrils poisoned the air around. Now he twisted himself into a circle, then stretched himself out on the ground like the trunk of a fallen tree. As he moved onward, Cadmus retreated before him, holding his spear opposite to the monster's opened jaws. The serpent snapped at the weapon and attempted to bite its iron point. At last Cadmus, watching his chance, thrust the spear at a moment when the animal's head thrown back came against the trunk of a tree, and so

succeeded in pinning him to its side. His weight bent the tree as he
struggled in the agonies of death.

While Cadmus stood over his conquered foe, contemplating its
vast size, a voice was heard (from whence he knew not, but he heard
it distinctly) commanding him to take the dragon's teeth and sow
them in the earth. He obeyed. He made a furrow in the ground, and
planted the teeth, destined to produce a crop of men. Scarce had he
done so when the clods began to move, and the points of spears
to appear above the surface. Next helmets with their nodding
plumes came up, and next the shoulders and breasts and limbs of
men with weapons, and in time a harvest of armed warriors. Cadmus,
alarmed, prepared to encounter a new enemy, but one of them said
to him, "Meddle not with our civil war." With that he who had
spoken smote one of his earth-born brothers with a sword, and he
himself fell pierced with an arrow from another. The latter fell
victim to a fourth, and in like manner the whole crowd dealt with
each other till all fell, slain with mutual wounds, except five survivors. One of these cast away his weapons and said, "Brothers, let
us live in peace!" These five joined with Cadmus in building his
city, to which they gave the name of Thebes.

Cadmus obtained in marriage Harmonia, the daughter of Venus.
The gods left Olympus to honour the occasion with their presence,
and Vulcan presented the bride with a necklace of surpassing brilliancy, his own workmanship. But a fatality hung over the family
of Cadmus in consequence of his killing the serpent sacred to Mars.
Semele and Ino, his daughters, and Actæon and Pentheus, his grandchildren, all perished unhappily, and Cadmus and Harmonia quitted
Thebes, now grown odious to them, and emigrated to the country of
the Enchelians, who received them with honour and made Cadmus
their king. But the misfortunes of their children still weighed upon
their minds; and one day Cadmus exclaimed, "If a serpent's life is
so dear to the gods, I would I were myself a serpent." No sooner had
he uttered the words than he began to change his form. Harmonia
beheld it and prayed to the gods to let her share his fate. Both became serpents. They live in the woods, but mindful of their origin,
they neither avoid the presence of man nor do they ever injure any
one.

There is a tradition that Cadmus introduced into Greece the
letters of the alphabet which were invented by the Phœnicians. This
is alluded to by Byron, where, addressing the modern Greeks, he
says:

"You have the letters Cadmus gave,
Think you he meant them for a slave?"

Milton, describing the serpent which tempted Eve, is reminded of the serpents of the classical stories and says:

> ..."—pleasing was his shape,
> And lovely: never since the serpent kind
> Lovelier; not those that in Illyria changed
> Hermione and Cadmus, nor the god
> In Epidaurus."

For an explanation of the last allusion, see EPIDAURUS.

THE MYRMIDONS

The Myrmidons were the soldiers of Achilles, in the Trojan war. From them all zealous and unscrupulous followers of a political chief are called by that name, down to this day. But the origin of the Myrmidons would not give one the idea of a fierce and bloody race, but rather of a laborious and peaceful one.

Cephalus, king of Athens, arrived in the island of Ægina to seek assistance of his old friend and ally Æacus, the king, in his war with Minos, king of Crete. Cephalus was most kindly received, and the desired assistance readily promised. "I have people enough," said Æacus, "to protect myself and spare you such a force as you need." "I rejoice to see it," replied Cephalus, "and my wonder has been raised, I confess, to find such a host of youths as I see around me, all apparently of about the same age. Yet there are many individuals whom I previously knew, that I look for now in vain. What has become of them?" Æacus groaned, and replied with a voice of sadness, "I have been intending to tell you, and will now do so, without more delay, that you may see how from the saddest beginning a happy result sometimes flows. Those whom you formerly knew are now dust and ashes! A plague sent by angry Juno devastated the land. She hated it because it bore the name of one of her husband's female favourites. While the disease appeared to spring from natural causes we resisted it as we best might, by natural remedies; but it soon appeared that the pestilence was too powerful for our efforts, and we yielded. At the beginning the sky seemed to settle down upon the earth, and thick clouds shut in the heated air. For four months together a deadly south wind prevailed. The disorder affected the wells and springs; thousands of snakes crept over the land and shed their poison in the fountains. The force of the disease was first spent on the lower animals—dogs, cattle, sheep, and birds. The luckless ploughman wondered to see his oxen fall in the midst of their work, and lie helpless in the unfinished furrow. The wool fell from the bleating sheep, and their bodies pined away. The horse, once foremost in the race, contested the palm no more, but groaned at his

stall and died an inglorious death. The wild boar forgot his rage,
the stag his swiftness, the bears no longer attacked the herds. Everything languished; dead bodies lay in the roads, the fields, and the
woods; the air was poisoned by them. I tell you what is hardly
credible, but neither dogs nor birds would touch them, nor starving
wolves. Their decay spread the infection. Next the disease attacked
the country people, and then the dwellers in the city. At first the
cheek was flushed, and the breath drawn with difficulty. The tongue
grew rough and swelled, and the dry mouth stood open with its veins
enlarged and gasped for the air. Men could not bear the heat of their
clothes or their beds, but preferred to lie on the bare ground; and
the ground did not cool them, but, on the contrary, they heated the
spot where they lay. Nor could the physicians help, for the disease
attacked them also, and the contact of the sick gave them infection,
so that the most faithful were the first victims. At last all hope of
relief vanished, and men learned to look upon death as the only deliverer from disease. Then they gave way to every inclination, and
cared not to ask what was expedient, for nothing was expedient. All
restraint laid aside, they crowded around the wells and fountains
and drank till they died, without quenching thirst. Many had not
strength to get away from the water, but died in the midst of the
stream, and others would drink of it notwithstanding. Such was their
weariness of their sick beds that some would creep forth, and if not
strong enough to stand, would die on the ground. They seemed to
hate their friends, and got away from their homes, as if, not knowing
the cause of their sickness, they charged it on the place of their
abode. Some were seen tottering along the road, as long as they could
stand, while others sank on the earth, and turned their dying eyes
around to take a last look, then closed them in death.

"What heart had I left me, during all this, or what ought I to have
had, except to hate life and wish to be with my dead subjects? On
all sides lay my people strewn like over-ripened apples beneath the
tree, or acorns under the storm-shaken oak. You see yonder a temple
on the height. It is sacred to Jupiter. O how many offered prayers
there, husbands for wives, fathers for sons, and died in the very act
of supplication! How often, while the priest made ready for sacrifice,
the victim fell, struck down by disease without waiting for the blow!
At length all reverence for sacred things was lost. Bodies were thrown
out unburied, wood was wanting for funeral piles, men fought with
one another for the possession of them. Finally there were none left
to mourn; sons and husbands, old men and youths, perished alike
unlamented.

"Standing before the altar I raised my eyes to heaven. 'O Jupiter,'

I said, 'if thou art indeed my father, and art not ashamed of thy offspring, give me back my people, or take me also away!' At these
words a clap of thunder was heard. 'I accept the omen,' I cried; 'O
may it be a sign of a favourable disposition towards me!' By chance
there grew by the place where I stood an oak with wide-spreading
branches, sacred to Jupiter. I observed a troop of ants busy with
their labour, carrying minute grains in their mouths and following
one another in a line up the trunk of the tree. Observing their numbers with admiration, I said, 'Give me, O father, citizens as numerous
as these, and replenish my empty city.' The tree shook and gave a
rustling sound with its branches, though no wind agitated them. I
trembled in every limb, yet I kissed the earth and the tree. I would
not confess to myself that I hoped, yet I did hope. Night came on
and sleep took possession of my frame oppressed with cares. The
tree stood before me in my dreams, with its numerous branches all
covered with living, moving creatures. It seemed to shake its limbs
and throw down over the ground a multitude of those industrious
grain-gathering animals, which appeared to gain in size, and grow
larger and larger, and by and by to stand erect, lay aside their superfluous legs and their black colour, and finally to assume the human
form. Then I awoke, and my first impulse was to chide the gods who
had robbed me of a sweet vision and given me no reality in its place.
Being still in the temple, my attention was caught by the sound of
many voices without; a sound of late unusual to my ears. While I
began to think I was yet dreaming, Telamon, my son, throwing open
the temple gates, exclaimed: 'Father, approach, and behold things
surpassing even your hopes!' I went forth; I saw a multitude of men
such as I had seen in my dream, and they were passing in procession
in the same manner. While I gazed with wonder and delight they approached, and kneeling hailed me as their king. I paid my vows to
Jove, and proceeded to allot the vacant city to the new-born race,
and to parcel out the fields among them. I called them Myrmidons,
from the ant (myrmex) from which they sprang. You have seen
these persons; their dispositions resemble those which they had in
their former shape. They are a diligent and industrious race, eager
to gain, and tenacious of their gains. Among them you may recruit
your forces. They will follow you to the war, young in years and
bold in heart."

This description of the plague is copied by Ovid from the account
which Thucydides, the Greek historian, gives of the plague of Athens.
The historian drew from life, and all the poets and writers of fiction
since his day, when they have had occasion to describe a similar
scene, have borrowed their details from him.

CHAPTER XIII

NISUS AND SCYLLA—ECHO AND NARCISSUS—CLYTIE—
HERO AND LEANDER

NISUS AND SCYLLA

MINOS, king of Crete, made war upon Megara. Nisus was king of Megara, and Scylla was his daughter. The siege had now lasted six months and the city still held out, for it was decreed by fate that it should not be taken so long as a certain purple lock, which glittered among the hair of King Nisus, remained on his head. There was a tower on the city walls, which overlooked the plain where Minos and his army were encamped. To this tower Scylla used to repair, and look abroad over the tents of the hostile army. The siege had lasted so long that she had learned to distinguish the persons of the leaders. Minos, in particular, excited her admiration. Arrayed in his helmet, and bearing his shield, she admired his graceful deportment; if he threw his javelin skill seemed combined with force in the discharge; if he drew his bow Apollo himself could not have done it more gracefully. But when he laid aside his helmet, and in his purple robes bestrode his white horse with its gay caparisons, and reined in its foaming mouth, the daughter of Nisus was hardly mistress of herself; she was almost frantic with admiration. She envied the weapon that he grasped, the reins that he held. She felt as if she could, if it were possible, go to him through the hostile ranks; she felt an impulse to cast herself down from the tower into the midst of his camp, or to open the gates to him, or to do anything else, so only it might gratify Minos. As she sat in the tower, she talked thus with herself: "I know not whether to rejoice or grieve at this sad war. I grieve that Minos is our enemy; but I rejoice at any cause that brings him to my sight. Perhaps he would be willing to grant us peace, and receive me as a hostage. I would fly down, if I could, and alight in his camp, and tell him that we yield ourselves to his mercy. But then, to betray my father! No! rather would I never see Minos again. And yet no doubt it is sometimes the best thing for a city to be conquered, when the conqueror is clement and generous. Minos certainly has right on his side. I think we shall be conquered; and if that must be the end of it, why should not love unbar the gates to him, instead of leaving it to be done by war? Better spare delay and slaughter if we can. And O if any one should wound or kill Minos! No one surely would have the heart to do it; yet ignorantly, not knowing him, one might. I will, I will surrender myself to him, with my country as a dowry, and so put an end to the war. But how? The gates are guarded, and my father keeps the keys; he only stands in my way. O that it might please the gods to take him away! But why ask the gods to do it? Another woman, loving as I do, would remove with her own hands whatever stood in the way of her love. And can any other woman dare more than I? I would encounter fire and sword to gain my object; but here there is no need of fire and sword. I only need my father's purple lock. More precious than gold to me, that will give me all I wish."

While she thus reasoned night came on, and soon the whole palace was buried in sleep. She entered her father's bedchamber and cut off the fatal lock; then passed out of the city and entered the enemy's camp. She demanded to be led to the king, and thus addressed him: "I am Scylla, the daughter of Nisus. I surrender to you my country and my father's house. I ask no reward but yourself: for love of you I have done it. See here the purple lock! With this I give you my father and his kingdom." She held out her hand with the fatal spoil. Minos shrunk back and refused to touch it. "The gods destroy thee, infamous woman," he exclaimed; "disgrace of our time! May neither earth nor sea yield thee a resting-place! Surely, my Crete, where Jove himself was cradled, shall not be polluted with such a monster!" Thus he said, and gave orders that equitable terms should be allowed to the conquered city, and that the fleet should immediately sail from the island.

Scylla was frantic. "Ungrateful man," she exclaimed, "is it thus you leave me?—me who have given you victory,—who have sacrificed for you parent and country! I am guilty, I confess, and deserve to die, but not by your hand." As the ships left the shore, she leaped into the water, and seizing the rudder of the one which carried Minos, she was borne along an unwelcome companion of their course. A sea-eagle soaring aloft,—it was her father who had been changed into that form,—seeing her, pounced down upon her, and struck her with his beak and claws. In terror she let go the ship and would have fallen into the water, but some pitying deity changed her into a bird. The sea-eagle still cherishes the old animosity; and whenever he espies her in his lofty flight you may see him dart down upon her, with beak and claws, to take vengeance for the ancient crime.

ECHO AND NARCISSUS

Echo was a beautiful nymph, fond of the woods and hills, where she devoted herself to woodland sports. She was a favourite of Diana, and attended her in the chase. But Echo had one failing; she was fond of talking, and whether in chat or argument, would have the last word. One day Juno was seeking her husband, who, she had reason to fear, was amusing himself among the nymphs. Echo by her talk contrived to detain the goddess till the nymphs made their escape. When Juno discovered it, she passed sentence upon Echo in these words: "You shall forfeit the use of that tongue with which you have cheated me, except for that one purpose you are so fond of—*reply*. You shall still have the last word, but no power to speak first."

This nymph saw Narcissus, a beautiful youth, as he pursued the chase upon the mountains. She loved him and followed his footsteps. O how she longed to address him in the softest accents, and win him to converse! but it was not in her power. She waited with impatience for him to speak first, and had her answer ready. One day the youth, being separated from his companions, shouted aloud, "Who's here?" Echo replied, "Here." Narcissus looked around, but seeing no one, called out, "Come." Echo answered, "Come." As no one came, Narcissus called again, "Why do you shun me?" Echo asked the same question. "Let us join one another," said the youth. The maid answered with all her heart in the same words, and hastened to the spot, ready to throw her arms about his neck. He started back, exclaiming, "Hands off! I would rather die than you should have me!" "Have me," said she; but it was all in vain. He left her, and she went to hide her blushes in the recesses of the woods. From that time forth she lived in caves and among mountain cliffs. Her form faded with grief, till at last all her flesh shrank away. Her bones were changed into rocks and there was nothing left of her but her voice. With that she is still ready to reply to any one who calls her, and keeps up her old habit of having the last word.

Narcissus's cruelty in this case was not the only instance. He shunned all the rest of the nymphs, as he had done poor Echo. One day a maiden who had in vain endeavoured to attract him uttered a prayer that he might some time or other feel what it was to love and meet no return of affection. The avenging goddess heard and granted the prayer.

There was a clear fountain, with water like silver, to which the shepherds never drove their flocks, nor the mountain goats resorted, nor any of the beasts of the forests; neither was it defaced with fallen leaves or branches; but the grass grew fresh around it, and the rocks sheltered it from the sun. Hither came one day the youth, fatigued with hunting, heated and thirsty. He stooped down to drink, and saw his own image in the water; he thought it was some beautiful water-spirit living in the fountain. He stood gazing with admiration at those bright eyes, those locks curled like the locks of

Bacchus or Apollo, the rounded cheeks, the ivory neck, the parted lips, and the glow of health and exercise over all. He fell in love with himself. He brought his lips near to take a kiss; he plunged his arms in to embrace the beloved object. It fled at the touch, but returned again after a moment and renewed the fascination. He could not tear himself away; he lost all thought of food or rest, while he hovered over the brink of the fountain gazing upon his own image. He talked with the supposed spirit: "Why, beautiful being, do you shun me? Surely my face is not one to repel you. The nymphs love me, and you yourself look not indifferent upon me. When I stretch forth my arms you do the same; and you smile upon me and answer my beckonings with the like." His tears fell into the water and disturbed the image. As he saw it depart, he exclaimed, "Stay, I entreat you! Let me at least gaze upon you, if I may not touch you." With this, and much more of the same kind, he cherished the flame that consumed him, so that by degrees he lost his colour, his vigour, and the beauty which formerly had so charmed the nymph Echo. She kept near him, however, and when he exclaimed, "Alas! alas!" she answered him with the same words. He pined away and died; and when his shade passed the Stygian river, it leaned over the boat to catch a look of itself in the waters. The nymphs mourned for him, especially the water-nymphs; and when they smote their breasts Echo smote hers also. They prepared a funeral pile and would have burned the body, but it was nowhere to be found; but in its place a flower, purple within, and surrounded with white leaves, which bears the name and preserves the memory of Narcissus.

Milton alludes to the story of Echo and Narcissus in the Lady's song in "Comus." She is seeking her brothers in the forest, and sings to attract their attention:

> "Sweet Echo, sweetest nymph, that liv'st unseen
> Within thy aëry shell
> By slow Meander's margent green,
> And in the violet-embroidered vale,
> Where the love-lorn nightingale
> Nightly to thee her sad song mourneth well;
> Canst thou not tell me of a gentle pair
> That likest thy Narcissus are?
> O, if thou have
> Hid them in some flowery cave,
> Tell me but where,
> Sweet queen of parly, daughter of the sphere,
> So may'st thou be translated to the skies,
> And give resounding grace to all heaven's harmonies."

Milton has imitated the story of Narcissus in the account which he makes Eve give of the first sight of herself reflected in the fountain.

"That day I oft remember when from sleep
I first awaked, and found myself reposed
Under a shade on flowers, much wondering where
And what I was, whence thither brought, and how
Not distant far from thence a murmuring sound
Of waters issued from a cave, and spread
Into a liquid plain, then stood unmoved
Pure as the expanse of heaven; I thither went
With unexperienced thought, and laid me down
On the green bank, to look into the clear
Smooth lake that to me seemed another sky.
As I bent down to look, just opposite
A shape within the watery gleam appeared,
Bending to look on me. I started back;
It started back; but pleased I soon returned,
Pleased it returned as soon with answering looks
Of sympathy and love. There had I fixed
Mine eyes till now, and pined with vain desire,
Had not a voice thus warned me: 'What thou seest,
What there thou seest, fair creature, is thyself;" etc.
                                    Paradise Lost, Book IV.

No one of the fables of antiquity has been oftener alluded to by
the poets than that of Narcissus. Here are two epigrams which treat
it in different ways. The first is by Goldsmith:

"ON A BEAUTIFUL YOUTH, STRUCK BLIND BY LIGHTNING

"Sure 'twas by Providence designed
    Rather in pity than in hate,
That he should be like Cupid blind,
    To save him from Narcissus' fate."

The other is by Cowper:

"ON AN UGLY FELLOW

"Beware, my friend, of crystal brook
Or fountain, lest that hideous hook,
    Thy nose, thou chance to see;
Narcissus' fate would then be thine,
And self-detested thou would'st pine,
    As self-enamoured he."

CLYTIE

Clytie was a water-nymph and in love with Apollo, who made her
no return. So she pined away, sitting all day long upon the cold
ground, with her unbound tresses streaming over her shoulders.
Nine days she sat and tasted neither food nor drink, her own tears
and the chilly dew her only food. She gazed on the sun when he rose,
and as he passed through his daily course to his setting; she saw
no other object, her face turned constantly on him. At last, they

say, her limbs rooted in the ground, her face became a flower,[1] which turns on its stem so as always to face the sun throughout its daily course; for it retains to that extent the feeling of the nymph from whom it sprang.

Hood, in his "Flowers," thus alludes to Clytie:

"I will not have the mad Clytie,
    Whose head is turned by the sun;
The tulip is a courtly quean,
    Whom therefore I will shun;

The cowslip is a country wench,
    The violet is a nun;—
But I will woo the dainty rose,
    The queen of every one."

The sunflower is a favourite emblem of constancy. Thus Moore uses it:

"The heart that has truly loved never forgets,
    But as truly loves on to the close;
As the sunflower turns on her god when he sets
    The same look that she turned when he rose."

HERO AND LEANDER

Leander was a youth of Abydos, a town of the Asian side of the strait which separates Asia and Europe. On the opposite shore, in the town of Sestos, lived the maiden Hero, a priestess of Venus. Leander loved her, and used to swim the strait nightly to enjoy the company of his mistress, guided by a torch which she reared upon the tower for the purpose. But one night a tempest arose and the sea was rough; his strength failed, and he was drowned. The waves bore his body to the European shore, where Hero became aware of his death, and in her despair cast herself down from the tower into the sea and perished.

The following sonnet is by Keats:

"ON A PICTURE OF LEANDER
"Come hither all sweet maidens soberly,
    Down looking aye, and with a chasten'd light
    Hid in the fringes of your eyelids white,
And meekly let your fair hands joinèd be,
As if so gentle that ye could not see,
    Untouch'd, a victim of your beauty bright,
    Sinking away to his young spirit's night,
Sinking bewilder'd 'mid the dreary sea.
'Tis young Leander toiling to his death.

[1] The sunflower.

Nigh swooning he doth purse his weary lips
For Hero's cheek, and smiles against her smile.
O horrid dream! see how his body dips
Dead-heavy; arms and shoulders gleam awhile;
He's gone; up bubbles all his amorous breath!"

The story of Leander's swimming the Hellespont was looked
upon as fabulous, and the feat considered impossible, till Lord Byron
proved its possibility by performing it himself. In the "Bride of
Abydos" he says,

"These limbs that buoyant wave hath borne."

The distance in the narrowest part is almost a mile, and there
is a constant current setting out from the Sea of Marmora into the
Archipelago. Since Byron's time the feat has been achieved by
others; but it yet remains a test of strength and skill in the art
of swimming sufficient to give a wide and lasting celebrity to any
one of our readers who may dare to make the attempt and succeed
in accomplishing it.

In the beginning of the second canto of the same poem, Byron thus
alludes to this story:

"The winds are high on Helle's wave,
    As on that night of stormiest water,
When Love, who sent, forgot to save
The young, the beautiful, the brave,
    The lonely hope of Sestos' daughter.
O, when alone along the sky
The turret-torch was blazing high,
Though rising gale and breaking foam,
And shrieking sea-birds warned him home;
And clouds aloft and tides below,
With signs and sounds forbade to go,
He could not see, he would not hear
Or sound or sight foreboding fear.
His eye but saw that light of love,
The only star it hailed above;
His ear but rang with Hero's song,
'Ye waves, divide not lovers long.'
That tale is old, but love anew
May nerve young hearts to prove as true."

CHAPTER XIV

MINERVA—NIOBE

MINERVA

MINERVA, the goddess of wisdom, was the daughter of Jupiter.
She was said to have leaped forth from his brain, mature, and in
complete armour. She presided over the useful and ornamental arts,

both those of men—such as agriculture and navigation—and those of women,—spinning, weaving, and needlework. She was also a warlike divinity; but it was defensive war only that she patronized, and she had no sympathy with Mars's savage love of violence and bloodshed. Athens was her chosen seat, her own city, awarded to her as the prize of a contest with Neptune, who also aspired to it. The tale ran that in the reign of Cecrops, the first king of Athens, the two deities contended for the possession of the city. The gods decreed that it should be awarded to that one who produced the gift most useful to mortals. Neptune gave the horse; Minerva produced the olive. The gods gave judgment that the olive was the more useful of the two, and awarded the city to the goddess; and it was named after her, Athens, her name in Greek being Athene.

There was another contest, in which a mortal dared to come in competition with Minera. That mortal was Arachne, a maiden who had attained such skill in the arts of weaving and embroidery that the nymphs themselves would leave their groves and fountains to come and gaze upon her work. It was not only beautiful when it was done, but beautiful also in the doing. To watch her, as she took the wool in its rude state and formed it into rolls, or separated it with her fingers and carded it till it looked as light and soft as a cloud, or twirled the spindle with skilful touch, or wove the web, or, after it was woven, adorned it with her needle, one would have said that Minerva herself had taught her. But this she denied, and could not bear to be thought a pupil even of a goddess. "Let Minerva try her skill with mine," said she; "if beaten I will pay the penalty." Minerva heard this and was displeased. She assumed the form of an old woman and went and gave Arachne some friendly advice. "I have had much experience," said she, "and I hope you will not despise my counsel. Challenge your fellow-mortals as you will, but do not compete with a goddess. On the contrary, I advise you to ask her forgiveness for what you have said, and as she is merciful perhaps she will pardon you." Arachne stopped her spinning and looked at the old dame with anger in her countenance. "Keep your counsel," said she, "for your daughters or handmaids; for my part I know what I say, and I stand to it. I am not afraid of the goddess; let her try her skill, if she dare venture." "She comes," said Minerva; and dropping her disguise stood confessed. The nymphs bent low in homage, and all the bystanders paid reverence. Arachne alone was unterrified. She blushed, indeed; a sudden colour dyed her cheek, and then she grew pale. But she stood to her resolve, and with a foolish conceit of her own skill rushed on her fate. Minerva forbore no longer nor interposed any further advice. They proceed to the contest. Each takes her

ϯ lation and attaches the web to the beam. Then the slender shuttle
is passed in and out among the threads. The reed with its fine teeth
strikes up the woof into its place and compacts the web. Both work
with speed; their skilful hands move rapidly, and the excitement
of the contest makes the labour light. Wool of Tyrian dye is con-
trasted with that of other colours, shaded off into one another so
adroitly that the joining deceives the eye. Like the bow, whose
long arch tinges the heavens, formed by sunbeams reflected from
the shower,[1] in which, where the colours meet they seem as one,
but at a little distance from the point of contact are wholly different.

Minerva wrought on her web the scene of her contest with
Neptune. Twelve of the heavenly powers are represented, Jupiter,
with august gravity, sitting in the midst. Neptune, the ruler of the
sea, holds his trident, and appears to have just smitten the earth,
from which a horse has leaped forth. Minerva depicted herself
with helmed head, her Ægis covering her breast. Such was the central circle; and in the four corners were represented incidents
illustrating the displeasure of the gods at such presumptuous mortals as had dared to contend with them. These were meant as
warnings to her rival to give up the contest before it was too late.

Arachne filled her web with subjects designedly chosen to exhibit
the failings and errors of the gods. One scene represented Leda
caressing the swan, under which form Jupiter had disguised himself; and another, Danaë, in the brazen tower in which her father
had imprisoned her, but where the god effected his entrance in
the form of a golden shower. Still another depicted Europa deceived by Jupiter under the disguise of a bull. Encouraged by the
tameness of the animal Europa ventured to mount his back, whereupon Jupiter advanced into the sea and swam with her to Crete.
You would have thought it was a real bull, so naturally was it
wrought, and so natural the water in which it swam. She seemed
to look with longing eyes back upon the shore she was leaving, and
to call to her companions for help. She appeared to shudder with
terror at the sight of the heaving waves, and to draw back her feet
from the water.

Arachne filled her canvas with similar subjects, wonderfully well
done, but strongly marking her presumption and impiety. Minerva could not forbear to admire, yet felt indignant at the insult.
She struck the web with her shuttle and rent it in pieces; she then
touched the forehead of Arachne and made her feel her guilt and
shame. She could not endure it and went and hanged herself.
Minerva pitied her as she saw her suspended by a rope. "Live,"

---

[1] This correct description of the rainbow is literally translated from Ovid.

she said, "guilty woman! and that you may preserve the memory of this lesson, continue to hang, both you and your descendants, to all future times." She sprinkled her with the juices of aconite, and immediately her hair came off, and her nose and ears likewise. Her form shrank up, and her head grew smaller yet; her fingers cleaved to her side and served for legs. All the rest of her is body, out of which she spins her thread, often hanging suspended by it, in the same attitude as when Minerva touched her and transformed her into a spider.

Spenser tells the story of Arachne in his "Muiopotmos," adhering very closely to his master Ovid, but improving upon him in the conclusion of the story. The two stanzas which follow tell what was done after the goddess had depicted her creation of the olive tree:

> "Amongst these leaves she made a Butterfly,
> With excellent device and wondrous slight,
> Fluttering among the olives wantonly,
> That seemed to live, so like it was in sight;
> The velvet nap which on his wings doth lie,
> The silken down with which his back is dight,
> His broad outstretched horns, his hairy thighs,
> His glorious colours, and his glistening eyes."[1]

> "Which when Arachne saw, as overlaid
> And mastered with workmanship so rare,
> She stood astonied long, ne aught gainsaid;
> And with fast-fixed eyes on her did stare,
> And by her silence, sign of one dismayed,
> The victory did yield her as her share:
> Yet did she inly fret and felly burn,
> And all her blood to poisonous rancour turn."

And so the metamorphosis is caused by Arachne's own mortification and vexation, and not by any direct act of the goddess.

The following specimen of old-fashioned gallantry is by Garrick:

> "UPON A LADY'S EMBROIDERY
>
> "Arachne once, as poets tell,
> A goddess at her art defied,
> And soon the daring mortal fell
> The hapless victim of her pride.
>
> "O, then beware Arachne's fate;
> Be prudent, Chloe, and submit,
> For you'll most surely meet her hate,
> Who rival both her art and wit."

[1] Sir James Mackintosh says of this, "Do you think that even a Chinese could paint the gay colours of a butterfly with more minute exactness than the following lines: 'The velvet nap,' etc.?"—*Life,* Vol. II. 246.

Tennyson, in his "Palace of Art," describing the works of art with which the palace was adorned, thus alludes to Europa:

> "... sweet Europa's mantle blew unclasped
> From off her shoulder, backward borne,
> From one hand drooped a crocus, one hand grasped
> The mild bull's golden horn."

In his "Princess" there is this allusion to Danaë:

> "Now lies the earth all Danaë to the stars,
> And all thy heart lies open unto me."

NIOBE

The fate of Arachne was noised abroad through all the country, and served as a warning to all presumptuous mortals not to compare themselves with the divinities. But one, and she a matron too, failed to learn the lesson of humility. It was Niobe, the queen of Thebes. She had indeed much to be proud of; but it was not her husband's fame, nor her own beauty, nor their great descent, nor the power of their kingdom that elated her. It was her children; and truly the happiest of mothers would Niobe have been if only she had not claimed to be so. It was on occasion of the annual celebration in honour of Latona and her offspring, Apollo and Diana,—when the people of Thebes were assembled, their brows crowned with laurel, bearing frankincense to the altars and paying their vows,—that Niobe appeared among the crowd. Her attire was splendid with gold and gems, and her aspect beautiful as the face of an angry woman can be. She stood and surveyed the people with haughty looks. "What folly," said she, "is this!—to prefer beings whom you never saw to those who stand before your eyes! Why should Latona be honoured with worship, and none be paid to me? My father was Tantalus, who was received as a guest at the table of the gods; my mother was a goddess. My husband built and rules this city, Thebes, and Phrygia is my paternal inheritance. Wherever I turn my eyes I survey the elements of my power; nor is my form and presence unworthy of a goddess. To all this let me add I have seven sons and seven daughters, and look for sons-in-law and daughters-in-law of pretensions worthy of my alliance. Have I not cause for pride? Will you prefer to me this Latona, the Titan's daughter, with her two children? I have seven times as many. Fortunate indeed am I, and fortunate I shall remain! Will any one deny this? My abundance is my security. I feel myself too strong for Fortune to subdue. She may take from me much; I shall still have much left. Were I to lose some of my children, I should hardly be left as poor as Latona with her two only. Away with you from these solemnities,—put off the laurel from your brows,—have done with this worship!" The people obeyed, and left the sacred services uncompleted.

The goddess was indignant. On the Cynthian mountain top where she dwelt she thus addressed her son and daughter: "My children, I who have been so proud of you both, and have been used to hold myself second to none of the goddesses except Juno alone, begin now to doubt whether I am indeed a goddess. I shall be deprived of my worship altogether unless you protect me." She was proceeding in this strain, but Apollo interrupted her. "Say no more," said he; "speech only delays punishment." So said Diana also. Darting through the air, veiled in clouds, they alighted on the towers of the city. Spread out before the gates was a broad plain, where the youth of the city pursued their warlike sports. The sons of Niobe were there with the rest,—some mounted on spirited horses richly caparisoned, some driving gay chariots. Ismenos, the first-born, as he guided his foaming steeds, struck with an arrow from above, cried out, "Ah me!" dropped the reins, and fell lifeless. Another, hearing the sound of the bow,—like the boatman who sees the storm gathering and makes all sail for the port.—gave the reins to his horses and attempted to escape. The inevitable arrow overtook him, as he fled. Two others, younger boys, just from their tasks, had gone to the playground to have a game of wrestling. As they stood breast to breast, one arrow pierced them both. They uttered a cry together, together cast a parting look around them, and together breathed their last. Alphenor, an elder brother, seeing them fall, hastened to the spot to render assistance, and fell stricken in the act of brotherly duty. One only was left, Ilioneus. He raised his arms to heaven to try whether prayer might not avail. "Spare me, ye gods!" he cried, addressing all, in his ignorance that all needed not his intercessions; and Apollo would have spared him, but the arrow had already left the string, and it was too late.

The terror of the people and grief of the attendants soon made Niobe acquainted with what had taken place. She could hardly think it possible; she was indignant that the gods had dared, and amazed that they had been able to do it. Her husband, Amphion, overwhelmed with the blow, destroyed himself. Alas! how different was this Niobe from her who had so lately driven away the people from the sacred rites, and held her stately course through the city, the envy of her friends, now the pity even of her foes! She knelt over the lifeless bodies, and kissed now one, now another of her dead sons. Raising her pallid arms to heaven, "Cruel Latona," said she, "feed full your rage with my anguish! Satiate your hard heart, while I follow to the grave my seven sons. Yet where is your triumph? Bereaved as I am, I am still richer than you, my conqueror." Scarce had she spoken, when the bow sounded and struck terror into all hearts except Niobe's alone. She was brave from excess of grief. The sisters stood in garments of mourning over the biers of their dead brothers. One fell, struck by an arrow, and died on the corpse she was bewailing. Another, attempting to console her mother, suddenly ceased to speak, and sank lifeless to the earth. A third tried to escape by flight, a fourth by concealment, another stood trembling, uncertain what course to take. Six were now dead, and only one remained, whom the mother held clasped in her arms, and covered as it were with her whole body. "Spare me one, and that the youngest! O spare me one of so many!" she cried; and while she spoke, that one fell dead. Desolate she sat, among sons, daughters, husband, all dead, and seemed torpid with grief. The breeze moved not her hair, no colour was on her cheek, her eyes glared fixed and immovable, there was no sign of life about her. Her very tongue cleaved to the roof of her mouth, and her veins ceased to convey the tide of life. Her neck bent not, her arms made no gesture, her foot no step. She was changed to stone, within and without. Yet tears continued to flow; and borne on a whirlwind to her native mountain, she still remains, a mass of rock, from which a trickling stream flows, the tribute of her never-ending grief.

The story of Niobe has furnished Byron with a fine illustration of the fallen condition of modern Rome:

"The Niobe of nations! there she stands,
    Childless and crownless in her voiceless woe;
An empty urn within her withered hands,
        Whose holy dust was scattered long ago;
The Scipios' tomb contains no ashes now:
The very sepulchres lie tenantless
Of their heroic dwellers; dost thou flow,
    Old Tiber! through a marble wilderness?
Rise with thy yellow waves, and mantle her distress."
                                                Childe Harold, IV. 79.

As an illustration of this story there is a celebrated statue in the imperial gallery of Florence. It is the principal figure of a group supposed to have been originally arranged in the pediment of a temple. The figure of the mother clasped by the arm of her terrified child is one of the most admired of the ancient statues. It ranks with the Laocoön and the Apollo among the masterpieces of art. The following is a translation of a Greek epigram supposed to relate to this statue:

"To stone the gods have changed her, but in vain;
The sculptor's art has made her breathe again."

Tragic as is the story of Niobe, we cannot forbear to smile at the use Moore has made of it in "Rhymes on the Road":

> " 'Twas in his carriage the sublime
> Sir Richard Blackmore used to rhyme,
> And, if the wits don't do him wrong,
> 'Twixt death and epics passed his time,
> Scribbling and killing all day long;
> Like Phœbus in his car at ease,
> Now warbling forth a lofty song,
> Now murdering the young Niobes."

Sir Richard Blackmore was a physician, and at the same time a very prolific and very tasteless poet, whose works are now forgotten, unless when recalled to mind by some wit like Moore for the sake of a joke.

CHAPTER XV

THE GRÆÆ AND GORGONS—PERSEUS—MEDUSA—ATLAS— ANDROMEDA

THE GRÆÆ AND GORGONS

THE Grææ were three sisters who were gray-haired from their birth, whence their name. The Gorgons were monstrous females with huge teeth like those of swine, brazen claws, and snaky hair. None of these beings make much figure in mythology except Medusa, the Gorgon, whose story we shall next advert to. We mention them chiefly to introduce an ingenious theory of some modern writers, namely, that the Gorgons and Grææ were only personifications of the terrors of the sea, the former denoting the *strong* billows of the wide open main, and the latter the *white*-crested waves that dash against the rocks of the coast. Their names in Greek signify the above epithets.

PERSEUS AND MEDUSA

Perseus was the son of Jupiter and Danaë. His grandfather Acrisius, alarmed by an oracle which had told him that his daughter's child would be the instrument of his death, caused the mother and child to be shut up in a chest and set adrift on the sea. The chest floated towards Seriphus, where it was found by a fisherman who conveyed the mother and infant to Polydectes, the king of the country, by whom they were treated with kindness. When Perseus was grown up Polydectes sent him to attempt the conquest of Medusa, a terrible monster who had laid waste the country. She was once a beautiful maiden whose hair was her chief glory, but as she dared to vie in beauty with Minerva, the goddess deprived her of her charms and changed her beautiful ringlets into hissing serpents. She became a cruel monster of so frightful an aspect that no living thing could behold her without being turned into stone. All around the cavern where she dwelt might be seen the stony figures of men and animals which had chanced to catch a glimpse of her and had been petrified with the sight. Perseus, favoured by Minerva and Mercury, the former of whom lent him her shield and the latter his winged shoes, approached Medusa while she slept and taking care not to look directly at her, but guided by her image reflected in the bright shield which he bore, he cut off her head and gave it to Minerva, who fixed it in the middle of her Ægis.

Milton, in his "Comus," thus alludes to the Ægis:

> "What was that snakyheaded Gorgon-shield
> That wise Minerva wore, unconquered virgin,
> Wherewith she freezed her foes to congealed stone,
> But rigid looks of chaste austerity,
> And noble grace that dashed brute violence
> With sudden adoration and blank awe!"

Armstrong, the poet of the "Art of Preserving Health," thus describes the effect of frost upon the waters:

> "Now blows the surly North and chills throughout
> The stiffening regions, while by stronger charms
> Than Circe e'er or fell Medea brewed,
> Each brook that wont to prattle to its banks
> Lies all bestilled and wedged betwixt its banks,
> Nor moves the withered reeds...
> The surges baited by the fierce North-east,
> Tossing with fretful spleen their angry heads,
> E'en in the foam of all their madness struck
> To monumental ice.
>
>   Such execution,
> So stern, so sudden, wrought the grisly aspect
> Of terrible Medusa,
> When wandering through the woods she turned to stone
> Their savage tenants; just as the foaming Lion
> Sprang furious on his prey, her speedier power
> Outran his haste,
> And fixed in that fierce attitude he stands
> Like Rage in marble!"—*Imitations of Shakespeare.*

PERSEUS AND ATLAS

After the slaughter of Medusa, Perseus, bearing with him the head of the Gorgon, flew far and wide, over land and sea. As night came on, he reached the western limit of the earth, where the sun

goes down. Here he would gladly have rested till morning. It was
the realm of King Atlas, whose bulk surpassed that of all other men.
He was rich in flocks and herds and had no neighbour or rival to
dispute his state. But his chief pride was in his gardens, whose fruit
was of gold, hanging from golden branches, half hid with golden
leaves. Perseus said to him, "I come as a guest. If you honour
illustrious descent, I claim Jupiter for my father; if mighty deeds,
I plead the conquest of the Gorgon. I seek rest and food." But Atlas
remembered that an ancient prophecy had warned him that a son
f Jove should one day rob him of his golden apples. So he answered, "Begone! or neither your false claims of glory nor parentage
shall protect you;" and he attempted to thrust him out. Perseus,
finding the giant too strong for him, said, "Since you value my
friendship so little, deign to accept a present;" and turning his face
away, he held up the Gorgon's head. Atlas, with all his bulk, was
changed into stone. His beard and hair became forests, his arms
and shoulders cliffs, his head a summit, and his bones rocks. Each
part increased in bulk till he became a mountain, and (such was
the pleasure of the gods) heaven with all its stars rests upon his
shoulders.

THE SEA-MONSTER

Perseus, continuing his flight, arrived at the country of the
Æthiopians, of which Cepheus was king. Cassiopeia his queen,
proud of her beauty, had dared to compare herself to the Sea-
Nymphs, which roused their indignation to such a degree that they
sent a prodigious sea-monster to ravage the coast. To appease the
deities, Cepheus was directed by the oracle to expose his daughter
Andromeda to be devoured by the monster. As Perseus looked down
from his aerial height he beheld the virgin chained to a rock, and
waiting the approach of the serpent. She was so pale and motionless
that if it had not been for her flowing tears and her hair that
moved in the breeze, he would have taken her for a marble statue.
He was so startled at the sight that he almost forgot to wave his
wings. As he hovered over her he said, "O virgin, undeserving of
those chains, but rather of such as bind fond lovers together, tell
me, I beseech you, your name, and the name of your country, and
why you are thus bound." At first she was silent from modesty,
and, if she could, would have hid her face with her hands; but when
he repeated his questions, for fear she might be thought guilty
of some fault which she dared not tell, she disclosed her name and
that of her country, and her mother's pride of beauty. Before she
had done speaking, a sound was heard off upon the water, and the
sea-monster appeared, with his head raised above the surface, cleav-

ing the waves with his broad breast. The virgin shrieked, the father and mother who had now arrived at the scene, wretched both, but the mother more justly so, stood by, not able to afford protection, but only to pour forth lamentations and to embrace the victim. Then spoke Perseus: "There will be time enough for tears; this hour is all we have for rescue. My rank as the son of Jove and my renown as the slayer of the Gorgon might make me acceptable as a suitor; but I will try to win her by services rendered, if the gods will only be propitious. If she be rescued by my valour, I demand that she be my reward." The parents consent (how could they hesitate?) and promise a royal dowry with her.

And now the monster was within the range of a stone thrown by a skilful slinger, when with a sudden bound the youth soared into the air. As an eagle, when from his lofty flight he sees a serpent basking in the sun, pounces upon him and seizes him by the neck to prevent him from turning his head round and using his fangs, so the youth darted down upon the back of the monster and plunged his sword into its shoulder. Irritated by the wound, the monster raised himself into the air, then plunged into the depth; then, like a wild boar surrounded by a pack of barking dogs, turned swiftly from side to side, while the youth eluded its attacks by means of his wings. Wherever he can find a passage for his sword between the scales he makes a wound, piercing now the side, now the flank, as it slopes towards the tail. The brute spouts from his nostrils water mixed with blood. The wings of the hero are wet with it, and he dares no longer trust to them. Alighting on a rock which rose above the waves, and holding on by a projecting fragment, as the monster floated near he gave him a death stroke. The people who had gathered on the shore shouted so that the hills reëchoed with the sound. The parents, transported with joy, embraced their future son-in-law, calling him their deliverer and the saviour of their house, and the virgin, both cause and reward of the contest, descended from the rock.

Cassiopeia was an Æthiopian, and consequently, in spite of her boasted beauty, black; at least so Milton seems to have thought, who alludes to this story in his "Penseroso," where he addresses Melancholy as the

> "...goddess, sage and holy,
> Whose saintly visage is too bright
> To hit the sense of human sight,
> And, therefore, to our weaker view,
> O'erlaid with black, staid Wisdom's hue.
> Black, but such as in esteem
> Prince Memnon's sister might beseem.

> Or that starred Æthiop queen that strove
> To set her beauty's praise above
> The sea-nymphs, and their powers offended."

Cassiopeia is called "the starred Æthiop queen" because after her death she was placed among the stars, forming the constellation of that name. Though she attained this honour, yet the Sea-Nymphs, her old enemies, prevailed so far as to cause her to be placed in that part of the heaven near the pole, where every night she is half the time held with her head downward, to give her a lesson of humility.

Memnon was an Æthiopian prince, of whom we shall tell in a future chapter.

THE WEDDING FEAST

The joyful parents, with Perseus and Andromeda, repaired to the palace, where a banquet was spread for them, and all was joy and festivity. But suddenly a noise was heard of warlike clamour, and Phineus, the betrothed of the virgin, with a party of his adherents, burst in, demanding the maiden as his own. It was in vain that Cepheus remonstrated—"You should have claimed her when she lay bound to the rock, the monster's victim. The sentence of the gods dooming her to such a fate dissolved all engagements, as death itself would have done." Phineus made no reply, but hurled his javelin at Perseus, but it missed its mark and fell harmless. Perseus would have thrown his in turn, but the cowardly assailant ran and took shelter behind the altar. But his act was a signal for an onset by his band upon the guests of Cepheus. They defended themselves and a general conflict ensued, the old king retreating from the scene after fruitless expostulations, calling the gods to witness that he was guiltless of this outrage on the rights of hospitality.

Perseus and his friends maintained for some time the unequal contest; but the numbers of the assailants were too great for them, and destruction seemed inevitable, when a sudden thought struck Perseus,—"I will make my enemy defend me." Then with a loud voice he exclaimed, "If I have any friend here let him turn away his eyes!" and held aloft the Gorgon's head. "Seek not to frighten us with your jugglery," said Thescelus, and raised his javelin in the act to throw, and became stone in the very attitude. Ampyx was about to plunge his sword into the body of a prostrate foe, but his arm stiffened and he could neither thrust forward nor withdraw it. Another, in the midst of a vociferous challenge, stopped, his mouth open, but no sound issuing. One of Perseus's friends, Aconteus, caught sight of the Gorgon and stiffened like the rest. Astyages struck him with his sword, but instead of wounding, it recoiled with a ringing noise.

Phineus beheld this dreadful result of his unjust aggression, and felt confounded. He called aloud to his friends, but got no answer; he touched them and found them stone. Falling on his knees and stretching out his hands to Perseus, but turning his head away, he begged for mercy. "Take all," said he, "give me but my life." "Base coward," said Perseus, "thus much I will grant you; no weapon shall touch you; moreover, you shall be preserved in my house as a memorial of these events." So saying, he held the Gorgon's head to the side where Phineus was looking, and in the very form in which he knelt, with his hands outstretched and face averted, he became fixed immovably, a mass of stone!

The following allusion to Perseus is from Milman's "Samor":

"As 'mid the fabled Libyan bridal stood
Perseus in stern tranquillity of wrath,
Half stood, half floated on his ankle-plumes
Out-swelling, while the bright face on his shield
Looked into stone the raging fray; so rose,
But with no magic arms, wearing alone
Th' appalling and control of his firm look,
The Briton Samor; at his rising awe
Went abroad, and the riotous hall was mute."

CHAPTER XVI

MONSTERS

GIANTS, SPHINX, PEGASUS AND CHIMÆRA, CENTAURS, GRIFFIN, AND PYGMIES

MONSTERS, in the language of mythology, were beings of unnatural proportions or parts, usually regarded with terror, as possessing immense strength and ferocity, which they employed for the injury and annoyance of men. Some of them were supposed to combine the members of different animals; such were the Sphinx and Chimæra; and to these all the terrible qualities of wild beasts were attributed, together with human sagacity and faculties. Others, as the giants, differed from men chiefly in their size; and in this particular we must recognize a wide distinction among them. The human giants, if so they may be called, such as the Cyclops, Antæus, Orion, and others, must be supposed not to be altogether disproportioned to human beings, for they mingled in love and strife with them. But the super-human giants, who warred with the gods, were of vastly larger dimensions. Tityus, we are told, when stretched on the plain, covered nine acres, and Enceladus required the whole of Mount Ætna to be laid upon him to keep him down.

We have already spoken of the war which the giants waged against the gods, and of its result. While this war lasted the giants proved a formidable enemy. Some of them, like Briareus, had a hundred arms; others, like Typhon, breathed out fire. At one time they put the gods to such fear that they fled into Egypt and hid themselves under various forms. Jupiter took the form of a ram, whence he was afterwards worshipped in Egypt as the god Ammon, with curved horns. Apollo became a crow, Bacchus a goat, Diana a cat, Juno a cow, Venus a fish, Mercury a bird. At another time the giants attempted to climb up into heaven, and for that purpose took up the mountain Ossa and piled it on Pelion.[1] They were at last subdued by thunderbolts, which Minerva invented, and taught Vulcan and his Cyclops to make for Jupiter.

THE SPHINX

Laius, king of Thebes, was warned by an oracle that there was danger to his throne and life if his new-born son should be suffered to grow up. He therefore committed the child to the care of a herdsman with orders to destroy him; but the herdsman, moved with pity, yet not daring entirely to disobey, tied up the child by the feet and left him hanging to the branch of a tree. In this condition the infant was found by a peasant, who carried him to his master and mistress, by whom he was adopted and called Œdipus, or Swollen-foot.

Many years afterwards Laius being on his way to Delphi, accompanied only by one attendant, met in a narrow road a young man also driving in a chariot. On his refusal to leave the way at their command the attendant killed one of his horses, and the stranger, filled with rage, slew both Laius and his attendant. The young man was Œdipus, who thus unknowingly became the slayer of his own father.

Shortly after this event the city of Thebes was afflicted with a monster which infested the highroad. It was called the Sphinx. It had the body of a lion and the upper part of a woman. It lay crouched on the top of a rock, and arrested all travellers who came that way, proposing to them a riddle, with the condition that those who could solve it should pass safe, but those who failed should be killed. Not one had yet succeeded in solving it, and all had been slain. Œdipus was not daunted by these alarming accounts, but boldly advanced to the trial. The Sphinx asked him, "What animal is that which in the morning goes on four feet, at noon on two, and

[1] See Proverbial Expressions, page 289.

in the evening upon three?" Œdipus replied, "Man, who in child-hood creeps on hands and knees, in manhood walks erect, and in old age with the aid of a staff." The Sphinx was so mortified at the solving of her riddle that she cast herself down from the rock and perished.

The gratitude of the people for their deliverance was so great that they made Œdipus their king, giving him in marriage their queen Jocasta. Œdipus, ignorant of his parentage, had already become the slayer of his father; in marrying the queen he became the husband of his mother. These horrors remained undiscovered, till at length Thebes was afflicted with famine and pestilence, and the oracle being consulted, the double crime of Œdipus came to light. Jocasta put an end to her own life, and Œdipus, seized with madness, tore out his eyes and wandered away from Thebes, dreaded and aban-doned by all except his daughters, who faithfully adhered to him, till after a tedious period of miserable wandering he found the termination of his wretched life.

PEGASUS AND THE CHIMÆRA

When Perseus cut off Medusa's head, the blood sinking into the earth produced the winged horse Pegasus. Minerva caught and tamed him and presented him to the Muses. The fountain Hippo-crene, on the Muses' mountain Helicon, was opened by a kick from his hoof.

The Chimæra was a fearful monster, breathing fire. The fore part of its body was a compound of the lion and the goat, and the hind part a dragon's. It made great havoc in Lycia, so that the king, Iobates, sought for some hero to destroy it. At that time there arrived at his court a gallant young warrior, whose name was Bel-lerophon. He brought letters from Prœtus, the son-in-law of Iobates, recommending Bellerophon in the warmest terms as an uncon-querable hero, but added at the close a request to his father-in-law to put him to death. The reason was that Prœtus was jealous of him, suspecting that his wife Antea looked with too much admira-tion on the young warrior. From this instance of Bellerophon being unconsciously the bearer of his own death warrant, the expression "Bellerophontic letters" arose, to describe any species of com-munication which a person is made the bearer of, containing matter prejudicial to himself.

Iobates, on perusing the letters, was puzzled what to do, not will-ing to violate the claims of hospitality, yet wishing to oblige his son-in-law. A lucky thought occurred to him, to send Bellerophon to combat with the Chimæra. Bellerophon accepted the proposal, but before proceeding to the combat consulted the soothsayer Polyidus, who advised him to procure if possible the horse Pegasus for the conflict. For this purpose he directed him to pass the night in the temple of Minerva. He did so, and as he slept Minerva came to him and gave him a golden bridle. When he awoke the bridle remained `n his hand. Minerva also showed him Pegasus drinking at the well of Pirene, and at sight of the bridle the winged steed came willingly and suffered himself to be taken. Bellerophon mounted him, rose with him into the air, soon found the Chimæra, and gained an easy victory over the monster.

After the conquest of the Chimæra Bellerophon was exposed to further trials and labours by his unfriendly host, but by the aid of Pegasus he triumphed in them all, till at length Iobates, seeing that the hero was a special favourite of the gods, gave him his daughter in marriage and made him his successor on the throne. At last Bellerophon by his pride and presumption drew upon himself the anger of the gods; it is said he even attempted to fly up into heaven on his winged steed, but Jupiter sent a gadfly which stung Pegasus and made him throw his rider, who became lame and blind in consequence. After this Bellerophon wandered lonely through the Aleian field, avoiding the paths of men, and died miserably.

Milton alludes to Bellerophon in the beginning of the seventh book of "Paradise Lost":

> "Descend from Heaven, Urania, by that name
> If rightly thou art called, whose voice divine
> Following, above the Olympian hill I soar,
> Above the flight of Pegasean wing.
>   Upled by thee,
> Into the Heaven of Heavens I have presumed,
> An earthly guest, and drawn empyreal air
> (Thy tempering); with like safety guided down
> Return me to my native element;
> Lest, from this flying steed unreined (as once
> Bellerophon, though from a lower clime),
> Dismounted, on the Aleian field I fall,
> Erroneous there to wander and forlorn."

Young, in his "Night Thoughts," speaking of the sceptic, says:

> "He whose blind thought futurity denies,
> Unconscious bears, Bellerophon, like thee
> His own indictment; he condemns himself.
> Who reads his bosom reads immortal life,
> Or nature there; imposing on her sons,
> Has written fables; man was made a lie."
>   Vol. II., p. 12.

Pegasus, being the horse of the Muses, has always been at the service of the poets. Schiller tells a pretty story of his having been sold by a needy poet and put to the cart and the plough. He was not fit for such service, and his clownish master could make nothing of him. But a youth stepped forth and asked leave to try him. As soon as he was seated on his back the horse, which had appeared at first vicious, and afterwards spirit-broken, rose kingly, a spirit, a god, unfolded the splendour of his wings, and soared towards heaven. Our own poet Longfellow also records an adventure of this famous steed in his "Pegasus in Pound."

Shakespeare alludes to Pegasus in "Henry IV.," where Vernon describes Prince Henry:

> "I saw young Harry, with his beaver on,
> His cuishes on his thighs, gallantly armed,
> Rise from the ground like feathered Mercury,
> And vaulted with such ease into his seat,
> As if an angel dropped down from the clouds,
> To turn and wind a fiery Pegasus,
> And witch the world with noble horsemanship."

THE CENTAURS

These monsters were represented as men from the head to the loins, while the remainder of the body was that of a horse. The ancients were too fond of a horse to consider the union of his nature with man's as forming a very degraded compound, and accordingly the Centaur is the only one of the fancied monsters of antiquity to which any good traits are assigned. The Centaurs were admitted to the companionship of man, and at the marriage of Pirithous with Hippodamia they were among the guests. At the feast Eurytion, one of the Centaurs, becoming intoxicated with the wine, attempted to offer violence to the bride; the other Centaurs followed his example, and a dreadful conflict arose in which several of them were slain. This is the celebrated battle of the Lapithæ and Centaurs, a favourite subject with the sculptors and poets of antiquity.

But not all the Centaurs were like the rude guests of Pirithous. Chiron was instructed by Apollo and Diana, and was renowned for his skill in hunting, medicine, music, and the art of prophecy. The most distinguished heroes of Grecian story were his pupils. Among the rest the infant Æsculapius was intrusted to his charge by Apollo, his father. When the sage returned to his home bearing the infant, his daughter Ocyrhoe came forth to meet him, and at sight of the child burst forth into a prophetic strain (for she was a prophetess), foretelling the glory that he was to achieve. Æsculapius when grown up became a renowned physician, and even in one instance succeeded in restoring the dead to life. Pluto resented this, and Jupiter, at his request, struck the bold physician with lightning, and killed him, but after his death received him into the number of the gods.

Chiron was the wisest and justest of all the Centaurs, and at his death Jupiter placed him among the stars as the constellation Sagittarius.

THE PYGMIES

The Pygmies were a nation of dwarfs, so called from a Greek word which means the cubit or measure of about thirteen inches, which was said to be the height of these people. They lived near the sources of the Nile, or according to others, in India. Homer tells us that the cranes used to migrate every winter to the Pygmies' country, and their appearance was the signal of bloody warfare to the puny inhabitants, who had to take up arms to defend their cornfields against the rapacious strangers. The Pygmies and their enemies the Cranes form the subject of several works of art.

Later writers tell of an army of Pygmies which finding Hercules asleep, made preparations to attack him, as if they were about to attack a city. But the hero, awaking, laughed at the little warriors, wrapped some of them up in his lion's skin, and carried them to Eurystheus.

Milton uses the Pygmies for a simile, "Paradise Lost," Book I.:

"...like that Pygmæan race
Beyond the Indian mount, or fairy elves
Whose midnight revels by a forest side,
Or fountain, some belated peasant sees
(Or dreams he sees), while overhead the moon
Sits arbitress, and nearer to the earth
Wheels her pale course; they on their mirth and dance
Intent, with jocund music charm his ear.
At once with joy and fear his heart rebounds."

THE GRIFFIN, OR GRYPHON

The Griffin is a monster with the body of a lion, the head and wings of an eagle, and back covered with feathers. Like birds it builds its nest, and instead of an egg lays an agate therein. It has long claws and talons of such a size that the people of that country make them into drinking-cups. India was assigned as the native country of the Griffins. They found gold in the mountains and built their nests of it, for which reason their nests were very tempting to the hunters, and they were forced to keep vigilant guard over them.

Their instinct led them to know where buried treasures lay, and they did their best to keep plunderers at a distance. The Arimaspians, among whom the Griffins flourished, were a one-eyed people of Scythia.

Milton borrows a simile from the Griffins, "Paradise Lose," Book II.:

> "As when a Gryphon through the wilderness
> With wingèd course, o'er hill and moory dale,
> Pursues the Arimaspian, who by stealth
> Had from his wakeful custody purloined
> The guarded gold," etc.

CHAPTER XVII

THE GOLDEN FLEECE—MEDEA

THE GOLDEN FLEECE

IN very ancient times there lived in Thessaly a king and queen named Athamas and Nephele. They had two children, a boy and a girl. After a time Athamas grew indifferent to his wife, put her away, and took another. Nephele suspected danger to her children from the influence of the step-mother, and took measures to send them out of her reach. Mercury assisted her, and gave her a ram with a *golden fleece*, on which she set the two children, trusting that the ram would convey them to a place of safety. The ram vaulted into the air with the children on his back, taking his course to the East, till when crossing the strait that divides Europe and Asia, the girl, whose name was Helle, fell from his back into the sea, which from her was called the Hellespont,—now the Dardanelles. The ram continued his career till he reached the kingdom of Colchis, on the eastern shore of the Black Sea, where he safely landed the boy Phryxus, who was hospitably received by Æetes, king of the country. Phryxus sacrificed the ram to Jupiter, and gave the *Golden Fleece* to Æetes, who placed it in a consecrated grove, under the care of a sleepless dragon.

There was another kingdom in Thessaly near to that of Athamas, and ruled over by a relative of his. The king Æson, being tired of the cares of government, surrendered his crown to his brother Pelias on condition that he should hold it only during the minority of Jason, the son of Æson. When Jason was grown up and came to demand the crown from his uncle, Pelias pretended to be willing to yield it, but at the same time suggested to the young man the glorious adventure of going in quest of the Golden Fleece, which it was well known was in the kingdom of Colchis, and was, as Pelias pretended, the rightful property of their family. Jason was pleased with the thought and forthwith made preparations for the expedition. At that time the only species of navigation known to the Greeks consisted of small boats or canoes hollowed out from trunks of trees, so that when Jason employed Argus to build him a vessel capable of containing fifty men, it was considered a gigantic undertaking. It was accomplished, however, and the vessel named "Argo," from the name of the builder. Jason sent his invitation to all the adventurous young men of Greece, and soon found himself at the head of a band of bold youths, many of whom afterwards were renowned among the heroes and demigods of Greece. Hercules, Theseus, Orpheus, and Nestor were among them. They are called the Argonauts, from the name of their vessel.

The "Argo" with her crew of heroes left the shores of Thessaly and having touched at the Island of Lemnos, thence crossed to Mysia and thence to Thrace. Here they found the sage Phineus, and from him received instruction as to their future course. It seems the entrance of the Euxine Sea was impeded by two small rocky islands, which floated on the surface, and in their tossings and heavings occasionally came together, crushing and grinding to atoms any object that might be caught between them. They were called the Symplegades, or Clashing Islands. Phineus instructed the Argonauts how to pass this dangerous strait. When they reached the islands they let go a dove, which took her way between the rocks, and passed in safety, only losing some feathers of her tail. Jason and his men seized the favourable moment of the rebound, plied their oars with vigour, and passed safe through, though the islands closed behind them, and actually grazed their stern. They now rowed along the shore till they arrived at the eastern end of the sea, and landed at the kingdom of Colchis.

Jason made known his message to the Colchian king, Æetes, who consented to give up the golden fleece if Jason would yoke to the plough two fire-breathing bulls with brazen feet, and sow the teeth of the dragon which Cadmus had slain, and from which it was well known that a crop of armed men would spring up, who would turn their weapons against their producer. Jason accepted the conditions, and a time was set for making the experiment. Previously, however, he found means to plead his cause to Medea, daughter of the king. He promised her marriage, and as they stood before the altar of Hecate, called the goddess to witness his oath. Medea yielded, and by her aid, for she was a potent sorceress, he was furnished with a charm, by which he could encounter safely the breath of the fire-breathing bulls and the weapons of the armed men.

At the time appointed, the people assembled at the grove of

Mars, and the king assumed his royal seat, while the multitude
covered the hill-sides. The brazen-footed bulls rushed in, breathing fire from their nostrils that burned up the herbage as they
passed. The sound was like the roar of a furnace, and the smoke
like that of water upon quick-lime. Jason advanced boldly to meet
them. His friends, the chosen heroes of Greece, trembled to behold
him. Regardless of the burning breath, he soothed their rage with
his voice, patted their necks with fearless hand, and adroitly
slipped over them the yoke, and compelled them to drag the plough.
The Colchians were amazed; the Greeks shouted for joy. Jason
next proceeded to sow the dragon's teeth and plough them in. And
soon the crop of armed men sprang up, and, wonderful to relate!
no sooner had they reached the surface than they began to brandish
their weapons and rush upon Jason. The Greeks trembled for their
hero, and even she who had provided him a way of safety and
taught him how to use it, Medea herself, grew pale with fear. Jason
for a time kept his assailants at bay with his sword and shield,
till, finding their numbers overwhelming, he resorted to the charm
which Medea had taught him, seized a stone and threw it in the
midst of his foes. They immediately turned their arms against one
another, and soon there was not one of the dragon's brood left alive.
The Greeks embraced their hero, and Medea, if she dared, would
have embraced him too.

It remained to lull to sleep the dragon that guarded the fleece,
and this was done by scattering over him a few drops of a preparation which Medea had supplied. At the smell he relaxed his rage,
stood for a moment motionless, then shut those great round eyes,
that had never been known to shut before, and turned over on
his side, fast asleep. Jason seized the fleece and with his friends
and Medea accompanying, hastened to their vessel before Æetes
the king could arrest their departure, and made the best of their
way back to Thessaly, where they arrived safe, and Jason delivered
the fleece to Pelias, and dedicated the "Argo" to Neptune. What
became of the fleece afterwards we do not know, but perhaps it
was found after all, like many other golden prizes, not worth the
trouble it had cost to procure it.

This is one of those mythological tales, says a late writer, in
which there is reason to believe that a substratum of truth exists,
though overlaid by a mass of fiction. It probably was the first
important maritime expedition, and like the first attempts of the
kind of all nations, as we know from history, was probably of a
half-piratical character. If rich spoils were the result it was enough
to give rise to the idea of the golden fleece.

Another suggestion of a learned mythologist, Bryant, is that it is a corrupt tradition of the story of Noah and the ark. The name "Argo" seems to countenance this, and the incident of the dove is another confirmation.

Pope, in his "Ode on St. Cecilia's Day," thus celebrates the launching of the ship "Argo," and the power of the music of Orpheus, whom he calls the Thracian:

"So when the first bold vessel dared the seas,
    High on the stern the Thracian raised his strain,
While Argo saw her kindred trees
    Descend from Pelion to the main.
Transported demigods stood round,
And men grew heroes at the sound."

In Dyer's poem of "The Fleece" there is an account of the ship "Argo" and her crew, which gives a good picture of this primitive maritime adventure:

"From every region of Ægea's shore
The brave assembled; those illustrious twins
Castor and Pollux; Orpheus, tuneful bard;
Zetes and Calais, as the wind in speed;
Strong Hercules and many a chief renowned.
On deep Ioclos' sandy shore they thronged,
Gleaming in armour, ardent of exploits;
And soon, the laurel cord and the huge stone
Uplifting to the deck, unmoored the bark;
Whose keel of wondrous length the skilful hand
Of Argus fashioned for the proud attempt;
And in the extended keel a lofty mast
Upraised, and sails full swelling; to the chiefs
Unwonted objects. Now first, now they learned
Their bolder steerage over ocean wave,
Led by the golden stars, as Chiron's art
Had marked the sphere celestial," etc.

Hercules left the expedition at Mysia, for Hylas, a youth beloved by him, having gone for water, was laid hold of and kept by the nymphs of the spring, who were fascinated by his beauty. Hercules went in quest of the lad, and while he was absent the "Argo" put to sea and left him. Moore, in one of his songs, makes a beautiful allusion to this incident:

"When Hylas was sent with his urn to the fount,
    Through fields full of light and with heart full of play,
Light rambled the boy over meadow and mount,
    And neglected his task for the flowers in the way.

"Thus many like me, who in youth should have tasted
    The fountain that runs by Philosophy's shrine,
Their time with the flowers on the margin have wasted,
    And left their light urns all as empty as mine."

MEDEA AND ÆSON

Amid the rejoicings for the recovery of the Golden Fleece, Jason felt that one thing was wanting, the presence of Æson, his father, who was prevented by his age and infirmities from taking part in them. Jason said to Medea, "My spouse, would that your arts, whose power I have seen so mighty for my aid, could do me one further service, take some years from my life and add them to my father's." Medea replied, "Not at such a cost shall it be done, but if my art avails me, his life shall be lengthened without abridging yours." The next full moon she issued forth alone, while all creatures slept; not a breath stirred the foliage, and all was still. To the stars she addressed her incantations, and to the moon; to Hecate,[1] the goddess of the under-world, and to Tellus the goddess of the earth, by whose power plants potent for enchantment are produced. She invoked the gods of the woods and caverns, of mountains and valleys, of lakes and rivers, of winds and vapours. While she spoke the stars shone brighter, and presently a chariot descended through the air, drawn by flying serpents. She ascended it, and borne aloft made her way to distant regions, where potent plants grew which she knew how to select for her purpose. Nine nights she employed in her search, and during that time came not within the doors of her palace nor under any roof, and shunned all intercourse with mortals.

She next erected two altars, the one to Hecate, the other to Hebe, the goddess of youth, and sacrificed a black sheep, pouring libations of milk and wine. She implored Pluto and his stolen bride that they would not hasten to take the old man's life. Then she directed that Æson should be led forth, and having thrown him into a deep sleep by a charm, had him laid on a bed of herbs, like one dead. Jason and all others were kept away from the place, that no profane eyes might look upon her mysteries. Then, with streaming hair, she thrice moved round the altars, dipped flaming twigs in the blood, and laid them thereon to burn. Meanwhile the cauldron with its contents was got ready. In it she put magic herbs, with seeds and flowers of acrid juice, stones from the distant east, and sand from the shore of all-surrounding ocean; hoar frost, gathered by moonlight, a screech owl's head and wings, and the entrails of a wolf. She added fragments of the shells of tortoises, and the liver of stags—animals

---

[1] Hecate was a mysterious divinity sometimes identified with Diana and sometimes with Proserpine. As Diana represents the moonlight splendour of night, so Hecate represents its darkness and terrors. She was the goddess of sorcery and witchcraft, and was believed to wander by night along the earth, seen only by the dogs, whose barking told her approach.

tenacious of life—and the head and beak of a crow, that outlives nine generations of men. These with many other things "without a name" she boiled together for her purposed work, stirring them up with a dry olive branch; and behold! the branch when taken out instantly became green, and before long was covered with leaves and a plentiful growth of young olives; and as the liquor boiled and bubbled, and sometimes ran over, the grass wherever the sprinklings fell shot forth with a verdure like that of spring.

Seeing that all was ready, Medea cut the throat of the old man and let out all his blood, and poured into his mouth and into his wound the juices of her cauldron. As soon as he had completely imbibed them, his hair and beard laid by their whiteness and assumed the blackness of youth; his paleness and emaciation were gone; his veins were full of blood, his limbs of vigour and robustness. Æson is amazed at himself, and remembers that such as he now is, he was in his youthful days, forty years before.

Medea used her arts here for a good purpose, but not so in another instance, where she made them the instruments of revenge. Pelias, our readers will recollect, was the usurping uncle of Jason, and had kept him out of his kingdom. Yet he must have had some good qualities, for his daughters loved him, and when they saw what Medea had done for Æson, they wished her to do the same for their father. Medea pretended to consent, and prepared her cauldron as before. At her request an old sheep was brought and plunged into the cauldron. Very soon a bleating was heard in the kettle, and when the cover was removed, a lamb jumped forth and ran frisking away into the meadow. The daughters of Pelias saw the experiment with delight, and appointed a time for their father to undergo the same operation. But Medea prepared her cauldron for him in a very different way. She put in only water and a few simple herbs. In the night she with the sisters entered the bed chamber of the old king, while he and his guards slept soundly under the influence of a spell cast upon them by Medea. The daughters stood by the bedside with their weapons drawn, but hesitated to strike, till Medea chid their irresolution. Then turning away their faces, and giving random blows, they smote him with their weapons. He, starting from his sleep, cried out, "My daughters, what are you doing? Will you kill your father?" Their hearts failed them and their weapons fell from their hands, but Medea struck him a fatal blow, and prevented his saying more.

Then they placed him in the cauldron, and Medea hastened to depart in her serpent-drawn chariot before they discovered her treachery, or their vengeance would have been terrible. She escaped, however, but had little enjoyment of the fruits of her crime. Jason, for whom she had done so much, wishing to marry Creusa, princess of Corinth, put away Medea. She, enraged at his ingratitude, called on the gods for vengeance, sent a poisoned robe as a gift to the bride, and then killing her own children, and setting fire to the palace, mounted her serpent-drawn chariot and fled to Athens, where she married King Ægeus, the father of Theseus, and we shall meet her again when we come to the adventures of that hero.

The incantations of Medea will remind the reader of those of the witches in "Macbeth." The following lines are those which seem most strikingly to recall the ancient model:

> "Round about the cauldron go;
> In the poisoned entrails throw.
>
> Fillet of a fenny snake
> In the cauldron boil and bake;
> Eye of newt and toe of frog,
> Wool of bat and tongue of dog,
> Adder's fork and blind-worm's sting,
> Lizard's leg and howlet's wing;
>
> Maw of ravening salt-sea shark,
> Root of hemlock digged in the dark," etc.
>
> *Macbeth,* Act IV. Scene 1.

And again:

> *Macbeth.*—What is't you do?
> *Witches.*—A deed without a name.

There is another story of Medea almost too revolting for record even of a sorceress, a class of persons to whom both ancient and modern poets have been accustomed to attribute every degree of atrocity. In her flight from Colchis she had taken her young brother Absyrtus with her. Finding the pursuing vessels of Æetes gaining upon the Argonauts, she caused the lad to be killed and his limbs to be strewn over the sea. Æetes on reaching the place found these sorrowful traces of his murdered son; but while he tarried to collect the scattered fragments and bestow upon them an honourable inter-ment, the Argonauts escaped.

In the poems of Campbell will be found a translation of one of the choruses of the tragedy of "Medea," where the poet Euripides has taken advantage of the occasion to pay a glowing tribute to Athens, his native city. It begins thus:

> "O haggard queen! to Athens dost thou guide
> Thy glowing chariot, steeped in kindred gore;
> Or seek to hide thy damned parricide
> Where peace and justice dwell for evermore?"

CHAPTER XVIII

MELEAGER AND ATALANTA

ONE of the heroes of the Argonautic expedition was Meleager, son of Œneus and Althea, king and queen of Calydon. Althea, when her son was born, beheld the three destinies, who as they spun their fatal thread, foretold that the life of the child should last no longer than a brand then burning upon the hearth. Althea seized and quenched the brand, and carefully preserved it for years, while Meleager grew to boyhood, youth and manhood. It chanced, then, that Œneus, as he offered sacrifices to the gods, omitted to pay due honours to Diana; and she, indignant at the neglect, sent a wild boar of enormous size to lay waste the fields of Calydon. Its eyes shone with blood and fire, its bristles stood like threatening spears, its tusks were like those of Indian elephants. The growing corn was trampled, the vines and olive trees laid waste, the flocks and herds were driven in wild confusion by the slaughtering foe. All common aid seemed vain; but Meleager called on the heroes of Greece to join in a bold hunt for the ravenous monster. Theseus and his friend Pirithous, Jason, Peleus, afterwards the father of Achilles, Telamon the father of Ajax, Nestor, then a youth, but who in his age bore arms with Achilles and Ajax in the Trojan war—these and many more joined in the enterprise. With them came Atalanta, the daughter of Iasius, king of Arcadia. A buckle of polished gold confined her vest, an ivory quiver hung on her left shoulder, and her left hand bore the bow. Her face blent feminine beauty with the best graces of martial youth. Meleager saw and loved.

But now already they were near the monster's lair. They stretched strong nets from tree to tree; they uncoupled their dogs, they tried to find the footprints of their quarry in the grass. From the wood was a descent to marshy grounds. Here the boar, as he lay among the reeds, heard the shouts of his pursuers, and rushed forth against them. One and another is thrown down and slain. Jason throws his spear, with a prayer to Diana for success; and the favouring goddess allows the weapon to touch, but not to wound, removing the steel point of the spear in its flight. Nestor, assailed, seeks and finds safety in the branches of a tree. Telamon rushes on, but stumbling at a projecting root, falls prone. But an arrow from Atalanta at length for the first time tastes the monster's blood. It is a slight wound, but Meleager sees and joyfully proclaims it. Anceus, excited to envy by the praise given to a female, loudly proclaims his own valour, and defies alike the boar and the goddess who had sent it; but as he rushes on, the infuriated beast lays him low with a mortal wound. Theseus throws his lance, but it is turned aside by a projecting bough. The dart of Jason misses its object, and kills instead one of their own dogs. But Meleager, after one unsuccessful stroke, drives his spear into the monster's side, then rushes on and despatches him with repeated blows.

Then rose a shout from those around; they congratulated the conqueror, crowding to touch his hand. He, placing his foot upon the head of the slain boar, turned to Atalanta and bestowed on her the head and the rough hide which were the trophies of his success. But at this, envy excited the rest to strife. Plexippus and Toxeus, the brothers of Meleager's mother, beyond the rest opposed the gift, and snatched from the maiden the trophy she had received. Meleager, kindling with rage at the wrong done to himself, and still more at the insult offered to her whom he loved, forgot the claims of kindred, and plunged his sword into the offenders' hearts.

As Althea bore gifts of thankfulness to the temples for the victory of her son, the bodies of her murdered brothers met her sight. She shrieks, and beats her breast, and hastens to change the garments of rejoicing for those of mourning. But when the author of the deed is known, grief gives way to the stern desire of vengeance on her son. The fatal brand, which once she rescued from the flames, the brand which the destinies had linked with Meleager's life, she brings forth, and commands a fire to be prepared. Then four times she essays to place the brand upon the pile; four times draws back, shuddering at the thought of bringing destruction on her son. The feelings of the mother and the sister contend within her. Now she is pale at the thought of the proposed deed, now flushed again with anger at the act of her son. As a vessel, driven in one direction by the wind, and in the opposite by the tide, the mind of Althea hangs suspended in uncertainty. But now the sister prevails above the mother, and she begins as she holds the fatal wood: "Turn, ye Furies, goddesses of punishment! turn to behold the sacrifice I bring! Crime must atone for crime. Shall Œneus rejoice in his victor son, while the house of Thestius is desolate? But, alas! to what deed am I borne along? Brothers, forgive a mother's weakness! my hand fails me. He deserves death, but not that I should destroy him. But shall he then live, and triumph, and reign over Calydon, while you, my brothers, wander unavenged among the shades? No! thou hast lived by my gift; die, now, for thine own crime. Return the life which twice I gave thee, first at thy birth, again when I snatched this brand from the flames. O that thou hadst then died! Alas! evil is the conquest; but, brothers, ye have conquered." And, turning away her face, she threw the fatal wood upon the burning pile.

It gave, or seemed to give, a deadly groan. Meleager, absent and unknowing of the cause, felt a sudden pang. He burns, and only by courageous pride conquers the pain which destroys him. He mourns only that he perishes by a bloodless and unhonoured death. With his last breath he calls upon his aged father, his brother, and his fond sisters, upon his beloved Atalanta, and upon his mother, the unknown cause of his fate. The flames increase, and with them the pain of the hero. Now both subside; now both are quenched. The brand is ashes, and the life of Meleager is breathed forth to the wandering winds.

Althea, when the deed was done, laid violent hands upon herself. The sisters of Meleager mourned their brother with uncontrollable grief; till Diana, pitying the sorrows of the house that once had aroused her anger, turned them into birds.

ATALANTA

The innocent cause of so much sorrow was a maiden whose face you might truly say was boyish for a girl, yet too girlish for a boy. Her fortune had been told, and it was to this effect: "Atalanta, do not marry; marriage will be your ruin." Terrified by this oracle, she fled the society of men, and devoted herself to the sports of the chase. To all suitors (for she had many) she imposed a condition which was generally effectual in relieving her of their persecutions,— "I will be the prize of him who shall conquer me in the race; but death must be the penalty of all who try and fail." In spite of this hard condition some would try. Hippomenes was to be judge of the race. "Can it be possible that any will be so rash as to risk so much for a wife?" said he. But when he saw her lay aside her robe for the race, he changed his mind, and said, "Pardon me, youths, I knew not the prize you were competing for." As he surveyed them he wished them all to be beaten, and swelled with envy of any one that seemed at all likely to win. While such were his thoughts, the virgin darted forward. As she ran she looked more beautiful than ever. The breezes seemed to give wings to her feet; her hair flew over her shoulders, and the gay fringe of her garment fluttered behind her. A ruddy hue tinged the whiteness of her skin, such as a crimson curtain casts on a marble wall. All her competitors were distanced, and were put to death without mercy. Hippomenes, not daunted by this result, fixing his eyes on the virgin, said, "Why boast of beating those laggards? I offer myself for the contest." Atalanta looked at him with a pitying countenance, and hardly knew whether she would rather conquer him or not. "What god can tempt one so young and handsome to throw himself away? I pity him, not for his beauty (yet he is beautiful), but for his youth. I wish he would give up the race, or if he will be so mad, I hope he may outrun me." While she hesitates, revolving these thoughts, the spectators grow impatient for the race, and her father prompts her to prepare. Then Hippomenes addressed a prayer to Venus: "Help me, Venus, for you have led me on." Venus heard and was propitious.

In the garden of her temple, in her own island of Cyprus, is a tree with yellow leaves and yellow branches and golden fruit. Hence she gathered three golden apples, and unseen by any one else, gave them to Hippomenes, and told him how to use them. The signal is given; each starts from the goal and skims over the sand. So light their tread, you would almost have thought they might run over the river surface or over the waving grain without sinking. The cries of the spectators cheered Hippomenes,—"Now, now, do your best! haste, haste! you gain on her! relax not! one more effort!" It was doubtful whether the youth or the maiden heard these cries with the greater pleasure. But his breath began to fail him, his throat was dry, the goal yet far off. At that moment he threw down one of the golden apples. The virgin was all amazement. She stopped to pick it up. Hippomenes shot ahead. Shouts burst forth from all sides. She redoubled her efforts, and soon overtook him. Again he threw an apple. She stopped again, but again came up with him. The goal was near; one chance only remained. "Now, goddess," said he, "prosper your gift!" and threw the last apple off at one side. She looked at it, and hesitated; Venus impelled her to turn aside for it. She did so, and was vanquished. The youth carried off his prize.

But the lovers were so full of their own happiness that they forgot to pay due honour to Venus; and the goddess was provoked at their ingratitude. She caused them to give offence to Cybele. That powerful goddess was not to be insulted with impunity. She took from them their human form and turned them into animals of characters resembling their own: of the huntress-heroine, triumphing in the blood of her lovers, she made a lioness, and of her lord and master a lion, and yoked them to her car, where they are still to be seen in all representations, in statuary or painting, of the goddess Cybele.

Cybele is the Latin name of the goddess called by the Greeks Rhea and Ops. She was the wife of Cronos and mother of Zeus. In works of art she exhibits the matronly air which distinguishes Juno and Ceres. Sometimes she is veiled, and seated on a throne with lions at her side, at other times riding in a chariot drawn by lions. She wears a mural crown, that is, a crown whose rim is carved in the form of towers and battlements. Her priests were called Corybantes.

Byron, in describing the city of Venice, which is built on a low island in the Adriatic Sea, borrows an illustration from Cybele:

"She looks a sea-Cybele fresh from ocean,
Rising with her tiara of proud towers
At airy distance, with majestic motion,
A ruler of the waters and their powers."
Childe Harold, IV.

In Moore's "Rhymes on the Road," the poet, speaking of Alpine scenery, alludes to the story of Atalanta and Hippomenes thus:

"Even here, in this region of wonders, I find
That light-footed Fancy leaves Truth far behind,
Or at least, like Hippomenes, turns her astray
By the golden illusions he flings in her way."

CHAPTER XIX

HERCULES—HEBE AND GANYMEDE

HERCULES

HERCULES was the son of Jupiter and Alcmena. As Juno was always hostile to the offspring of her husband by mortal mothers, she declared war against Hercules from his birth. She sent two serpents to destroy him as he lay in his cradle, but the precocious infant strangled them with his own hands. He was, however, by the arts of Juno rendered subject to Eurystheus and compelled to perform all his commands. Eurystheus enjoined upon him a succession of desperate adventures, which are called the "Twelve Labours of Hercules." The first was the fight with the Nemean lion. The valley of Nemea was infested by a terrible lion. Eurystheus ordered Hercules to bring him the skin of this monster. After using in vain his club and arrows against the lion, Hercules strangled the animal with his hands. He returned carrying the dead lion on his shoulders; but Eurystheus was so frightened at the sight of it and at this proof of the prodigious strength of the hero, that he ordered him to deliver the account of his exploits in future outside the town.

His next labour was the slaughter of the Hydra. This monster ravaged the country of Argos, and dwelt in a swamp near the well of Amymone. This well had been discovered by Amymone when the country was suffering from drought, and the story was that Neptune, who loved her, had permitted her to touch the rock with his trident, and a spring of three outlets burst forth. Here the Hydra took up his position, and Hercules was sent to destroy him. The Hydra had nine heads, of which the middle one was immortal. Hercules struck off its heads with his club, but in the place of the head knocked off, two new ones grew forth each time. At length with the assistance of his faithful servant Iolaus, he burned away the heads of the Hydra, and buried the ninth or immortal one under a huge rock.

Another labour was the cleaning of the Augean stables. Augeas, king of Elis, had a herd of three thousand oxen, whose stalls had not been cleansed for thirty years. Hercules brought the rivers Alpheus and Peneus through them, and cleansed them thoroughly in one day.

His next labour was of a more delicate kind. Admeta, the daughter of Eurystheus, longed to obtain the girdle of the queen of the Amazons, and Eurystheus ordered Hercules to go and get it. The Amazons were a nation of women. They were very warlike and held several flourishing cities. It was their custom to bring up only the female children; the boys were either sent away to the neighbouring nations or put to death. Hercules was accompanied by a number of volunteers, and after various adventures at last reached the country of the Amazons. Hippolyta, the queen, received him kindly, and consented to yield him her girdle, but Juno, taking the form of an Amazon, went and persuaded the rest that the strangers were carrying off their queen. They instantly armed and came in great numbers down to the ship. Hercules, thinking that Hippolyta had acted treacherously, slew her, and taking her girdle made sail homewards.

Another task enjoined him was to bring to Eurystheus the oxen of Geryon, a monster with three bodies, who dwelt in the island of Erytheia (the red), so called because it lay at the west, under the rays of the setting sun. This description is thought to apply to Spain, of which Geryon was king. After traversing various countries, Hercules reached at length the frontiers of Libya and Europe, where he raised the two mountains of Calpe and Abyla, as monuments of his progress, or, according to another account, rent one mountain into two and left half on each side, forming the straits of Gibraltar, the two mountains being called the Pillars of Hercules. The oxen were guarded by the giant Eurytion and his two-headed dog, but Hercules killed the giant and his dog and brought away the oxen in safety to Eurystheus.

The most difficult labour of all was getting the golden apples of the Hesperides, for Hercules did not know where to find them. These were the apples which Juno had received at her wedding from the goddess of the Earth, and which she had intrusted to the keeping of the daughters of Hesperus, assisted by a watchful dragon. After various adventures Hercules arrived at Mount Atlas in Africa. Atlas was one of the Titans who had warred against the gods, and after they were subdued, Atlas was condemned to bear on his shoulders the weight of the heavens. He was the father of the Hesperides, and Hercules thought might, if any one could, find the apples and bring them to him. But how to send Atlas away from his post, or bear up the heavens while he was gone? Hercules took the burden on his own shoulders, and sent Atlas to seek the apples. He returned with them, and though somewhat reluctantly, took his burden upon his shoulders again, and let Hercules return with the apples to Eurystheus.

Milton, in his "Comus," makes the Hesperides the daughters of Hesperus and niece of Atlas:

> "...amidst the gardens fair
> Of Hesperus and his daughters three,
> That sing about the golden tree."

The poets, led by the analogy of the lovely appearance of the western sky at sunset, viewed the west as a region of brightness and glory. Hence they placed in it the Isles of the Blest, the ruddy Isle Erytheia, on which the bright oxen of Geryon were pastured, and the Isle of the Hesperides. The apples are supposed by some to be the oranges of Spain, of which the Greeks had heard some obscure accounts.

A celebrated exploit of Hercules was his victory over Antæus. Antæus, the son of Terra, the Earth, was a mighty giant and wrestler, whose strength was invincible so long as he remained in contact with his mother Earth. He compelled all strangers who came to his country to wrestle with him, on condition that if conquered (as they all were) they should be put to death. Hercules encountered him, and finding that it was of no avail to throw him, for he always rose with renewed strength from every fall, he lifted him up from the earth and strangled him in the air.

Cacus was a huge giant, who inhabited a cave on Mount Aventine, and plundered the surrounding country. When Hercules was driving home the oxen of Geryon, Cacus stole part of the cattle, while the hero slept. That their footprints might not serve to show where they had been driven, he dragged them backward by their tails to his cave; so their tracks all seemed to show that they had gone in the opposite direction. Hercules was deceived by this stratagem, and would have failed to find his oxen, if it had not happened that in driving the remainder of the herd past the cave where the stolen ones were concealed, those within began to low, and were thus discovered. Cacus was slain by Hercules.

The last exploit we shall record was bringing Cerberus from the lower world. Hercules descended into Hades, accompanied by Mercury and Minerva. He obtained permission from Pluto to carry Cerberus to the upper air, provided he could do it without the use of weapons; and in spite of the monster's struggling, he seized him, held him fast, and carried him to Eurystheus, and afterwards brought him back again. When he was in Hades he obtained the liberty of Theseus, his admirer and imitator, who had been detained a prisoner there for an unsuccessful attempt to carry off Proserpine.

Hercules in a fit of madness killed his friend Iphitus, and was condemned for this offence to become the slave of Queen Omphale for three years. While in this service the hero's nature seemed changed. He lived effeminately, wearing at times the dress of a woman, and spinning wool with the hand-maidens of Omphale, while the queen wore his lion's skin. When this service was ended he married Dejanira and lived in peace with her three years. On one occasion as he was travelling with his wife, they came to a river, across which the Centaur Nessus carried travellers for a stated fee. Hercules himself forded the river, but gave Dejanira to Nessus to be carried across. Nessus attempted to run away with her, but Hercules heard her cries and shot an arrow into the heart of Nessus. The dying Centaur told Dejanira to take a portion of his blood and keep it, as it might be used as a charm to preserve the love of her husband.

Dejanira did so, and before long fancied she had occasion to use it. Hercules in one of his conquests had taken prisoner a fair maiden, named Iole, of whom he seemed more fond than Dejanira approved. When Hercules was about to offer sacrifices to the gods in honour of his victory, he sent to his wife for a white robe to use on the occasion. Dejanira, thinking it a good opportunity to try her love-spell, steeped the garment in the blood of Nessus. We are to suppose she took care to wash out all traces of it, but the magic power remained, and as soon as the garment became warm on the body of Hercules the poison penetrated into all his limbs and caused him the most intense agony. In his frenzy he seized Lichas, who had brought him the fatal robe, and hurled him into the sea. He wrenched off the garment, but it stuck to his flesh, and with it he tore away whole pieces of his body. In this state he embarked on board a ship and was conveyed home. Dejanira, on seeing what she had unwittingly done, hung herself. Hercules, prepared to die, ascended

Mount Œta, where he built a funeral pile of trees, gave his bow and arrows to Philoctetes, and laid himself down on the pile, his head resting on his club, and his lion's skin spread over him. With a countenance as serene as if he were taking his place at a festal board he commanded Philoctetes to apply the torch. The flames spread apace and soon invested the whole mass.

Milton thus alludes to the frenzy of Hercules:

> "As when Alcides [1] from Œchalia crowned
> With conquest, felt the envenomed robe, and tore,
> Through pain, up by the roots Thessalian pines
> And Lichas from the top of Œta threw
> Into the Euboic Sea."

The gods themselves felt troubled at seeing the champion of the earth so brought to his end. But Jupiter with cheerful countenance thus addressed them: "I am pleased to see your concern, my princes, and am gratified to perceive that I am the ruler of a loyal people, and that my son enjoys your favour. For although your interest in him arises from his noble deeds, yet it is not the less gratifying to me. But now I say to you, Fear not. He who conquered all else is not to be conquered by those flames which you see blazing on Mount Œta. Only his mother's share in him can perish; what he derived from me is immortal. I shall take him, dead to earth, to the heavenly shores, and I require of you all to receive him kindly. If any of you feel grieved at his attaining this honour, yet no one can deny that he has deserved it." The gods all gave their assent; Juno only heard the closing words with some displeasure that she should be so particularly pointed at, yet not enough to make her regret the determination of her husband. So when the flames had consumed the mother's share of Hercules, the diviner part, instead of being injured thereby, seemed to start forth with new vigour, to assume a more lofty port and a more awful dignity. Jupiter enveloped him in a cloud, and took him up in a four-horse chariot to dwell among the stars. As he took his place in heaven, Atlas felt the added weight.

Juno, now reconciled to him, gave him her daughter Hebe in marriage.

The poet Schiller, in one of his pieces called the "Ideal and Life," illustrates the contrast between the practical and the imaginative in some beautiful stanzas, of which the last two may be thus translated:

> "Deep degraded to a coward's slave,
> Endless contests bore Alcides brave,

[1] Alcides, a name of Hercules.

Through the thorny path of suffering led;
Slew the Hydra, crushed the lion's might,
Threw himself, to bring his friend to light,
Living, in the skiff that bears the dead.
All the torments, every toil of earth
Juno's hatred on him could impose,
Well he bore them, from his fated birth
To life's grandly mournful close.

"Till the god, the earthly part forsaken,
From the man in flames asunder taken,
Drank the heavenly ether's purer breath.
Joyous in the new unwonted lightness,
Soared he upwards to celestial brightness,
Earth's dark heavy burden lost in death.
High Olympus gives harmonious greeting
To the hall where reigns his sire adored;
Youth's bright goddess, with a blush at meeting,
Gives the nectar to her lord."

S. G. B.

HEBE AND GANYMEDE

Hebe, the daughter of Juno, and goddess of youth, was cup-bearer to the gods. The usual story is that she resigned her office on becoming the wife of Hercules. But there is another statement which our countryman Crawford, the sculptor, has adopted in his group of Hebe and Ganymede, now in the Athenæum gallery. According to this, Hebe was dismissed from her office in consequence of a fall which she met with one day when in attendance on the gods. Her successor was Ganymede, a Trojan boy, whom Jupiter, in the disguise of an eagle, seized and carried off from the midst of his playfellows on Mount Ida, bore up to heaven, and installed in the vacant place.

Tennyson, in his "Palace of Art," describes among the decorations on the walls a picture representing this legend:

"There, too, flushed Ganymede, his rosy thigh
   Half buried in the eagle's down,
Sole as a flying star shot through the sky
   Above the pillared town."

And in Shelley's "Prometheus" Jupiter calls to his cup-bearer thus:

"Pour forth heaven's wine, Idæan Ganymede,
And let it fill the Dædal cups like fire."

The beautiful legend of the "Choice of Hercules" may be found in the "Tatler," No. 97.

CHAPTER XX

THESEUS—DÆDALUS—CASTOR AND POLLUX

THESEUS

THESEUS was the son of Ægeus, king of Athens, and of Æthra, daughter of the king of Trœzen. He was brought up at Trœzen, and when arrived at manhood was to proceed to Athens and present himself to his father. Ægeus on parting from Æthra, before the birth of his son, placed his sword and shoes under a large stone and directed her to send his son to him when he became strong enough to roll away the stone and take them from under it. When she thought the time had come, his mother led Theseus to the stone, and he removed it with ease and took the sword and shoes. As the roads were infested with robbers, his grandfather pressed him earnestly to take the shorter and safer way to his father's country— by sea; but the youth, feeling in himself the spirit and the soul of a hero, and eager to signalize himself like Hercules, with whose fame all Greece then rang, by destroying the evil-doers and monsters that oppressed the country, determined on the more perilous and adventurous journey by land.

His first day's journey brought him to Epidaurus, where dwelt a man named Periphetes, a son of Vulcan. This ferocious savage always went armed with a club of iron, and all travellers stood in terror of his violence. When he saw Theseus approach he assailed him, but speedily fell beneath the blows of the young hero, who took possession of his club and bore it ever afterwards as a memorial of his first victory.

Several similar contests with the petty tyrants and marauders of the country followed, in all of which Theseus was victorious. One of these evil-doers was called Procrustes, or the Stretcher. He had an iron bedstead, on which he used to tie all travellers who fell into his hands. If they were shorter than the bed, he stretched their limbs to make them fit it; if they were longer than the bed, he lopped off a portion. Theseus served him as he had served others.

Having overcome all the perils of the road, Theseus at length reached Athens, where new dangers awaited him. Medea, the sorceress, who had fled from Corinth after her separation from Jason, had become the wife of Ægeus, the father of Theseus. Knowing by her arts who he was, and fearing the loss of her influence with her husband if Theseus should be acknowledged as his son, she filled the mind of Ægeus with suspicions of the young stranger, and induced him to present him a cup of poison; but at the moment

when Theseus stepped forward to take it, the sight of the sword
which he wore discovered to his father who he was, and prevented
the fatal draught. Medea, detected in her arts, fled once more from
deserved punishment, and arrived in Asia, where the country afterwards called Media, received its name from her. Theseus was
acknowledged by his father, and declared his successor.

The Athenians were at that time in deep affliction, on account
of the tribute which they were forced to pay to Minos, king of
Crete. This tribute consisted of seven youths and seven maidens,
who were sent every year to be devoured by the Minotaur, a monster with a bull's body and a human head. It was exceedingly
strong and fierce, and was kept in a labyrinth constructed by
Dædalus, so artfully contrived that whoever was enclosed in it
could by no means find his way out unassisted. Here the Minotaur
roamed, and was fed with human victims.

Theseus resolved to deliver his countrymen from this calamity,
or to die in the attempt. Accordingly, when the time of sending
off the tribute came, and the youths and maidens were, according to
custom, drawn by lot to be sent, he offered himself as one of the
victims, in spite of the entreaties of his father. The ship departed
under black sails, as usual, which Theseus promised his father
to change for white, in case of his returning victorious. When they
arrived in Crete, the youths and maidens were exhibited before
Minos; and Ariadne, the daughter of the king, being present, became deeply enamoured of Theseus, by whom her love was readily
returned. She furnished him with a sword, with which to encounter
the Minotaur, and with a clue of thread by which he might find
his way out of the labyrinth. He was successful, slew the Minotaur,
escaped from the labyrinth, and taking Ariadne as the companion
of his way, with his rescued companions sailed for Athens. On
their way they stopped at the island of Naxos, where Theseus abandoned Ariadne, leaving her asleep.[1] His excuse for this ungrateful
treatment of his benefactress was that Minerva appeared to him
in a dream and commanded him to do so.

On approaching the coast of Attica, Theseus forgot the signal
appointed by his father, and neglected to raise the white sails, and
the old king, thinking his son had perished, put an end to his own
life. Theseus thus became king of Athens.

One of the most celebrated of the adventures of Theseus is his
expedition against the Amazons. He assailed them before they had
recovered from the attack of Hercules, and carried off their queen
Antiope. The Amazons in their turn invaded the country of Athens

[1] One of the finest pieces of sculpture in Italy, the recumbent Ariadne of
the Vatican, represents this incident. A copy is in the Athenæum gallery,
Boston.

and penetrated into the city itself; and the final battle in which Theseus overcame them was fought in the very midst of the city. This battle was one of the favourite subjects of the ancient sculptors, and is commemorated in several works of art that are still extant.

The friendship between Theseus and Pirithous was of a most intimate nature, yet it originated in the midst of arms. Pirithous had made an irruption into the plain of Marathon, and carried off the herds of the king of Athens. Theseus went to repel the plunderers. The moment Pirithous beheld him, he was seized with admiration; he stretched out his hand as a token of peace, and cried, "Be judge thyself—what satisfaction dost thou require?" "Thy friendship," replied the Athenian, and they swore inviolable fidelity. Their deeds corresponded to their professions, and they ever continued true brothers in arms. Each of them aspired to espouse a daughter of Jupiter. Theseus fixed his choice on Helen, then but a child, afterwards so celebrated as the cause of the Trojan war, and with the aid of his friend he carried her off. Pirithous aspired to the wife of the monarch of Erebus; and Theseus, though aware of the danger, accompanied the ambitious lover in his descent to the underworld. But Pluto seized and set them on an enchanted rock at his palace gate, where they remained till Hercules arrived and liberated Theseus, leaving Pirithous to his fate.

After the death of Antiope, Theseus married Phædra, daughter of Minos, king of Crete. Phædra saw in Hippolytus, the son of Theseus, a youth endowed with all the graces and virtues of his father, and of an age corresponding to her own. She loved him, but he repulsed her advances, and her love was changed to hate. She used her influence over her infatuated husband to cause him to be jealous of his son, and he imprecated the vengeance of Neptune upon him. As Hippolytus was one day driving his chariot along the shore, a sea-monster raised himself above the waters, and frightened the horses so that they ran away and dashed the chariot to pieces. Hippolytus was killed, but by Diana's assistance Æsculapius restored him to life. Diana removed Hippolytus from the power of his deluded father and false stepmother, and placed him in Italy under the protection of the nymph Egeria.

Theseus at length lost the favour of his people, and retired to the court of Lycomedes, king of Scyros, who at first received him kindly, but afterwards treacherously slew him. In a later age the Athenian general Cimon discovered the place where his remains were laid, and caused them to be removed to Athens, where they were deposited in a temple called the Theseum, erected in honour of the hero.

The queen of the Amazons whom Theseus espoused is by some called Hippolyta. That is the name she bears in Shakespeare's "Midsummer Night's Dream,"—the subject of which is the festivities attending the nuptials of Theseus and Hippolyta.

Mrs. Hemans has a poem on the ancient Greek tradition that the "Shade of Theseus" appeared strengthening his countrymen at the battle of Marathon.

Theseus is a semi-historical personage. It is recorded of him that he united the several tribes by whom the territory of Attica was then possessed into one state, of which Athens was the capital. In commemoration of this important event, he instituted the festival of Panathenæa, in honour of Minerva, the patron deity of Athens. This festival differed from the other Grecian games chiefly in two particulars. It was peculiar to the Athenians, and its chief feature was a solemn procession in which the Peplus, or sacred robe of Minerva, was carried to the Parthenon, and suspended before the statue of the goddess. The Peplus was covered with embroidery, worked by select virgins of the noblest families in Athens. The procession consisted of persons of all ages and both sexes. The old men carried olive branches in their hands, and the young men bore arms. The young women carried baskets on their heads, containing the sacred utensils, cakes, and all things necessary for the sacrifices. The procession formed the subject of the bas-reliefs which embellished the outside of the temple of the Parthenon. A considerable portion of these sculptures is now in the British Museum among those known as the "Elgin marbles."

OLYMPIC AND OTHER GAMES

It seems not inappropriate to mention here the other celebrated national games of the Greeks. The first and most distinguished were the Olympic, founded, it was said, by Jupiter himself. They were celebrated at Olympia in Elis. Vast numbers of spectators flocked to them from every part of Greece, and from Asia, Africa and Sicily. They were repeated every fifth year in midsummer, and continued five days. They gave rise to the custom of reckoning time and dating events by Olympiads. The first Olympiad is generally considered as corresponding with the year 776 B.C. The Pythian games were celebrated in the vicinity of Delphi, the Isthmian on the Corinthian Isthmus, the Nemean at Nemea, a city of Argolis.

The exercises in these games were of five sorts: running, leaping, wrestling, throwing the quoit, and hurling the javelin, or boxing. Besides these exercises of bodily strength and agility there were contests in music, poetry and eloquence. Thus these games furnished poets, musicians and authors the best opportunities to present their productions to the public, and the fame of the victors was diffused far and wide.

DÆDALUS

The labyrinth from which Theseus escaped by means of the clew of Ariadne was built by Dædalus, a most skilful artificer. It was an edifice with numberless winding passages and turnings opening into one another, and seeming to have neither beginning nor end, like the river Mæander, which returns on itself, and flows now onward, now backward, in its course to the sea. Dædalus built the labyrinth for King Minos, but afterwards lost the favour of the king, and was shut up in a tower. He contrived to make his escape from his prison, but could not leave the island by sea, as the king kept strict watch on all the vessels, and permitted none to sail without being carefully searched. "Minos may control the land and sea," said Dædalus, "but not the regions of the air. I will try that way." So he set to work to fabricate wings for himself and his young son Icarus. He wrought feathers together, beginning with the smallest and adding larger, so as to form an increasing surface. The larger ones he secured with thread and the smaller with wax, and gave the whole a gentle curvature like the wings of a bird. Icarus, the boy, stood and looked on, sometimes running to gather up the feathers which the wind had blown away, and then handling the wax and working it over with his fingers, by his play impeding his father in his labours. When at last the work was done, the artist, waving his wings, found himself buoyed upward, and hung suspended, poising himself on the beaten air. He next equipped his son in the same manner and taught him how to fly, as a bird tempts her young ones from the lofty nest into the air. When all was prepared for flight he said, "Icarus, my son, I charge you to keep at a moderate height, for if you fly too low the damp will clog your wings, and if too high the heat will melt them. Keep near me and you will be safe." While he gave him these instructions and fitted the wings to his shoulders, the face of the father was wet with tears, and his hands trembled. He kissed the boy, not knowing that it was for the last time. Then rising on his wings, he flew off, encouraging him to follow, and looked back from his own flight to see how his son managed his wings. As they flew the ploughman stopped his work to gaze, and the shepherd leaned on his staff and watched them, astonished at the sight, and thinking they were gods who could thus cleave the air.

They passed Samos and Delos on the left and Lebynthos on

the right, when the boy, exulting in his career, began to leave the guidance of his companion and soar upward as if to reach heaven. The nearness of the blazing sun softened the wax which held the feathers together, and they came off. He fluttered with his arms, but no feathers remained to hold the air. While his mouth uttered cries to his father it was submerged in the blue waters of the sea, which thenceforth was called by his name. His father cried, "Icarus, Icarus, where are you?" At last he saw the feathers floating on the water, and bitterly lamenting his own arts, he buried the body and called the land Icaria in memory of his child. Dædalus arrived safe in Sicily, where he built a temple to Apollo, and hung up his wings, an offering to the god.

Dædalus was so proud of his achievements that he could not bear the idea of a rival. His sister had placed her son Perdix under his charge to be taught the mechanical arts. He was an apt scholar and gave striking evidences of ingenuity. Walking on the sea-shore he picked up the spine of a fish. Imitating it, he took a piece of iron and notched it on the edge, and thus invented the *saw*. He put two pieces of iron together, connecting them at one end with a rivet, and sharpening the other ends, and made a pair of *compasses*. Dædalus was so envious of his nephew's performances that he took an opportunity, when they were together one day on the top of a high tower, to push him off. But Minerva, who favours ingenuity, saw him falling, and arrested his fate by changing him into a bird called after his name, the Partridge. This bird does not build his nest in the trees, nor take lofty flights, but nestles in the hedges, and mindful of his fall, avoids high places.

The death of Icarus is told in the following lines by Darwin:

"... with melting wax and loosened strings
Sunk hapless Icarus on unfaithful wings;
Headlong he rushed through the affrighted air,
With limbs distorted and dishevelled hair;
His scattered plumage danced upon the wave,
And sorrowing Nereids decked his watery grave;
O'er his pale corse their pearly sea-flowers shed,
And strewed with crimson moss his marble bed;
Struck in their coral towers the passing bell,
And wide in ocean tolled his echoing knell."

CASTOR AND POLLUX

Castor and Pollux were the offspring of Leda and the Swan, under which disguise Jupiter had concealed himself. Leda gave birth to an egg from which sprang the twins. Helen, so famous afterwards as the cause of the Trojan war, was their sister.

When Theseus and his friend Pirithous had carried off Helen from Sparta, the youthful heroes, Castor and Pollux, with their followers, hastened to her rescue. Theseus was absent from Attica and the brothers were successful in recovering their sister.

Castor was famous for taming and managing horses, and Pollux for skill in boxing. They were united by the warmest affection and inseparable in all their enterprises. They accompanied the Argonautic expedition. During the voyage a storm arose, and Orpheus prayed to the Samothracian gods, and played on his harp, whereupon the storm ceased and stars appeared on the heads of the brothers. From this incident, Castor and Pollux came afterwards to be considered the patron deities of seamen and voyagers, and the lambent flames, which in certain states of the atmosphere play round the sails and masts of vessels, were called by their names.

After the Argonautic expedition, we find Castor and Pollux engaged in a war with Idas and Lynceus. Castor was slain, and Pollux, inconsolable for the loss of his brother, besought Jupiter to be permitted to give his own life as a ransom for him. Jupiter so far consented as to allow the two brothers to enjoy the boon of life alternately, passing one day under the earth and the next in the heavenly abodes. According to another form of the story, Jupiter rewarded the attachment of the brothers by placing them among the stars as Gemini the Twins.

They received divine honours under the name of Dioscuri (sons of Jove). They were believed to have appeared occasionally in later times, taking part with one side or the other, in hard-fought fields, and were said on such occasions to be mounted on magnificent white steeds. Thus in the early history of Rome they are said to have assisted the Romans at the battle of Lake Regillus, and after the victory a temple was erected in their honour on the spot where they appeared.

Macaulay, in his "Lays of Ancient Rome," thus alludes to the legend:

> "So like they were, no mortal
>   Might one from other know;
> White as snow their armour was,
>   Their steeds were white as snow.
> Never on earthly anvil
>   Did such rare armour gleam,
> And never did such gallant steeds
>   Drink of an earthly stream.
>
> "Back comes the chief in triumph
>   Who in the hour of fight

Hath seen the great twin Brethren
   In harness on his right.
Safe comes the ship to haven,
   Through billows and through gales,
If once the great Twin Brethren
   Sit shining on the sails."

CHAPTER XXI

BACCHUS—ARIADNE

BACCHUS

BACCHUS was the son of Jupiter and Semele. Juno, to gratify
her resentment against Semele, contrived a plan for her destruc‹
tion. Assuming the form of Beroë, her aged nurse, she insinuated
doubts whether it was indeed Jove himself who came as a lover.
Heaving a sigh, she said, "I hope it will turn out so, but I can't
help being afraid. People are not always what they pretend to be.
If he is indeed Jove, make him give some proof of it. Ask him
to come arrayed in all his splendours, such as he wears in heaven.
That will put the matter beyond a doubt." Semele was persuaded
to try the experiment. She asks a favour, without naming what
it is. Jove gives his promise, and confirms it with the irrevocable
oath, attesting the river Styx, terrible to the gods themselves.
Then she made known her request. The god would have stopped
her as she spake, but she was too quick for him. The words
escaped, and he could neither unsay his promise nor her request.
In deep distress he left her and returned to the upper regions.
There he clothed himself in his splendours, not putting on all his
terrors, as when he overthrew the giants, but what is known
among the gods as his lesser panoply. Arrayed in this, he entered
the chamber of Semele. Her mortal frame could not endure the
splendours of the immortal radiance. She was consumed to ashes.

Jove took the infant Bacchus and gave him in charge to the
Nysæan nymphs, who nourished his infancy and childhood, and
for their care were rewarded by Jupiter by being placed, as the
Hyades, among the stars. When Bacchus grew up he discovered
the culture of the vine and the mode of extracting its precious
juice; but Juno struck him with madness, and drove him forth
a wanderer through various parts of the earth. In Phrygia the
goddess Rhea cured him and taught him her religious rites, and
he set out on a progress through Asia, teaching the people the
cultivation of the vine. The most famous part of his wanderings
is his expedition to India, which is said to have lasted several
years. Returning in triumph, he undertook to introduce his wor‹

ship into Greece, but was opposed by some princes, who dreaded
its introduction on account of the disorder and madness it brought
with it.

As he approached his native city Thebes, Pentheus the king,
who had no respect for the new worship, forbade its rites to be
performed. But when it was known that Bacchus was advancing,
men and women, but chiefly the latter, young and old, poured
forth to meet him and to join his triumphal march.

Mr. Longfellow in his "Drinking Song" thus describes the march
of Bacchus:

> "Fauns with youthful Bacchus follow;
>   Ivy crowns that brow, supernal
> As the forehead of Apollo,
>   And possessing youth eternal.

> "Round about him fair Bacchantes,
>   Bearing cymbals, flutes and thyrses,
> Wild from Naxian groves of Zante's
>   Vineyards, sing delirious verses."

It was in vain Pentheus remonstrated, commanded and threatened. "Go," said he to his attendants, "seize this vagabond leader
of the rout and bring him to me. I will soon make him confess
his false claim of heavenly parentage and renounce his counterfeit worship." It was in vain his nearest friends and wisest counsellors remonstrated and begged him not to oppose the god. Their
remonstrances only made him more violent.

But now the attendants returned whom he had despatched to
seize Bacchus. They had been driven away by the Bacchanals,
but had succeeded in taking one of them prisoner, whom, with
his hands tied behind him, they brought before the king. Pentheus,
beholding him with wrathful countenance, said "Fellow! you shall
speedily be put to death, that your fate may be a warning to
others; but though I grudge the delay of your punishment, speak,
tell us who you are, and what are these new rites you presume
to celebrate."

The prisoner, unterrified, responded, "My name is Acetes;
my country is Mæonia; my parents were poor people, who had no
fields or flocks to leave me, but they left me their fishing rods
and nets and their fisherman's trade. This I followed for some
time, till growing weary of remaining in one place, I learned the
pilot's art and how to guide my course by the stars. It happened
as I was sailing for Delos we touched at the island of Dia and
went ashore. Next morning I sent the men for fresh water, and
myself mounted the hill to observe the wind; when my men returned bringing with them a prize, as they thought. a boy of

delicate appearance, whom they had found asleep. They judged
he was a noble youth, perhaps a king's son, and they might get
a liberal ransom for him. I observed his dress, his walk, his face.
There was something in them which I felt sure was more than
mortal. I said to my men, 'What god there is concealed in that
form I know not, but some one there certainly is. Pardon us,
gentle deity, for the violence we have done you, and give success to
our undertakings.' Dictys, one of my best hands for climbing
the mast and coming down by the ropes, and Melanthus, my
steersman, and Epopeus, the leader of the sailor's cry, one and all
exclaimed, 'Spare your prayers for us.' So blind is the lust of
gain! When they proceeded to put him on board I resisted them.
'This ship shall not be profaned by such impiety,' said I. 'I have
a greater share in her than any of you.' But Lycabas, a turbulent fellow, seized me by the throat and attempted to throw me
overboard, and I scarcely saved myself by clinging to the ropes.
The rest approved the deed.

"Then Bacchus (for it was indeed he), as if shaking off his
drowsiness, exclaimed, 'What are you doing with me? What is
this fighting about? Who brought me here? Where are you going
to carry me?' One of them replied, 'Fear nothing; tell us where
you wish to go and we will take you there.' 'Naxos is my home,'
said Bacchus; 'take me there and you shall be well rewarded.'
They promised so to do, and told me to pilot the ship to Naxos.
Naxos lay to the right, and I was trimming the sails to carry
us there, when some by signs and others by whispers signified
to me their will that I should sail in the opposite direction, and
take the boy to Egypt to sell him for a slave. I was confounded
and said, 'Let some one else pilot the ship;' withdrawing myself
from any further agency in their wickedness. They cursed me,
and one of them, exclaiming, 'Don't flatter yourself that we de-
pend on you for our safety,' took my place as pilot, and bore
away from Naxos.

"Then the god, pretending that he had just become aware of
their treachery, looked out over the sea and said in a voice of
weeping, 'Sailors, these are not the shores you promised to take
me to; yonder island is not my home. What have I done that
you should treat me so? It is small glory you will gain by cheating
a poor boy.' I wept to hear him, but the crew laughed at both of
us, and sped the vessel fast over the sea. All at once—strange as
it may seem, it is true,—the vessel stopped, in the mid sea, as
fast as if it was fixed on the ground. The men, astonished, pulled
at their oars, and spread more sail, trying to make progress by
the aid of both, but all in vain. Ivy twined round the oars and

hindered their motion, and clung to the sails, with heavy clusters of berries. A vine, laden with grapes, ran up the mast, and along the sides of the vessel. The sound of flutes was heard and the odour of fragrant wine spread all around. The god himself had a chaplet of vine leaves, and bore in his hand a spear wreathed with ivy. Tigers crouched at his feet, and forms of lynxes and spotted panthers played around him. The men were seized with terror or madness; some leaped overboard; others preparing to do the same beheld their companions in the water undergoing a change, their bodies becoming flattened and ending in a crooked tail. One exclaimed, 'What miracle is this!' and as he spoke his mouth widened, his nostrils expanded, and scales covered all his body. Another, endeavouring to pull the oar, felt his hands shrink up and presently to be no longer hands but fins; another, trying to raise his arms to a rope, found he had no arms, and curving his mutilated body jumped into the sea. What had been his legs became the two ends of a crescent-shaped tail. The whole crew became dolphins and swam about the ship, now upon the surface, now under it, scattering the spray, and spouting the water from their broad nostrils. Of twenty men I alone was left. Trembling with fear, the god cheered me. 'Fear not,' said he; 'steer towards Naxos.' I obeyed, and when we arrived there, I kindled the altars and celebrated the sacred rites of Bacchus."

Pentheus here exclaimed, "We have wasted time enough on this silly story. Take him away and have him executed without delay." Acetes was led away by the attendants and shut up fast in prison; but while they were getting ready the instruments of execution the prison doors came open of their own accord and the chains fell from his limbs, and when they looked for him he was nowhere to be found.

Pentheus would take no warning, but instead of sending others, determined to go himself to the scene of the solemnities. The mountain Citheron was all alive with worshippers, and the cries of the Bacchanals resounded on every side. The noise roused the anger of Pentheus as the sound of a trumpet does the fire of a war-horse. He penetrated through the wood and reached an open space where the chief scene of the orgies met his eyes. At the same moment the women saw him; and first among them his own mother, Agave, blinded by the god, cried out, "See there the wild boar, the hugest monster that prowls in these woods! Come on, sisters! I will be the first to strike the wild boar." The whole band rushed upon him, and while he now talks less arrogantly, now excuses himself, and now confesses his crime and implores pardon, they press upon him and wound him. In vain

he cries to his aunts to protect him from his mother. Autonoë
seized one arm, Ino the other, and between them he was torn to
pieces, while his mother shouted, "Victory! Victory! we have done
it; the glory is ours!"

So the worship of Bacchus was established in Greece.

There is an allusion to the story of Bacchus and the mariners in
Milton's "Comus," at line 46. The story of Circe will be found
in Chapter XXIX.

> "Bacchus that first from out the purple grapes
> Crushed the sweet poison of misused wine,
> After the Tuscan mariners transformed,
> Coasting the Tyrrhene shore as the winds listed
> On Circe's island fell; (who knows not Circe,
> The daughter of the Sun? whose charmed cup
> Whoever tasted lost his upright shape,
> And downward fell into a grovelling swine.)"

ARIADNE

We have seen in the story of Theseus how Ariadne, the daughter of King Minos, after helping Theseus to escape from the
labyrinth, was carried by him to the island of Naxos and was
left there asleep, while the ungrateful Theseus pursued his way
home without her. Ariadne, on waking and finding herself deserted, abandoned herself to grief. But Venus took pity on her,
and consoled her with the promise that she should have an immortal lover, instead of the mortal one she had lost.

The island where Ariadne was left was the favourite island of
Bacchus, the same that he wished the Tyrrhenian mariners to
carry him to, when they so treacherously attempted to make prize
of him. As Ariadne sat lamenting her fate, Bacchus found her,
consoled her, and made her his wife. As a marriage present he
gave her a golden crown, enriched with gems, and when she died,
he took her crown and threw it up into the sky. As it mounted
the gems grew brighter and were turned into stars, and preserving its form Ariadne's crown remains fixed in the heavens as a
constellation, between the kneeling Hercules and the man who
holds the serpent.

Spenser alludes to Ariadne's crown, though he has made some
mistakes in his mythology. It was at the wedding of Pirithous,
and not Theseus, that the Centaurs and Lapithæ quarrelled.

> "Look how the crown which Ariadne wore
> Upon her ivory forehead that same day
> That Theseus her unto his bridal bore,
> Then the bold Centaurs made that bloody fray

With the fierce Lapiths which did them dismay;
Being now placed in the firmament,
Through the bright heaven doth her beams display,
And is unto the stars an ornament,
Which round about her move in order excellent."

CHAPTER XXII

THE RURAL DEITIES—ERISICHTHON—RHŒCUS—THE
WATER DEITIES—THE CAMENÆ—THE WINDS

THE RURAL DEITIES

PAN, the god of woods and fields, of flocks and shepherds, dwelt in grottos, wandered on the mountains and in valleys, and amused himself with the chase or in leading the dances of the nymphs. He was fond of music, and was, as we have seen, the inventor of the syrinx, or shepherd's pipe, which he himself played in a masterly manner. Pan, like other gods who dwelt in forests, was dreaded by those whose occupations caused them to pass through the woods by night, for the gloom and loneliness of such scenes dispose the mind to superstitious fears. Hence sudden fright without any visible cause was ascribed to Pan, and called a Panic terror.

As the name of the god signifies *all*, Pan came to be considered a symbol of the universe and personification of Nature; and later still to be regarded as a representative of all the gods and of heathenism itself.

Sylvanus and Faunus were Latin divinities, whose characteristics are so nearly the same as those of Pan that we may safely consider them as the same personage under different names.

The wood-nymphs, Pan's partners in the dance, were but one class of nymphs. There were besides them the Naiads, who presided over brooks and fountains, the Oreads, nymphs of mountains and grottos, and the Nereids, sea-nymphs. The three last named were immortal, but the wood-nymphs, called Dryads or Hamadryads, were believed to perish with the trees which had been their abode and with which they had come into existence. It was therefore an impious act wantonly to destroy a tree, and in some aggravated cases was severely punished, as in the instance of Erisichthon, which we are about to record.

Milton in his glowing description of the early creation, thus alludes to Pan as the personification of Nature:

"... Universal Pan,
Knit with the Graces and the Hours in dance,
Led on the eternal spring."

And describing Eve's abode:

> "...In shadier bower,
> More sacred or sequestered, though but feigned,
> Pan or Sylvanus never slept, nor nymph
> Nor Faunus haunted."
>
> *Paradise Lost*, B. 1V.

It was a pleasing trait in the old Paganism that it loved to trace in every operation of nature the agency of deity. The imagination of the Greeks peopled all the regions of earth and sea with divinities, to whose agency it attributed those phenomena which our philosophy ascribes to the operation of the laws of nature. Sometimes in our poetical moods we feel disposed to regret the change, and to think that the heart has lost as much as the head has gained by the substitution. The poet Wordsworth thus strongly expresses this sentiment:

> "...Great God, I'd rather be
> A Pagan, suckled in a creed outworn,
> So might I, standing on this pleasant lea,
> Have glimpses that would make me less forlorn;
> Have sight of Proteus rising from the sea,
> And hear old Triton blow his wreathed horn."

Schiller, in his poem "Die Götter Griechenlands," expresses his regret for the overthrow of the beautiful mythology of ancient times in a way which has called forth an answer from a Christian poet, Mrs. E. Barrett Browning, in her poem called "The Dead Pan." The two following verses are a specimen:

> "By your beauty which confesses
> Some chief Beauty conquering you,
> By our grand heroic guesses
> Through your falsehood at the True,
> We will weep *not!* earth shall roll
> Heir to each god's aureole,
>   And Pan is dead.

> "Earth outgrows the mythic fancies
> Sung beside her in her youth;
> And those debonaire romances
> Sound but dull beside the truth.
> Phœbus' chariot course is run!
> Look up, poets, to the sun!
>   Pan, Pan is dead."

These lines are founded on an early Christian tradition that when the heavenly host told the shepherds at Bethlehem of the birth of Christ, a deep groan, heard through all the isles of Greece, told that the great Pan was dead, and that all the royalty of Olympus was dethroned and the several deities were sent wandering in cold and darkness. So Milton in his "Hymn on the Nativity":

> "The lonely mountains o'er
>   And the resounding shore,
>   A voice of weeping heard and loud lament;
>   From haunted spring and dale,
>   Edged with poplar pale,
>   The parting Genius is with sighing sent;
>   With flower-enwoven tresses torn,
>   The nymphs in twilight shade of tangled thickets mourn."

ERISICHTHON

Erisichthon was a profane person and a despiser of the gods. On one occasion he presumed to violate with the axe a grove sacred to Ceres. There stood in this grove a venerable oak, so large that it seemed a wood in itself, its ancient trunk towering aloft, whereon votive garlands were often hung and inscriptions carved expressing the gratitude of suppliants to the nymph of the tree. Often had the Dryads danced round it hand in hand. Its trunk measured fifteen cubits round, and it overtopped the other trees as they overtopped the shrubbery. But for all that, Erisichthon saw no reason why he should spare it and he ordered his servants to cut it down. When he saw them hesitate he snatched an axe from one, and thus impiously exclaimed: "I care not whether it be a tree beloved of the goddess or not; were it the goddess herself it should come down if it stood in my way." So saying, he lifted the axe and the oak seemed to shudder and utter a groan. When the first blow fell upon the trunk blood flowed from the wound. All the bystanders were horror-struck, and one of them ventured to remonstrate and hold back the fatal axe. Erisichthon, with a scornful look, said to him, "Receive the reward of your piety;" and turned against him the weapon which he had held aside from the tree, gashed his body with many wounds, and cut off his head. Then from the midst of the oak came a voice, "I who dwell in this tree am a nymph beloved of Ceres, and dying by your hands forewarn you that punishment awaits you." He desisted not from his crime, and at last the tree, sundered by repeated blows and drawn by ropes, fell with a crash and prostrated a great part of the grove in its fall.

The Dryads, in dismay at the loss of their companion and at seeing the pride of the forest laid low, went in a body to Ceres, all clad in garments of mourning, and invoked punishment upon Erisichthon. She nodded her assent, and as she bowed her head the grain ripe for harvest in the laden fields bowed also. She planned a punishment so dire that one would pity him, if such a culprit as he could be pitied—to deliver him over to Famine. As Ceres herself could not approach Famine, for the Fates have ordained that these two goddesses shall never come together, she called an Oread from her mountain and spoke to her in these words: "There is a place in the farthest part of ice-clad Scythia, a sad and sterile region without trees and without crops. Cold dwells there, and Fear and Shuddering, and Famine. Go and tell the last to take possession of the bowels of Erisichthon. Let not abundance subdue her, nor the power of my gifts drive her away. Be not alarmed at the distance" (for Famine dwells very far from Ceres), "but take my chariot. The dragons are fleet and obey the rein, and will take you through the air in a short time." So she gave her the reins, and she drove away and soon reached Scythia. On arriving at Mount Caucasus she stopped the dragons and found Famine in a stony field, pulling up with teeth and claws the scanty herbage. Her hair was rough, her eyes sunk, her face pale, her lips blanched, her jaws covered with dust, and her skin drawn tight, so as to show all her bones. As the Oread saw her afar off (for she did not dare to come near), she delivered the commands of Ceres; and, though she stopped as short a time as possible, and kept her distance as well as she could, yet she began to feel hungry, and turned the dragons' heads and drove back to Thessaly.

Famine obeyed the commands of Ceres and sped through the air to the dwelling of Erisichthon, entered the bedchamber of the guilty man, and found him asleep. She enfolded him with her wings and breathed herself into him, infusing her poison into his veins. Having discharged her task, she hastened to leave the land of plenty and returned to her accustomed haunts. Erisichthon still slept, and in his dreams craved food, and moved his jaws as if eating. When he awoke, his hunger was raging. Without a moment's delay he would have food set before him, of whatever kind earth, sea, or air produces; and complained of hunger even while he ate. What would have sufficed for a city or a nation, was not enough for him. The more he ate the more he craved. His hunger was like the sea, which receives all the rivers, yet is never filled; or like fire, that burns all the fuel that is heaped upon it, yet is still voracious for more.

His property rapidly diminished under the unceasing demands of his appetite, but his hunger continued unabated. At length he had spent all and had only his daughter left, a daughter worthy of a better parent. *Her too he sold.* She scorned to be a slave of a purchaser and as she stood by the seaside raised her hands in prayer to Neptune. He heard her prayer, and though her new master was not far off and had his eye upon her a moment before, Neptune changed her form and made her assume that of a fisherman busy at his occupation. Her master, looking for her and seeing her in her altered form, addressed her and said, "Good fisherman, whither went the maiden whom I saw just now, with hair dishevelled and in humble garb, standing about where you stand? Tell me truly; so may your luck be good and not a fish nibble at your hook and get away." She perceived that her prayer was answered and rejoiced inwardly at hearing herself inquired of about herself. She replied, "Pardon me, stranger, but I have been so intent upon my line that I have seen nothing else; but I wish I may never catch another fish if I believe any woman or other person except myself to have been hereabouts for some time." He was deceived and went his way, thinking his slave had escaped. Then she resumed her own form. Her father was well pleased to find her still with him, and the money too that he got by the sale of her; so he sold her again. But she was changed by the favour of Neptune as often as she was sold, now into a horse, now a bird, now an ox, and now a stag—got away from her purchasers and came home. By this base method the starving father procured food; but not enough for his wants, and at last hunger compelled him to devour his limbs, and he strove to nourish his body by eating his body, till death relieved him from the vengeance of Ceres.

RHŒCUS

The Hamadryads could appreciate services as well as punish injuries. The story of Rhœcus proves this. Rhœcus, happening to see an oak just ready to fall, ordered his servants to prop it up. The nymph, who had been on the point of perishing with the tree, came and expressed her gratitude to him for having saved her life and bade him ask what reward he would. Rhœcus boldly asked her love and the nymph yielded to his desire. She at the same time charged him to be constant and told him that a bee should be her messenger and let him know when she would admit his society. One time the bee came to Rhœcus when he was playing at draughts and he carelessly brushed it away. This so incensed the nymph that she deprived him of sight.

Our countryman, J. R. Lowell, has taken this story for the subject of one of his shorter poems. He introduces it thus:

"Hear now this fairy legend of old Greece,
As full of freedom, youth and beauty still,
As the immortal freshness of that grace
Carved for all ages on some Attic frieze."

THE WATER DEITIES

Oceanus and Tethys were the Titans who ruled over the watery elements. When Jove and his brothers overthrew the Titans and assumed their power, Neptune and Amphitrite succeeded to the dominion of the waters in place of Oceanus and Tethys.

NEPTUNE

Neptune was the chief of the water deities. The symbol of his power was the trident, or spear with three points, with which he used to shatter rocks, to call forth or subdue storms, to shake the shores and the like. He created the horse and was the patron of horse races. His own horses had brazen hoofs and golden manes. They drew his chariot over the sea, which became smooth before him, while the monsters of the deep gambolled about his path.

AMPHITRITE

Amphitrite was the wife of Neptune. She was the daughter of Nereus and Doris, and the mother of Triton. Neptune, to pay his court to Amphitrite, came riding on a dolphin. Having won her he rewarded the dolphin by placing him among the stars.

NEREUS AND DORIS

Nereus and Doris were the parents of the Nereids, the most celebrated of whom were Amphitrite, Thetis, the mother of Achilles, and Galatea, who was loved by the Cyclops Polyphemus. Nereus was distinguished for his knowledge and his love of truth and justice, whence he was termed an elder; the gift of prophecy was also assigned to him.

TRITON AND PROTEUS

Triton was the son of Neptune and Amphitrite, and the poets made him his father's trumpeter. Proteus was also a son of Neptune. He, like Nereus, is styled a sea-elder for his wisdom and knowledge of future events. His peculiar power was that of changing his shape at will.

THETIS

Thetis, the daughter of Nereus and Doris, was so beautiful that Jupiter himself sought her in marriage; but having learned from

Prometheus the Titan that Thetis should bear a son who should
be greater than his father, Jupiter desisted from his suit and
decreed that Thetis should be the wife of a mortal. By the aid
of Chiron the Centaur, Peleus succeeded in winning the goddess
for his bride and their son was the renowned Achilles. In our
chapter on the Trojan war it will appear that Thetis was a faithful mother to him, aiding him in all difficulties, and watching over
his interests from the first to the last.

LEUCOTHEA AND PALÆMON

Ino, the daughter of Cadmus and wife of Athamas, flying from
her frantic husband with her little son Melicertes in her arms,
sprang from a cliff into the sea. The gods, out of compassion,
make her a goddess of the sea, under the name of Leucothea, and
him a god, under that of Palæmon. Both were held powerful to
save from shipwreck and were invoked by sailors. Palæmon was
usually represented riding on a dolphin. The Isthmian games
were celebrated in his honour. He was called Portunus by the
Romans, and believed to have jurisdiction of the ports and shores.

Milton alludes to all these deities in the song at the conclusion
of "Comus":

"Sabrina fair, . . .
Listen and appear to us,
In name of great Oceanus;
By the earth-shaking Neptune's mace,
And Tethys' grave, majestic pace;
By hoary Nereus' wrinkled look,
And the Carpathian wizard's hook,[1]

By scaly Triton's winding shell,
And old soothsaying Glaucus' spell,
By Leucothea's lovely hands,
And her son who rules the strands;
By Thetis' tinsel-slippered feet,
And the songs of Sirens sweet;" etc.

Armstrong, the poet of the "Art of Preserving Health," under
the inspiration of Hygeia, the goddess of health, thus celebrates
the Naiads. Pæon is a name both of Apollo and Æsculapius.

"Come, ye Naiads! to the fountains lead!
Propitious maids! the task remains to sing
Your gifts (so Pæon, so the powers of Health
Command), to praise your crystal element.
O comfortable streams! with eager lips
And trembling hands the languid thirsty quaff
New life in you; fresh vigour fills their veins.

[1] Proteus.

No warmer cups the rural ages knew,
None warmer sought the sires of humankind;
Happy in temperate peace their equal days
Felt not the alternate fits of feverish mirth
And sick dejection; still serene and pleased,
Blessed with divine immunity from ills,
Long centuries they lived; their only fate
Was ripe old age, and rather sleep than death."

THE CAMENÆ

By this name the Latins designated the Muses, but included under it also some other deities, principally nymphs of fountains. Egeria was one of them, whose fountain and grotto are still shown. It was said that Numa, the second king of Rome, was favoured by this nymph with secret interviews, in which she taught him those lessons of wisdom and of law which he embodied in the institutions of his rising nation. After the death of Numa the nymph pined away and was changed into a fountain.

Byron, in "Childe Harold," Canto IV., thus alludes to Egeria and her grotto:

"Here didst thou dwell, in this enchanted cover,
   Egeria! all thy heavenly bosom beating
For the far footsteps of thy mortal lover;
   The purple midnight veiled that mystic meeting
With her most starry canopy;" etc.

Tennyson, also, in his "Palace of Art," gives us a glimpse of the royal lover expecting the interview:

"Holding one hand against his ear,
   To list a footfall ere he saw
The wood-nymph, stayed the Tuscan king to hear
   Of wisdom and of law."

THE WINDS

When so many less active agencies were personified, it is not to be supposed that the winds failed to be so. They were Boreas or Aquilo, the north wind; Zephyrus or Favonius, the west; Notus or Auster, the south; and Eurus, the east. The first two have been chiefly celebrated by the poets, the former as the type of rudeness, the latter of gentleness. Boreas loved the nymph Orithyia, and tried to play the lover's part, but met with poor success. It was hard for him to breathe gently, and sighing was out of the question. Weary at last of fruitless endeavours, he acted out his true character, seized the maiden and carried her off. Their children were Zetes and Calais, winged warriors, who accompanied the

Argonautic expedition, and did good service in an encounter with those monstrous birds the Harpies.

Zephyrus was the lover of Flora. Milton alludes to them in "Paradise Lost," where he describes Adam waking and contemplating Eve still asleep.

> "... He on his side
> Leaning half raised, with looks of cordial love,
> Hung over her enamoured, and beheld
> Beauty which, whether waking or asleep,
> Shot forth peculiar graces; then with voice,
> Mild as when Zephyrus on Flora breathes,
> Her hand soft touching, whispered thus: 'Awake!
> My fairest, my espoused, my latest found,
> Heaven's last, best gift, my ever-new delight.'"

Dr. Young, the poet of the "Night Thoughts," addressing the idle and luxurious, says:

> "Ye delicate! who nothing can support
> (Yourselves most insupportable) for whom
> The winter rose must blow, ...
> .... and silky soft
> Favonius breathe still softer or be chid!"

CHAPTER XXIII

ACHELOUS AND HERCULES—ADMETUS AND ALCESTIS— ANTIGONE—PENELOPE

ACHELOUS AND HERCULES

THE river-god Achelous told the story of Erisichthon to Theseus and his companions, whom he was entertaining at his hospitable board, while they were delayed on their journey by the overflow of his waters. Having finished his story, he added, "But why should I tell of other persons' transformations when I myself am an instance of the possession of this power? Sometimes I become a serpent, and sometimes a bull, with horns on my head. Or I should say I once could do so; but now I have but one horn, having lost one." And here he groaned and was silent.

Theseus asked him the cause of his grief, and how he lost his horn. To which question the river-god replied as follows: "Who likes to tell of his defeats? Yet I will not hesitate to relate mine, comforting myself with the thought of the greatness of my conqueror, for it was Hercules. Perhaps you have heard of the fame of Dejanira, the fairest of maidens, whom a host of suitors strove to win. Hercules and myself were of the number, and the rest

yielded to us two. He urged in his behalf his descent from Jove
and his labours by which he had exceeded the exactions of Juno,
his stepmother. I, on the other hand, said to the father of the
maiden, 'Behold me, the king of the waters that flow through your
land. I am no stranger from a foreign shore, but belong to the
country, a part of your realm. Let it not stand in my way that
royal Juno owes me no enmity nor punishes me with heavy tasks.
As for this man, who boasts himself the son of Jove, it is either a
false pretence, or disgraceful to him if true, for it cannot be true
except by his mother's shame.' As I said this Hercules scowled
upon me, and with difficulty restrained his rage. 'My hand will
answer better than my tongue,' said he. 'I yield to you the victory
in words, but trust my cause to the strife of deeds.' With that he
advanced towards me, and I was ashamed, after what I had said,
to yield. I threw off my green vesture and presented myself for
the struggle. He tried to throw me, now attacking my head, now
my body. My bulk was my protection, and he assailed me in vain.
For a time we stopped, then returned to the conflict. We each kept
our position, determined not to yield, foot to foot, I bending over
him, clenching his hand in mine, with my forehead almost touching
his. Thrice Hercules tried to throw me off, and the fourth time he
succeeded, brought me to the ground, and himself upon my back.
I tell you the truth, it was as if a mountain had fallen on me. I
struggled to get my arms at liberty, panting and reeking with
perspiration. He gave me no chance to recover, but seized my
throat. My knees were on the earth and my mouth in the dust.

"Finding that I was no match for him in the warrior's art, I
resorted to others and glided away in the form of a serpent. I
curled my body in a coil and hissed at him with my forked tongue.
He smiled scornfully at this, and said, 'It was the labour of my
infancy to conquer snakes.' So saying he clasped my neck with his
hands. I was almost choked, and struggled to get my neck out of
his grasp. Vanquished in this form, I tried what alone remained to
me and assumed the form of a bull. He grasped my neck with his
arm, and dragging my head down to the ground, overthrew me on
the sand. Nor was this enough. His ruthless hand rent my horn
from my head. The Naiads took it, consecrated it, and filled it
with fragrant flowers. Plenty adopted my horn and made it her
own, and called it 'Cornucopia.' "

The ancients were fond of finding a hidden meaning in their
mythological tales. They explain this fight of Achelous with Hercules by saying Achelous was a river that in seasons of rain overflowed its banks. When the fable says that Achelous loved Dejanira,

and sought a union with her, the meaning is that the river in its windings flowed through part of Dejanira's kingdom. It was said to take the form of a snake because of its winding, and of a bull because it made a brawling or roaring in its course. When the river swelled, it made itself another channel. Thus its head was horned. Hercules prevented the return of these periodical overflows by embankments and canals; and therefore he was said to have vanquished the river-god and cut off his horn. Finally, the lands formerly subject to overflow, but now redeemed, became very fertile. and this is meant by the horn of plenty.

There is another account of the origin of the Cornucopia. Jupiter at his birth was committed by his mother Rhea to the care of the daughters of Melisseus, a Cretan king. They fed the infant deity with the milk of the goat Amalthea. Jupiter broke off one of the horns of the goat and gave it to his nurses, and endowed it with the wonderful power of becoming filled with whatever the possessor might wish.

The name of Amalthea is also given by some writers to the mother of Bacchus. It is thus used by Milton, "Paradise Lost," Book IV.:

> "...That Nyseian isle,
> Girt with the river Triton, where old Cham,
> Whom Gentiles Ammon call, and Libyan Jove,
> Hid Amalthea and her florid son,
> Young Bacchus, from his stepdame Rhea's eye."

ADMETUS AND ALCESTIS

Æsculapius, the son of Apollo, was endowed by his father with such skill in the healing art that he even restored the dead to life. At this Pluto took alarm, and prevailed on Jupiter to launch a thunderbolt at Æsculapius. Apollo was indignant at the destruction of his son, and wreaked his vengeance on the innocent workmen who had made the thunderbolt. These were the Cyclopses, who have their workshop under Mount Ætna, from which the smoke and flames of their furnaces are constantly issuing. Apollo shot his arrows at the Cyclopses, which so incensed Jupiter that he condemned him as a punishment to become the servant of a mortal for the space of one year. Accordingly Apollo went into the service of Admetus, king of Thessaly, and pastured his flocks for him on the verdant banks of the river Amphrysos.

Admetus was a suitor, with others, for the hand of Alcestis, the daughter of Pelias, who promised her to him who should come for her in a chariot drawn by lions and boars. This task Admetus performed by the assistance of his divine herdsman, and was made happy in the possession of Alcestis. But Admetus fell ill, and being near to death, Apollo prevailed on the Fates to spare him on condition that some one would consent to die in his stead. Admetus, in his joy at this reprieve, thought little of the ransom, and perhaps remembering the declarations of attachment which he had often heard from his courtiers and dependents fancied that it would be easy to find a substitute. But it was not so. Brave warriors, who would willingly have perilled their lives for their prince, shrunk from the thought of dying for him on the bed of sickness; and old servants who had experienced his bounty and that of his house from their childhood up, were not willing to lay down the scanty remnant of their days to show their gratitude. Men asked, "Why does not one of his parents do it? They cannot in the course of nature live much longer, and who can feel like them the call to rescue the life they gave from an untimely end?" But the parents, distressed though they were at the thought of losing him, shrunk from the call. Then Alcestis, with a generous self-devotion, proffered herself as the substitute. Admetus, fond as he was of life, would not have submitted to receive it at such a cost; but there was no remedy. The condition imposed by the Fates had been met, and the decree was irrevocable. Alcestis sickened as Admetus revived, and she was rapidly sinking to the grave.

Just at this time Hercules arrived at the Palace of Admetus, and found all the inmates in great distress for the impending loss of the devoted wife and beloved mistress. Hercules, to whom no labour was too arduous, resolved to attempt her rescue. He went and lay in wait at the door of the chamber of the dying queen, and when Death came for his prey, he seized him and forced him to resign his victim. Alcestis recovered, and was restored to her husband.

Milton alludes to the story of Alcestis in his Sonnet "on his deceased wife":

> "Methought I saw my late espoused saint
>   Brought to me like Alcestis from the grave,
>   Whom Jove's great son to her glad husband gave,
> Rescued from death by force, though pale and faint."

J. R. Lowell has chosen the "Shepherd of King Admetus" for the subject of a short poem. He makes that event the first introduction of poetry to men.

> "Men called him but a shiftless youth,
>   In whom no good they saw,
> And yet unwittingly, in truth,
>   They made his careless words their law.

"And day by day more holy grew
Each spot where he had trod,
Till after-poets only knew
Their first-born brother was a god."

ANTIGONE

A large proportion both of the interesting persons and of the exalted acts of legendary Greece belongs to the female sex. Antigone was as bright an example of filial and sisterly fidelity as was Alcestis of connubial devotion. She was the daughter of Œdipus and Jocasta, who with all their descendants were the victims of an unrelenting fate, dooming them to destruction. Œdipus in his madness had torn out his eyes, and was driven forth from his kingdom Thebes, dreaded and abandoned by all men, as an object of divine vengeance. Antigone, his daughter, alone shared his wanderings and remained with him till he died, and then returned to Thebes.

Her brothers, Eteocles and Polynices, had agreed to share the kingdom between them, and reign alternately year by year. The first year fell to the lot of Eteocles, who, when his time expired, refused to surrender the kingdom to his brother. Polynices fled to Adrastus, king of Argos, who gave him his daughter in marriage, and aided him with an army to enforce his claim to the kingdom. This led to the celebrated expedition of the "Seven against Thebes," which furnished ample materials for the epic and tragic poets of Greece.

Amphiaraus, the brother-in-law of Adrastus, opposed the enterprise, for he was a soothsayer, and knew by his art that no one of the leaders except Adrastus would live to return. But Amphiaraus, on his marriage to Eriphyle, the king's sister, had agreed that whenever he and Adrastus should differ in opinion, the decision should be left to Eriphyle. Polynices, knowing this, gave Eriphyle the collar of Harmonia, and thereby gained her to his interest. This collar or necklace was a present which Vulcan had given to Harmonia on her marriage with Cadmus, and Polynices had taken it with him on his flight from Thebes. Eriphyle could not resist so tempting a bribe, and by her decision the war was resolved on, and Amphiaraus went to his certain fate. He bore his part bravely in the contest, but could not avert his destiny. Pursued by the enemy, he fled along the river, when a thunderbolt launched by Jupiter opened the ground, and he, his chariot, and his charioteer were swallowed up.

It would not be in place here to detail all the acts of heroism or atrocity which marked the contest; but we must not omit to record the fidelity of Evadne as an offset to the weakness of Eriphyle.

Capaneus, the husband of Evadne, in the ardour of the fight declared that he would force his way into the city in spite of Jove himself. Placing a ladder against the wall he mounted, but Jupiter, offended at his impious language, struck him with a thunderbolt. When his obsequies were celebrated, Evadne cast herself on his funeral pile and perished.

Early in the contest Eteocles consulted the soothsayer Tiresias as to the issue. Tiresias in his youth had by chance seen Minerva bathing. The goddess in her wrath deprived him of his sight, but afterwards relenting gave him in compensation the knowledge of future events. When consulted by Eteocles, he declared that victory should fall to Thebes if Menœceus, the son of Creon, gave himself a voluntary victim. The heroic youth, learning the response, threw away his life in the first encounter.

The siege continued long, with various success. At length both hosts agreed that the brothers should decide their quarrel by single combat. They fought and fell by each other's hands. The armies then renewed the fight, and at last the invaders were forced to yield, and fled, leaving their dead unburied. Creon, the uncle of the fallen princes, now become king, caused Eteocles to be buried with distinguished honour, but suffered the body of Polynices to lie where it fell, forbidding every one on pain of death to give it burial.

Antigone, the sister of Polynices, heard with indignation the revolting edict which consigned her brother's body to the dogs and vultures, depriving it of those rites which were considered essential to the repose of the dead. Unmoved by the dissuading counsel of an affectionate but timid sister, and unable to procure assistance, she determined to brave the hazard, and to bury the body with her own hands. She was detected in the act, and Creon gave orders that she should be buried alive, as having deliberately set at naught the solemn edict of the city. Her lover, Hæmon, the son of Creon, unable to avert her fate, would not survive her, and fell by his own hand.

Antigone forms the subject of two fine tragedies of the Grecian poet Sophocles. Mrs. Jameson, in her "Characteristics of Women," has compared her character with that of Cordelia, in Shakspeare's "King Lear."

The following is the lamentation of Antigone over Œdipus, when death has at last relieved him from his sufferings:

> "Alas! I only wished I might have died
> With my poor father; wherefore should I ask
> For longer life?
> O. I was fond of misery with him;

> E'en what was most unlovely grew beloved
> When he was with me. O my dearest father,
> Beneath the earth now in deep darkness hid,
> Worn as thou wert with age, to me thou still
> Wast dear, and shalt be ever."
>
> *Francklin's Sophocles.*

PENELOPE

Penelope is another of those mythic heroines whose beauties were rather those of character and conduct than of person. She was the daughter of Icarius, a Spartan prince. Ulysses, king of Ithaca, sought her in marriage, and won her, over all competitors. When the moment came for the bride to leave her father's house, Icarius, unable to bear the thoughts of parting with his daughter, tried to persuade her to remain with him, and not accompany her husband to Ithaca. Ulysses gave Penelope her choice, to stay or go with him. Penelope made no reply, but dropped her veil over her face. Icarius urged her no further, but when she was gone erected a statue to Modesty on the spot where they parted.

Ulysses and Penelope had not enjoyed their union more than a year when it was interrupted by the events which called Ulysses to the Trojan war. During his long absence, and when it was doubtful whether he still lived, and highly improbable that he would ever return, Penelope was importuned by numerous suitors, from whom there seemed no refuge but in choosing one of them for her husband. Penelope, however, employed every art to gain time, still hoping for Ulysses' return. One of her arts of delay was engaging in the preparation of a robe for the funeral canopy of Laertes, her husband's father. She pledged herself to make her choice among the suitors when the robe was finished. During the day she worked at the robe, but in the night she undid the work of the day. This is the famous Penelope's web, which is used as a proverbial expression for anything which is perpetually doing but never done. The rest of Penelope's history will be told when we give an account of her husband's adventures.

CHAPTER XXIV

ORPHEUS AND EURYDICE—ARISTÆUS—AMPHION—LINUS— THAMYRIS—MARSYAS—MELAMPUS—MUSÆUS

ORPHEUS AND EURYDICE

ORPHEUS was the son of Apollo and the Muse Calliope. He was presented by his father with a lyre and taught to play upon it, which he did to such perfection that nothing could withstand the charm of his music. Not only his fellow-mortals, but wild beasts were softened by his strains, and gathering round him laid by their fierceness, and stood entranced with his lay. Nay, the very trees and rocks were sensible to the charm. The former crowded round him and the latter relaxed somewhat of their hardness, softened by his notes.

Hymen had been called to bless with his presence the nuptials of Orpheus with Eurydice; but though he attended, he brought no happy omens with him. His very torch smoked and brought tears into their eyes. In coincidence with such prognostics, Eurydice, shortly after her marriage, while wandering with the nymphs, her companions, was seen by the shepherd Aristæus, who was struck by her beauty and made advances to her. She fled, and in flying trod upon a snake in the grass, was bitten in the foot, and died. Orpheus sang his grief to all who breathed the upper air, both gods and men, and finding it all unavailing resolved to seek his wife in the regions of the dead. He descended by a cave situated on the side of the promontory of Tænarus and arrived at the Stygian realm. He passed through crowds of ghosts and presented himself before the throne of Pluto and Proserpine. Accompanying the words with the lyre, he sung, "O deities of the under-world, to whom all we who live must come, hear my words, for they are true. I come not to spy out the secrets of Tartarus, nor to try my strength against the three-headed dog with snaky hair who guards the entrance. I come to seek my wife, whose opening years the poisonous viper's fang has brought to an untimely end. Love has led me here, Love, a god all powerful with us who dwell on the earth, and, if old traditions say true, not less so here. I implore you by these abodes full of terror, these realms of silence and un-created things, unite again the thread of Eurydice's life. We all are destined to you, and sooner or later must pass to your domain. She too, when she shall have filled her term of life, will rightly be yours. But till then grant her to me, I beseech you. If you deny me, I cannot return alone; you shall triumph in the death of us both."

As he sang these tender strains, the very ghosts shed tears. Tantalus, in spite of his thirst, stopped for a moment his efforts for water, Ixion's wheel stood still, the vulture ceased to tear the giant's liver, the daughters of Danaus rested from their task of drawing water in a sieve, and Sisyphus sat on his rock to listen. Then for the first time, it is said, the cheeks of the Furies were wet with tears. Proserpine could not resist, and Pluto himself gave way. Eurydice was called. She came from among the new-arrived ghosts, limping with her wounded foot. Orpheus was permitted to take her away with him on one condition, that he should not turn around to look at her till they should have reached the upper air. Under this condition they proceeded on their way, he leading, she following, through passages dark and steep, in total silence, till they had nearly reached the outlet into the cheerful upper world, when Orpheus, in a moment of forgetfulness, to assure himself that she was still following, cast a glance behind him, when instantly she was borne away. Stretching out their arms to embrace each other, they grasped only the air! Dying now a second time, she yet cannot reproach her husband, for how can she blame his impatience to behold her? "Farewell," she said, "a last farewell,"— and was hurried away, so fast that the sound hardly reached his ears.

Orpheus endeavoured to follow her, and besought permission to return and try once more for her release; but the stern ferryman repulsed him and refused passage. Seven days he lingered about the brink, without food or sleep; then bitterly accusing of cruelty the powers of Erebus, he sang his complaints to the rocks and mountains, melting the hearts of tigers and moving the oaks from their stations. He held himself aloof from womankind, dwelling constantly on the recollection of his sad mischance. The Thracian maidens tried their best to captivate him, but he repulsed their advances. They bore with him as long as they could; but finding him insensible one day, excited by the rites of Bacchus, one of them exclaimed, "See yonder our despiser!" and threw at him her javelin. The weapon, as soon as it came within the sound of his lyre, fell harmless at his feet. So did also the stones that they threw at him. But the women raised a scream and drowned the voice of the music, and then the missiles reached him and soon were stained with his blood. The maniacs tore him limb from limb, and threw his head and his lyre into the river Hebrus, down which they floated, murmuring sad music, to which the shores responded a plaintive symphony. The Muses gathered up the fragments of his body and buried them at Libethra, where the nightingale is said to sing over his grave more sweetly than in any other part of Greece. His lyre was placed by Jupiter among the stars. His shade passed a second time to Tartarus, where he sought out his Eurydice and embraced her with eager arms. They roam the happy fields together now, sometimes he leading, sometimes she; and Orpheus gazes as much as he will upon her, no longer incurring a penalty for a thoughtless glance.

The story of Orpheus has furnished Pope with an illustration of the power of music, for his "Ode for St. Cecilia's Day." The following stanza relates the conclusion of the story:

"But soon, too soon the lover turns his eyes;
Again she falls, again she dies, she dies!
How wilt thou now the fatal sisters move?
No crime was thine, if 'tis no crime to love.
     Now under hanging mountains,
     Beside the falls of fountains,
     Or where Hebrus wanders,
     Rolling in meanders,
          All alone,
          He makes his moan,
          And calls her ghost,
     For ever, ever, ever lost!
Now with furies surrounded,
Despairing, confounded,
He trembles, he glows,
Amidst Rhodope's snows.
See, wild as the winds o'er the desert he flies;
Hark! Hæmus resounds with the Bacchanals' cries.
          Ah, see, he dies!
Yet even in death Eurydice he sung,
Eurydice still trembled on his tongue:
     Eurydice the woods
     Eurydice the floods
     Eurydice the rocks and hollow mountains rung."

The superior melody of the nightingale's song over the grave of
Orpheus is alluded to by Southey in his "Thalaba":

"Then on his ear what sounds
     Of harmony arose!
Far music and the distance-mellowed song
     From bowers of merriment;
     The waterfall remote;
The murmuring of the leafy groves;
     The single nightingale
Perched in the rosier by, so richly toned,
That never from that most melodious bird
Singing a love song to his brooding mate,
Did Thracian shepherd by the grave
Of Orpheus hear a sweeter melody,
Though there the spirit of the sepulchre
     All his own power infuse, to swell
     The incense that he loves."

ARISTÆUS, THE BEE-KEEPER

Man avails himself of the instincts of the inferior animals for
his own advantage. Hence sprang the art of keeping bees. Honey
must first have been known as a wild product, the bees building
their structures in hollow trees or holes in the rocks, or any similar
cavity that chance offered. Thus occasionally the carcass of a dead
animal would be occupied by the bees for that purpose. It was no
doubt from some such incident that the superstition arose that the

bees were engendered by the decaying flesh of the animal; and Virgil, in the following story, shows how this supposed fact may be turned to account for renewing the swarm when it has been lost by disease or accident.

Aristæus, who first taught the management of bees, was the son of the water-nymph Cyrene. His bees had perished, and he resorted for aid to his mother. He stood at the river side and thus addressed her: "O mother, the pride of my life is taken from me! I have lost my precious bees. My care and skill have availed me nothing, and you, my mother, have not warded off from me the blow of misfortune." His mother heard these complaints as she sat in her palace at the bottom of the river, with her attendant nymphs around her. They were engaged in female occupations, spinning and weaving, while one told stories to amuse the rest. The sad voice of Aristæus interrupting their occupation, one of them put her head above the water and seeing him, returned and gave information to his mother, who ordered that he should be brought into her presence. The river at her command opened itself and let him pass in, while it stood curled like a mountain on either side. He descended to the region where the fountains of the great rivers lie; he saw the enormous receptacles of waters and was almost deafened with the roar, while he surveyed them hurrying off in various directions to water the face of the earth. Arriving at his mother's apartment, he was hospitably received by Cyrene and her nymphs, who spread their table with the richest dainties. They first poured out libations to Neptune, then regaled themselves with the feast, and after that Cyrene thus addressed him: "There is an old prophet named Proteus, who dwells in the sea and is a favourite of Neptune, whose herd of sea-calves he pastures. We nymphs hold him in great respect, for he is a learned sage and knows all things, past, present, and to come. He can tell you, my son, the cause of the mortality among your bees and how you may remedy it. But he will not do it voluntarily, however you may entreat him. You must compel him by force. If you seize him and chain him, he will answer your questions in order to get released, for he cannot by all his arts get away if you hold fast the chains. I will carry you to his cave, where he comes at noon to take his midday repose. Then you may easily secure him. But when he finds himself captured, his resort is to a power he possesses of changing himself into various forms. He will become a wild boar or a fierce tiger, a scaly dragon or lion with yellow mane. Or he will make a noise like the crackling of flames or the rush of water, so as to tempt you to let go the chain, when he will make his escape. But you have only to keep him fast bound, and at last when he finds all his arts unavail-

ing, he will return to his own figure and obey your commands."
So saying she sprinkled her son with fragrant nectar, the beverage
of the gods, and immediately an unusual vigour filled his frame,
and courage his heart, while perfume breathed all around him.

The nymph led her son to the prophet's cave and concealed him
among the recesses of the rocks, while she herself took her place
behind the clouds. When noon came and the hour when men and
herds retreat from the glaring sun to indulge in quiet slumber,
Proteus issued from the water, followed by his herd of sea-calves
which spread themselves along the shore. He sat on the rock and
counted his herd; then stretched himself on the floor of the cave
and went to sleep. Aristæus hardly allowed him to get fairly asleep
before he fixed the fetters on him and shouted aloud. Proteus,
waking and finding himself captured, immediately resorted to his
arts, becoming first a fire, then a flood, then a horrible wild beast,
in rapid succession. But finding all would not do, he at last resumed his own form and addressed the youth in angry accents:
"Who are you, bold youth, who thus invade my abode, and what
do you want with me?" Aristæus replied, "Proteus, you know
already, for it is needless for any one to attempt to deceive you.
And do you also cease your efforts to elude me. I am led hither by
divine assistance, to know from you the cause of my misfortune
and how to remedy it." At these words the prophet, fixing on him
his grey eyes with a piercing look, thus spoke: "You receive the
merited reward of your deeds, by which Eurydice met her death,
for in flying from you she trod upon a serpent, of whose bite she
died. To avenge her death, the nymphs, her companions, have sent
this destruction to your bees. You have to appease their anger,
and thus it must be done: Select four bulls, of perfect form and
size, and four cows of equal beauty, build four altars to the nymphs,
and sacrifice the animals, leaving their carcasses in the leafy grove.
To Orpheus and Eurydice you shall pay such funeral honours as
may allay their resentment. Returning after nine days, you will
examine the bodies of the cattle slain and see what will befall."
Aristæus faithfully obeyed these directions. He sacrificed the
cattle, he left their bodies in the grove, he offered funeral honours
to the shades of Orpheus and Eurydice; then returning on the
ninth day he examined the bodies of the animals, and, wonderful
to relate! a swarm of bees had taken possession of one of the
carcasses and were pursuing their labours there as in a hive.

In "The Task," Cowper alludes to the story of Aristæus, when
speaking of the ice-palace built by the Empress Anne of Russia.
He has been describing the fantastic forms which ice assumes in
connection with waterfalls. etc.:

"Less worthy of applause though more admired
Because a novelty, the work of man,
Imperial mistress of the fur-clad Russ,
Thy most magnificent and mighty freak,
The wonder of the north. No forest fell
When thou wouldst build, no quarry sent its stores
T' enrich thy walls; but thou didst hew the floods
And make thy marble of the glassy wave.
In such a palace Aristæus found
Cyrene, when he bore the plaintive tale
Of his lost bees to her maternal ear."

Milton also appears to have had Cyrene and her domestic scene in his mind when he describes to us Sabrina, the nymph of the river Severn, in the Guardian-spirit's song in "Comus":

"Sabrina fair!
Listen where thou art sitting
Under the glassy, cool, translucent wave
In twisted braids of lilies knitting
The loose train of thy amber-drooping hair;
Listen for dear honour's sake,
Goddess of the silver lake!
Listen and save."

The following are other celebrated mythical poets and musicians, some of whom were hardly inferior to Orpheus himself:

AMPHION

Amphion was the son of Jupiter and Antiope, queen of Thebes. With his twin brother Zethus, he was exposed at birth on Mount Cithæron, where they grew up among the shepherds, not knowing their parentage. Mercury gave Amphion a lyre and taught him to play upon it, and his brother occupied himself in hunting and tending the flocks. Meanwhile Antiope, their mother, who had been treated with great cruelty by Lycus, the usurping king of Thebes, and by Dirce, his wife, found means to inform her children of their rights and to summon them to her assistance. With a band of their fellow-herdsmen they attacked and slew Lycus, and tying Dirce by the hair of her head to a bull, let him drag her till she was dead.[1] Amphion, having become king of Thebes, fortified the city with a wall. It is said that when he played on his lyre the stones moved of their own accord and took their places in the wall.

See Tennyson's poem of "Amphion" for an amusing use made of this story.

[1] The punishment of Dirce is the subject of a celebrated group of statuary now in the Museum at Naples.

LINUS

Linus was the instructor of Hercules in music, but having one day reproved his pupil rather harshly, he roused the anger of Hercules, who struck him with his lyre and killed him.

THAMYRIS

An ancient Thracian bard, who in his presumption challenged the Muses to a trial of skill, and being overcome in the contest, was deprived by them of his sight. Milton alludes to him with other blind bards, when speaking of his own blindness, "Paradise Lost," Book III. 35.

MARSYAS

Minerva invented the flute, and played upon it to the delight of all the celestial auditors; but the mischievous urchin Cupid having dared to laugh at the queer face which the goddess made while playing, Minerva threw the instrument indignantly away, and it fell down to earth and was found by Marsyas. He blew upon it, and drew from it such ravishing sounds that he was tempted to challenge Apollo himself to a musical contest. The god of course triumphed, and punished Marsyas by flaying him alive.

MELAMPUS

Melampus was the first mortal endowed with prophetic powers. Before his house there stood an oak tree containing a serpent's nest. The old serpents were killed by the servants, but Melampus took care of the young ones and fed them carefully. One day when he was asleep under the oak the serpents licked his ears with their tongues. On awaking he was astonished to find that he now understood the language of birds and creeping things. This knowledge enabled him to foretell future events, and he became a renowned soothsayer. At one time his enemies took him captive and kept him strictly imprisoned. Melampus in the silence of the night heard the woodworms in the timbers talking together, and found out by what they said that the timbers were nearly eaten through and the roof would soon fall in. He told his captors and demanded to be let out, warning them also. They took his warning, and thus escaped destruction, and rewarded Melampus and held him in high honour.

MUSÆUS

A semi-mythological personage who was represented by one tradition to be the son of Orpheus. He is said to have written sacred poems and oracles. Milton couples his name with that of Orpheus in his "Il Penseroso":

> "But O, sad virgin, that thy power
> Might raise Musæus from his bower,
> Or bid the soul of Orpheus sing
> Such notes as warbled to the string,
> Drew iron tears down Pluto's cheek,
> And made Hell grant what love did seek."

CHAPTER XXV

ARION—IBYCUS—SIMONIDES—SAPPHO

THE poets whose adventures compose this chapter were real persons some of whose works yet remain, and their influence on poets who succeeded them is yet more important than their poetical remains. The adventures recorded of them in the following stories rest on the same authority as other narratives of the "Age of Fable," that is, of the poets who have told them. In their present form, the first two are translated from the German, Arion from Schlegel, and Ibycus from Schiller.

ARION

Arion was a famous musician, and dwelt at the court of Periander, king of Corinth, with whom he was a great favourite. There was to be a musical contest in Sicily, and Arion longed to compete for the prize. He told his wish to Periander, who besought him like a brother to give up the thought. "Pray stay with me," he said, "and be contented. He who strives to win may lose." Arion answered, "A wandering life best suits the free heart of a poet. The talent which a god bestowed on me, I would fain make a source of pleasure to others. And if I win the prize, how will the enjoyment of it be increased by the consciousness of my widespread fame!" He went, won the prize, and embarked with his wealth in a Corinthian ship for home. On the second morning after setting sail, the wind breathed mild and fair. "O Periander," he exclaimed, "dismiss your fears! Soon shall you forget them in my embrace. With what lavish offerings will we display our gratitude to the gods, and how merry will we be at the festal board!" The wind and sea continued propitious. Not a cloud dimmed the firmament.

He had not trusted too much to the ocean—but he had to man. He overheard the seamen exchanging hints with one another, and found they were plotting to possess themselves of his treasure. Presently they surrounded him loud and mutinous, and said, "Arion, you must die! If you would have a grave on shore, yield yourself to die on this spot; but if otherwise, cast yourself into the sea." "Will nothing satisfy you but my life?" said he. "Take my gold, and welcome, I willingly buy my life at that price." "No, no; we cannot spare you. Your life would be too dangerous to us. Where could we go to escape from Periander, if he should know that you had been robbed by us? Your gold would be of little use to us, if, on returning home, we could never more be free from fear." "Grant me, then," said he, "a last request, since nought will avail to save my life, that I may die, as I have lived, as becomes a bard. When I shall have sung my death song, and my harp-strings shall have ceased to vibrate, then I will bid farewell to life, and yield uncomplaining to my fate." This prayer, like the others, would have been unheeded,—they thought only of their booty,— but to hear so famous a musician, that moved their rude hearts. "Suffer me," he added, "to arrange my dress. Apollo will not favour me unless I be clad in my minstrel garb."

He clothed his well-proportioned limbs in gold and purple fair to see, his tunic fell around him in graceful folds, jewels adorned his arms, his brow was crowned with a golden wreath, and over his neck and shoulders flowed his hair perfumed with odours. His left hand held the lyre, his right the ivory wand with which he struck its chords. Like one inspired, he seemed to drink the morning air and glitter in the morning ray. The seamen gazed with admiration. He strode forward to the vessel's side and looked down into the deep blue sea. Addressing his lyre, he sang, "Companion of my voice, come with me to the realm of shades. Though Cerberus may growl, we know the power of song can tame his rage. Ye heroes of Elysium, who have passed the darkling flood,—ye happy souls, soon shall I join your band. Yet can ye relieve my grief? Alas, I leave my friend behind me. Thou, who didst find thy Eurydice, and lose her again as soon as found; when she had vanished like a dream, how didst thou hate the cheerful light! I must away, but I will not fear. The gods look down upon us. Ye who slay me unoffending, when I am no more, your time of trembling shall come. Ye Nereids, receive your guest, who throws himself upon your mercy!" So saying, he sprang into the deep sea. The waves covered him, and the seamen held on their way, fancying themselves safe from all danger of detection.

But the strains of his music had drawn round him the inhabitants of the deep to listen, and Dolphins followed the ship as if chained by a spell. While he struggled in the waves, a Dolphin offered him his back, and carried him mounted thereon safe to shore. At the spot where he landed, a monument of brass was afterwards erected upon the rocky shore, to preserve the memory of the event.

When Arion and the dolphin parted, each to his own element, Arion thus poured forth his thanks: "Farewell, thou faithful, friendly fish! Would that I could reward thee; but thou canst not wend with me, nor I with thee. Companionship we may not have. May Galatea, queen of the deep, accord thee her favour, and thou, proud of the burden, draw her chariot over the smooth mirror of the deep."

Arion hastened from the shore, and soon saw before him the towers of Corinth. He journeyed on, harp in hand, singing as he went, full of love and happiness, forgetting his losses, and mindful only of what remained, his friend and his lyre. He entered the hospitable halls, and was soon clasped in the embrace of Periander. "I come back to thee, my friend," he said. "The talent which a god bestowed has been the delight of thousands, but false knaves have stripped me of my well-earned treasure; yet I retain the consciousness of widespread fame." Then he told Periander all the wonderful events that had befallen him, who heard him with amazement. "Shall such wickedness triumph?" said he. "Then in vain is power lodged in my hands. That we may discover the criminals, you must remain here in concealment, and so they will approach without suspicion." When the ship arrived in the harbour, he summoned the mariners before him. "Have you heard anything of Arion?" he inquired. "I anxiously look for his return." They replied, "We left him well and prosperous in Tarentum." As they said these words, Arion stepped forth and faced them. His well-proportioned limbs were arrayed in gold and purple fair to see, his tunic fell around him in graceful folds, jewels adorned his arms, his brow was crowned with a golden wreath, and over his neck and shoulders flowed his hair perfumed with odours; his left hand held the lyre, his right the ivory wand with which he struck its chords. They fell prostrate at his feet, as if a lightning bolt had struck them. "We meant to murder him, and he has become a god. O Earth, open and receive us!" Then Periander spoke. "He lives, the master of the lay! Kind Heaven protects the poet's life. As for you, I invoke not the spirit of vengeance; Arion wishes not your blood. Ye slaves of avarice, begone! Seek some barbarous land, and never may aught beautiful delight your souls!"

Spenser represents Arion, mounted on his dolphin, accompanying the train of Neptune and Amphitrite:

"Then was there heard a most celestial sound
Of dainty music which did next ensue,
And, on the floating waters as enthroned,
Arion with his harp unto him drew
The ears and hearts of all that goodly crew;
Even when as yet the dolphin which him bore
Through the Ægean Seas from pirates' view,
Stood still, by him astonished at his lore,
And all the raging seas for joy forgot to roar."

Byron, in his "Childe Harold," Canto II., alludes to the story of
Arion, when, describing his voyage, he represents one of the seamen
making music to entertain the rest:

"The moon is up; by Heaven a lovely eve!
Long streams of light o'er dancing waves expand;
Now lads on shore may sigh and maids believe;
Such be our fate when we return to land!
Meantime some rude Arion's restless hand
Wakes the brisk harmony that sailors love;
A circle there of merry listeners stand,
Or to some well-known measure featly move
Thoughtless as if on shore they still were free to rove."

IBYCUS

In order to understand the story of Ibycus which follows it is
necessary to remember, first, that the theatres of the ancients were
immense fabrics capable of containing from ten to thirty thousand
spectators, and as they were used only on festal occasions, and
admission was free to all, they were usually filled. They were without
roofs and open to the sky, and the performances were in the daytime.
Secondly, the appalling representation of the Furies is not exaggerated in the story. It is recorded that Æschylus, the tragic poet,
having on one occasion represented the Furies in a chorus of fifty
performers, the terror of the spectators was such that many fainted
and were thrown into convulsions, and the magistrates forbade a
like representation for the future.

Ibycus, the pious poet, was on his way to the chariot races and
musical competitions held at the Isthmus of Corinth, which attracted
all of Grecian lineage. Apollo had bestowed on him the gift of song,
the honeyed lips of the poet, and he pursued his way with lightsome
step, full of the god. Already the towers of Corinth crowning the
height appeared in view, and he had entered with pious awe the
sacred grove of Neptune. No living object was in sight, only a flock
of cranes flew overhead taking the same course as himself in their
migration to a southern clime. "Good luck to you, ye friendly
squadrons," he exclaimed, "my companions from across the sea. I
take your company for a good omen. We come from far and fly in

search of hospitality. May both of us meet that kind reception which shields the stranger guest from harm!"

He paced briskly on, and soon was in the middle of the wood. There suddenly, at a narrow pass, two robbers stepped forth and barred his way. He must yield or fight. But his hand, accustomed to the lyre, and not to the strife of arms, sank powerless. He called for help on men and gods, but his cry reached no defender's ear. "Then here must I die," said he, "in a strange land, unlamented, cut off by the hand of outlaws, and see none to avenge my cause." Sore wounded, he sank to the earth, when hoarse screamed the cranes overhead. "Take up my cause, ye cranes," he said, "since no voice but yours answers to my cry." So saying he closed his eyes in death.

The body, despoiled and mangled, was found, and though disfigured with wounds, was recognized by the friend in Corinth who had expected him as a guest. "Is it thus I find you restored to me?" he exclaimed. "I who hoped to entwine your temples with the wreath of triumph in the strife of song!"

The guests assembled at the festival heard the tidings with dismay. All Greece felt the wound, every heart owned its loss. They crowded round the tribunal of the magistrates, and demanded vengeance on the murderers and expiation with their blood.

But what trace or mark shall point out the perpetrator from amidst the vast multitude attracted by the splendour of the feast? Did he fall by the hands of robbers or did some private enemy slay him? The all-discerning sun alone can tell, for no other eye beheld it. Yet not improbably the murderer even now walks in the midst of the throng, and enjoys the fruits of his crime, while vengeance seeks for him in vain. Perhaps in their own temple's enclosure he defies the gods, mingling freely in this throng of men that now presses into the amphitheatre.

For now crowded together, row on row, the multitude fills the seats till it seems as if the very fabric would give way. The murmur of voices sounds like the roar of the sea, while the circles widening in their ascent rise tier on tier, as if they would reach the sky.

And now the vast assemblage listens to the awful voice of the chorus personating the Furies, which in solemn guise advances with measured step, and moves around the circuit of the theatre. Can they be mortal women who compose that awful group, and can that vast concourse of silent forms be living beings?

The choristers, clad in black, bore in their fleshless hands torches blazing with a pitchy flame. Their cheeks were bloodless, and in place of hair writhing and swelling serpents curled around their brows. Forming a circle, these awful beings sang their hymns, rending the hearts of the guilty, and enchaining all their faculties. It rose and swelled, overpowering the sound of the instruments, stealing the judgment, palsying the heart, curdling the blood.

"Happy the man who keeps his heart pure from guilt and crime! Him we avengers touch not; he treads the path of life secure from us. But woe! woe! to him who has done the deed of secret murder. We, the fearful family of Night, fasten ourselves upon his whole being. Thinks he by flight to escape us? We fly still faster in pursuit, twine our snakes around his feet, and bring him to the ground. Unwearied we pursue; no pity checks our course; still on and on, to the end of life, we give him no peace nor rest." Thus the Eumenides sang, and moved in solemn cadence, while stillness like the stillness of death sat over the whole assembly as if in the presence of superhuman beings; and then in solemn march completing the circuit of the theatre, they passed out at the back of the stage.

Every heart fluttered between illusion and reality, and every breast panted with undefined terror, quailing before the awful power that watches secret crimes and winds unseen the skein of destiny. At that moment a cry burst forth from one of the uppermost benches —"Look! look! comrade, yonder are the cranes of Ibycus!" And suddenly there appeared sailing across the sky a dark object which a moment's inspection showed to be a flock of cranes flying directly over the theatre. "Of Ibycus! did he say?" The beloved name revived the sorrow in every breast. As wave follows wave over the face of the sea, so ran from mouth to mouth the words, "Of Ibycus! him whom we all lament, whom some murderer's hand laid low! What have the cranes to do with him?" And louder grew the swell of voices, while like a lightning's flash the thought sped through every heart, "Observe the power of the Eumenides! The pious poet shall be avenged! the murderer has informed against himself. Seize the man who uttered that cry and the other to whom he spoke!"

The culprit would gladly have recalled his words, but it was too late. The faces of the murderers, pale with terror, betrayed their guilt. The people took them before the judge, they confessed their crime, and suffered the punishment they deserved.

SIMONIDES

Simonides was one of the most prolific of the early poets of Greece, but only a few fragments of his compositions have descended to us. He wrote hymns, triumphal odes, and elegies. In the last species of composition he particularly excelled. His genius was inclined to the pathetic, and none could touch with truer effect the chords of human sympathy. The "Lamentation of Danaë," the most important of the fragments which remain of his poetry, is based upon the tradition that Danaë and her infant son were confined by order of her father, Acrisius, in a chest and set adrift on the sea. The chest floated towards the island of Seriphus, where both were rescued by Dictys, a fisherman, and carried to Polydectes, king of the country, who received and protected them. The child, Perseus, when grown up became a famous hero, whose adventures have been recorded in a previous chapter.

Simonides passed much of his life at the courts of princes, and often employed his talents in panegyric and festal odes, receiving his reward from the munificence of those whose exploits he cele-brated. This employment was not derogatory, but closely resembles that of the earliest bards, such as Demodocus, described by Homer, or of Homer himself, as recorded by tradition.

On one occasion, when residing at the court of Scopas, king of Thessaly, the prince desired him to prepare a poem in celebration of his exploits, to be recited at a banquet. In order to diversify his theme, Simonides, who was celebrated for his piety, introduced into his poem the exploits of Castor and Pollux. Such digressions were not unusual with the poets on similar occasions, and one might suppose an ordinary mortal might have been content to share the praises of the sons of Leda. But vanity is exacting; and as Scopas sat at his festal board among his courtiers and sycophants, he grudged every verse that did not rehearse his own praises. When Simonides approached to receive the promised reward Scopas be-stowed but half the expected sum, saying, "Here is payment for my portion of thy performance; Castor and Pollux will doubtless com-pensate thee for so much as relates to them." The disconcerted poet returned to his seat amidst the laughter which followed the great man's jest. In a little time he received a message that two young men on horseback were waiting without and anxious to see him. Simonides hastened to the door, but looked in vain for the visitors. Scarcely, however, had he left the banqueting hall when the roof fell in with a loud crash, burying Scopas and all his guests beneath the ruins. On inquiring as to the appearance of the young men who had sent for him, Simonides was satisfied that they were no other than Castor and Pollux themselves.

SAPPHO

Sappho was a poetess who flourished in a very early age of Greek literature. Of her works few fragments remain, but they are enough to establish her claim to eminent poetical genius. The story of

Sappho commonly alluded to is that she was passionately in love with a beautiful youth named Phaon, and failing to obtain a return of affection she threw herself from the promontory of Leucadia into the sea, under a superstition that those who should take that "Lover's-leap" would, if not destroyed, be cured of their love.

Byron alludes to the story of Sappho in "Childe Harold," Canto II.:

> "Childe Harold sailed and passed the barren spot
> Where sad Penelope o'erlooked the wave,
> And onward viewed the mount, not yet forgot,
> The lover's refuge and the Lesbian's grave.
> Dark Sappho! could not verse immortal save
> That breast imbued with such immortal fire?

> " 'Twas on a Grecian autumn's gentle eve
> Childe Harold hailed Leucadia's cape afar;" etc.

Those who wish to know more of Sappho and her "leap" are referred to the "Spectator," Nos. 223 and 229. See also Moore's "Evenings in Greece."

CHAPTER XXVI

ENDYMION—ORION—AURORA AND TITHONUS—ACIS AND GALATEA

ENDYMION was a beautiful youth who fed his flock on Mount Latmos. One calm, clear night, Diana, the moon, looked down and saw him sleeping. The cold heart of the virgin goddess was warmed by his surpassing beauty, and she came down to him, kissed him, and watched over him while he slept.

Another story was that Jupiter bestowed on him the gift of perpetual youth united with perpetual sleep. Of one so gifted we can have but few adventures to record. Diana, it was said, took care that his fortunes should not suffer by his inactive life, for she made his flock increase, and guarded his sheep and lambs from the wild beasts.

The story of Endymion has a peculiar charm from the human meaning which it so thinly veils. We see in Endymion the young poet, his fancy and his heart seeking in vain for that which can satisfy them, finding his favourite hour in the quiet moonlight, and nursing there beneath the beams of the bright and silent witness the melancholy and the ardour which consume him. The story suggests aspiring and poetic love, a life spent more in dreams than in reality, and an early and welcome death.—*S. G. B.*

The "Endymion" of Keats is a wild and fanciful poem, containing some exquisite poetry, as this, to the moon:

".. . The sleeping kine
Couched in thy brightness dream of fields divine.
Innumerable mountains rise, and rise,
Ambitious for the hallowing of thine eyes,
And yet thy benediction passeth not
One obscure hiding-place, one little spot
Where pleasure may be sent; the nested wren
Has thy fair face within its tranquil ken;" etc., etc.

Dr. Young, in the "Night Thoughts," alludes to Endymion thus:

".. . These thoughts, O Night, are thine;
From thee they came like lovers' secret sighs,
While others slept. So Cynthia, poets feign,
In shadows veiled, soft, sliding from her sphere,
Her shepherd cheered, of her enamoured less
Than I of thee."

Fletcher, in the "Faithful Shepherdess," tells:

"How the pale Phœbe, hunting in a grove,
First saw the boy Endymion, from whose eyes
She took eternal fire that never dies;
How she conveyed him softly in a sleep,
His temples bound with poppy, to the steep
Head of old Latmos, where she stoops each night,
Gilding the mountain with her brother's light,
To kiss her sweetest."

ORION

Orion was the son of Neptune. He was a handsome giant and a mighty hunter. His father gave him the power of wading through the depths of the sea, or, as others say, of walking on its surface.

Orion loved Merope, the daughter of Œnopion, king of Chios, and sought her in marriage. He cleared the island of wild beasts, and brought the spoils of the chase as presents to his beloved; but as Œnopion constantly deferred his consent, Orion attempted to gain possession of the maiden by violence. Her father, incensed at this conduct, having made Orion drunk, deprived him of his sight and cast him out on the seashore. The blinded hero followed the sound of a Cyclops' hammer till he reached Lemnos, and came to the forge of Vulcan, who, taking pity on him, gave him Kedalion, one of his men, to be his guide to the abode of the sun. Placing Kedalion on his shoulders, Orion proceeded to the east, and there meeting the sun-god, was restored to sight by his beam.

After this he dwelt as a hunter with Diana, with whom he was a favourite, and it is even said she was about to marry him. Her brother was highly displeased and often chid her, but to no purpose. One day, observing Orion wading through the sea with his head just above the water, Apollo pointed it out to his sister and maintained that she could not hit that black thing on the sea. The archer-goddess discharged a shaft with fatal aim. The waves rolled the dead body of Orion to the land, and bewailing her fatal error with many tears, Diana placed him among the stars, where he appears as a giant, with a girdle, sword, lion's skin, and club. Sirius, his dog, follows him, and the Pleiads fly before him.

The Pleiads were daughters of Atlas, and nymphs of Diana's train. One day Orion saw them and became enamoured and pursued them. In their distress they prayed to the gods to change their form, and Jupiter in pity turned them into pigeons, and then made them a constellation in the sky. Though their number was seven, only six stars are visible, for Electra, one of them, it is said left her place that she might not behold the ruin of Troy, for that city was founded by her son Dardanus. The sight had such an effect on her sisters that they have looked pale ever since.

Mr. Longfellow has a poem on the "Occultation of Orion." The following lines are those in which he alludes to the mythic story. We must premise that on the celestial globe Orion is represented as robed in a lion's skin and wielding a club. At the moment the stars of the constellation, one by one, were quenched in the light of the moon, the poet tells us

> "Down fell the red skin of the lion
> Into the river at his feet.
> His mighty club no longer beat
> The forehead of the bull; but he
> Reeled as of yore beside the sea,
> When blinded by Œnopion
> > He sought the blacksmith at his forge,
> > And climbing up the narrow gorge,
> Fixed his blank eyes upon the sun."

Tennyson has a different theory of the Pleiads:

> "Many a night I saw the Pleiads, rising through the mellow shade,
> Glitter like a swarm of fire-flies tangled in a silver braid"
> > > *Locksley Hall.*

Byron alludes to the lost Pleiad:

> "Like the lost Pleiad seen no more below."

See also Mrs. Hemans's verses on the same subject.

AURORA AND TITHONUS

The goddess of the Dawn, like her sister the Moon, was at times inspired with the love of mortals. Her greatest favourite was Tithonus son of Laomedon, king of Troy. She stole him away, and prevailed on Jupiter to grant him immortality; but, forgetting to have youth joined in the gift, after some time she began to discern, to her great mortification, that he was growing old. When his hair was quite white she left his society; but he still had the range of her palace, lived on ambrosial food, and was clad in celestial raiment. At length he lost the power of using his limbs, and then she shut him up in his chamber, whence his feeble voice might at times be heard. Finally she turned him into a grasshopper.

Memnon was the son of Aurora and Tithonus. He was king of the Æthiopians, and dwelt in the extreme east, on the shore of Ocean. He came with his warriors to assist the kindred of his father in the war of Troy. King Priam received him with great honours, and listened with admiration to his narrative of the wonders of the ocean shore.

The very day after his arrival, Memnon, impatient of repose, led his troops to the field. Antilochus, the brave son of Nestor, fell by his hand, and the Greeks were put to flight, when Achilles appeared and restored the battle. A long and doubtful contest ensued between him and the son of Aurora; at length victory declared for Achilles, Memnon fell, and the Trojans fled in dismay.

Aurora, who from her station in the sky had viewed with apprehension the danger of her son, when she saw him fall, directed his brothers, the Winds, to convey his body to the banks of the river Esepus in Paphlagonia. In the evening Aurora came, accompanied by the Hours and the Pleiads, and wept and lamented over her son. Night, in sympathy with her grief, spread the heaven with clouds; all nature mourned for the offspring of the Dawn. The Æthiopians raised his tomb on the banks of the stream in the grove of the Nymphs, and Jupiter caused the sparks and cinders of his funeral pile to be turned into birds, which, dividing into two flocks, fought over the pile till they fell into the flames. Every year at the anniversary of his death they return and celebrate his obsequies in like manner. Aurora remains inconsolable for the loss of her son. Her tears still flow, and may be seen at early morning in the form of dew-drops on the grass.

Unlike most of the marvels of ancient mythology, there still exist some memorials of this. On the banks of the river Nile, in Egypt, are two colossal statues, one of which is said to be the statue of Memnon. Ancient writers record that when the first rays of the rising sun fall upon this statue a sound is heard to issue from it, which they compare to the snapping of a harp-string. There is some doubt about the identification of the existing statue with the one described by the ancients, and the mysterious sounds are still more doubtful. Yet there are not wanting some modern testimonies to their being still audible. It has been suggested that sounds produced by confined air making its escape from crevices or caverns in the rocks may have given some ground for the story. Sir Gardner Wilkinson, a late traveller, of the highest authority, examined the statue itself, and discovered that it was hollow, and that "in the lap of the statue is a stone, which on being struck emits a metallic sound, that might still be made use of to deceive a visitor who was predisposed to believe its powers."

The vocal statue of Memnon is a favourite subject of allusion with the poets. Darwin, in his "Botanic Garden," says:

> "So to the sacred Sun in Memnon's fane
> Spontaneous concords choired the matin strain;
> Touched by his orient beam responsive rings
> The living lyre and vibrates all its strings;
> Accordant aisles the tender tones prolong,
> And holy echoes swell the adoring song."
>
> Book I., l. 182.

ACIS AND GALATEA

Scylla was a fair virgin of Sicily, a favourite of the Sea-Nymphs. She had many suitors, but repelled them all, and would go to the grotto of Galatea, and tell her how she was persecuted. One day the goddess, while Scylla dressed her hair, listened to the story, and then replied, "Yet, maiden, your persecutors are of the not ungentle race of men, whom, if you will, you can repel; but I, the daughter of Nereus, and protected by such a band of sisters, found no escape from the passion of the Cyclops but in the depths of the sea;" and tears stopped her utterance, which when the pitying maiden had wiped away with her delicate finger, and soothed the goddess, "Tell me, dearest," said she, "the cause of your grief." Galatea then said, "Acis was the son of Faunus, and a Naiad. His father and mother loved him dearly, but their love was not equal to mine. For the beautiful youth attached himself to me alone, and he was just sixteen years old, the down just beginning to darken his cheeks. As much as I sought his society, so much did the Cyclops seek mine; and if you ask me whether my love for Acis or my hatred of Polyphemus was the stronger, I cannot tell you; they were in equal measure. O Venus, how great is thy power! this fierce giant, the terror of the woods, whom no hapless stranger escaped unharmed, who defied even Jove himself, learned to feel what love was, and, touched with a passion for me, forgot his flocks and his well-stored caverns. Then for the first time he began to take some care of his appearance, and to try to make himself agreeable; he harrowed those coarse locks of his with a comb, and mowed his beard with a sickle, looked at his harsh features in the water, and composed his countenance. His love of slaughter, his fierceness and thirst of blood prevailed no more, and ships that touched at his island went away in safety. He paced up and down the sea-shore, imprinting huge tracks with his heavy tread, and, when weary, lay tranquilly in his cave.

"There is a cliff which projects into the sea, which washes it on either side. Thither one day the huge Cyclops ascended, and sat down while his flocks spread themselves around. Laying down his staff, which would have served for a mast to hold a vessel's sail, and taking his instrument compacted of numerous pipes, he made the hills and the waters echo the music of his song. I lay hid under a rock by the side of my beloved Acis, and listened to the distant strain. It was full of extravagant praises of my beauty, mingled with passionate reproaches of my coldness and cruelty.

"When he had finished he rose up, and, like a raging bull that cannot stand still, wandered off into the woods. Acis and I thought no more of him, till on a sudden he came to a spot which gave him a view of us as we sat. 'I see you,' he exclaimed, 'and I will make this the last of your love-meetings.' His voice was a roar such as an angry Cyclops alone could utter. Ætna trembled at the sound. I, overcome with terror, plunged into the water. Acis turned and fled, crying, 'Save me, Galatea, save me, my parents!' The Cyclops pursued him, and tearing a rock from the side of the mountain hurled it at him. Though only a corner of it touched him, it overwhelmed him.

"All that fate left in my power I did for Acis. I endowed him with the honours of his grandfather, the river-god. The purple blood flowed out from under the rock, but by degrees grew paler and looked like the stream of a river rendered turbid by rains, and in time it became clear. The rock cleaved open, and the water, as it gushed from the chasm, uttered a pleasing murmur."

Thus Acis was changed into a river, and the river retains the name of Acis.

Dryden, in his "Cymon and Iphigenia," has told the story of a clown converted into a gentleman by the power of love, in a way that shows traces of kindred to the old story of Galatea and the Cyclops.

> "What not his father's care nor tutor's art
> Could plant with pains in his unpolished heart,
> The best instructor, Love, at once inspired,
> As barren grounds to fruitfulness are fired.
> Love taught him shame, and shame with love at strife
> Soon taught the sweet civilities of life."

CHAPTER XXVII

THE TROJAN WAR

MINERVA was the goddess of wisdom, but on one occasion she did a very foolish thing; she entered into competition with Juno and Venus for the prize of beauty. It happened thus: At the nuptials of Peleus and Thetis all the gods were invited with the exception of Eris, or Discord. Enraged at her exclusion, the goddess threw a golden apple among the guests, with the inscription, "For the fairest." Thereupon Juno, Venus, and Minerva each claimed the apple. Jupiter, not willing to decide in so delicate a matter, sent the goddesses to Mount Ida, where the beautiful shepherd Paris was tending his flocks, and to him was committed the decision. The goddesses accordingly appeared before him. Juno promised him power and riches, Minerva glory and renown in war, and Venus the fairest of women for his wife, each attempting to bias his decision in her own favour. Paris decided in favour of Venus and gave her the golden apple, thus making the two other goddesses his enemies. Under the protection of Venus, Paris sailed to Greece, and was hospitably received by Menelaus, king of Sparta. Now Helen, the wife of Menelaus, was the very woman whom Venus had destined for Paris, the fairest of her sex. She had been sought as a bride by numerous suitors, and before her decision was made known, they all, at the suggestion of Ulysses, one of their number, took an oath that they would defend her from all injury and avenge her cause if necessary. She chose Menelaus, and was living with him happily when Paris became their guest. Paris, aided by Venus, persuaded her to elope with him, and carried her to Troy, whence arose the famous Trojan war, the theme of the greatest poems of antiquity, those of Homer and Virgil.

Menelaus called upon his brother chieftains of Greece to fulfil their pledge, and join him in his efforts to recover his wife. They generally came forward, but Ulysses, who had married Penelope, and was very happy in his wife and child, had no disposition to embark in such a troublesome affair. He therefore hung back and Palamedes was sent to urge him. When Palamedes arrived at Ithaca Ulysses pretended to be mad. He yoked an ass and an ox together to the plough and began to sow salt. Palamedes, to try him, placed the infant Telemachus before the plough, whereupon the father turned the plough aside, showing plainly that he was no madman, and after that could no longer refuse to fulfil his promise. Being now himself gained for the undertaking, he lent his aid to bring in other reluctant chiefs, especially Achilles. This hero was the son of that Thetis at whose marriage the apple of Discord had been thrown among the goddesses. Thetis was herself one of the immortals, a sea-nymph, and knowing that her son was fated to perish before Troy if he went on the expedition, she endeavoured to prevent his going. She sent him away to the court of King Lycomedes, and induced him to conceal himself in the disguise of a maiden among the daughters of the king. Ulysses, hearing he was there, went disguised as a merchant to the palace and offered for sale female ornaments, among which he had placed some arms. While the king's daughters were engrossed with the other contents of the merchant's pack, Achilles handled the weapons and thereby betrayed himself to the keen eye of Ulysses, who found no great difficulty in persuading him to disregard his mother's prudent counsels and join his countrymen in the war.

Priam was king of Troy, and Paris, the shepherd and seducer of Helen, was his son. Paris had been brought up in obscurity, because there were certain ominous forebodings connected with him from his infancy that he would be the ruin of the state. These forebodings seemed at length likely to be realized, for the Grecian armament now in preparation was the greatest that had ever been fitted out. Agamemnon, king of Mycenæ, and brother of the injured Menelaus, was chosen commander-in-chief. Achilles was their most illustrious warrior. After him ranked Ajax, gigantic in size and of great courage, but dull of intellect; Diomede, second only to Achilles in all the qualities of a hero; Ulysses, famous for his sagacity; and Nestor, the oldest of the Grecian chiefs, and one to whom they all looked up for counsel. But Troy was no feeble enemy. Priam, the king, was now old, but he had been a wise prince and had strengthened his state by good government at home and numerous alliances with his neighbours. But the principal stay and support of his throne was his son Hector, one of the noblest characters painted by heathen antiquity. He felt, from the first, a presentiment of the fall of his country, but still persevered in his heroic resistance, yet by no means justified the wrong which brought this danger upon her. He was united in marriage with Andromache, and as a husband and father his character was not less admirable than as a warrior. The principal leaders on the side of the Trojans, besides Hector, were Æneas and Deiphobus, Glaucus and Sarpedon.

After two years of preparation the Greek fleet and army assembled in the port of Aulis in Bœotia. Here Agamemnon in hunting killed a stag which was sacred to Diana, and the goddess in return visited the army with pestilence, and produced a calm which prevented the ships from leaving the port. Calchas, the soothsayer, thereupon announced that the wrath of the virgin goddess could only be appeased by the sacrifice of a virgin on her altar, and that none other but the daughter of the offender would be acceptable. Agamemnon, however reluctant, yielded his consent, and the maiden Iphigenia was sent for under the pretence that she was to be married to Achilles. When she was about to be sacrificed the goddess relented and snatched her away, leaving a hind in her place, and Iphigenia, enveloped in a cloud, was carried to Tauris, where Diana made her priestess of her temple.

Tennyson, in his "Dream of Fair Women," makes Iphigenia thus describe her feelings at the moment of sacrifice:

"I was cut off from hope in that sad place,
  Which yet to name my spirit loathes and fears;
My father held his hand upon his face;
  I, blinded by my tears,

"Still strove to speak; my voice was thick with sighs,
  As in a dream. Dimly I could descry
The stern black-bearded kings, with wolfish eyes,
  Waiting to see me die.

"The tall masts quivered as they lay afloat,
  The temples and the people and the shore;
One drew a sharp knife through my tender throat
  Slowly,—and—nothing more."

The wind now proving fair the fleet made sail and brought the forces to the coast of Troy. The Trojans came to oppose their landing, and at the first onset Protesilaus fell by the hand of Hector. Protesilaus had left at home his wife, Loadamia, who was most tenderly attached to him. When the news of his death reached her she implored the gods to be allowed to converse with him only three hours. The request was granted. Mercury led Protesilaus back to the upper world, and when he died a second time Laodamia died with him. There was a story that the nymphs planted elm trees round his grave which grew very well till they were high enough to command a view of Troy, and then withered away, while fresh branches sprang from the roots.

Wordsworth has taken the story of Protesilaus and Laodamia for the subject of a poem. It seems the oracle had declared that victory should be the lot of that party from which should fall the first victim to the war. The poet represents Protesilaus, on his brief return to earth, as relating to Laodamia the story of his fate:

" 'The wished-for wind was given; I then revolved
  The oracle, upon the silent sea;
And if no worthier led the way, resolved
  That of a thousand vessels mine should be
The foremost prow impressing to the strand,—
Mine the first blood that tinged the Trojan sand.

" 'Yet bitter, ofttimes bitter was the pang
   When of thy loss I thought, beloved wife!
On thee too fondly did my memory hang,
   And on the joys we shared in mortal life,
The paths which we had trod,—these fountains, flowers;
My new planned cities and unfinished towers.

" 'But should suspense permit the foe to cry,
   "Behold they tremble! haughty their array,
Yet of their number no one dares to die?"
   In soul I swept the indignity away:
Old frailties then recurred: but lofty thought
In act embodied my deliverance wrought.'

.   .   .   .

"...upon the side
   Of Hellespont (such faith was entertained)
A knot of spiry trees for ages grew
   From out the tomb of him for whom she died;
And ever when such stature they had gained
That Ilium's walls were subject to their view,
The trees' tall summits withered at the sight,
A constant interchange of growth and blight!"

"THE ILIAD"

The war continued without decisive results for nine years. Then
an event occurred which seemed likely to be fatal to the cause of
the Greeks, and that was a quarrel between Achilles and Agamemnon. It is at this point that the great poem of Homer, "The Iliad,"
begins. The Greeks, though unsuccessful against Troy, had taken
the neighbouring and allied cities, and in the division of the spoil a
female captive, by name Chryseis, daughter of Chryses, priest of
Apollo, had fallen to the share of Agamemnon. Chryses came bearing
the sacred emblems of his office, and begged the release of his
daughter. Agamemnon refused. Thereupon Chryses implored Apollo
to afflict the Greeks till they should be forced to yield their prey.
Apollo granted the prayer of his priest, and sent pestilence into the
Grecian camp. Then a council was called to deliberate how to allay
the wrath of the gods and avert the plague. Achilles boldly charged
their misfortunes upon Agamemnon as caused by his withholding
Chryseis. Agamemnon, enraged, consented to relinquish his captive,
but demanded that Achilles should yield to him in her stead Briseis,
a maiden who had fallen to Achilles' share in the division of the
spoil. Achilles submitted, but forthwith declared that he would take
no further part in the war. He withdrew his forces from the general
camp and openly avowed his intention of returning home to Greece.

The gods and goddesses interested themselves as much in this
famous war as the parties themselves. It was well known to them
that fate had decreed that Troy should fall, at last, if her enemies

should persevere and not voluntarily abandon the enterprise. Yet there was room enough left for chance to excite by turns the hopes and fears of the powers above who took part with either side. Juno and Minerva, in consequence of the slight put upon their charms by Paris, were hostile to the Trojans; Venus for the opposite cause favoured them. Venus enlisted her admirer Mars on the same side, but Neptune favoured the Greeks. Apollo was neutral, sometimes taking one side, sometimes the other, and Jove himself, though he loved the good King Priam, yet exercised a degree of impartiality; not, however, without exceptions.

Thetis, the mother of Achilles, warmly resented the injury done to her son. She repaired immediately to Jove's palace and besought him to make the Greeks repent of their injustice to Achilles by granting success to the Trojan arms. Jupiter consented, and in the battle which ensued the Trojans were completely successful. The Greeks were driven from the field and took refuge in their ships.

Then Agamemnon called a council of his wisest and bravest chiefs. Nestor advised that an embassy should be sent to Achilles to persuade him to return to the field; that Agamemnon should yield the maiden, the cause of the dispute, with ample gifts to atone for the wrong he had done. Agamemnon consented, and Ulysses, Ajax and Phœnix were sent to carry to Achilles the penitent message. They performed that duty, but Achilles was deaf to their entreaties. He positively refused to return to the field, and persisted in his resolution to embark for Greece without delay.

The Greeks had constructed a rampart around their ships, and now instead of besieging Troy they were in a manner besieged themselves, within their rampart. The next day after the unsuccessful embassy to Achilles, a battle was fought, and the Trojans, favoured by Jove, were successful, and succeeded in forcing a passage through the Grecian rampart, and were about to set fire to the ships. Neptune, seeing the Greeks so pressed, came to their rescue. He appeared in the form of Calchas the prophet, encouraged the warriors with his shouts, and appealed to each individually till he raised their ardour to such a pitch that they forced the Trojans to give way. Ajax performed prodigies of valour, and at length encountered Hector. Ajax shouted defiance, to which Hector replied, and hurled his lance at the huge warrior. It was well aimed and struck Ajax, where the belts that bore his sword and shield crossed each other on the breast. The double guard prevented its penetrating and it fell harmless. Then Ajax, seizing a huge stone, one of those that served to prop the ships, hurled it at Hector. It struck him in the neck and stretched him on the plain. His followers instantly seized him and bore him off, stunned and wounded.

While Neptune was thus aiding the Greeks and driving back the Trojans, Jupiter saw nothing of what was going on, for his attention had been drawn from the field by the wiles of Juno. That goddess had arrayed herself in all her charms, and to crown all had borrowed of Venus her girdle, called "Cestus," which had the effect to heighten the wearer's charms to such a degree that they were quite irresistible. So prepared, Juno went to join her husband, who sat on Olympus watching the battle. When he beheld her she looked so charming that the fondness of his early love revived, and, forgetting the contending armies and all other affairs of state, he thought only of her and let the battle go as it would.

But this absorption did not continue long, and when, upon turning his eyes downward, he beheld Hector stretched on the plain almost lifeless from pain and bruises, he dismissed Juno in a rage, commanding her to send Iris and Apollo to him. When Iris came he sent her with a stern message to Neptune, ordering him instantly to quit the field. Apollo was despatched to heal Hector's bruises and to inspirit his heart. These orders were obeyed with such speed that, while the battle still raged, Hector returned to the field and Neptune betook himself to his own dominions.

An arrow from Paris's bow wounded Machaon, son of Æsculapius, who inherited his father's art of healing, and was therefore of great value to the Greeks as their surgeon, besides being one of their bravest warriors. Nestor took Machaon in his chariot and conveyed him from the field. As they passed the ships of Achilles, that hero, looking out over the field, saw the chariot of Nestor and recognized the old chief, but could not discern who the wounded chief was. So calling Patroclus, his companion and dearest friend, he sent him to Nestor's tent to inquire.

Patroclus, arriving at Nestor's tent, saw Machaon wounded, and having told the cause of his coming would have hastened away, but Nestor detained him, to tell him the extent of the Grecian calamities. He reminded him also how, at the time of departing for Troy, Achilles and himself had been charged by their respective fathers with different advice: Achilles to aspire to the highest pitch of glory, Patroclus, as the elder, to keep watch over his friend, and to guide his inexperience. "Now," said Nestor, "is the time for such influence. If the gods so please, thou mayest win him back to the common cause; but if not let him at least send his soldiers to the field, and come thou, Patroclus, clad in his armour, and perhaps the very sight of it may drive back the Trojans."

Patroclus was strongly moved with this address, and hastened back to Achilles, revolving in his mind all he had seen and heard.

He told the prince the sad condition of affairs at the camp of their late associates: Diomede, Ulysses, Agamemnon, Machaon, all wounded, the rampart broken down, the enemy among the ships preparing to burn them, and thus to cut off all means of return to Greece. While they spoke the flames burst forth from one of the ships. Achilles, at the sight, relented so far as to grant Patroclus his request to lead the Myrmidons (for so were Achilles' soldiers called) to the field, and to lend him his armour, that he might thereby strike more terror into the minds of the Trojans. Without delay the soldiers were marshalled, Patroclus put on the radiant armour and mounted the chariot of Achilles, and led forth the men ardent for battle. But before he went, Achilles strictly charged him that he should be content with repelling the foe. "Seek not," said he, "to press the Trojans without me, lest thou add still more to the disgrace already mine." Then exhorting the troops to do their best he dismissed them full of ardour to the fight.

Patroclus and his Myrmidons at once plunged into the contest where it raged hottest; at the sight of which the joyful Grecians shouted and the ships re-echoed the acclaim. The Trojans, at the sight of the well-known armour, struck with terror, looked everywhere for refuge. First those who had got possession of the ship and set it on fire left and allowed the Grecians to retake it and extinguish the flames. Then the rest of the Trojans fled in dismay. Ajax, Menelaus, and the two sons of Nestor performed prodigies of valour. Hector was forced to turn his horses' heads and retire from the enclosure, leaving his men entangled in the fosse to escape as they could. Patroclus drove them before him, slaying many, none daring to make a stand against him.

At last Sarpedon, son of Jove, ventured to oppose himself in fight to Patroclus. Jupiter looked down upon him and would have snatched him from the fate which awaited him, but Juno hinted that if he did so it would induce all others of the inhabitants of heaven to interpose in like manner whenever any of their offspring were endangered; to which reason Jove yielded. Sarpedon threw his spear, but missed Patroclus, but Patroclus threw his with better success. It pierced Sarpedon's breast and he fell, and, calling to his friends to save his body from the foe, expired. Then a furious contest arose for the possession of the corpse. The Greeks succeeded and stripped Sarpedon of his armour; but Jove would not allow the remains of his son to be dishonoured, and by his command Apollo snatched from the midst of the combatants the body of Sarpedon and committed it to the care of the twin brothers Death and Sleep, by whom it was transported to Lycia, the native land of Sarpedon, where it received due funeral rites.

Thus far Patroclus had succeeded to his utmost wish in repelling the Trojans and relieving his countrymen, but now came a change of fortune. Hector, borne in his chariot, confronted him. Patroclus threw a vast stone at Hector, which missed its aim, but smote Cebriones, the charioteer, and knocked him from the car. Hector leaped from the chariot to rescue his friend, and Patroclus also descended to complete his victory. Thus the two heroes met face to face. At this decisive moment the poet, as if reluctant to give Hector the glory, records that Phœbus took part against Patroclus. He struck the helmet from his head and the lance from his hand. At the same moment an obscure Trojan wounded him in the back, and Hector, pressing forward, pierced him with his spear. He fell mortally wounded.

Then arose a tremendous conflict for the body of Patroclus, but his armour was at once taken possession of by Hector, who retiring a short distance divested himself of his own armour and put on that of Achilles, then returned to the fight. Ajax and Menelaus defended the body, and Hector and his bravest warriors struggled to capture it. The battle raged with equal fortunes, when Jove enveloped the whole face of heaven with a dark cloud. The lightning flashed, the thunder roared, and Ajax, looking round for some one whom he might despatch to Achilles to tell him of the death of his friend, and of the imminent danger that his remains would fall into the hands of the enemy, could see no suitable messenger. It was then that he exclaimed in those famous lines so often quoted,

> "Father of heaven and earth! deliver thou
> Achaia's host from darkness; clear the skies;
> Give day; and, since thy sovereign will is such,
> Destruction with it; but, O, give us day."
>
> *Cowper.*

Or, as rendered by Pope,

> "...Lord of earth and air!
> O king! O father! hear my humble prayer!
> Dispel this cloud, the light of heaven restore;
> Give me to see and Ajax asks no more;
> If Greece must perish we thy will obey,
> But let us perish in the face of day."

Jupiter heard the prayer and dispersed the clouds. Then Ajax sent Antilochus to Achilles with the intelligence of Patroclus's death, and of the conflict raging for his remains. The Greeks at last succeeded in bearing off the body to the ships, closely pursued by Hector and Æneas and the rest of the Trojans.

Achilles heard the fate of his friend with such distress that Antilochus feared for a while that he would destroy himself. His groans reached the ears of his mother, Thetis, far down in the deeps of ocean where she abode, and she hastened to him to inquire the cause. She found him overwhelmed with self-reproach that he had indulged his resentment so far, and suffered his friend to fall a victim to it. But his only consolation was the hope of revenge. He would fly instantly in search of Hector. But his mother reminded him that he was now without armour, and promised him, if he would but wait till the morrow, she would procure for him a suit of armour from Vulcan more than equal to that he had lost. He consented, and Thetis immediately repaired to Vulcan's palace. She found him busy at his forge making tripods for his own use, so artfully constructed that they moved forward of their own accord when wanted, and retired again when dismissed. On hearing the request of Thetis, Vulcan immediately laid aside his work and hastened to comply with her wishes. He fabricated a splendid suit of armour for Achilles, first a shield adorned with elaborate devices, then a helmet crested with gold, then a corselet and greaves of impenetrable temper, all perfectly adapted to his form, and of consummate workmanship. It was all done in one night, and Thetis, receiving it, descended with it to earth and laid it down at Achilles' feet at the dawn of day.

The first glow of pleasure that Achilles had felt since the death of Patroclus was at the sight of this splendid armour. And now, arrayed in it, he went forth into the camp, calling all the chiefs to council. When they were all assembled he addressed them. Renouncing his displeasure against Agamemnon and bitterly lamenting the miseries that had resulted from it, he called on them to proceed at once to the field. Agamemnon made a suitable reply, laying all the blame on Ate, the goddess of discord; and thereupon complete reconcilement took place between the heroes.

Then Achilles went forth to battle inspired with a rage and thirst for vengeance that made him irresistible. The bravest warriors fled before him or fell by his lance. Hector, cautioned by Apollo, kept aloof; but the god, assuming the form of one of Priam's sons. Lycaon, urged Æneas to encounter the terrible warrior. Æneas, though he felt himself unequal, did not decline the combat. He hurled his spear with all his force against the shield, the work of Vulcan. It was formed of five metal plates; two were of brass, two of tin, and one of gold. The spear pierced two thicknesses, but was stopped in the third. Achilles threw his with better success. It pierced through the shield of Æneas, but glanced near his shoulder and made no wound. Then Æneas seized a stone, such as two men of modern times could hardly lift, and was about to throw it, and Achilles, with sword drawn, was about to rush upon him, when Neptune, who looked out upon the contest, moved with pity

for Æneas, who he saw would surely fall a victim if not speedily
rescued, spread a cloud between the combatants, and lifting Æneas
from the ground, bore him over the heads of warriors and steeds
to the rear of the battle. Achilles, when the mist cleared away,
looked round in vain for his adversary, and acknowledging the
prodigy, turned his arms against other champions. But none dared
stand before him, and Priam looking down from the city walls
beheld his whole army in full flight towards the city. He gave
command to open wide the gates to receive the fugitives, and to
shut them as soon as the Trojans should have passed, lest the
enemy should enter likewise. But Achilles was so close in pursuit
that that would have been impossible if Apollo had not, in the
form of Agenor, Priam's son, encountered Achilles for a while,
then turned to fly, and taken the way apart from the city. Achilles
pursued and had chased his supposed victim far from the walls,
when Apollo disclosed himself, and Achilles, perceiving how he
had been deluded, gave up the chase.

But when the rest had escaped into the town Hector stood without determined to await the combat. His old father called to him
from the walls and begged him to retire nor tempt the encounter.
His mother, Hecuba, also besought him to the same effect, but all
in vain. "How can I," said he to himself, "by whose command
the people went to this day's contest, where so many have fallen,
seek safety for myself against a single foe? But what if I offer him
to yield up Helen and all her treasures and ample of our own
beside? Ah, no! it is too late. He would not even hear me through,
but slay me while I spoke." While he thus ruminated, Achilles
approached, terrible as Mars, his armour flashing lightning as he
moved. At that sight Hector's heart failed him and he fled. Achilles
swiftly pursued. They ran, still keeping near the walls, till they had
thrice encircled the city. As often as Hector approached the walls
Achilles intercepted him and forced him to keep out in a wider
circle. But Apollo sustained Hector's strength and would not let
him sink in weariness. Then Pallas, assuming the form of Deiphobus, Hector's bravest brother, appeared suddenly at his side.
Hector saw him with delight, and thus strengthened stopped his
flight and turned to meet Achilles. Hector threw his spear, which
struck the shield of Achilles and bounded back. He turned to
receive another from the hand of Deiphobus, but Deiphobus was
gone. Then Hector understood his doom and said, "Alas! it is
plain this is my hour to die! I thought Deiphobus at hand, but
Pallas deceived me, and he is still in Troy. But I will not fall
inglorious." So saying he drew his falchion from his side and
rushed at once to combat. Achilles, secure behind his shield,

waited the approach of Hector. When he came within reach of his spear, Achilles choosing with his eye a vulnerable part where the armour leaves the neck uncovered, aimed his spear at that part and Hector fell, death-wounded, and feebly said, "Spare my body! Let my parents ransom it, and let me receive funeral rites from the sons and daughters of Troy." To which Achilles replied, "Dog, name not ransom nor pity to me, on whom you have brought such dire distress. No! trust me, nought shall save thy carcass from the dogs. Though twenty ransoms and thy weight in gold were offered, I would refuse it all."

So saying he stripped the body of its armour, and fastening cords to the feet tied them behind his chariot, leaving the body to trail along the ground. Then mounting the chariot he lashed the steeds and so dragged the body to and fro before the city. What words can tell the grief of King Priam and Queen Hecuba at this sight! His people could scarce restrain the old king from rushing forth. He threw himself in the dust and besought them each by name to give him way. Hecuba's distress was not less violent. The citizens stood round them weeping. The sound of the mourning reached the ears of Andromache, the wife of Hector, as she sat among her maidens at work, and anticipating evil she went forth to the wall. When she saw the sight there presented, she would have thrown herself headlong from the wall, but fainted and fell into the arms of her maidens. Recovering, she bewailed her fate, picturing to herself her country ruined, herself a captive, and her son dependent for his bread on the charity of strangers.

When Achilles and the Greeks had taken their revenge on the killer of Patroclus they busied themselves in paying due funeral rites to their friend. A pile was erected, and the body burned with due solemnity; and then ensued games of strength and skill, chariot races, wrestling, boxing and archery. Then the chiefs sat down to the funeral banquet and after that retired to rest. But Achilles neither partook of the feast nor of sleep. The recollection of his lost friend kept him awake, remembering their companionship in toil and dangers, in battle or on the perilous deep. Before the earliest dawn he left his tent, and joining to his chariot his swift steeds, he fastened Hector's body to be dragged behind. Twice he dragged him round the tomb of Patroclus, leaving him at length stretched in the dust. But Apollo would not permit the body to be torn or disfigured with all this abuse, but preserved it free from all taint or defilement.

While Achilles indulged his wrath in thus disgracing brave Hector, Jupiter in pity summoned Thetis to his presence. He told her to go to her son and prevail on him to restore the body of Hector to his friends. Then Jupiter sent Iris to King Priam to encourage him to go to Achilles and beg the body of his son. Iris delivered her message, and Priam immediately prepared to obey. He opened his treasuries and took out rich garments and cloths, with ten talents in gold and two splendid tripods and a golden cup of matchless workmanship. Then he called to his sons and bade them draw forth his litter and place in it the various articles designed for a ransom to Achilles. When all was ready, the old king with a single companion as aged as himself, the herald Idæus, drove forth from the gates, parting there with Hecuba, his queen, and all his friends, who lamented him as going to certain death.

But Jupiter, beholding with compassion the venerable king, sent Mercury to be his guide and protector. Mercury, assuming the form of a young warrior, presented himself to the aged couple, and while at the sight of him they hesitated whether to fly or yield, the god approached, and grasping Priam's hand offered to be their guide to Achilles' tent. Priam gladly accepted his offered service, and he, mounting the carriage, assumed the reins and soon conveyed them to the tent of Achilles. Mercury's wand put to sleep all the guards, and without hindrance he introduced Priam into the tent where Achilles sat, attended by two of his warriors. The old king threw himself at the feet of Achilles, and kissed those terrible hands which had destroyed so many of his sons. "Think, O Achilles," he said, "of thy own father, full of days like me, and trembling on the gloomy verge of life. Perhaps even now some neighbour chief oppresses him and there is none at hand to succour him in his distress. Yet doubtless knowing that Achilles lives he still rejoices, hoping that one day he shall see thy face again. But no comfort cheers me, whose bravest sons, so late the flower of Ilium, all have fallen. Yet one I had, one more than all the rest the strength of my age, whom, fighting for his country, thou hast slain. I come to redeem his body, bringing inestimable ransom with me. Achilles! reverence the gods! recollect thy father! for his sake show compassion to me!" These words moved Achilles, and he wept remembering by turns his absent father and his lost friend. Moved with pity of Priam's silver locks and beard, he raised him from the earth, and thus spake: "Priam, I know that thou hast reached this place conducted by some god, for without aid divine no mortal even in his prime of youth had dared the attempt. I grant thy request, moved thereto by the evident will of Jove." So saying he arose, and went forth with his two friends, and unloaded of its charge the litter, leaving two mantles and a robe for the covering of the body, which they placed on the litter, and spread the garments over it, that not unveiled it should be borne back to Troy. Then Achilles dismissed the old king with his attendants, having first pledged himself to allow a truce of twelve days for the funeral solemnities.

As the litter approached the city and was descried from the walls, the people poured forth to gaze once more on the face of their hero. Foremost of all, the mother and the wife of Hector came, and at the sight of the lifeless body renewed their lamentations. The people all wept with them, and to the going down of the sun there was no pause or abatement of their grief.

The next day preparations were made for the funeral solemnities. For nine days the people brought wood and built the pile, and on the tenth they placed the body on the summit and applied the torch; while all Troy thronging forth encompassed the pile. When it had completely burned, they quenched the cinders with wine, collected the bones and placed them in a golden urn, which they buried in the earth, and reared a pile of stones over the spot.

> "Such honours Ilium to her hero paid,
> And peaceful slept the mighty Hector's shade."
> *Pope.*

CHAPTER XXVIII

THE FALL OF TROY—RETURN OF THE GREEKS—
AGAMEMNON, ORESTES AND ELECTRA

THE FALL OF TROY

THE story of the Iliad ends with the death of Hector, and it is from the Odyssey and later poems that we learn the fate of the other heroes. After the death of Hector, Troy did not immediately fall, but receiving aid from new allies still continued its resistance. One of these allies was Memnon, the Æthiopian prince, whose story we have already told. Another was Penthesilea, queen of the Amazons, who came with a band of female warriors. All the authorities attest their valour and the fearful effect of their war cry. Penthesilea slew many of the bravest warriors, but was at last slain by Achilles. But when the hero bent over his fallen foe, and contemplated her beauty, youth and valour, he bitterly regretted his victory. Thersites, an insolent brawler and demagogue, ridiculed his grief, and was in consequence slain by the hero.

Achilles by chance had seen Polyxena, daughter of King Priam, perhaps on occasion of the truce which was allowed the Trojans for the burial of Hector. He was captivated with her charms, and to win her in marriage agreed to use his influence with the Greeks to grant peace to Troy. While in the temple of Apollo, negotiating the marriage, Paris discharged at him a poisoned arrow, which, guided by Apollo, wounded Achilles in the heel, the only vulnerable part about him. For Thetis his mother had dipped him when an infant in the river Styx, which made every part of him invulnerable except the heel by which she held him.[1]

The body of Achilles so treacherously slain was rescued by Ajax and Ulysses. Thetis directed the Greeks to bestow her son's armour on the hero who of all the survivors should be judged most deserving of it. Ajax and Ulysses were the only claimants; a select number of the other chiefs were appointed to award the prize. It was awarded to Ulysses, thus placing wisdom before valour, whereupon Ajax slew himself. On the spot where his blood sank into the earth a flower sprang up, called the hyacinth, bearing on its leaves the first two letters of the name of Ajax, Ai, the Greek for "woe." Thus Ajax is a claimant with the boy Hyacinthus for the honour of giving birth to this flower. There is a species of Larkspur which represents the hyacinth of the poets in preserving the memory of this event, the Delphinium Ajacis—Ajax's Larkspur.

It was now discovered that Troy could not be taken but by the aid of the arrows of Hercules. They were in possession of Philoctetes, the friend who had been with Hercules at the last and lighted his funeral pyre. Philoctetes had joined the Grecian expedition against Troy, but had accidentally wounded his foot with one of the poisoned arrows, and the smell from his wound proved so offensive that his companions carried him to the isle of Lemnos and left him there. Diomed was now sent to induce him to rejoin the army. He succeeded. Philoctetes was cured of his wound by Machaon, and Paris was the first victim of the fatal arrows. In his distress Paris bethought him of one whom in his prosperity he had forgotten. This was the nymph Œnone, whom he had married when a youth, and had abandoned for the fatal beauty Helen. Œnone remembering the wrongs she had suffered, refused to heal the wound, and Paris went back to Troy and died. Œnone quickly repented, and hastened after him with remedies, but came too late, and in her grief hung herself.[2]

There was in Troy a celebrated statue of Minerva called the Palladium. It was said to have fallen from heaven, and the belief was that the city could not be taken so long as this statue remained within it. Ulysses and Diomed entered the city in disguise and

[1] The story of the invulnerability of Achilles is not found in Homer, and is inconsistent with his account. For how could Achilles require the aid of celestial armour if he were invulnerable?

[2] Tennyson has chosen Œnone as the subject of a short poem; but he has omitted the most poetical part of the story, the return of Paris wounded, her cruelty and subsequent repentance.

succeeded in obtaining the Palladium, which they carried off to the Grecian camp.

But Troy still held out, and the Greeks began to despair of ever subduing it by force, and by advice of Ulysses resolved to resort to stratagem. They pretended to be making preparations to abandon the siege, and a portion of the ships were withdrawn and lay hid behind a neighbouring island. The Greeks then constructed an immense *wooden horse,* which they gave out was intended as a propitiatory offering to Minerva, but in fact was filled with armed men. The remaining Greeks then betook themselves to their ships and sailed away, as if for a final departure. The Trojans, seeing the encampment broken up and the fleet gone, concluded the enemy to have abandoned the siege. The gates were thrown open, and the whole population issued forth rejoicing at the long-prohibited liberty of passing freely over the scene of the late encampment. The great *horse* was the chief object of curiosity. All wondered what it could be for. Some recommended to take it into the city as a trophy; others felt afraid of it.

While they hesitate, Laocoön, the priest of Neptune, exclaims, "What madness, citizens, is this? Have you not learned enough of Grecian fraud to be on your guard against it? For my part, I fear the Greeks even when they offer gifts." [1] So saying he threw his lance at the horse's side. It struck, and a hollow sound reverberated like a groan. Then perhaps the people might have taken his advice and destroyed the fatal horse and all its contents; but just at that moment a group of people appeared, dragging forward one who seemed a prisoner and a Greek. Stupefied with terror, he was brought before the chiefs, who reassured him, promising that his life should be spared on condition of his returning true answers to the questions asked him. He informed them that he was a Greek, Sinon by name, and that in consequence of the malice of Ulysses he had been left behind by his countrymen at their departure. With regard to the wooden horse, he told them that it was a propitiatory offering to Minerva, and made so huge for the express purpose of preventing its being carried within the city; for Calchas the prophet had told them that if the Trojans took possession of it they would assuredly triumph over the Greeks. This language turned the tide of the people's feelings and they began to think how they might best secure the monstrous horse and the favourable auguries connected with it, when suddenly a prodigy occurred which left no room to doubt. There appeared, advancing over the sea, two immense serpents. They came upon the land, and the crowd fled in all directions. The serpents advanced directly to

[1] See Proverbial Expressions, page 289.

the spot where Laocoön stood with his two sons. They first attacked the children, winding round their bodies and breathing
their pestilential breath in their faces. The father, attempting to
rescue them, is next seized and involved in the serpents' coils. He
struggles to tear them away, but they overpower all his efforts and
strangle him and the children in their poisonous folds. This event
was regarded as a clear indication of the displeasure of the gods
at Laocoön's irreverent treatment of the wooden horse, which they
no longer hesitated to regard as a sacred object, and prepared to
introduce with due solemnity into the city. This was done with
songs and triumphal acclamations, and the day closed with festivity. In the night the armed men who were enclosed in the body
of the horse, being let out by the traitor Sinon, opened the gates
of the city to their friends, who had returned under cover of the
night. The city was set on fire; the people, overcome with feasting
and sleep, put to the sword, and Troy completely subdued.

One of the most celebrated groups of statuary in existence is
that of Laocoön and his children in the embrace of the serpents.
The original is in the Vatican at Rome. The following lines are
from the "Childe Harold" of Byron:

> "Now turning to the Vatican go see
> Laocoön's torture dignifying pain;
> A father's love and mortal's agony
> With an immortal's patience blending;—vain
> The struggle! vain against the coiling strain
> And gripe and deepening of the dragon's grasp
> The old man's clinch; the long envenomed chain
> Rivets the living links; the enormous asp
> Enforces pang on pang and stifles gasp on gasp."

The comic poets will also occasionally borrow a classical allusion. The following is from Swift's "Description of a City Shower":

> "Boxed in a chair the beau impatient sits,
> While spouts run clattering o'er the roof by fits,
> And ever and anon with frightful din
> The leather sounds; he trembles from within.
> So when Troy chairmen bore the wooden steed
> Pregnant with Greeks impatient to be freed,
> (Those bully Greeks, who, as the moderns do,
> Instead of paying chairmen, run them through);
> Laocoön struck the outside with a spear,
> And each imprisoned champion quaked with fear."

King Priam lived to see the downfall of his kingdom and was
slain at last on the fatal night when the Greeks took the city. He
had armed himself and was about to mingle with the combatants,
but was prevailed on by Hecuba. his aged queen, to take refuge

with herself and his daughters as a suppliant at the altar of Jupiter. While there, his youngest son Polites, pursued by Pyrrhus, the son of Achilles, rushed in wounded, and expired at the feet of his father; whereupon Priam, overcome with indignation, hurled his spear with feeble hand against Pyrrhus,[1] and was forthwith slain by him.

Queen Hecuba and her daughter Cassandra were carried captives to Greece. Cassandra had been loved by Apollo, and he gave her the gift of prophecy; but afterwards offended with her, he rendered the gift unavailing by ordaining that her predictions should never be believed. Polyxena, another daughter, who had been loved by Achilles, was demanded by the ghost of that warrior, and was sacrificed by the Greeks upon his tomb.

MENELAUS AND HELEN

Our readers will be anxious to know the fate of Helen, the fair but guilty occasion of so much slaughter. On the fall of Troy Menelaus recovered possession of his wife, who had not ceased to love him, though she had yielded to the might of Venus and deserted him for another. After the death of Paris she aided the Greeks secretly on several occasions, and in particular when Ulysses and Diomed entered the city in disguise to carry off the Palladium. She saw and recognized Ulysses, but kept the secret and even assisted them in obtaining the image. Thus she became reconciled to her husband, and they were among the first to leave the shores of Troy for their native land. But having incurred the displeasure of the gods they were driven by storms from shore to shore of the Mediterranean, visiting Cyprus, Phœnicia and Egypt. In Egypt they were kindly treated and presented with rich gifts, of which Helen's share was a golden spindle and a basket on wheels. The basket was to hold the wool and spools for the queen's work.

Dyer, in his poem of the "Fleece," thus alludes to this incident:

> "...many yet adhere
> To the ancient distaff, at the bosom fixed,
> Casting the whirling spindle as they walk.
>
> .   .   .   .   .
>
> This was of old, in no inglorious days,
> The mode of spinning, when the Egyptian prince
> A golden distaff gave that beauteous nymph,
> Too beauteous Helen; no uncourtly gift."

[1] Pyrrhus's exclamation, "Not such aid nor such defenders does the time require," has become proverbial. See Proverbial Expressions, page 289.

Milton also alludes to a famous recipe for an invigorating draught, called Nepenthe, which the Egyptian queen gave to Helen:

"Not that Nepenthes which the wife of Thone
In Egypt gave to Jove-born Helena,
Is of such power to stir up joy as this,
To life so friendly or so cool to thirst."

Comus.

Menelaus and Helen at length arrived in safety at Sparta, resumed their royal dignity, and lived and reigned in splendour; and when Telemachus, the son of Ulysses, in search of his father, arrived at Sparta, he found Menelaus and Helen celebrating the marriage of their daughter Hermione to Neoptolemus, son of Achilles.

AGAMEMNON, ORESTES AND ELECTRA

Agamemnon, the general-in-chief of the Greeks, the brother of Menelaus, and who had been drawn into the quarrel to avenge his brother's wrongs, not his own, was not so fortunate in the issue. During his absence his wife Clytemnestra had been false to him, and when his return was expected, she with her paramour, Ægisthus, laid a plan for his destruction, and at the banquet given to celebrate his return, murdered him.

It was intended by the conspirators to slay his son Orestes also, a lad not yet old enough to be an object of apprehension, but from whom, if he should be suffered to grow up, there might be danger. Electra, the sister of Orestes, saved her brother's life by sending him secretly away to his uncle Strophius, King of Phocis. In the palace of Strophius Orestes grew up with the king's son Pylades, and formed with him that ardent friendship which has become proverbial. Electra frequently reminded her brother by messengers of the duty of avenging his father's death, and when grown up he consulted the oracle of Delphi, which confirmed him in his design. He therefore repaired in disguise to Argos, pretending to be a messenger from Strophius, who had come to announce the death of Orestes, and brought the ashes of the deceased in a funeral urn. After visiting his father's tomb and sacrificing upon it, according to the rites of the ancients, he made himself known to his sister Electra, and soon after slew both Ægisthus and Clytemnestra.

This revolting act, the slaughter of a mother by her son, though alleviated by the guilt of the victim and the express command of the gods, did not fail to awaken in the breasts of the ancients the same abhorrence that it does in ours. The Eumenides, avenging deities, seized upon Orestes, and drove him frantic from land to land. Pylades accompanied him in his wanderings and watched over him. At length, in answer to a second appeal to the oracle, he was directed to go to Tauris in Scythia, and to bring thence a statue of Diana which was believed to have fallen from heaven. Accordingly Orestes and Pylades went to Tauris, where the bar-barous people were accustomed to sacrifice to the goddess all strangers who fell into their hands. The two friends were seized and carried bound to the temple to be made victims. But the priestess of Diana was no other than Iphigenia, the sister of Orestes, who, our readers will remember, was snatched away by Diana at the moment when she was about to be sacrificed. As-certaining from the prisoners who they were, Iphigenia disclosed herself to them, and the three made their escape with the statue of the goddess, and returned to Mycenæ.

But Orestes was not yet relieved from the vengeance of the Erinyes. At length he took refuge with Minerva at Athens. The goddess afforded him protection, and appointed the court of Areopagus to decide his fate. The Erinyes brought forward their accusation, and Orestes made the command of the Delphic oracle his excuse. When the court voted and the voices were equally divided, Orestes was acquitted by the command of Minerva.

Byron, in "Childe Harold," Canto IV., alludes to the story of Orestes:

"O thou who never yet of human wrong
Left the unbalanced scale, great Nemesis!
Thou who didst call the Furies from the abyss,
And round Orestes bade them howl and hiss,
For that unnatural retribution,—just
Had it but been from hands less near,—in this,
Thy former realm, I call thee from the dust!"

One of the most pathetic scenes in the ancient drama is that in which Sophocles represents the meeting of Orestes and Electra, on his return from Phocis. Orestes, mistaking Electra for one of the domestics, and desirous of keeping his arrival a secret till the hour of vengeance should arrive, produces the urn in which his ashes are supposed to rest. Electra, believing him to be really dead, takes the urn and, embracing it, pours forth her grief in language full of tenderness and despair.

Milton in one of his sonnets, says:

"...The repeated air
Of sad Electra's poet had the power
To save the Athenian walls from ruin bare."

This alludes to the story that when, on one occasion, the city of Athens was at the mercy of her Spartan foes, and it was proposed to destroy it, the thought was rejected upon the accidental quotation, by some one, of a chorus of Euripides.

TROY

After hearing so much about the city of Troy and its heroes, the reader will perhaps be surprised to learn that the exact site of that famous city is still a matter of dispute. There are some vestiges of tombs on the plain which most nearly answers to the description given by Homer and the ancient geographers, but no other evidence of the former existence of a great city. Byron thus describes the present appearance of the scene:

> "The winds are high, and Helle's tide
> Rolls darkly heaving to the main;
> And night's descending shadows hide
> That field with blood bedewed in vain,
> The desert of old Priam's pride,
> The tombs, sole relics of his reign.
> All—save immortal dreams that could beguile
> The blind old man of Scio's rocky isle."
> *Bride of Abydos.*

CHAPTER XXIX

ADVENTURES OF ULYSSES—THE LOTUS-EATERS—CYCLOPSES—CIRCE —SIRENS—SCYLLA AND CHARYBDIS—CALYPSO

RETURN OF ULYSSES

THE romantic poem of the Odyssey is now to engage our attention. It narrates the wanderings of Ulysses (Odysseus in the Greek language) in his return from Troy to his own kingdom Ithaca.

From Troy the vessels first made land at Ismarus, city of the Ciconians, where, in a skirmish with the inhabitants, Ulysses lost six men from each ship. Sailing thence, they were overtaken by a storm which drove them for nine days along the sea till they reached the country of the Lotus-eaters. Here, after watering, Ulysses sent three of his men to discover who the inhabitants were. These men on coming among the Lotus-eaters were kindly entertained by them, and were given some of their own food, the lotus-plant, to eat. The effect of this food was such that those who partook of it lost all thoughts of home and wished to remain in that country. It was by main force that Ulysses dragged these men away, and he was even obliged to tie them under the benches of his ships.[1]

"How sweet it were, hearing the downward stream
With half-shut eyes ever to seem
Falling asleep in a half-dream!
To dream and dream, like yonder amber light
Which will not leave the myrrh-bush on the height;
To hear each other's whispered speech;
Eating the Lotos, day by day,
To watch the crisping ripples on the beach,
And tender curving lines of creamy spray:
To lend our hearts and spirits wholly
To the influence of mild-minded melancholy;
To muse and brood and live again in memory,
With those old faces of our infancy
Heaped over with a mound of grass,
Two handfuls of white dust, shut in an urn of brass."

They next arrived at the country of the Cyclopses. The Cyclopses were giants, who inhabited an island of which they were the only possessors. The name means "round eye," and these giants were so called because they had but one eye, and that placed in the middle of the forehead. They dwelt in caves and fed on the wild productions of the island and on what their flocks yielded, for they were shepherds. Ulysses left the main body of his ships at anchor, and with one vessel went to the Cyclopses' island to explore for supplies. He landed with his companions, carrying with them a jar of wine for a present, and coming to a large cave they entered it, and finding no one within examined its contents. They found it stored with the richest of the flock, quantities of cheese, pails and bowls of milk, lambs and kids in their pens, all in nice order. Presently arrived the master of the cave, Polyphemus, bearing an immense bundle of firewood, which he threw down before the cavern's mouth. He then drove into the cave the sheep and goats to be milked, and, entering, rolled to the cave's mouth an enormous rock, that twenty oxen could not draw. Next he sat down and milked his ewes, preparing a part for cheese, and setting the rest aside for his customary drink. Then, turning round his great eye, he discerned the strangers, and growled out to them, demanding who they were, and where from. Ulysses replied most humbly, stating that they were Greeks, from the great expedition that had lately won so much glory in the conquest of Troy; that they were now on their way home, and finished by imploring his hospitality in the name of the gods. Polyphemus deigned no answer, but reaching out his hand seized two of the Greeks, whom he hurled against the side of the cave, and

[1] Tennyson in the "Lotos-eaters," has charmingly expressed the dreamy, languid feeling which the lotus food is said to have produced.

dashed out their brains. He proceeded to devour them with great relish, and having made a hearty meal, stretched himself out on the floor to sleep. Ulysses was tempted to seize the opportunity and plunge his sword into him as he slept, but recollected that it would only expose them all to certain destruction, as the rock with which the giant had closed up the door was far beyond their power to remove, and they would therefore be in hopeless imprisonment. Next morning the giant seized two more of the Greeks, and despatched them in the same manner as their companions, feasting on their flesh till no fragment was left. He then moved away the rock from the door, drove out his flocks, and went out, carefully replacing the barrier after him. When he was gone Ulysses planned how he might take vengeance for his murdered friends, and effect his escape with his surviving companions. He made his men prepare a massive bar of wood cut by the Cyclops for a staff, which they found in the cave. They sharpened the end of it, and seasoned it in the fire, and hid it under the straw on the cavern floor. Then four of the boldest were selected, with whom Ulysses joined himself as a fifth. The Cyclops came home at evening, rolled away the stone and drove in his flock as usual. After milking them and making his arrangements as before, he seized two more of Ulysses' companions and dashed their brains out, and made his evening meal upon them as he had on the others. After he had supped, Ulysses approaching him handed him a bowl of wine, saying, "Cyclops, this is wine; taste and drink after thy meal of men's flesh." He took and drank it, and was hugely delighted with it, and called for more. Ulysses supplied him once again, which pleased the giant so much that he promised him as a favour that he should be the last of the party devoured. He asked his name, to which Ulysses replied, "My name is Noman."

After his supper the giant lay down to repose, and was soon found asleep. Then Ulysses with his four select friends thrust the end of the stake into the fire till it was all one burning coal, then poising it exactly above the giant's only eye, they buried it deeply into the socket, twirling it round as a carpenter does his auger. The howling monster with his outcry filled the cavern, and Ulysses with his aids nimbly got out of his way and concealed themselves in the cave. He, bellowing, called aloud on all the Cyclopses dwelling in the caves around him, far and near. They on his cry flocked round the den, and inquired what grievous hurt had caused him to sound such an alarm and break their slumbers. He replied, "O friends, I die, and Noman gives the blow." They answered, "If no man hurts thee it is the stroke of Jove, and thou must bear it." So saying, they left him groaning.

Next morning the Cyclops rolled away the stone to let his flock out to pasture, but planted himself in the door of the cave to feel of all as they went out, that Ulysses and his men should not escape with them. But Ulysses had made his men harness the rams of the flock three abreast, with osiers which they found on the floor of the cave. To the middle ram of the three one of the Greeks suspended himself, so protected by the exterior rams on either side. As they passed, the giant felt of the animals' backs and sides, but never thought of their bellies; so the men all passed safe, Ulysses himself being on the last one that passed. When they had got a few paces from the cavern, Ulysses and his friends released themselves from their rams, and drove a good part of the flock down to the shore to their boat. They put them aboard with all haste, then pushed off from the shore, and when at a safe distance Ulysses shouted out, "Cyclops, the gods have well requited thee for thy atrocious deeds. Know it is Ulysses to whom thou owest thy shameful loss of sight." The Cyclops, hearing this, seized a rock that projected from the side of the mountain, and rending it from its bed he lifted it high in the air, then exerting all his force, hurled it in the direction of the voice. Down came the mass, just clearing the vessel's stern. The ocean, at the plunge of the huge rock, heaved the ship towards the land, so that it barely escaped being swamped by the waves. When they had with the utmost difficulty pulled off shore, Ulysses was about to hail the giant again, but his friends besought him not to do so. He could not forbear, however, letting the giant know that they had escaped his missile, but waited till they had reached a safer distance than before. The giant answered them with curses, but Ulysses and his friends plied their oars vigorously, and soon regained their companions.

Ulysses next arrived at the island of Æolus. To this monarch Jupiter had intrusted the government of the winds, to send them forth or retain them at his will. He treated Ulysses hospitably, and at his departure gave him, tied up in a leathern bag with a silver string, such winds as might be hurtful and dangerous, commanding fair winds to blow the barks towards their country. Nine days they sped before the wind, and all that time Ulysses had stood at the helm, without sleep. At last quite exhausted he lay down to sleep. While he slept, the crew conferred together about the mysterious bag, and concluded it must contain treasures given by the hospitable King Æolus to their commander. Tempted to secure some portion for themselves, they loosed the string, when immediately the winds rushed forth. The ships were driven far from their course, and back again to the island they had just left. Æolus was so indignant at their folly that he refused to assist them further, and they were obliged to labour over their course once more by means of their oars.

The Læstrygonians

Their next adventure was with the barbarous tribe of Læstrygonians. The vessels all pushed into the harbour, tempted by the secure appearance of the cove, completely land-locked; only Ulysses moored his vessel without. As soon as the Læstrygonians found the ships completely in their power they attacked them, heaving huge stones which broke and overturned them, and with their spears despatched the seamen as they struggled in the water. All the vessels with their crews were destroyed, except Ulysses' own ship, which had remained outside, and finding no safety but in flight, he exhorted his men to ply their oars vigorously, and they escaped.

With grief for their slain companions mixed with joy at their own escape, they pursued their way till they arrived at the Ææan isle, where Circe dwelt, the daughter of the sun. Landing here, Ulysses climbed a hill, and gazing round saw no signs of habitation except in one spot at the centre of the island, where he perceived a palace embowered with trees. He sent forward one-half of his crew, under the command of Eurylochus, to see what prospect of hospitality they might find. As they approached the palace, they found themselves surrounded by lions, tigers, and wolves, not fierce, but tamed by Circe's art, for she was a powerful magician. All these animals had once been men, but had been changed by Circe's enchantments into the forms of beasts. The sounds of soft music were heard from within, and a sweet female voice singing. Eurylochus called aloud and the goddess came forth and invited them in; they all gladly entered except Eurylochus, who suspected danger. The goddess conducted her guests to a seat, and had them served with wine and other delicacies. When they had feasted heartily, she touched them one by one with her wand, and they became immediately changed into *swine*, in "head, body, voice, and bristles," yet with their intellects as before. She shut them in her sties and supplied them with acorns and such other things as swine love.

Eurylochus hurried back to the ship and told the tale. Ulysses thereupon determined to go himself, and try if by any means he might deliver his companions. As he strode onward alone, he met a youth who addressed him familiarly, appearing to be acquainted with his adventures. He announced himself as Mercury, and informed Ulysses of the arts of Circe, and of the danger of approaching her. As Ulysses was not to be dissuaded from his attempt, Mercury provided him with a sprig of the plant Moly, of wonderful power to resist sorceries, and instructed him how to act. Ulysses proceeded, and reaching the palace was courteously received by Circe, who entertained him as she had done his companions, and after he had eaten and drank, touched him with her wand, saying, "Hence, seek the sty and wallow with thy friends." But he, instead of obeying, drew his sword and rushed upon her with fury in his countenance. She fell on her knees and begged for mercy. He dictated a solemn oath that she would release his companions and practise no further harm against him or them; and she repeated it, at the same time promising to dismiss them all in safety after hospitably entertaining them. She was as good as her word. The men were restored to their shapes, the rest of the crew summoned from the shore, and the whole magnificently entertained day after day, till Ulysses seemed to have forgotten his native land, and to have reconciled himself to an inglorious life of ease and pleasure.

At length his companions recalled him to nobler sentiments, and he received their admonition gratefully. Circe aided their departure, and instructed them how to pass safely by the coast of the Sirens. The Sirens were sea-nymphs who had the power of charming by their song all who heard them, so that the unhappy mariners were irresistibly impelled to cast themselves into the sea to their destruction. Circe directed Ulysses to fill the ears of his seamen with wax, so that they should not hear the strain; and to cause himself to be bound to the mast, and his people to be strictly enjoined, whatever he might say or do, by no means to release him till they should have passed the Sirens' island. Ulysses obeyed these directions. He filled the ears of his people with wax, and suffered them to bind him with cords firmly to the mast. As they approached the Sirens' island, the sea was calm, and over the waters came the notes of music so ravishing and attractive that Ulysses struggled to get loose, and by cries and signs to his people begged to be released; but they, obedient to his previous orders, sprang forward and bound him still faster. They held on their course, and the music grew fainter till it ceased to be heard, when with joy Ulysses gave his companions the signal to unseal their ears, and they relieved him from his bonds.

The imagination of a modern poet, Keats, has discovered for us the thoughts that passed through the brains of the victims of Circe, after their transformation. In his "Endymion" he represents one of them, a monarch in the guise of an elephant, addressing the sorceress in human language, thus:

"I sue not for my happy crown again;
I sue not for my phalanx on the plain;
I sue not for my lone, my widowed wife;
I sue not for my ruddy drops of life,
My children fair, my lovely girls and boys;
I will forget them; I will pass these joys,

Ask nought so heavenward; so too—too high;
Only I pray, as fairest boon, to die;
To be delivered from this cumbrous flesh,
From this gross, detestable, filthy mesh,
And merely given to the cold, bleak air.
Have mercy, goddess! Circe, feel my prayer!"

Scylla and Charybdis

Ulysses had been warned by Circe of the two monsters Scylla and Charybdis. We have already met with Scylla in the story of Glaucus, and remember that she was once a beautiful maiden and was changed into a snaky monster by Circe. She dwelt in a cave high up on the cliff, from whence she was accustomed to thrust forth her long necks (for she had six heads), and in each of her mouths seize one of the crew of every vessel passing within reach. The other terror, Charybdis, was a gulf, nearly on a level with the water. Thrice each day the water rushed into a frightful chasm, and thrice was disgorged. Any vessel coming near the whirlpool when the tide was rushing in must inevitably be ingulfed; not Neptune himself could save it.

On approaching the haunt of the dread monsters, Ulysses kept strict watch to discover them. The roar of the waters as Charybdis ingulfed them, gave warning at a distance, but Scylla could nowhere be discerned. While Ulysses and his men watched with anxious eyes the dreadful whirlpool, they were not equally on their guard from the attack of Scylla, and the monster, darting forth her snaky heads, caught six of his men, and bore them away, shrieking, to her den. It was the saddest sight Ulysses had yet seen; to behold his friends thus sacrificed and hear their cries, unable to afford them any assistance.

Circe had warned him of another danger. After passing Scylla and Charybdis the next land he would make was Thrinakia, an island whereon were pastured the cattle of Hyperion, the Sun, tended by his daughters Lampetia and Phaëthusa. These flocks must not be violated, whatever the wants of the voyagers might be. If this injunction were transgressed destruction was sure to fall on the offenders.

Ulysses would willingly have passed the island of the Sun without stopping, but his companions so urgently pleaded for the rest and refreshment that would be derived from anchoring and passing the night on shore, that Ulysses yielded. He bound them, however, with an oath that they would not touch one of the animals of the sacred flocks and herds, but content themselves with what provision they yet had left of the supply which Circe had put on board. So long as this supply lasted the people kept their oath, but contrary winds detained them at the island for a month, and after consuming all their stock of provisions, they were forced to rely upon the birds and fishes they could catch. Famine pressed them, and at length one day, in the absence of Ulysses, they slew some of the cattle, vainly attempting to make amends for the deed by offering from them a portion to the offended powers. Ulysses, on his return to the shore, was horror-struck at perceiving what they had done, and the more so on account of the portentous signs which followed. The skins crept on the ground, and the joints of meat lowed on the spits while roasting.

The wind becoming fair they sailed from the island. They had not gone far when the weather changed, and a storm of thunder and lightning ensued. A stroke of lightning shattered their mast, which in its fall killed the pilot. At last the vessel itself came to pieces. The keel and mast floating side by side, Ulysses formed of them a raft, to which he clung, and, the wind changing, the waves bore him to Calypso's island. All the rest of the crew perished.

The following allusion to the topics we have just been considering is from Milton's "Comus," line 252:

> "...I have often heard
> My mother Circe and the Sirens three,
> Amidst the flowery-kirtled Naiades,
> Culling their potent herbs and baneful drugs,
> Who as they sung would take the prisoned soul
> And lap it in Elysium. Scylla wept,
> And chid her barking waves into attention,
> And fell Charybdis murmured soft applause."

Scylla and Charybdis have become proverbial, to denote opposite dangers which beset one's course. See Proverbial Expressions, p. 289.

CALYPSO

Calypso was a sea-nymph, which name denotes a numerous class of female divinities of lower rank, yet sharing many of the attributes of the gods. Calypso received Ulysses hospitably, entertained him magnificently, became enamoured of him, and wished to retain him for ever, conferring on him immortality. But he persisted in his resolution to return to his country and his wife and son. Calypso at last received the command of Jove to dismiss him. Mercury brought the message to her, and found her in her grotto, which is thus described by Homer:

> "A garden vine, luxuriant on all sides,
> Mantled the spacious cavern, cluster-hung
> Profuse; four fountains of serenest lymph,
> Their sinuous course pursuing side by side,

> Strayed all around, and everywhere appeared
> Meadows of softest verdure, purpled o'er
> With violets; it was a scene to fill
> A god from heaven with wonder and delight."

Calypso with much reluctance proceeded to obey the commands of Jupiter. She supplied Ulysses with the means of constructing a raft, provisioned it well for him, and gave him a favouring gale. He sped on his course prosperously for many days, till at length, when in sight of land, a storm arose that broke his mast, and threatened to rend the raft asunder. In this crisis he was seen by a compassionate sea-nymph, who in the form of a cormorant alighted on the raft, and presented him a girdle, directing him to bind it beneath his breast, and if he should be compelled to trust himself to the waves, it would buoy him up and enable him by swimming to reach the land.

Fénelon, in his romance of "Telemachus," has given us the adventures of the son of Ulysses in search of his father. Among other places at which he arrived, following on his father's footsteps, was Calypso's isle, and, as in the former case, the goddess tried every art to keep him with her, and offered to share her immortality with him. But Minerva, who in the shape of Mentor accompanied him and governed all his movements, made him repel her allurements, and when no other means of escape could be found, the two friends leaped from a cliff into the sea, and swam to a vessel which lay becalmed off shore. Byron alludes to this leap of Telemachus and Mentor in the following stanza:

> "But not in silence pass Calypso's isles,
> The sister tenants of the middle deep;
> There for the weary still a haven smiles,
> Though the fair goddess long has ceased to weep,
> And o'er her cliffs a fruitless watch to keep
> For him who dared prefer a mortal bride.
> Here too his boy essayed the dreadful leap,
> Stern Mentor urged from high to yonder tide;
> While thus of both bereft the nymph-queen doubly sighed."

CHAPTER XXX

THE PHÆACIANS—FATE OF THE SUITORS

THE PHÆACIANS

ULYSSES clung to the raft while any of its timbers kept together, and when it no longer yielded him support, binding the girdle around him, he swam. Minerva smoothed the billows before him and sent him a wind that rolled the waves towards the shore. The surf beat high on the rocks and seemed to forbid approach; but at length finding calm water at the mouth of a gentle stream, he landed, spent with toil, breathless and speechless and almost dead. After some time, reviving, he kissed the soil, rejoicing, yet at a loss what course to take. At a short distance he perceived a wood to which he turned his steps. There, finding a covert sheltered by intermingling branches alike from the sun and the rain, he collected a pile of leaves and formed a bed, on which he stretched himself, and heaping the leaves over him, fell asleep.

The land where he was thrown was Scheria, the country of the Phæacians. These people dwelt originally near the Cyclopses; but being oppressed by that savage race, they migrated to the isle of Scheria, under the conduct of Nausithoüs, their king. They were, the poet tells us, a people akin to the gods, who appeared manifestly and feasted among them when they offered sacrifices and did not conceal themselves from solitary wayfarers when they met them. They had abundance of wealth and lived in the enjoyment of it undisturbed by the alarms of war, for as they dwelt remote from gain-seeking men, no enemy ever approached their shores, and they did not even require to make use of bows and quivers. Their chief employment was navigation. Their ships, which went with the velocity of birds, were endued with intelligence; they knew every port and needed no pilot. Alcinoüs, the son of Nausithoüs, was now their king, a wise and just sovereign, beloved by his people.

Now it happened that the very night on which Ulysses was cast ashore on the Phæacian island, and while he lay sleeping on his bed of leaves, Nausicaa, the daughter of the king, had a dream sent by Minerva, reminding her that her wedding-day was not far distant, and that it would be but a prudent preparation for that event to have a general washing of the clothes of the family. This was no slight affair, for the fountains were at some distance, and the garments must be carried thither. On awaking, the princess hastened to her parents to tell them what was on her mind; not alluding to her wedding-day, but finding other reasons equally good. Her father readily assented and ordered the grooms to furnish forth a wagon for the purpose. The clothes were put therein, and the queen mother placed in the wagon, likewise, an abundant supply of food and wine. The princess took her seat and plied the lash, her attendant virgins following her on foot. Arrived at the river side, they turned out the mules to graze, and unlading the carriage, bore the garments down to the water, and working with cheerfulness and alacrity soon despatched their labour. Then having spread the garments on the shore to dry, and having themselves bathed, they sat down to enjoy their meal; after which they rose and amused themselves with a game of ball, the princess singing to them while they played. But when they had refolded the apparel and were about to resume their way to the town, Minerva caused the ball thrown by the princess to fall into the water, whereat they all screamed and Ulysses awaked at the sound.

Now we must picture to ourselves Ulysses, a shipwrecked mariner, but a few hours escaped from the waves, and utterly destitute of clothing, awaking and discovering that only a few bushes were interposed between him and a group of young maidens whom, by their deportment and attire, he discovered to be not mere peasant girls, but of a higher class. Sadly needing help, how could he yet venture, naked as he was, to discover himself and make his wants known? It certainly was a case worthy of the interposition of his patron goddess Minerva, who never failed him at a crisis. Breaking off a leafy branch from a tree, he held it before him and stepped out from the thicket. The virgins at sight of him fled in all directions, Nausicaa alone excepted, for *her* Minerva aided and endowed with courage and discernment. Ulysses, standing respectfully aloof, told his sad case, and besought the fair object (whether queen or goddess he professed he knew not) for food and clothing. The princess replied courteously, promising present relief and her father's hospitality when he should become acquainted with the facts. She called back her scattered maidens, chiding their alarm, and reminding them that the Phæacians had no enemies to fear. This man, she told them, was an unhappy wanderer, whom it was a duty to cherish, for the poor and stranger are from Jove. She bade them bring food and clothing, for some of her brothers' garments were among the contents of the wagon. When this was done, and Ulysses, retiring to a sheltered place, had washed his body free from the sea-foam, clothed and refreshed himself with food, Pallas dilated his form and diffused grace over his ample chest and manly brows.

The princess, seeing him, was filled with admiration, and scrupled not to say to her damsels that she wished the gods would send her such a husband. To Ulysses she recommended that he should repair to the city, following herself and train so far as the way lay through the fields; but when they should approach the city she desired that he would no longer be seen in her company, for she feared the remarks which rude and vulgar people might make on seeing her return accompanied by such a gallant stranger. To avoid which she directed him to stop at a grove adjoining the city, in which were a farm and garden belonging to the king. After allowing time for the princess and her companions to reach the city, he was then to pursue his way thither, and would be easily guided by any he might meet to the royal abode.

Ulysses obeyed the directions and in due time proceeded to the city, on approaching which he met a young woman bearing a pitcher forth for water. It was Minerva, who had assumed that form. Ulysses accosted her and desired to be directed to the palace of Alcinoüs the king. The maiden replied respectfully, offering to be his guide; for the palace, she informed him, stood near her father's dwelling. Under the guidance of the goddess, and by her power enveloped in a cloud which shielded him from observation, Ulysses passed among the busy crowd, and with wonder observed their harbour, their ships, their forum (the resort of heroes), and their battlements, till they came to the palace, where the goddess, having first given him some information of the country, king, and people he was about to meet, left him. Ulysses, before entering the courtyard of the palace, stood and surveyed the scene. Its splendour astonished him. Brazen walls stretched from the entrance to the interior house, of which the doors were gold, the doorposts silver, the lintels silver ornamented with gold. On either side were figures of mastiffs wrought in gold and silver, standing in rows as if to guard the approach. Along the walls were seats spread through all their length with mantles of finest texture, the work of Phæacian maidens. On these seats the princes sat and feasted, while golden statues of graceful youths held in their hands lighted torches which shed radiance over the scene. Full fifty female menials served in household offices, some employed to grind the corn, others to wind off the purple wool or ply the loom. For the Phæacian women as far exceeded all other women in household arts as the mariners of that country did the rest of mankind in the management of ships. Without the court a spacious garden lay, four acres in extent. In it grew many a lofty tree, pomegranate, pear, apple, fig, and olive. Neither winter's cold nor summer's drought arrested their growth, but they flourished in constant succession, some budding while others were maturing. The vineyard was equally prolific. In one quarter you might see the vines, some in blossom, some loaded with ripe grapes, and in another observe the vintagers treading the wine press. On the garden's borders flowers of all hues bloomed all the year round, arranged with neatest art. In the midst two fountains poured forth their waters, one flowing by artificial channels over all the garden, the other conducted through the courtyard of the palace, whence every citizen might draw his supplies.

Ulysses stood gazing in admiration, unobserved himself, for the cloud which Minerva spread around him still shielded him. At length, having sufficiently observed the scene, he advanced with rapid step into the hall where the chiefs and senators were assembled, pouring libation to Mercury, whose worship followed the evening meal. Just then Minerva dissolved the cloud and disclosed him to the assembled chiefs. Advancing to the place where the queen sat, he knelt at her feet and implored her favour and assistance to enable him to return to his native country. Then withdrawing, he seated himself in the manner of suppliants, at the hearth side.

For a time none spoke. At last an aged statesman, addressing the king, said, "It is not fit that a stranger who asks our hospitality should be kept waiting in suppliant guise, none welcoming him. Let him therefore be led to a seat among us and supplied with food and wine." At these words the king rising gave his hand to Ulysses and led him to a seat, displacing thence his own son to make room for the stranger. Food and wine were set before him and he ate and refreshed himself.

The king then dismissed his guests, notifying them that the next day he would call them to council to consider what had best be done for the stranger.

When the guests had departed and Ulysses was left alone with the king and queen, the queen asked him who he was and whence he came, and (recognizing the clothes which he wore as those which her maidens and herself had made) from whom he received those garments. He told them of his residence in Calypso's isle and his departure thence; of the wreck of his raft, his escape by swimming, and of the relief afforded by the princess. The parents heard approvingly, and the king promised to furnish a ship in which his guest might return to his own land.

The next day the assembled chiefs confirmed the promise of the king. A bark was prepared and a crew of stout rowers selected, and all betook themselves to the palace, where a bounteous repast was provided. After the feast the king proposed that the young men should show their guest their proficiency in manly sports, and all went forth to the arena for games of running, wrestling, and other exercises. After all had done their best, Ulysses being challenged to show what he could do, at first declined, but being taunted by one of the youths, seized a quoit of weight far heavier than any of the Phæacians had thrown, and sent it farther than the utmost throw of theirs. All were astonished, and viewed their guest with greatly increased respect.

After the games they returned to the hall, and the herald led in Demodocus, the blind bard,

> "... Dear to the Muse,
> Who yet appointed him both good and ill,
> Took from his sight, but gave him strains divine."

He took for his theme the "Wooden Horse," by means of which the Greeks found entrance into Troy. Apollo inspired him, and he sang so feelingly the terrors and the exploits of that eventful time that all were delighted, but Ulysses was moved to tears. Observing which,

Alcinoüs, when the song was done, demanded of him why at the mention of Troy his sorrows awaked. Had he lost there a father, or brother, or any dear friend? Ulysses replied by announcing himself by his true name, and at their request, recounted the adventures which had befallen him since his departure from Troy. This narrative raised the sympathy and admiration of the Phæacians for their guest to the highest pitch. The king proposed that all the chiefs should present him with a gift, himself setting the example. They obeyed, and vied with one another in loading the illustrious stranger with costly gifts.

The next day Ulysses set sail in the Phæacian vessel, and in a short time arrived safe at Ithaca, his own island. When the vessel touched the strand he was asleep. The mariners, without waking him, carried him on shore, and landed with him the chest containing his presents, and then sailed away.

Neptune was so displeased at the conduct of the Phæacians in thus rescuing Ulysses from his hands that on the return of the vessel to port he transformed it into a rock, right opposite the mouth of the harbour.

Homer's description of the ships of the Phæacians has been thought to look like an anticipation of the wonders of modern steam navigation. Alcinoüs says to Ulysses,

"Say from what city, from what regions tossed,
And what inhabitants those regions boast?
So shalt thou quickly reach the realm assigned,
In wondrous ships, self-moved, instinct with mind;
No helm secures their course, no pilot guides;
Like man intelligently they plough the tides,
Conscious of every coast and every bay
That lies beneath the sun's all-seeing ray."

Odyssey, Book VIII.

Lord Carlisle, in his "Diary in the Turkish and Greek Waters," thus speaks of Coriu, which he considers to be the ancient Phæacian island:

"The sites explain the 'Odyssey.' The temple of the sea-god could not have been more fitly placed, upon a grassy platform of the most elastic turf, on the brow of a crag commanding the harbour, and channel, and ocean. Just at the entrance of the inner harbour there is a picturesque rock with a small convent perched upon it, which by one legend is the transformed pinnace of Ulysses.

"Almost the only river in the island is just at the proper distance from the probable site of the city and palace of the king, to justify the princess Nausicaa having had resort to her chariot and to luncheon when she went with the maidens of the court to wash their garments."

Fate of the Suitors

Ulysses had now been away from Ithaca for twenty years, and when he awoke he did not recognize his native land. Minerva appeared to him in the form of a young shepherd, informed him where he was, and told him the state of things at his palace. More than a hundred nobles of Ithaca and of the neighbouring islands had been for years suing for the hand of Penelope, his wife, imagining him dead, and lording it over his palace and people, as if they were owners of both. That he might be able to take vengeance upon them, it was important that he should not be recognized. Minerva accordingly metamorphosed him into an unsightly beggar, and as such he was kindly received by Eumæus, the swine-herd, a faithful servant of his house.

Telemachus, his son, was absent in quest of his father. He had gone to the courts of the other kings, who had returned from the Trojan expedition. While on the search, he received counsel from Minerva to return home. He arrived and sought Eumæus to learn something of the state of affairs at the palace before presenting himself among the suitors. Finding a stranger with Eumæus, he treated him courteously, though in the garb of a beggar, and promised him assistance. Eumæus was sent to the palace to inform Penelope privately of her son's arrival, for caution was necessary with regard to the suitors, who, as Telemachus had learned, were plotting to intercept and kill him. When Eumæus was gone, Minerva presented herself to Ulysses, and directed him to make himself known to his son. At the same time she touched him, removed at once from him the appearance of age and penury, and gave him the aspect of vigorous manhood that belonged to him. Telemachus viewed him with astonishment, and at first thought he must be more than mortal. But Ulysses announced himself as his father, and accounted for the change of appearance by explaining that it was Minerva's doing.

> "... Then threw Telemachus
> His arms around his father's neck and wept.
> Desire intense of lamentation seized.
> On both; soft murmurs uttering, each indulged
> His grief."

The father and son took counsel together how they should get the better of the suitors and punish them for their outrages. It was arranged that Telemachus should proceed to the palace and mingle with the suitors as formerly; that Ulysses should also go as a beggar, a character which in the rude old times had different privileges from what we concede to it now. As traveller and storyteller, the beggar was admitted in the halls of chieftains, and often treated like a guest; though sometimes, also, no doubt, with contumely. Ulysses charged his son not to betray, by any display of unusual interest in him, that he knew him to be other than he seemed, and even if he saw him insulted, or beaten, not to interpose otherwise than he might do for any stranger. At the palace they found the usual scene of feasting and riot going on. The suitors pretended to receive Telemachus with joy at his return, though secretly mortified at the failure of their plots to take his life. The old beggar was permitted to enter, and provided with a portion from the table. A touching incident occurred as Ulysses entered the courtyard of the palace. An old dog lay in the yard almost dead with age, and seeing a stranger enter, raised his head, with ears erect. It was Argus, Ulysses' own dog, that he had in other days often led to the chase.

> "... Soon as he perceived
> Long-lost Ulysses nigh, down fell his ears
> Clapped close, and with his tail glad sign ue gave
> Of gratulation, impotent to rise,
> And to approach his master as of old.
> Ulysses, noting him, wiped off a tear
> Unmarked.
> ... Then his destiny released
> Old Argus, soon as he had lived to see
> Ulysses in the twentieth year restored."

As Ulysses sat eating his portion in the hall, the suitors began to exhibit their insolence to him. When he mildly remonstrated, one of them raised a stool and with it gave him a blow. Telemachus had hard work to restrain his indignation at seeing his father so treated in his own hall, but remembering his father's injunctions, said no more than what became him as master of the house, though young, and protector of his guests.

Penelope had protracted her decision in favour of either of her suitors so long that there seemed to be no further pretence for delay. The continued absence of her husband seemed to prove that his return was no longer to be expected. Meanwhile her son had grown up, and was able to manage his own affairs. She therefore consented to submit the question of her choice to a trial of skill among the suitors. The test selected was shooting with the bow. Twelve rings were arranged in a line, and he whose arrow was sent through the whole twelve was to have the queen for his prize. A bow that one of his brother heroes had given to Ulysses in former times was brought from the armoury, and with its quiver full of arrows was laid in the hall. Telemachus had taken care that all other weapons should be removed, under pretence that in the heat of competition there was danger, in some rash moment, of putting them to an improper use.

All things being prepared for the trial, the first thing to be done was to bend the bow in order to attach the string. Telemachus endeavoured to do it, but found all his efforts fruitless; and modestly confessing that he had attempted a task beyond his strength, he yielded the bow to another. *He* tried it with no better success, and, amidst the laughter and jeers of his companions, gave it up. Another tried it and another; they rubbed the bow with tallow, but all to no purpose; it would not bend. Then spoke Ulysses, humbly suggesting that he should be permitted to try; for, said he, "beggar as I am, I was once a soldier, and there is still some strength in these old limbs of mine." The suitors hooted with derision, and commanded to turn him out of the hall for his insolence. But Telemachus spoke up for him, and, merely to gratify the old man, bade him try. Ulysses took the bow, and handled it with the hand of a master. With ease he adjusted the cord to its notch, then fitting an arrow to the bow he drew the string and sped the arrow unerring through the rings.

Without allowing them time to express their astonishment, he said, "Now for another mark!" and aimed direct at the most insolent one of the suitors. The arrow pierced through his throat and he fell dead. Telemachus, Eumæus, and another faithful follower, well armed, now sprang to the side of Ulysses. The suitors, in amazement, looked round for arms, but found none, neither was there any way of escape, for Eumæus had secured the door. Ulysses left them not long in uncertainty; he announced himself as the long-lost chief, whose house they had invaded, whose substance they had squandered, whose wife and son they had persecuted for ten long years; and told them he meant to have ample vengeance. All were slain, and Ulysses was left master of his palace and possessor of his kingdom and his wife.

Tennyson's poem of "Ulysses" represents the old hero, after his dangers past and nothing left but to stay at home and be happy, growing tired of inaction and resolving to set forth again in quest of new adventures:

> "...Come, my friends,
> 'Tis not too late to seek a newer world.
> Push off, and sitting well in order smite
> The sounding furrows; for my purpose holds
> To sail beyond the sunset, and the baths
> Of all the western stars, until I die.
> It may be that the gulfs will wash us down;
> It may be we shall touch the Happy Isles,
> And see the great Achilles whom we knew;" etc.

CHAPTER XXXI

ADVENTURES OF ÆNEAS—THE HARPIES—DIDO—PALINURIUS

ADVENTURES OF ÆNEAS

WE have followed one of the Grecian heroes, Ulysses, in his wanderings on his return home from Troy, and now we propose to share the fortunes of the remnant of the *conquered* people, under their chief Æneas, in their search for a new home, after the ruin of their native city. On that fatal night when the wooden horse disgorged its contents of armed men, and the capture and conflagration of the city were the result, Æneas made his escape from the scene of destruction, with his father, and his wife, and young son. The father, Anchises, was too old to walk with the speed required, and Æneas took him upon his shoulders.[1] Thus burdened, leading his son and followed by his wife, he made the best of his way out of the burning city; but, in the confusion, his wife was swept away and lost.

On arriving at the place of rendezvous, numerous fugitives, of both sexes, were found, who put themselves under the guidance of Æneas. Some months were spent in preparation, and at length they embarked. They first landed on the neighboring shores of Thrace, and were preparing to build a city, but Æneas was deterred by a prodigy. Preparing to offer sacrifice, he tore some twigs from one of the bushes. To his dismay the wounded part dropped blood. When he repeated the act a voice from the ground cried out to him, "Spare me, Æneas; I am your kinsman, Polydore, here murdered with many arrows, from which a bush has grown, nourished with my blood." These words recalled to the recollection of Æneas that Polydore was a young prince of Troy, whom his father had sent with ample treasures to the neighbouring land of Thrace, to be there brought up, at a distance from the horrors of war. The king to whom he was sent had murdered him and seized his treasures. Æneas and his companions, considering the land accursed by the stain of such a crime, hastened away.

They next landed on the island of Delos, which was once a floating island, till Jupiter fastened it by adamantine chains to the bottom of the sea. Apollo and Diana were born there, and the island was sacred to Apollo. Here Æneas consulted the oracle of Apollo, and received an answer, ambiguous as usual,—"Seek your ancient mother; there the race of Æneas shall dwell, and reduce all other nations to their sway." The Trojans heard with joy and

[1] See Proverbial Expressions, page 289.

immediately began to ask one another, "Where is the spot intended by the oracle?" Anchises remembered that there was a tradition that their forefathers came from Crete and thither they resolved to steer. They arrived at Crete and began to build their city, but sickness broke out among them, and the fields that they had planted failed to yield a crop. In this gloomy aspect of affairs Æneas was warned in a dream to leave the country and seek a western land, called Hesperia, whence Dardanus, the true founder of the Trojan race, had originally migrated. To Hesperia, now called Italy, therefore, they directed their future course, and not till after many adventures and the lapse of time sufficient to carry a modern navigator several times round the world, did they arrive there.

Their first landing was at the island of the Harpies. These were disgusting birds with the heads of maidens, with long claws and faces pale with hunger. They were sent by the gods to torment a certain Phineus, whom Jupiter had deprived of his sight, in punishment of his cruelty; and whenever a meal was placed before him the Harpies darted down from the air and carried it off. They were driven away from Phineus by the heroes of the Argonautic expedition, and took refuge in the island where Æneas now found them.

When they entered the port the Trojans saw herds of cattle roaming over the plain. They slew as many as they wished and prepared for a feast. But no sooner had they seated themselves at the table than a horrible clamour was heard in the air, and a flock of these odious harpies came rushing down upon them, seizing in their talons the meat from the dishes and flying away with it. Æneas and his companions drew their swords and dealt vigorous blows among the monsters, but to no purpose, for they were so nimble it was almost impossible to hit them, and their feathers were like armour impenetrable to steel. One of them, perched on a neighbouring cliff, screamed out, "Is it thus, Trojans, you treat us innocent birds, first slaughter our cattle and then make war on ourselves?" She then predicted dire sufferings to them in their future course, and having vented her wrath flew away. The Trojans made haste to leave the country, and next found themselves coasting along the shore of Epirus. Here they landed, and to their astonishment learned that certain Trojan exiles, who had been carried there as prisoners, had become rulers of the country. Andromache, the widow of Hector, became the wife of one of the victorious Grecian chiefs, to whom she bore a son. Her husband dying, she was left regent of the country, as guardian of her son, and had married a fellow-captive, Helenus, of the royal race of

Troy. Helenus and Andromache treated the exiles with the utmost hospitality, and dismissed them loaded with gifts.

From hence Æneas coasted along the shore of Sicily and passed the country of the Cyclopses. Here they were hailed from the shore by a miserable object, whom by his garments, tattered as they were, they perceived to be a Greek. He told them he was one of Ulysses' companions, left behind by that chief in his hurried departure. He related the story of Ulysses' adventure with Polyphemus, and besought them to take him off with them as he had no means of sustaining his existence where he was but wild berries and roots, and lived in constant fear of the Cyclopses. While he spoke Polyphemus made his appearance; "a terrible monster, shapeless, vast, whose only eye had been put out." [1] He walked with cautious steps, feeling his way with a staff, down to the seaside, to wash his eye-socket in the waves. When he reached the water, he waded out towards them, and his immense height enabled him to advance far into the sea, so that the Trojans, in terror, took to their oars to get out of his way. Hearing the oars, Polyphemus shouted after them, so that the shores resounded, and at the noise the other Cyclopses came forth from their caves and woods and lined the shore, like a row of lofty pine trees. The Trojans plied their oars and soon left them out of sight.

Æneas had been cautioned by Helenus to avoid the strait guarded by the monsters Scylla and Charybdis. There Ulysses, the reader will remember, had lost six of his men, seized by Scylla while the navigators were wholly intent upon avoiding Charybdis. Æneas, following the advice of Helenus, shunned the dangerous pass and coasted along the island of Sicily.

Juno, seeing the Trojans speeding their way prosperously towards their destined shore, felt her old grudge against them revive, for she could not forget the slight that Paris had put upon her, in awarding the prize of beauty to another. "In heavenly minds can such resentments dwell!" [1] Accordingly she hastened to Æolus, the ruler of the winds,—the same who supplied Ulysses with favouring gales, giving him the contrary ones tied up in a bag. Æolus obeyed the goddess and sent forth his sons, Boreas, Typhon, and the other winds, to toss the ocean. A terrible storm ensued and the Trojan ships were driven out of their course towards the coast of Africa. They were in imminent danger of being wrecked, and were separated, so that Æneas thought that all were lost except his own.

At this crisis, Neptune, hearing the storm raging, and knowing that he had given no orders for one, raised his head above the

[1] See Proverbial Expressions, page 290.

waves, and saw the fleet of Æneas driving before the gale. Knowing the hostility of Juno, he was at no loss to account for it, but
his anger was not the less at this interference in his province. He
called the winds and dismissed them with a severe reprimand. He
then soothed the waves, and brushed away the clouds from before
the face of the sun. Some of the ships which had got on the rocks
he prised off with his own trident, while Triton and a sea-nymph,
putting their shoulders under others, set them afloat again. The
Trojans, when the sea became calm, sought the nearest shore, which
was the coast of Carthage, where Æneas was so happy as to find
that one by one the ships all arrived safe, though badly shaken.

Waller, in his "Panegyric to the Lord Protector" (Cromwell),
alludes to this stilling of the storm by Neptune:

> "Above the waves, as Neptune showed his face,
> To chide the winds and save the Trojan race,
> So has your Highness, raised above the rest,
> Storms of ambition tossing us repressed."

DIDO

Carthage, where the exiles had now arrived, was a spot on the
coast of Africa opposite Sicily, where at that time a Tyrian colony
under Dido, their queen, were laying the foundations of a state
destined in later ages to be the rival of Rome itself. Dido was the
daughter of Belus, king of Tyre, and sister of Pygmalion, who
succeeded his father on the throne. Her husband was Sichæus, a
man of immense wealth, but Pygmalion, who coveted his treasures, caused him to be put to death. Dido, with a numerous body
of friends and followers, both men and women, succeeded in effect-
ing their escape from Tyre, in several vessels, carrying with them
the treasures of Sichæus. On arriving at the spot which they selected as the seat of their future home, they asked of the natives
only so much land as they could enclose with a bull's hide. When
this was readily granted, she caused the hide to be cut into strips,
and with them enclosed a spot on which she built a citadel, and
called it Byrsa (a hide). Around this fort the city of Carthage rose,
and soon became a powerful and flourishing place.

Such was the state of affairs when Æneas with his Trojans arrived there. Dido received the illustrious exiles with friendliness and
hospitality. "Not unacquainted with distress," she said, "I have
learned to succour the unfortunate." [1] The queen's hospitality displayed itself in festivities at which games of strength and skill
were exhibited. The strangers contended for the palm with her

[1] See Proverbial Expressions, page 290.

own subjects, on equal terms, the queen declaring that whether the victor were "Trojan or Tyrian should make no difference to her." [1] At the feast which followed the games, Æneas gave at her request a recital of the closing events of the Trojan history and his own adventures after the fall of the city. Dido was charmed with his discourse and filled with admiration of his exploits. She conceived an ardent passion for him, and he for his part seemed well content to accept the fortunate chance which appeared to offer him at once a happy termination of his wanderings, a home, a kingdom, and a bride. Months rolled away in the enjoyment of pleasant inter- course, and it seemed as if Italy and the empire destined to be founded on its shores were alike forgotten. Seeing which, Jupiter despatched Mercury with a message to Æneas recalling him to a sense of his high destiny, and commanding him to resume his voyage.

Æneas parted from Dido, though she tried every allurement and persuasion to detain him. The blow to her affection and her pride was too much for her to endure, and when she found that he was gone, she mounted a funeral pile which she had caused to be erected, and having stabbed herself was consumed with the pile. The flames rising over the city were seen by the departing Trojans. and, though the cause was unknown, gave to Æneas some intima- tion of the fatal event.

The following epigram we find in "Elegant Extracts":

FROM THE LATIN
"Unhappy, Dido, was thy fate
In first and second married state!
One husband caused thy flight by dying,
Thy death the other caused by flying."

PALINURUS

After touching at the island of Sicily, where Acestes, a prince of Trojan lineage, bore sway, who gave them a hospitable recep- tion, the Trojans re-embarked, and held on their course for Italy. Venus now interceded with Neptune to allow her son at last to attain the wisned-for goal and find an end of his perils on the deep. Neptune consented, stipulating only for one life as a ran- som for the rest. The victim was Palinurus, the pilot. As he sat watching the stars, with his hand on the helm, Somnus sent by Neptune approached in the guise of Phorbas and said: "Palinurus, the breeze is fair, the water smooth, and the ship sails steadily on her course. Lie down awhile and take needful rest. I will stand at

[1] See Proverbial Expressions, page 290.

the helm in your place." Palinurus replied, "Tell me not of smooth seas or favouring winds,—me who have seen so much of their treachery. Shall I trust Æneas to the chances of the weather and the winds?" And he continued to grasp the helm and to keep his eyes fixed on the stars. But Somnus waved over him a branch moistened with Lethæan dew, and his eyes closed in spite of all his efforts. Then Somnus pushed him overboard and he fell: but keeping his hold upon the helm, it came away with him. Neptune was mindful of his promise and kept the ship on her track without helm or pilot, till Æneas discovered his loss, and, sorrowing deeply for his faithful steersman, took charge of the ship himself.

There is a beautiful allusion to the story of Palinurus in Scott's "Marmion," Introduction to Canto I., where the poet, speaking of the recent death of William Pitt, says:

"O, think how, to his latest day,
   When death just hovering claimed his prey,
   With Palinure's unaltered mood,
   Firm at his dangerous post he stood;
   Each call for needful rest repelled,
   With dying hand the rudder held,
   Till in his fall, with fateful sway,
   The steerage of the realm gave way."

The ships at last reached the shores of Italy, and joyfully did the adventurers leap to land. While his people were employed in making their encampment Æneas sought the abode of the Sibyl. It was a cave connected with a temple and grove, sacred to Apollo and Diana. While Æneas contemplated the scene, the Sibyl accosted him. She seemed to know his errand, and under the influence of the deity of the place, burst forth in a prophetic strain, giving dark intimations of labours and perils through which he was destined to make his way to final success. She closed with the encouraging words which have become proverbial: "Yield not to disasters, but press onward the more bravely."[1] Æneas replied that he had prepared himself for whatever might await him. He had but one request to make. Having been directed in a dream to seek the abode of the dead in order to confer with his father, Anchises, to receive from him a revelation of his future fortunes and those of his race, he asked her assistance to enable him to accomplish the task. The Sibyl replied, "The descent to Avernus is easy: the gate of Pluto stands open night and day; but to retrace one's steps and return to the upper air, that is the toil, that the difficulty."[1] She instructed him to seek in the forest a tree on which grew a golden branch. This branch was to be plucked

[1] See Proverbial Expressions, page 290.

off and borne as a gift to Proserpine, and if fate was propitious
it would yield to the hand and quit its parent trunk, but otherwise
no force could rend it away. If torn away, another would succeed.[1]

Æneas followed the directions of the Sibyl. His mother, Venus,
sent two of her doves to fly before him and show him the way,
and by their assistance he found the tree, plucked the branch, and
hastened back with it to the Sibyl.

CHAPTER XXXII

THE INFERNAL REGIONS—THE SIBYL

The Infernal Regions

As at the commencement of our series we have given the pagan
account of the creation of the world, so as we approach its conclusion we present a view of the regions of the dead, depicted by
one of their most enlightened poets, who drew his doctrines from
their most esteemed philosophers. The region where Virgil locates
the entrance to this abode is perhaps the most strikingly adapted
to excite ideas of the terrific and preternatural of any on the face
of the earth. It is the volcanic region near Vesuvius, where the
whole country is cleft with chasms, from which sulphurous flames
arise, while the ground is shaken with pent-up vapours, and mysterious sounds issue from the bowels of the earth. The lake Avernus
is supposed to fill the crater of an extinct volcano. It is circular,
half a mile wide, and very deep, surrounded by high banks, which
in Virgil's time were covered with a gloomy forest. Mephitic vapours rise from its waters, so that no life is found on its banks,
and no birds fly over it. Here, according to the poet, was the cave
which afforded access to the infernal regions, and here Æneas offered sacrifices to the infernal deities, Proserpine, Hecate, and the
Furies. Then a roaring was heard in the earth, the woods on the
hill-tops were shaken, and the howling of dogs announced the approach of the deities. "Now," said the Sibyl, "summon up your
courage, for you will need it." She descended into the cave, and
Æneas followed. Before the threshold of hell they passed through
a group of beings who are enumerated as Griefs and avenging
Cares, pale Diseases and melancholy Age, Fear and Hunger that
tempt to crime, Toil, Poverty, and Death,—forms horrible to view.
The Furies spread the couches there, and Discord, whose hair was
of vipers tied up with a bloody fillet. Here also were the monsters,
Briareus, with his hundred arms, Hydras hissing, and Chimæras
breathing fire. Æneas shuddered at the sight, drew his sword and

[1] See Proverbial Expressions, page 290.

would have struck, but the Sibyl restrained him. They then came to the black river Cocytus, where they found the ferryman, Charon old and squalid, but strong and vigorous, who was receiving passengers of all kinds into his boat, magnanimous heroes, boys and unmarried girls, as numerous as the leaves that fall at autumn, or the flocks that fly southward at the approach of winter. They stood pressing for a passage and longing to touch the opposite shore. But the stern ferryman took in only such as he chose, driving the rest back. Æneas, wondering at the sight, asked the Sibyl, "Why this discrimination?" She answered, "Those who are taken or board the bark are the souls of those who have received due burial rites; the host of others who have remained unburied are not permitted to pass the flood but wander a hundred years, and flit to and fro about the shore, till at last they are taken over." Æneas grieved at recollecting some of his own companions who had perished in the storm. At that moment he beheld Palinurus, his pilot, who fell overboard and was drowned. He addressed him and asked him the cause of his misfortune. Palinurus replied that the rudder was carried away, and he, clinging to it, was swept away with it. He besought Æneas most urgently to extend to him his hand and take him in company to the opposite shore. But the Sibyl rebuked him for the wish thus to transgress the laws of Pluto; but consoled him by informing him that the people of the shore where his body had been wafted by the waves should be stirred up by prodigies to give it due burial, and that the promontory should bear the name of Cape Palinurus, which it does to this day. Leaving Palinurus consoled by these words, they approached the boat. Charon, fixing his eyes sternly upon the advancing warrior, demanded by what right he, living and armed, approached that shore. To which the Sibyl replied that they would commit no violence, that Æneas's only object was to see his father, and finally exhibited the golden branch at sight of which Charon's wrath relaxed, and he made haste to turn his bark to the shore, and receive them on board. The boat, adapted only to the light freight of bodiless spirits, groaned under the weight of the hero. They were soon conveyed to the opposite shore. There they were encountered by the three-headed dog, Cerberus, with his necks bristling with snakes. He barked with all his three throats till the Sibyl threw him a medicated cake which he eagerly devoured, and then stretched himself out in his den and fell asleep. Æneas and the Sibyl sprang to land. The first sound that struck their ears was the wailing of young children, who had died on the threshold of life, and near to these were they who had perished under false charges. Minos presides over them as judge, and examines the deeds of each. The next class was of those who had died by their own hand, hating life and seeking refuge in death. O how willingly would they now endure poverty, labour, and any other infliction, if they might but return to life! Next were situated the regions of sadness, divided off into retired paths, leading through groves of myrtle. Here roamed those who had fallen victims to unrequited love, not freed from pain even by death itself. Among these, Æneas thought he descried the form of Dido, with a wound still recent. In the dim light he was for a moment uncertain, but approaching, perceived it was indeed herself. Tears fell from his eyes, and he addressed her in the accents of love. "Unhappy Dido! was then the rumour true that you had perished? and was I, alas! the cause? I call the gods to witness that my departure from you was reluctant, and in obedience to the commands of Jove; nor could I believe that my absence would cost you so dear. Stop, I beseech you, and refuse me not a last farewell." She stood for a moment with averted countenance, and eyes fixed on the ground, and then silently passed on, as insensible to his pleadings as a rock. Æneas followed for some distance; then, with a heavy heart, rejoined his companion and resumed his route.

They next entered the fields where roam the heroes who have fallen in battle. Here they saw many shades of Grecian and Trojan warriors. The Trojans thronged around him, and could not be satisfied with the sight. They asked the cause of his coming, and plied him with innumerable questions. But the Greeks, at the sight of his armour glittering through the murky atmosphere, recognized the hero, and filled with terror turned their backs and fled, as they used to do on the plains of Troy.

Æneas would have lingered long with his Trojan friends, but the Sibyl hurried him away. They next came to a place where the road divided, the one leading to Elysium, the other to the regions of the condemned. Æneas beheld on one side the walls of a mighty city, around which Phlegethon rolled its fiery waters. Before him was the gate of adamant that neither gods nor men can break through. An iron tower stood by the gate, on which Tisiphone, the avenging Fury, kept guard. From the city were heard groans, and the sound of the scourge, the creaking of iron, and the clanking of chains. Æneas, horror-struck, inquired of his guide what crimes were those whose punishments produced the sounds he heard? The Sibyl answered, "Here is the judgment hall of Rhadamanthus, who brings to light crimes done in life, which the perpetrator vainly thought impenetrably hid. Tisiphone applies her whip of scorpions, and delivers the offender over to her sister Furies." At this moment with horrid clang the brazen gates unfolded, and Æneas saw within a Hydra with fifty heads guarding the entrance. The Sibyl told him that the gulf of Tartarus descended deep, so that its recesses were as far beneath their feet as heaven was high above their heads. In the bottom of this pit, the Titan race, who warred against the gods, lie prostrate; Salmoneus, also, who presumed to vie with Jupiter, and built a bridge of brass over which he drove his chariot that the sound might resemble thunder, launching flaming brands at his people in imitation of lightning, till Jupiter struck him with a real thunderbolt, and taught him the difference between mortal weapons and divine. Here, also, is Tityus, the giant, whose form is so immense that as he lies he stretches over nine acres, while a vulture preys upon his liver, which as fast as it is devoured grows again, so that his punishment will have no end.

Æneas saw groups seated at tables loaded with dainties, while near by stood a Fury who snatched away the viands from their lips as fast as they prepared to taste them. Others beheld suspended over their heads huge rocks, threatening to fall, keeping them in a state of constant alarm. These were they who had hated their brothers, or struck their parents, or defrauded the friends who trusted them, or who, having grown rich, kept their money to themselves, and gave no share to others; the last being the most numerous class. Here also were those who had violated the marriage vow, or fought in a bad cause, or failed in fidelity to their employers. Here was one who had sold his country for gold, another who perverted the laws, making them say one thing to-day and another to-morrow.

Ixion was there, fastened to the circumference of a wheel ceaselessly revolving; and Sisyphus, whose task was to roll a huge stone up to a hill-top, but when the steep was well-nigh gained, the rock, repulsed by some sudden force, rushed again headlong down to the plain. Again he toiled at it, while the sweat bathed all his weary limbs, but all to no effect. There was Tantalus, who stood in a pool, his chin level with the water, yet he was parched with thirst, and found nothing to assuage it; for when he bowed his hoary head, eager to quaff, the water fled away, leaving the ground at his feet all dry. Tall trees laden with fruit stooped their heads to him, pears, pomegranates, apples, and luscious figs; but when with a sudden grasp he tried to seize them winds whirled them high above his reach.

The Sibyl now warned Æneas it was time to turn from these melancholy regions and seek the city of the blessed. They passed through a middle tract of darkness, and came upon the Elysian fields, the groves where the happy reside. They breathed a freer air, and saw all objects clothed in a purple light. The region has a sun and stars of its own. The inhabitants were enjoying themselves in various ways, some in sports on the grassy turf, in games of strength or skill, others dancing or singing. Orpheus struck the chords of his lyre, and called forth ravishing sounds. Here Æneas saw the founders of the Trojan state, magnanimous heroes who lived in happier times. He gazed with admiration on the war chariots and glittering arms now reposing in disuse. Spears stood fixed in the ground, and the horses, unharnessed, roamed over the plain. The same pride in splendid armour and generous steeds which the old heroes felt in life, accompanied them here. He saw another group feasting and listening to the strains of music. They were in a laurel grove, whence the great river Po has its origin, and flows out among men. Here dwelt those who fell by wounds received in their country's cause, holy priests also, and poets who have uttered thoughts worthy of Apollo, and others who have contributed to cheer and adorn life by their discoveries in the useful arts, and have made their memory blessed by rendering service to mankind. They wore snow-white fillets about their brows. The Sibyl addressed a group of these, and inquired where Anchises was to be found. They were directed where to seek him, and soon found him in a verdant valley, where he was contemplating the ranks of his posterity, their destinies and worthy deeds to be achieved in coming times. When he recognized Æneas approaching, he stretched out both hands to him, while tears flowed freely. "Have you come at last," said he, "long expected, and do I behold you after such perils past? O my son, how have I trembled for you as I have watched your career!" To which Æneas replied, "O father! your image was always before me to guide and guard me." Then he endeavoured to enfold his father in his embrace, but his arms enclosed only an unsubstantial image.

Æneas perceived before him a spacious valley, with trees gently waving to the wind, a tranquil landscape, through which the river Lethe flowed. Along the banks of the stream wandered a countless multitude, numerous as insects in the summer air. Æneas, with surprise, inquired who were these. Anchises answered, "They are souls to which bodies are to be given in due time. Meanwhile they dwell on Lethe's bank, and drink oblivion of their former lives." "O father!" said Æneas, "is it possible that any can be so in love with life as to wish to leave these tranquil seats for the upper world?" Anchises replied by explaining the plan of creation. The Creator, he told him, originally made the material of which souls are composed of the four elements, fire, air, earth, and water, all which when united took the form of the most excellent part, fire,

and became *flame*. This material was scattered like seed among
the heavenly bodies, the sun, moon, and stars. Of this seed the
inferior gods created man and all other animals, mingling it with
various proportions of earth, by which its purity was alloyed and
reduced. Thus, the more earth predominates in the composition the
less pure is the individual; and we see men and women with their
full-grown bodies have not the purity of childhood. So in proportion to the time which the union of body and soul has lasted is the
impurity contracted by the spiritual part. This impurity must
be purged away after death, which is done by ventilating the souls
in the current of winds, or merging them in water, or burning out
their impurities by fire. Some few, of whom Anchises intimates
that he is one, are admitted at once to Elysium, there to remain.
But the rest, after the impurities of earth are purged away, are
sent back to life endowed with new bodies, having had the remembrance of their former lives effectually washed away by the
waters of Lethe. Some, however, there still are, so thoroughly
corrupted, that they are not fit to be intrusted with human bodies,
and these are made into brute animals, lions, tigers, cats, dogs,
monkeys, etc. This is what the ancients called Metempsychosis, or
the transmigration of souls; a doctrine which is still held by the
natives of India, who scruple to destroy the life even of the most
insignificant animal, not knowing but it may be one of their relations in an altered form.

Anchises, having explained so much, proceeded to point out to
Æneas individuals of his race, who were hereafter to be born, and
to relate to him the exploits they should perform in the world.
After this he reverted to the present, and told his son of the events
that remained to him to be accomplished before the complete establishment of himself and his followers in Italy. Wars were to be
waged, battles fought, a bride to be won, and in the result a
Trojan state founded, from which should arise the Roman power,
to be in time the sovereign of the world.

Æneas and the Sibyl then took leave of Anchises, and returned
by some short cut, which the poet does not explain, to the upper
world.

ELYSIUM

Virgil, we have seen, places his Elysium under the earth, and
assigns it for a residence to the spirits of the blessed. But in Homer
Elysium forms no part of the realms of the dead. He places it on
the west of the earth, near Ocean, and describes it as a happy
land, where there is neither snow, nor cold, nor rain, and always
fanned by the delightful breezes of Zephyrus. Hither favoured

heroes pass without dying and live happy under the rule of Rhada-manthus. The Elysium of Hesiod and Pindar is in the Isles of the Blessed, or Fortunate Islands, in the Western Ocean. From these sprang the legend of the happy island Atlantis. This bliss-ful region may have been wholly imaginary, but possibly may have sprung from the reports of some storm-driven mariners who had caught a glimpse of the coast of America.

J. R. Lowell, in one of his shorter poems, claims for the present age some of the privileges of that happy realm. Addressing the Past, he says:

> "Whatever of true life there was in thee,
> Leaps in our age's veins.
>   .   .   .   .
> Here, 'mid the bleak waves of our strife and care,
>   Float the green 'Fortunate Isles,'
> Where all thy hero-spirits dwell and share
>   Our martyrdoms and toils.
>   The present moves attended
> With all of brave and excellent and fair
>   That made the old time splendid."

Milton also alludes to the same fable in "Paradise Lost," Book III. l. 568:

> "Like those Hesperian gardens famed of old,
> Fortunate fields and groves and flowery vales,
> Thrice happy isles."

And in Book II. he characterizes the rivers of Erebus according to the meaning of their names in the Greek language:

> "Abhorrèd Styx, the flood of deadly hate,
> Sad Acheron of sorrow black and deep;
> Cocytus named of lamentation loud
> Heard on the rueful stream; fierce Phlegethon
> Whose waves of torrent fire inflame with rage.
> Far off from these a slow and silent stream,
> Lethe, the river of oblivion, rolls
> Her watery labyrinth, whereof who drinks
> Forthwith his former state and being forgets,
> Forgets both joy and grief, pleasure and pain."

THE SIBYL

As Æneas and the Sibyl pursued their way back to earth, he said to her, "Whether thou be a goddess or a mortal beloved of the gods, by me thou shalt always be held in reverence. When I reach the upper air I will cause a temple to be built to thy honour, and will myself bring offerings." "I am no goddess," said the Sibyl; "I have no claim to sacrifice or offering. I am mortal; yet if I could have accepted the love of Apollo I might have been immortal. He promised me the fulfilment of my wish, if I would consent to be his. I took a handful of sand, and holding it forth, said, 'Grant me to see as many birthdays as there are sand grains in my hand.' Unluckily I forgot to ask for enduring youth. This also he would have granted, could I have accepted his love, but offended at my refusal, he allowed me to grow old. My youth and youthful strength fled long ago. I have lived seven hundred years, and to equal the number of the sand-grains I have still to see three hundred springs and three hundred harvests. My body shrinks up as years increase, and in time, I shall be lost to sight, but my voice will remain, and future ages will respect my sayings."

These concluding words of the Sibyl alluded to her prophetic power. In her cave she was accustomed to inscribe on leaves gathered from the trees the names and fates of individuals. The leaves thus inscribed were arranged in order within the cave, and might be consulted by her votaries. But if perchance at the opening of the door the wind rushed in and dispersed the leaves the Sibyl gave no aid in restoring them again, and the oracle was irreparably lost.

The following legend of the Sibyl is fixed at a later date. In the reign of one of the Tarquins there appeared before the king a woman who offered him nine books for sale. The king refused to purchase them, whereupon the woman went away and burned three of the books, and returning offered the remaining books for the same price she had asked for the nine. The king again rejected them; but when the woman, after burning three books more, returned and asked for the three remaining the same price which she had before asked for the nine, his curiosity was excited, and he purchased the books. They were found to contain the destinies of the Roman state. They were kept in the temple of Jupiter Capitolinus, preserved in a stone chest, and allowed to be inspected only by special officers appointed for that duty, who, on great occasions, consulted them and interpreted their oracles to the people.

There were various Sibyls; but the Cumæan Sibyl, of whom Ovid and Virgil write, is the most celebrated of them. Ovid's story of her life protracted to one thousand years may be intended to represent the various Sibyls as being only reappearances of one and the same individual.

Young, in the "Night Thoughts," alludes to the Sibyl. Speaking of Worldly Wisdom, he says:

"If future fate she plans 'tis all in leaves,
Like Sibyl, unsubstantial, fleeting bliss;
At the first blast it vanishes in air.

As worldly schemes resemble Sibyl's leaves,
The good man's days to Sibyl's books compare,
The price still rising as in number less."

CHAPTER XXXIII

ÆNEAS IN ITALY

CAMILLA—EVANDER—NISUS AND EURYALUS—
MEZENTIUS—TURNUS

ÆNEAS, having parted from the Sibyl and rejoined his fleet, coasted along the shores of Italy and cast anchor in the mouth of the Tiber. The poet, having brought his hero to this spot, the destined termination of his wanderings, invokes his Muse to tell him the situation of things at that eventful moment. Latinus, third in descent from Saturn, ruled the country. He was now old and had no male descendant, but had one charming daughter, Lavinia, who was sought in marriage by many neighbouring chiefs, one of whom, Turnus, king of the Rutulians, was favoured by the wishes of her parents. But Latinus had been warned in a dream by his father Faunus, that the destined husband of Lavinia should come from a foreign land. From that union should spring a race destined to subdue the world.

Our readers will remember that in the conflict with the Harpies one of those half-human birds had threatened the Trojans with dire sufferings. In particular she predicted that before their wanderings ceased they should be pressed by hunger to devour their tables. This portent now came true; for as they took their scanty meal, seated on the grass, the men placed their hard biscuit on their laps, and put thereon whatever their gleanings in the woods supplied. Having despatched the latter they finished by eating the crusts. Seeing which, the boy Iulus said playfully, "See, we are eating our tables." Æneas caught the words and accepted the omen. "All hail, promised land!" he exclaimed, "this is our home, this our country." He then took measures to find out who were the present inhabitants of the land, and who their rulers. A hundred chosen men were sent to the village of Latinus, bearing presents and a request for friendship and alliance. They went and were favourably received. Latinus immediately concluded that the Trojan hero was no other than the promised son-in-law announced by the oracle. He cheerfully granted his alliance and sent back the messengers mounted on steeds from his stables, and loaded with gifts and friendly messages.

Juno, seeing things go thus prosperously for the Trojans, felt her old animosity revive, summons Alecto from Erebus, and sent her to stir up discord. The Fury first took possession of the queen, Amata, and roused her to oppose in every way the new alliance. Alecto then speeded to the city of Turnus, and assuming the form of an old priestess, informed him of the arrival of the foreigners and of the attempts of their prince to rob him of his bride. Next she turned her attention to the camp of the Trojans. There she saw the boy Iulus and his companions amusing themselves with hunting. She sharpened the scent of the dogs, and led them to rouse up from the thicket a tame stag, the favourite of Silvia, the daughter of Tyrrheus, the king's herdsman. A javelin from the hand of Iulus wounded the animal, and he had only strength left to run homewards, and died at his mistress's feet. Her cries and tears roused her brothers and the herdsmen, and they, seizing whatever weapons came to hand, furiously assaulted the hunting party. These were protected by their friends, and the herdsmen were finally driven back with the loss of two of their number.

These things were enough to rouse the storm of war, and the queen, Turnus, and the peasants all urged the old king to drive the strangers from the country. He resisted as long as he could, but, finding his opposition unavailing, finally gave way and retreated to his retirement.

Opening the Gates of Janus

It was the custom of the country, when war was to be undertaken, for the chief magistrate, clad in his robes of office, with solemn pomp to open the gates of the temple of Janus, which were kept shut as long as peace endured. His people now urged the old king to perform that solemn office, but he refused to do so. While they contested, Juno herself, descending from the skies, smote the doors with irresistible force, and burst them open. Immediately the whole country was in a flame. The people rushed from every side breathing nothing but war.

Turnus was recognized by all as leader; others joined as allies, chief of whom was Mezentius, a brave and able soldier, but of detestable cruelty. He had been the chief of one of the neighbouring cities, but his people drove him out. With him was joined his son Lausus, a generous youth, worthy of a better sire.

Camilla

Camilla, the favourite of Diana, a huntress and warrior, after the fashion of the Amazons, came with her band of mounted followers, including a select number of her own sex, and ranged herself on the side of Turnus. This maiden had never accustomed her fingers to the distaff or the loom, but had learned to endure the toils of war, and in speed to outstrip the wind. It seemed as if she might run over the standing corn without crushing it, or over the surface of the water without dipping her feet. Camilla's history had been singular from the beginning. Her father, Metabus, driven from his city by civil discord, carried with him in his flight his infant daughter. As he fled through the woods, his enemies in hot pursuit, he reached the bank of the river Amazenus, which, swelled by rain, seemed to debar a passage. He paused for a moment, then decided what to do. He tied the infant to his lance with wrappers of bark, and poising the weapon in his upraised hand, thus addressed Diana: "Goddess of the woods! I consecrate this maid to you"; then hurled the weapon with its burden to the opposite bank. The spear flew across the roaring water. His pursuers were already upon him, but he plunged into the river and swam across, and found the spear, with the infant safe on the other side. Thenceforth he lived among the shepherds and brought up his daughter in woodland arts. While a child she was taught to use the bow and throw the javelin. With her sling she could bring down the crane or the wild swan. Her dress was a tiger's skin. Many mothers sought her for a daughter-in-law, but she continued faithful to Diana and repelled the thought of marriage.

EVANDER

Such were the formidable allies that ranged themselves against Æneas. It was night and he lay stretched in sleep on the bank of the river under the open heavens. The god of the stream, Father Tiber, seemed to raise his head above the willows and to say, "O goddess-born, destined possessor of the Latin realms, this is the promised land, here is to be your home, here shall terminate the hostility of the heavenly powers, if only you faithfully persevere. There are friends not far distant. Prepare your boats and row up my stream; I will lead you to Evander, the Arcadian chief. He has long been at strife with Turnus and the Rutulians, and is prepared to become an ally of yours. Rise! offer your vows to Juno, and deprecate her anger. When you have achieved your victory then think of me." Æneas woke and paid immediate obedience to the friendly vision. He sacrificed to Juno, and invoked the god of the river and all his tributary fountains to lend their aid. Then for the first time a vessel filled with armed warriors floated on the stream of the Tiber. The river smoothed its waves, and bade its current flow gently, while, impelled by the vigorous strokes of the rowers, the vessels shot rapidly up the stream.

About the middle of the day they came in sight of the scattered

buildings of the infant town, where in after times the proud city of
Rome grew, whose glory reached the skies. By chance the old king,
Evander, was that day celebrating annual solemnities in honour of
Hercules and all the gods. Pallas, his son, and all the chiefs of the
little commonwealth stood by. When they saw the tall ship gliding
onward near the wood, they were alarmed at the sight, and rose
from the tables. But Pallas forbade the solemnities to be interrupted,
and seizing a weapon, stepped forward to the river's bank. He called
aloud, demanding who they were, and what their object. Æneas,
holding forth an olive-branch, replied, "We are Trojans, friends
to you, and enemies to the Rutulians. We seek Evander, and offer
to join our arms with yours." Pallas, in amaze at the sound of so
great a name, invited them to land, and when Æneas touched the
shore he seized his hand, and held it long in friendly grasp. Proceeding through the wood, they joined the king and his party and
were most favourably received. Seats were provided for them at the
tables, and the repast proceeded.

INFANT ROME

When the solemnities were ended all moved towards the city. The
king, bending with age, walked between his son and Æneas, taking
the arm of one or the other of them, and with much variety of pleasing talk shortening the way. Æneas with delight looked and listened,
observing all the beauties of the scene, and learning much of heroes
renowned in ancient times. Evander said, "These extensive groves
were once inhabited by fauns and nymphs, and a rude race of men
who sprang from the trees themselves, and had neither laws nor
social culture. They knew not how to yoke the cattle nor raise a
harvest, nor provide from present abundance for future want; but
browsed like beasts upon the leafy boughs, or fed voraciously on
their hunted prey. Such were they when Saturn, expelled from
Olympus by his sons, came among them and drew together the fierce
savages, formed them into society and gave them laws. Such peace
and plenty ensued that men ever since have called his reign the
golden age; but by degrees far other times succeeded, and the thirst
of gold and the thirst of blood prevailed. The land was a prey to
successive tyrants, till fortune and resistless destiny brought me
hither, an exile from my native land, Arcadia."

Having thus said, he showed him the Tarpeian rock, and the rude
spot then overgrown with bushes where in after times the Capitol
rose in all its magnificence. He next pointed to some dismantled
walls, and said, "Here stood Janiculum, built by Janus, and there
Saturnia, the town of Saturn." Such discourse brought them to the

cottage of poor Evander, whence they saw the lowing herds roaming over the plain where now the proud and stately Forum stands. They entered, and a couch was spread for Æneas, well stuffed with leaves, and covered with the skin of a Libyan bear.

Next morning, awakened by the dawn and the shrill song of birds beneath the eaves of his low mansion, old Evander rose. Clad in a tunic, and a panther's skin thrown over his shoulders, with sandals on his feet and his good sword girded to his side, he went forth to seek his guest. Two mastiffs followed him, his whole retinue and body guard. He found the hero attended by his faithful Achates, and, Pallas, soon joining them, the old king spoke thus:

"Illustrious Trojan, it is but little we can do in so great a cause. Our state is feeble, hemmed in on one side by the river, on the other by the Rutulians. But I propose to ally you with a people numerous and rich, to whom fate has brought you at the propitious moment. The Etruscans hold the country beyond the river. Mezentius was their king, a monster of cruelty, who invented unheard-of torments to gratify his vengeance. He would fasten the dead to the living, hand to hand and face to face, and leave the wretched victims to die in that dreadful embrace. At length the people cast him out, him and his house. They burned his palace and slew his friends. He escaped and took refuge with Turnus, who protects him with arms. The Etruscans demand that he shall be given up to deserved punishment, and would ere now have attempted to enforce their demand; but the priests restrain them, telling them that it is the will of heaven that no native of the land shall guide them to victory, and that their destined leader must come from across the sea. They have offered the crown to me, but I am too old to undertake such great affairs, and my son is native-born, which precludes him from the choice. You, equally by birth and time of life, and fame in arms, pointed out by the gods, have but to appear to be hailed at once as their leader. With you I will join Pallas, my son, my only hope and comfort. Under you he shall learn the art of war, and strive to emulate your great exploits."

Then the king ordered horses to be furnished for the Trojan chiefs, and Æneas, with a chosen band of followers and Pallas accompanying, mounted and took the way to the Etruscan city,[1] having sent back the rest of his party in the ships. Æneas and his band safely arrived at the Etruscan camp and were received with open arms by Tarchon and his countrymen.

[1] The poet here inserts a famous line which is thought to imitate in its sound the galloping of horses. It may be thus translated: "Then struck the hoofs of the steeds on the ground with a four-footed trampling."—See Proverbial Expressions, page 290.

NISUS AND EURYALUS

In the meanwhile Turnus had collected his bands and made all necessary preparations for the war. Juno sent Iris to him with a message inciting him to take advantage of the absence of Æneas and surprise the Trojan camp. Accordingly the attempt was made, but the Trojans were found on their guard, and having received strict orders from Æneas not to fight in his absence, they lay still in their intrenchments, and resisted all the efforts of the Rutulians to draw them into the field. Night coming on, the army of Turnus, in high spirits at their fancied superiority, feasted and enjoyed them-selves, and finally stretched themselves on the field and slept secure.

In the camp of the Trojans things were far otherwise. There all was watchfulness and anxiety and impatience for Æneas's return. Nisus stood guard at the entrance of the camp, and Euryalus, a youth distinguished above all in the army for graces of person and fine qualities, was with him. These two were friends and brothers in arms. Nisus said to his friend, "Do you perceive what confidence and carelessness the enemy display? Their lights are few and dim, and the men seem all oppressed with wine or sleep. You know how anxiously our chiefs wish to send to Æneas, and to get intelligence from him. Now, I am strongly moved to make my way through the enemy's camp and to go in search of our chief. If I succeed, the glory of the deed will be reward enough for me, and if they judge the service deserves anything more, let them pay it to you."

Euryalus, all on fire with the love of adventure, replied, "Would you, then, Nisus, refuse to share your enterprise with me? And shall I let you go into such danger alone? Not so my brave father brought me up, nor so have I planned for myself when I joined the standard of Æneas, and resolved to hold my life cheap in compari-son with honour." Nisus replied, "I doubt it not, my friend; but you know the uncertain event of such an undertaking, and whatever may happen to me, I wish you to be safe. You are younger than I and have more of life in prospect. Nor can I be the cause of such grief to your mother, who has chosen to be here in the camp with you rather than stay and live in peace with the other matrons in Acestes' city." Euryalus replied, "Say no more. In vain you seek arguments to dissuade me. I am fixed in the resolution to go with you. Let us lose no time." They called the guard, and committing the watch to them, sought the general's tent. They found the chief officers in consultation, deliberating how they should send notice to Æneas of their situation. The offer of the two friends was gladly ac-cepted, themselves loaded with praises and promised the most liberal rewards in case of success. Iulus especially addressed Euryalus,

assuring him of his lasting friendship. Euryalus replied, "I have but
one boon to ask. My aged mother is with me in the camp. For me
she left the Trojan soil, and would not stay behind with the other
matrons at the city of Acestes. I go now without taking leave of her.
I could not bear her tears nor set at nought her entreaties. But do
thou, I beseech you, comfort her in her distress. Promise me that
and I shall go more boldly into whatever dangers may present themselves." Iulus and the other chiefs were moved to tears, and promised to do all his request. "Your mother shall be mine," said Iulus,
"and all that I have promised to you shall be made good to her, if
you do not return to receive it."

The two friends left the camp and plunged at once into the midst
of the enemy. They found no watch, no sentinels posted, but, all
about, the sleeping soldiers strewn on the grass and among the
wagons. The laws of war at that early day did not forbid a brave
man to slay a sleeping foe, and the two Trojans slew, as they passed,
such of the enemy as they could without exciting alarm. In one tent
Euryalus made prize of a helmet brilliant with gold and plumes.
They had passed through the enemy's ranks without being discovered, but now suddenly appeared a troop directly in front of
them, which, under Volscens, their leader, were approaching the
camp. The glittering helmet of Euryalus caught their attention, and
Volscens hailed the two, and demanded who and whence they were.
They made no answer, but plunged into the wood. The horsemen
scattered in all directions to intercept their flight. Nisus had eluded
pursuit and was out of danger, but Euryalus being missing he turned
back to seek him. He again entered the wood and soon came within
sound of voices. Looking through the thicket he saw the whole band
surrounding Euryalus with noisy questions. What should he do?
how extricate the youth, or would it be better to die with him?

Raising his eyes to the moon, which now shone clear, he said,
"Goddess! favour my effort!" and aiming his javelin at one of the
leaders of the troop, struck him in the back and stretched him on
the plain with a death-blow. In the midst of their amazement another weapon flew and another of the party fell dead. Volscens, the
leader, ignorant whence the darts came, rushed sword in hand upon
Euryalus. "You shall pay the penalty of both," he said, and would
have plunged the sword into his bosom, when Nisus, who from his
concealment saw the peril of his friend, rushed forward exclaiming,
" 'Twas I, 'twas I; turn your swords against me, Rutulians, I did
it; he only followed me as a friend." While he spoke the sword fell,
and pierced the comely bosom of Euryalus. His head fell on his
shoulder, like a flower cut down by the plough. Nisus rushed upon

Volscens and plunged his sword into his body, and was himself slain
on the instant by numberless blows.

MEZENTIUS

Æneas, with his Etrurian allies, arrived on the scene of action in
time to rescue his beleaguered camp; and now the two armies being
nearly equal in strength, the war began in good earnest. We cannot
find space for all the details, but must simply record the fate of the
principal characters whom we have introduced to our readers. The
tyrant Mezentius, finding himself engaged against his revolting subjects, raged like a wild beast. He slew all who dared to withstand
him, and put the multitude to flight wherever he appeared. At last
he encountered Æneas, and the armies stood still to see the issue.
Mezentius threw his spear, which striking Æneas's shield glanced
off and hit Anthor. He was a Grecian by birth, who had left Argos,
his native city, and followed Evander into Italy. The poet says of
him with simple pathos which has made the words proverbial, "He
fell, unhappy, by a wound intended for another, looked up to the
skies, and dying remembered sweet Argos." [1] Æneas now in turn
hurled his lance. It pierced the shield of Mezentius, and wounded
him in the thigh. Lausus, his son, could not bear the sight, but rushed
forward and interposed himself, while the followers pressed round
Mezentius and bore him away. Æneas held his sword suspended
over Lausus and delayed to strike, but the furious youth pressed on
and he was compelled to deal the fatal blow. Lausus fell, and Æneas
bent over him in pity. "Hapless youth," he said, "what can I do for
you worthy of your praise? Keep those arms in which you glory,
and fear not but that your body shall be restored to your friends,
and have due funeral honours." So saying, he called the timid followers and delivered the body into their hands.

Mezentius meanwhile had been borne to the river-side, and
washed his wound. Soon the news reached him of Lausus's death,
and rage and despair supplied the place of strength. He mounted his
horse and dashed into the thickest of the fight, seeking Æneas. Having found him, he rode round him in a circle, throwing one javelin
after another, while Æneas stood fenced with his shield, turning
every way to meet them. At last, after Mezentius had three times
made the circuit, Æneas threw his lance directly at the horse's head.
It pierced his temples and he fell, while a shout from both armies
rent the skies. Mezentius asked no mercy, but only that his body
might be spared the insults of his revolted subjects, and be buried

[1] See Proverbial Expressions, page 290.

in the same grave with his son. He received the fatal stroke not
unprepared, and poured out his life and his blood together.

PALLAS, CAMILLA, TURNUS

While these things were doing in one part of the field, in another
Turnus encountered the youthful Pallas. The contest between champions so unequally matched could not be doubtful. Pallas bore himself bravely, but fell by the lance of Turnus. The victor almost
relented when he saw the brave youth lying dead at his feet, and
spared to use the privilege of a conqueror in despoiling him of his
arms. The belt only, adorned with studs and carvings of gold, he
took and clasped round his own body. The rest he remitted to the
friends of the slain.

After the battle there was a cessation of arms for some days to
allow both armies to bury their dead. In this interval Æneas challenged Turnus to decide the contest by single combat, but Turnus
evaded the challenge. Another battle ensued, in which Camilla, the
virgin warrior, was chiefly conspicuous. Her deeds of valor surpassed
those of the bravest warriors, and many Trojans and Etruscans fell
pierced with her darts or struck down by her battle-axe. At last an
Etruscan named Aruns, who had watched her long, seeking for some
advantage, observed her pursuing a flying enemy whose splendid
armour offered a tempting prize. Intent on the chase she observed
not her danger, and the javelin of Aruns struck her and inflicted a
fatal wound. She fell and breathed her last in the arms of her attendant maidens. But Diana, who beheld her fate, suffered not her
slaughter to be unavenged. Aruns, as he stole away, glad but frightened, was struck by a secret arrow, launched by one of the nymphs
of Diana's train, and died ignobly and unknown.

At length the final conflict took place between Æneas and Turnus.
Turnus had avoided the contest as long as he could, but at last,
impelled by the ill success of his arms and by the murmurs of his
followers, he braced himself to the conflict. It could not be doubtful.
On the side of Æneas were the expressed decree of destiny, the aid
of his goddess-mother at every emergency, and impenetrable armour
fabricated by Vulcan, at her request, for her son. Turnus, on the
other hand, was deserted by his celestial allies, Juno having been
expressly forbidden by Jupiter to assist him any longer. Turnus
threw his lance, but it recoiled harmless from the shield of Æneas.
The Trojan hero then threw his, which penetrated the shield of
Turnus, and pierced his thigh. Then Turnus's fortitude forsook
him and he begged for mercy; and Æneas would have given him
life, but at the instant his eye fell on the belt of Pallas, which Turnus

had taken from the slaughtered youth. Instantly his rage revived, and exclaiming, "Pallas immolates thee with this blow," he thrust him through with his sword.

Here the poem of the "Æneid" closes, and we are left to infer that Æneas, having triumphed over his foes, obtained Lavinia for his bride. Tradition adds that he founded his city, and called it after her name, Lavinium. His son Iulus founded Alba Longa, which was the birthplace of Romulus and Remus and the cradle of Rome itself.

There is an allusion to Camilla in those well-known lines of Pope, in which, illustrating the rule that "the sound should be an echo to the sense," he says:

> "When Ajax strives some rock's vast weight to throw,
> The line too labours and the words move slow.
> Not so when swift Camilla scours the plain,
> Flies o'er the unbending corn or skims along the main."
>
> *Essay on Criticism.*

CHAPTER XXXIV

PYTHAGORAS—EGYPTIAN DEITIES—ORACLES

PYTHAGORAS

THE teachings of Anchises to Æneas, respecting the nature of the human soul, were in conformity with the doctrines of the Pythagoreans. Pythagoras (born five hundred and forty years B.C.) was a native of the island of Samos, but passed the chief portion of his life at Crotona in Italy. He is therefore sometimes called "the Samian," and sometimes "the philosopher of Crotona." When young he travelled extensively, and it is said visited Egypt, where he was instructed by the priests in all their learning, and afterwards journeyed to the East, and visited the Persian and Chaldean Magi, and the Brahmins of India.

At Crotona, where he finally established himself, his extraordinary qualities collected round him a great number of disciples. The inhabitants were notorious for luxury and licentiousness, but the good effects of his influence were soon visible. Sobriety and temperance succeeded. Six hundred of the inhabitants became his disciples and enrolled themselves in a society to aid each other in the pursuit of wisdom, uniting their property in one common stock for the benefit of the whole. They were required to practise the greatest purity and simplicity of manners. The first lesson they learned was *silence;* for a time they were required to be only hearers. "He [Pythagoras] said so" (*Ipse dixit*), was to be held by them as sufficient, without any proof. It was only the advanced pupils, after years of patient submission, who were allowed to ask questions and to state objections.

Pythagoras considered *numbers* as the essence and principle of all things, and attributed to them a real and distinct existence; so that, in his view, they were the elements out of which the universe was constructed. How he conceived this process has never been satisfactorily explained. He traced the various forms and phenomena of the world to numbers as their basis and essence. The "Monad" or *unit* he regarded as the source of all numbers. The number *Two* was imperfect, and the cause of increase and division. *Three* was called the number of the whole because it had a beginning, middle, and end. *Four,* representing the square, is in the highest degree perfect; and *Ten,* as it contains the sum of the four prime numbers, comprehends all musical and arithmetical proportions, and denotes the system of the world.

As the numbers proceed from the monad, so he regarded the pure and simple essence of the Deity as the source of all the forms of nature. Gods, demons, and heroes are emanations of the Supreme, and there is a fourth emanation, the human soul. This is immortal, and when freed from the fetters of the body passes to the habitation of the dead, where it remains till it returns to the world, to dwell in some other human or animal body, and at last, when sufficiently purified, it returns to the source from which it proceeded. This doctrine of the transmigration of souls (metempsychosis), which was originally Egyptian and connected with the doctrine of reward and punishment of human actions, was the chief cause why the Pythagoreans killed no animals. Ovid represents Pythagoras addressing his disciples in these words: "Souls never die, but always on quitting one abode pass to another. I myself can remember that in the time of the Trojan war I was Euphorbus, the son of Panthus, and fell by the spear of Menelaus. Lately being in the temple of Juno, at Argos, I recognized my shield hung up there among the trophies. All things change, nothing perishes. The soul passes hither and thither, occupying now this body, now that, passing from the body of a beast into that of a man, and thence to a beast's again. As wax is stamped with certain figures, then melted, then stamped anew with others, yet is always the same wax, so the soul, being always the same, yet wears, at different times, different forms. Therefore, if the love of kindred is not extinct in your bosoms, forbear, I entreat you, to violate the life of those who may haply be your own relatives."

Shakespeare, in the "Merchant of Venice," makes Gratiano allude to the metempsychosis, where he says to Shylock:

> "Thou almost mak'st me waver in my faith,
> To hold opinion with Pythagoras,
> That souls of animals infuse themselves
> Into the trunks of men; thy currish spirit
> Governed a wolf, who, hanged for human slaughter,
> Infused his soul in thee; for thy desires
> Are wolfish, bloody, starved and ravenous."

The relation of the notes of the musical scale to numbers, whereby harmony results from vibrations in equal times, and discord from the reverse, led Pythagoras to apply the word "harmony" to the visible creation, meaning by it the just adaptation of parts to each other. This is the idea which Dryden expresses in the beginning of his "Song for St. Cecilia's Day":

> "From harmony, from heavenly harmony
> This everlasting frame began;
> From harmony to harmony
> Through all the compass of the notes it ran,
> The Diapason closing full in Man."

In the centre of the universe (he taught) there was a central fire, the principle of life. The central fire was surrounded by the earth, the moon, the sun, and the five planets. The distances of the various heavenly bodies from one another were conceived to correspond to the proportions of the musical scale. The heavenly bodies, with the gods who inhabited them, were supposed to perform a choral dance round the central fire, "not without song." It is this doctrine which Shakespeare alludes to when he makes Lorenzo teach astronomy to Jessica in this fashion:

> "Look, Jessica, see how the floor of heaven
> Is thick inlaid with patines of bright gold!
> There's not the smallest orb that thou behold'st
> But in his motion like an angel sings,
> Still quiring to the young-eyed cherubim;
> Such harmony is in immortal souls!
> But whilst this muddy vesture of decay
> Doth grossly close it in we cannot hear it."
>
> *Merchant of Venice.*

The spheres were conceived to be crystalline or glassy fabrics arranged over one another like a nest of bowls reversed. In the substance of each sphere one or more of the heavenly bodies was supposed to be fixed, so as to move with it. As the spheres are transparent we look through them and see the heavenly bodies which they contain and carry round with them. But as these spheres cannot move on one another without friction, a sound is thereby produced which is of exquisite harmony, too fine for mortal ears to recognize. Milton, in his "Hymn on the Nativity," thus alludes to the music of the spheres:

> "Ring out, ye crystal spheres!
> Once bless our human ears
>   (If ye have power to charm our senses so);
> And let your silver chime
> Move in melodious time;
>   And let the bass of Heaven's deep organ blow;
> And with your ninefold harmony
> Make up full concert to the angelic symphony."

Pythagoras is said to have invented the lyre. Our own poet Longfellow, in "Verses to a Child," thus relates the story:

> "As great Pythagoras of yore,
> Standing beside the blacksmith's door,
> And hearing the hammers as they smote
> The anvils with a different note,
> Stole from the varying tones that hung
> Vibrant on every iron tongue,
> The secret of the sounding wire,
> And formed the seven-chorded lyre."

See also the same poet's "Occultation of Orion"—

> "The Samian's great Æolian lyre."

SYBARIS AND CROTONA

Sybaris, a neighbouring city to Crotona, was as celebrated for luxury and effeminacy as Crotona for the reverse. The name has become proverbial. J. R. Lowell uses it in this sense in his charming little poem "To the Dandelion":

> "Not in mid June the golden-cuirassed bee
> Feels a more summer-like, warm ravishment
>   In the white lily's breezy tent
> (His conquered Sybaris) than I when first
> From the dark green thy yellow circles burst."

A war arose between the two cities, and Sybaris was conquered and destroyed. Milo, the celebrated athlete, led the army of Crotona. Many stories are told of Milo's vast strength, such as his carrying a heifer of four years old upon his shoulders and afterwards eating the whole of it in a single day. The mode of his death is thus related: As he was passing through a forest he saw the trunk of a tree which had been partially split open by wood-cutters, and attempted to rend it further; but the wood closed upon his hands and held him fast, in which state he was attacked and devoured by wolves.

Byron, in his "Ode to Napoleon Bonaparte," alludes to the story of Milo:

> "He who of old would rend the oak
> Deemed not of the rebound;
> Chained by the trunk he vainly broke,
> Alone, how looked he round!"

EGYPTIAN DEITIES

The Egyptians acknowledged as the highest deity Amun, afterwards called Zeus, or Jupiter Ammon. Amun manifested himself in his word or will, which created Kneph and Athor, of different sexes. From Kneph and Athor proceeded Osiris and Isis. Osiris was worshipped as the god of the sun, the source of warmth, life, and fruitfulness, in addition to which he was also regarded as the god of the Nile, who annually visited his wife, Isis (the Earth), by means of an inundation. Serapis or Hermes is sometimes represented as identical with Osiris, and sometimes as a distinct divinity, the ruler of Tartarus and god of medicine. Anubis is the guardian god, represented with a dog's head, emblematic of his character of fidelity and watchfulness. Horus or Harpocrates was the son of Osiris. He is represented seated on a Lotus flower, with his finger on his lips, as the god of Silence.

In one of Moore's "Irish Melodies" is an allusion to Harpocrates:

> "Thyself shall, under some rosy bower,
> Sit mute, with thy finger on thy lip;
> Like him, the boy, who born among
> The flowers that on the Nile-stream blush,
> Sits ever thus,—his only song
> To Earth and Heaven, 'Hush all, hush!'"

MYTH OF OSIRIS AND ISIS

Osiris and Isis were at one time induced to descend to the earth to bestow gifts and blessings on its inhabitants. Isis showed them first the use of wheat and barley, and Osiris made the instruments of agriculture and taught men the use of them, as well as how to harness the ox to the plough. He then gave men laws, the institution of marriage, a civil organization, and taught them how to worship the gods. After he had thus made the valley of the Nile a happy country, he assembled a host with which he went to bestow his blessings upon the rest of the world. He conquered the nations everywhere, but not with weapons, only with music and eloquence. His brother, Typhon saw this, and filled with envy and malice sought during his absence to usurp his throne. But Isis, who held the reins of government, frustrated his plans. Still more embittered, he now resolved to kill his brother. This he did in the following manner: Having organized a conspiracy of seventy-two members, he went with them to the feast which was celebrated in honour of the king's return. He then caused a box or chest to be brought in, which had been made to fit exactly the size of Osiris, and declared that he would give that chest of precious wood to whomsoever could get into it. The rest tried in vain, but no sooner was Osiris in it than Typhon and his companions closed the lid and flung the chest into the Nile. When Isis heard of the cruel murder she wept and mourned, and then with her hair shorn, clothed in black and beating her breast, she sought diligently for the body of her husband. In this search she was materially assisted by Anubis, the son of Osiris and Nephthys. They sought in vain for some time; for when the chest, carried by the waves to the shores of Byblos, had become entangled in the reeds that grew at the edge of the water, the divine power that dwelt in the body of Osiris imparted such strength to the shrub that it grew into a mighty tree, enclosing in its trunk the coffin of the god. This tree with its sacred deposit was shortly after felled, and erected as a column in the palace of the king of Phœnicia. But at length by the aid of Anubis and the sacred birds, Isis ascertained these facts, and then went to the royal city. There she offered herself at the palace as a servant, and being admitted, threw off her disguise and appeared as the goddess, surrounded with thunder and lightning. Striking the column with her wand she caused it to split open and give up the sacred coffin. This she seized and returned with it, and concealed it in the depth of a forest, but Typhon discovered it, and cutting the body into fourteen pieces scattered them hither and thither. After a tedious search, Isis found thirteen pieces, the fishes of the Nile having eaten the other. This she replaced by an imitation of sycamore wood, and buried the body at Philoe, which became ever after the great burying place of the nation, and the spot to which pilgrimages were made from all parts of the country. A temple of surpassing magnificence was also erected there in honour of the god, and at every place where one of his limbs had been found minor temples and tombs were built to commemorate the event. Osiris became after that the tutelar deity of the Egyptians. His soul was supposed always to inhabit the body of the bull Apis, and at his death to transfer itself to his successor.

Apis, the Bull of Memphis, was worshipped with the greatest reverence by the Egyptians. The individual animal who was held to be Apis was recognized by certain signs. It was requisite that he should be quite black. have a white square mark on the forehead, another, in the form of an eagle, on his back, and under his tongue a lump somewhat in the shape of a scarabæus or beetle. As soon as a bull thus marked was found by those sent in search of him, he was placed in a building facing the east, and was fed with milk for four months. At the expiration of this term the priests repaired at new moon, with great pomp, to his habitation and saluted him Apis. He was placed in a vessel magnificently decorated and conveyed down the Nile to Memphis, where a temple, with two chapels and a court for exercise, was assigned to him. Sacrifices were made to him, and once every year, about the time when the Nile began to rise, a golden cup was thrown into the river, and a grand festival was held to celebrate his birthday. The people believed that during this festival the crocodiles forgot their natural ferocity and became harmless. There was, however, one drawback to his happy lot: he was not permitted to live beyond a certain period, and if, when he had attained the age of twenty-five years, he still survived, the priests drowned him in the sacred cistern and then buried him in the temple of Serapis. On the death of this bull, whether it occurred in the course of nature or by violence, the whole land was filled with sorrow and lamentations, which lasted until his successor was found.

We find the following item in one of the newspapers of the day:

"The Tomb of Apis.—The excavations going on at Memphis bid fair to make that buried city as interesting as Pompeii. The monster tomb of Apis is now open, after having lain unknown for centuries."

Milton, in his "Hymn on the Nativity," alludes to the Egyptian deities, not as imaginary beings, but as real demons, put to flight by the coming of Christ.

> "The brutish gods of Nile as fast,
> Isis and Horus and the dog Anubis haste.
> Nor is Osiris seen
> In Memphian grove or green
> Trampling the unshowered [1] grass with lowings loud;
> Nor can he be at rest
> Within his sacred chest;
> Nought but profoundest hell can be his shroud.
> In vain with timbrel'd anthems dark
> The sable-stoled sorcerers bear his worshipped ark."

Isis was represented in statuary with the head veiled, a symbol of mystery. It is this which Tennyson alludes to in "Maud," IV. 8:

> "For the drift of the Maker is dark, an Isis hid by the veil," etc.

[1] There being no rain in Egypt, the grass is "unshowered," and the country depends for its fertility upon the overflowings of the Nile. The ark alluded to in the last line is shown by pictures still remaining on the walls of the Egyptian temples to have been borne by the priests in their religious processions. It probable represented the chest in which Osiris was placed.

ORACLES

Oracle was the name used to denote the place where answers were supposed to be given by any of the divinities to those who consulted them respecting the future. The word was also used to signify the response which was given.

The most ancient Grecian oracle was that of Jupiter at Dodona. According to one account, it was established in the following manner: Two black doves took their flight from Thebes in Egypt. One flew to Dodona in Epirus, and alighting in a grove of oaks, it proclaimed in human language to the inhabitants of the district that they must establish there an oracle of Jupiter. The other dove flew to the temple of Jupiter Ammon in the Libyan Oasis, and delivered a similar command there. Another account is, that they were not doves, but priestesses, who were carried off from Thebes in Egypt by the Phœnicians, and set up oracles at the Oasis and Dodona. The responses of the oracle were given from the trees, by the branches rustling in the wind, the sounds being interpreted by the priests.

But the most celebrated of the Grecian oracles was that of Apollo at Delphi, a city built on the slopes of Parnassus in Phocis.

It had been observed at a very early period that the goats feeding on Parnassus were thrown into convulsions when they approached a certain long deep cleft in the side of the mountain. This was owing to a peculiar vapour arising out of the cavern, and one of the goatherds was induced to try its effects upon himself. Inhaling the intoxicating air, he was affected in the same manner as the cattle had been, and the inhabitants of the surrounding country, unable to explain the circumstance, imputed the convulsive ravings to which he gave utterance while under the power of the exhalations to a divine inspiration. The fact was speedily circulated widely, and a temple was erected on the spot. The prophetic influence was at first variously attributed to the goddess Earth, to Neptune, Themis, and others, but it was at length assigned to Apollo, and to him alone. A priestess was appointed whose office it was to inhale the hallowed air, and who was named the Pythia. She was prepared for this duty by previous ablution at the fountain of Castalia, and being crowned with laurel was seated upon a tripod similarly adorned, which was placed over the chasm whence the divine afflatus proceeded. Her inspired words while thus situated were interpreted by the priests.

ORACLE OF TROPHONIUS

Besides the oracles of Jupiter and Apollo, at Dodona and Delphi, that of Trophonius in Bœotia was held in high estimation. Tropho nius and Agamedes were brothers. They were distinguished architects, and built the temple of Apollo at Delphi, and a treasury for King Hyrieus. In the wall of the treasury they placed a stone, in such a manner that it could be taken out; and by this means, from time to time, purloined the treasure. This amazed Hyrieus, for his locks and seals were untouched, and yet his wealth continually diminished. At length he set a trap for the thief and Agamedes was caught.

Trophonius, unable to extricate him, and fearing that when found he would be compelled by torture to discover his accomplice, cut off his head. Trophonius himself is said to have been shortly afterwards swallowed up by the earth.

The oracle of Trophonius was at Lebadea in Bœotia. During a great drought the Bœotians, it is said, were directed by the god at Delphi to seek aid of Trophonius at Lebadea. They came thither, but could find no oracle. One of them, however, happening to see a swarm of bees, followed them to a chasm in the earth, which proved to be the place sought.

Peculiar ceremonies were to be performed by the person who came to consult the oracle. After these preliminaries, he descended into the cave by a narrow passage. This place could be entered only in the night. The person returned from the cave by the same narrow passage, but walking backwards. He appeared melancholy and dejected; and hence the proverb which was applied to a person lowspirited and gloomy, "He has been consulting the oracle of Trophonius."

ORACLE OF ÆSCULAPIUS

There were numerous oracles of Æsculapius, but the most celebrated one was at Epidaurus. Here the sick sought responses and the recovery of their health by sleeping in the temple. It has been inferred from the accounts that have come down to us that the treatment of the sick resembled what is now called Animal Magnetism or Mesmerism.

Serpents were sacred to Æsculapius, probably because of a superstition that those animals have a faculty of renewing their youth by a change of skin.

The worship of Æsculapius was introduced into Rome in a time of great sickness, and an embassy sent to the temple of Epidaurus to entreat the aid of the god. Æsculapius was propitious and on the return of the ship accompanied it in the form of a serpent. Arriving in the river Tiber, the serpent glided from the vessel and took possession of an island in the river, and a temple was there erected to his honour.

ORACLE OF APIS

At Memphis the sacred bull Apis gave answer to those who consulted him by the manner in which he received or rejected what was presented to him. If the bull refused food from the hand of the inquirer it was considered an unfavourable sign, and the contrary when he received it.

It has been a question whether oracular responses ought to be ascribed to mere human contrivance or to the agency of evil spirits. The latter opinion has been most general in past ages. A third theory has been advanced since the phenomena of Mesmerism have attracted attention, that something like the mesmeric trance was induced in the Pythoness, and the faculty of clairvoyance really called into action.

Another question is as to the time when the Pagan oracles ceased to give responses. Ancient Christian writers assert that they became silent at the birth of Christ, and were heard no more after that date. Milton adopts this view in his "Hymn on the Nativity," and in lines of solemn and elevated beauty pictures the consternation of the heathen idols at the advent of the Saviour:

"The oracles are dumb;
  No voice or hideous hum
    Rings through the archèd roof in words deceiving.
Apollo from his shrine
Can no more divine,
  With hollow shriek the steep of Delphos leaving.
No nightly trance or breathèd spell
Inspires the pale-eyed priest from the prophetic cell."

In Cowper's poem of "Yardley Oak" there are some beautiful mythological allusions. The former of the two following is to the fable of Castor and Pollux; the latter is more appropriate to our present subject. Addressing the acorn he says,

"Thou fell'st mature; and in the loamy clod,
Swelling with vegetative force instinct,
Didst burst thine egg, as theirs the fabled Twins
Now stars; two lobes protruding, paired exact;
A leaf succeeded and another leaf,
And, all the elements thy puny growth
Fostering propitious, thou becam'st a twig.
Who lived when thou wast such? O, couldst thou speak,
As in Dodona once thy kindred trees
Oracular, I would not curious ask
The future, best unknown, but at thy mouth
Inquisitive, the less ambiguous past."

Tennyson, in his "Talking Oak," alludes to the oaks of Dodona in these lines:

> "And I will work in prose and rhyme,
>   And praise thee more in both
>   Than bard has honored beech or lime,
>   Or that Thessalian growth
>   In which the swarthy ring-dove sat
>   And mystic sentence spoke;" etc.

Byron alludes to the oracle of Delphi where, speaking of Rousseau, whose writings he conceives did much to bring on the French revolution, he says,

> "For then he was inspired, and from him came,
>   As from the Pythian's mystic cave of yore,
>   Those oracles which set the world in flame,
>   Nor ceased to burn till kingdoms were no more."

CHAPTER XXXV

ORIGIN OF MYTHOLOGY—STATUES OF GODS AND GODDESSES—POETS OF MYTHOLOGY

ORIGIN OF MYTHOLOGY

HAVING reached the close of our series of stories of Pagan mythology, an inquiry suggests itself. "Whence came these stories? Have they a foundation in truth, or are they simply dreams of the imagination?" Philosophers have suggested various theories of the subject; and 1. The Scriptural theory; according to which all mythological legends are derived from the narratives of Scriptures, though the real facts have been disguised and altered. Thus Deucalion is only another name for Noah, Hercules for Samson, Arion for Jonah, etc. Sir Walter Raleigh, in his "History of the World," says, "Jubal, Tubal, and Tubal-Cain were Mercury, Vulcan, and Apollo, inventors of Pasturage, Smithing, and Music. The Dragon which kept the golden apples was the serpent that beguiled Eve. Nimrod's tower was the attempt of the Giants against Heaven." There are doubtless many curious coincidences like these, but the theory cannot without extravagance be pushed so far as to account for any great proportion of the stories.

2. The Historical theory; according to which all the persons mentioned in mythology were once real human beings, and the legends and fabulous traditions relating to them are merely the additions and embellishments of later times. Thus the story of Æolus, the king and god of the winds, is supposed to have risen from the fact that Æolus was the ruler of some islands in the Tyrrhenian Sea, where he reigned as a just and pious king, and taught the natives the use of sails for ships, and how to tell from the signs of the atmos-

phere the changes of the weather and the winds. Cadmus, who, the legend says, sowed the earth with dragon's teeth, from which sprang a crop of armed men, was in fact an emigrant from Phœnicia, and brought with him into Greece the knowledge of the letters of the alphabet, which he taught to the natives. From these rudiments of learning sprung civilization, which the poets have always been prone to describe as a deterioration of man's first estate, the Golden Age of innocence and simplicity.

3. The Allegorical theory supposes that all the myths of the ancients were allegorical and symbolical, and contained some moral, religious, or philosophical truth or historical fact, under the form of an allegory, but came in process of time to be understood literally. Thus Saturn, who devours his own children, is the same power whom the Greeks called Cronos (Time), which may truly be said to destroy whatever it has brought into existence. The story of Io is interpreted in a similar manner. Io is the moon, and Argus the starry sky, which, as it were, keeps sleepless watch over her. The fabulous wanderings of Io represent the continual revolutions of the moon, which also suggested to Milton the same idea.

> "To behold the wandering moon
> Riding near her highest noon,
> Like one that had been led astray
> In the heaven's wide, pathless way."
>
> *Il Penseroso.*

4. The Physical theory; according to which the elements of air, fire, and water were originally the objects of religious adoration, and the principal deities were personifications of the powers of nature. The transition was easy from a personification of the elements to the notion of supernatural beings presiding over and governing the different objects of nature. The Greeks, whose imagination was lively, peopled all nature with invisible beings, and supposed that every object, from the sun and sea to the smallest fountain and rivulet, was under the care of some particular divinity. Wordsworth, in his "Excursion," has beautifully developed this view of Grecian mythology:

> "In that fair clime the lonely herdsman, stretched
> On the soft grass through half a summer's day,
> With music lulled his indolent repose;
> And, in some fit of weariness, if he,
> When his own breath was silent, chanced to hear
> A distant strain far sweeter than the sounds
> Which his poor skill could make, his fancy fetched
> Even from the blazing chariot of the Sun
> A beardless youth who touched a golden lute,
> And filled the illumined groves with ravishment.
> The mighty hunter, lifting up his eyes

Toward the crescent Moon, with grateful heart
Called on the lovely Wanderer who bestowed
That timely light to share his joyous sport;
And hence a beaming goddess with her nymphs
Across the lawn and through the darksome grove
(Not unaccompanied with tuneful notes
By echo multiplied from rock or cave)
Swept in the storm of chase, as moon and stars
Glance rapidly along the clouded heaven
When winds are blowing strong. The Traveller slaked
His thirst from rill or gushing fount, and thanked
The Naiad. Sunbeams upon distant hills
Gliding apace with shadows in their train,
Might, with small help from fancy, be transformed
Into fleet Oreads sporting visibly.
The Zephyrs, fanning, as they passed, their wings,
Lacked not for love fair objects whom they wooed
With gentle whisper. Withered boughs grotesque,
Stripped of their leaves and twigs by hoary age,
From depth of shaggy covert peeping forth
In the low vale, or on steep mountain side;
And sometimes intermixed with stirring horns
Of the live deer, or goat's depending beard;
These were the lurking Satyrs, a wild brood
Of gamesome deities; or Pan himself,
That simple shepherd's awe-inspiring god."

All the theories which have been mentioned are true to a certain extent. It would therefore be more correct to say that the mythology of a nation has sprung from all these sources combined than from any one in particular. We may add also that there are many myths which have arisen from the desire of man to account for those natural phenomena which he cannot understand; and not a few have had their rise from a similar desire of giving a reason for the names of places and persons.

STATUES OF THE GODS

To adequately represent to the eye the ideas intended to be conveyed to the mind under the several names of deities was a task which called into exercise the highest powers of genius and art. Of to many attempts *four* have been most celebrated, the first two known to us only by the descriptions of the ancients, the others still extant and the acknowledged masterpieces of the sculptor's art.

THE OLYMPIAN JUPITER

The statue of the Olympian Jupiter by Phidias was considered the highest achievement of this department of Grecian art. It was of colossal dimensions, and was what the ancients called "chryselephantine"; that is, composed of ivory and gold; the parts representing flesh being of ivory laid on a core of wood or stone, while the drapery and other ornaments were of gold. The height of the figure was forty feet, on a pedestal twelve feet high. The god was represented seated on his throne. His brows were crowned with a wreath of olive, and he held in his right hand a sceptre, and in his left a statue of Victory. The throne was of cedar, adorned with gold and precious stones.

The idea which the artist essayed to embody was that of the supreme deity of the Hellenic (Grecian) nation, enthroned as a conqueror, in perfect majesty and repose, and ruling with a nod the subject world. Phidias avowed that he took his idea from the representation which Homer gives in the first book of the "Iliad," in the passage thus translated by Pope:

> "He spoke and awful bends his sable brows,
> Shakes his ambrosial curls and gives the nod,
> The stamp of fate and sanction of the god.
> High heaven with reverence the dread signal took,
> And all Olympus to the centre shook." [1]

THE MINERVA OF THE PARTHENON

This was also the work of Phidias. It stood in the Parthenon, or temple of Minerva at Athens. The goddess was represented standing. In one hand she held a spear, in the other a statue of Victory. Her helmet, highly decorated, was surmounted by a Sphinx. The statue was forty feet in height, and, like the Jupiter, composed of ivory and gold. The eyes were of marble, and probably painted to represent the iris and pupil. The Parthenon, in which this statue stood, was also constructed under the direction and superintendence of Phidias. Its exterior was enriched with sculptures, many of them from the hand of Phidias. The Elgin marbles, now in the British Museum, are a part of them.

[1] Cowper's version is less elegant, but truer to the original:
> "He ceased, and under his dark brows the nod
> Vouchsafed of confirmation. All around
> The sovereign's everlasting head his curls
> Ambrosial shook, and the huge mountain reeled."

It may interest our readers to see how this passage appears in another famous version, that which was issued under the name of Tickell, contemporaneously with Pope's, and which, being by many attributed to Addison, led to the quarrel which ensued between Addison and Pope:
> "This said, his kingly brow the sire inclined;
> The large black curls fell awful from behind,
> Thick shadowing the stern forehead of the god;
> Olympus trembled at the almighty nod."

Both the Jupiter and Minerva of Phidias are lost, but there is good ground to believe that we have, in several extant statues and busts, the artist's conceptions of the countenances of both. They are characterized by grave and dignified beauty, and freedom from any transient expression, which in the language of art is called *repose*.

THE VENUS DE' MEDICI

The Venus of the Medici is so called from its having been in the possession of the princes of that name in Rome when it first attracted attention, about two hundred years ago. An inscription on the base records it to be the work of Cleomenes, an Athenian sculptor of 200 B.C., but the authenticity of the inscription is doubtful. There is a story that the artist was employed by public authority to make a statue exhibiting the perfection of female beauty, and to aid him in his task the most perfect forms the city could supply were furnished him for models. It is this which Thomson alludes to in his "Summer":

> "So stands the statue that enchants the world;
> So bending tries to veil the matchless boast,
> The mingled beauties of exulting Greece."

Byron also alludes to this statue. Speaking of the Florence Museum, he says:

> "There, too, the goddess loves in stone, and fills
> The air around with beauty;" etc.

And in the next stanza,

> "Blood, pulse, and breast confirm the Dardan shepherd's prize."

See this last allusion explained in Chapter XXVII.

THE APOLLO BELVEDERE

The most highly esteemed of all the remains of ancient sculpture is the statue of Apollo, called the Belvedere, from the name of the apartment of the Pope's palace at Rome in which it was placed. The artist is unknown. It is supposed to be a work of Roman art, of about the first century of our era. It is a standing figure, in marble, more than seven feet high, naked except for the cloak which is fastened around the neck and hangs over the extended left arm. It is supposed to represent the god in the moment when he has shot the arrow to destroy the monster Python. (See Chapter III.) The victorious divinity is in the act of stepping forward. The left arm, which seems to have held the bow, is outstretched, and the head is turned in the same direction. In attitude and proportion the graceful majesty of the figure is unsurpassed. The effect is completed by the countenance, where on the perfection of youthful godlike beauty there dwells the consciousness of triumphant power.

THE DIANA A LA BICHE

The Diana of the Hind, in the palace of the Louvre, may be considered the counterpart to the Apollo Belvedere. The attitude much resembles that of the Apollo, the sizes correspond and also the style of execution. It is a work of the highest order, though by no means equal to the Apollo. The attitude is that of hurried and eager motion, the face that of a huntress in the excitement of the chase. The left hand is extended over the forehead of the Hind, which runs by her side, the right arm reaches backward over the shoulder to draw an arrow from the quiver.

THE POETS OF MYTHOLOGY

Homer, from whose poems of the "Iliad" and "Odyssey" we have taken the chief part of our chapters of the Trojan war and the return of the Grecians, is almost as mythical a personage as the heroes he celebrates. The traditionary story is that he was a wandering minstrel, blind and old, who travelled from place to place singing his lays to the music of his harp, in the courts of princes or the cottages of peasants, and dependent upon the voluntary offerings of his hearers for support. Byron calls him "The blind old man of Scio's rocky isle," and a well-known epigram, alluding to the uncertainty of the fact of his birthplace, says:

"Seven wealthy towns contend for Homer dead,
Through which the living Homer begged his bread."

These seven were Smyrna, Scio, Rhodes, Colophon, Salamis, Argos, and Athens.

Modern scholars have doubted whether the Homeric poems are the work of any single mind. This arises from the difficulty of believing that poems of such length could have been committed to writing at so early an age as that usually assigned to these, an age earlier than the date of any remaining inscriptions or coins, and when no materials capable of containing such long productions were yet introduced into use. On the other hand it is asked how poems of such length could have been handed down from age to age by means of the memory alone. This is answered by the statement that there was a professional body of men, called Rhapsodists, who recited the poems of others, and whose business it was to commit to memory and rehearse for pay the national and patriotic legends.

The prevailing opinion of the learned, at this time, seems to be that the framework and much of the structure of the poems belongs to Homer, but that there are numerous interpolations and additions by other hands.

The date assigned to Homer, on the authority of Herodotus, is 850 B.C.

VIRGIL

Virgil, called also by his surname, Maro, from whose poem of the "Æneid" we have taken the story of Æneas, was one of the great poets who made the reign of the Roman emperor Augustus so celebrated, under the name of the Augustan age. Virgil was born in Mantua in the year 70 B.C. His great poem is ranked next to those of Homer, in the highest class of poetical composition, the Epic. Virgil is far inferior to Homer in originality and invention, but superior to him in correctness and elegance. To critics of English lineage Milton alone of modern poets seems worthy to be classed with these illustrious ancients. His poem of "Paradise Lost," from which we have borrowed so many illustrations, is in many respects equal, in some superior, to either of the great works of antiquity. The following epigram of Dryden characterizes the three poets with as much truth as it is usual to find in such pointed criticism:

"ON MILTON.

"Three poets in three different ages born,
Greece, Italy, and England did adorn.
The first in loftiness of soul surpassed,
The next in majesty, in both the last.
The force of nature could no further go;
To make a third she joined the other two."

From Cowper's "Table Talk":

"Ages elapsed ere Homer's lamp appeared,
And ages ere the Mantuan swan was heard.
To carry nature lengths unknown before,
To give a Milton birth, asked ages more.
Thus genius rose and set at ordered times,
And shot a dayspring into distant climes,
Ennobling every region that he chose;
He sunk in Greece, in Italy he rose,
And, tedious years of Gothic darkness past,
Emerged all splendour in our isle at last.
Thus lovely Halcyons dive into the main,
Then show far off their shining plumes again."

OVID,

often alluded to in poetry by his other name of Naso, was born in the year 43 B.C. He was educated for public life and held some offices

of considerable dignity, but poetry was his delight, and he early
resolved to devote himself to it. He accordingly sought the society
of the contemporary poets, and was acquainted with Horace and saw
Virgil, though the latter died when Ovid was yet too young and
undistinguished to have formed his acquaintance. Ovid spent an
easy life at Rome in the enjoyment of a competent income. He was
intimate with the family of Augustus, the emperor, and it is supposed that some serious offence given to some member of that family
was the cause of an event which reversed the poet's happy circumstances and clouded all the latter portion of his life. At the age of
fifty he was banished from Rome, and ordered to betake himself to
Tomi, on the borders of the Black Sea. Here, among the barbarous
people and in a severe climate, the poet, who had been accustomed
to all the pleasures of a luxurious capital and the society of his most
distinguished contemporaries, spent the last ten years of his life,
worn out with grief and anxiety. His only consolation in exile was
to address his wife and absent friends, and his letters were all
poetical. Though these poems (the "Tristia" and "Letters from
Pontus") have no other topic than the poet's sorrow's, his exquisite
taste and fruitful invention have redeemed them from the charge of
being tedious, and they are read with pleasure and even with sympathy.

The two great works of Ovid are his "Metamorphoses" and his
"Fasti." They are both mythological poems, and from the former
we have taken most of our stories of Grecian and Roman mythology.
A late writer thus characterizes these poems:

"The rich mythology of Greece furnished Ovid, as it may still
furnish the poet, the painter, and the sculptor, with materials for
his art. With exquisite taste, simplicity, and pathos he has narrated
the fabulous traditions of early ages, and given to them that appearance of reality which only a master-hand could impart. His pictures
of nature are striking and true; he selects with care that which is
appropriate; he rejects the superfluous; and when he has completed
his work, it is neither defective nor redundant. The 'Metamorphoses'
are read with pleasure by youth, and are re-read in more advanced
age with still greater delight. The poet ventured to predict that his
poem would survive him, and be read wherever the Roman name was
known."

The prediction above alluded to is contained in the closing lines
of the "Metamorphoses," of which we give a literal translation
below:

> "And now I close my work, which not the ire
> Of Jove, nor tooth of time, nor sword, nor fire
> Shall bring to nought. Come when it will that day
> Which o'er the body, not the mind, has sway,

And snatch the remnant of my life away,
My better part above the stars shall soar,
And my renown endure for evermore.
Where'er the Roman arms and arts shall spread,
There by the people shall my book be read;
And, if aught true in poet's visions be,
My name and fame have immortality."

CHAPTER XXXVI

MODERN MONSTERS—THE PHŒNIX—BASILISK—UNICORN—
—SALAMANDER

MODERN MONSTERS

THERE is a set of imaginary beings which seem to have been the successors of the "Gorgons, Hydras, and Chimeras dire" of the old superstitions, and, having no connection with the false gods of Paganism, to have continued to enjoy an existence in the popular belief after Paganism was superseded by Christianity. They are mentioned perhaps by the classical writers, but their chief popularity and currency seem to have been in more modern times. We seek our accounts of them not so much in the poetry of the ancients as in the old natural history books and narrations of travellers. The accounts which we are about to give are taken chiefly from the Penny Cyclopedia.

THE PHŒNIX

Ovid tells the story of the Phœnix as follows: "Most beings spring from other individuals; but there is a certain kind which reproduces itself. The Assyrians call it the Phœnix. It does not live on fruit or flowers, but on frankincense and odoriferous gums. When it has lived five hundred years, it builds itself a nest in the branches of an oak, or on the top of a palm tree. In this it collects cinnamon, and spikenard, and myrrh, and of these materials builds a pile on which it deposits itself, and dying, breathes out its last breath amidst odours. From the body of the parent bird, a young Phœnix issues forth, destined to live as long a life as its predecessor. When this has grown up and gained sufficient strength, it lifts its nest from the tree (its own cradle and its parent's sepulchre), and carries it to the city of Heliopolis in Egypt, and deposits it in the temple of the Sun."

Such is the account given by a poet. Now let us see that of a philosophic historian. Tacitus says, "in the consulship of Paulus Fabius (A.D. 34) the miraculous bird known to the world by the name of the Phœnix, after disappearing for a series of ages, revisited Egypt. It was attended in its flight by a group of various birds, all attracted by the novelty, and gazing with wonder at so beautiful an appearance." He then gives an account of the bird, not varying materially from the preceding, but adding some details. "The first care of the young bird as soon as fledged, and able to trust to his wings, is to perform the obsequies of his father. But this duty is not undertaken rashly. He collects a quantity of myrrh, and to try his strength makes frequent excursions with a load on his back. When he has gained sufficient confidence in his own vigour, he takes up the body of his father and flies with it to the altar of the Sun, where he leaves it to be consumed in flames of fragrance." Other writers add a few particulars. The myrrh is compacted in the form of an egg, in which the dead Phœnix is enclosed. From the mouldering flesh of the dead bird a worm springs, and this worm, when grown large, is transformed into a bird. Herodotus *describes* the bird, though he says, "I have not seen it myself, except in a picture. Part of his plumage is gold-coloured, and part crimson; and he is for the most part very much like an eagle in outline and bulk."

The first writer who disclaimed a belief in the existence of the Phœnix was Sir Thomas Browne, in his "Vulgar Errors," published in 1646. He was replied to a few years later by Alexander Ross, who says, in answer to the objection of the Phœnix so seldom making his appearance, "His instinct teaches him to keep out of the way of the tyrant of the creation, *man*, for if he were to be got at, some wealthy glutton would surely devour him, though there were no more in the world."

Dryden in one of his early poems has this allusion to the Phœnix:

"So when the new-born Phœnix first is seen
Her feathered subjects all adore their queen,
And while she makes her progress through the East,
From every grove her numerous train 's increased;
Each poet of the air her glory sings,
And round him the pleased audience clap their wings."

Milton, in "Paradise Lost," Book V., compares the angel Raphael descending to earth to a Phœnix:

"...Down thither, prone in flight
He speeds, and through the vast ethereal sky
Sails between worlds and worlds, with steady wing,
Now on the polar winds, then with quick fan
Winnows the buxom air; till within soar
Of towering eagles, to all the fowls he seems
A Phœnix, gazed by all; as that sole bird
When, to enshrine his relics in the sun's
Bright temple, to Egyptian Thebes he flies."

The Cockatrice, or Basilisk

This animal was called the king of the serpents. In confirmation of his royalty, he was said to be endowed with a crest, or comb upon the head, constituting a crown. He was supposed to be produced from the egg of a cock hatched under toads or serpents. There were several species of this animal. One species burned up whatever they approached; a second were a kind of wandering Medusa's heads, and their look caused an instant horror which was immediately followed by death. In Shakespeare's play of "Richard the Third," Lady Anne, in answer to Richard's compliment on her eyes, says "Would tney were basilisk's, to strike thee dead!"

The basilisks were called kings of serpents because all other serpents and snakes, behaving like good subjects, and wisely not wishing to be burned up or struck dead, fled the moment they heard the distant hiss of their king, although they might be in full feed upon the most delicious prey, leaving the sole enjoyment of the banquet to the royal monster.

The Roman naturalist Pliny thus describes him. "He does not impel his body, like other serpents, by a multiplied flexion, but advances lofty and upright. He kills the shrubs, not only by contact, but by breathing on them, and splits the rocks, such power of evil is there in him." It was formerly believed that if killed by a spear from on horseback the power of the poison conducted through the weapon killed not only the rider, but the horse also. To this Lucan alludes in these lines:

> "What though the Moor the basilisk hath slain,
> And pinned him lifeless to the sandy plain,
> Up through the spear the subtle venom flies,
> The hand imbibes it, and the victor dies."

Such a prodigy was not likely to be passed over in the legends of the saints. Accordingly we find it recorded that a certain holy man, going to a fountain in the desert, suddenly beheld a basilisk. He immediately raised his eyes to heaven, and with a pious appeal to the Deity laid the monster dead at his feet.

These wonderful powers of the basilisk are attested by a host of learned persons, such as Galen, Avicenna, Scaliger, and others. Occasionally one would demur to some part of the tale while he admitted the rest. Jonston, a learned physician, sagely remarks, "I would scarcely believe that it kills with its look, for who could have seen it and lived to tell the story?" The worthy sage was not aware that those who went to hunt the basilisk of this sort took with them a mirror, which reflected back the deadly glare upon its author, and by a kind of poetical justice slew the basilisk with his own weapon.

But what was to attack this terrible and unapproachable monster? There is an old saying that "everything has its enemy"—and the cockatrice quailed before the weasel. The basilisk might look daggers, the weasel cared not, but advanced boldly to the conflict. When bitten, the weasel retired for a moment to eat some rue, which was the only plant the basilisks could not wither, returned with renewed strength and soundness to the charge, and never left the enemy till he was stretched dead on the plain. The monster, too, as if conscious of the irregular way in which he came into the world, was supposed to have a great antipathy to a cock; and well he might, for as soon as he heard the cock crow he expired.

The basilisk was of some use after death. Thus we read that its carcass was suspended in the temple of Apollo, and in private houses, as a sovereign remedy against spiders, and that it was also hung up in the temple of Diana, for which reason no swallow ever dared enter the sacred place.

The reader will, we apprehend, by this time have had enough of absurdities, but still we can imagine his anxiety to know what a cockatrice was like. The following is from Aldrovandus, a celebrated naturalist of the sixteenth century, whose work on natural history, in thirteen folio volumes, contains with much that is valuable a large proportion of fables and inutilities. In particular he is so ample on the subject of the cock and the bull that from his practice, all rambling, gossiping tales of doubtful credibility are called *cock and bull stories*.

Shelley, in his "Ode to Naples," full of the enthusiasm excited by the intelligence of the proclamation of a Constitutional Government at Naples, in 1820, thus uses an allusion to the basilisk:

> "What though Cimmerian anarchs dare blaspheme
> Freedom and thee? a new Actæon's error
> Shall theirs have been,—devoured by their own hounds!
>   Be thou like the imperial basilisk,
> Killing thy foe with unapparent wounds!
>   Gaze on oppression, till at that dread risk,
>   Aghast she pass from the earth's disk.
> Fear not, but gaze,—for freemen mightier grow,
> And slaves more feeble, gazing on their foe."

The Unicorn

Pliny, the Roman naturalist, out of whose account of the unicorn most of the modern unicorns have been described and figured, records it as "a very ferocious beast, similar in the rest of its body to a horse, with the head of a deer, the feet of an elephant, the tail of a boar, a deep, bellowing voice, and a single black horn, two cubits in length, standing out in the middle of its forehead." He adds that "it cannot be taken alive"; and some such excuse may have been necessary in those days for not producing the living animal upon the arena of the amphitheatre.

The unicorn seems to have been a sad puzzle to the hunters, who hardly knew how to come at so valuable a piece of game. Some described the horn as movable at the will of the animal, a kind of small sword, in short, with which no hunter who was not exceedingly cunning in fence could have a chance. Others maintained that all the animal's strength lay in its horn, and that when hard pressed in pursuit, it would throw itself from the pinnacle of the highest rocks horn foremost, so as to pitch upon it, and then quietly march off not a whit the worse for its fall.

But it seems they found out how to circumvent the poor unicorn at last. They discovered that it was a great lover of purity and innocence, so they took the field with a young *virgin*, who was placed in the unsuspecting admirer's way. When the unicorn spied her, he approached with all reverence, crouched beside her, and laying his head in her lap, fell asleep. The treacherous virgin then gave a signal, and the hunters made in and captured the simple beast.

Modern zoologists, disgusted as they well may be with such fables as these, disbelieved generally the existence of the unicorn. Yet there are animals bearing on their heads a bony protuberance more or less like a horn, which may have given rise to the story. The rhinoceros horn, as it is called, is such a protuberance, though it does not exceed a few inches in height, and is far from agreeing with the descriptions of the horn of the unicorn. The nearest approach to a horn in the middle of the forehead is exhibited in the bony protuberance on the forehead of the giraffe; but this also is short and blunt, and is not the only horn of the animal, but a third horn, standing in front of the two others. In fine, though it would be presumptuous to deny the existence of a one-horned quadruped other than the rhinoceros, it may be safely stated that the insertion of a long and solid horn in the living forehead of a horse-like or deer-like animal is as near an impossibility as anything can be.

The Salamander

The following is from the "Life of Benvenuto Cellini," an Italian artist of the sixteenth century, written by himself: "When I was about five years of age, my father, happening to be in a little room in which they had been washing, and where there was a good fire of oak burning, looked into the flames and saw a little animal resembling a lizard, which could live in the hottest part of that element.

Instantly perceiving what it was, he called for my sister and me, and, after he had shown us the creature, he gave me a box on the ear. I fell a-crying, while he, soothing me with caresses, spoke these words: 'My dear child, I do not give you that blow for any fault you have committed, but that you may recollect that the little creature you see in the fire is a salamander; such a one as never was beheld before to my knowledge.' So saying he embraced me, and gave me some money."

It seems unreasonable to doubt a story of which Signor Cellini was both an eye and ear witness. Add to which the authority of numerous sage philosophers, at the head of whom are Aristotle and Pliny, affirms this power of the salamander. According to them, the animal not only resists fire, but extinguishes it, and when he sees the flame charges it as an enemy which he well knows how to vanquish.

That the skin of an animal which could resist the action of fire should be considered proof against that element is not to be wondered at. We accordingly find that a cloth made of the skin of salamanders (for there really is such an animal, a kind of lizard) was incombustible, and very valuable for wrapping up such articles as were too precious to be intrusted to any other envelopes. These fire-proof cloths were actually produced, said to be made of salamander's wool, though the knowing ones detected that the substance of which they were composed was asbestos, a mineral, which is in fine filaments capable of being woven into a flexible cloth.

The foundation of the above fables is supposed to be the fact that the salamander really does secrete from the pores of his body a milky juice, which when he is irritated is produced in considerable quantity, and would doubtless, for a few moments, defend the body from fire. Then it is a hibernating animal, and in winter retires to some hollow tree or other cavity, where it coils itself up and remains in a torpid state till the spring again calls it forth. It may therefore sometimes be carried with the fuel to the fire, and wake up only time enough to put forth all its faculties for its defence. Its viscous juice would do good service, and all who profess to have seen it, acknowledge that it got out of the fire as fast as its legs could carry it; indeed, too fast for them ever to make prize of one, except in one instance, and in that one the animal's feet and some parts of its body were badly burned.

Dr. Young, in the "Night Thoughts," with more quaintness than good taste, compares the sceptic who can remain unmoved in the contemplation of the starry heavens to a salamander unwarmed in the fire:

"An undevout astronomer is mad!

. . . . . .

"O, what a genius must inform the skies!
And is Lorenzo's salamander-heart
Cold and untouched amid these sacred fires?"

CHAPTER XXXVII

EASTERN MYTHOLOGY—ZOROASTER—HINDU MYTHOLOGY—CASTES
—BUDDHA—GRAND LAMA

ZOROASTER

OUR knowledge of the religion of the ancient Persians is principally derived from the Zendavesta, or sacred books of that people.
Zoroaster was the founder of their religion, or rather the reformer
of the religion which preceded him. The time when he lived is doubtful, but it is certain that his system became the dominant religion
of Western Asia from the time of Cyrus (550 B.C.) to the conquest
of Persia by Alexander the Great. Under the Macedonian monarchy
the doctrines of Zoroaster appear to have been considerably corrupted by the introduction of foreign opinions, but they afterwards
recovered their ascendency.

Zoroaster taught the existence of a supreme being, who created
two other mighty beings and imparted to them as much of his own
nature as seemed good to him. Of these, Ormuzd (called by the
Greeks Oromasdes) remained faithful to his creator, and was regarded as the source of all good, while Ahriman (Arimanes) rebelled, and became the author of all evil upon the earth. Ormuzd
created man and supplied him with all the materials of happiness;
but Ahriman marred this happiness by introducing evil into the
world, and creating savage beasts and poisonous reptiles and plants.
In consequence of this, evil and good are now mingled together in
every part of the world, and the followers of good and evil—the
adherents of Ormuzd and Ahriman—carry on incessant war. But
this state of things will not last for ever. The time will come when
the adherents of Ormuzd shall everywhere be victorious, and Ahriman and his followers be consigned to darkness for ever.

The religious rites of the ancient Persians were exceedingly simple.
They used neither temples, altars, nor statues, and performed their
sacrifices on the tops of mountains. They adored fire, light, and the
sun as emblems of Ormuzd, the source of all light and purity, but
did not regard them as independent deities. The religious rites and
ceremonies were regulated by the priests, who were called Magi.

The learning of the Magi was connected with astrology and enchantment, in which they were so celebrated that their name was
applied to all orders of magicians and enchanters.

Wordsworth thus alludes to the worship of the Persians:

> "...the Persian,—zealous to reject
> Altar and Image, and the inclusive walls
> And roofs of temples built by human hands,—
> The loftiest heights ascending, from their tops,
> With myrtle-wreathed Tiara on his brows,
> Presented sacrifice to Moon and Stars,
> And to the Winds and mother Elements,
> And the whole circle of the Heavens, for him
> A sensitive existence and a God."
>
> *Excursion,* Book IV.

In "Childe Harold" Byron speaks thus of the Persian worship:

> "Not vainly did the early Persian make
> His altar the high places and the peak
> Of earth-o'er-gazing mountains, and thus take
> A fit and unwalled temple, there to seek
> The Spirit, in whose honour shrines are weak,
> Upreared of human hands. Come and compare
> Columns and idol-dwellings, Goth or Greek,
> With Nature's realms of worship, earth and air,
> Nor fix on fond abodes to circumscribe thy prayer."
>
> III. 91.

The religion of Zoroaster continued to flourish even after the introduction of Christianity, and in the third century was the dominant faith of the East, till the rise of the Mahometan power and the
conquest of Persia by the Arabs in the seventh century, who compelled the greater number of the Persians to renounce their ancient
faith. Those who refused to abandon the religion of their ancestors
fled to the deserts of Kerman and to Hindustan, where they still
exist under the name of Parsees, a name derived from Paris, the
ancient name of Persia. The Arabs call them Guebers, from an Arabic
word signifying unbelievers. At Bombay the Parsees are at this day
a very active, intelligent, and wealthy class. For purity of life,
honesty, and conciliatory manners, they are favourably distinguished. They have numerous temples to Fire, which they adore as
the symbol of the divinity.

The Persian religion makes the subject of the finest tale in Moore's
"Lalla Rookh," the "Fire Worshippers." The Gueber chief says:

> "Yes! I am of that impious race,
> Those slaves of Fire, that morn and even
> Hail their creator's dwelling-place
> Among the living lights of heaven:

Yes! I am of that outcast crew
To Iran and to vengeance true,
Who curse the hour your Arabs came
To desecrate our shrines of flame,
And swear before God's burning eye
To break our country's chains or die."

HINDU MYTHOLOGY

The religion of the Hindus is professedly founded on the Vedas. To these books of their scripture they attach the greatest sanctity, and state that Brahma himself composed them at the creation. But the present arrangement of the Vedas is attributed to the sage Vyasa, about five thousand years ago.

The Vedas undoubtedly teach the belief of one supreme God. The name of this deity is Brahma. His attributes are represented by the three personified powers of *creation, preservation,* and *destruction,* which under the respective names of Brahma, Vishnu, and Siva form the *Trimurti* or triad of principal Hindu gods. Of the inferior gods the most important are: 1. Indra, the god of heaven, of thunder, lightning, storm, and rain; 2. Agni, the god of fire; 3. Yama, the god of the infernal regions; 4. Surya, the god of the sun.

Brahma is the creator of the universe, and the source from which all the individual deities have sprung, and into which all will ultimately be absorbed. "As milk changes to curd, and water to ice, so is Brahma variously transformed and diversified, without aid of exterior means of any sort." The human soul, according to the Vedas, is a portion of the supreme ruler, as a spark is of the fire.

VISHNU

Vishnu occupies the second place in the triad of the Hindus, and is the personification of the preserving principle. To protect the world in various epochs of danger, Vishnu descended to the earth in different incarnations, or bodily forms, which descents are called Avatars. They are very numerous, but ten are more particularly specified. The first Avatar was as Matsya, the Fish, under which form Vishnu preserved Manu, the ancestor of the human race, during a universal deluge. The second Avatar was in the form of a Tortoise, which form he assumed to support the earth when the gods were churning the sea for the beverage of immortality, Amrita.

We may omit the other Avatars, which were of the same general character, that is, interpositions to protect the right or to punish wrong-doers, and come to the ninth, which is the most celebrated of the Avatars of Vishnu, in which he appeared in the human form of Krishna, an invincible warrior, who by his exploits relieved the earth from the tyrants who oppressed it.

Buddha is by the followers of the Brahminical religion regarded as a delusive incarnation of Vishnu, assumed by him in order to induce the Asuras, opponents of the gods, to abandon the sacred ordinances of the Vedas, by which means they lost their strength and supremacy.

Kalki is the name of the *tenth* Avatar, in which Vishnu will appear at the end of the present age of the world to destroy all vice and wickedness, and to restore mankind to virtue and purity.

SIVA

Siva is the third person of the Hindu triad. He is the personification of the destroying principle. Though the third name, he is, in respect to the number of his worshippers and the extension of his worship, before either of the others. In the Puranas (the scriptures of the modern Hindu religion) no allusion is made to the original power of this god as a destroyer; that power not being to be called into exercise till after the expiration of twelve millions of years, or when the universe will come to an end; and Mahadeva (another name for Siva) is rather the representative of regeneration than of destruction.

The worshippers of Vishnu and Siva form two sects, each of which proclaims the superiority of its favourite deity, denying the claims of the other, and Brahma, the creator, having finished his work, seems to be regarded as no longer active, and has now only one temple in India, while Mahadeva and Vishnu have many. The worshippers of Vishnu are generally distinguished by a greater tenderness for life, and consequent abstinence from animal food, and a worship less cruel than that of the followers of Siva.

JUGGERNAUT

Whether the worshippers of Juggernaut are to be reckoned among the followers of Vishnu or Siva, our authorities differ. The temple stands near the shore, about three hundred miles southwest of Calcutta. The idol is a carved block of wood, with a hideous face, painted black, and a distended blood-red mouth. On festival days the throne of the image is placed on a tower sixty feet high, moving on wheels. Six long ropes are attached to the tower, by which the people draw it along. The priests and their attendants stand round the throne on the tower, and occasionally turn to the worshippers with songs and gestures. While the tower moves along numbers of the devout worshippers throw themselves on the ground, in order to be crushed by the wheels, and the multitude shout in approbation of the act, as a pleasing sacrifice to the idol. Every year, particularly at two great festivals in March and July, pilgrims flock in crowds to the temple. Not less than seventy or eighty thousand people are said to visit the place on these occasions, when all castes eat together.

CASTES

The division of the Hindus into classes or castes, with fixed occupations, existed from the earliest times. It is supposed by some to have been founded upon conquest, the first three castes being composed of a foreign race, who subdued the natives of the country and reduced them to an inferior caste. Others trace it to the fondness of perpetuating, by descent from father to son, certain offices or occupations.

The Hindu tradition gives the following account of the origin of the various castes: At the creation Brahma resolved to give the earth inhabitants who should be direct emanations from his own body. Accordingly from his mouth came forth the eldest born, Brahma (the priest), to whom he confided the four Vedas; from his right arm issued Shatriya (the warrior), and from his left, the warrior's wife. His thighs produced Vaissyas, male and female (agriculturists and traders), and lastly from his feet sprang Sudras (mechanics and labourers).

The four sons of Brahma, so significantly brought into the world, became the fathers of the human race, and heads of their respective castes. They were commanded to regard the four Vedas as containing all the rules of their faith, and all that was necessary to guide them in their religious ceremonies. They were also commanded to take rank in the order of their birth, the Brahmans uppermost, as having sprung from the head of Brahma.

A strong line of demarcation is drawn between the first three castes and the Sudras. The former are allowed to receive instruction from the Vedas, which is not permitted to the Sudras. The Brahmans possess the privilege of teaching the Vedas, and were in former times in exclusive possession of all knowledge. Though the sovereign of the country was chosen from the Shatriya class, also called Rajputs, the Brahmans possessed the real power, and were the royal counsellors, the judges and magistrates of the country; their persons and property were inviolable; and though they committed the greatest crimes, they could only be banished from the kingdom. They were to be treated by sovereigns with the greatest respect, for "a Brahman, whether learned or ignorant, is a powerful divinity."

When the Brahman arrives at years of maturity it becomes his duty to marry. He ought to be supported by the contributions of the rich, and not to be obliged to gain his subsistence by any laborious or productive occupation. But as all the Brahmans could not be maintained by the working classes of the community, it was found necessary to allow them to engage in productive employments.

We need say little of the two intermediate classes, whose rank and privileges may be readily inferred from their occupations. The Sudras or fourth class are bound to servile attendance on the higher classes, especially the Brahmans, but they may follow mechanical occupations and practical arts, as painting and writing, or become traders or husbandmen. Consequently they sometimes grow rich, and it will also sometimes happen that Brahmans become poor. That fact works its usual consequence, and rich Sudras sometimes employ poor Brahmans in menial occupations.

There is another class lower even than the Sudras, for it is not one of the original pure classes, but springs from an unauthorized union of individuals of different castes. These are the Pariahs, who are employed in the lowest services and treated with the utmost severity. They are compelled to do what no one else can do without pollution. They are not only considered unclean themselves, but they render unclean everything they touch. They are deprived of all civil rights, and stigmatized by particular laws regulating their mode of life, their houses, and their furniture. They are not allowed to visit the pagodas or temples of the other castes, but have their own pagodas and religious exercises. They are not suffered to enter the houses of the other castes; if it is done incautiously or from necessity, the place must be purified by religious ceremonies. They must not appear at public markets, and are confined to the use of particular wells, which they are obliged to surround with bones of animals, to warn others against using them. They dwell in miserable hovels, distant from cities and villages, and are under no restrictions in regard to food, which last is not a privilege, but a mark of ignominy, as if they were so degraded that nothing could pollute them. The three higher castes are prohibited entirely the use of flesh. The fourth is allowed to use all kinds except beef, but only the lowest caste is allowed every kind of food without restriction.

BUDDHA

Buddha, whom the Vedas represent as a delusive incarnation of Vishnu, is said by his followers to have been a mortal sage, whose name was Gautama, called also by the complimentary epithets of Sakyasinha, the Lion, and Buddha, the Sage.

By a comparison of the various epochs assigned to his birth, it is inferred that he lived about one thousand years before Christ.

He was the son of a king; and when in conformity to the usage of the country he was, a few days after his birth, presented before the altar of a deity, the image is said to have inclined its head as a presage of the future greatness of the new-born prophet. The child soon developed faculties of the first order, and became equally distinguished by the uncommon beauty of his person. No sooner had he grown to years of maturity than he began to reflect deeply on the depravity and misery of mankind, and he conceived the idea of retiring from society and devoting himself to meditation. His father in vain opposed this design. Buddha escaped the vigilance of his guards, and having found a secure retreat, lived for six years undisturbed in his devout contemplations. At the expiration of that period he came forward at Benares as a religious teacher. At first some who heard him doubted of the soundness of his mind; but his doctrines soon gained credit, and were propagated so rapidly that Buddha himself lived to see them spread all over India. He died at the age of eighty years.

The Buddhists reject entirely the authority of the Vedas, and the religious observances prescribed in them and kept by the Hindus. They also reject the distinction of castes, and prohibit all bloody sacrifices, and allow animal food. Their priests are chosen from all classes; they are expected to procure their maintenance by perambulation and begging, and among other things it is their duty to endeavour to turn to some use things thrown aside as useless by others, and to discover the medicinal power of plants. But in Ceylon three orders of priests are recognized; those of the highest order are usually men of high birth and learning, and are supported at the principal temples, most of which have been richly endowed by the former monarchs of the country.

For several centuries after the appearance of Buddha, his sect seems to have been tolerated by the Brahmans, and Buddhism appears to have penetrated the peninsula of Hindustan in every direction, and to have been carried to Ceylon, and to the eastern peninsula. But afterwards it had to endure in India a long-continued persecution, which ultimately had the effect of entirely abolishing it in the country where it had originated, but to scatter it widely over adjacent countries. Buddhism appears to have been introduced into China about the year 65 of our era. From China it was subsequently extended to Corea, Japan, and Java.

THE GRAND LAMA

It is a doctrine alike of the Brahminical Hindus and of the Buddhist sect that the confinement of the human soul, an emana- tion of the divine spirit, in a human body, is a state of misery, and the consequence of frailties and sins committed during former existences. But they hold that some few individuals have appeared on this earth from time to time, not under the necessity of ter- restrial existence, but who voluntarily descended to the earth to promote the welfare of mankind. These individuals have gradually assumed the character of reappearances of Buddha himself, in which capacity the line is continued till the present day, in the sev- eral Lamas of Thibet, China, and other countries where Buddhism prevails. In consequence of the victories of Gengis Khan and his successors, the Lama residing in Thibet was raised to the dignity of chief pontiff of the sect. A separate province was assigned to him as his own territory, and besides his spiritual dignity he be- came to a limited extent a temporal monarch. He is styled the Dalai Lama.

The first Christian missionaries who proceeded to Thibet were surprised to find there in the heart of Asia a pontifical court and several other ecclesiastical institutions resembling those of the Roman Catholic church. They found convents for priests and nuns; also processions and forms of religious worship, attended with much pomp and splendour; and many were induced by these simi- larities to consider Lamaism as a sort of degenerated Christianity. It is not improbable that the Lamas derived some of these prac- tices from the Nestorian Christians, who were settled in Tartary when Buddhism was introduced into Thibet.

PRESTER JOHN

An early account, communicated probably by travelling mer- chants, of a Lama or spiritual chief among the Tartars, seems to have occasioned in Europe the report of a Presbyter or Prester John, a Christian pontiff resident in Upper Asia. The Pope sent a mission in search of him, as did also Louis IX of France, some years later, but both missions were unsuccessful, though the small communities of Nestorian Christians, which they did find, served to keep up the belief in Europe that such a personage did exist somewhere in the East. At last in the fifteenth century, a Portu-guese traveller, Pedro Covilham, happening to hear that there was a Christian prince in the country of the Abessines (Abyssinia), not far from the Red Sea, concluded that this must be the true Prester John. He accordingly went thither, and penetrated to the court of the king, whom he calls Negus. Milton alludes to him in "Paradise Lost," Book XI., where, describing Adam's vision of his descendants in their various nations and cities, scattered over the face of the earth, he says,—

> "... Nor did his eyes not ken
> Th' empire of Negus, to his utmost port,
> Ercoco, and the less maritime kings,
> Mombaza and Quiloa and Melind."

CHAPTER XXXVIII

NORTHERN MYTHOLOGY—VALHALLA—THE VALKYRIOR

Northern Mythology

THE stories which have engaged our attention thus far relate to the mythology of southern regions. But there is another branch of ancient superstitions which ought not to be entirely overlooked, especially as it belongs to the nations from which we, through our English ancestors, derive our origin. It is that of the northern nations, called Scandinavians, who inhabited the countries now known as Sweden, Denmark, Norway, and Iceland. These mytho-logical records are contained in two collections called the Eddas, of which the oldest is in poetry and dates back to the year 1056, the more modern or prose Edda being of the date of 1640.

According to the Eddas there was once no heaven above nor earth beneath, but only a bottomless deep, and a world of mist in which flowed a fountain. Twelve rivers issued from this fountain, and when they had flowed far from their source, they froze into ice, and one layer accumulating over another, the great deep was filled up.

Southward from the world of mist was the world of light. From this flowed a warm wind upon the ice and melted it. The vapours rose in the air and formed clouds, from which sprang Ymir, the Frost giant and his progeny, and the cow Audhumbla, whose milk afforded nourishment and food to the giant. The cow got nourish-ment by licking the hoar frost and salt from the ice. While she was one day licking the salt stones there appeared at first the hair of a man, on the second day the whole head, and on the third the entire form endowed with beauty, agility, and power. This new being was a god, from whom and his wife, a daughter of the giant race, sprang the three brothers Odin, Vili, and Ve. They slew the giant Ymir, and out of his body formed the earth, of his blood the seas, of his bones the mountains, of his hair the trees, of his skull the heavens, and of his brain clouds, charged with hail and snow. Of Ymir's eyebrows the gods formed Midgard (mid earth), destined to become the abode of man.

Odin then regulated the periods of day and night and the seasons by placing in the heavens the sun and moon, and appointing to them their respective courses. As soon as the sun began to shed its rays upon the earth, it caused the vegetable world to bud and sprout. Shortly after the gods had created the world they walked by the side of the sea, pleased with their new work, but found that it was still incomplete, for it was without human beings. They therefore took an ash tree and made a man out of it, and they made a woman out of an alder, and called the man Aske and the woman Embla. Odin then gave them life and soul, Vili reason and motion, and Ve bestowed upon them the senses, expressive features, and speech. Midgard was then given them as their residence, and they became the progenitors of the human race.

The mighty ash tree Ygdrasill was supposed to support the whole universe. It sprang from the body of Ymir, and had three immense roots, extending one into Asgard (the dwelling of the gods), the other into Jotunheim (the abode of the giants), and the third to Niffleheim (the regions of darkness and cold). By the side of each of these roots is a spring, from which it is watered. The root that extends into Asgard is carefully tended by the three Norns, goddesses, who are regarded as the dispensers of fate. They are Urdur (the past), Verdandi (the present), Skuld (the future). The spring at the Jotunheim side is Ymir's well, in which wisdom and wit lie hidden, but that of Niffleheim feeds the adder Nidhogge (darkness), which perpetually gnaws at the root. Four harts run across the branches of the tree and bite the buds; they represent the four winds. Under the tree lies Ymir, and when he tries to shake off its weight the earth quakes.

Asgard is the name of the abode of the gods, access to which is only gained by crossing the bridge Bifrost (the rainbow). Asgard consists of golden and silver palaces, the dwellings of the gods, but the most beautiful of these is Valhalla, the residence of Odin. When seated on his throne he overlooks all heaven and earth. Upon his shoulders are the ravens Hugin and Munin, who fly every day over the whole world, and on their return report to him all they have seen and heard. At his feet lie his two wolves, Geri and Freki, to whom Odin gives all the meat that is set before him, for he himself stands in no need of food. Mead is for him both food and drink. He invented the Runic characters, and it is the business of the Norns to engrave the runes of fate upon a metal shield. From Odin's name, spelt Woden, as it sometimes is, came Wednesday, the name of the fourth day of the week.

Odin is frequently called Alfdaur (All-father), but this name is sometimes used in a way that shows that the Scandinavians had an idea of a deity superior to Odin, uncreated and eternal.

Of the Joys of Valhalla

Valhalla is the great hall of Odin, wherein he feasts with his chosen heroes, all those who have fallen bravely in battle, for all who die a peaceful death are excluded. The flesh of the boar Schrimnir is served up to them, and is abundant for all. For although this boar is cooked every morning, he becomes whole again every night. For drink the heroes are supplied abundantly with mead from the she-goat Heidrum. When the heroes are not feasting they amuse themselves with fighting. Every day they ride out into the court or field and fight until they cut each other in pieces. This is their pastime; but when meal time comes they recover from their wounds and return to feast in Valhalla.

The Valkyrior

The Valkyrior are warlike virgins, mounted upon horses and armed with helmets and spears. Odin, who is desirous to collect a great many heroes in Valhalla, to be able to meet the giants in a day when the final contest must come, sends down to every battle-field to make choice of those who shall be slain. The Valkyrior are his messengers, and their name means "Choosers of the slain." When they ride forth on their errand, their armour sheds a strange flickering light, which flashes up over the northern skies, making what men call the "Aurora Borealis," or "Northern Lights." [1]

Of Thor and the Other Gods

Thor, the thunderer, Odin's eldest son, is the strongest of gods and men, and possesses three very precious things. The first is a hammer, which both the Frost and the Mountain giants know to their cost, when they see it hurled against them in the air, for it has split many a skull of their fathers and kindred. When thrown,

---

[1] Gray's ode, "The Fatal Sisters," is founded on this superstition.

it returns to his hand of its own accord. The second rare thing
he possesses is called the belt of strength. When he girds it about
him his divine might is doubled. The third, also very precious, is
his iron gloves, which he puts on whenever he would use his mallet
efficiently. From Thor's name is derived our word Thursday.

Frey is one of the most celebrated of the gods. He presides over
rain and sunshine and all the fruits of the earth. His sister Freya
is the most propitious of the goddesses. She loves music, spring,
and flowers, and is particularly fond of the Elves (fairies). She is
very fond of love ditties, and all lovers would do well to invoke
her.

Bragi is the god of poetry, and his song records the deeds of
warriors. His wife, Iduna, keeps in a box the apples which the
gods, when they feel old age approaching, have only to taste of
to become young again.

Heimdall is the watchman of the gods, and is therefore placed
on the borders of heaven to prevent the giants from forcing their
way over the bridge Bifrost (the rainbow). He requires less sleep
than a bird, and sees by night as well as by day a hundred miles
around him. So acute is his ear that no sound escapes him, for he
can even hear the grass grow and the wool on a sheep's back.

OF LOKI AND HIS PROGENY

There is another deity who is described as the calumniator of
the gods and the contriver of all fraud and mischief. His name is
Loki. He is handsome and well made, but of a very fickle mood and
most evil disposition. He is of the giant race, but forced himself
into the company of the gods, and seems to take pleasure in
bringing them into difficulties, and in extricating them out of the
danger by his cunning, wit and skill. Loki has three children. The
first is the wolf Fenris, the second the Midgard serpent, the third
Hela (Death). The gods were not ignorant that these monsters
were growing up, and that they would one day bring much evil
upon gods and men. So Odin deemed it advisable to send one to
bring them to him. When they came he threw the serpent into
that deep ocean by which the earth is surrounded. But the monster
had grown to such an enormous size that holding his tail in his
mouth he encircles the whole earth. Hela he cast into Niffleheim,
and gave her power over nine worlds or regions, into which she
distributes those who are sent to her; that is, all who die of sickness
or old age. Her hall is called Elvidner. Hunger is her table, Starvation her knife, Delay her man, Slowness her maid, Precipice her
threshold, Care her bed, and Burning Anguish forms the hangings

of the apartments. She may easily be recognized, for her body is half flesh colour and half blue, and she has a dreadfully stern and forbidding countenance.

The wolf Fenris gave the gods a great deal of trouble before they succeeded in chaining him. He broke the strongest fetters as if they were made of cobwebs. Finally the gods sent a messenger to the mountain spirits, who made for them the chain called Gleipnir. It is fashioned of six things, viz., the noise made by the footfall of a cat, the beards of women, the roots of stones, the breath of fishes, the nerves (sensibilities) of bears, and the spittle of birds. When finished it was as smooth and soft as a silken string. But when the gods asked the wolf to suffer himself to be bound with this apparently slight ribbon, he suspected their design, fearing that it was made by enchantment. He therefore only consented to be bound with it upon condition that one of the gods put his hand in his (Fenris's) mouth as a pledge that the band was to be removed again. Tyr (the god of battles) alone had courage enough to do this. But when the wolf found that he could not break his fetters, and that the gods would not release him, he bit off Tyr's hand, and he has ever since remained one-handed.

How Thor Paid the Mountain Giant His Wages

Once on a time, when the gods were constructing their abodes and had already finished Midgard and Valhalla, a certain artificer came and offered to build them a residence so well fortified that they should be perfectly safe from the incursions of the Frost giants and the giants of the mountains. But he demanded for his reward the goddess Freya, together with the sun and moon. The gods yielded to his terms, provided he would finish the whole work himself without any one's assistance, and all within the space of one winter. But if anything remained unfinished on the first day of summer he should forfeit the recompense agreed on. On being told these terms the artificer stipulated that he should be allowed the use of his horse Svadilfari, and this by the advice of Loki was granted to him. He accordingly set to work on the first day of winter, and during the night let his horse draw stone for the building. The enormous size of the stones struck the gods with astonishment, and they saw clearly that the horse did one-half more of the toilsome work than his master. Their bargain, however, had been concluded, and confirmed by solemn oaths, for without these precautions a giant would not have thought himself safe among the gods, especially when Thor should return from an expedition he had then undertaken against the evil demons.

As the winter drew to a close, the building was far advanced, and the bulwarks were sufficiently nigh and massive to render the place impregnable. In short, when it wanted but three days to summer, the only part that remained to be finished was the gateway. Then sat the gods on their seats of justice and entered into consultation, inquiring of one another who among them could have advised to give Freya away, or to plunge the heavens in darkness by permitting the giant to carry away the sun and the moon.

They all agreed that no one but Loki, the author of so many evil deeds, could have given such bad counsel, and that he should be put to a cruel death if he did not contrive some way to prevent the artificer from completing his task and obtaining the stipulated recompense. They proceeded to lay hands on Loki, who in his fright promised upon oath that, let it cost him what it would, he would so manage matters that the man should lose his reward. That very night when the man went with Svadilfari for building stone, a mare suddenly ran out of a forest and began to neigh. The horse thereat broke loose and ran after the mare into the forest, which obliged the man also to run after his horse, and thus between one and another the whole night was lost, so that at dawn the work had not made the usual progress. The man, seeing that he must fail of completing his task, resumed his own gigantic stature, and the gods now clearly perceived that it was in reality a mountain giant who had come amongst tnem. Feeling no longer bound by their oaths, they called on Thor, who immediately ran to their assistance, and lifting up his mallet, paid the workman his wages, not with the sun and moon, and not even by sending him back to Jotunheim, for with the first blow he shattered the giant's skull to pieces and hurled him headlong into Niffleheim.

THE RECOVERY OF THE HAMMER

Once upon a time it happened that Thor's hammer fell into the possession of the giant Thrym, who buried it eight fathoms deep under the rocks of Jotunheim. Thor sent Loki to negotiate with Thrym, but he could only prevail so far as to get the giant's promise to restore the weapon if Freya would consent to be his bride. Loki returned and reported the result of his mission, but the goddess of love was quite horrified at the idea of bestowing her charms on the king of the Frost giants. In this emergency Loki persuaded Thor to dress himself in Freya's clothes and accompany him to Jotunheim. Thrym received his veiled bride with due courtesy, but was greatly surprised at seeing her eat for her supper eight salmons and a full grown ox, besides other delicacies, washing the whole down with three tuns of mead. Loki, however, assured him that she had not tasted anything for eight long nights, so great was her desire to see her lover, the renowned ruler of Jotunheim. Thrym had at length the curiosity to peep under his bride's veil, but started back in affright and demanded why Freya's eyeballs glistened with fire. Loki repeated the same excuse and the giant was satisfied. He ordered the hammer to be brought in and laid on the maiden's lap. Thereupon Thor threw off his disguise, grasped his redoubted weapon, and slaughtered Thrym and all his followers.

Frey also possessed a wonderful weapon, a sword which would of itself spread a field with carnage whenever the owner desired it. Frey parted with this sword, but was less fortunate than Thor and never recovered it. It happened in this way: Frey once mounted Odin's throne, from whence one can see over the whole universe, and looking round saw far off in the giant's kingdom a beautiful maid, at the sight of whom he was struck with sudden sadness, insomuch that from that moment he could neither sleep, nor drink, nor speak. At last Skirnir, his messenger, drew his secret from him, and undertook to get him the maiden for his bride, if he would give him his sword as a reward. Frey consented and gave him the sword, and Skirnir set off on his journey and obtained the maiden's promise that within nine nights she would come to a certain place and there wed Frey. Skirnir having reported the success of his errand, Frey exclaimed:

> "Long is one night,
> Long are two nights,
> But how shall I hold out three?
> Shorter hath seemed
> A month to me oft
> Than of this longing time the half."

So Frey obtained Gerda, the most beautiful of all women, for his wife, but he lost his sword.

This story, entitled "Skirnir For," and the one immediately preceding it, "Thrym's Quida," will be found poetically told in Longfellow's "Poets and Poetry of Europe."

CHAPTER XXXIX

THOR'S VISIT TO JOTUNHEIM

THOR'S VISIT TO JOTUNHEIM, THE GIANT'S COUNTRY

ONE day the god Thor, with his servant Thialfi, and accompanied by Loki, set out on a journey to the giant's country. Thialfi was of all men the swiftest of foot. He bore Thor's wallet, containing their provisions. When night came on they found themselves in an immense forest, and searched on all sides for a place where they might pass the night, and at last came to a very large hall, with an entrance that took the whole breadth of one end of the building. Here they lay down to sleep, but towards midnight were alarmed by an earthquake which shook the whole edifice. Thor, rising up, called on his companions to seek with him a place of safety. On the right they found an adjoining chamber, into which the others entered, but Thor remained at the doorway with his mallet in his hand, prepared to defend himself, whatever might happen. A terrible groaning was heard during the night, and at dawn of day Thor went out and found lying near him a huge giant, who slept and snored in the way that had alarmed them so. It is said that for once Thor was afraid to use his mallet, and as the giant soon waked up, Thor contented himself with simply asking his name.

"My name is Skrymir," said the giant, "but I need not ask thy name, for I know that thou art the god Thor. But what has become of my glove?" Thor then perceived that what they had taken overnight for a hall was the giant's glove, and the chamber where his two companions had sought refuge was the thumb. Skrymir then proposed that they should travel in company, and Thor consenting, they sat down to eat their breakfast, and when they had done, Skrymir packed all the provisions into one wallet, threw it over his shoulder, and strode on before them, taking such tremendous strides that they were hard put to it to keep up with him. So they travelled the whole day, and at dusk Skrymir chose a place for them to pass the night in under a large oak tree. Skrymir then told them he would lie down to sleep. "But take ye the wallet," he added, "and prepare your supper."

Skrymir soon fell asleep and began to snore strongly; but when Thor tried to open the wallet, he found the giant had tied it up so tight he could not untie a single knot. At last Thor became wroth, and grasping his mallet with both hands he struck a furious blow on the giant's head. Skrymir, awakening, merely asked whether a leaf had not fallen on his head, and whether they had supped and were ready to go to sleep. Thor answered that they were just going to sleep, and so saying went and laid himself down under another tree. But sleep came not that night to Thor, and when Skrymir snored again so loud that the forest re-echoed with the noise, he arose, and grasping his mallet launched it with such force at the giant's skull that it made a deep dint in it. Skrymir, awakening, cried out, "What's the matter? Are there any birds perched on this tree? I felt some moss from the branches fall on my head. How fares it with thee, Thor?" But Thor went away hastily, saying that he had just then awoke, and that as it was only midnight, there was still time for sleep. He, however, resolved that if he had an opportunity of striking a third blow, it should settle all matters between them. A little before daybreak he perceived that Skrymir was again fast asleep, and again grasping his mallet, he dashed it with such violence that it forced its way into the giant's skull up to the handle. But Skrymir sat up, and stroking his cheek said, "An acorn fell on my head. What! Art thou awake, Thor? Methinks it is time for us to get up and dress ourselves; but you have not now a long way before you to the city called Utgard. I have heard you whispering to one another that I am not a man of small dimensions; but if you come to Utgard you will see there many men much taller than I. Wherefore I advise you, when you come there, not to make too much of yourselves, for the followers of Utgard-Loki will not brook the boasting of such little fellows as you are. You must take the road that leads eastward, mine lies northward, so we must part here."

Hereupon he threw his wallet over his shoulders and turned away from them into the forest, and Thor had no wish to stop him or to ask for any more of his company.

Thor and his companions proceeded on their way, and towards noon descried a city standing in the middle of a plain. It was so lofty that they were obliged to bend their necks quite back on their shoulders in order to see to the top of it. On arriving they entered the city, and seeing a large palace before them with the door wide open, they went in, and found a number of men of prodigious stature, sitting on benches in the hall. Going further, they came before the king, Utgard-Loki, whom they saluted with great respect. The king, regarding them with a scornful smile, said, "If I do not mistake me, that stripling yonder must be the god Thor." Then addressing himself to Thor, he said, "Perhaps thou mayst be more than thou appearest to be. What are the feats that thou and thy fellows deem yourselves skilled in, for no one is permitted to remain here who does not, in some feat or other, excel all other men?"

"The feat that I know," said Loki, "is to eat quicker than any one else, and in this I am ready to give a proof against any one here who may choose to compete with me."

"That will indeed be a feat," said Utgard-Loki, "if thou performest what thou promisest, and it shall be tried forthwith."

He then ordered one of his men who was sitting at the farther end of the bench, and whose name was Logi, to come forward and try his skill with Loki. A trough filled with meat having been set on the hall floor, Loki placed himself at one end, and Logi at the other, and each of them began to eat as fast as he could, until they met in the middle of the trough. But it was found that Loki had only eaten the flesh, while his adversary had devoured both flesh and bone, and the trough to boot. All the company therefore adjudged that Loki was vanquished.

Utgard-Loki then asked what feat the young man who accompanied Thor could perform. Thialfi answered that he would run a race with any one who might be matched against him. The king observed that skill in running was something to boast of, but if the youth would win the match he must display great agility. He then arose and went with all who were present to a plain where there was good ground for running on, and calling a young man named Hugi, bade him run a match with Thialfi. In the first course Hugi so much outstripped his competitor that he turned back and met him not far from the starting place. Then they ran a second and a third time, but Thialfi met with no better success.

Utgard-Loki then asked Thor in what feats he would choose to give proofs of that prowess for which he was so famous. Thor answered that he would try a drinking match with any one. Utgard-Loki bade his cupbearer bring the large horn which his followers were obliged to empty when they had trespassed in any way against the law of the feast. The cupbearer having presented it to Thor, Utgard-Loki said, "Whoever is a good drinker will empty that horn at a single draught, though most men make two of it, but the most puny drinker can do it in three."

Thor looked at the horn, which seemed of no extraordinary size though somewhat long; however, as he was very thirsty, he set it to his lips, and without drawing breath, pulled as long and as deeply as he could, that he might not be obliged to make a second draught of it; but when he set the horn down and looked in, he could scarcely perceive that the liquor was diminished.

After taking breath, Thor went to it again with all his might, but when he took the horn from his mouth, it seemed to him that he had drunk rather less than before, although the horn could now be carried without spilling.

"How now, Thor?" said Utgard-Loki; "thou must not spare thyself; if thou meanest to drain the horn at the third draught thou must pull deeply; and I must needs say that thou wilt not be called so mighty a man here as thou art at home if thou showest no greater prowess in other feats than methinks will be shown in this."

Thor, full of wrath, again set the horn to his lips, and did his best to empty it; but on looking in found the liquor was only a little lower, so he resolved to make no further attempt, but gave back the horn to the cupbearer.

"I now see plainly," said Utgard-Loki, "that thou art not quite so stout as we thought thee: but wilt thou try any other feat, though methinks thou art not likely to bear any prize away with thee hence."

"What new trial hast thou to propose?" said Thor.

"We have a very trifling game here," answered Utgard-Loki, "in which we exercise none but children. It consists in merely lifting my cat from the ground; nor should I have dared to mention such a feat to the great Thor if I had not already observed that thou art by no means what we took thee for."

As he finished speaking, a large grey cat sprang on the hall floor. Thor put his hand under the cat's belly and did his utmost to raise him from the floor, but the cat, bending his back, had, notwithstanding all Thor's efforts, only one of his feet lifted up, seeing which Thor made no further attempt.

"This trial has turned out," said Utgard-Loki, "just as I imagined it would. The cat is large, but Thor is little in comparison to our men."

"Little as ye call me," answered Thor, "let me see who among you will come hither now I am in wrath and wrestle with me."

"I see no one here," said Utgard-Loki, looking at the men sitting on the benches, "who would not think it beneath him to wrestle with thee; let somebody, however, call hither that old crone, my nurse Elli, and let Thor wrestle with her if he will. She has thrown to the ground many a man not less strong than this Thor is."

A toothless old woman then entered the hall, and was told by Utgard-Loki to take hold of Thor. The tale is shortly told. The more Thor tightened his hold on the crone the firmer she stood. At length after a very violent struggle Thor began to lose his footing, and was finally brought down upon one knee. Utgard-Loki then told them to desist, adding that Thor had now no occasion to ask any one else in the hall to wrestle with him, and it was also getting late; so he showed Thor and his companions to their seats, and they passed the night there in good cheer.

The next morning, at break of day, Thor and his companions dressed themselves and prepared for their departure. Utgard-Loki ordered a table to be set for them, on which there was no lack of victuals or drink. After the repast Utgard-Loki led them to the gate of the city, and on parting asked Thor how he thought his journey had turned out, and whether he had met with any men stronger than himself. Thor told him that he could not deny but that he had brought great shame on himself. "And what grieves me most," he added, "is that ye will call me a person of little worth."

"Nay," said Utgard-Loki, "it behooves me to tell thee the truth, now thou art out of the city, which so long as I live and have my way thou shalt never enter again. And, by my troth, had I known beforehand that thou hadst so much strength in thee, and wouldst have brought me so near to a great mishap, I would not have suffered thee to enter this time. Know then that I have all along deceived thee by my illusions; first in the forest, where I tied up the wallet with iron wire so that thou couldst not untie it. After this thou gavest me three blows with thy mallet; the first, though the least, would have ended my days had it fallen on me, but I slipped aside and thy blows fell on the mountain, where thou wilt find three glens, one of them remarkably deep. These are the dints made by thy mallet. I have made use of similar illusions in the contests you have had with my followers. In the first, Loki, like hunger itself, devoured all that was set before him, but Logi was in reality nothing else than Fire, and therefore consumed not only the meat, but the trough which held it. Hugi, with whom Thialfi contended in running, was Thought, and it was impossible for Thialfi to keep pace with that. When thou in thy turn didst attempt to empty the horn, thou didst perform, by my troth, a deed so marvellous that had I not seen it myself I should never have believed it. For one end of that horn reached the sea, which thou wast not aware of, but when thou comest to the shore thou wilt perceive how much the sea has sunk by thy draughts. Thou didst perform a feat no less wonderful by lifting up the cat, and to tell thee the truth, when we saw that one of his paws was off the floor, we were all of us terror-stricken, for what thou tookest for a cat was in reality the Midgard serpent that encompasseth the earth, and he was so stretched by thee that he was barely long enough to enclose it between his head and tail. Thy wrestling with Elli was also a most astonishing feat, for there was never yet a man, nor ever will be, whom Old Age, for such in fact was Elli, will not sooner or later lay low. But now, as we are going to part, let me tell thee that it will be better for both of us if thou never come near me again, for shouldst thou do so, I shall again defend myself by other illusions, so that thou wilt only lose thy labour and get no fame from the contest with me."

On hearing these words Thor in a rage laid hold of his mallet and would have launched it at him, but Utgard-Loki had disappeared, and when Thor would have returned to the city to destroy it, he found nothing around him but a verdant plain.

CHAPTER XL

THE DEATH OF BALDUR—THE ELVES—RUNIC LETTERS— SKALDS—ICELAND

THE DEATH OF BALDUR

BALDUR the Good, having been tormented with terrible dreams indicating that his life was in peril, told them to the assembled gods, who resolved to conjure all things to avert from him the threatened danger. Then Frigga, the wife of Odin, exacted an oath from fire and water, from iron and all other metals, from stones, trees, diseases, beasts, birds, poisons, and creeping things, that none of them would do any harm to Baldur. Odin, not satisfied with all this, and feeling alarmed for the fate of his son, determined to consult the prophetess Angerbode, a giantess, mother of Fenris, Hela, and the Midgard serpent. She was dead, and Odin was forced to seek her in Hela's dominions. This Descent of Odin forms the subject of Gray's fine ode beginning:

> "Uprose the king of men with speed
> And saddled straight his coal-black steed."

But the other gods, feeling that what Frigga had done was quite sufficient, amused themselves with using Baldur as a mark, some hurling darts at him, some stones, while others hewed at him with their swords and battle-axes; for do what they would, none of them could harm him. And this became a favourite pastime with them and was regarded as an honour shown to Baldur. But when Loki beheld the scene he was sorely vexed that Baldur was not hurt. Assuming, therefore, the shape of a woman, he went to Fensalir, the mansion of Frigga. That goddess, when she saw the pretended woman, inquired of her if she knew what the gods were doing at their meetings. She replied that they were throwing darts and stones at Baldur, without being able to hurt him. "Ay," said Frigga, "neither stones, nor sticks, nor anything else can hurt Baldur, for I have exacted an oath from all of them." "What," exclaimed the woman, "have all things sworn to spare Baldur?" "All things," replied

Frigga, "except one little shrub that grows on the eastern side of Valhalla, and is called Mistletoe, and which I thought too young and feeble to crave an oath from."

As soon as Loki heard this he went away, and resuming his natural shape, cut off the mistletoe, and repaired to the place where the gods were assembled. There he found Hodur standing apart, without partaking of the sports, on account of his blindness, and going up to him, said, "Why dost thou not also throw something at Baldur?"

"Because I am blind," answered Hodur, "and see not where Baldur is, and have, moreover, nothing to throw."

"Come, then," said Loki, "do like the rest, and show honour to Baldur by throwing this twig at him, and I will direct thy arm towards the place where he stands."

Hodur then took the mistletoe, and under the guidance of Loki, darted it at Baldur, who, pierced through and through, fell down lifeless. Surely never was there witnessed, either among gods or men, a more atrocious deed than this. When Baldur fell, the gods were struck speechless with horror, and then they looked at each other and all were of one mind to lay hands on him who had done the deed, but they were obliged to delay their vengeance out of respect for the sacred place where they were assembled. They gave vent to their grief by loud lamentations. When the gods came to themselves, Frigga asked who among them wished to gain all her love and good will. "For this," said she, "shall he have who will ride to Hel and offer Hela a ransom if she will let Baldur return to Asgard." Whereupon Hermod, surnamed the Nimble, the son of Odin, offered to undertake the journey. Odin's horse, Sleipnir, which has eight legs and can outrun the wind, was then led forth, on which Hermod mounted and galloped away on his mission. For the space of nine days and as many nights he rode through deep glens so dark that he could not discern anything, until he arrived at the river Gyoll, which he passed over on a bridge covered with glittering gold. The maiden who kept the bridge asked him his name and lineage, telling him that the day before five bands of dead persons had ridden over the bridge, and did not shake it as much as he alone. "But," she added, "thou hast not death's hue on thee; why then ridest thou here on the way to Hel?"

"I ride to Hel," answered Hermod, "to seek Baldur. Hast thou perchance seen him pass this way?"

She replied, "Baldur hath ridden over Gyoll's bridge, and yonder lieth the way he took to the abodes of death."

Hermod pursued his journey until he came to the barred gates of Hel. Here he alighted, girthed his saddle tighter, and remounting clapped both spurs to his horse, who cleared the gate by a tremendous leap without touching it. Hermod then rode on to the palace, where he found his brother Baldur occupying the most distinguished seat in the hall, and passed the night in his company. The next morning he besought Hela to let Baldur ride home with him, assuring her that nothing but lamentations were to be heard among the gods. Hela answered that it should now be tried whether Baldur was so beloved as he was said to be. "If, therefore," she added, "all things in the world, both living and lifeless, weep for him, then shall he return to life; but if any one thing speak against him or refuse to weep, he shall be kept in Hel."

Hermod then rode back to Asgard and gave an account of all he had heard and witnessed.

The gods upon this despatched messengers throughout the world to beg everything to weep in order that Baldur might be delivered from Hel. All things very willingly complied with this request, both men and every other living being, as well as earths, and stones, and trees, and metals, just as we have all seen these things weep when they are brought from a cold place into a hot one. As the messengers were returning, they found an old hag named Thaukt sitting in a cavern, and begged her to weep Baldur out of Hel. But she answered:

> "Thaukt will wail
> With dry tears
> Baldur's bale-fire.
> Let Hela keep her own."

It was strongly suspected that this hag was no other than Loki himself, who never ceased to work evil among gods and men. So Baldur was prevented from coming back to Asgard.[1]

THE FUNERAL OF BALDUR

The gods took up the dead body and bore it to the seashore where stood Baldur's ship "Hringham," which passed for the largest in the world. Baldur's dead body was put on the funeral pile, on board the ship, and his wife Nanna was so struck with grief at the sight that she broke her heart, and her body was burned on the same pile with her husband's. There was a vast concourse of various kinds of people at Baldur's obsequies. First came Odin accompanied by Frigga, the Valkyrior, and his ravens; then Frey in his car drawn by Gullinbursti, the boar; Heimdall rode his horse Gulltopp, and Freya drove in her chariot drawn by cats. There were also a great many Frost giants and giants of the mountain present. Baldur's horse was led

---

[1] In Longfellow's Poems will be found a poem entitled "Tegner's Drapa," upon the subject of Baldur's death.

to the pile fully caparisoned and consumed in the same flames with his master.

But Loki did not escape his deserved punishment. When he saw how angry the gods were, he fled to the mountain, and there built himself a hut with four doors, so that he could see every approaching danger. He invented a net to catch the fishes, such as fishermen have used since his time. But Odin found out his hiding-place and the gods assembled to take him. He, seeing this, changed himself into a salmon, and lay hid among the stones of the brook. But the gods took his net and dragged the brook, and Loki, finding he must be caught, tried to leap over the net; but Thor caught him by the tail and compressed it, so that salmons ever since have had that part remarkably fine and thin. They bound him with chains and suspended a serpent over his head, whose venom falls upon his face drop by drop. His wife Siguna sits by his side and catches the drops as they fall, in a cup; but when she carries it away to empty it, the venom falls upon Loki, which makes him howl with horror, and twist his body about so violently that the whole earth shakes, and this produces what men call earthquakes.

The Elves

The Edda mentions another class of beings, inferior to the gods, but still possessed of great power; these were called Elves. The white spirits, or Elves of Light, were exceedingly fair, more brilliant than the sun, and clad in garments of a delicate and transparent texture. They loved the light, were kindly disposed to mankind, and generally appeared as fair and lovely children. Their country was called Alfheim, and was the domain of Freyr, the god of the sun, in whose light they were always sporting.

The black or Night Elves were a different kind of creatures. Ugly, long-nosed dwarfs, of a dirty brown colour, they appeared only at night, for they avoided the sun as their most deadly enemy, because whenever his beams fell upon any of them they changed them immediately into stones. Their language was the echo of solitudes, and their dwelling-places subterranean caves and clefts. They were supposed to have come into existence as maggots produced by the decaying flesh of Ymir's body, and were afterwards endowed by the gods with a human form and great understanding. They were particularly distinguished for a knowledge of the mysterious powers of nature, and for the runes which they carved and explained. They were the most skilful artificers of all created beings, and worked in metals and in wood. Among their most noted works were Thor's hammer, and the ship "Skidbladnir," which they gave to Freyr, and which was so

large that it could contain all the deities with their war and household implements, but so skilfully was it wrought that when folded
together it could be put into a side pocket.

RAGNAROK, THE TWILIGHT OF THE GODS

It was a firm belief of the northern nations that a time would come
when all the visible creation, the gods of Valhalla and Niffleheim, the
inhabitants of Jotunheim, Alfheim, and Midgard, together with their
habitations, would be destroyed. The fearful day of destruction will
not, however, be without its forerunners. First will come a triple
winter, during which snow will fall from the four corners of the
heavens, the frost be very severe, the wind piercing, the weather
tempestuous, and the sun impart no gladness. Three such winters
will pass away without being tempered by a single summer. Three
other similar winters will then follow, during which war and discord
will spread over the universe. The earth itself will be frightened and
begin to tremble, the sea leave its basin, the heavens tear asunder,
and men perish in great numbers, and the eagles of the air feast upon
their still quivering bodies. The wolf Fenris will now break his
bands, the Midgard serpent rise out of her bed in the sea, and Loki,
released from his bonds, will join the enemies of the gods. Amidst the
general devastation the sons of Muspelheim will rush forth under
their leader Surtur, before and behind whom are flames and burning
fire. Onward they ride over Bifrost, the rainbow bridge, which breaks
under the horses' hoofs. But they, disregarding its fall, direct their
course to the battlefield called Vigrid. Thither also repair the wolf
Fenris, the Midgard serpent, Loki with all the followers of Hela, and
the Frost giants.

Heimdall now stands up and sounds the Giallar horn to assemble
the gods and heroes for the contest. The gods advance, led on by
Odin, who engages the wolf Fenris, but falls a victim to the monster,
who is, however, slain by Vidar, Odin's son. Thor gains great renown
by killing the Midgard serpent, but recoils and falls dead, suffocated
with the venom which the dying monster vomits over him. Loki and
Heimdall meet and fight till they are both slain. The gods and their
enemies having fallen in battle, Surtur, who has killed Freyr, darts
fire and flames over the world, and the whole universe is burned up.
The sun becomes dim, the earth sinks into the ocean, the stars fall
from heaven, and time is no more.

After this Alfadur (the Almighty) will cause a new heaven and a
new earth to arise out of the sea. The new earth filled with abundant
supplies will spontaneously produce its fruits without labour or care.

Wickedness and misery will no more be known, but the gods and men will live happily together.

RUNIC LETTERS

One cannot travel far in Denmark, Norway, or Sweden without meeting with great stones of different forms, engraven with char- acters called Runic, which appear at first sight very different from all we know. The letters consist almost invariably of straight lines, in the shape of little sticks either singly or put together. Such sticks were in early times used by the northern nations for the purpose of ascertaining future events. The sticks were shaken up, and from the figures that they formed a kind of divination was derived.

The Runic characters were of various kinds. They were chiefly used for magical purposes. The noxious, or, as they called them, the *bitter* runes, were employed to bring various evils on their enemies; the favourable averted misfortune. Some were medicinal, others employed to win love, etc. In later times they were frequently used for inscriptions, of which more than a thousand have been found. The language is a dialect of the Gothic, called Norse, still in use in Iceland. The inscriptions may therefore be read with certainty, but hitherto very few have been found which throw the least light on history. They are mostly epitaphs on tombstones.

Gray's ode on the "Descent of Odin" contains an allusion to the use of Runic letters for incantation:

"Facing to the northern clime,
Thrice he traced the Runic rhyme;
Thrice pronounced, in accents dread
The thrilling verse that wakes the dead,
Till from out the hollow ground
Slowly breathed a sullen sound."

THE SKALDS

The Skalds were the bards and poets of the nation, a very im- portant class of men in all communities in an early stage of civiliza- tion. They are the depositaries of whatever historic lore there is, and it is their office to mingle something of intellectual gratification with the rude feasts of the warriors, by rehearsing, with such accomplish- ments of poetry and music as their skill can afford, the exploits of their heroes, living or dead. The compositions of the Skalds were called Sagas, many of which have come down to us, and contain valuable materials of history, and a faithful picture of the state of society at the time to which they relate.

ICELAND

The Eddas and Sagas have come to us from Iceland. The following extract from Carlyle's lectures on "Heroes and Hero Worship" gives an animated account of the region where the strange stories we have been reading had their origin. Let the reader contrast it for a moment with Greece, the parent of classical mythology:

"In that strange island, Iceland,—burst up, the geologists say, by fire from the bottom of the sea, a wild land of barrenness and lava, swallowed many months of every year in black tempests, yet with a wild, gleaming beauty in summer time, towering up there stern and grim in the North Ocean, with its snow yokuls [mountains], roaring geysers [boiling springs], sulphur pools, and horrid volcanic chasms, like the waste, chaotic battlefield of Frost and Fire,—where, of all places, we least looked for literature or written memorials,—the record of these things was written down. On the seaboard of this wild land is a rim of grassy country, where cattle can subsist, and men by means of them and of what the sea yields; and it seems they were poetic men these, men who had deep thoughts in them and uttered musically their thoughts. Much would be lost had Iceland not been burst up from the sea, not been discovered by the Northmen!"

CHAPTER XLI

THE DRUIDS—IONA

DRUIDS

THE Druids were the priests or ministers of religion among the ancient Celtic nations in Gaul, Britain, and Germany. Our information respecting them is borrowed from notices in the Greek and Roman writers, compared with the remains of Welsh and Gaelic poetry still extant.

The Druids combined the functions of the priest, the magistrate, the scholar, and the physician. They stood to the people of the Celtic tribes in a relation closely analogous to that in which the Brahmans of India, the Magi of Persia, and the priests of the Egyptians stood to the people respectively by whom they were revered.

The Druids taught the existence of one god, to whom they gave a name "Be' al," which Celtic antiquaries tell us means "the life of everything," or "the source of all beings," and which seems to have affinity with the Phœnician Baal. What renders this affinity more striking is that the Druids as well as the Phœnicians identified this, their supreme deity, with the *Sun*. Fire was regarded as a symbol of

the divinity. The Latin writers assert that the Druids also worshipped numerous inferior gods.

They used no images to represent the object of their worship, nor
did they meet in temples or buildings of any kind for the performance of their sacred rites. A circle of stones (each stone
generally of vast size), enclosing an area of from twenty feet to
thirty yards in diameter, constituted their sacred place. The most
celebrated of these now remaining is Stonehenge, on Salisbury Plain,
England.

These sacred circles were generally situated near some stream, or
under the shadow of a grove or widespreading oak. In the centre
of the circle stood the Cromlech or altar, which was a large stone,
placed in the manner of a table upon other stones set up on end.
The Druids had also their high places, which were large stones or
piles of stones on the summits of hills. These were called Cairns,
and were used in the worship of the deity under the symbol of the
sun.

That the Druids offered sacrifices to their deity there can be no
doubt. But there is some uncertainty as to what they offered, and
of the ceremonies connected with their religious services we know
almost nothing. The classical (Roman) writers affirm that they
offered on great occasions human sacrifices; as for success in war
or for relief from dangerous diseases. Cæsar has given a detailed
account of the manner in which this was done. "They have images
of immense size, the limbs of which are framed with twisted twigs
and filled with living persons. These being set on fire, those within
are encompassed by the flames." Many attempts have been made
by Celtic writers to shake the testimony of the Roman historians
to this fact, but without success.

The Druids observed two festivals in each year. The former took
place in the beginning of May, and was called Beltane or "fire of
God." On this occasion a large fire was kindled on some elevated
spot, in honour of the sun, whose returning beneficence they thus
welcomed after the gloom and desolation of winter. Of this custom
a trace remains in the name given to Whitsunday in parts of Scotland to this day. Sir Walter Scott uses the word in the "Boat Song"
in the "Lady of the Lake":

> "Ours is no sapling, chance sown by the fountain,
> Blooming at Beltane in winter to fade;" etc.

The other great festival of the Druids was called "Samh' in," or
"fire of peace," and was held on Hallow-eve (first of November),
which still retains this designation in the Highlands of Scotland.
On this occasion the Druids assembled in solemn conclave, in the
most central part of the district, to discharge the judicial functions

of their order. All questions, whether public or private, all crimes against person or property, were at this time brought before them for adjudication. With these judicial acts were combined certain superstitious usages, especially the kindling of the sacred fire, from which all the fires in the district, which had been beforehand scrupulously extinguished, might be relighted. This usage of kindling fires on Hallow-eve lingered in the British islands long after the establishment of Christianity.

Besides these two great annual festivals, the Druids were in the habit of observing the full moon, and especially the sixth day of the moon. On the latter they sought the Mistletoe, which grew on their favourite oaks, and to which, as well as to the oak itself, they ascribed a peculiar virtue and sacredness. The discovery of it was an occasion of rejoicing and solemn worship. "They call it," says Pliny, "by a word in their language, which means 'heal-all,' and having made solemn preparation for feasting and sacrifice under the tree, they drive thither two milk-white bulls, whose horns are then for the first time bound. The priest then, robed in white, ascends the tree, and cuts off the mistletoe with a golden sickle. It is caught in a white mantle, after which they proceed to slay the victims, at the same time praying that God would render his gift prosperous to those to whom he had given it." They drink the water in which it has been infused, and think it a remedy for all diseases. The mistletoe is a parasitic plant, and is not always nor often found on the oak, so that when it is found it is the more precious.

The Druids were the teachers of morality as well as of religion. Of their ethical teaching a valuable specimen is preserved in the Triads of the Welsh Bards, and from this we may gather that their views of moral rectitude were on the whole just, and that they held and inculcated many very noble and valuable principles of conduct. They were also the men of science and learning of their age and people. Whether they were acquainted with letters or not has been disputed, though the probability is strong that they were, to some extent. But it is certain that they committed nothing of their doctrine, their history, or their poetry to writing. Their teaching was oral, and their literature (if such a word may be used in such a case) was preserved solely by tradition. But the Roman writers admit that "they paid much attention to the order and laws of nature, and investigated and taught to the youth under their charge many things concerning the stars and their motions, the size of the world and the lands, and concerning the might and power of the immortal gods."

Their history consisted in traditional tales, in which the heroic deeds of their forefathers were celebrated. These were apparently in verse, and thus constituted part of the poetry as well as the history of the Druids. In the poems of Ossian we have, if not the actual productions of Druidical times, what may be considered faithful representations of the songs of the Bards.

The Bards were an essential part of the Druidical hierarchy. One author, Pennant, says, "The Bards were supposed to be endowed with powers equal to inspiration. They were the oral historians of all past transactions, public and private. They were also accomplished genealogists," etc.

Pennant gives a minute account of the Eisteddfods or sessions of the Bards and minstrels, which were held in Wales for many centuries, long after the Druidical priesthood in its other departments became extinct. At these meetings none but Bards of merit were suffered to rehearse their pieces, and minstrels of skill to perform. Judges were appointed to decide on their respective abilities, and suitable degrees were conferred. In the earlier period the judges were appointed by the Welsh princes, and after the conquest of Wales, by commission from the kings of England. Yet the tradition is that Edward I, in revenge for the influence of the Bards in animating the resistance of the people to his sway, persecuted them with great cruelty. This tradition has furnished the poet Gray with the subject of his celebrated ode, the "Bard."

There are still occasional meetings of the lovers of Welsh poetry and music, held under the ancient name. Among Mrs. Hemans' poems is one written for an Eisteddfod, or meeting of Welsh Bards, held in London, May 22, 1822. It begins with a description of the ancient meeting, of which the following lines are a part:

> "... midst the eternal cliffs, whose strength defied
> The crested Roman in his hour of pride;
> And where the Druid's ancient cromlech frowned,
> And the oaks breathed mysterious murmurs round,
> There thronged the inspired of yore! on plain or height,
> In the sun's face, beneath the eye of light,
> And baring unto heaven each noble head,
> Stood in the circle, where none else might tread."

The Druidical system was at its height at the time of the Roman invasion under Julius Cæsar. Against the Druids, as their chief enemies, these conquerors of the world directed their unsparing fury. The Druids, harassed at all points on the mainland, retreated to Anglesey and Iona, where for a season they found shelter and continued their now dishonoured rites.

The Druids retained their predominance in Iona and over the adjacent islands and mainland until they were supplanted and their superstitions overturned by the arrival of St. Columba, the apostle of the Highlands, by whom the inhabitants of that district were first led to profess Christianity.

IONA

One of the smallest of the British Isles, situated near a rugged and barren coast, surrounded by dangerous seas, and possessing no sources of internal wealth, Iona has obtained an imperishable place in history as the seat of civilization and religion at a time when the darkness of heathenism hung over almost the whole of Northern Europe. Iona or Icolmkill is situated at the extremity of the island of Mull, from which it is separated by a strait of half a mile in breadth, its distance from the mainland of Scotland being thirty-six miles.

Columba was a native of Ireland, and connected by birth with the princes of the land. Ireland was at that time a land of gospel light, while the western and northern parts of Scotland were still immersed in the darkness of heathenism. Columba with twelve friends landed on the island of Iona in the year of our Lord 563, having made the passage in a wicker boat covered with hides. The Druids who occupied the island endeavoured to prevent his settling there, and the savage nations on the adjoining shores incommoded him with their hostility, and on several occasions endangered his life by their attacks. Yet by his perseverance and zeal he surmounted all opposition, procured from the king a gift of the island, and established there a monastery of which he was the abbot. He was unwearied in his labours to disseminate a knowledge of the Scriptures throughout the Highlands and islands of Scotland, and such was the reverence paid him that though not a bishop, but merely a presbyter and monk, the entire province with its bishops was subject to him and his successors. The Pictish monarch was so impressed with a sense of his wisdom and worth that he held him in the highest honour, and the neighbouring chiefs and princes sought his counsel and availed themselves of his judgment in settling their disputes.

When Columba landed on Iona he was attended by twelve followers whom he had formed into a religious body of which he was the head. To these, as occasion required, others were from time to time added, so that the original number was always kept up. Their institution was called a monastery and the superior an abbot, but the system had little in common with the monastic institutions of later times. The name by which those who submitted to the rule were known was that of Culdees, probably from the Latin "cultores Dei"—worshippers of God. They were a body of religious persons associated together for the purpose of aiding each other in the

common work of preaching the gospel and teaching youth, as well
as maintaining in themselves the fervour of devotion by united
exercises of worship. On entering the order certain vows were taken
by the members, but they were not those which were usually imposed
by monastic orders, for of these, which are three—celibacy, poverty,
and obedience,—the Culdees were bound to none except the third.
To poverty they did not bind themselves; on the contrary they
seem to have laboured diligently to procure for themselves and those
dependent on them the comforts of life. Marriage also was allowed
them, and most of them seem to have entered into that state. True,
their wives were not permitted to reside with them at the institution,
but they had a residence assigned to them in an adjacent locality.
Near Iona there is an island which still bears the name of "Eilen
nam ban," women's island, where their husbands seem to have resided with them, except when duty required their presence in the
school or the sanctuary.

Campbell, in his poem of "Reullura," alludes to the married
monks of Iona:

> "...The pure Culdees
>   Were Albyn's earliest priests of God,
> Ere yet an island of her seas
>   By foot of Saxon monk was trod,
> Long ere her churchmen by bigotry
> Were barred from holy wedlock's tie.
> 'Twas then that Aodh, famed afar,
>   In Iona preached the word with power,
> And Reullura, beauty's star,
>   Was the partner of his bower."

In one of his "Irish Melodies," Moore gives the legend of St.
Senanus and the lady who sought shelter on the island, but was
repulsed:

> "O, haste and leave this sacred isle,
> Unholy bark, ere morning smile;
> For on thy deck, though dark it be,
>   A female form I see;
> And I have sworn this sainted sod
> Shall ne'er by woman's foot be trod."

In these respects and in others the Culdees departed from the
established rules of the Romish church, and consequently were
deemed heretical. The consequence was that as the power of the
latter advanced that of the Culdees was enfeebled. It was not, however, till the thirteenth century that the communities of the Culdees
were suppressed and the members dispersed. They still continued to
labour as individuals, and resisted the inroads of Papal usurpation

as they best might till the light of the Reformation dawned on the world.

Iona, from its position in the western seas, was exposed to the assaults of the Norwegian and Danish rovers by whom those seas were infested, and by them it was repeatedly pillaged, its dwellings burned, and its peaceful inhabitants put to the sword. These unfavourable circumstances led to its gradual decline, which was expedited by the subversion of the Culdees throughout Scotland. Under the reign of Popery the island became the seat of a nunnery, the ruins of which are still seen. At the Reformation, the nuns were allowed to remain, living in community, when the abbey was dismantled.

Iona is now chiefly resorted to by travellers on account of the numerous ecclesiastical and sepulchral remains which are found upon it. The principal of these are the Cathedral or Abbey Church and the Chapel of the Nunnery. Besides these remains of ecclesiastical antiquity, there are some of an earlier date, and pointing to the existence on the island of forms of worship and belief different from those of Christianity. These are the circular Cairns which are found in various parts, and which seem to have been of Druidical origin. It is in reference to all these remains of ancient religion that Johnson exclaims, "That man is little to be envied whose patriotism would not gain force upon the plains of Marathon, or whose piety would not grow warmer amid the ruins of Iona."

In the "Lord of the Isles," Scott beautifully contrasts the church on Iona with the cave of Staffa, opposite:

> "Nature herself, it seemed, would raise
> A minster to her Maker's praise!
> Not for a meaner use ascend
> Her columns, or her arches bend;
> Nor of a theme less solemn tells
> That mighty surge that ebbs and swells,
> And still between each awful pause,
> From the high vault an answer draws,
> In varied tone, prolonged and high,
> That mocks the organ's melody;
> Nor doth its entrance front in vain
> To old Iona's holy fane,
> That Nature's voice might seem to say,
> Well hast thou done, frail child of clay!
> Thy humble powers that stately shrine
> Tasked high and hard—but witness mine!"

CHAPTER XLII

BEOWULF

ALTHOUGH the manuscript which contains the epic of Beowulf was written about 1000 A.D., the poem itself was known and had been elaborated upon for centuries by minstrels who recited the heroic exploits of the son of Ecgtheow and nephew of Hygelac, King of the Geats, whose kingdom was what is now Southern Sweden.

In his boyhood Beowulf gave evidence of the great feats of strength and courage which in manhood made him the deliverer of Hrothgar, King of Denmark, from the monster, Grendel, and later in his own kingdom from the fiery dragon which dealt Beowulf a mortal blow.

Beowulf's first renown followed his conquest of many sea-monsters while he swam for seven days and nights before he came to the country of the Finns. Helping to defend the land of the Hetware, he killed many of the enemy and again showed his prowess as a swimmer by bringing to his ship the armor of thirty of his slain pursuers. Offered the crown of his native land, Beowulf, just entering manhood, refused it in favor of Heardred, the young son of the queen. Instead, he acted as guardian and counsellor until the boy-king grew old enough to rule alone.

For twelve years, Hrothgar, King of Denmark, suffered while his kingdom was being ravaged by a devouring monster, named Grendel. This Grendel bore a charmed life against all weapons forged by man. He lived in the wastelands and nightly prowled out to visit the hall of Hrothgar, carrying off and slaughtering many of the guests.

Beowulf, hearing from mariners of Grendel's murderous visits, sailed from Geatland with fourteen stalwart companions to render Hrothgar the help of his great strength. Landing on the Danish coast, Beowulf was challenged as a spy. He persuaded the coast-guards to let him pass, and he was received and feasted by King Hrothgar. When the king and his court retired for the night, Beowulf and his companions were left alone in the hall. All but Beowulf fell asleep. Grendel entered. With a stroke he killed one of Beowulf's sleeping men, but Beowulf, unarmed, wrestled with the monster and by dint of his great strength managed to tear Grendel's arm out at the shoulder. Grendel, mortally wounded, retreated, leaving a bloody trail from the hall to his lair.

All fear of another attack by Grendel allayed. the Danes returned to the hall, and Beowulf and his companions were sheltered elsewhere. Grendel's mother came to avenge the fatal injury to her monster son and carried off a Danish nobleman and Grendel's torn-off paw. Following the blood trail, Beowulf went forth to despatch the mother. Armed with his sword, Hrunting, he came to the water's edge. He plunged in and swam to a chamber under the sea. There he fought with Grendel's mother, killing her with an old sword he found in the sea cavern. Nearby was Grendel's body. Beowulf cut off its head and brought it back as a trophy to King Hrothgar. Great was the rejoicing in the hall and greater was Beowulf's welcome when he returned to Geatland, where he was given great estates and many high honors.

Shortly afterward, Heardred, the boy-king, was killed in the war with the Swedes. Beowulf succeeded him to the throne.

For fifty years Beowulf ruled his people in peace and serenity. Then suddenly a dragon, furious at having his treasure stolen from his hoard in a burial mound, began to ravage Beowulf's kingdom. Like Grendel, this monster left its den at night on its errand of murder and pillage.

Beowulf, now an aged monarch, resolved to do battle, unaided, with the dragon. He approached the entrance to its den, whence boiling steam issued forth. Undaunted, Beowulf strode forward shouting his defiance. The dragon came out, sputtering flames from its mouth. The monster rushed upon Beowulf with all its fury and almost crushed him in its first charge. So fearful grew the struggle that all but one of Beowulf's men deserted and fled for their lives. Wiglaf remained to help his aged monarch. Another rush of the dragon shattered Beowulf's sword and the monster's fangs sunk into Beowulf's neck. Wiglaf, rushing into the struggle, helped the dying Beowulf to kill the dragon.

Before his death, Beowulf named Wiglaf his successor to the throne of Geatland and ordered that his own ashes be placed in a memorial shrine at the top of a high cliff commanding the sea. Beowulf's body was burned on a vast funeral pyre, while twelve Geats rode around the mound singing their sorrow and their praise for the good and great man, Beowulf.

PROVERBIAL EXPRESSIONS

No. 1. Page 37
MATERIEM superabat opus.—*Ovid.*
The workmanship surpassed the material.

No. 2. Page 37
Facies non omnibus una,
Nec diversa tamen, qualem decet esse sororum.—*Ovid.*
Their faces were not all alike, nor yet unlike, but such as those of sisters ought to be.

No. 3. Page 39
Medio tutissimus ibis.—*Ovid.*
You will go most safely in the middle.

No. 4. Page 41
Hic situs est Phaëton, currus auriga paterni,
Quem si non tenuit, magnis tamen excidit ausis.—*Ovid.*
Here lies Phaëton, the driver of his father's chariot, which if he failed to manage, yet he fell in a great undertaking.

No. 5. Page 102
Imponere Pelio Ossam.—*Virgil.*
To pile Ossa upon Pelion.

No. 6. Page 185
Timeo Danaos et dona ferentes.—*Virgil.*
I fear the Greeks even when they offer gifts.

No. 7. Page 187
Non tali auxilio nec defensoribus istis
Tempus eget.—*Virgil.*
Not such aid nor such defenders does the time require.

No. 8. Page 197
Incidit in Scyllam, cupiens vitare Charybdim.
He runs on Scylla, wishing to avoid Charybdis.

No. 9. Page 207
Sequitur patrem, non passibus æquis.—*Virgil.*
He follows his father with unequal steps.

No. 10. Page 209

Monstrum horrendum, informe, ingens, cui lumen ademptum.—*Virgil.*

A horrible monster, misshapen, vast, whose only eye had been put out.

No. 11. Page 209

Tantæne animis cœlestibus iræ?—*Virgil.*

In heavenly minds can such resentments dwell?

No. 12. Page 210

Haud ignara mali, miseris succurrere disco.—*Virgil.*

Not unacquainted with distress, I have learned to succour the unfortunate.

No. 13. Page 211

Tros, Tyriusve mihi nullo discrimine agetur.—*Virgil.*

Whether Trojan or Tyrian shall make no difference to me.

No. 14. Page 212

Tu ne cede malis, sed contra audentior ito.—*Virgil.*

Yield thou not to adversity, but press on the more bravely.

No. 15. Page 212

Facilis descensus Averni;
Noctes atque dies patet atri janua Ditis;
Sed revocare gradum, superasque evadere ad auras,
Hoc opus, hic labor est.—*Virgil.*

The descent to Avernus is easy; the gate of Pluto stands open night and day; but to retrace one's steps and return to the upper air, that is the toil, that the difficulty.

No. 16. Page 213

Uno avulso non deficit alter.—*Virgil.*

When one is torn away another succeeds.

No. 17. Page 225

Quadrupedante putrem sonitu quatit ungula campum.—*Virgil.*

Then struck the hoofs of the steeds on the ground with a four-footed trampling.

No. 18. Page 228

Sternitur infelix alieno vulnere, cœlumque
Adspicit et moriens dulces reminiseitur Argos.—*Virgil.*

He falls, unhappy, by a wound intended for another; looks up to the skies, and dying remembers sweet Argos.

INDEX OF NAMES

Absyrtus, 113
Aby'dos, 89
Ace'tes, 166
Acha'tes, 225
Achelo'us, 144
Achilles, 171
Acis, 169
Acon'teus, 100
Actæon, 33
Adme'ta, 119
Adme'tus, 146
Ado'nis, 58
Adrastus, 148
Æ'acus, 80
Æe'tes, 108
Æge'us, 124
Ægis, 97
Ægisthus 188
Æne'as, 172, 207
Æ'olus, 193, 209
Æscula'pius, 105, 238
Æson, 107
Æthiopians, 8
Æthra, 124
Agame'des, 238
Agamemnon, 172, 188
Aga've, 134
Age'nor, 77
Agla'ia, 13
Agni, 256
Ah'riman, 254
Ajax, 172
Alces'tis, 146
Alci'des, 122
Alcin'o-us, 199
Alcme'na, 118
Alecto, 13
Alexander. See Paris
Alfa'dur, 264
Alphe'us, 50
Althæ'a, 114
Amalthe'a, 146
Am'azons, 119, 125
Ambro'sia, 9
Ammon, 102
Amphiara'us, 148

Amphi'on, 94, 156
Amphitri'te, 141
Ampyx, 100
Amri'ta, 256
Amymo'ne, 118
Anaxar'ete, 67
Ance'us, 114
Anchi'ses, 207
Andræ'mon, 57
Androm'ache, 172, 208
Androm'eda, 98
Anemo'ne, 59
Antæ'us, 120
Ante'a, 103
An'teros, 11
Antig'one, 148
Anti'ope, 125, 156
Anu'bis, 234
Aphrodi'te, 11
Apis, 235, 239
Apollo, 11, 21
Aq'uilo, 143
Arach'ne, 90
Arcas, 32
Areop'agus, 189
Ares, 11
Arethu'sa, 50
Argo, 108
Ar'gonauts, 108
Argus, 29, 108, 205
Ariad'ne, 125, 135
Arima'nes, 254
Arimas'pians, 107
Ari'on, 158
Aristæ'us, 151, 153
Ar'temis, 11
Ascræ'an—Hesiod
Asgard, 263
Aske, 263
Astræ'a, 18
Asty'ages, 100
Atalan'ta, 114
Ate, 179
Ath'amas, 107
Athe'ne, 11
Atlan'tis, 219

Atlas, 97
At'ropos, 13
Audhum'bla, 262
Au'geas, 119
Aulis, 172
Auro'ra, 168
Auster, 143
Av'atar, 256
Bacchanals, 132
Bacchus, 12, 131
Bac'trian sage—Zoro-
  aster
Baldur, 274
Bards, 282
Basilisk, 250
Baucis, 44
Beller'ophon, 103
Bello'na, 14
Beltane, 281
Beowulf, 287
Ber'oë, 131
Bifrost, 263
Bo'reas, 143
Bragi, 265
Brahma, 256
Brazen age, 17
Bria'reus, 10
Brise'is, 174
Buddha, 260
Byrsa, 210
Cacus, 120
Cadmus, 77
Cadu'ceus, 12
Cai'cus, 40
Cal'a-is, 143
Calchas, 172
Calli'ope, 12
Callisto, 31
Cal'ydon, 114
Calypso, 197
Came'næ, 143
Camil'la, 222, 229
Cap'aneus, 149
Cassandra, 187
Cassiope'ia, 98
Castes, 258

Castor, 129
Ce'crops, 90
Ce'leus, 48
Centaurs, 105
Ceph'alus, 26, 80
Ce'pheus, 98
Cer'berus, 121
Ce'res, 12, 48
Cestus, 11, 176
Ce-yx, 60
Chaos, 15
Charon, 214
Charyb'dis, 196, 209
Chimæra, 103
Chiron, 105
Chryse'is, 174
Chryses, 174
Cir'ce, 53, 194
Clio, 12
Clotho, 13
Clym'ene, 36
Clytemnes'tra, 188
Clyt'i-e, 87
Cockatrice, 250
Columba, 284
Cornucopia, 146
Corybantes, 118
Cranes, 106
Creon, 149
Cre-u'sa, 113
Cromlech, 281
Cronos, 13
Culdees, 285
Cupid, 11, 68
Cy'ane, 49
Cyb'e-le, 117
Cyclo'pses, 146, 191, 209
Cyn'osure, 32
Cyre'ne, 154
Dæd'alus, 128
Dalai Lama, 261
Dan'a-e, 91, 96, 163
Daphne, 21
Dar'danus, 208
Dawn, 168
Deiph'obus, 172
Dejani'ra, 144
Delos, 36, 207
Del'phi, 7, 237
Deme'ter, 12
Demod'ocus, 202
Deuca'lion, 19
Dia'na, 33
Dictys, 133
Dido, 210

Diomed, } 172
Diomede, } 184
Dio'ne, 11
Diony'sus, 12
Dioscu'ri, 130
Dirce, 156
Dis, 10
Dodo'na, 237
Doris, 141
Druids, 280
Dryads, 136
Dry'ope, 56
Ecgtheow, 287
Echo, 84
Edda, 262
Ege'ria, 143
Electra, 167, 188
Eleusinian mysteries, 51
Eleusis, 51
Elgin marbles, 127, 243
Elli, 272
Elves, 277
Elysium, 218
Embla, 263
Encel'adus, 102
Endym'ion, 165
Epidau'rus, 238
Epime'theus, 16
Epo'peus, 133
Er'ato, 13
Er'ebus—the infernal
    regions
Erid'anus, 41
Erin'nyes, 13, 189
Eriph'yle, 148
Eris, 171
Erisich'thon, 138
Eros, 9
Ete'ocles, 149
Eumæ'us, 204
Eumen'ides, 13, 163 189
Euphros'yne, 13
Euro'pa, 91
Eury'alus, 227
Euryd'ice, 150
Euryn'ome, 10
Eurys'theus, 119
Euryt'ion, 105
Eurus, 143
Euter'pe, 12
Evadne, 149
Evan'der, 223
Famine, 139
Fates, 13
Faunus, 14, 136

Favo'nius, 143
Fenris, 265
Flora, 14, 144
Freki, 264
Frey, 265
Freya, 265
Frigga, 274
Furies, 13, 161
Galatea, 169
Gan'ymede, 123
Gautama, 260
Gem'ini, 130
Genius, 64
Geri, 263
Ger'yon, 119
Giallar horn, 278
Giants, 101
Glaucus, 52, 172
Golden age, 17
Golden fleece, 107
Gordian knot, 44
Gorgons, 96
Graces, 13
Grææ, 96
Grendel, 287
Griffin, 106
Guebers, 255
Hades, 121
Hæmon, 149
Halcy'one, 60
Hamad'ryads, 136
Harmo'nia, 79, 148
Harpies, 208
Harpoc'rates, 234
Heardred, 287
Hæbe, 123
Hebrus, 152
Hec'ate, 108
Hector, 172
Hec'uba, 186
Heidrum, 264
Heimdall, 265
Hela, 265
Helen, 171, 187
Hel'enus, 209
Heli'ades, 42
Hel'icon, 40
Hellas, 8
Helle, 107
Hel'lespont, 107
Hephæs'tus, 10
Hera, 10
Hercules, 118
Hermes, 12
Hermod, 275

Hero, 88
Hespe'ria, 208
Hesper'ides, 119
Hes'perus, 119
Hestia, 14
Hindus, 256
Hippocre'ne, 103
Hippodami'a, 105
Hippol'yta, 119
Hippol'ytus, 126
Hippom'enes, 116
Hodur, 275
Homer, 246
Horus, 234
Hrothgar, 287
Hrunting, 288
Hugi, 271
Hugin, 263
Hyacin'thus, 59
Hy'ades, 131
Hydra, 118
Hyge'ia, 142
Hygelac, 287
Hylas, 110
Hymen, 151
Hyperbo'reans, 8
Hype'rion, } 10, 196
Hyperi'on, }
Iap'etus, 10
Ia'sius, 114
Ib'ycus, 161
Ica'rius, 150
Ic'arus, 128
Ida, 171
Idas, 130
Idu'na, 265
Iliad, 174
Ilion. See Troy.
Ili'oneus, 94
Indra, 256
Ino, 142
Io, 28
Iob'ates, 103
Iola'us, 119
I'ole, 121
Io'na, 284
Iphigeni'a, 173, 189
Iphis, 67
Iph'itus, 121
Iris, 10, 62
Iron age, 17
Isis, 234
Isme'nos, 94
Isthmian games, 127
Ith'aca, 203

Ixi'on, 151, 216
Janus, 14
Jason, 107
Jocasta, 103, 148
Jotunheim, 263
Jove, 9
Juggernaut, 257
Juno, 10, 28, 171
Ju'piter, 9
Lab'yrinth, 125
Lach'esis, 13
Læstrygo'nians, 194
La'ius, 102
Lama, 261
Laoc'oön, 185
Laodami'a, 173
Lap'ithæ, 105
Lares, 14
Larva, 14
Lati'nus, 221
Latmos, 165
Lato'na, 34, 93
Lausus, 228
Lavin'ia, 221
Lean'der, 88
Leda, 91
Lemur, 14
Lesbian—Sappho
Lethe, 217
Leucothe'a, 142
Liber, 14
Libe'thra, 152
Lichas, 121
Linus, 157
Logi, 271
Loki, 265
Lotis, 57
Lotus eaters, 190
Luci'na, 14
Ly'cabas, 133
Lycome'des, 126, 172
Lycus, 156
Lyn'ceus, 130
Macha'on, 176
Mæander, 128
Mæoni'des. See Homer.
Magi, 254
Mahade'va, 257
Maia, 12
Mantu'an swain. See
Virgil
Manu, 256
Maro. See Virgil
Mars, 11
Mar'syas, 157

Mede'a, 108, 111
Medu'sa, 96
Megæ'ra, 13
Melampus, 157
Melan'thus, 133
Melea'ger, 114
Melicer'tes, 142
Melisseus, 146
Melpom'ene, 12
Memnon, 168
Menela'us, 171, 187
Menœ'ceus, 149
Mentor, 198
Mercury, 12
Mer'ope, 166
Metani'ra, 49
Metempsycho'sis, 218
Metis, 10
Mezen'tius, 228
Midas, 42
Midgard, 263
Milky way, 18
Milo, 233
Miner'va, 89, 171
Minos, 80, 125, 128
Min'otaur, 125
Mistletoe, 275, 282
Mnemos'yne, 10
Momus, 13
Monsters, 101
Mor'pheus, 63
Mul'ciber, 14
Musæus, 158
Muses, 12
Myr'midons, 80
Na'iads, 142
Nanna, 276
Narcissus, 84
Nausic'aa, 199
Negus, 262
Ne'mean games, 127
Ne'mean lion, 158
Nem'esis, 13
Neoptol'emus, 188
Nepenthe, 188
Neph'ele, 107
Neptune, 141
Ne'reids, 41, 141
Ne'reus, 41, 141
Nessus, 121
Nestor, 172
Nidhogge, 263
Niffleheim, 263
Ni'obe, 93
Nisus, 83, 226

Norns, 263
Numa, 143
Nymphs, 136
Nysæ'an nymphs, 131
Oce'anus, 141
Odin, 263
Od'yssey, 183
Œd'ipus, 102, 148
Œ'neus, 114
Œno'ne, 184
Œno'pion, 166
Œta, 122
Olympiads, 127
Olympic games, 127
Olympus, 7
Om'phale, 121
Ophi'on, 10
Ops, 117
Oracles, 237
O'reads, 136
Ores'tes, 188
Ori'on, 166
Orithyi'a, 143
Ormuzd, 254
Or'pheus, 150
Oromas'des, 254
Osi'ris, 234
Ossa, 102
Os'sian, 283
Ov'id, 246
Pacto'lus, 43
Pæon, 142
Palæ'mon, 142
Palame'des, 171
Pa'les, 14
Palinu'rus, 211
Palla'dium, 184
Pallas, 11, 229
Pan, 13, 43, 136
Panathenæ'a, 127
Pando'ra, 15
Parcæ. See Fates
Pa'riahs, 259
Paris, 171
Parnas'sus, 19, 237
Parsees, 255
Par'thenon, 127
Patro'clus, 176
Peg'asus, 103
Pe'leus, 114
Pe'lias 107, 146
Pe'lion 102
Pena'tes 14
Penel'ope, 150, 205
Pe'neus, 22

Penthesile'a, 183
Pen'theus, 132
Pe'plus, 127
Periander, 158
Periphe'tes, 124
Perseph'one, 12
Per'seus, 96
Phæacians, 199
Phædra, 126
Pha'eton, 36
Phaon, 165
Phile'mon, 44
Philocte'tes, 122, 184
Phin'eus, 100, 108
Phœbus, 11
Phœnix, 248
Phryxus, 107
Pirith'o-us, 105, 126
Ple'iads, 167
Plenty, 145
Plexip'pus, 115
Pluto, 48
Plutus, 13
Poli'tes, 187
Pollux, 129
Polydec'tes, 96
Pol'ydore, 207
Polyhym'nia, 13
Polyi'dus, 104
Polyni'ces, 148
Polyphe'mus, 209
Polyx'ena, 183, 187
Pomo'na, 14, 26, 65
Portu'nus, 142
Posei'don, 10
Prester John, 261
Pri'am, 172
Pro'cris, 26
Procrus'tes, 124
Prome'theus, 15
Pros'erpine, }
Proser'pine, } 47
Protesila'us, 173
Pro'teus, 141, 154
Psyche, 68
Pura'nas, 257
Pygma'lion, 35, 210
Pygmies, 106
Pyl'ades, 189
Pyr'amus, 24
Pyrrha, 19
Pyrrhus, 187
Pythag'oras, 230
Pyth'ia, 237
Pythian games, 127

Python, 22
Quiri'nus, 14
Rhadaman'thus, 215
Rhea, 10
Rhœcus, 140
Sabri'na, 156
Sagitta'rius, 106
Sakyasin'ha, 260
Salamander, 252
Sa'mian sage, 230
Sappho, 164
Sarpe'don, 172, 177
Saturn, 10, 13
Satyrs, 13
Scylla, 52, 196
Sem'ele, 131
Sera'pis, 234
Shatriy'a, 258
Sibyl, 212, 219
Sichæus, 210
Sile'nus, 42
Silver age, 17
Simon'ides, 163
Sinon, 186
Sirens, 195
Sir'ius, 167
Sis'yphus, 274
Siva, 257
Skalds, 279
Skidbladnir, 277
Skirnir, 268
Skrymir, 269
Skuld, 263
Sleipnir, 279
Somnus, 62, 211
Sphinx, 102
Stonehenge, 281
Styx, 131
Sudra, 253
Surtur, 278
Surya, 256
Syb'aris, 233
Sylva'nus, 66, 136
Sympleg'ades, 108
Syrinx, 29
Tan'talus, 93, 216
Tar'tarus, 216
Tauris, 173, 189
Tel'amon, 114
Telem'achus, 198, 204
Tellus, 111
Ter'minus, 14
Terpsich'ore, 12
Terra, 120
Te'thys, 31, 141

Thali'a, 13
Tham'yris, 157
Thebes, 77
Themis, 13
Thersi'tes, 183
Thes'celus, 100
The'seus, 124
Thes'tius, 115
The'tis, 141, 175, 179
Thialfi, 269
Thisbe, 24
Thor, 265
Thrym, 267
Tire'sias, 149
Tisiph'one, 13, 215
Titans, 9, 16
Titho'nus, 167
Tit'yus, 101
Tox'eus, 115

Triptol'emus, 50
Triton, 141
Tropho'nius, 238
Troy, 171
Turnus, 229
Typhon, 47, 234
Tyr, 266
Ulysses, 150, 171, 190
Unicorn, 251
Urania, 13
Urdur, 263
Utgard, 270
Utgard-Loki, 270
Vaissya, 258
Valhalla, 263
Valkyr'ior, 264
Vedas, 256
Venus, 11, 58, 171
Verdandi, 263

Vertumnus 65
Vesta, 14
Virgil, 246
Vishnu, 256
Vulcan, 10
Vya'sa, 256
Wiglaf, 288
Winds, 143
Woden, 264
Wooden horse, 185
Yama, 256
Ygdrasill, 263
Ymir, 262
Zendaves'ta, 254
Zeph'yrus, 60, 144
Zetes, 143
Zethus, 156
Zeus, 9
Zoroas'ter, 254

THE AGE OF CHIVALRY
OR
LEGENDS OF KING ARTHUR

Throngs of knights and barons bold,
In weeds of peace high triumphs hold,
With store of ladies, whose bright eyes
Rain influence and judge the prize.
MILTON.

PREFACE

IN a former work the compiler of this volume endeavored to impart the pleasures of classical learning to the English reader, by presenting the stories of Pagan mythology in a form adapted to modern taste. In the present volume the attempt has been made to treat in the same way the stories of the second "age of fable," the age which witnessed the dawn of the several states of Modern Europe.

It is believed that this presentation of a literature which held unrivalled sway over the imaginations of our ancestors, for many centuries, will not be without benefit to the reader, in addition to the amusement it may afford. The tales, though not to be trusted for their facts, are worthy of all credit as pictures of manners; and it is beginning to be held that the manners and modes of thinking of an age are a more important part of its history than the conflicts of its peoples, generally leading to no result. Besides this, the literature of romance is a treasure-house of poetical material, to which modern poets frequently resort. The Italian poets, Dante and Ariosto, the English, Spenser, Scott, and Tennyson, and our own Longfellow and Lowell, are examples of this.

These legends are so connected with each other, so consistently adapted to a group of characters strongly individualized in Arthur, Launcelot, and their compeers, and so lighted up by the fires of imagination and invention, that they seem as well adapted to the poet's purpose as the legends of the Greek and Roman mythology. And if every well-educated young person is expected to know the story of the Golden Fleece, why is the quest of the Sangreal less worthy of his acquaintance? Or if an allusion to the shield of Achilles ought not to pass unapprehended, why should one to Excalibar, the famous sword of Arthur:—

> "Of Arthur, who, to upper light restored,
> With that terrific sword,
> Which yet he brandishes for future war,
> Shall lift his country's fame above the polar star?" [1]

It is an additional recommendation of our subject, that it tends to cherish in our minds the idea of the source from which we sprung. We are entitled to our full share in the glories and

[1] Wordsworth.

recollections of the land of our forefathers, down to the time of colonization thence. The associations which spring from this source must be fruitful of good influences; among which not the least valuable is the increased enjoyment which such associations afford to the American traveller when he visits England, and sets his foot upon any of her renowned localities.

The readers of Tennyson are invited to peruse in these legends the originals of those stories which the poet has clothed in the drapery of verse, and given to the public in his "Idylls of the King," and in shorter poems. Perhaps some of them may be found more intelligible for our plain narrative of the same events.

THOMAS BULFINCH.

BOSTON, 1858.

PART I

KING ARTHUR AND HIS KNIGHTS

KING ARTHUR AND HIS KNIGHTS

CHAPTER I

INTRODUCTION

ON the decline of the Roman power, about five centuries after
Christ, the countries of Northern Europe were left almost destitute
of a national government. Numerous chiefs, more or less powerful, held local sway, as far as each could enforce his dominion,
and occasionally those chiefs would unite for a common object;
but, in ordinary times, they were much more likely to be found
in hostility to one another. In such a state of things, the rights of
the humbler classes of society were at the mercy of every assailant;
and it is plain that, without some check upon the lawless power of
the chiefs, society must have relapsed into barbarism. Such checks
were found, first, in the rivalry of the chiefs themselves, whose
mutual jealousy made them restraints upon one another; secondly,
in the influence of the Church, which, by every motive, pure
or selfish, was pledged to interpose for the protection of the
weak; and lastly, in the generosity and sense of right which, however crushed under the weight of passion and selfishness, dwell
naturally in the heart of man. From this last source sprang
Chivalry, which framed an ideal of the heroic character, combining
invincible strength and valor, justice, modesty, loyalty to superiors,
courtesy to equals, compassion to weakness, and devotedness to
the Church; an ideal which, if never met with in real life, was
acknowledged by all as the highest model for emulation.

The word Chivalry is derived from the French *cheval*, a horse.
The word *knight*, which originally meant boy or servant, was
particularly applied to a young man after he was admitted to the
privilege of bearing arms. This privilege was conferred on youths
of family and fortune only, for the mass of the people were not
furnished with arms. The knight then was a mounted warrior, a
man of rank, or in the service and maintenance of some man of
rank, generally possessing some independent means of support,
but often relying mainly on the gratitude of those whom he served
for the supply of his wants, and often, no doubt, resorting to the
means which power confers on its possessor.

In time of war the knight was, with his followers, in the camp
of his sovereign, or commanding in the field, or holding some
castle for him. In time of peace he was often in attendance at
his sovereign's court, gracing with his presence the banquets and
tournaments with which princes cheered their leisure. Or he
was traversing the country in quest of adventure, professedly bent
on redressing wrongs and enforcing rights, sometimes in fulfilment
of some vow of religion or of love. These wandering knights were
called knights-errant; they were welcome guests in the castles of
the nobility, for their presence enlivened the dulness of those
secluded abodes, and they were received with honor at the abbeys,
which often owed the best part of their revenues to the patronage
of the knights; but if no castle or abbey or hermitage were at
hand, their hardy habits made it not intolerable to them to lie
down, supperless, at the foot of some wayside cross, and pass
the night.

It is evident that the justice administered by such an instrumentality must have been of the rudest description. The force
whose legitimate purpose was to redress wrongs, might easily be
perverted to inflict them. Accordingly, we find in the romances,
which, however fabulous in facts, are true as pictures of manners,
that a knightly castle was often a terror to the surrounding country;
that its dungeons were full of oppressed knights and ladies, waiting
for some champion to appear to set them free, or to be ransomed
with money; that hosts of idle retainers were ever at hand to enforce
their lord's behests, regardless of law and justice; and that the
rights of the unarmed multitude were of no account. This con-
trariety of fact and theory in regard to chivalry will account for the
opposite impressions which exist in men's minds respecting it. While
it has been the theme of the most fervid eulogium on the one part,
it has been as eagerly denounced on the other. On a cool estimate,
we cannot but see reason to congratulate ourselves that it has given
way in modern times to the reign of law, and that the civil magistrate, if less picturesque, has taken the place of the mailed champion.

THE TRAINING OF A KNIGHT

The preparatory education of candidates for knighthood was
long and arduous. At seven years of age the noble children were
usually removed from their father's house to the court or castle of
their future patron, and placed under the care of a governor, who
taught them the first articles of religion, and respect and reverence
for their lords and superiors, and initiated them in the ceremonies of
a court. They were called *pages*, *valets* or *varlets*, and their office

was to carve, to wait at table, and to perform other menial services, which were not then considered humiliating. In their leisure hours they learned to dance and play on the harp, were instructed in the mysteries of *woods* and *rivers,* that is, in hunting, falconry, and fishing, and in wrestling, tilting with spears, and performing other military exercises on horseback. At fourteen the page became an esquire, and began a course of severer and more laborious exercises. To vault on a horse in heavy armor; to run, to scale walls, and spring over ditches, under the same encumbrance; to wrestle, to wield the battle-axe for a length of time, without raising the visor or taking breath; to perform with grace all the evolutions of horse-manship,—were necessary preliminaries to the reception of knight-hood, which was usually conferred at twenty-one years of age, when the young man's education was supposed to be completed. In the meantime, the esquires were no less assiduously engaged in acquiring all those refinements of civility which formed what was in that age called *courtesy.* The same castle in which they received their education was usually thronged with young persons of the other sex, and the page was encouraged, at a very early age, to select some lady of the court as the mistress of his heart, to whom he was taught to refer all his sentiments, words, and actions. The service of his mistress was the glory and occupation of a knight, and her smiles, bestowed at once by affection and gratitude, were held out as the recompense of his well-directed valor. Religion united its influence with those of loyalty and love, and the order of knighthood, endowed with all the sanctity and religious awe that attended the priesthood, became an object of ambition to the great-est sovereigns.

The ceremonies of initiation were peculiarly solemn. After under-going a severe fast, and spending whole nights in prayer, the can-didate confessed, and received the sacrament. He then clothed himself in snow-white garments, and repaired to the church, or the hall, where the ceremony was to take place, bearing a knightly sword suspended from his neck, which the officiating priest took and blessed, and then returned to him. The candidate then, with folded arms, knelt before the presiding knight, who, after some questions about his motives and purposes in requesting admission, administered to him the oaths, and granted his request. Some of the knights present, sometimes even ladies and damsels, handed to him in succession the spurs, the coat of mail, the hauberk, the armlet and gauntlet, and lastly he girded on the sword. He then knelt again before the president, who, rising from his seat, gave him the "accolade," which consisted of three strokes, with the flat of a sword, on the shoulder or neck of the candidate, accompanied by the words: "In the name of God, of St. Michael, and St. George, I make thee a knight; be valiant, courteous, and loyal!" Then he received his helmet, his shield, and spear; and thus the investiture ended.

FREEMEN, VILLAINS, SERFS, AND CLERKS

The other classes of which society was composed were, first, *free-men,* owners of small portions of land, independent, though they sometimes voluntarily became the vassals of their more opulent neighbors, whose power was necessary for their protection. The other two classes, which were much the most numerous, were either serfs or villains, both of which were slaves.

The *serfs* were in the lowest state of slavery. All the fruits of their labor belonged to the master whose land they tilled, and by whom they were fed and clothed.

The *villains* were less degraded. Their situation seems to have resembled that of the Russian peasants at this day. Like the serfs, they were attached to the soil, and were transferred with it by purchase; but they paid only a fixed rent to the landlord, and had a right to dispose of any surplus that might arise from their industry.

The term *clerk* was of very extensive import. It comprehended, originally, such persons only as belonged to the clergy, or clerical order, among whom, however, might be found a multitude of married persons, artisans or others. But in process of time a much wider rule was established; every one that could read being accounted a *clerk,* or *clericus,* and allowed the "benefit of clergy," that is, exemption from capital and some other forms of punishment, in case of crime.

TOURNAMENTS

The splendid pageant of a tournament between knights, its gaudy accessories and trappings, and its chivalrous regulations, originated in France. Tournaments were repeatedly condemned by the Church, probably on account of the quarrels they led to, and the often fatal results. The "joust," or "just," was different from the tournament. In these, knights fought with their lances, and their object was to unhorse their antagonists; while the tournaments were intended for a display of skill and address in evolutions, and with various weapons, and greater courtesy was observed in the regulations. By these it was forbidden to wound the horse, or to use the point of the sword, or to strike a knight after he had raised his visor, or unlaced his helmet. The ladies encouraged their knights in these exercises; they bestowed prizes, and the conqueror's feats were the theme of romance and song. The stands overlooking the ground, of course, were varied in the shapes of towers, terraces, galleries, and pensile gardens, magnificently decorated with tapestry, pavilions, and banners. Every combatant proclaimed the name of the lady whose *servant d'amour* he was. He was wont to look up to the stand, and strengthen his courage by the sight of the bright eyes that were raining their influence on him from above. The knights also carried *favors*, consisting of scarfs, veils, sleeves, bracelets, clasps,—in short, some piece of female habiliment,—attached to their helmets, shields, or armor. If, during the combat, any of these appendages were dropped or lost, the fair donor would at times send her knight new ones, especially if pleased with his exertions.

Mail Armor

Mail armor, of which the hauberk is a species, and which derived its name from *maille*, a French word for *mesh*, was of two kinds, *plate* or *scale* mail, and *chain* mail. It was originally used for the protection of the body only, reaching no lower than the knees. It was shaped like a carter's frock, and bound round the waist by a girdle. Gloves and hose of mail were afterwards added, and a hood, which, when necessary, was drawn over the head, leaving the face alone uncovered. To protect the skin from the impression of the iron network of the chain mail, a quilted lining was employed, which, however, was insufficient, and the bath was used to efface the marks of the armor.

The hauberk was a complete covering of double chain mail. Some hauberks opened before, like a modern coat; others were closed like a shirt.

The chain mail of which they were composed was formed by a number of iron links, each link having others inserted into it, the whole exhibiting a kind of network, of which (in some instances at least) the meshes were circular, with each link separately riveted.

The hauberk was proof against the most violent blow of a sword; but the point of a lance might pass through the meshes, or drive the iron into the flesh. To guard against this, a thick and well-stuffed doublet was worn underneath, under which was commonly added an iron breastplate. Hence the expression "to pierce both plate and mail," so common in the earlier poets.

Mail armor continued in general use till about the year 1300,

when it was gradually supplanted by plate armor, or suits consisting of pieces or plates of solid iron, adapted to the different parts
of the body.

Shields were generally made of wood, covered with leather, or
some similar substance. To secure them, in some sort, from being
cut through by the sword, they were surrounded with a hoop of
metal.

HELMETS

The helmet was composed of two parts: the *headpiece*, which
was strengthened within by several circles of iron; and the *visor*,
which, as the name implies, was a sort of grating to see through, so
contrived as, by sliding in a groove, or turning on a pivot, to be
raised or lowered at pleasure. Some helmets had a further im-
provement called a *bever*, from the Italian *bevere*, to drink. The
ventayle, or "air-passage," is another name for this.

To secure the helmet from the possibility of falling, or of being
struck off, it was tied by several laces to the meshes of the hauberk; consequently, when a knight was overthrown, it was necessary to undo these laces before he could be put to death; though
this was sometimes effected by lifting up the skirt of the hauberk,
and stabbing him in the belly. The instrument of death was a
small dagger, worn on the right side.

ROMANCES

In ages when there were no books, when noblemen and princes
themselves could not read, history or tradition was monopolized
by the story-tellers. They inherited, generation after generation,
the wondrous tales of their predecessors, which they retailed to
the public with such additions of their own as their acquired
information supplied them with. Anachronisms became of course
very common, and errors of geography, of locality, of manners,
equally so. Spurious genealogies were invented, in which Arthur
and his knights, and Charlemagne and his paladins, were made
to derive their descent from Æneas, Hector, or some other of
the Trojan heroes.

With regard to the derivation of the word *Romance*, we trace
it to the fact that the dialects which were formed in Western
Europe, from the admixture of Latin with the native languages,
took the name of *Langue Romaine*. The French language was
divided into two dialects. The river Loire was their common
boundary. In the provinces to the south of that river the affirma-
tive, *yes*, was expressed by the word *oc*; in the north it was

called *oil* (*oui*); and hence Dante has named the southern language *langue d'oc*, and the northern *langue d'oil*. The latter, which was carried into England by the Normans, and is the origin of the present French, may be called the French Romane; and the former the Provençal, or Provencial Romane, because it was spoken by the people of Provence and Languedoc, southern provinces of France.

These dialects were soon distinguished by very opposite characters. A soft and enervating climate, a spirit of commerce encouraged by an easy communication with other maritime nations, the influx of wealth, and a more settled government, may have tended to polish and soften the diction of the Provencials, whose poets, under the name of Troubadours, were the masters of the Italians, and particularly of Petrarch. Their favorite pieces were *Sirventes* (satirical pieces), love-songs, and *Tensons*, which last were a sort of dialogue in verse between two poets, who questioned each other on some refined points of love's casuistry. It seems the Provencials were so completely absorbed in these delicate questions as to neglect and despise the composition of fabulous histories of adventure and knighthood, which they left in a great measure to the poets of the northern part of the kingdom, called Trouveurs.

At a time when chivalry excited universal admiration, and when all the efforts of that chivalry were directed against the enemies of religion, it was natural that literature should receive the same impulse, and that history and fable should be ransacked to furnish examples of courage and piety that might excite increased emulation. Arthur and Charlemagne were the two heroes selected for this purpose. Arthur's pretensions were that he was a brave, though not always a successful warrior; he had withstood with great resolution the arms of the infidels, that is to say of the Saxons, and his memory was held in the highest estimation by his countrymen, the Britons, who carried with them into Wales, and into the kindred country of Armorica, or Brittany, the memory of his exploits, which their national vanity insensibly exaggerated, till the little prince of the Silures (South Wales) was magnified into the conqueror of England, of Gaul, and of the greater part of Europe. His genealogy was gradually carried up to an imaginary Brutus, and to the period of the Trojan war, and a sort of chronicle was composed in the Welsh, or Armorican language, which, under the pompous title of the History of the Kings of Britain, was translated into Latin by Geoffrey of Monmouth, about the year 1150. The Welsh critics consider the ma

terial of the work to have been an older history, written by St.
Talian, Bishop of St. Asaph, in the seventh century.

As to Charlemagne, though his real merits were sufficient to
secure his immortality, it was impossible that his *holy wars*
against the Saracens should not become a favorite topic for
fiction. Accordingly, the fabulous history of these wars was written, probably towards the close of the eleventh century, by a
monk, who, thinking it would add dignity to his work to embel-
lish it with a contemporary name, boldly ascribed it to Turpin,
who was Archbishop of Rheims about the year 773.

These fabulous chronicles were for a while imprisoned in
languages of local only or of professional access. Both Turpin
and Geoffrey might indeed be read by ecclesiastics, the sole
Latin scholars of those times, and Geoffrey's British original
would contribute to the gratification of Welshmen; but neither
could become extensively popular till translated into some language of general and familiar use. The Anglo-Saxon was at that
time used only by a conquered and enslaved nation; the Spanish
and Italian languages were not yet formed; the Norman French
alone was spoken and understood by the nobility in the greater
part of Europe, and therefore was a proper vehicle for the new
mode of composition.

That language was fashionable in England before the Conquest, and became, after that event, the only language used at
the court of London. As the various conquests of the Normans,
and the enthusiastic valor of that extraordinary people, had
familiarized the minds of men with the most marvellous events,
their poets eagerly seized the fabulous legends of Arthur and
Charlemagne, translated them into the language of the day, and
soon produced a variety of imitations. The adventures attributed
to these monarchs, and to their distinguished warriors, together
with those of many other traditionary or imaginary heroes,
composed by degrees that formidable body of marvellous histories which, from the dialect in which the most ancient of them
were written, were called Romances.

METRICAL ROMANCES

The earliest form in which romances appear is that of a rude
kind of verse. In this form it is supposed they were sung or
recited at the feasts of princes and knights in their baronial
halls. The following specimen of the language and style of Robert
de Beauvais, who flourished in 1257, is from Sir Walter Scott's
Introduction to the Romance of Sir Tristram:

"Ne voil pas emmi dire,
Ici diverse la matyere,
Entre ceus qui solent cunter,
E de la cunte Tristran parler."

"I will not say too much about it,
So diverse is the matter,
Among those who are in the habit of telling
And relating the story of Tristran."

This is a specimen of the language which was in use among the nobility of England in the ages immediately after the Norman conquest. The following is a specimen of the English that existed at the same time among the common people. Robert de Brunne, speaking of his Latin and French authorities, says:—

"Als thai haf wryten and sayd
Haf I alle in myn Inglis layd,
In symple speeche as I couthe,
That is lightest in manne's mouthe.
Alle for the luf of symple men,
That strange Inglis cannot ken."

The "strange Inglis" being the language of the previous specimen.

It was not till toward the end of the thirteenth century that the *prose* romances began to appear. These works generally began with disowning and discrediting the sources from which in reality they drew their sole information. As every romance was supposed to be a real history, the compilers of those in prose would have forfeited all credit if they had announced themselves as mere copyists of the minstrels. On the contrary, they usually state that, as the popular poems upon the matter in question contain many "lesings," they had been induced to translate the real and true history of such or such a knight from the original Latin or Greek, or from the ancient British or Armorican authorities, which authorities existed only in their own assertion.

A specimen of the style of the prose romance may be found in the following extract from one of the most celebrated and latest of them, the Morte d'Arthur of Sir Thomas Mallory, of the date of 1485. From this work much of the contents of this volume has been drawn, with as close an adherence to the original style as was thought consistent with our plan of adapting our narrative to the taste of modern readers.

"It is notoyrly knowen thorugh the vnyuersal world that there been ix worthy and the best that ever were. That is to wete thre paynyms, thre Jewes, and thre crysten men. As for the paynyms, they were tofore the Incarnacyon of Cryst whiche were named, the fyrst Hector of Troye; the second Alysaunder the grete, and

the thyrd Julyus Cezar, Emperour of Rome, of whome thystoryes
ben well kno and had. And as for the thre Jewes whyche also
were tofore thyncarnacyon of our Lord, of whome the fyrst was
Duc Josue, whyche brought the chyldren of Israhel into the londe
of beheste; the second Dauyd, kyng of Jherusalem, and the thyrd
Judas Machabeus; of these thre the byble reherceth al theyr noble
hystoryes and actes. And sythe the sayd Incarnacyon haue ben
the noble crysten men stalled and admytted thorugh the vnyuersal
world to the nombre of the ix beste and worthy, of whome was
fyrst the noble Arthur, whose noble actes I purpose to wryte in
this present book here folowyng. The second was Charlemayn, or
Charles the grete, of whome thystorye is had in many places both
in frensshe and englysshe, and the thyrd and last was Godefray of
boloyn."

The Mabinogeon

It has been well known to the literati and antiquarians of
Europe, that there exist in the great public libraries voluminous
manuscripts of romances and tales once popular, but which on
the invention of printing had already become antiquated and
fallen into neglect. They were therefore never printed, and seldom
perused even by the learned, until about half a century ago, when
attention was again directed to them, and they were found very
curious monuments of ancient manners, habits, and modes of
thinking. Several have since been edited, some by individuals, as
Sir Walter Scott and the poet Southey, others by antiquarian
societies. The class of readers which could be counted on for such
publications was so small that no inducement of profit could be
found to tempt editors and publishers to give them to the world.
It was therefore only a few, and those the most accessible, which
were put in print. There was a class of manuscripts of this kind
which were known, or rather suspected, to be both curious and
valuable, but which it seemed almost hopeless ever to see in
fair printed English. These were the Welsh popular tales, called
Mabinogeon, a plural word, the singular being *Mabinogi,* a tale.
Manuscripts of these were contained in the Bodleian Library at
Oxford, and elsewhere, but the difficulty was to find translators
and editors. The Welsh is a spoken language among the peasantry
of Wales, but is entirely neglected among the learned, unless they
are natives of the principality. Of the few Welsh scholars none
were found who took sufficient interest in this branch of learning
to give these productions to the English public. Southey and Scott,
and others who, like them, loved the old romantic legends of their
country, often urged upon the Welsh literati the duty of reproduc-

ing the Mabinogeon. Southey, in the preface to his edition of
Morte d'Arthur, says: "The specimens which I have seen are
exceedingly curious; nor is there a greater desideratum in British
literature than an edition of these tales, with a literal version, and
such comments as Mr. Davies of all men is best qualified to give.
Certain it is that many of the Round Table fictions originated in
Wales, or in Bretagne, and probably might still be traced there."

Again, in a letter to Sir Charles W. W. Wynn, dated 1819,
he says:—

"I begin almost to despair of ever seeing more of the Mabinogeon; and yet, if some competent Welshman could be found to
edit it carefully, with as literal a version as possible, I am sure
it might be made worth his while by a subscription, printing a
small edition at a high price, perhaps two hundred at five guineas.
I myself would gladly subscribe at that price per volume for such
an edition of the whole of your genuine remains in prose and verse.
Till some such collection is made, the 'gentlemen of Wales' ought
to be prohibited from wearing a leek; ay, and interdicted from
toasting cheese also. Your bards would have met with better usage
if they had been Scotchmen."

Sharon Turner and Sir Walter Scott also expressed a similar
wish for the publication of the Welsh manuscripts. The former
took part in an attempt to effect it, through the instrumentality
of a Mr. Owen, a Welshman, but, we judge, by what Southey
says of him, imperfectly acquainted with English. Southey's language is, "William Owen lent me three parts of the Mabinogeon,
delightfully translated into so Welsh an idiom and syntax that
such a translation is as instructive as an original." In another
letter he adds, "Let Sharon make his language grammatical, but
not alter their idiom in the slightest point."

It is possible Mr. Owen did not proceed far in an undertaking
which, so executed, could expect but little popular patronage. It
was not till an individual should appear possessed of the requisite
knowledge of the two languages, of enthusiasm sufficient for the
task, and of pecuniary resources sufficient to be independent of the
booksellers and of the reading public, that such a work could be
confidently expected. Such an individual has, since Southey's day
and Scott's, appeared in the person of Lady Charlotte Guest, an
English lady united to a gentleman of property in Wales, who,
having acquired the language of the principality, and become
enthusiastically fond of its literary treasures, has given them to
the English reader, in a dress which the printer's and the en-
graver's arts have done their best to adorn. In four royal octave
volumes containing the Welsh originals, the translation, and ample

illustrations from Fench, German, and other contemporary and affiliated literature, the Mabinogeon is spread before us. To the antiquarian and the student of language and ethnology an invaluable treasure, it yet can hardly, in such a form, win its way to popular acquaintance. We claim no other merit than that of bringing it to the knowledge of our readers, of abridging its details, of selecting its most attractive portions, and of faithfully preserving throughout the style in which Lady Guest has clothed her legends. For this service we hope that our readers will confess we have laid them under no light obligation.

CHAPTER II

THE MYTHICAL HISTORY OF ENGLAND

ACCORDING to the earliest accounts, Albion, a giant, and son of Neptune, a contemporary of Hercules, ruled over the island, to which he gave his name. Presuming to oppose the progress of Hercules in his western march, he was slain by him.

Another story is that Histion, the son of Japhet, the son of Noah, had four sons,—Francus, Romanus, Alemannus, and Britto, from whom descended the French, Roman, German, and British people.

Rejecting these and other like stories, Milton gives more regard to the story of Brutus, the Trojan, which, he says, is supported by "descents of ancestry long continued, laws and exploits not plainly seeming to be borrowed or devised, which on the common belief have wrought no small impression; defended by many, denied utterly by few." The principal authority is Geoffrey of Monmouth, whose history, written in the twelfth century, purports to be a translation of a history of Britain, brought over from the opposite shore of France, which, under the name of Brittany, was chiefly peopled by natives of Britain, who from time to time emigrated thither, driven from their own country by the inroads of the Picts and Scots. According to this authority, Brutus was the son of Silvius, and he of Ascanius, the son of Æneas, whose flight from Troy and settlement in Italy will be found narrated in "The Age of Fable."

Brutus, at the age of fifteen, attending his father to the chase, unfortunately killed him with an arrow. Banished therefor by his kindred, he sought refuge in that part of Greece where Helenus, with a band of Trojan exiles, had become established. But Helenus was now dead, and the descendants of the Trojans were oppressed by Pandrasus, the king of the country. Brutus, being kindly received among them, so throve in virtue and in arms as to win the regard of all the eminent of the land above all others of his age. In consequence of this the Trojans not only began to hope, but secretly to persuade him to lead them the way to liberty. To encourage them they had the promise of help from Assaracus, a noble Greek youth, whose mother was a Trojan. He had suffered wrong at the hands of the king, and for that reason the more willingly cast in his lot with the Trojan exiles.

Choosing a fit opportunity, Brutus with his countrymen withdrew to the woods and hills, as the safest place from which to expostulate, and sent this message to Pandrasus: "That the Trojans, holding it unworthy of their ancestors to serve in a foreign land, had retreated to the woods, choosing rather a savage life than a slavish one. If that displeased him, then, with his leave, they would depart to some other country." Pandrasus, not expecting so bold a message from the sons of captives, went in pursuit of them, with such forces as he could gather, and met them on the banks of the Achelous, where Brutus got the advantage, and took the king captive. The result was, that the terms demanded by the Trojans were granted; the king gave his daughter Imogen in marriage to Brutus, and furnished shipping, money, and fit provision for them all to depart from the land.

The marriage being solemnized, and shipping from all parts got together, the Trojans, in a fleet of no less than three hundred and twenty sail, betook themselves to the sea. On the third day they arrived at a certain island, which they found destitute of inhabitants, though there were appearances of former habitation, and among the ruins a temple of Diana. Brutus, here performing sacrifice at the shrine of the goddess, invoked an oracle for his guidance, in these lines:—

"Goddess of shades, and huntress, who at will
Walk'st on the rolling sphere, and through the deep;
On thy third realm, the earth, look now and tell
What land, what seat of rest, thou bidd'st me seek;
What certain seat where I may worship thee
For aye, with temples vowed and virgin choirs."

To whom, sleeping before the altar, Diana, in a vision thus answered:—

"Brutus! far to the west, in the ocean wide,
Beyond the realm of Gaul, a land there lies,
Seagirt it lies, where giants dwelt of old;
Now, void, it fits thy people: thither bend
Thy course; there shalt thou find a lasting seat;
There to thy sons another Troy shall rise,
And kings be born of thee, whose dreaded might
Shall save the world, and conquer nations bold."

Brutus, guided now, as he thought, by Divine direction, sped his course towards the west, and, arriving at a place on the Tyrrhene sea, found there the descendants of certain Trojans who with Antenor came into Italy, of whom Corineus was the chief. These joined company, and the ships pursued their way till they arrived at the mouth of the river Loire, in France, where the expedition landed, with a view to a settlement, but were so rudely assaulted by the inhabitants that they put to sea again, and arrived at a part of the coast of Britain now called Devonshire, where Brutus felt convinced that he had found the promised end of his voyage, landed his colony, and took possession.

The island, not yet Britain, but Albion, was in a manner desert and inhospitable, occupied only by a remnant of the giant race whose excessive force and tyranny had destroyed the others. The Trojans encountered these and extirpated them, Corineus in particular signalizing himself by his exploits against them; from whom Cornwall takes its name, for that region fell to his lot, and there the hugest giants dwelt, lurking in rocks and caves, till Corineus rid the land of them.

Brutus built his capital city, and called it Trojanova (New Troy), changed in time to Trinovantum, now London;[1] and, having governed the isle twenty-four years, died, leaving three sons, Locrine, Albanact, and Camber. Locrine had the middle part, Camber the west, called Cambria from him, and Albanact Albania, now Scotland. Locrine was married to Guendolen, the daughter of Corineus; but, having seen a fair maid named Estrildis, who had been brought captive from Germany, he became enamored of her, and had by her a daughter, whose name was Sabra. This matter was kept secret while Corineus lived; but after his death, Locrine divorced Guendolen, and made Estrildis his queen. Guendolen, all in rage, departed to Cornwall, where Madan, her son, lived, who had been brought up by Corineus, his grandfather. Gathering an army of her father's friends and subjects, she gave battle to her husband's forces, and Locrine was slain. Guendolen caused her rival, Estrildis, with her daughter Sabra, to be thrown into the river, from which cause the river thenceforth bore the maiden's name, which by length of time is now changed into Sabrina or Severn. Milton alludes to this in his address to the river—and in

"Severn swift, guilty of maiden's death";—

his "Comus" tells the story with a slight variation, thus:—

[1] "For noble Britons sprong from Trojans bold,
And Troynovant was built of old Troy's ashes cold."
SPENSER, Book III. Canto IX. 38.

"There is a gentle nymph not far from hence,
That with moist curb sways the smooth Severn stream;
Sabrina is her name, a virgin pure:
Whilom she was the daughter of Locrine,
That had the sceptre from his father, Brute.
She, guiltless damsel, flying the mad pursuit
Of her enragéd step-dame, Guendolen,
Commended her fair innocence to the flood,
That stayed her flight with his cross-flowing course.
The water-nymphs that in the bottom played
Held up their pearléd wrists and took her in,
Bearing her straight to aged Nereus' hall,
Who, piteous of her woes, reared her lank head,
And gave her to his daughters to imbathe
In nectared lavers strewed with asphodel,
And through the porch and inlet of each sense
Dropped in ambrosial oils till she revived,
And underwent a quick, immortal change,
Made goddess of the river," etc.

If our readers ask when all this took place, we must answer, in
the first place, that mythology is not careful of dates; and next
that, as Brutus was the great-grandson of Æneas, it must have
been not far from a century subsequent to the Trojan war, or
about 1100 years before the invasion of the island by Julius Cæsar.
This long interval is filled with the names of princes whose chief
occupation was in warring with one another. Some few, whose
names remain connected with places, or embalmed in literature, we
will mention.

BLADUD

Bladud built the city of Bath, and dedicated the medicinal
waters to Minerva. He was a man of great invention, and practised
the arts of magic, till, having made him wings to fly, he fell down
upon the temple of Apollo, in Trinovant, and so died, after twenty
years' reign.

LEIR

Leir, who next reigned, built Leicester, and called it after his
name. He had no male issue, but only three daughters. When
grown old, he determined to divide his kingdom among his daughters, and bestow them in marriage. But first, to try which of them
loved him best, he determined to ask them solemnly in order, and
judge of the warmth of their affection by their answers. Goneril,
the eldest, knowing well her father's weakness, made answer that
she loved him, "above her soul." "Since thou so honorest my declining age," said the old man, "to thee and to thy husband I
give the third part of my realm." Such good success for a few

words soon uttered was ample instruction to Regan, the second daughter, what to say. She therefore, to the same question replied, that "she loved him more than all the world beside"; and so received an equal reward with her sister. But Cordeilla, the youngest, and hitherto the best beloved, too honest to profess in words more than she felt in her heart, was not moved from the solid purpose of a sincere and virtuous answer, and replied: "Father, my love towards you is as my duty bids. They who pretend beyond this flatter." When the old man, sorry to hear this, and wishing her to recall these words, persisted in asking, she still restrained her expressions so as to say rather less than more than the truth. Then Leir, all in a passion, burst forth: "Since thou hast not reverenced thy aged father like thy sisters, think not to have any part in my kingdom or what else I have";—and without delay, giving in marriage his other daughters, Goneril to the Duke of Albany, and Regan to the Duke of Cornwall, he divides his kingdom between them. Cordeilla, portionless, married the prince of France, who shortly after succeeded his father upon the throne.

King Leir went to reside with his eldest daughter, attended only by a hundred knights. But in a short time his attendants, being complained of as too numerous and disorderly, are reduced to thirty. Resenting that affront, the old king betakes him to his second daughter; but she, instead of soothing his wounded pride, takes part with her sister, and refuses to admit a retinue of more than five. Then back he returns to the other, who now will not receive him with more than one attendant. Then the remembrance of Cordeilla comes to his thoughts, and he takes his journey into France to seek her, with little hope of kind consideration from one whom he had so injured, but to pay her the last recompense he can render,—confession of his injustice. When Cordeilla is informed of his approach, and of his sad condition, she pours forth true filial tears. And, not willing that her own or others' eyes should see him in that forlorn condition, she sends one of her trusted servants to meet him, and convey him privately to some comfortable abode, and to furnish him with such state as befitted his dignity. After which Cordeilla, with the king her husband, went in state to meet him, and, after an honorable reception, the king permitted his wife Cordeilla to go with an army and set her father again upon his throne. They prospered, subdued the wicked sisters and their consorts, and Leir obtained the crown and held it three years. Cordeilla succeeded him, and reigned five years; but the sons of her sisters, after that, rebelled against her, and she lost both her crown and life.

Shakespeare has chosen this story as the subject of his tragedy of King Lear, varying its details in some respects. The madness of Lear, and the ill success of Cordeilla's attempt to reinstate her father, are the principal variations, and those in the names will also be noticed. Our narrative is drawn from Milton's History; and thus the reader will perceive that the story of Leir has had the distinguished honor of being told by the two acknowledged chiefs of British literature.

FERREX AND PORREX

Ferrex and Porrex were brothers, who held the kingdom after Leir. They quarrelled about the supremacy, and Porrex expelled his brother, who, obtaining aid from Suard, king of the Franks, returned and made war upon Porrex. Ferrex was slain in battle, and his forces dispersed. When their mother came to hear of her son's death, who was her favorite, she fell into a great rage, and conceived a mortal hatred against the survivor. She took, there-fore, her opportunity when he was asleep, fell upon him, and, with the assistance of her women, tore him in pieces. This horrid story would not be worth relating, were it not for the fact that it has furnished the plot for the first tragedy which was written in the English language. It was entitled Gorboduc, but in the second edition Ferrex and Porrex, and was the production of Thomas Sackville, afterwards Earl of Dorset, and Thomas Norton, a barrister. Its date was 1561.

DUNWALLO MOLMUTIUS

This is the next name of note. Molmutius established the Mol-mutine laws, which bestowed the privilege of sanctuary on temples, cities, and the roads leading to them, and gave the same protection to ploughs, extending a religious sanction to the labors of the field. Shakespeare alludes to him in Cymbeline, Act III, Sc. I.:—

> "Molmutius made our laws;
> Who was the first of Britain which did put
> His brows within a golden crown, and called
> Himself a king."

BRENNUS AND BELINUS,

the sons of Molmutius, succeeded him. They quarrelled, and Bren-nus was driven out of the island, and took refuge in Gaul, where he met with such favor from the king of the Allobroges, that he gave him his daughter in marriage, and made him his partner on the throne. Brennus is the name which the Roman historians give to the famous leader of the Gauls who took Rome in the time of Camillus. Geoffrey of Monmouth claims the glory of the conquest for the British prince, after he had become king of the Allobroges.

ELIDURE

After Belinus and Brennus there reigned several kings of little note, and then came Elidure. Arthgallo, his brother, being king, gave great offence to his powerful nobles, who rose against him, deposed him, and advanced Elidure to the throne. Arthgallo fled, and endeavored to find assistance in the neighboring kingdoms to reinstate him, but found none. Elidure reigned prosperously and wisely. After five years' possession of the kingdom, one day, when hunting, he met in the forest his brother, Arthgallo, who had been deposed. After long wandering, unable longer to bear the poverty to which he was reduced, he had returned to Britain, with only ten followers, designing to repair to those who had formerly been his friends. Elidure, at the sight of his brother in distress, forgetting all animosities, ran to him, and embraced him. He took Arthgallo home with him, and concealed him in the palace. After this he feigned himself sick, and, calling his nobles about him, induced them, partly by persuasion, partly by force, to consent to his abdicating the kingdom, and reinstating his brother on the throne. The agreement being ratified, Elidure took the crown from his own head, and put it on his brother's head. Arthgallo after this reigned ten years, well and wisely, exercising strict justice towards all men.

He died, and left the kingdom to his sons, who reigned with various fortunes, but were not long-lived, and left no offspring, so that Elidure was again advanced to the throne, and finished the course of his life in just and virtuous actions, receiving the name of *the pious,* from the love and admiration of his subjects.

Wordsworth has taken the story of Artegal and Elidure for the subject of a poem, which is No. 2 of "Poems founded on the Affections."

LUD

After Elidure the Chronicle names many kings, but none of special note, till we come to Lud, who greatly enlarged Trinovant, his capital, and surrounded it with a wall. He changed its name, bestowing upon it his own, so that thenceforth it was called Lud's town, afterwards London. Lud was buried by the gate of the city called after him Ludgate. He had two sons, but they were not old enough at the time of their father's death to sustain the cares of government, and therefore their uncle Caswallaun, or Cassibellaunus, succeeded to the kingdom. He was a brave and magnificent prince, so that his fame reached to distant countries.

CASSIBELLAUNUS

About this time it happened (as is found in the Roman histories) that Julius Cæsar, having subdued Gaul, came to the shore opposite Britain. And having resolved to add this island also to his conquest, he prepared ships and transported his army across the sea, to the mouth of the river Thames. Here he was met by Cassibellaun, with all his forces, and a battle ensued, in which Nennius, the brother of Cassibellaun, engaged in single combat with Cæsar. After several furious blows given and received, the sword of Cæsar stuck so fast in the shield of Nennius, that it could not be pulled out, and, the combatants being separated by the intervention of the troops, Nennius remained possessed of this trophy. At last, after the greater part of the day was spent, the Britons poured in so fast that Cæsar was forced to retire to his camp and fleet. And finding it useless to continue the war any longer at that time, he returned to Gaul.

Shakespeare alludes to Cassibellaunus, in Cymbeline:—

> "The famed Cassibelan, who was once at point
> (O giglot fortune!) to master Cæsar's sword,
> Made Lud's town with rejoicing fires bright,
> And Britons strut with courage."

KYMBELINUS, OR CYMBELINE

Cæsar, on a second invasion of the island, was more fortunate, and compelled the Britons to pay tribute. Cymbeline, the nephew of the king, was delivered to the Romans as a hostage for the faithful fulfilment of the treaty, and, being carried to Rome by Cæsar, he was there brought up in the Roman arts and accomplishments. Being afterwards restored to his country, and placed on the throne, he was attached to the Romans, and continued through all his reign at peace with them. His sons, Guiderius and Arviragus, who make their appearance in Shakespeare's play of Cymbeline, succeeded their father, and, refusing to pay tribute to the Romans, brought on another invasion. Guiderius was slain, but Arviragus afterward made terms with the Romans, and reigned prosperously many years.

ARMORICA

The next event of note is the conquest and colonization of Armorica, by Maximus, a Roman general, and Conan, lord of Miniadoc or Denbigh-land, in Wales. The name of the country was changed to Brittany, or Lesser Britain; and so completely was it possessed by the British colonists, that the language became assimilated to that spoken in Wales, and it is said that to this day the peasantry of the two countries can understand each other when speaking their native language.

The Romans eventually succeeded in establishing themselves in the island, and after the lapse of several generations they became blended with the natives so that no distinction existed between the two races. When at length the Roman armies were withdrawn from Britain, their departure was a matter of regret to the inhabitants, as it left them without protection against the barbarous tribes, Scots, Picts, and Norwegians, who harassed the country incessantly. This was the state of things when the era of King Arthur began.

The adventure of Albion, the giant, with Hercules is alluded to by Spenser, Faery Queene, Book IV., Canto XI.:—

> "For Albion the son of Neptune was;
> Who for the proof of his great puissance,
> Out of his Albion did on dry foot pass,
> Into old Gaul that now is cleped France,
> To fight with Hercules, that did advance
> To vanquish all the world with matchless might;
> And there his mortal part by great mischance
> Was slain."

CHAPTER III

ARTHUR

WE shall begin our history of King Arthur by giving those particulars of his life which appear to rest on historical evidence; and then proceed to record those legends concerning him which form the earliest portion of British literature.

Arthur was a prince of the tribe of Britons called Silures, whose country was South Wales,—the son of Uther, named Pendragon, a title given to an elective sovereign, paramount over the many kings of Britain. He appears to have commenced his martial career about the year 500, and was raised to the Pendragonship about ten years later. He is said to have gained twelve victories over the Saxons.

The most important of them was that of Badon, by some supposed to be Bath, by others Berkshire. This was the last of his battles with the Saxons, and checked their progress so effectually that Arthur experienced no more annoyance from them, and reigned in peace, until the revolt of his nephew Modred, twenty years later, which led to the fatal battle of Camlan, in Cornwall, in 542. Modred was slain, and Arthur, mortally wounded, was conveyed by sea to Glastonbury, where he died, and was buried. Tradition preserved the memory of the place of his interment within the abbey, as we are told by Giraldus Cambrensis, who was present when the grave was opened by command of Henry II. in 1150, and saw the bones and sword of the monarch, and a leaden cross let into his tombstone, with the inscription in rude Roman letters, "Here lies buried the famous King Arthur, in the island Avolonia." This story has been elegantly versified by Warton. A popular traditional belief was long entertained among the Britons that Arthur was not dead, but had been carried off to be healed of his wounds in Fairy-land, and that he would reappear to avenge his countrymen, and reinstate them in the sovereignty of Britain. In Wharton's Ode a bard relates to King Henry the traditional story of Arthur's death, and closes with these lines:—

> "Yet in vain a paynim foe
> Armed with fate the mighty blow;
> For when he fell, the Elfin queen,
> All in secret and unseen,
> O'er the fainting hero +hrew
> Her mantle of ambrosial blue,
> And bade her spirits bear him far,
> In Merlin's agate-axled car,
> To her green isle's enamelled steep,
> Far in the navel of the deep.
> O'er his wounds she sprinkled dew
> From flowers that in Arabia grew.
>
>   .   .   .   .   .
>
> There he reigns a mighty king,
> Thence to Britain shall return,
> If right prophetic rolls I learn,
> Borne on victory's spreading plume,
> His ancient sceptre to resume,
> His knightly table to restore,
> And brave the tournaments of yore."

After this narration another bard came forward, who recited a different story:—

> "When Arthur bowed his haughty crest,
> No princess veiled in azure vest
> Snatched him, by Merlin's powerful spell,
> In groves of golden bliss to dwell;

> But when he fell, with wingèd speed,
> His champions, on a milk-white steed,
> From the battle's hurricane
> Bore him to Joseph's towered fane,[1]
>
> In the fair vale of Avalon;
> There, with chanted orison
> And the long blaze of tapers clear,
> The stoled fathers met the bier;
> Through the dim aisles, in order dread
> Of martial woe, the chief they led,
> And deep entombed in holy ground,
> Before the altar's solemn bound."

It must not be concealed, that the very existence of Arthur has been denied by some. Milton says of him: "As to Arthur, more renowned in songs and romances than in true stories, who he was, and whether ever any such reigned in Britain, hath been doubted heretofore, and may again, with good reason." Modern critics, however, admit that there was a prince of this name, and find proof of it in the frequent mention of him in the writings of the Welsh bards. But the Arthur of romance, according to Mr. Owen, a Welsh scholar and antiquarian, is a mythological person. "Arthur," he says, "is the Great Bear, as the name literally implies (Arctos, Arcturus), and perhaps this constellation, being so near the pole, and visibly describing a circle in a small space, is the origin of the famous Round Table." Let us now turn to the history of King Arthur, as recorded by the romantic chroniclers.

Constans, king of Britain, had three sons, Moines, Ambrosius, otherwise called Uther, and Pendragon. Moines, soon after his accession to the crown, was vanquished by the Saxons, in consequence of the treachery of his seneschal, Vortigern, and growing unpopular, through misfortune, he was killed by his subjects, and the traitor Vortigern chosen in his place.

Vortigern was soon after defeated in a great battle by Uther and Pendragon, the surviving brothers of Moines, and Pendragon ascended the throne.

This prince had great confidence in the wisdom of Merlin, and made him his chief adviser. About this time a dreadful war arose between the Saxons and Britons. Merlin obliged the royal brothers

---

[1] Glastonbury Abbey, said to be founded by Joseph of Arimathea, in a spot anciently called the island or valley of Avalonia.

Tennyson, in his Palace of Art, alludes to the legend of Arthur's rescue by the Fairy queen, thus:—

> "Or mythic Uther's deeply wounded son,
> In some fair space of sloping greens,
> Lay dozing in the vale of Avalon,
> And watched by weeping queens."

to swear fidelity to each other, but predicted that one of them must fall in the first battle. The Saxons were routed, and Pendragon, being slain, was succeeded by Uther, who now assumed, in addition to his own name, the appellation of Pendragon.

Merlin still continued a favorite counsellor. At the request of Uther, he transported by magic art enormous stones from Ireland, to form the sepulchre of Pendragon. These stones constitute the monument now called Stonehenge, on Salisbury Plain.

Merlin next proceeded to Carlisle to prepare the Round Table, at which he seated an assemblage of the great nobles of the country. The companions admitted to this high order were bound by oath to assist each other at the hazard of their own lives, to attempt singly the most perilous adventures, to lead, when necessary, a life of monastic solitude, to fly to arms at the first summons, and never to retire from battle till they had defeated the enemy, unless night intervened and separated the combatants.

Soon after this institution, the king invited all his barons to the celebration of a great festival, which he proposed holding annually at Carlisle.

As the knights had obtained the sovereign's permission to bring their ladies along with them, the beautiful Igerne accompanied her husband, Gerlois, Duke of Tintadiel, to one of these anniversaries. The king became deeply enamored of the Duchess, and disclosed his passion; but Igerne repelled his advances, and revealed his solicitations to her husband. On hearing this, the Duke instantly removed from court with Igerne, and without taking leave of Uther. The king complained to his council of this want of duty, and they decided that the Duke should be summoned to court, and, if refractory, should be treated as a rebel. As he refused to obey the citation, the king carried war into the estates of his vassal, and besieged him in the strong castle of Tintadiel. Merlin transformed the king into the likeness of Gerlois, and enabled him to have many stolen interviews with Igerne. At length the Duke was killed in battle, and the king espoused Igerne.

From this union sprang Arthur, who succeeded his father, Uther, upon the throne.

ARTHUR CHOSEN KING

Arthur, though only fifteen years old at his father's death, was elected king, at a general meeting of the nobles. It was not done without opposition, for there were many ambitious competitors; but Bishop Brice, a person of great sanctity, on Christmas eve addressed the assembly, and represented that it would well become them, at that solemn season, to put up their prayers for some token which should manifest the intentions of Providence respecting their future sovereign. This was done, and with such success, that the service was scarcely ended, when a miraculous stone was discovered, before the church door, and in the stone was firmly fixed a sword, with the following words engraven on its hilt:—

"I am hight Escalibore,
Unto a king fair tresore."

Bishop Brice, after exhorting the assembly to offer up their thanksgivings for this signal miracle, proposed a law, that whoever should be able to draw out the sword from the stone, should be acknowledged as sovereign of the Britons; and his proposal was decreed by general acclamation. The tributary kings of Uther, and the most famous knights, successively put their strength to the proof, but the miraculous sword resisted all their efforts. It stood till Candlemas; it stood till Easter, and till Pentecost, when the best knights in the kingdom usually assembled for the annual tournament. Arthur, who was at that time serving in the capacity of squire to his foster-brother, Sir Kay, attended his master to the lists. Sir Kay fought with great valor and success, but had the misfortune to break his sword, and sent Arthur to his mother for a new one. Arthur hastened home, but did not find the lady; but having observed near the church a sword sticking in a stone, he galloped to the place, drew out the sword with great ease, and delivered it to his master. Sir Kay would willingly have assumed to himself the distinction conferred by the possession of the sword; but when, to confirm the doubters, the sword was replaced in the stone, he was utterly unable to withdraw it, and it would yield a second time to no hand but Arthur's. Thus decisively pointed out by Heaven as their king, Arthur was by general consent proclaimed as such, and an early day appointed for his solemn coronation.

Immediately after his election to the crown, Arthur found himself opposed by eleven kings and one duke, who with a vast army were actually encamped in the forest of Rockingham. By Merlin's advice Arthur sent an embassy to Brittany to solicit aid of King Ban and King Bohort, two of the best knights in the world. They accepted the call, and with a powerful army crossed the sea, landing at Portsmouth, where they were received with great rejoicing. The rebel kings were still superior in numbers; but Merlin by a powerful enchantment, caused all their tents to fall down at once, and in the confusion Arthur with his allies fell upon them and totally routed them.

After defeating the rebels, Arthur took the field against the

Saxons. As they were too strong for him unaided, he sent an embassy to Armorica, beseeching the assistance of Hoel, who soon after brought over an army to his aid. The two kings joined their forces, and sought the enemy, whom they met, and both sides prepared for a decisive engagement. "Arthur himself," as Geoffrey of Monmouth relates, "dressed in a breastplate worthy of so great a king, places on his head a golden helmet engraved with the semblance of a dragon. Over his shoulders he throws his shield called Priwen, on which a picture of the Holy Virgin constantly recalled her to his memory. Girt with Caliburn, a most excellent sword, and fabricated in the isle of Avalon, he graces his right hand with the lance named Ron. This was a long and broad spear, well contrived for slaughter." After a severe conflict, Arthur, calling on the name of the Virgin, rushes into the midst of his enemies, and destroys multitudes of them with the formidable Caliburn, and puts the rest to flight. Hoel, being detained by sickness, took no part in this battle.

This is called the victory of Mount Badon, and, however disguised by fable, it is regarded by historians as a real event.

The feats performed by Arthur at the battle of Badon Mount are thus celebrated in Drayton's verse:—

> "They sung how he himself at Badon bore, that day,
> When at the glorious goal his British scepter lay;
> Two dais together how the battle stronglie stood;
> Pendragon's worthie son, who waded there in blood,
> Three hundred Saxons slew with his owne valiant hand."
>
> *Song IV.*

MERLIN

> "—— The most famous man of all those times,
> Merlin, who knew the range of all their arts,
> Had built the King his havens, ships and halls,
> Was also Bard, and knew the starry heavens;
> The people called him wizard."—TENNYSON.

Now Merlin, of whom we have already heard somewhat and shall hear more, was the son of no mortal father, but of an Incubus, one of a class of beings not absolutely wicked, but far from good, who inhabit the regions of the air. Merlin's mother was a virtuous young woman, who, on the birth of her son, intrusted him to a priest, who hurried him to the baptismal fount, and so saved him from sharing the lot of his father, though he retained many marks of his unearthly origin.

At this time Vortigern reigned in Britain. He was a usurper, who had caused the death of his sovereign, Moines, and driven the two brothers of the late king, whose names were Uther and Pendragon.

into banishment. Vortigern, who lived in constant fear of the return of the rightful heirs of the kingdom, began to erect a strong tower for defence. The edifice, when brought by the workmen to a certain height, three times fell to the ground, without any apparent cause. The king consulted his astrologers on this wonderful event, and learned from them that it would be necessary to bathe the cornerstone of the foundation with the blood of a child born without a mortal father.

In search of such an infant, Vortigern sent his messengers all over the kingdom, and they by accident discovered Merlin, whose lineage seemed to point him out as the individual wanted. They took him to the king; but Merlin, young as he was, explained to the king the absurdity of attempting to rescue the fabric by such means, for he told him the true cause of the instability of the tower was its being placed over the den of two immense dragons, whose combats shook the earth above them. The king ordered his workmen to dig beneath the tower, and when they had done so they discovered two enormous serpents, the one white as milk, the other red as fire. The multitude looked on with amazement, till the serpents, slowly rising from their den, and expanding their enormous folds, began the combat, when every one fled in terror, except Merlin, who stood by clapping his hands and cheering on the conflict. The red dragon was slain, and the white one, gliding through a cleft in the rock, disappeared.

These animals typified, as Merlin afterwards explained, the invasion of Uther and Pendragon, the rightful princes, who soon after landed with a great army. Vortigern was defeated, and afterwards burned alive in the castle he had taken such pains to construct. On the death of Vortigern, Pendragon ascended the throne. Merlin became his chief adviser, and often assisted the king by his magical arts. Among other endowments, he had the power to transform himself into any shape he pleased. At one time he appeared as a dwarf, at others as a damsel, a page, or even a greyhound or a stag. This faculty he often employed for the service of the king, and sometimes also for the diversion of the court and the sovereign.

Merlin continued to be a favorite counsellor through the reigns of Pendragon, Uther, and Arthur, and at last disappeared from view, and was no more found among men, through the treachery of his mistress, Viviane, the Fairy, which happened in this wise.

Merlin, having become enamored of the fair Viviane, the Lady of the Lake, was weak enough to impart to her various important secrets of his art, being impelled by a fatal destiny, of which he was at the same time fully aware. The lady, however, was not content with his devotion, unbounded as it seems to have been, but "cast about," the Romance tells us, how she might "detain him for ever-more," and one day addressed him in these terms: "Sir, I would that we should make a fair place and a suitable, so contrived by art and by cunning that it might never be undone, and that you and I should be there in joy and solace." "My lady," said Merlin, "I will do all this." "Sir," said she, "I would not have you do it, but you shall teach me, and I will do it, and then it will be more to my mind." "I grant you this," said Merlin. Then he began to devise, and the damsel put it all in writing. And when he had devised the whole, then had the damsel full great joy, and showed him greater semblance of love than she had ever before made, and they sojourned together a long while. At length it fell out that, as they were going one day in hand through the forest of Brécéliande, they found a bush of white-thorn, which was laden with flowers; and they seated themselves, under the shade of this white-thorn, upon the grass, and Merlin laid his head upon the damsel's lap, and fell asleep. Then the damsel rose, and made a ring with her wimple round the bush, and round Merlin, and began her enchantments, such as he himself had taught her; and nine times she made the ring, and nine times she made the enchantment, and then she went and sat down by him, and placed his head again upon her lap. And when he awoke, and looked round him, it seemed to him that he was enclosed in the strongest tower in the world, and laid upon a fair bed. Then said he to the dame: "My lady, you have deceived me, unless you abide with me, for no one hath power to unmake this tower but you alone." She then promised that she would be often there, and in this she held her covenant with him. And Merlin never went out of that tower where his Mistress Viviane had enclosed him; but she entered and went out again when she listed.

After this event Merlin was never more known to hold converse with any mortal but Viviane, except on one occasion. Arthur, having for some time missed him from his court, sent several of his knights in search of him, and among the number Sir Gawain, who met with a very unpleasant adventure while engaged in this quest. Happening to pass a damsel on his road, and neglecting to salute her, she revenged herself for his incivility by transforming him into a hideous dwarf. He was bewailing aloud his evil fortune as he went through the forest of Brécéliande, when suddenly he heard the voice of one groaning on his right hand; and, looking that way, he could see nothing save a kind of smoke, which seemed like air, and through which he could not pass. Merlin then addressed him from out the smoke, and told him by what misadventure he was imprisoned there. "Ah, sir!" he added, "you will never see me more, and that grieves me, but I cannot remedy it; I shall never more speak to you, nor to any other person, save only my mistress. But do thou hasten to King Arthur, and charge him from me to undertake, without delay, the quest of the Sacred Graal. The knight is already born, and has received knighthood at his hands, who is destined to accomplish this quest." And after this he comforted Gawain under his transformation, assuring him that he should speedily be disenchanted; and he predicted to him that he should find the king at Carduel, in Wales, on his return, and that all the other knights who had been on like quest would arrive there the same day as himself. And all this came to pass as Merlin had said.

Merlin is frequently introduced in the tales of chivalry, but it is chiefly on great occasions, and at a period subsequent to his death, or magical disappearance. In the romantic poems of Italy, and in Spenser, Merlin is chiefly represented as a magical artist. Spenser represents him as the artificer of the impenetrable shield and other armor of Prince Arthur (Faery Queene, Book I., Canton vii.), and of a mirror, in which a damsel viewed her lover's shade. The Fountain of Love, in the Orlando Innamorato, is described as his work; and in the poem of Ariosto we are told of a hall adorned with prophetic paintings, which demons had executed in a single night, under the direction of Merlin.

The following legend is from Spenser's Faery Queene (Book III., Canto iii.):—

CAER-MERDIN, OR CAERMARTHEN (IN WALES), MERLIN'S TOWER, AND THE
IMPRISONED FIENDS

Forthwith themselves disguising both, in straunge
And base attire, that none might them bewray,
To Maridunum, that is now by chaunge
Of name Caer-Merdin called, they took their way:
There the wise Merlin, whylome wont (they say)
To make his wonne, low underneath the ground
In a deep delve, far from the view of day,
That of no living wight he mote be found,
Whenso he counselled with his sprights encompassed round.

And if thou ever happen that same way
To travel, go to see that dreadful place;
It is a hideous hollow cave (they say)
Under a rock that lies a little space,
From the swift Barry, tombling down apace
Amongst the woody hills of Dynevor;
But dare not thou, I charge, in any case,
To enter into that same baleful bower,
For fear the cruel fiends should thee unwares devour.

But standing high aloft, low lay thine ear,
And there such ghastly noise of iron chains
And brazen cauldrons thou shalt rumbling hear,
Which thousand sprites with long enduring pains

Do toss, that it will stun thy feeble brains;
And oftentimes great groans, and grievous stounds,
When too huge toil and labor them constrains;
And oftentimes loud strokes and ringing sounds
From under that deep rock most horribly rebounds.

The cause some say is this. A little while
Before that Merlin died, he did intend
A brazen wall in compas to compile
About Caermerdin, and did it commend
Unto these sprites to bring to perfect end;
During which work the Lady of the Lake,
Whom long he loved, for him in haste did send;
Who, thereby forced his workmen to forsake,
Them bound till his return their labor not to slack.

In the meantime, through that false lady's train,
He was surprised, and buried under beare,[1]
Ne ever to his work returned again;
Natheless those fiends may not their work forbear,
So greatly his commandëment they fear;
But there do toil and travail day and night,
Until that brazen wall they up do rear.
For Merlin had in magic more insight
Than ever him before or after living wight.

GUENEVER

"Leodogran, the King of Cameliard,
Had one fair daughter, and none other child,
And she was fairest of all flesh on earth,
Guenevere, and in her his one delight."
                                        TENNYSON.

Merlin had planned for Arthur a marriage with the daughter of
King Laodegan [2] of Carmalide. By his advice Arthur paid a visit to
the court of that sovereign, attended only by Merlin and by thirty-
nine knights whom the magician had selected for that service. On
their arrival they found Laodegan and his peers sitting in council,
endeavoring, but with small prospect of success, to devise means
for resisting the impending attack of Ryence, King of Ireland, who,
with fifteen tributary kings and an almost innumerable army, had
nearly surrounded the city. Merlin, who acted as leader of the band
of British knights, announced them as strangers, who came to offer
the king their services in his wars; but under the express condition
that they should be at liberty to conceal their names and quality
until they should think proper to divulge them. These terms were

[1] *Buried under beare.* Buried under something which enclosed him like a
coffin or bier.

[2] The spelling of these proper names is very often only a matter of taste. I
think, however, *Leodogran* and *Guenevere* are less common than *Laodegan* and
Guenever.

thought very strange, but were thankfully accepted, and the strangers, after taking the usual oath to the king, retired to the lodging which Merlin had prepared for them.

A few days after this, the enemy, regardless of a truce into which they had entered with King Laodegan, suddenly issued from their camp and made an attempt to surprise the city. Cleodalis, the king's general, assembled the royal forces with all possible despatch. Arthur and his companions also flew to arms, and Merlin appeared at their head, bearing a standard on which was emblazoned a terrific dragon. Merlin advanced to the gate, and commanded the porter to open it, which the porter refused to do, without the king's order. Merlin thereupon took up the gate, with all its appurtenances of locks, bars, and bolts, and directed his troop to pass through, after which he replaced it in perfect order. He then set spurs to his horse, and dashed, at the head of the little troop, into a body of two thousand Pagans. The disparity of numbers being so enormous, Merlin cast a spell upon the enemy, so as to prevent their seeing the small number of their assailants; notwithstanding which the British knights were hard pressed. But the people of the city, who saw from the walls this unequal contest, were ashamed of leaving the small body of strangers to their fate, so they opened the gate and sallied forth. The numbers were now more nearly equal, and Merlin revoked his spell, so that the two armies encountered on fair terms. Where Arthur, Ban, Bohort, and the rest fought, the king's army had the advantage; but in another part of the field the king himself was surrounded and carried off by the enemy. This sad sight was seen by Guenever, the fair daughter of the king, who stood on the city wall and looked at the battle. She was in dreadful distress, tore her hair, and swooned away.

But Merlin, aware of what passed in every part of the field, suddenly collected his knights, led them out of the battle, intercepted the passage of the party who were carrying away the king, charged them with irresistible impetuosity, cut in pieces or dispersed the whole escort, and rescued the king. In the fight Arthur encountered Caulang, a giant fifteen feet high, and the fair Guenever, who already began to feel a strong interest in the handsome young stranger, trembled for the issue of the contest. But Arthur, dealing a dreadful blow on the shoulder of the monster, cut through his neck so that his head hung over on one side, and in this condition his horse carried him about the field, to the great horror and dismay of the Pagans. Guenever could not refrain from expressing aloud her wish that the gentle knight, who dealt with giants so dexterously, were destined to become her husband, and the wish was echoed by her

attendants. The enemy soon turned their backs, and fled with pre-
cipitation, closely pursued by Laodegan and his allies.

After the battle Arthur was disarmed and conducted to the bath
by the Princess Guenever, while his friends were attended by the
other ladies of the court. After the bath the knights were conducted
to a magnificent entertainment, at which they were diligently served
by the same fair attendants. Laodegan, more and more anxious to
know the name and quality of his generous deliverers, and occasionally forming a secret wish that the chief of his guests might be
captivated by the charms of his daughter, appeared silent and pen-
sive, and was scarcely roused from his reverie by the banter of his
courtiers. Arthur, having had an opportunity of explaining to Guenever his great esteem for her merit, was in the joy of his heart, and
was still further delighted by hearing from Merlin the late exploits
of Gawain at London, by means of which his immediate return to
his dominions was rendered unnecessary, and he was left at liberty
to protract his stay at the court of Laodegan. Every day contributed
to increase the admiration of the whole court for the gallant strangers, and the passion of Guenever for their chief; and when at last
Merlin announced to the king that the object of the visit of the
party was to procure a bride for their leader, Laodegan at once
presented Guenever to Arthur, telling him that, whatever might be
his rank, his merit was sufficient to entitle him to the possession
of the heiress of Carmalide. Arthur accepted the lady with the
utmost gratitude, and Merlin then proceeded to satisfy the king
of the rank of his son-in-law; upon which Laodegan, with all his
barons, hastened to do homage to their lawful sovereign, the successor of Uther Pendragon. The fair Guenever was then solemnly
betrothed to Arthur, and a magnificent festival was proclaimed,
which lasted seven days. At the end of that time, the enemy appearing again with renewed force, it became necessary to resume military
operations.[1]

We must now relate what took place at or near London while
Arthur was absent from his capital. At this very time a band of
young heroes were on their way to Arthur's court, for the purpose
of receiving knighthood from him. They were Gawain and his three
brothers, nephews of Arthur, sons of King Lot, and Galachin, another nephew, son of King Nanters. King Lot had been one of the
rebel chiefs whom Arthur had defeated, but he now hoped by means
of the young men to be reconciled to his brother-in-law. He equipped

---

[1] Guenever, the name of Arthur's queen, also written Genievre and Geneura,
is familiar to all who are conversant with chivalric lore. It is to her adventures,
and those of her true knight, Sir Launcelot, that Dante alludes in the beautiful
episode of Francesca da Rimini.

his sons and his nephew with the utmost magnificence, giving them a splendid retinue of young men, sons of earls and barons, all mounted on the best horses, with complete suits of choice armor. They numbered in all seven hundred, but only nine had yet received the order of knighthood; the rest were candidates for that honor, and anxious to earn it by an early encounter with the enemy. Gawain, the leader, was a knight of wonderful strength; but what was most remarkable about him was that his strength was greater at certain hours of the day than at others. From nine o'clock till noon his strength was doubled, and so it was from three to even-song; for the rest of the time it was less remarkable, though at all times surpassing that of ordinary men.

After a march of three days they arrived in the vicinity of London, where they expected to find Arthur and his court; and very unexpectedly fell in with a large convoy belonging to the enemy, consisting of numerous carts and wagons, all loaded with provisions, and escorted by three thousand men, who had been collecting spoil from all the country round. A single charge from Gawain's impetuous cavalry was sufficient to disperse the escort and to recover the convoy, which was instantly despatched to London. But before long a body of seven thousand fresh soldiers advanced to the attack of the five princes and their little army. Gawain, singling out a chief named Choas, of gigantic size, began the battle by splitting him from the crown of the head to the breast. Galachin encountered King Sanagran, who was also very huge, and cut off his head. Agrivain and Gahariet also performed prodigies of valor. Thus they kept the great army of assailants at bay, though hard pressed, till of a sudden they perceived a strong body of the citizens advancing from London, where the convoy which had been recovered by Gawain had arrived, and informed the mayor and citizens of the danger of their deliverer. The arrival of the Londoners soon decided the contest. The enemy fled in all directions, and Gawain and his friends, escorted by the grateful citizens, entered London, and were received with acclamations.

After the great victory of Mount Badon, by which the Saxons were for the time effectually put down, Arthur turned his arms against the Scots and Picts, whom he routed at Lake Lomond, and compelled to sue for mercy. He then went to York to keep his Christmas, and employed himself in restoring the Christian churches which the Pagans had rifled and overthrown. The following summer he conquered Ireland, and then made a voyage with his fleet to Iceland, which he also subdued. The kings of Gothland and of the Orkneys came voluntarily and made their submission, promising to pay tribute. Then he returned to Britain, where, having established the kingdom, he dwelt twelve years in peace.

During this time he invited over to him all persons whatsoever that were famous for valor in foreign nations, and augmented the number of his domestics, and introduced such politeness into his court as people of the remotest countries thought worthy of their imitation. So that there was not a nobleman who thought himself of any consideration unless his clothes and arms were made in the same fashion as those of Arthur's knights.

Finding himself so powerful at home, Arthur began to form designs for extending his power abroad. So, having prepared his fleet, he first attempted Norway, that he might procure the crown of it for Lot, his sister's husband. Arthur landed in Norway, fought a great battle with the king of that country, defeated him, and pursued the victory till he had reduced the whole country under his dominion, and established Lot upon the throne. Then Arthur made a voyage to Gaul and laid siege to the city of Paris. Gaul was at that time a Roman province, and governed by Flollo, the Tribune. When the siege of Paris had continued a month, and the people began to suffer from famine, Flollo challenged Arthur to single combat, proposing to decide the conquest in that way. Arthur gladly accepted the challenge, and slew his adversary in the contest, upon which the citizens surrendered the city to him. After the victory Arthur divided his army into two parts, one of which he committed to the conduct of Hoel, whom he ordered to march into Aquitaine, while he with the other part should endeavor to subdue the other provinces. At the end of nine years, in which time all the parts of Gaul were entirely reduced, Arthur returned to Paris, where he kept his court, and calling an assembly of the clergy and people, established peace and the just administration of the laws in that kingdom. Then he bestowed Normandy upon Bedver, his butler, and the province of Andegavia upon Kay, his steward,[1] and several others upon his great men that attended him. And, having settled the peace of the cities and countries, he returned back in the beginning of spring to Britain.

Upon the approach of the feast of Pentecost, Arthur, the better to

---

[1] This name, in the French romances, is spelled Queux, which means *head cook*. This would seem to imply that it was a title, and not a name; yet the personage who bore it is never mentioned by any other. He is the chief, if not the only, comic character among the heroes of Arthur's court. He is the Seneschal or Steward, his duties also embracing those of chief of the cooks. In the romances his general character is a compound of valor and buffoonery, always ready to fight, and generally getting the worst of the battle. He is also sarcastic and abusive in his remarks, by which he often gets into trouble. Yet Arthur seems to have an attachment to him, and often takes his advice. which is generally wrong.

demonstrate his joy after such triumphant successes, and for the more solemn observation of that festival, and reconciling the minds of the princes that were now subject to him, resolved during that season to hold a magnificent court, to place the crown upon his head, and to invite all the kings and dukes under his subjection to the solemnity. And he pitched upon Caerleon, the City of Legions, as the proper place for his purpose. For, besides its great wealth above the other cities,[1] its situation upon the river Usk, near the Severn sea, was most pleasant and fit for so great a solemnity. For on one side it was washed by that noble river, so that the kings and princes from the countries beyond the seas might have the convenience of sailing up to it. On the other side the beauty of the meadows and groves, and magnificence of the royal palaces, with lofty gilded roofs that adorned it, made it even rival the grandeur of Rome. It was also famous for two churches, whereof one was adorned with a choir of virgins, who devoted themselves wholly to the service of God, and the other maintained a convent of priests. Besides, there was a college of two hundred philosophers, who, being learned in astronomy and the other arts, were diligent in observing the courses of the stars, and gave Arthur true predictions of the events that would happen. In this place, therefore, which afforded such delights, were preparations made for the ensuing festival.

Ambassadors were then sent into several kingdoms, to invite to court the princes both of Gaul and of the adjacent islands. Accordingly there came Augusel, king of Albania, now Scotland, Cadwallo, king of Venedotia, now North Wales, Sater, king of Demetia, now South Wales; also the archbishops of the metropolitan sees, London and York, and Dubricius, bishop of Caerleon, the City of Legions. This prelate, who was primate of Britain, was so eminent for his piety that he could cure any sick person by his prayers. There were

---

[1] Several cities are allotted to King Arthur by the romance-writers. The principal are Caerleon, Camelot, and Carlisle.

Caerleon derives its name from its having been the station of one of the legions during the dominion of the Romans. It is called by Latin writers Urbs Legionum, the City of Legions,—the former word being rendered into Welsh by *Caer,* meaning city, and the latter contracted into *lleon.* The river Usk retains its name in modern geography, and there is a town or city of Caerleon upon it, though the city of Cardiff is thought to be the scene of Arthur's court. Chester also bears the Welsh name of Caerleon; for Chester, derived from *castra,* Latin for *camp,* is the designation of military headquarters.

Camelot is thought to be Winchester.

Shalott is Guildford.

Hamo's Port is Southampton.

Carlisle is the city still retaining that name, near the Scottish border. But this name is also sometimes applied to other places, which were, like itself, military stations.

also the counts of the principal cities, and many other worthies of no less dignity.

From the adjacent islands came Guillamurius, king of Ireland, Gunfasius, king of the Orkneys, Malvasius, king of Iceland, Lot, king of Norway, Bedver the butler, Duke of Normandy, Kay the sewer, Duke of Andegavia; also the twelve peers of Gaul, and Hoel, Duke of the Armorican Britons, with his nobility, who came with such a train of mules, horses, and rich furniture, as is difficult to describe. Besides these, there remained no prince of any consideration on this side of Spain who came not upon this invitation, and no wonder, when Arthur's munificence, which was celebrated over the whole world, made him beloved by all people.

When all were assembled, upon the day of the solemnity, the archbishops were conducted to the palace in order to place the crown upon the king's head. Then Dubricius, inasmuch as the court was held in his diocese, made himself ready to celebrate the office. As soon as the king was invested with his royal habiliments, he was conducted in great pomp to the metropolitan church, having four kings, viz., of Albania, Cornwall, Demetia, and Venedotia, bearing four golden swords before him. On another part was the queen, dressed out in her richest ornaments, conducted by the archbishops and bishops to the Church of Virgins; the four queens, also, of the kings last mentioned, bearing before her four white doves, according to ancient custom. When the whole procession was ended, so transporting was the harmony of the musical instruments and voices, whereof there was a vast variety in both churches, that the knights who attended were in doubt which to prefer, and therefore crowded from one to the other by turns, and were far from being tired of the solemnity, though the whole day had been spent in it. At last, when divine service was over at both churches, the king and queen put off their crowns, and, putting on their lighter ornaments, went to the banquet. When they had all taken their seats according to precedence, Kay the sewer, in rich robes of ermine, with a thousand young noblemen all in like manner clothed in rich attire, served up the dishes. From another part Bedver the butler was followed by the same number of attendants, who waited with all kinds of cups and drinking-vessels. And there was food and drink in abundance, and everything was of the best kind, and served in the best manner. For at that time Britain had arrived at such a pitch of grandeur that in riches, luxury, and politeness it far surpassed all other kingdoms.

As soon as the banquets were over they went into the fields without the city, to divert themselves with various sports, such as shooting with bows and arrows, tossing the pike, casting of heavy stones and rocks, playing at dice, and the like, and all these inoffensively, and without quarrelling. In this manner were three days spent, and after that they separated, and the kings and noblemen departed to their several homes.

After this Arthur reigned five years in peace. Then came ambassadors from Lucius Tiberius, Procurator under Leo, Emperor of Rome, demanding tribute. But Arthur refused to pay tribute, and prepared for war. As soon as the necessary dispositions were made, he committed the government of his kingdom to his nephew Modred and to Queen Guenever, and marched with his army to Hamo's Port, where the wind stood fair for him. The army crossed over in safety, and landed at the mouth of the river Barba. And there they pitched their tents to wait the arrival of the kings of the islands.

As soon as all the forces were arrived, Arthur marched forward to Augustodunum, and encamped on the banks of the river Alba. Here repeated battles were fought, in all which the Britons, under their valiant leaders, Hoel, Duke of Armorica, and Gawain, nephew to Arthur, had the advantage. At length Lucius Tiberius determined to retreat, and wait for the Emperor Leo to join him with fresh troops. But Arthur, anticipating this event, took possession of a certain valley, and closed up the way of retreat to Lucius, compelling him to fight a decisive battle, in which Arthur lost some of the bravest of his knights and most faithful followers. But on the other hand Lucius Tiberius was slain, and his army totally defeated. The fugitives dispersed over the country, some to the by-ways and woods, some to the cities and towns, and all other places where they could hope for safety.

Arthur stayed in those parts till the next winter was over, and employed his time in restoring order and settling the government. He then returned into England, and celebrated his victories with great splendor.

Then the king established all his knights, and to them that were not rich he gave lands, and charged them all never to do outrage nor murder, and always to flee treason; also, by no means to be cruel, but to give mercy unto him that asked mercy, upon pain of forfeiture of their worship and lordship; and always to do ladies, damosels, and gentlewomen service, upon pain of death. Also that no man take battle in a wrongful quarrel, for no law, nor for any world's goods. Unto this were all the knights sworn of the Table Round, both old and young. And at every year were they sworn at the high feast of Pentecost.

King Arthur Slays the Giant of St. Michael's Mount

While the army was encamped in Brittany, awaiting the arrival of the kings, there came a countryman to Arthur, and told him that a giant, whose cave was in a neighboring mountain, called St. Michael's Mount, had for a long time been accustomed to carry off the children of the peasants, to devour them. "And now he hath taken the Duchess of Brittany, as she rode with her attendants, and hath carried her away in spite of all they could do." "Now, fellow," said King Arthur, "canst thou bring me there where this giant haunteth?" "Yea, sure," said the good man; "lo, yonder where thou seest two great fires, there shalt thou find him, and more treasure than I suppose is in all France beside." Then the king called to him Sir Bedver and Sir Kay, and commanded them to make ready horse and harness for himself and them; for after evening he would ride on pilgrimage to St. Michael's Mount.

So they three departed, and rode forth till they came to the foot of the mount. And there the king commanded them to tarry, for he would himself go up into that mount. So he ascended the hill till he came to a great fire, and there he found an aged woman sitting by a new-made grave, making great sorrow. Then King Arthur saluted her, and demanded of her wherefore she made such lamentation; to whom she answered: "Sir Knight, speak low, for yonder is a devil, and if he hear thee speak he will come and destroy thee. For ye cannot make resistance to him, he is so fierce and so strong. He hath murdered the Duchess, which here lieth, who was the fairest of all the world, wife to Sir Hoel, Duke of Brittany." "Dame," said the king, "I come from the noble conqueror, King Arthur, to treat with that tyrant." "Fie on such treaties," said she; "he setteth not by the king, nor by no man else." "Well," said Arthur, "I will accomplish my message for all your fearful words." So he went forth by the crest of the hill, and saw where the giant sat at supper, gnawing on the limb of a man, and baking his broad limbs at the fire, and three fair damsels lying bound, whose lot it was to be devoured in their turn. When King Arthur beheld that he had great compassion on them, so that his heart bled for sorrow. Then he hailed the giant, saying, "He that all the world ruleth give thee short life and shameful death. Why hast thou murdered this Duchess? Therefore come forth, thou caitiff, for this day thou shalt die by my hand." Then the giant started up, and took a great club, and smote at the king, and smote off his coronal; and then the king struck him in the belly with his sword, and made a fearful wound. Then the giant threw away his club, and caught the king in his arms, so that he crushed his ribs. Then the three maidens kneeled down and prayed for help and comfort for Arthur. And Arthur weltered and wrenched, so that he was one while under, and another time above. And so weltering and wallowing they rolled down the hill, and ever as they weltered Arthur smote him with his dagger; and it fortuned they came to the place where the two knights were. And when they saw the king fast in the giant's arms they came and loosed him. Then the king commanded Sir Kay to smite off the giant's head, and to set it on the truncheon of a spear, and fix it on the barbican, that all the people might see and behold it. This was done, and anon it was known through all the country, wherefor the people came and thanked the king. And he said, "Give your thanks to God; and take ye the giant's spoil and divide it among you." And King Arthur caused a church to be builded on that hill, in honor of St. Michael.

King Arthur Gets a Sword from the Lady of the Lake

One day King Arthur rode forth, and on a sudden he was ware of three churls chasing Merlin to have slain him. And the king rode unto them and bade them, "Flee, churls!" Then were they afraid when they saw a knight, and fled. "O Merlin," said Arthur, "here hadst thou been slain, for all thy crafts, had I not been by." "Nay," said Merlin, "not so, for I could save myself if I would; but thou art more near thy death than I am." So, as they went thus talking, King Arthur perceived where sat a knight on horseback, as if to guard the pass. "Sir knight," said Arthur, "for what cause abidest thou here?" Then the knight said, "There may no knight ride this way unless he joust with me, for such is the custom of the pass." "I will amend that custom," said the king. Then they ran together, and they met so hard that their spears were shivered. Then they drew their swords and fought a strong battle, with many great strokes. But at length the sword of the knight smote King Arthur's sword in two pieces. Then said the knight unto Arthur, "Thou art in my power, whether to save thee or slay thee, and unless thou yield thee as overcome and recreant thou shalt die." "As for death," said King Arthur, "welcome be it when it cometh; but to yield me unto thee as recreant I will not." Then he leapt upon the knight, and took him by the middle and threw him down; but the knight was a passing strong man, and anon he brought Arthur under him, and would have razed off his helm to slay him. Then said Merlin, "Knight, hold thy hand, for this knight is a man of more worship than thou art aware of." "Why, who is he?" said the knight. "It is King Arthur." Then would he have slain him for dread of his wrath, and lifted up his sword to slay him; and therewith Merlin cast an enchantment on the knight, so that he fell to the earth in a great sleep. Then Merlin took up King Arthur and set him on his horse. "Alas!" said Arthur, "what hast thou done, Merlin? hast thou slain this good knight by thy crafts?" "Care ye not," said Merlin; "he is wholer than ye be. He is only asleep, and will wake in three hours."

Right so the king and he departed, and went unto an hermit that was a good man and a great leech. So the hermit searched all his wounds and gave him good salves; so the king was there three days, and then were his wounds well amended that he might ride and go, and so departed. And as they rode Arthur said, "I have no sword." "No force," said Merlin; "hereby is a sword that shall be yours." So they rode till they came to a lake, the which was a fair water and broad, and in the midst of the lake Arthur was ware of an arm clothed in white samite, that held a fair sword in that hand. "So," said Merlin, "yonder is that sword that I spake of." With that they saw a damsel going upon the lake. "What damsel is that?" said Arthur. "That is the Lady of the Lake," said Merlin; "and within that lake is a rock, and therein is as fair a place as any on earth, and richly beseen, and this damsel will come to you anon, and then speak ye fair to her and she will give thee that sword." Anon withal came the damsel unto Arthur and saluted him, and he her again. "Damsel," said Arthur, "what sword is that that yonder the arm holdeth above the waves? I would it were mine, for I have no sword." "Sir Arthur king," said the damsel, "that sword is mine, and if ye will give me a gift when I ask it you ye shall have it." "By my faith," said Arthur, "I will give ye what gift ye shall ask." "Well," said the damsel, "go you into yonder barge and row your-self to the sword, and take it and the scabbard with you, and I will ask my gift when I see my time." So Arthur and Merlin alighted, and tied their horses to two trees, and so they went into the ship, and when they came to the sword that the hand held, Arthur took it by the handles, and took it with him. And the arm and the hand went under the water.

Then they returned unto the land and rode forth. And Sir Arthur looked on the sword and liked it right well.

So they rode unto Caerleon, whereof his knights were passing glad. And when they heard of his adventures they marvelled that he would jeopard his person so alone. But all men of worship said it was a fine thing to be under such a chieftain as would put his person in adventure as other poor knights did.

CHAPTER IV

CARADOC BRIEFBRAS; OR, CARADOC WITH THE SHRUNKEN ARM

CARADOC was the son of Ysenne, the beautiful niece of Arthur. He was ignorant who his father was, till it was discovered in the following manner: When the youth was of proper years to receive the honors of knighthood, King Arthur held a grand court for the purpose of knighting him. On this occasion a strange knight presented himself, and challenged the knights of Arthur's court to exchange blow for blow with him. His proposal was this,—to lay his neck on a block for any knight to strike, on condition that, if he survived the blow, the knight should submit in turn to the same experiment. Sir Kay, who was usually ready to accept all challenges, pronounced this wholly unreasonable, and declared that he would not accept it for all the wealth in the world. And when the knight offered his sword, with which the operation was to be performed, no person ventured to accept it, till Caradoc, growing angry at the disgrace which was thus incurred by the Round Table, threw aside his mantle and took it. "Do you do this as one of the best knights?" said the stranger. "No," he replied, "but as one of the most foolish." The stranger lays his head upon the block, receives a blow which sends it rolling from his shoulders, walks after it, picks it up, replaces it with great success, and says he will return when the court shall be assembled next year, and claim his turn. When the anniversary arrived both parties were punctual to their engagement. Great entreaties were used by the king and queen, and the whole court, in behalf of Caradoc, but the stranger was inflexible. The young knight laid his head upon the block, and more than once desired him to make an end of the business, and not keep him longer in so disagreeable a state of expectation. At last the stranger strikes him gently with the side of the sword, bids him rise, and reveals to him the fact that he is his father, the enchanter Eliaures, and that he gladly owns him for a son, having proved his courage, and fidelity to his word.

But the favor of enchanters is short-lived and uncertain. Eliaures fell under the influence of a wicked woman, who, to satisfy her pique against Caradoc, persuaded the enchanter to fasten on his arm a serpent, which remained there sucking at his flesh and blood, no human skill sufficing either to remove the reptile or alleviate the torments which Caradoc endured.

Caradoc was betrothed to Guimier, sister to his bosom friend Cador, and daughter to the king of Cornwall. As soon as they were informed of his deplorable condition, they set out for Nantes, where

Caradoc's castle was, that Guimier might attend upon him. When
Caradoc heard of their coming his first emotion was that of joy and
love. But soon he began to fear that the sight of his emaciated form
and of his sufferings would disgust Guimier; and this apprehension
became so strong that he departed secretly from Nantes, and hid
himself in a hermitage. He was sought far and near by the knights
of Arthur's court, and Cador made a vow never to desist from the
quest till he should have found him. After long wandering, Cador
discovered his friend in the hermitage, reduced almost to a skeleton,
and apparently near his death. All other means of relief having
already been tried in vain, Cador at last prevailed on the enchanter
Eliaures to disclose the only method which could avail for his rescue.
A maiden must be found, his equal in birth and beauty, and loving
him better than herself, so that she would expose herself to the same
torment to deliver him. Two vessels were then to be provided, the
one filled with sour wine and the other with milk. Caradoc must
enter the first, so that the wine should reach his neck, and the maiden
must get into the other, and, exposing her bosom upon the edge of
the vessel, invite the serpent to forsake the withered flesh of his
victim for this fresh and inviting food. The vessels were to be
placed three feet apart, and as the serpent crossed from one to the
other a knight was to cut him in two. If he failed in his blow, Caradoc
would indeed be delivered, but it would only be to see his fair
champion suffering the same cruel and hopeless torment. The sequel
may be easily foreseen. Guimier willingly exposed herself to the
perilous adventure, and Cador, with a lucky blow, killed the serpent.
The arm, in which Caradoc had suffered so long, recovered its
strength, but not its shape, in consequence of which he was called
Caradoc Briefbras, Caradoc of the Shrunken Arm.

Caradoc and Guimier are the hero and heroine of the ballad of
the Boy and the Mantle, which follows.

THE BOY AND THE MANTLE

In Carlisle dwelt King Arthur,
  A prince of passing might,
And there maintained his Table
  Beset with many a knight.

And there he kept his Christmas,
  With mirth and princely cheer,
When lo! a strange and cunning boy
  Before him did appear.

A kirtle and a mantle
  This boy had him upon,
With brooches, rings, and ouches,
  Full daintily bedone.

He had a sash of silk
  About his middle meet;
And thus with seemly curtesie
  He did King Arthur greet:

"God speed thee, brave King Arthur,
  Thus feasting in thy bower,
And Guenever, thy goodly queen,
  That fair and peerless flower.

"Ye gallant lords and lordlings,
  I wish you all take heed,
Lest what ye deem a blooming rose
  Should prove a cankered weed."

Then straightway from his bosom
  A little wand he drew;
And with it eke a mantle,
  Of wondrous shape and hue.

"Now have thou here, King Arthur,
  Have this here of me,
And give unto thy comely queen,
  All shapen as you see.

"No wife it shall become,
  That once hath been to blame."
Then every knight in Arthur's court
  Sly glancèd at his dame.

And first came Lady Guenever,
  The mantle she must try.
This dame she was new-fangled,[1]
  And of a roving eye.

When she had taken the mantle,
  And all with it was clad,
From top to toe it shivered down,
  As though with shears beshred.

One while it was too long,
  Another while too short,
And wrinkled on the shoulders,
  In most unseemly sort.

Now green, now red it seemed,
  Then all of sable hue;
"Beshrew me," quoth King Arthur,
  "I think thou be'st not true!"

Down she threw the mantle,
  No longer would she stay;
But, storming like a fury,
  To her chamber flung away.

She cursed the rascal weaver,
  That had the mantle wrought;
And doubly cursed the froward **imp**
  Who thither had **it** brought.

[1] New-fangled,—fond of novelty.

"I had rather live in deserts,
  Beneath the greenwood tree,
Than here, base king, among thy grooms,
  The sport of them and thee."

Sir Kay called forth his lady,
  And bade her to come near:
"Yet, dame, if thou be guilty,
  I pray thee now forbear."

This lady, pertly giggling,
  With forward step came on,
And boldly to the little boy
  With fearless face is gone.

When she had taken the mantle,
  With purpose for to wear,
It shrunk up to her shoulder,
  And left her back all bare.

Then every merry knight,
  That was in Arthur's court,
Gibed and laughed and flouted,
  To see that pleasant sport.

Down she threw the mantle,
  No longer bold or gay,
But, with a face all pale and wan,
  To her chamber slunk away.

Then forth came an old knight
  A-pattering o'er his creed,
And proffered to the little boy
  Five nobles to his meed:

"And all the time of Christmas
  Plum-porridge shall be thine,
If thou wilt let my lady fair
  Within the mantle shine."

A saint his lady seemed,
  With step demure and slow,
And gravely to the mantle
  With mincing face doth go.

When she the same had taken
  That was so fine and thin,
It shrivelled all about her,
  And showed her dainty skin.

Ah! little did her mincing,
  Or his long prayers bestead;
She had no more hung on her
  Than a tassel and a thread.

Down she threw the mantle,
  With terror and dismay,
And with a face of scarlet
  To her chamber hied away.

Sir Cradock called his lady,
    And bade her to come near;
"Come win this mantle, lady,
    And do me credit here:

"Come win this mantle, lady,
    For now it shall be thine,
If thou hast never done amiss,
    Since first I made thee mine."

The lady, gently blushing,
    With modest grace came on;
And now to try the wondrous charm
    Courageously is gone.

When she had ta'en the mantle,
    And put it on her back,
About the hem it seemed
    To wrinkle and to crack.

"Lie still," she cried, "O mantle!
    And shame me not for naught;
I'll freely own whate'er amiss
    Or blameful I have wrought.

"Once I kissed Sir Cradock
    Beneath the greenwood tree;
Once I kissed Sir Cradock's mouth,
    Before he married me."

When she had thus her shriven,
    And her worst fault had told,
The mantle soon became her,
    Right comely as it should.

Most rich and fair of color,
    Like gold it glittering shone,
And much the knights in Arthur's court
    Admired her every one.

The ballad goes on to tell of two more trials of a similar kind,
made by means of a boar's head and a drinking-horn, in both of
which the result was equally favorable with the first to Sir Cradock
and his lady. It then concludes as follows:—

Thus boar's head, horn, and mantle
    Were this fair couple's meed;
And all such constant lovers,
    God send them well to speed.
                    Percy's Reliques.

CHAPTER V

SIR GAWAIN

Sir Gawain was nephew to King Arthur, by his sister Morgana,
married to Lot. king of Orkney, who was by Arthur made king of

Norway. Sir Gawain was one of the most famous knights of the Round Table, and is characterized by the romancers as the *sage* and *courteous* Gawain. To this Chaucer alludes in his "Squiere's Tale," which the strange knight "saluteth" all the court—

> "With so high reverence and observance,
> As well in speeche as in countenance,
> That Gawain, with his olde curtesie,
> Though he were come agen out of faërie,
> Ne coude him not amenden with a word."

Gawain's brothers were Agravain, Gaharet, and Gareth.

SIR GAWAIN'S MARRIAGE

Once upon a time King Arthur held his court in merry Carlisle, when a damsel came before him and craved a boon. It was for vengeance upon a caitiff knight, who had made her lover captive and despoiled her of her lands. King Arthur commanded to bring him his sword, Excalibar, and to saddle his steed, and rode forth without delay to right the lady's wrong. Ere long he reached the castle of the grim baron, and challenged him to the conflict. But the castle stood on magic ground, and the spell was such that no knight could tread thereon but straight his courage fell and his strength decayed. King Arthur felt the charm, and before a blow was struck his sturdy limbs lost their strength, and his head grew faint. He was fain to yield himself prisoner to the churlish knight, who refused to release him except upon condition that he should return at the end of a year, and bring a true answer to the question, "What thing is it which women most desire?" or in default thereof surrender himself and his lands. King Arthur accepted the terms, and gave his oath to return at the time appointed. During the year the king rode east, and he rode west, and inquired of all whom he met what thing it is which all women most desire. Some told him riches; some pomp and state; some mirth; some flattery; and some a gallant knight. But in the diversity of answers he could find no sure dependence. The year was well nigh spent when, one day, as he rode thoughtfully through a forest, he saw sitting beneath a tree a lady of such hideous aspect that he turned away his eyes, and when she greeted him in seemly sort made no answer. "What wight art thou," the lady said, "that will not speak to me? It may chance that I may resolve thy doubts, though I be not fair of aspect." "If thou wilt do so," said King Arthur, "choose what reward thou wilt, thou grim lady, and it shall be given thee." "Swear me this upon thy faith," she said, and Arthur swore it. Then the lady told him the secret, and demanded her reward, which was that the king should find some fair and courtly knight to be her husband.

King Arthur hastened to the grim baron's castle and told him one by one all the answers which he had received from his various advisers, except the last, and not one was admitted as the true one. "Now yield thee, Arthur," the giant said, "for thou hast not paid thy ransom, and thou and thy lands are forfeited to me." Then King Arthur said:—

> "Yet hold thy hand, thou proud baron,
>   I pray thee hold thy hand.
> And give me leave to speak once more,
>   In rescue of my land.
> This morn, as I came over a moor,
>   I saw a lady set,
> Between an oak and a green holly,
>   All clad in red scarlet.
> She says *all women would have their will*,
>   This is their chief desire;
> Now yield, as thou art a baron true,
>   That I have paid my hire."

"It was my sister that told thee this," the churlish baron exclaimed. "Vengeance light on her! I will some time or other do her as ill a turn."

King Arthur rode homeward, but not light of heart; for he remembered the promise he was under to the loathly lady to give her one of his young and gallant knights for a husband. He told his grief to Sir Gawain, his nephew, and he replied, "Be not sad, my lord, for I will marry the loathly lady." King Arthur replied:—

> "Now nay, now nay, good Sir Gawaine,
>   My sister's son ye be;
> The loathly lady's all too grim,
>   And all too foule for thee."

But Gawain persisted, and the king at last, with sorrow of heart, consented that Gawain should be his ransom. So, one day, the king and his knights rode to the forest, met the loathly lady, and brought her to the court. Sir Gawain stood the scoffs and jeers of his companions as he best might, and the marriage was solemnized, but not with the usual festivities. Chaucer tells us:—

> "There was no joye, ne feste at alle;
> There n'as but hevinesse and mochel sorwe,
> For prively he wed her on the morwe,
> And all day after hid him as an owle,
> So wo was him his wife loked so foule!" [1]

---

[1] *N'as* is *not was*, contracted; in modern phrase, *there was not*. *Mochel sorwe* is *much sorrow: morwe* is *morrow*.

When night came, and they were alone together, Sir Gawain could not conceal his aversion; and the lady asked him why he sighed so heavily, and turned away his face. He candidly confessed it was on account of three things, her age, her ugliness, and her low degree. The lady, not at all offended, replied with excellent arguments to all his objections. She showed him that with age is discretion, with ugliness security from rivals, and that all true gentility depends, not upon the accident of birth, but upon the character of the individual.

Sir Gawain made no reply; but, turning his eyes on his bride, what was his amazement to perceive that she wore no longer the unseemly aspect that had so distressed him. She then told him that the form she had worn was not her true form, but a disguise imposed upon her by a wicked enchanter, and that she was condemned to wear it until two things should happen; one, that she should obtain some young and gallant knight to be her husband. This having been done, one half of the charm was removed. She was now at liberty to wear her true form for half the time, and she bade him choose whether he would have her fair by day and ugly by night, or the reverse. Sir Gawain would fain have had her look her best by night, when he alone should see her, and show her repulsive visage, if at all, to others. But she reminded him how much more pleasant it would be to her to wear her best looks in the throng of knights and ladies by day. Sir Gawain yielded, and gave up his will to hers. This alone was wanting to dissolve the charm. The lovely lady now with joy assured him that she should change no more; but as she now was so would she remain by night as well as by day.

> "Sweet blushes stayned her rud-red cheek,
>   Her eyen were black as sloe,
> The ripening cherrye swelled her lippe,
>   And all her neck was snow.
> Sir Gawain kist that ladye faire
>   Lying upon the sheete,
> And swore, as he was a true knight,
>   The spice was never so swete."

The dissolution of the charm which had held the lady also released her brother, the "grim baron," for he too had been implicated in it. He ceased to be a churlish oppressor, and became a gallant and generous knight as any at Arthur's court.

CHAPTER VI

LAUNCELOT OF THE LAKE

KING BAN, of Brittany, the faithful ally of Arthur, was attacked by his enemy Claudas, and, after a long war, saw himself reduced to the possession of a single fortress, where he was besieged by his enemy. In this extremity he determined to solicit the assistance of Arthur, and escaped in a dark night, with his wife Helen and his infant son Launcelot, leaving his castle in the hands of his seneschal, who immediately surrendered the place to Claudas. The flames of his burning citadel reached the eyes of the unfortunate monarch during his flight, and he expired with grief. The wretched Helen, leaving her child on the brink of a lake, flew to receive the last sighs of her husband, and on returning perceived the little Launcelot in the arms of a nymph, who, on the approach of the queen, threw herself into the lake with the child. This nymph was Viviane, mistress of the enchanter Merlin, better known by the name of the Lady of the Lake. Launcelot received his appellation from having been educated at the court of this enchantress, whose palace was situated in the midst, not of a real, but, like the appearance which deceives the African traveller, of an imaginary lake, whose deluding resemblance served as a barrier to her residence. Here she dwelt not alone, but in the midst of a numerous retinue, and a splendid court of knights and damsels.

The queen, after her double loss, retired to a convent, where she was joined by the widow of Bohort, for this good king had died of grief on hearing of the death of his brother Ban. His two sons, Lionel and Bohort, were rescued by a faithful knight, and arrived in the shape of greyhounds at the palace of the lake, where, having resumed their natural form, they were educated along with their cousin Launcelot.

The fairy, when her pupil had attained the age of eighteen, conveyed him to the court of Arthur, for the purpose of demanding his admission to the honor of knighthood; and at the first appearance of the youthful candidate the graces of his person, which were not inferior to his courage and skill in arms, made an instantaneous and indelible impression on the heart of Guenever, while her charms inspired him with an equally ardent and constant passion. The mutual attachment of these lovers exerted, from that time forth, an influence over the whole history of Arthur. For the sake of Guenever Launcelot achieved the conquest of Northumberland, defeated Gal-lehaut, King of the Marches, who afterwards become his most faithful friend and ally, exposed himself in numberless encounters. and brought hosts of prisoners to the feet of his sovereign.

After King Arthur was come from Rome into England all the knights of the Table Round resorted unto him, and made him many jousts and tournaments. And in especial Sir Launcelot of the Lake, in all tournaments and jousts and deeds of arms, both for life and death, passed all other knights, and was never overcome, except it were by treason or enchantment; and he increased marvellously in worship, wherefore Queen Guenever had him in great favor, above all other knights. And for certain he loved the queen again above all other ladies; and for her he did many deeds of arms, and saved her from peril through his noble chivalry. Thus Sir Launcelot rested him long with play and game, and then he thought to prove himself in strange adventures; so he bade his nephew, Sir Lionel, to make him ready,—"for we two will seek adventures." So they mounted on their horses, armed at all sights, and rode into a forest, and so into a deep plain. And the weather was hot about noon, and Sir Launcelot had great desire to sleep. Then Sir Lionel espied a great apple-tree that stood by a hedge, and he said: "Brother, yonder is a fair shadow,—there may we rest us and our horses." "It is well said," replied Sir Launcelot. So they there alighted, and Sir Launcelot laid him down, and his helm under his head, and soon was asleep passing fast. And Sir Lionel waked while he slept. And presently there came three knights riding as fast as ever they might ride, and there followed them but one knight. And Sir Lionel thought he never saw so great a knight before. So within a while this great knight overtook one of those knights, and smote him so that he fell to the earth. Then he rode to the second knight and smote him, and so he did to the third knight. Then he alighted down, and bound all the three knights fast with their own bridles. When Sir Lionel saw him do thus he thought to assay him, and made him ready, silently, not to awake Sir Launcelot, and rode after the strong knight, and bade him turn. And the other smote Sir Lionel so hard that horse and man fell to the earth; and then he alighted down, and bound Sir Lionel, and threw him across his own horse; and so he served them all four, and rode with them away to his own castle. And when he came there, he put them in a deep prison, in which were many more knights in great distress.

Now while Sir Launcelot lay under the apple-tree sleeping there came by him four queens of great estate. And that the heat should not grieve them, there rode four knights about them, and bare a cloth of green silk, on four spears, betwixt them and the sun. And the queens rode on four white mules.

Thus as they rode they heard by them a great horse grimly neigh. Then they were aware of a sleeping knight, that lay all armed under an apple-tree; and as the queens looked on his face they knew it was Sir Launcelot. Then they began to strive for that knight, and each one said she would have him for her love. "We will not strive," said Morgane le Fay, that was King Arthur's sister, "for I will put an enchantment upon him, that he shall not wake for six hours, and we will take him away to my castle; and then when he is surely within my hold I will take the enchantment from him, and then let him choose which of us he will have for his love." So the enchantment was cast upon Sir Launcelot. And then they laid him upon his shield, and bare him so on horseback between two knights, and brought him unto the castle and laid him in a chamber, and at night they sent him his supper.

And on the morning came early those four queens, richly dight, and bade him good morning, and he them again. "Sir knight," they said, "thou must understand that thou art our prisoner; and we know thee well, that thou art Sir Launcelot of the Lake, King Ban's son, and that thou art the noblest knight living. And we know well that there can no lady have thy love but one, and that is Queen Guenever; and now thou shalt lose her forever, and she thee; and therefore it behooveth thee now to choose one of us. I am the Queen Morgane le Fay, and here is the Queen of North Wales, and the Queen of Eastland, and the Queen of the Isles. Now choose one of us which thou wilt have, for if thou choose not in this prison thou shalt die." "This is a hard case," said Sir Launcelot, "that either I must die or else choose one of you; yet had I liever to die in this prison with worship than have to have one of you for my paramour, for ye be false enchantresses." "Well," said the queens, "is this your answer, that ye will refuse us?" "Yea, on my life it is," said Sir Launcelot. Then they departed, making great sorrow.

Then at noon came a damsel unto him with his dinner, and asked him, "What cheer?" "Truly, fair damsel," said Sir Launcelot, "never so ill." "Sir," said she, "if you will be ruled by me, I will help you out of this distress. If ye will promise me to help my father on Tuesday next, who hath made a tournament betwixt him and the king of North Wales; for the last Tuesday my father lost the field." "Fair maiden," said Sir Launcelot, "tell me what is your father's name, and then will I give you an answer." "Sir knight," she said, "my father is King Bagdemagus." "I know him well," said Sir Launcelot, "for a noble king and a good knight, and, by the faith of my body, I will be ready to do your father and you service at that day."

So she departed, and came on the next morning early and found him ready, and brought him out of twelve locks, and brought him to his own horse, and lightly he saddled him, and so rode forth.

And on the Tuesday next he came to a little wood where the tournament should be. And there were scaffolds and holds, that lords and ladies might look on, and give the prize. Then came into the field the king of North Wales, with eightscore helms, and King Bagdemagus came with fourscore helms. And then they couched their spears, and came together with a great dash, and there were overthrown at the first encounter twelve of King Bagdemagus's party and six of the king of North Wales's party, and King Bagdemagus's party had the worse.

With that came Sir Launcelot of the Lake, and thrust in with his spear in the thickest of the press; and he smote down five knights ere he held his hand; and he smote down the king of North Wales, and he brake his thigh in that fall. And then the knights of the king of North Wales would joust no more; and so the gree was given to King Bagdemagus.

And Sir Launcelot rode forth with King Bagdemagus unto his castle; and there he had passing good cheer, both with the king and with his daughter. And on the morn he took his leave, and told the king he would go and seek his brother, Sir Lionel, that went from him when he slept. So he departed, and by adventure he came to the same forest where he was taken sleeping. And in the highway he met a damsel riding on a white palfrey, and they saluted each other. "Fair damsel," said Sir Launcelot, "know ye in this country any adventures?" "Sir Knight," said the damsel, "here are adventures near at hand, if thou durst pursue them." "Why should I not prove adventures?" said Sir Launcelot, "since for that came I hither." "Sir," said she, "hereby dwelleth a knight that will not be overmatched for any man I know, except thou overmatch him. His name is Sir Turquine, and, as I understand, he is a deadly enemy of King Arthur, and he has in his prison good knights of Arthur's court three score and more, that he hath won with his own hands." "Damsel," said Launcelot, "I pray you bring me unto this knight." So she told him, "Hereby, within this mile, is his castle, and by it on the left hand is a ford for horses to drink of, and over that ford there groweth a fair tree, and on that tree hang many shields that good knights wielded aforetime, that are now prisoners: and on the tree hangeth a basin of copper and latten, and if thou strike upon that basin thou shalt hear tidings." And Sir Launcelot departed, and rode as the damsel had shown him, and shortly he came to the ford, and the tree where hung the shields and basin. And among the shields he saw Sir Lionel's and Sir Hector's shield, besides many others of knights that he knew.

Then Sir Launcelot struck on the basin with the butt of his spear; and long he did so, but he saw no man. And at length he was ware of a great knight that drove a horse before him, and across the horse there lay an armed knight bounden. And as they came near Sir Launcelot thought he should know the captive knight. Then Sir Launcelot saw that it was Sir Gaheris, Sir Gawain's brother, a knight of the Table Round. "Now, fair knight," said Sir Launcelot, "put that wounded knight off the horse, and let him rest awhile, and let us two prove our strength. For, as it is told me, thou hast done great despite and shame unto knights of the Round Table, therefore now defend thee." "If thou be of the Table Round," said Sir Turquine, "I defy thee and all thy fellowship." "That is overmuch said," said Sir Launcelot.

Then they put their spears in the rests, and came together with their horses as fast as they might run. And each smote the other in the middle of their shields, so that their horses fell under them, and the knights were both staggered; and as soon as they could clear their horses, they drew out their swords and came together eagerly, and each gave the other many strong strokes, for neither shield nor harness might withstand their strokes. So within a while both had grimly wounds, and bled grievously. Then at the last they were breathless both, and stood leaning upon their swords. "Now, fellow," said Sir Turquine, "thou art the stoutest man that ever I met with, and best breathed; and so be it thou be not the knight that I hate above all other knights, the knight that slew my brother, Sir Caradoc, I will gladly accord with thee; and for thy love I will deliver all the prisoners that I have."

"What knight is he that thou hatest so above others?" "Truly," said Sir Turquine, "his name is Sir Launcelot of the Lake." "I am Sir Launcelot of the Lake, King Ban's son of Benwick, and very knight of the Table Round; and now I defy thee do thy best." "Ah" said Sir Turquine, "Launcelot, thou art to me the most welcome that ever was knight; for we shall never part till the one of us be dead." And then they hurtled together like two wild bulls, rashing and lashing with their swords and shields, so that sometimes they fell, as it were, headlong. Thus they fought two hours and more, till the ground where they fought was all bepurpled with blood.

Then at the last Sir Turquine waxed sore faint, and gave somewhat aback, and bare his shield full low for weariness. That spied Sir Launcelot, and leapt then upon him fiercely as a lion, and took

him by the beaver of his helmet, and drew him down on his knees.
And he rased off his helm, and smote his neck in sunder.

And Sir Gaheris, when he saw Sir Turquine slain, said, "Fair
lord, I pray you tell me your name, for this day I say ye are the
best knight in the world, for ye have slain this day in my sight
the mightiest man and the best knight except you that ever I saw."
"Sir, my name is Sir Launcelot du Lac, that ought to help you of
right for King Arthur's sake, and in especial for Sir Gawain's sake,
your own dear brother. Now I pray you, that ye go into yonder
castle, and set free all the prisoners ye find there, for I am sure
ye shall find there many knights of the Table Round, and especially
my brother Sir Lionel. I pray you greet them all from me, and tell
them I bid them take there such stuff as they find; and tell my
brother to go unto the court and abide me there, for by the feast
of Pentecost I think to be there; but at this time I may not stop,
for I have adventures on hand." So he departed, and Sir Gaheris
rode into the castle, and took the keys from the porter, and hastily
opened the prison door and let out all the prisoners. There was Sir
Kay, Sir Brandeles, and Sir Galynde, Sir Bryan and Sir Alyduke,
Sir Hector de Marys and Sir Lionel, and many more. And when
they saw Sir Gaheris, they all thanked him, for they thought, because
he was wounded, that he had slain Sir Turquine. "Not so," said Sir
Gaheris; "it was Sir Launcelot that slew him, right worshipfully;
I saw it with mine eyes."

Sir Launcelot rode till at nightfall he came to a fair castle, and
therein he found an old gentlewoman, who lodged him with good-
will, and there he had good cheer for him and his horse. And when
time was, his host brought him to a fair chamber over the gate to
his bed. Then Sir Launcelot unarmed him, and set his harness by
him, and went to bed, and anon he fell asleep. And soon after, there
came one on horseback and knocked at the gate in great haste; and
when Sir Launcelot heard this, he arose and looked out of the
window, and saw by the moonlight three knights riding after that
one man, and all three lashed on him with their swords, and that
one knight turned on them knightly again and defended himself.
"Truly," said Sir Launcelot, "yonder one knight will I help, for it
is shame to see three knights on one." Then he took his harness
and went out at the window by a sheet down to the four knights;
and he said aloud, "Turn you knights unto me, and leave your
fighting with that knight." Then the knights left Sir Kay, for it was
he they were upon, and turned unto Sir Launcelot, and struck many
great strokes at Sir Launcelot, and assailed him on every side. Then
Sir Kay addressed him to help Sir Launcelot, but he said, "Nay,
sir, I will none of your help; let me alone with them." So Sir Kay

suffered him to do his will, and stood one side. And within six strokes, Sir Launcelot had stricken them down.

Then they all cried, "Sir knight, we yield us unto you." "As to that," said Sir Launcelot, "I will not take your yielding unto me. If so be ye will yield you unto Sir Kay the seneschal, I will save your lives, but else not." "Fair knight," then they said, "we will do as thou commandest us." "Then shall ye," said Sir Launcelot, "on Whitsunday next, go unto the court of King Arthur, and there shall ye yield you unto Queen Guenever, and say that Sir Kay sent you thither to be her prisoners." "Sir," they said, "it shall be done, by the faith of our bodies;" and then they swore, every knight upon his sword. And so Sir Launcelot suffered them to depart.

On the morn Sir Launcelot rose early and left Sir Kay sleeping; and Sir Launcelot took Sir Kay's armor and his shield, and armed him, and went to the stable and took his horse, and so he departed. Then soon after arose Sir Kay and missed Sir Launcelot. And then he espied that he had taken his armor and his horse. "Now, by my faith, I know well," said Sir Kay, "that he will grieve some of King Arthur's knights, for they will deem that it is I, and will be bold to meet him. But by cause of his armor I am sure I shall ride in peace." Then Sir Kay thanked his host and departed.

Sir Launcelot rode in a deep forest, and there he saw four knights under an oak, and they were of Arthur's court. There was Sir Sagramour le Desirus and Hector de Marys, and Sir Gawain and Sir Uwaine. As they spied Sir Launcelot, they judged by his arms it had been Sir Kay. "Now, by my faith," said Sir Sagramour, "I will prove Sir Kay's might;" and got his spear in his hand, and came toward Sir Launcelot. Therewith Sir Launcelot couched his spear against him, and smote Sir Sagramour so sore that horse and man fell both to the earth. Then said Sir Hector, "Now shall ye see what I may do with him." But he fared worse than Sir Sagramour, for Sir Launcelot's spear went through his shoulder and bare him from his horse to the ground. "By my faith," said Sir Uwaine, "yonder is a strong knight, and I fear he hath slain Sir Kay, and taken his armor." And therewith Sir Uwaine took his spear in hand, and rode toward Sir Launcelot; and Sir Launcelot met him on the plain and gave him such a buffet that he was staggered, and wist not where he was. "Now see I well," said Sir Gawain, "that I must encounter with that knight." Then he adjusted his shield, and took a good spear in his hand, and Sir Launcelot knew him well. Then they let run their horses with all their mights, and each knight smote the other in the middle of his shield. But Sir Gawain's spear broke, and Sir Launcelot charged so sore upon him that his horse fell over backward. Then Sir Launcelot rode away smiling with himself, and he said, "Good luck be with him that made this spear, for never came a better into my hand." Then the four knights went each to the other and comforted one another. "What say ye to this adventure," said Sir Gawain, "that one spear hath felled us all four?" "I dare lay my head it is Sir Launcelot," said Sir Hector; "I know it by his riding."

And Sir Launcelot rode through many strange countries, till, by fortune, he came to a fair castle; and as he passed beyond the castle, he thought he heard two bells ring. And then he perceived how a falcon came flying over his head toward a high elm; and she had long lunys [1] about her feet, and she flew unto the elm to take her perch, and the lunys got entangled in a bough; and when she would have taken her flight, she hung by the legs fast, and Sir Launcelot saw how she hung and beheld the fair falcon entangled, and he was sorry for her. Then came a lady out of the castle and cried aloud, "O Launcelot, Launcelot, as thou art the flower of all knights, help me to get my hawk; for if my hawk be lost, my lord will slay me, he is so hasty." "What is your lord's name?" said Sir Launcelot. "His name is Sir Phelot, a knight that belongeth to the king of North Wales." "Well, fair lady, since ye know my name, and require me of knighthood to help you, I will do what I may to get your hawk; and yet, in truth, I am an ill climber and the tree is passing high and few boughs to help me." And therewith Sir Launcelot alighted and tied his horse to a tree, and prayed the lady to unarm him. And when he was unarmed, he put off his jerkin, and with might and force he clomb up to the falcon, and tied the lunys to a rotten bough, and threw the hawk down with it; and the lady got the hawk in her hand. Then suddenly there came out of the castle her husband all armed, and with his naked sword in his hand, and said, "O Knight Launcelot, now have I got thee as I would;" and stood at the boll of the tree to slay him. "Ah, lady!" said Sir Launcelot, "why have ye betrayed me?" "She hath done," said Sir Phelot, "but as I commanded her; and therefore there is none other way but thine hour is come, and thou must die." "That were shame unto thee," said Sir Launcelot; "thou an armed knight to slay a naked man by treason." "Thou gettest none other grace," said Sir Phelot, "and therefore help thyself if thou canst." "Alas!" said Sir Launcelot, "that ever a knight should die weaponless!" And therewith he turned his eyes upward and downward; and over his head he saw a big bough leafless, and he brake it off from the trunk. And then he came lower, and watched how his own horse stood; and suddenly he leapt on the further side of his horse from the knight. Then Sir Phelot lashed at him eagerly, meaning to have

[1] *Lunys,* the string with which the falcon is held.

slain him. But Sir Launcelot put away the stroke with the big bough, and smote Sir Phelot therewith on the side of the head, so that he fell down in a swoon to the ground. Then Sir Launcelot took his sword out of his hand and struck his head from the body. Then said the lady, "Alas! why hast thou slain my husband?" "I am not the cause," said Sir Launcelot, "for with falsehood ye would have slain me, and now it is fallen on yourselves." Thereupon Sir Launcelot got all his armor and put it upon him hastily for fear of more resort, for the knight's castle was so nigh. And as soon as he might, he took his horse and departed, and thanked God he had escaped that adventure.

And two days before the feast of Pentecost, Sir Launcelot came home; and the king and all the court were passing glad of his coming. And when Sir Gawain, Sir Uwaine, Sir Sagramour, and Sir Hector de Marys saw Sir Launcelot in Sir Kay's armor, then they wist well it was he that smote them down, all with one spear. Then there was laughing and merriment among them; and from time to time came all the knights that Sir Turquine had prisoners, and they all honored and worshipped Sir Launcelot. Then Sir Gaheris said, "I saw all the battle from the beginning to the end," and he told King Arthur all how it was. Then Sir Kay told the king how Sir Launcelot had rescued him, and how he "made the knights yield to me, and not to him." And there they were, all three, and confirmed it all. "And by my faith," said Sir Kay, "because Sir Launcelot took my harness and left me his, I rode in peace, and no man would have to do with me."

And so at that time Sir Launcelot had the greatest name of any knight of the world, and most was he honored of high and low.

CHAPTER VII

THE STORY OF LAUNCELOT.—THE ADVENTURE OF THE CART

So it befell in the month of May, Queen Guenever called unto her knights of the Table Round, and she gave them warning that early upon the morrow she would ride on maying into the woods and fields beside Westminster. "And I warn you that there be none of you but that he be well horsed, and that ye be all clothed in green, either in silk, either in cloth, and I shall bring with me ten ladies, and every knight shall have a lady behind him, and every knight shall have a squire and two yeomen, and I will that ye all be well horsed." So they made them ready in the freshest manner, and these were the names of the knights: Sir Kay the seneschal, Sir Agravaine, Sir Brandeles, Sir Sagramour le Desirus, Sir Dodynas le

Sauvage, Sir Ozanna le Cure Hardy, Sir Ladynas of the Forest Savage, Sir Perseant of Inde, Sir Ironside that was called the knight of the red lawns, and Sir Pelleas the lover; and these ten knights made them ready in the freshest manner to ride with the queen. And so upon the morn they took their horses, with the queen, and rode on maying in woods and meadows, as it pleased them, in great joy and delight; for the queen had cast to have been again with King Arthur at the furthest by ten of the clock, and so was that time her purpose. Then there was a knight, that knight Meleagans, and he was son unto King Bagdemagus, and this knight had at that time a castle, of the gift of King Arthur, within seven miles of Westminster; and this knight Sir Meleagans loved passing well Queen Guenever, and so had he done long and many years. And he had lain in a wait for to steal away the queen, but evermore he forbore, because of Sir Launcelot, for in no wise would he meddle with the queen if Sir Launcelot were in her company, or else if he were near at hand to her. And at that time was such a custom the queen rode never without a great fellowship of men of arms about her; and they were many good knights, and the most part were young men that would have worship, and they were called the queen's knights, and never in no battle, tournament, nor joust, they bare none of them no manner of acknowledging of their own arms, but plain white shields, and thereby they were called the queen's knights. And then when it happed any of them to be of great worship by his noble deeds, then at the next feast of Pentecost, if there were any slain or dead, as there was no year that these failed, but some were dead, then was there chosen in his stead the most men of worship that were called the queen's knights. And thus they came up all first, or they were renowned men of worship, both Sir Launcelot and the remnant of them.

But this knight, Sir Meleagans, had espied the queen well and her purpose, and how Sir Launcelot was not with her, and how she had no men of arms with her but the ten noble knights all arrayed in green for maying. Then he provided him a twenty men of arms and an hundred archers, for to destroy the queen and her knights, for he thought that time was the best season to take the queen. So as the queen had mayed and all her knights, all were bedashed with herbs, mosses, and flowers, in the best manner and freshest. Right so came out of a wood Sir Meleagans with an eight-score men well harnessed, as they should fight in a battle of arrest, and bade the queen and her knights abide, for maugre their heads they should abide. "Traitor knight," said Queen Guenever, "what castest thou for to do? Wilt thou shame thyself? Bethink thee how thou art a king's son, and knight of the Table Round, and thou to be about to dishonor the noble king that made thee knight; thou shamest all knighthood and thyself, and me. I let thee wit, me shalt thou never shame, for I had lever cut my throat in twain than thou shouldst dishonor me." "As for all this language," said Sir Meleagans, "be it as it may, for wit you well, madam, I have loved you many a year, and never or now could I get you at such an advantage as I do now, and therefore I will take you as I find you." Then spake all the ten noble knights at once, and said: "Sir Meleagans, wit thou well ye are about to jeopard your worship to dishonor, and also ye cast to jeopard our persons; howbeit we be unarmed, ye have us at great avail, for it seemeth by you that ye have laid watch upon us; but rather than ye should put the queen to shame, and us all, we had as lief to depart from our lives, for if we other ways did we should be ashamed forever." Then Sir Meleagans said, "Dress you as well as you can, and keep the queen." Then all the ten knights of the Table Round drew their swords, and the other let run at them with their spears, and the ten knights manly abode them, and smote away their spears, that no spear did them none harm. Then they lashed together with swords, and anon Sir Kay, Sir Sagramour, Sir Agravaine, Sir Dodynas, Sir Ladynas, and Sir Ozanna were smitten to the earth with grimly wounds. Then Sir Brandiles, and Sir Persant, Sir Ironside, and Sir Pelleas fought long, and they were sorely wounded; for these ten knights or ever they were laid to the ground slew forty men of the boldest and best of them. So when the queen saw her knights thus dolefully wounded, and needs must be slain at the last, then for pity and sorrow she cried, "Sir Meleagans, slay not my noble knights, and I will go with thee upon this covenant, that thou save them, and suffer them not to be no more hurt, with this, that they be led with me wheresoever thou leadest me; for I will rather slay myself than I will go with thee, unless that these my noble knights may be in my presence." "Madam," said Meleagans, "for your sake they shall be led with you into mine own castle, with that ye will be ruled and ride with me." Then the queen prayed the four knights to leave their fighting, and she and they would not part. "Madam," said Sir Pelleas, "we will do as ye do, for as for me I take no force of my life nor death." For Sir Pelleas gave such buffets that none armor might hold him.

Then by the queen's commandment they left battle, and dressed the wounded knights on horseback, some sitting, some overthwart their horses, that it was pity to behold them. And then Sir Meleagans charged the queen and all her knights that none of all her fellowship should depart from her; for full sore he dreaded Sir Launcelot du Lac. lest he should have any knowledging. All this espied the queen and privily she called unto her a child of her chamber, that was swiftly horsed, to whom she said, "Go thou, when thou seest thy time, and bear this ring to Sir Launcelot du Lac, and pray him, as he loveth me, that he will see me, and rescue me if ever he will have joy of me; and spare thou not thy horse," said the queen, "neither for water nor for land." So the child espied his time, and lightly he took his horse with the spurs, and departed as fast as he might. And when Sir Meleagans saw him so flee he understood that it was by the queen's commandment for to warn Sir Launcelot. Then they that were best horsed chased him, and shot at him, but from them all the child went suddenly; and then Sir Meleagans said unto the queen, "Madam, ye are about to betray me, but I shall ordain for Sir Launcelot that he shall not come lightly to you." And then he rode with her and them all to his castle in all the haste that he might. And by the way Sir Meleagans laid in an ambushment the best archers that he might get in his country, to the number of thirty, to await upon Sir Launcelot, charging them that if they saw such a manner of knight come by the way upon a white horse, that in any wise they slay his horse, but in no manner of wise have not ado with him bodily, for he was overhard to be overcome. So this was done, and they were come to his castle, but in no wise the queen would never let none of the ten knights and her ladies out of her sight, but always they were in her presence. So when the child was departed from the fellowship of Sir Meleagans, within awhile he came to Westminster. And anon he found Sir Launcelot. And when he had told him his message, and delivered him the queen's ring, "Alas!" said Sir Launcelot, "now am I shamed forever, unless that I may rescue that noble lady from dishonor." Then eagerly he asked his armor, and ever the child told Sir Launcelot how the ten knights fought marvellously, and how Sir Pelleas, and Sir Ironside, and Sir Brandiles, and Sir Persant of Inde fought strongly, but as for Sir Pelleas there might none withstand him, and how they all fought till at last they were laid to the earth, and then the queen made appointment for to save their lives, and go with Sir Meleagans. "Alas!" said Sir Launcelot, "that most noble lady that she should be so destroyed! I had lever," said Sir Launcelot, "than all France that I had been there well armed." So when Launcelot was armed and upon his horse, he prayed the child of the queen's chamber to warn Sir Lavaine how suddenly he was departed, and for what cause,—"and pray him, as he loveth me, that he will hie him after me, and that he stint not until he come to the castle where Sir Meleagans abideth or dwelleth, for there," said Launcelot, "shall he hear of me if I am a man living, and rescue the queen and her ten knights, the which he traitorously hath taken, and that shall I prove upon his head, and all them that hold with him."

Then Sir Launcelot rode as fast as he might, and he took the water at Westminster, and made his horse to swim over Thames at Lambeth. And then within a while he came to the place where the ten knights had fought with Sir Meleagans, and then Sir Launcelot followed that track until he came to a wood, and there was a straight way, and there the thirty archers bade Sir Launcelot turn again, and follow no longer that track. "What commandment have ye thereto," said Sir Launcelot, "to cause me, that am a knight of the Round Table, to leave my right way?" "This way shalt thou leave, or else thou shalt go it on thy foot, for wit thou well thy horse shall be slain." "That is little mastery," said Launcelot, "to slay my horse, but as for myself, when my horse is slain, I give right nought for you, not if ye were five hundred more." So then they shot Sir Launcelot's horse, and smote him with many arrows. And then Sir Launcelot avoided his horse and went on foot; but there were so many ditches and hedges betwixt them and him that he might meddle with none of them. "Alas, for shame," said Sir Launcelot, "that ever one knight should betray another knight, but it is an old saw, 'A good man is never in danger but when he is in danger of a coward.' " Then Sir Launcelot went a while, and then he was foul cumbered of his armor, his shield, and his spear, and all that belonged to him. Wit ye well he was sore annoyed, and full loth he was to leave anything that belonged to him, for he dreaded sore the treason of Sir Meleagans. And then by fortune there came by a cart that came thither for to fetch wood.

Now at this time carts were but little used save for carrying offal or such like, and for conveying criminals to execution. But Sir Launcelot took no thought save of rescuing the queen. "Say me, carter," said he, "what shall I give thee for to suffer me to leap into thy cart, and that thou shalt bring me unto a castle within this two mile?" "Thou shalt not come within my cart," said the carter, "for I am sent for to fetch wood for my lord Sir Meleagans." "With him would I speak." "Thou shalt not go with me," said the carter. Then Sir Launcelot lept to him, and gave him such a buffet that he fell to the earth stark dead. Then the other carter, his fellow, thought to have gone the same way, and then he cried, "Fair lord, save my life, and I shall bring you where you will."

So then Sir Launcelot placed himself in the cart, and only lamented that with much jolting he made but little progress. Then it happened Sir Gawain passed by, and seeing an armed knight travelling in that unusual way, he drew near to see who it might be. Then Sir Launcelot told him how the queen had been carried off, and how, in hastening to her rescue, his horse had been disabled, and he had been compelled to avail himself of the cart rather than give up his enterprise. Then Sir Gawain said, "Surely it is unworthy of a knight to travel in such sort!" but Sir Launcelot heeded him not.

At nightfall they arrived at a castle, and the lady thereof came out at the head of her damsels to welcome Sir Gawain. But to admit his companion, whom she supposed to be a criminal, or at least a prisoner, it pleased her not; however, to oblige Sir Gawain, she consented. At supper Sir Launcelot came near being consigned to the kitchen, and was only admitted to the lady's table at the earnest solicitation of Sir Gawain. Neither would the damsels prepare a bed for him. He seized the first he found unoccupied, and was left undisturbed.

Next morning he saw from the turrets of the castle a train accompanying a lady, whom he imagined to be the queen. Sir Gawain thought it might be so, and became equally eager to depart. The lady of the castle supplied Sir Launcelot with a horse, and they traversed the plain at full speed. They learned from some travellers whom they met that there were two roads which led to the castle of Sir Meleagans. Here therefore the friends separated. Sir Launcelot found his way beset with obstacles, which he encountered successfully, but not without much loss of time. As evening approached he was met by a young and sportive damsel, who gayly proposed to him a supper at her castle. The knight, who was hungry and weary, accepted the offer, though with no very good grace. He followed the lady to her castle, and ate voraciously of her supper, but was quite impenetrable to all her amorous advances. Suddenly' the scene changed, and he was assailed by six furious ruffians, whom he dealt with so vigorously that most of them were speedily disabled, when again there was a change, and he found himself alone with his fair hostess, who informed him that she was none other than his guardian fairy, who had but subjected him to tests of his courage and fidelity. The next day the fairy brought him on his road, and before parting gave him a ring, which she told him would by its changes of color disclose to him all enchantments, and enable him to subdue them.

Sir Launcelot pursued his journey, being but little troubled save by the taunts of travellers, who all seemed to have learned by some means his disgraceful drive in the cart. One, more insolent than the rest, had the audacity to interrupt him during dinner, and even to risk a battle in support of his pleasantry. Launcelot, after an easy victory, only doomed him to be carted in his turn.

At night he was received at another castle, with great apparent hospitality, but found himself in the morning in a dungeon and loaded with chains. Consulting his ring, and finding that this was an enchantment, he burst his chains, seized his armor in spite of the visionary monsters who attempted to defend it, broke open the gates of the tower, and continued his journey. At length his progress was checked by a wide and rapid torrent, which could only be passed on a narrow bridge, on which a false step would prove his destruction. Launcelot, leading his horse by the bridle, and making him swim by his side, passed over the bridge, and was attacked, as soon as he reached the bank, by a lion and a leopard, both of which he slew, and then, exhausted and bleeding, seated himself on the grass, and endeavored to bind up his bounds, when he was accosted by Brademagus, the father of Meleagans, whose castle was then in sight, and at no great distance. The king, no less courteous than his son was haughty and insolent, after complimenting Sir Launcelot on the valor and skill he had displayed in the perils of the bridge and the wild beasts, offered him his assistance, and informed him that the queen was safe in his castle, but could only be rescued by encountering Meleagans. Launcelot demanded the battle for the next day, and accordingly it took place, at the foot of the tower, and under the eyes of the fair captive. Launcelot was enfeebled by his wounds, and fought not with his usual spirit, and the contest for a time was doubtful; till Guenever exclaimed, "Ah, Launcelot! my knight, truly have I been told that thou art no longer worthy of me!" These words instantly revived the drooping knight; he resumed at once his usual superiority, and soon laid at his feet his haughty adversary.

He was on the point of sacrificing him to his resentment when Guenever, moved by the entreaties of Brademagus, ordered him to withhold the blow, and he obeyed. The castle and its prisoners were now at his disposal. Launcelot hastened to the apartment of the queen, threw himself at her feet, and was about to kiss her hand, when she exclaimed, "Ah, Launcelot! why do I see thee again, yet feel thee to be no longer worthy of me, after having been disgracefully drawn about the country in a ——" She had not time to finish the phrase, for her lover suddenly started from her, and bitterly lamenting that he had incurred the displeasure of his sovereign lady, rushed out of the castle, threw his sword and his shield to the right and left, ran furiously into the woods, and disappeared.

It seems that the story of the abominable cart, which haunted Launcelot at every step, had reached the ears of Sir Kay, who had told it to the queen, as a proof that her knight must have been dishonored. But Guenever had full leisure to repent the haste with which she had given credit to the tale. Three days elapsed, during which Launcelot wandered without knowing where he went, till at last he began to reflect that his mistress had doubtless been deceived by misrepresentation, and that it was his duty to set her right. He therefore returned, compelled Meleagans to release his prisoners, and, taking the road by which they expected the arrival of Sir Gawain, had the satisfaction of meeting him the next day; after which the whole company proceeded gayly towards Camelot.

CHAPTER VIII

THE STORY OF LAUNCELOT.—THE LADY OF SHALOTT

KING ARTHUR proclaimed a solemn tournament to be held at Winchester. The king, not less impatient than his knights for this festival, set off some days before to superintend the preparations, leaving the queen with her court at Camelot. Sir Launcelot, under pretence of indisposition, remained behind also. His intention was to attend the tournament in disguise; and having communicated his project to Guenever, he mounted his horse, set off without any attendant, and, counterfeiting the feebleness of age, took the most unfrequented road to Winchester, and passed unnoticed as an old knight who was going to be a spectator of the sports. Even Arthur and Gawain, who happened to behold him from the windows of a castle under which he passed, were the dupes of his disguise. But an accident betrayed him. His horse happened to stumble, and the hero, forgetting for a moment his assumed character, recovered the animal with a strength and agility so peculiar to himself, that they instantly recognized the inimitable Launcelot. They suffered him, however, to proceed on his journey without interruption, convinced that his extraordinary feats of arms must discover him at the approaching festival.

In the evening Launcelot was magnificently entertained as a stranger knight at the neighboring castle of Shalott. The lord of this castle had a daughter of exquisite beauty, and two sons lately received into the order of knighthood, one of whom was at that time ill in bed, and thereby prevented from attending the tournament, for which both brothers had long made preparations. Launcelot offered to attend the other, if he were permitted to borrow the armor of the invalid, and the lord of Shalott, without knowing the name of his guest, being satisfied from his appearance that his son could not have a better assistant in arms, most thankfully accepted the offer. In the meantime the young lady, who had been much struck by the first appearance of the stranger knight, continued to survey him with increased attention, and before the conclusion of supper, became so deeply enamored of him, that, after frequent changes of color, and other symptoms which Sir Launcelot could not possibly mistake, she was obliged to retire to her chamber, and seek relief in tears. Sir Launcelot hastened to convey to her, by means of her brother, the information that his heart was already disposed of, but that it would be his pride and pleasure to act as her knight at the approaching tournament. The lady, obliged to be satisfied with that courtesy, presented him her scarf to be worn at the tournament.

Launcelot set off in the morning with the young knight, who, on their approaching Winchester, carried him to the castle of a lady, sister to the lord of Shalott, by whom they were hospitably entertained. The next day they put on their armor, which was perfectly plain, and without any device, as was usual to youths during the first year of knighthood, their shields being only painted red, as some color was necessary to enable them to be recognized by their attendants. Launcelot wore on his crest the scarf of the maid of Shalott, and, thus equipped, proceeded to the tournament, where the knights were divided into two companies, the one commanded by Sir Galehaut, the other by King Arthur. Having surveyed the combat for a short time from without the lists, and observed that Sir Galehaut's party began to give way, they joined the press and attacked the royal knights, the young man choosing such adversaries as were suited to his strength, while his companion selected the principal champions of the Round Table, and successively overthrew Gawain, Bohort, and Lionel. The astonishment of the spectators was extreme, for it was thought that no one but Launcelot could possess such invincible force; yet the favor on his crest seemed to preclude the possibility of his being thus disguised, for Launcelot had never been known to wear the badge of any but his sovereign lady. At length Sir Hector, Launcelot's brother, engaged him, and, after a dreadful combat, wounded him dangerously in the head, but was himself completely stunned by a blow on the helmet, and felled to the ground; after which the conqueror rode off at full speed, attended by his companion.

They returned to the castle of Shalott, where Launcelot was attended with the greatest care by the good earl, by his two sons, and, above all, by his fair daughter, whose medical skill probably much hastened the period of his recovery. His health was almost completely restored, when Sir Hector, Sir Bohort, and Sir Lionel, who, after the return of the court to Camelot, had undertaken the quest of their relation, discovered him walking on the walls of the castle. Their meeting was very joyful; they passed three days in the castle amidst constant festivities, and bantered each other on the events of the tournament. Launcelot, though he began by vowing vengeance against the author of his wound, yet ended by declaring that he felt rewarded for the pain by the pride he took in witnessing his brother's extraordinary prowess. He then dismissed them with a message to the queen, promising to follow immediately, it being necessary that he should first take a formal leave of his kind hosts, as well as of the fair maid of Shalott.

The young lady, after vainly attempting to detain him by her tears and solicitations, saw him depart without leaving her any ground for hope.

It was early summer when the tournament took place; but some months had passed since Launcelot's departure, and winter was now near at hand. The health and strength of the Lady of Shalott had gradually sunk, and she felt that she could not live apart from the object of her affections. She left the castle, and, descending to the river's brink, placed herself in a boat, which she loosed from its moorings, and suffered to bear her down the current toward Camelot.

One morning, as Arthur and Sir Lionel looked from the window of the tower, the walls of which were washed by a river, they descried a boat richly ornamented, and covered with an awning of cloth of gold, which appeared to be floating down the stream without any human guidance. It struck the shore while they watched it, and they hastened down to examine it. Beneath the awning they discovered the dead body of a beautiful woman, in whose features Sir Lionel easily recognized the lovely maid of Shalott. Pursuing their search, they discovered a purse richly embroidered with gold and jewels, and within the purse a letter, which Arthur opened, and found addressed to himself and all the knights of the Round Table, stating that Launcelot of the Lake, the most accomplished of knights and most beautiful of men, but at the same time the most cruel and inflexible, had by his rigor produced the death of the wretched maiden, whose love was no less invincible than his cruelty.

The king immediately gave orders for the interment of the lady, with all the honors suited to her rank, at the same time explaining to the knights the history of her affection for Launcelot, which moved the compassion and regret of all.

Tennyson has chosen the story of the Lady of Shalott for the subject of a poem:—

"There she weaves by night and day
A magic web with colors gay.
She has heard a whisper say
A curse is on her if she stay
To look down to Camelot.

She knows not what the curse may be,
And so she weaveth steadily,
And little other care hath she,
The Lady of Shalott.

"And moving thro' a mirror clear
That hangs before her all the year,
Shadows of the world appear.
There she sees the highway near
Winding down to Camelot:
There the river eddy whirls,
And there the surly village churls,
And the red cloaks of market girls
Pass onward from Shalott.

"Sometimes a troop of damsels glad,
An abbot on an ambling pad,
Sometimes a curly shepherd lad,
Or long-haired page in crimson clad
Goes by to towered Camelot.
And sometimes thro' the mirror blue
The knights come riding two and two:
She has no loyal knight and true,
The Lady of Shalott.

"But in her web she still delights
To weave the mirror's magic sights,
For often thro' the silent nights
A funeral, with plumes and lights
And music, went to Camelot:
Or when the moon was overhead,
Came two young lovers lately wed;
'I am half sick of shadows,' said
The Lady of Shalott."

The poem goes on as the story: the lady sees Launcelot, he rides
away, and she afterward dies and floats down the river in a boat
to Camelot. The poem ends as follows:—

"Under tower and balcony,
By garden wall and gallery,
A gleaming shape she floated by
Dead-pale between the houses high,
Silent unto Camelot.
Out upon the wharves they came,
Knight and burgher, lord and dame,
And round the prow they read her name,
The Lady of Shalott.

"Who is this? and what is here?
And in the lighted palace near
Died the sound of royal cheer;
And they crossed themselves for fear
All the knights at Camelot:
But Launcelot mused a little space;
He said 'She has a lovely face;
God in his mercy lend her grace,
The Lady of Shalott.'"

The story of "Elaine, the fair, Elaine, the lovable, Elaine, the lily-maid of Astolat," one of the earliest of the "Idylls of the King," is of course the same tale as the Lady of Shalott.

CHAPTER IX

THE STORY OF LAUNCELOT.—QUEEN GUENEVER'S PERIL

It happened at this time that Queen Guenever was thrown into great peril of her life. A certain squire who was in her immediate service, having some cause of animosity to Sir Gawain, determined to destroy him by poison at a public entertainment. For this purpose he concealed the poison in an apple of fine appearance, which he placed on the top of several others, and put the dish before the queen, hoping that, as Sir Gawain was the knight of greatest dignity, she would present the apple to him. But it happened that a Scottish knight of high distinction, who arrived on that day, was seated next to the queen, and to him, as a stranger, she presented the apple, which he had no sooner eaten than he was seized with dreadful pain, and fell senseless. The whole court was of course thrown into confusion; the knights rose from table, darting looks of indignation at the wretched queen, whose tears and protestations were unable to remove their suspicions. In spite of all that could be done the knight died, and nothing remained but to order a magnificent funeral and monument for him, which was done.

Some time after, Sir Mador, brother of the murdered knight, arrived at Arthur's court in quest of him. While hunting in the forest he by chance came to the spot where the monument was erected, read the inscription, and returned to court determined on immediate and signal vengeance. He rode into the hall, loudly accused the queen of treason, and insisted on her being given up to punishment, unless she should find, by a certain day, a knight hardy enough to risk his life in support of her innocence. Arthur, powerful as he was, did not dare to deny the appeal, but was compelled, with a heavy heart, to accept it, and Mador sternly took his departure, leaving the royal couple plunged in terror and anxiety.

During all this time Launcelot was absent, and no one knew where he was. He had fled in anger from his fair mistress, upon being reproached by her with his passion for the Lady of Shalott, which she had hastily inferred from his wearing her scarf at the tournament. He took up his abode with a hermit in the forest, and resolved to think no more of the cruel beauty, whose conduct he thought must flow from a wish to get rid of him. Yet calm reflection had somewhat cooled his indignation, and he had begun to wish, though hardly able to hope, for a reconciliation, when the news of Sir Mador's challenge fortunately reached his ears. The intelligence revived his spirits, and he began to prepare with the utmost cheerfulness for a contest which, if successful, would insure him at once the affection of his mistress and the gratitude of his sovereign.

The sad fate of the Lady of Shalott had ere this completely acquitted Launcelot in the queen's mind of all suspicion of his fidelity, and she lamented most grievously her foolish quarrel with him, which now, at her time of need, deprived her of her most efficient champion.

As the day appointed by Sir Mador was fast approaching, it became necessary that she should procure a champion for her defence; and she successively adjured Sir Hector, Sir Lionel, Sir Bohort, and Sir Gawain to undertake the battle. She fell on her knees before them, called Heaven to witness her innocence of the crime alleged against her, but was sternly answered by all that they could not fight to maintain the innocence of one whose act, and the fatal consequences of it, they had seen with their own eyes. She retired, therefore, dejected and disconsolate; but the sight of the fatal pile on which, if guilty, she was doomed to be burned, exciting her to fresh effort, she again repaired to Sir Bohort, threw herself at his feet, and, piteously calling on him for mercy, fell into a swoon. The brave knight was not proof against this. He raised her up, and hastily promised that he would undertake her cause, if no other or better champion should present himself. He then summoned his friends, and told them his resolution; and as a mortal combat with Sir Mador was a most fearful enterprise, they agreed to accompany him in the morning to the hermitage in the forest, where he proposed to receive absolution from the hermit, and to make his peace with Heaven, before he entered the lists. As they approached the hermitage, they espied a knight riding in the forest, whom they at once recognized as Sir Launcelot. Overjoyed at the meeting, they quickly, in answer to his questions, confirmed the news of the queen's imminent danger, and received his instructions to return to court, to comfort her as well as they could, but to say nothing of his intention of undertaking her defence, which he meant to do in the character of an unknown adventurer.

On their return to the castle they found that mass was finished, and had scarcely time to speak to the queen before they were summoned into the hall to dinner. A general gloom was spread over the countenances of all the guests. Arthur himself was unable to conceal his dejection, and the wretched Guenever, motionless and bathed in tears, sat in trembling expectation of Sir Mador's appearance. Nor was it long ere he stalked into the hall, and with a voice of thunder, rendered more impressive by the general silence, demanded instant justice on the guilty party. Arthur replied with dignity, that little of the day was yet spent, and that perhaps a champion might yet be found capable of satisfying his thirst for battle. Sir Bohort now rose from table, and, shortly returning in complete armor, resumed his place, after receiving the embraces and thanks of the king, who now began to resume some degree of confidence. Sir Mador, growing impatient, again repeated his denunciations of vengeance, and insisted that the combat should no longer be postponed.

In the height of the debate there came riding into the hall a knight mounted on a black steed, and clad in black armor, with his visor down, and lance in hand. "Sir," said the king, "is it your will to alight and partake of our cheer?" "Nay, sir," he replied; "I come to save a lady's life. The queen hath ill bestowed her favors, and honored many a knight, that in her hour of need she should have none to take her part. Thou that darest accuse her of treachery stand forth, for to-day shalt thou need all thy might."

Sir Mador, though surprised, was not appalled by the stern challenge and formidable appearance of his antagonist, but prepared for the encounter. At the first shock both were unhorsed. They then drew their swords, and commenced a combat which lasted from noon till evening, when Sir Mador, whose strength began to fail, was felled to the ground by Launcelot, and compelled to sue for mercy. The victor, whose arm was already raised to terminate the life of his opponent, instantly dropped his sword, courteously lifted up the fainting Sir Mador, frankly confessing that he had never before encountered so formidable an enemy. The other, with similar courtesy, solemnly renounced all further projects of vengeance for his brother's death; and the two knights, now become fast friends, embraced each other with the greatest cordiality. In the meantime Arthur, having recognized Sir Launcelot, whose helmet was now unlaced, rushed down into the lists, followed by all his knights, to welcome and thank his deliverer. Guenever swooned with joy, and the place of combat suddenly exhibited a scene of the most tumultuous delight.

The general satisfaction was still further increased by the discovery of the real culprit. Having accidentally incurred some suspicion, he confessed his crime, and was publicly punished in the presence of Sir Mador.

The court now returned to the castle, which, with the title of "La Joyeuse Garde" bestowed upon it in memory of the happy event, was conferred on Sir Launcelot by Arthur, as a memorial of his gratitude.

So far of the Story of Sir Launcelot. Let us turn now to the Story of Sir Tristram of Lyonesse.

CHAPTER X

THE STORY OF TRISTRAM OF LYONESSE

MELIADUS was king of Leonois, or Lyonesse, a country famous in the annals of romance, which adjoined the kingdom of Cornwall, but has now disappeared from the map, having been, it is said, overwhelmed by the ocean. Meliadus was married to Isabella, sister of Mark, king of Cornwall. A fairy fell in love with him, and drew him away by enchantment while he was engaged in hunting. His queen set out in quest of him, but was taken ill on her journey, and died, leaving an infant son, whom, from the melancholy circumstances of his birth, she called Tristram.

Gouvernail, the queen's squire, who had accompanied her, took charge of the child, and restored him to his father, who had at length burst the enchantments of the fairy, and returned home. Meliadus, after seven years, married again, and the new queen, being jealous of the influence of Tristram with his father, laid plots for his life, which were discovered by Gouvernail, who, in consequence, fled with the boy to the court of the king of France, where Tristram was kindly received, and grew up improving in every gallant and knightly accomplishment, adding to his skill in arms the arts of music and of chess. In particular, he devoted himself to the chase and to all woodland sports, so that he became distinguished above all other chevaliers of the court for his knowledge of all that relates to hunting. No wonder that Belinda, the king's daughter, fell in love with him; but as he did not return her passion, she, in a sudden impulse of anger, excited her father against him, and he was banished the kingdom. The princess soon repented of her act, and in despair destroyed herself, having first written a most tender letter to Tristram, sending him at the same time a beautiful and sagacious dog, of which she was very fond, desiring him to keep it as a memorial of her. Meliadus was now dead, and as his queen, Tristram's stepmother, held the throne, Gouvernail was afraid to carry his pupil to his native country, and took him to Cornwall, to his uncle Mark, who gave him a kind reception.

King Mark resided at the castle of Tintadel, already mentioned in the history of Uther and Iguerne. In this court Tristram became distinguished in all the exercises incumbent on a knight; nor was it

ZEUS

PLATE I

VENUS, CERES AND JUNO
By RAPHAEL

PLATE II

SATURN
By VERONESE

PLATE III

PALLAS SUBDUING A CENTAUR

By BOTTICELLI

PLATE IV

LEDA AND THE SWAN
By MICHELANGELO

PLATE V

LAOCOÖN

PLATE VI

THE EDUCATION OF ACHILLES
By DELACROIX

PLATE VII

THE WINE OF CIRCE
By BURNE-JONES

PLATE VIII

THE RETURN OF ULYSSES
By PINTURICCHIO

PLATE IX

ÆNEAS CARRYING ANCHISES FROM TROY

By RAPHAEL

PLATE X

ÆNEAS IN THE UNDERWORLD

By BREUGHEL

PLATE XI

THE OATH OF KNIGHTHOOD
By ABBEY

PLATE XII

GALAHAD THE DELIVERER
By ABBEY

PLATE XIII

CHARLEMAGNE
By DÜRER

PLATE XIV

CHARLEMAGNE CROWNED EMPEROR AT ROME

By RETHEL

PLATE XV

THE BATTLE OF CORDOVA

PLATE XVI
By RETHEL

long before he had an opportunity of practically employing his valor and skill. Moraunt, a celebrated champion, brother to the queen of Ireland, arrived at the court, to demand tribute of King Mark. The knights of Cornwall are in ill repute, in romance, for their cowardice, and they exhibited it on this occasion. King Mark could find no champion who dared to encounter the Irish knight, till his nephew Tristram, who had not yet received the honors of knighthood, craved to be admitted to the order, offering at the same time to fight the battle of Cornwall against the Irish champion. King Mark assented with reluctance; Tristram received the accolade, which conferred knighthood upon him; and the place and time were assigned for the encounter.

Without attempting to give the details of this famous combat, the first and one of the most glorious of Tristram's exploits, we shall only say that the young knight, though severely wounded, cleft the head of Moraunt, leaving a portion of his sword in the wound. Moraunt, half dead with his wound and the disgrace of his defeat, hastened to hide himself in his ship, sailed away with all speed for Ireland, and died soon after arriving in his own country.

The kingdom of Cornwall was thus delivered from its tribute. Tristram, weakened by loss of blood, fell senseless. His friends flew to his assistance. They dressed his wounds, which in general healed readily; but the lance of Moraunt was poisoned, and one wound which it made yielded to no remedies, but grew worse day by day. The surgeons could do no more. Tristram asked permission of his uncle to depart, and seek for aid in the kingdom of Loegria (England). With his consent he embarked, and, after tossing for many days on the sea, was driven by the winds to the coast of Ireland. He landed, full of joy and gratitude that he had escaped the peril of the sea; took his rote,[1] and began to play. It was a summer evening, and the king of Ireland and his daughter, the beautiful Isoude, were at a window which overlooked the sea. The strange harper was sent for, and conveyed to the palace, where, finding that he was in Ireland, whose champion he had lately slain, he concealed his name, and called himself Tramtris. The queen undertook his cure, and by a medicated bath gradually restored him to health. His skill in music and in games occasioned his being frequently called to court, and he became instructor of the Princess Isoude in minstrelsy and poetry, who profited so well under his care, that she soon had no equal in the kingdom, except her instructor.

At this time a tournament was held, at which many knights of the Round Table, and others, were present. On the first day a Saracen prince, named Palamedes, obtained the advantage over all. They

[1] A musical instrument.

brought him to the court, and gave him a feast, at which Tristram, just recovering from his wound, was present. The fair Isoude appeared on this occasion in all her charms. Palamedes could not behold them without emotion, and made no effort to conceal his love. Tristram perceived it, and the pain he felt from jealousy taught him how dear the fair Isoude had already become to him.

Next day the tournament was renewed. Tristram, still feeble from his wound, rose during the night, took his arms, and concealed them in a forest near the place of the contest, and, after it had begun, mingled with the combatants. He overthrew all that encountered him, in particular Palamedes, whom he brought to the ground with a stroke of his lance, and then fought him hand to hand, bearing off the prize of the tourney. But his exertions caused his wound to reopen; he bled fast, and in this sad state, yet in triumph, they bore him to the palace. The fair Isoude devoted herself to his relief with an interest which grew more vivid day by day; and her skilful care soon restored him to health.

It happened one day that a damsel of the court, entering the closet where Tristram's arms were deposited, perceived that a part of the sword had been broken off. It occurred to her that the missing portion was like that which was left in the skull of Moraunt, the Irish champion. She imparted her thought to the queen, who compared the fragment taken from her brother's wound with the sword of Tristram, and was satisfied that it was part of the same, and that the weapon of Tristram was that which reft her brother's life. She laid her griefs and resentment before the king, who satisfied himself with his own eyes of the truth of her suspicions. Tristram was cited before the whole court, and reproached with having dared to present himself before them after having slain their kinsman. He acknowledged that he had fought with Moraunt to settle the claim for tribute, and said that it was by force of winds and waves alone that he was thrown on their coast. The queen demanded vengeance for the death of her brother; the fair Isoude trembled and grew pale, but a murmur rose from all the assembly that the life of one so handsome and so brave should not be taken for such a cause, and generosity finally triumphed over resentment in the mind of the king. Tristram was dismissed in safety, but commanded to leave the kingdom without delay, and never to return thither under pain of death. Tristram went back, with restored health, to Cornwall.

King Mark made his nephew give him a minute recital of his adventures. Tristram told him all minutely; but when he came to speak of the fair Isoude, he described her charms with a warmth and energy such as none but a lover could display. King Mark was fascinated with the description, and, choosing a favorable time, demanded a boon[1] of his nephew, who readily granted it. The king made him swear upon the holy reliques that he would fulfil his commands. Then Mark directed him to go to Ireland, and obtain for him the fair Isoude to be queen of Cornwall.

Tristram believed it was certain death for him to return to Ireland; and how could he act as ambassador for his uncle in such a cause? Yet, bound by his oath, he hesitated not for an instant. He only took the precaution to change his armor. He embarked for Ireland; but a tempest drove him to the coast of England, near Camelot, where King Arthur was holding his court, attended by the knights of the Round Table, and many others, the most illustrious in the world.

Tristram kept himself unknown. He took part in many jousts; he fought many combats, in which he covered himself with glory. One day he saw among those recently arrived the king of Ireland, father of the fair Isoude. This prince, accused of treason against his liege sovereign, Arthur, came to Camelot to free himself of the charge. Blaanor, one of the most redoubtable warriors of the Round Table, was his accuser, and Argius, the king, had neither youthful vigor nor strength to encounter him. He must therefore seek a champion to sustain his innocence. But the knights of the Round Table were not at liberty to fight against one another, unless in a quarrel of their own. Argius heard of the great renown of the unknown knight; he also was witness of his exploits. He sought him, and conjured him to adopt his defence, and on his oath declared that he was innocent of the crime of which he was accused. Tristram readily consented, and made himself known to the king, who on his part promised to reward his exertions, if successful, with whatever gift he might ask.

Tristram fought with Blaanor, and overthrew him, and held his life in his power. The fallen warrior called on him to use his right of conquest, and strike the fatal blow. "God forbid," said Tristram, "that I should take the life of so brave a knight!" He raised him up and restored him to his friends. The judges of the field decided that the king of Ireland was acquitted of the charge against him, and they led Tristram in triumph to his tent. King Argius, full of

---

[1] "Good faith was the very corner-stone of chivalry. Whenever a knight's word was pledged (it mattered not how rashly), it was to be redeemed at any price. Hence the sacred obligation of the *boon granted* by a knight to his suppliant. Instances without number occur in romance, in which a knight, by rashly granting an indefinite boon, was obliged to do or suffer something extremely to his prejudice. But it is not in romance alone that we find such singular instances of adherence to an indefinite promise. The history of the times presents authentic transactions equally embarrassing and absurd."— SCOTT, *note of Sir Tristram.*

gratitude, conjured Tristram to accompany him to his kingdom. They departed together, and arrived in Ireland; and the queen, forgetting her resentment for her brother's death, exhibited to the preserver of her husband's life nothing but gratitude and good-will.

How happy a moment for Isoude, who knew that her father had promised his deliverer whatever boon he might ask. But the unhappy Tristram gazed on her with despair, at the thought of the cruel oath which bound him. His magnanimous soul subdued the force of his love. He revealed the oath which he had taken, and with trembling voice demanded the fair Isoude for his uncle.

Argius consented, and soon all was prepared for the departure of Isoude. Brengwain, her favorite maid-of-honor, was to accompany her. On the day of departure the queen took aside this devoted attendant, and told her that she had observed that her daughter and Tristram were attached to one another, and that to avert the bad effects of this inclination she had procured from a powerful fairy a potent philter (love-draught), which she directed Brengwain to administer to Isoude and to King Mark on the evening of their marriage.

Isoude and Tristram embarked together. A favorable wind filled the sails and promised them a fortunate voyage. The lovers gazed upon one another, and could not repress their sighs. Love seemed to light up all his fires on their lips, as in their hearts. The day was warm; they suffered from thirst. Isoude first complained. Tristram descried the bottle containing the love-draught, which Brengwain had been so imprudent as to leave in sight. He took it, gave some of it to the charming Isoude, and drank the remainder himself. The dog Houdain licked the cup. The ship arrived in Cornwall, and Isoude was married to King Mark. The old monarch was delighted with his bride, and his gratitude to Tristram was unbounded. He loaded him with honors, and made him chamberlain of his palace, thus giving him access to the queen at all times.

In the midst of the festivities of the court which followed the royal marriage, an unknown minstrel one day presented himself, bearing a harp of peculiar construction. He excited the curiosity of King Mark by refusing to play upon it till he should grant him a boon. The king having promised to grant his request, the minstrel, who was none other than the Saracen knight, Sir Palamedes, the lover of the fair Isoude, sung to the harp a lay, in which he demanded Isoude as the promised gift. King Mark could not by the laws of knighthood withhold the boon. The lady was mounted on her horse and led away by her triumphant lover. Tristram, it is needless to say, was absent at the time, and did not return until their departure. When he heard what had taken place, he seized his rote, and hastened to the shore, where Isoude and her new master had already embarked. Tristram played upon his rote, and the sound reached the ears of Isoude, who became so deeply affected that Sir Palamedes was induced to return with her to land, that they might see the unknown musician. Tristram watched his opportunity, seized the lady's horse by the bridle, and plunged with her into the forest, tauntingly informing his rival that "what he had got by the harp he had lost by the rote." Palamedes pursued, and a combat was about to commence, the result of which must have been fatal to one or other of these gallant knights; but Isoude stepped between them, and, addressing Palamedes, said, "You tell me that you love me; you will not then deny me the request I am about to make?" "Lady," he replied, "I will perform your bidding." "Leave, then," said she, "this contest, and repair to King Arthur's court, and salute Queen Guenever for me; tell her that there are in the world but two ladies, herself and I, and two lovers, hers and mine; and come thou not in future in any place where I am." Palamedes burst into tears. "Ah, lady," said he, "I will obey you; but I beseech you that you will not forever steel your heart against me." "Palamedes," she replied, "may I never taste of joy again if I ever quit my first love." Palamedes then went his way. The lovers remained a week in concealment, after which Tristram restored Isoude to her husband, advising him in future to reward minstrels in some other way.

The king showed much gratitude to Tristram, but in the bottom of his heart he cherished bitter jealousy of him. One day Tristram and Isoude were alone together in her private chamber. A base and cowardly knight of the court, named Audret, spied them through a keyhole. They sat at a table of chess, but were not attending to the game. Andret brought the king, having first raised his suspicions, and placed him so as to watch their motions. The king saw enough to confirm his suspicions, and he burst into the apartment with his sword drawn, and had nearly slain Tristram before he was put on his guard. But Tristram avoided the blow, drew his sword, and drove before him the cowardly monarch, chasing him through all the apartments of the palace, giving him frequent blows with the flat of his sword, while he cried in vain to his knights to save him. They were not inclined, or did not dare to interpose in his behalf.

A proof of the great popularity of the tale of Sir Tristram is the fact that the Italian poets, Boiardo and Ariosto, have founded upon it the idea of the two enchanted fountains, which produced the opposite effects of love and hatred. Boiardo thus describes the fountain of hatred:—

> "Fair was that fountain, sculptured all of gold,
> With alabaster sculptured, rich and rare;
> And in its basin clear thou might'st behold
> The flowery marge reflected fresh and fair.
> Sage Merlin framed the font,—so legends bear,—
> When on fair Isoude doated Tristram brave,
> That the good errant knight, arriving there,
> Might quaff oblivion in the enchanted wave,
> And leave his luckless love, and 'scape his timeless grave.

> "But ne'er the warrior's evil fate allowed
> His steps that fountain's charmèd verge to gain,
> Though restless, roving on adventure proud,
> He traversed oft the land and oft the main."

.   .   .   .   .   .

CHAPTER XI

TRISTRAM AND ISOUDE

AFTER this affair Tristram was banished from the kingdom, and Isoude shut up in a tower which stood on the bank of a river. Tristram could not resolve to depart without some further communication with his beloved; so he concealed himself in the forest, till at last he contrived to attract her attention by means of twigs, which he curiously peeled and sent down the stream under her window. By this means many secret interviews were obtained. Tristram dwelt in the forest, sustaining himself by game, which the dog Houdain ran down for him; for this faithful animal was unequalled in the chase, and knew so well his master's wish for concealment that in the pursuit of his game he never barked. At length Tristram departed, but left Houdain with Isoude, as a remembrancer of him.

Sir Tristram wandered through various countries, achieving the most perilous enterprises, and covering himself with glory, yet unhappy at the separation from his beloved Isoude. At length King Mark's territory was invaded by a neighboring chieftain, and he was forced to summon his nephew to his aid. Tristram obeyed the call, put himself at the head of his uncle's vassals, and drove the enemy out of the country. Mark was full of gratitude, and Tristram, restored to favor and to the society of his beloved Isoude, seemed at the summit of happiness. But a sad reverse was at hand.

Tristram had brought with him a friend named Pheredin, son of the king of Brittany. This young knight saw Queen Isoude, and could not resist her charms. Knowing the love of his friend for the queen, and that that love was returned, Pheredin concealed his own, until his health failed, and he feared he was drawing near his end. He then wrote to the beautiful queen that he was dying for love of her.

The gentle Isoude, in a moment of pity for the friend of Tristram, returned him an answer so kind and compassionate that it restored him to life. A few days afterward Tristram found this letter. The most terrible jealousy took possession of his soul; he would have slain Pheredin, who with difficulty made his escape. Then Tristram mounted his horse, and rode to the forest, where for ten days he took no rest nor food. At length he was found by a damsel lying almost dead by the brink of a fountain. She recognized him, and tried in vain to rouse his attention. At last, recollecting his love for music, she went and got her harp, and played thereon. Tristram was roused from his reverie; tears flowed; he breathed more freely; he took the harp from the maiden, and sung this lay, with a voice broken with sobs:—

> "Sweet I sang in former days,
> Kind love perfected my lays:
> Now my art alone displays
> The woe that on my being preys.

> "Charming love, delicious power,
> Worshipped from my earliest hour,
> Thou who life on all dost shower,
> Love! my life thou dost devour.

> "In death's hour I beg of thee,
> Isoude, dearest enemy,
> Thou who erst couldst kinder be,
> When I'm gone, forget not me.

> "On my gravestone passers by
> Oft will read, as low I lie,
> 'Never wight in love could vie
> With Tristram, yet she let him die.' "

Tristram, having finished his lay, wrote it off and gave it to the damsel, conjuring her to present it to the queen.

Meanwhile Queen Isoude was inconsolable at the absence of Tristram. She discovered that it was caused by the fatal letter which she had written to Pheredin. Innocent, but in despair at the sad effects of her letter, she wrote another to Pheredin, charging him never to see her again. The unhappy lover obeyed this cruel decree. He plunged into the forest, and died of grief and love in a hermit's cell.

Isoude passed her days in lamenting the absence and unknown fate of Tristram. One day her jealous husband, having entered

her chamber unperceived, overheard her singing the following lay:—

"My voice to piteous wail is bent,
 My harp to notes of languishment;
 Ah, love! delightsome days be meant
 For happier wights, with hearts content.

"Ah, Tristram! far away from me,
 Art thou from restless anguish free?
 Ah! couldst thou so one moment be,
 From her who so much loveth thee?"

The king, hearing these words, burst forth in a rage; but Isoude
was too wretched to fear his violence. "You have heard me," she
said; "I confess it all. I love Tristram, and always shall love him.
Without doubt he is dead, and died for me. I no longer wish to
live. The blow that shall finish my misery will be most welcome."

The king was moved at the distress of the fair Isoude, and
perhaps the idea of Tristram's death tended to allay his wrath.
He left the queen in charge of her women, commanding them to
take especial care lest her despair should lead her to do harm
to herself.

Tristram, meanwhile, distracted as he was, rendered a most
important service to the shepherds by slaying a gigantic robber
named Taullas, who was in the habit of plundering their flocks
and rifling their cottages. The shepherds, in their gratitude to
Tristram, bore him in triumph to King Mark to have him bestow
on him a suitable reward. No wonder Mark failed to recognize
in the half-clad wild man before him his nephew Tristram; but
grateful for the service the unknown had rendered, he ordered
him to be well taken care of, and gave him in charge to the queen
and her women. Under such care Tristram rapidly recovered his
serenity and his health, so that the romancer tells us he became
handsomer than ever. King Mark's jealousy revived with Tristram's health and good looks, and, in spite of his debt of gratitude
so lately increased, he again banished him from the court.

Sir Tristram left Cornwall, and proceeded into the land of
Loegria (England) in quest of adventures. One day he entered
a wide forest. The sound of a little bell showed him that some
inhabitant was near. He followed the sound, and found a hermit,
who informed him that he was in the forest of Arnantes, belonging
to the fairy Viviane, the Lady of the Lake, who, smitten with love
for King Arthur, had found means to entice him to this forest,
where by enchantments she held him a prisoner, having deprived
him of all memory of who and what he was. The hermit informed
him that all the knights of the Round Table were out in search

of the king, and that he (Tristram) was now in the scene of the most grand and important adventures.

This was enough to animate Tristram in the search. He had not wandered far before he encountered a knight of Arthur's court, who proved to be Sir Kay the seneschal, who demanded of him whence he came. Tristram answering, "From Cornwall," Sir Kay did not let slip the opportunity of a joke at the expense of the Cornish knight. Tristram chose to leave him in his error, and even confirmed him in it; for meeting some other knights, Tristram declined to joust with them. They spent the night together at an abbey, where Tristram submitted patiently to all their jokes. The seneschal gave the word to his companions that they should set out early next day, and intercept the Cornish knight on his way, and enjoy the amusement of seeing his fright when they should insist on running a tilt with him. Tristram next morning found himself alone; he put on his armor, and set out to continue his quest. He soon saw before him the seneschal and the three knights, who barred the way, and insisted on a joust. Tristram excused himself a long time; at last he reluctantly took his stand. He encountered them, one after the other, and overthrew them all four, man and horse, and then rode off, bidding them not to forget their friend, the knight of Cornwall.

Tristram had not ridden far when he met a damsel, who cried out, "Ah, my lord! hasten forward, and prevent a horrid treason!" Tristram flew to her assistance, and soon reached a spot where he beheld a knight, whom three others had borne to the ground, and were unlacing his helmet in order to cut off his head.

Tristram flew to the rescue, and slew with one stroke of his lance one of the assailants. The knight, recovering his feet, sacrificed another to his vengeance, and the third made his escape. The rescued knight then raised the visor of his helmet, and a long white beard fell down upon his breast. The majesty and venerable air of this knight made Tristram suspect that it was none other than Arthur himself, and the prince confirmed his conjecture. Tristram would have knelt before him, but Arthur received him in his arms, and inquired his name and country; but Tristram declined to disclose them, on the plea that he was now on a quest requiring secrecy. At this moment the damsel who had brought Tristram to the rescue darted forward, and, seizing the king's hand, drew from his finger a ring, the gift of the fairy, and by that act dissolved the enchantment. Arthur, having recovered his reason and his memory, offered to Tristram to attach him to his court, and to confer honors and dignities upon him; but Tristram declined all, and only consented to accompany him till he should see him safe in the hands of his knights. Soon after, Hector de Marys rode up, and saluted the king, who on his part introduced him to Tristram as one of the bravest of his knights. Tristram took leave of the king and his faithful follower, and continued his quest.

We cannot follow Tristram through all the adventures which filled this epoch of his history. Suffice it to say, he fulfilled on all occasions the duty of a true knight, rescuing the oppressed, redressing wrongs, abolishing evil customs, and suppressing injustice, thus by constant action endeavoring to lighten the pains of absence from her he loved. In the meantime Isoude, separated from her dear Tristram, passed her days in languor and regret. At length she could no longer resist the desire to hear some news of her lover. She wrote a letter, and sent it by one of her damsels, niece of her faithful Brengwain. One day Tristram, weary with his exertions, had dismounted and laid himself down by the side of a fountain and fallen asleep. The damsel of Queen Isoude arrived at the same fountain, and recognized Passebreul, the horse of Tristram, and presently perceived his master, asleep. He was thin and pale, showing evident marks of the pain he suffered in separation from his beloved. She awaked him, and gave him the letter which she bore, and Tristram enjoyed the pleasure, so sweet to a lover, of hearing from and talking about the object of his affections. He prayed the damsel postpone her return till after the magnificent tournament which Arthur had proclaimed should have taken place, and conducted her to the castle of Persides, a brave and loyal knight, who received her with great consideration.

Tristram conducted the damsel of Queen Isoude to the tournament and had her placed in the balcony among the ladies of the queen. He then joined the tourney. Nothing could exceed his strength and valor. Launcelot admired him, and by a secret presentiment declined to dispute the honor of the day with a knight so gallant and so skilful. Arthur descended from the balcony to greet the conqueror; but the modest and devoted Tristram, content with having borne off the prize in the sight of the messenger of Isoude, made his escape with her, and disappeared.

The next day the tourney recommenced. Tristram assumed different armor, that he might not be known; but he was soon detected by the terrible blows that he gave. Arthur and Guenever had no doubt that it was the same knight who had borne off the prize of the day before. Arthur's gallant spirit was roused. After Launcelot of the Lake and Sir Gawain, he was accounted the best knight of the Round Table. He went privately and armed himself, and came into the tourney in undistinguished armor. He ran a joust with Tristram, whom he shook in his seat; but Tristram, who did not know him, threw him out of the saddle. Arthur recovered himself and, content with having made proof of the stranger knight, bade Launcelot finish the adventure, and vindicate the honor of the Round Table. Sir Launcelot, at the bidding of the monarch, assailed Tristram, whose lance was already broken in former encounters. But the law of this sort of combat was, that the knight, after having broken his lance, must fight with his sword, and must not refuse to meet with his shield the lance of his antagonist. Tristram met Launcelot's charge upon his shield, which that terrible lance could not fail to pierce. It inflicted a wound upon Tristram's side, and breaking, left the iron in the wound. But Tristram also with his sword smote so vigorously on Launcelot's casque that he cleft it, and wounded his head. The wound was not deep, but the blood flowed into his eyes, and blinded him for a moment, and Tristram, who thought himself mortally wounded, retired from the field. Launcelot declared to the king that he had never received such a blow in his life before.

Tristram hastened to Gouvernail, his squire, who drew forth the iron, bound up the wound, and gave him immediate ease. Tristram, after the tournament, kept retired in his tent, but Arthur, with the consent of the knights of the Round Table, decreed him the honors of the second day. But it was no longer a secret that the victor of the two days was the same individual, and Gouvernail, being questioned, confirmed the suspicions of Launcelot and Arthur, that it was no other than Sir Tristram of Lyonesse, the nephew of the king of Cornwall.

King Arthur, who desired to reward his distinguished valor, and knew that his uncle Mark had ungratefully banished him, would have eagerly availed himself of the opportunity to attach Tristram to his court,—all the knights of the Round Table declaring with acclamation that it would be impossible to find a more worthy companion. But Tristram had already departed in search of adventures, and the damsel of Queen Isoude returned to her mistress.

CHAPTER XII

THE STORY OF SIR TRISTRAM OF LYONESSE

SIR TRISTRAM rode through a forest, and saw ten men fighting, and one man did battle against nine. So he rode to the knights and cried to them, bidding them cease their battle, for they did themselves great shame, so many knights to fight against one. Then answered the master of the knights (his name was Sir Breuse sans Pitié, who was at that time the most villainous knight living): "Sir knight, what have ye to do to meddle with us? If ye be wise, depart on your way as you came, for this knight shall not escape us." "That were pity," said Sir Tristram, "that so good a knight should be slain so cowardly; therefore I warn you I will succor him with all my puissance."

Then Sir Tristram alighted off his horse, because they were on foot, that they should not slay his horse. And he smote on the right hand and on the left so vigorously, that well-nigh at every stroke he struck down a knight. At last they fled, with Breuse sans Pitié, into the tower, and shut Sir Tristram without the gate. Then Sir Tristram returned back to the rescued knight, and found him sitting under a tree, sore wounded. "Fair knight," said he, "how is it with you?" "Sir knight," said Sir Palamedes, for he it was, "I thank you for your great goodness, for ye have rescued me from death." "What is your name?" said Sir Tristram. He said, "My name is Sir Palamedes." "Say ye so?" said Sir Tristram; "now know that thou art the man in the world that I most hate; therefore make thee ready, for I will do battle with thee." "What is your name?" said Sir Palamedes. "My name is Sir Tristram, your mortal enemy." "It may be so," said Sir Palamedes; "but you have done overmuch for me this day, that I should fight with you. Moreover, it will be no honor for you to have to do with me, for you are fresh and I am wounded. Therefore, if you will needs have to do with me, assign me a day, and I shall meet you without fail." "You say well," said Sir Tristram; "now I assign you to meet me in the meadow by the river of Camelot, where Merlin set the monument." So they were agreed. Then they departed, and took their ways diverse. Sir Tristram passed through a great forest into a plain, till he came to a priory, and there he reposed him with a good man six days.

Then departed Sir Tristram, and rode straight into Camelot to the monument of Merlin, and there he looked about him for Sir Palamedes. And he perceived a seemly knight, who came riding against him all in white, with a covered shield. When he came nigh, Sir Tristram said aloud, "Welcome, sir knight, and well and truly have you kept your promise." Then they made ready their shields and spears, and came together with all the might of their horses, so fiercely, that both the horses and the knights fell to the earth. And as soon as they might, they quitted their horses, and struck together with bright swords as men of might, and each wounded the other wonderfully sore, so that the blood ran out upon the grass. Thus they fought for the space of four hours, and never one would speak to the other one word. Then at last spake the white knight, and said, "Sir, thou fightest wonderful well, as ever I saw knight; therefore, if it please you, tell me your name." "Why dost thou ask my name?" said Sir Tristram; "art thou not Sir Palamedes?" "No, fair knight," said he, "I am Sir Launcelot of the Lake." "Alas!" said Sir Tristram, "what have I done? for you are the man of the world that I love best." "Fair knight," said Sir Launcelot, "tell me your name." "Truly," said he, "my name is Sir Tristram de Lyonesse." "Alas! alas!" said Sir Launcelot, "what adventure has befallen me!" And therewith Sir Launcelot kneeled down, and yielded him up his sword; and Sir Tristram kneeled down, and yielded him up his sword; and so either gave other the degree. And then they both went to the stone, and sat them down upon it, and took off their helms, and each kissed the other a hundred times. And then anon they rode toward Camelot, and on the way they met with Sir Gawain and Sir Gaheris, that had made promise to Arthur never to come again to the court till they had brought Sir Tristram with them.

"Return again," said Sir Launcelot, "for your quest is done; for I have met with Sir Tristram. Lo, here he is in his own person." Then was Sir Gawain glad, and said to Sir Tristram, "Ye are welcome." With this came King Arthur, and when he wist there was Sir Tristram, he ran unto him, and took him by the hand, and said, "Sir Tristram, ye are as welcome as any knight that ever came to this court." Then Sir Tristram told the king how he came thither for to have had to do with Sir Palamedes, and how he had rescued him from Sir Breuse sans Pitié and the nine knights. Then King Arthur took Sir Tristram by the hand, and went to the Table Round, and Queen Guenever came, and many ladies with her, and all the ladies said with one voice, "Welcome, Sir Tristram." "Welcome," said the knights. "Welcome," said Arthur, "for one of the best knights, and the gentlest of the world, and the man of most worship; for of all manner of hunting thou bearest the prize, and of all measures of blowing thou art the beginning, and of all the terms of hunting and hawking ye are the inventor, and of all instruments of music ye are the best skilled; therefore, gentle knight," said Arthur, "ye are welcome to this court." And then King Arthur made Sir Tristram knight of the Table Round with great nobley and feasting as can be thought.

The Round Table had been made by the famous enchanter Merlin, and on it he had exerted all his skill and craft. Of the seats which surrounded it he had constructed thirteen, in memory of the thirteen Apostles. Twelve of these seats only could be occupied, and they only by knights of the highest fame; the thirteenth represented the seat of the traitor Judas. It remained always empty. It was called the *perilous seat* ever since a rash and haughty Saracen knight had dared to place himself in it, when the earth opened and swallowed him up.

A magic power wrote upon each seat the name of the knight who was entitled to sit in it. No one could succeed to a vacant seat unless he surpassed in valor and glorious deeds the knight who had occupied it before him; without this qualification he would be violently repelled by a hidden force. Thus proof was made of all those who presented themselves to replace any companions of the order who had fallen.

One of the principal seats, that of Moraunt of Ireland, had been vacant ten years, and his name still remained over it ever since the time when that distinguished champion fell beneath the sword of Sir Tristram. Arthur now took Tristram by the hand and led him to that seat. Immediately the most melodious sounds were heard, and exquisite perfumes filled the place; the name of Moraunt disappeared, and that of Tristram blazed forth in light. The rare modesty of Tristram had now to be subjected to a severe task; for the clerks charged with the duty of preserving the annals of the Round Table attended, and he was required by the law of his order to declare what feats of arms he had accomplished to entitle him to take that seat. This ceremony being ended, Tristram received the congratulations of all his companions. Sir Launcelot and Guenever took occasion to speak to him of the fair Isoude, and to express their wish that some happy chance might bring her to the kingdom of Loegria.

While Tristram was thus honored and caressed at the court of King Arthur, the most gloomy and malignant jealousy harassed the soul of Mark. He could not look upon Isoude without remembering that she loved Tristram, and the good fortune of his nephew goaded him to thoughts of vengeance. He at last resolved to go disguised into the kingdom of Loegria, attack Tristram by stealth, and put him to death. He took with him two knights, brought up in his court, who he thought were devoted to him; and, not willing to leave Isoude behind, named two of her maidens to attend her, together with her faithful Brengwain, and made them accompany him.

Having arrived in the neighborhood of Camelot, Mark imparted his plan to his two knights, but they rejected it with horror; nay, more, they declared that they would no longer remain in his service;

and left him, giving him reason to suppose that they should repair to the court to accuse him before Arthur. It was necessary for Mark to meet and rebut their accusation; so, leaving Isoude in an abbey, he pursued his way alone to Camelot.

Mark had not ridden far when he encountered a party of knights of Arthur's court, and would have avoided them, for he knew their habit of challenging to a joust every stranger knight whom they met. But it was too late. They had seen his armor, and recognized him as a Cornish knight, and at once resolved to have some sport with him. It happened they had with them, Daguenet, King Arthur's fool, who, though deformed and weak of body, was not wanting in courage. The knights as Mark approached laid their plan that Daguenet should personate Sir Launcelot of the Lake, and challenge the Cornish knight. They equipped him in armor belonging to one of their number who was ill, and sent him forward to the cross-road to defy the strange knight. Mark, who saw that his antagonist was by no means formidable in appearance, was not disinclined to the combat; but when the dwarf rode towards him, calling out that he was Sir Launcelot of the Lake, his fears prevailed, he put spurs to his horse, and rode away at full speed, pursued by the shouts and laughter of the party.

Meanwhile, Isoude, remaining at the abbey with her faithful Brengwain, found her only amusement in walking occasionally in a forest adjoining the abbey. There, on the brink of a fountain girdled with trees, she thought of her love, and sometimes joined her voice and her harp in lays reviving the memory of its pains or pleasures. One day the caitiff knight, Breuse the Pitiless, heard her voice, concealed himself, and drew near. She sang:—

"Sweet silence, shadowy bower, and verdant lair,
   Ye court my troubled spirit to repose,
Whilst I, such dear remembrance rises there,
   Awaken every echo with my woes.

"Within these woods, by Nature's hand arrayed,
   A fountain springs, and feeds a thousand flowers;
Ah! how my groans do all its murmurs aid!
   How my sad eyes do swell it with their showers!

"What doth my knight the while? to him is given
   A double meed; in love and arms' emprise,
Him the Round Table elevates to heaven!
   Tristram! ah me! he hears not Isoude's cries."

Breuse the Pitiless, who, like most other caitiffs, had felt the weight of Tristram's arm, and hated him accordingly, at hearing his name breathed forth by the beautiful songstress, impelled by a double impulse, rushed forth from his concealment and laid hands on his victim. Isoude fainted, and Brengwain filled the air with her shrieks. Breuse carried Isoude to the place where he had left his horse; but the animal had got away from his bridle, and was at some distance. He was obliged to lay down his fair burden, and go in pursuit of his horse. Just then a knight came up, drawn by the cries of Brengwain, and demanded the cause of her distress. She could not speak, but pointed to her mistress lying insensible on the ground.

Breuse had by this time returned, and the cries of Brengwain, renewed at seeing him, sufficiently showed the stranger the cause of the distress. Tristram spurred his horse towards Breuse, who, not unprepared, ran to the encounter. Breuse was unhorsed, and lay motionless, pretending to be dead; but when the stranger knight left him to attend to the distressed damsels, he mounted his horse, and made his escape.

The knight now approached Isoude, gently raised her head, drew aside the golden hair which covered her countenance, gazed thereon for an instant, uttered a cry, and fell back insensible. Brengwain came; her caress soon restored her mistress to life, and they then turned their attention to the fallen warrior. They raised his visor, and discovered the countenance of Sir Tristram. Isoude threw herself on the body of her lover, and bedewed his face with her tears. Their warmth revived the knight, and Tristram, on awaking, found himself in the arms of his dear Isoude.

It was the law of the Round Table that each knight after his admission should pass the next ten days in quest of adventures, during which time his companions might meet him in disguised armor, and try their strength with him. Tristram had now been out seven days, and in that time had encountered many of the best knights of the Round Table, and acquitted himself with honor. During the remaining three days Isoude remained at the abbey, under his protection, and then set out with her maidens, escorted by Sir Tristram, to rejoin King Mark at the court of Camelot.

This happy journey was one of the brightest epochs in the lives of Tristram and Isoude. He celebrated it by a lay upon the harp in a peculiar measure, to which the French give the name of *Triolet*:—

> "With fair Isoude, and with love,
>   Ah! how sweet the life I lead!
> How blest forever thus to rove,
> With fair Isoude, and with love!
> As she wills, I live and move,
> And cloudless days to days succeed:
> With fair Isoude, and with love,
>   Ah! how sweet the life I lead!

"Journeying on from break of day,
Feel you not fatigued, my fair?
Yon green turf invites to play;
Journeying on from day to day,
Ah! let us to that shade away,
Were it but to slumber there!
Journeying on from break of day,
Feel you not fatigued, my fair?"

They arrived at Camelot, where Sir Launcelot received them most cordially. Isoude was introduced to King Arthur and Queen Guenever, who welcomed her as a sister. As King Mark was held in arrest under the accusation of the two Cornish knights, Queen Isoude could not rejoin her husband, and Sir Launcelot placed his castle of La Joyeuse Garde at the disposal of his friends, who there took up their abode.

King Mark, who found himself obliged to confess the truth of the charge against him, or to clear himself by combat with his accusers, preferred the former, and King Arthur, as his crime had not been perpetrated, remitted the penalty, only enjoining upon him, under pain of his signal displeasure, to lay aside all thoughts of vengeance against his nephew. In the presence of the king and his court, all parties were formally reconciled; Mark and his queen departed for their home, and Tristram remained at Arthur's court.

CHAPTER XIII

END OF THE STORY OF SIR TRISTRAM OF LYONESSE

WHILE Sir Tristram and the fair Isoude abode yet at La Joyeuse Garde, Sir Tristram rode forth one day, without armor, having no weapon but his spear and his sword. And as he rode he came to a place where he saw two knights in battle, and one of them had gotten the better, and the other lay overthrown. The knight who had the better was Sir Palamedes. When Sir Palamedes knew Sir Tristram, he cried out, "Sir Tristram, now we be met, and ere we depart we will redress our old wrongs." "As for that," said Sir Tristram, "there never yet was Christian man that might make his boast that I ever fled from him, and thou that art a Saracen shalt never say that of me." And therewith Sir Tristram made his horse to run, and with all his might came straight upon Sir Palamedes, and broke his spear upon him. Then he drew his sword and struck at Sir Palamedes six great strokes, upon his helm. Sir Palamedes saw that Sir Tristram had not his armor on, and he marvelled at his rashness and his great folly; and said to himself, "If I meet and slay him I am ashamed wheresoever I go." Then Sir Tristram cried out and said, "Thou coward knight, why wilt thou not do battle with me? for have thou no doubt I shall endure all thy malice." "Ah, Sir Tristram!" said Sir Palamedes, "thou knowest I may not fight with thee for shame; for thou art here naked, and I am armed; now I require that thou answer me a question that I shall ask you." "Tell me what it is," said Sir Tristram. "I put the case," said Sir Palamedes, "that you were well armed, and I naked as ye be; what would you do to me now, by your true knighthood?" "Ah!" said Sir Tristram, "now I understand thee well, Sir Palamedes; and, as God me bless, what I shall say shall not be said for fear that I have of thee. But if it were so, thou shouldest depart from me, for I would not have to do with thee." "No more will I with thee," said Sir Palamedes, "and therefore ride forth on thy way." "As for that, I may choose," said Sir Tristram, "either to ride or to abide. But, Sir Palamedes, I marvel at one thing,—that thou art so good a knight, yet that thou wilt not be christened." "As for that," said Sir Palamedes, "I may not yet be christened, for a vow which I made many years ago; yet in my heart I believe in our Saviour and his mild mother Mary; but I have yet one battle to do, and when that is done I will be christened, with a good will." "By my head," said Sir Tristram, "as for that one battle, thou shalt seek it no longer; for yonder is a knight, whom you have smitten down. Now help me to be clothed in his armor, and I will soon fulfil thy vow." "As ye will," said Sir Palamedes, "so shall it be." So they rode both unto that knight that sat on a bank; and Sir Tristram saluted him, and he full weakly saluted him again. "Sir," said Sir Tristram, "I pray you to lend me your whole armor; for I am unarmed, and I must do battle with this knight." "Sir," said the hurt knight, "you shall have it, with a right good will." Then Sir Tristram unarmed Sir Galleron, for that was the name of the hurt knight, and he as well as he could helped to arm Sir Tristram. Then Sir Tristram mounted upon his own horse, and in his hand he took Sir Galleron's spear. Thereupon Sir Palamedes was ready, and so they came hurtling together, and each smote the other in the midst of their shields. Sir Palamedes' spear broke, and Sir Tristram smote down the horse. Then Sir Palamedes leapt from his horse, and drew out his sword. That saw Sir Tristram, and therewith he alighted and tied his horse to a tree. Then they came together as two wild beasts, lashing the one on the other, and so fought more than two hours; and often Sir Tristram smote such strokes at Sir Palamedes that he made him to kneel, and Sir Palamedes broke away Sir Tristram's shield, and wounded him. Then Sir Tristram was wroth out of measure, and he rushed to Sir Palamedes and wounded him passing sore through the shoulder. and by fortune smote Sir Palamedes' sword out of his hand. And if Sir Palamedes had stooped for his sword, Sir Tristram had slain him. Then Sir Palamedes stood and beheld his sword with a full sorrowful heart. "Now," said Sir Tristram, "I have thee at a vantage, as thou hadst me to-day; but it shall never be said, in court, or among good knights, that Sir Tristram did slay any knight that was weaponless: therefore take thou thy sword, and let us fight this battle to the end." Then spoke Sir Palamedes to Sir Tristram: "I have no wish to fight this battle any more. The offence that I have done unto you is not so great but that, if it please you, we may be friends. All that I have offended is for the love of the queen, La Belle Isoude, and I dare maintain that she is peerless among ladies; and for that offence ye have given me many grievous and sad strokes, and some I have given you again. Wherefore I require you, my lord Sir Tristram, forgive me all that I have offended you, and this day have me unto the next church; and first I will be clean confessed, and after that see you that I be truly baptized, and then we will ride together unto the court of my lord, King Arthur, so that we may be there at the feast of Pentecost." "Now take your horse," said Sir Tristram, "and as you have said, so shall it be done." So they took their horses, and Sir Galleron rode with them. When they came to the church of Carlisle, the bishop commanded to fill a great vessel with water; and when he had hallowed it, he then confessed Sir Palamedes clean, and christened him; and Sir Tristram and Sir Galleron were his god-fathers. Then soon after they departed, and rode toward Camelot, where the noble King Arthur and Queen Guenever were keeping a court royal. And the king and all the court were glad that Sir Palamedes was christened. Then Sir Tristram returned again to La Joyeuse Garde, and Sir Palamedes went his way.

Not long after these events Sir Gawain returned from Brittany, and related to King Arthur the adventure which befell him in the forest of Breciliande,—how Merlin had there spoken to him, and enjoined him to charge the king to go without delay upon the quest of the Holy Greal. While King Arthur deliberated, Tristram determined to enter upon the quest, and the more readily, as it was well known to him that this holy adventure would, if achieved, procure him the pardon of all his sins. He immediately departed for the kingdom of Brittany, hoping there to obtain from Merlin counsel as to the proper course to pursue to insure success.

On arriving in Brittany Tristram found King Hoel engaged in a war with a rebellious vassal, and hard pressed by his enemy. His best knights had fallen in a late battle, and he knew not where to turn for assistance. Tristram volunteered his aid. It

was accepted; and the army of Hoel, led by Tristram, and inspired by his example, gained a complete victory. The king,
penetrated by the most lively sentiments of gratitude, and having
informed himself of Tristram's birth, offered him his daughter in
marriage. The princess was beautiful and accomplished, and bore
the same name with the Queen of Cornwall; but this one is designated by the Romancers as Isoude of the White Hands, to distinguish her from Isoude the Fair.

How can we describe the conflict that agitated the heart of
Tristram? He adored the first Isoude, but his love for her was
hopeless, and not unaccompanied by remorse. Moreover, the
sacred quest on which he had now entered demanded of him perfect purity of life. It seemed as if a happy destiny had provided
for him, in the charming princess Isoude of the White Hands, the
best security for all his good resolutions. This last reflection determined him. They were married, and passed some months in tranquil happiness at the court of King Hoel. The pleasure which
Tristram felt in his wife's society increased day by day. An inward
grace seemed to stir within him from the moment when he took
the oath to go on the quest of the Holy Greal; it seemed even to
triumph over the power of the magic love-potion.

The war, which had been quelled for a time, now burst out
anew. Tristram, as usual, was foremost in every danger. The
enemy was worsted in successive conflicts, and at last shut himself up in his principal city. Tristram led on the attack of the
city. As he mounted a ladder to scale the walls, he was struck
on the head by a fragment of rock, which the besieged threw
down upon him. It bore him to the ground, where he lay insensible.

As soon as he recovered consciousness, he demanded to be carried to his wife. The princess, skilled in the art of surgery, would
not suffer any one but herself to touch her beloved husband. Her
fair hands bound up his wounds; Tristram kissed them with gratitude, which began to grow into love. At first the devoted cares
of Isoude seemed to meet with great success; but after awhile
these flattering appearances vanished, and, in spite of all her
care, the malady grew more serious day by day.

In this perplexity, an old squire of Tristram's reminded his
master that the princess of Ireland, afterward queen of Cornwall,
had once cured him under circumstances quite as discouraging.
He called Isoude of the White Hands to him, told her of his former
cure, added that he believed that the Queen Isoude could heal
him, and that he felt sure that she would come to his relief if
sent for.

Isoude of the White Hands consented that Gesnes, a trusty man and skilful navigator, should be sent to Cornwall. Tristram called him, and, giving him a ring, "Take this," he said, "to the Queen of Cornwall. Tell her that Tristram, near to death, demands her aid. If you succeed in bringing her with you, place white sails to your vessel on your return, that we may know of your success when the vessel first heaves in sight. But if Queen Isoude refuses, put on black sails; they will be the presage of my impending death."

Gesnes performed his mission successfully. King Mark happened to be absent from his capital, and the queen readily consented to return with the bark to Brittany. Gesnes clothed his vessel in the whitest of sails, and sped his way back to Brittany.

Meantime the wound of Tristram grew more desperate day by day. His strength, quite prostrated, no longer permitted him to be carried to the seaside daily, as had been his custom from the first moment when it was possible for the bark to be on the way homeward. He called a young damsel, and gave her in charge to keep watch in the direction of Cornwall, and to come and tell him the color of the sails of the first vessel she should see approaching.

When Isoude of the White Hands consented that the queen of Cornwall should be sent for, she had not known all the reasons which she had for fearing the influence which renewed intercourse with that princess might have on her own happiness. She had now learned more, and felt the danger more keenly. She thought, if she could only keep the knowledge of the queen's arrival from her husband, she might employ in his service any resources which her skill could supply, and still avert the dangers which she apprehended. When the vessel was seen approaching, with its white sails sparkling in the sun, the damsel, by command of her mistress, carried word to Tristram that the sails were black.

Tristram, penetrated with inexpressible grief, breathed a profound sigh, turned away his face, and said, "Alas, my beloved! we shall never see one another again!" Then he commended himself to God, and breathed his last.

The death of Tristram was the first intelligence which the queen of Cornwall heard on landing. She was conducted almost senseless into the chamber of Tristram, and expired holding him in her arms.

Tristram, before his death, had requested that his body should be sent to Cornwall, and that his sword, with a letter he had written, should be delivered to King Mark. The remains of Tristram and Isoude were embarked in a vessel, along with the sword, which was presented to the king of Cornwall. He was melted with tenderness when he saw the weapon which slew Moraunt of Ireland,—which had so often saved his life, and redeemed the honor of his kingdom. In the letter Tristram begged pardon of his uncle, and related the story of the amorous draught.

Mark ordered the lovers to be buried in his own chapel. From the tomb of Tristram there sprung a vine, which went along the walls, and descended into the grave of the queen. It was cut down three times, but each time sprung up again more vigorous than before, and this wonderful plant has ever since shaded the tombs of Tristram and Isoude.

———

Spenser introduces Sir Tristram in his Faery Queene. In Book VI., Canto ii., Sir Calidore encounters in the forest a young hunter, whom he thus describes:—

> "Him steadfastly he marked, and saw to be
> A goodly youth of amiable grace,
> Yet but a slender slip, that scarce did see
> Yet seventeen yeares; but tall and faire of face,
> That sure he deemed him borne of noble race.
> All in a woodman's jacket he was clad
> Of Lincoln greene, belayed with silver lace;
> And on his head an hood with aglets [1] sprad,
> And by his side his hunter's horne he hanging had.

> "Buskins he wore of costliest cordawayne,
> Pinckt upon gold, and paled part per part,[2]
> As then the guize was for each gentle swayne,
> In his right hand he held a trembling dart,
> Whose fellow he before had sent apart;
> And in his left he held a sharp bore-speare,
> With which he wont to launch the salvage heart
> Of many a lyon, and of many a beare,
> That first unto his hand in chase did happen neare."

Tristram is often alluded to by the Romancers as the great authority and model in all matters relating to the chase. In the Faery Queene, Tristram, in answer to the inquiries of Sir Calidore, informs him of his name and parentage, and concludes:—

> "All which my days I have not lewdly spent,
> Nor spilt the blossom of my tender years
> In idlesse; but, as was convenient,
> Have trained been with many noble feres
> In gentle thewes, and such like seemly leers; [3]

---

[1] *Aglets*, points or tags.

[2] *Pinckt upon gold*, etc., adorned with golden points, or eyelets, and regularly intersected with stripes. *Paled* (in heraldry), striped.

[3] *Feres*, companions; *thewes*, labors; *leers*, learning.

'Mongst which my most delight hath always been
To hunt the salvage chace, amongst my peers,
Of all that rangeth in the forest green
Of which none is to me unknown that yet was seen.

"Ne is there hawk which mantleth on her perch,
Whether high towering or accosting low,
But I the measure of her flight do search,
And all her prey, and all her diet know.
Such be our joys, which in these forests grow."

CHAPTER XIV

THE STORY OF PERCEVAL

"——Sir Percivale,
Whom Arthur and his knighthood called the Pure."

TENNYSON.

THE father and two elder brothers of Perceval had fallen in battle or tournaments, and hence, as the last hope of his family, his mother retired with him into a solitary region, where he was brought up in total ignorance of arms and chivalry. He was allowed no weapon but "a lyttel Scots spere," which was the only thing of all "her lordes faire gere" that his mother carried to the wood with her. In the use of this he became so skilful that he could kill with it not nly the animals of the chase for her table, but even birds on the wing. At length, however, Perceval was roused to a desire of military renown by seeing in the forest five knights who were in complete armor. He said to his mother, "Mother, what are those yonder?" "They are angels, my son," said she. "By my faith, I will go and become an angel with them." And Perceval went to the road and met them. "Tell me, good lad," said one of them, "sawest thou a knight pass this way either to-day or yesterday?" "I know not," said he, "what a knight is." "Such an one as I am," said the knight. "If thou wilt tell me what I ask thee, I will tell thee what thou askest me." "Gladly will I do so," said Sir Owain, for that was the knight's name. "What is this?" demanded Perceval, touch-ing the saddle. "It is a saddle," said Owain. Then he asked about all the accoutrements which he saw upon the men and the horses, and about the arms, and what they were for, and how they were used. And Sir Owain showed him all those things fully. And Perceval in return gave him such information as he had.

Then Perceval returned to his mother, and said to her, "Mother, those were not angels, but honorable knights." Then his mother swooned away. And Perceval went to the place where they kept the horses that carried firewood and provisions for the castle, and he took a bony, piebald horse, which seemed to him the strongest of them. And he pressed a pack into the form of a saddle, and with twisted twigs he imitated the trappings which he had seen upon the horses. When he came again to his mother the countess had recovered from her swoon. "My son," said she, "desirest thou to ride forth?" "Yes, with thy leave," said he. "Go forward then," she said, "to the court of Arthur, where there are the best and the noblest and the most bountiful of men, and tell him thou art Perceval, the son of Pelenore, and ask of him to bestow knighthood on thee. And whenever thou seest a church, repeat there thy pater-noster; and if thou see meat and drink, and hast need of them, thou mayest take them. If thou hear an outcry of one in distress, proceed toward it, especially if it be the cry of a woman, and render her what service thou canst. If thou see a fair jewel, win it, for thus shalt thou acquire fame; yet freely give it to another, for thus thou shalt obtain praise. If thou see a fair woman, pay court to her, for thus thou wilt obtain love."

After this discourse Perceval mounted the horse, and, taking a number of sharp-pointed sticks in his hand, he rode forth. And he rode far in the woody wilderness without food or drink. At last he came to an opening in the wood, where he saw a tent, and as he thought it might be a church he said his pater-noster to it. And he went toward it; and the door of the tent was open. And Perceval dismounted and entered the tent. In the tent he found a maiden sitting, with a golden frontlet on her forehead and a gold ring on her hand. And Perceval said, "Maiden, I salute you, for my mother told me whenever I met a lady I must respectfully salute her." Perceiving in one corner of the tent some food, two flasks full of wine, and some boar's flesh roasted, he said, "My mother told me, whenever I saw meat and drink to take it." And he ate greedily, for he was very hungry. "Sir, thou hadst best go quickly from here, for fear that my friends should come, and evil should befall you." But Perceval said, "My mother told me wheresoever I saw a fair jewel to take it," and he took the gold ring from her finger, and put it on his own; and he gave the maiden his own ring in exchange for hers; then he mounted his horse and rode away.

Perceval journeyed on till he arrived at Arthur's court. And it so happened that just at that time an uncourteous knight had offered Queen Guenever a gross insult. For when her page was serving the queen with a golden goblet, this knight struck the arm of the page and dashed the wine in the queen's face and over her stomacher. Then he said, "If any have boldness to avenge this insult to Guenever, let him follow me to the meadow." So the knight took his horse and rode to the meadow, carrying away the golden goblet. And all the household hung down their heads, and no one offered to follow the knight to take vengeance upon him. For it seemed to them that no one would have ventured on so daring an outrage unless he possessed such powers, through magic or charms, that none could be able to punish him. Just then, behold, Perceval entered the hall upon the bony, piebald horse, with his uncouth trappings. In the centre of the hall stood Kay the seneschal. "Tell me, tall man," said Perceval, "is that Arthur yonder?" "What wouldst thou with Arthur?" asked Kay. "My mother told me to go to Arthur and receive knighthood from him." "By my faith," said he, "thou art all too meanly equipped with horse and with arms." Then all the household began to jeer and laugh at him. But there was a certain damsel who had been a whole year at Arthur's court, and had never been known to smile. And the king's fool [1] had said that this damsel would not smile till she had seen him who would be the flower of chivalry. Now this damsel came up to Perceval and told him, smiling, that, if he lived, he would be one of the bravest and best of knights. "Truly," said Kay, "thou art ill taught to remain a year at Arthur's court, with choice of society, and smile on no one, and now before the face of Arthur and all his knights to call such a man as this the flower of knighthood;" and he gave her a box on the ear, that she fell senseless to the ground. Then said Kay to Perceval, "Go after the knight who went hence to the meadow, overthrow him and recover the golden goblet, and possess thyself of his horse and arms, and thou shalt have knighthood." "I will do so, tall man," said Perceval. So he turned his horse's head toward the meadow. And when he came there, the knight was riding up and down, proud of his strength and valor and noble mien. "Tell me," said the knight, "didst thou see any one coming after me from the court?" "The tall man that was there," said Perceval, "told me to come and overthrow thee, and to take from thee the goblet and thy horse and armor for myself." "Silence!" said the knight; "go back to the court, and tell Arthur either to come himself, or to send some other to fight with me; and unless he do so quickly, I will not wait for him." "By my faith," said Perceval, "choose thou whether it shall be willingly or unwillingly, for I will have the horse and the arms and the goblet." Upon this the knight ran at him furiously, and struck him a violent blow with the shaft of his spear, between the neck and the shoulder. "Ha, ha, lad!" said Perceval, "my mother's servants were not used to play with me in this wise; so thus will I play with thee." And

[1] A fool was a common appendage of the courts of those days when this romance was written. A fool was the ornament held in next estimation to a dwarf. He wore a white dress with a yellow bonnet, and carried a bell or *bawble* in his hand. Though called a fool, his words were often weighed and remembered as if there were a sort of oracular meaning in them.

he threw at him one of his sharp-pointed sticks, and it struck him in the eye, and came out at the back of his head, so that he fell down lifeless.

But at the court of Arthur, Sir Owain said to Kay, "Verily, thou wert ill advised when thou didst send that madman after the knight. For one of two things must befall him. He must either be overthrown or slain. If he is overthrown by the knight, he will be counted by him to be an honorable person of the court, and an eternal disgrace will it be to Arthur and his warriors. And if he is slain, the disgrace will be the same, and moreover his sin will be upon him; therefore will I go to see what has befallen him." So Sir Owain went to the meadow, and he found Perceval dragging the man about. "What art thou doing thus?" said Sir Owain. "This iron coat," said Perceval, "will never come from off him; not by my efforts, at any rate." And Sir Owain unfastened his armor and his clothes. "Here, my good soul," said he, "is a horse and armor better than thine. Take them joyfully, and come with me to Arthur to receive the order of knighthood, for thou dost merit it." And Owain helped Perceval to put it on, and taught him how to put his foot in the stirrup, and use the spur; for Perceval had never used stirrup nor spur, but rode without saddle, and urged on his horse with a stick. Then Owain would have had him return to the court to receive the praise that was his due; but Perceval said, "I will not come to the court till I have encountered the tall man that is there, to revenge the injury he did to the maiden. But take thou the goblet to Queen Guenever, and tell King Arthur that, wherever I am, I will be his vassal, and will do him what profit and service I can." And Sir Owain went back to the court, and related all these things to Arthur and Guenever, and to all the household.

And Perceval rode forward. And as he proceeded, behold a knight met him. "Whence comest thou?" said the knight. "I come from Arthur's court," said Perceval. "Art thou one of his men?" asked he. "Yes, by my faith," he answered. "A good service, truly, is that of Arthur." "Wherefore sayest thou so?" said Perceval. "I will tell thee," said he. "I have always been Arthur's enemy, and all such of his men as I have ever encountered I have slain." And without further parlance they fought, and it was not long before Perceval brought him to the ground, over his horse's crupper. Then the knight besought his mercy. "Mercy thou shalt have," said Perceval, "if thou wilt make oath to me that thou wilt go to Arthur's court and tell him that it was I that overthrew thee, for the honor of his service; and say that I will never come to the court until I have avenged the insult offered to the maiden." The knight pledged him his faith of this, and proceeded to the court of Arthur and said as he had promised, and conveyed the threat to Sir Kay.

And Perceval rode forward. And within that week he encountered sixteen knights, and overthrew them all shamefully. And they all went to Arthur's court, taking with them the same message which the first knight had conveyed from Perceval, and the same threat which he had sent to Sir Kay. And thereupon Sir Kay was reproved by Arthur; and Sir Kay was greatly grieved thereat.

And Perceval rode forward. And he came to a lake, on the side of which was a fair castle, and on the border of the lake he saw a hoary-headed man sitting upon a velvet cushion, and his attendants were fishing in the lake. When the hoary-headed man beheld Perceval approaching, he arose and went into the castle. Perceval rode to the castle, and the door was open, and he entered the hall. And the hoary-headed man received Perceval courteously, and asked him to sit by him on the cushion. When it was time, the tables were set, and they went to meat. And when they had finished their meat, the hoary-headed man asked Perceval if he knew how to fight with the sword. "I know not," said Perceval, "but were I to be taught, doubtless I should." "Whoever can play well with the cudgel and shield will also be able to fight with a sword." And the man had two sons; the one had yellow hair and the other auburn. "Arise, youths," said the old man, "and play with the cudgel and the shield." And so did they. "Tell me, my son," said the man, "which of the youths thinkest thou plays best?" "I think," said Perceval, "that the yellow-haired youth could draw blood if he chose." "Arise thou, then, and take the cudgel and the shield from the hand of the youth with the auburn hair, and draw blood from the yellow-haired youth if thou canst." So Perceval arose, and he lifted up his arm, and struck him such a mighty blow that he cut his forehead open from one side to the other. "Ah, my life," said the old man, "come, now, and sit down, for thou wilt become the best fighter with the sword of any in this island; and I am thy uncle, thy mother's brother; I am called King Pecheur.[1] Thou shalt remain with me a space, in order to learn the manners and customs of different countries, and courtesy and noble bearing. And this do thou remember: if thou seest aught to cause thy wonder, ask not the meaning of it; if no one has the courtesy to inform thee, the reproach will not fall upon thee, but upon me that am thy teacher." While Perceval and his uncle discoursed together, Perceval beheld two youths enter the hall, bearing a golden cup and a spear of mighty size, with blood dropping from its point to the ground. And when all the company saw this, they began to weep and lament.

[1] The word means both *fisher* and *sinner*.

But for all that, the man did not break off his discourse with Perceval. And as he did not tell him the meaning of what he saw, he forbore to ask him concerning it. Now the cup that Perceval saw was the Sangreal, and the spear the sacred spear; and afterwards King Pecheur removed with those sacred relics into a far country.

.   .   .   .

One evening Perceval entered a valley, and came to a hermit's cell; and the hermit welcomed him gladly, and there he spent the night. And in the morning he arose, and when he went forth, behold! a shower of snow had fallen in the night, and a hawk had killed a wild-fowl in front of the cell. And the noise of the horse had scared the hawk away, and a raven alighted on the bird. And Perceval stood and compared the blackness of the raven and the whiteness of the snow and the redness of the blood to the hair of the lady that best he loved, which was blacker than jet, and to her skin, which was whiter than the snow, and to the two red spots upon her cheeks, which were redder than the blood upon the snow.

Now Arthur and his household were in search of Perceval, and by chance they came that way. "Know ye," said Arthur, "who is the knight with the long spear that stands by the brook up yonder?" "Lord," said one of them, "I will go and learn who he is." So the youth came to the place where Perceval was, and asked him what he did thus, and who he was. But Perceval was so intent upon his thought that he gave him no answer. Then the youth thrust at Perceval with his lance; and Perceval turned upon him and struck him to the ground. And when the youth returned to the king, and told how rudely he had been treated, Sir Kay said, "I will go myself." And when he greeted Perceval, and got no answer, he spoke to him rudely and angrily. And Perceval thrust at him with his lance, and cast him down so that he broke his arm and his shoulder-blade. And while he lay thus stunned, his horse returned back at a wild and prancing pace.

Then said Sir Gawain, surnamed the Golden-Tongued, because he was the most courteous knight in Arthur's court: "It is not fitting that any should disturb an honorable knight from his thought unadvisedly; for either he is pondering some damage that he has sustained, or he is thinking of the lady he best loves. If it seem well to thee, lord, I will go and see if this knight has changed from his thought, and if he has, I will ask him courteously to come and visit thee."

And Perceval was resting on the shaft of his spear, pondering the same thought, and Sir Gawain came to him, and said, "If I thought it would be as agreeable to thee as it would be to me. I would converse with thee. I have also a message from Arthur unto thee, to pray thee to come and visit him. And two men have been before on this errand." "That is true," said Perceval, "and uncourteously they came. They attacked me, and I was annoyed thereat." Then he told him the thought that occupied his mind, and Gawain said, "This was not an ungentle thought, and I should marvel if it were pleasant for thee to be drawn from it." Then said Perceval, "Tell me, is Sir Kay in Arthur's court?" "He is," said Gawain; "and truly he is the knight who fought with thee last." "Verily," said Perceval, "I am not sorry to have thus avenged the insult to the smiling maiden." Then Perceval told him his name, and said, "Who art thou?" And he replied, "I am Gawain." "I am right glad to meet thee," said Perceval, "for I have everywhere heard of thy prowess and uprightness; and I solicit thy fellowship." "Thou shalt have it, by my faith; and grant me thine," said he. "Gladly will I do so," answered Perceval.

So they went together to Arthur, and saluted him. "Behold, lord," said Gawain, "him whom thou hast sought so long." "Welcome unto thee, chieftain," said Arthur. And hereupon there came the queen and her handmaidens, and Perceval saluted them. And they were rejoiced to see him, and bade him welcome. And Arthur did him great honor and respect, and they returned toward Caerleon.

CHAPTER XV

THE QUEST OF THE SANGREAL

"—The cup itself from which our Lord
Drank at the last sad supper with His own.
This from the blessed land of Aromat,
After the day of darkness, when the dead
Went wandering over Moriah—the good saint,
Arimathean Joseph, journeying, brought
To Glastonbury, where the winter thorn
Blossoms at Christmas, mindful of our Lord,
And there awhile abode; and if a man
Could touch or see it, he was healed at once,
By faith, of all his ills. But then the times
Grew to such evil that the holy cup
Was caught away to Heaven, and disappeared."

TENNYSON.

THE Sangreal was the cup from which our Saviour drank at his last supper. He was supposed to have given it to Joseph of Arimathea, who carried it to Europe, together with the spear with which the soldier pierced the Saviour's side. From generation to generation one of the descendants of Joseph of Arimathea had been devoted to the guardianship of these precious relics; but on the sole condition of leading a life of purity in thought, word, and deed. For a long time the Sangreal was visible to all pilgrims, and its presence conferred blessings upon the land in which it was preserved. But at length one of those holy men to whom its guardianship had descended so far forgot the obligation of his sacred office as to look with unhallowed eye upon a young female pilgrim whose robe was accidentally loosened as she knelt before him. The sacred lance instantly punished his frailty, spontaneously falling upon him, and inflicting a deep wound. The marvellous wound could by no means be healed, and the guardian of the Sangreal was ever after called "Le Roi Pecheur,"—the Sinner King. The Sangreal withdrew its visible presence from the crowds who came to worship, and an iron age succeeded to the happiness which its presence had diffused among the tribes of Britain.

We have told in the history of Merlin how that great prophet and enchanter sent a message to King Arthur by Sir Gawain, directing him to undertake the recovery of the Sangreal, informing him at the same time that the knight who should accomplish that sacred quest was already born, and of a suitable age to enter upon it. Sir Gawain delivered his message, and the king was anxiously revolving in his mind how best to achieve the enterprise, when, at the vigil of Pentecost, all the fellowship of the Round Table being met together at Camelot, as they sat at meat, suddenly there was heard a clap of thunder, and then a bright light burst forth, and every knight, as he looked on his fellow, saw him, in seeming, fairer than ever before. All the hall was filled with sweet odors, and every knight had such meat and drink as he best loved. Then there entered into the hall the Holy Greal, covered with white samite, so that none could see it, and it passed through the hall suddenly and disappeared. During this time no one spoke a word, but when they had recovered breath to speak, King Arthur said, "Certainly we ought greatly to thank the Lord for what He hath showed us this day." Then Sir Gawain rose up, and made a vow that for twelve months and a day he would seek the Sangreal, and not return till he had seen it, if so he might speed. When they of the Round Table heard Sir Gawain say so, they arose, the most part of them, and vowed the same. When King Arthur heard this he was greatly displeased, for he knew well that they might not gainsay their vows. "Alas!" said he to Sir Gawain, "you have nigh slain me with the vow and promise that ye have made, for ye have bereft me of the fairest fellowship that ever was seen together in any realm of the world; for when they shall depart hence, I am sure that all shall never meet more in this world."

SIR GALAHAD

At that time there entered the hall a good old man, and with him he brought a young knight, and these words he said: "Peace be with you, fair lords." Then the old man said unto King Arthur, "Sir, I bring you here a young knight that is of kings' lineage, and of the kindred of Joseph of Arimathea, being the son of Dame Elaine, the daughter of King Pelles, king of the foreign country." Now the name of the young knight was Sir Galahad, and he was the son of Sir Launcelot du Lac; but he had dwelt with his mother, at the court of King Pelles, his grandfather, till now he was old enough to bear arms, and his mother had sent him in the charge of a holy hermit to King Arthur's court. Then Sir Launcelot beheld his son, and had great joy of him. And Sir Bohort told his fellows, "Upon my life, this young knight shall come to great worship." The noise was great in all the court, so that it came to the queen. And she said, "I would fain see him, for he must needs be a noble knight, for so is his father." And the queen and her ladies all said that he resembled much unto his father; and he was seemly and demure as a dove, with all manner of good features, that in the whole world men might not find his match. And King Arthur said, "God make him a good man, for beauty faileth him not, as any that liveth."

Then the hermit led the young knight to the Siege Perilous; and he lifted up the cloth, and found there letters that said, "This is the seat of Sir Galahad, the good knight"; and he made him sit in that seat. And all the knights of the Round Table marvelled greatly at Sir Galahad, seeing him sit securely in that seat, and said, "This is he by whom the Sangreal shall be achieved, for there never sat one before in that seat without being mischieved."

On the next day the king said, "Now, at this quest of the Sangreal shall all ye of the Round Table depart, and never shall I see you again all together; therefore I will that ye all repair to the meadow of Camelot, for to joust and tourney yet once more before ye depart." But all the meaning of the king was to see Sir Galahad proved. So then were they all assembled in the meadow. Then Sir Galahad, by request of the king and queen, put on his harness and his helm, but shield would he take none for any prayer of the king. And the queen was in a tower, with all her ladies, to behold that tournament. Then Sir Galahad rode into the midst of the meadow; and there he began to break spears marvellously, so that all men had wonder of him, for he surmounted all knights that encountered with him, except two, Sir Launcelot and Sir Perceval. Then the king, at the queen's request, made him to alight, and presented him to the queen; and she said, "Never two men resembled one another more than he and Sir Launcelot, and therefore it is no marvel that he is like him in prowess."

Then the king and the queen went to the minster, and the knights followed them. And after the service was done, they put on their helms and departed, and there was great sorrow. They rode through the streets of Camelot, and there was weeping of the rich and poor; and the king turned away, and might not speak for weeping. And so they departed, and every knight took the way that him best liked.

Sir Galahad rode forth without shield, and rode four days, and found no adventure. And on the fourth day he came to a white abbey; and there he was received with great reverence, and led to a chamber. He met there two knights, King Bagdemagus and Sir Uwaine, and they made of him great solace. "Sirs," said Sir Galahad, "what adventure brought you hither?" "Sir," said they, "it is told us that within this place is a shield, which no man may bear unless he be worthy; and if one unworthy should attempt to bear it, it shall surely do him a mischief." Then King Bagdemagus said, "I fear not to bear it, and that shall ye see to-morrow."

So on the morrow they arose, and heard mass; then King Bagdemagus asked where the adventurous shield was. Anon a monk led him behind an altar, where the shield hung, as white as snow; but in the midst there was a red cross. Then King Bagdemagus took the shield, and bare it out of the minster; and he said to Sir Galahad, "If it please you, abide here till ye know how I shall speed."

Then King Bagdemagus and his squire rode forth; and when they had ridden a mile or two, they saw a goodly knight come towards them, in white armor, horse and all; and he came as fast as his horse might run, with his spear in the rest; and King Bagdemagus directed his spear against him, and broke it upon the white knight, but the other struck him so hard that he broke the mails, and thrust him through the right shoulder, for the shield covered him not, and so he bare him from his horse. Then the white knight turned his horse and rode away.

Then the squire went to King Bagdemagus, and asked him whether he were sore wounded or not. "I am sore wounded," said he, "and full hardly shall I escape death." Then the squire set him on his horse, and brought him to an abbey; and there he was taken down softly, and unarmed, and laid in a bed, and his wound was looked to, for he lay there long, and hardly escaped with his life. And the squire brought the shield back to the abbey.

The next day Sir Galahad took the shield, and within a while he came to the hermitage, where he met the white knight, and each saluted the other courteously. "Sir," said Sir Galahad, "can you tell me the marvel of the shield?" "Sir," said the white knight, "that shield belonged of old to the gentle knight, Joseph of Arimathea; and when he came to die, he said, 'Never shall man bear this shield about his neck but he shall repent it, unto the time that Sir Galahad, the good knight, bear it, the last of my lineage, the which shall do many marvellous deeds.' " And then the white knight vanished away.

SIR GAWAIN

After Sir Gawain departed, he rode many days, both toward and forward, and at last he came to the abbey where Sir Galahad took the white shield. And they told Sir Gawain of the marvellous adventure that Sir Galahad had done. "Truly," said Sir Gawain, "I am not happy that I took not the way that he went, for, if I may meet with him, I will not part from him lightly, that I may partake with him all the marvellous adventures which he shall achieve." "Sir," said one of the monks, "he will not be of your fellowship." "Why?" said Sir Gawain. "Sir," said he, "because ye be sinful, and he is blissful." Then said the monk, "Sir Gawain, thou must do penance for thy sins." "Sir, what penance shall I do?" "Such as I will show," said the good man. "Nay," said Sir Gawain, "I will do no penance, for we knights adventurous often suffer great woe and pain." "Well," said the good man; and he held his peace. And Sir Gawain departed.

Now it happened, not long after this, that Sir Gawain and Sir Hector rode together, and they came to a castle where was a great tournament. And Sir Gawain and Sir Hector joined themselves to the party that seemed the weaker, and they drove before them the other party. Then suddenly came into the lists a knight, bearing a white shield with a red cross, and by adventure he came by Sir Gawain, and he smote him so hard that he clave his helm and wounded his head, so that Sir Gawain fell to the earth. When Sir Hector saw that, he knew that the knight with the white shield was Sir Galahad, and he thought it no wisdom to abide with him, and also for natural love, that he was his uncle. Then Sir Galahad retired privily, so that none knew where he had gone. And Sir Hector raised up Sir Gawain, and said, "Sir, me seemeth your quest is done." "It is done," said Sir Gawain; "I shall seek no further." Then Gawain was borne into the castle, and unarmed, and laid in a rich bed, and a leech found to search his wound. And Sir Gawain and Sir Hector abode together, for Sir Hector would not away until Sir Gawain were whole.

Now Sir Galahad, after that the white knight had vanished away, rode till he came to a waste forest, and there he met with Sir Launcelot and Sir Perceval, but they knew him not, for he was new disguised. Right so, Sir Launcelot his father dressed his spear, and brake it upon Sir Galahad, and Sir Galahad smote him so again, that he smote down horse and man. And then he drew his sword, and dressed him to Sir Perceval, and smote him so on the helm that it rove to the coif of steel, and had not the sword swerved Sir Perceval had been slain, and with the stroke he fell out of his saddle. This joust was done before the hermitage where a recluse dwelled. And when she saw Sir Galahad ride, she said, "God be with thee, best knight of the world. Ah, certes," she said all aloud, that Launcelot and Perceval might hear it, "and yonder two knights had known thee as well as I do, they would not have encountered with thee." When Sir Galahad heard her say so he was sore adread to be known: therewith he smote his horse with his spurs, and rode at a great pace away from them. Then perceived they both that he was Sir Galahad, and up they got on their horses, and rode fast after him, but in a while he was out of their sight. And then they turned again with heavy cheer. "Let us spere some tidings," said Sir Perceval, "at yonder recluse." "Do as ye list," said Sir Launcelot. When Sir Perceval came to the recluse, she knew him well enough, and Sir Launcelot both.

But Sir Launcelot rode overthwart and endlong in a wild forest, and held no path, but as wild adventure led him. And at the last he came to a stony cross, which departed two ways in waste land, and by the cross was a stone that was of marble, but it was so dark that Sir Launcelot might not wit what it was. Then Sir Launcelot looked by him, and saw an old chapel, and there he thought to have found people. And Sir Launcelot tied his horse to a tree, and there he did off his shield, and hung it upon a tree. And then he went to the chapel door, and found it waste and broken. And within he found a fair altar full richly arrayed with cloth of clean silk, and there stood a fair, clean candlestick which bare six great candles, and the candlestick was of silver. And when Sir Launcelot saw this light, he had great will for to enter into the chapel, but he could find no place where he might enter: then was he passing heavy and dismayed. And he returned and came again to his horse, and took off his saddle and his bridle, and let him pasture; and unlaced his helm, and ungirded his sword, and laid him down to sleep upon his shield before the cross.

And as he lay, half waking and half sleeping, he saw come by him two palfreys, both fair and white, which bare a litter, on which lay a sick knight. And when he was nigh the cross, he there abode still. And Sir Launcelot heard him say, "O sweet Lord, when shall this sorrow leave me, and when shall the holy vessel come by me whereby

I shall be healed?" And thus a great while complained the knight, and Sir Launcelot heard it. Then Sir Launcelot saw the candlestick, with the lighted tapers, come before the cross, but he could see nobody that brought it. Also there came a salver of silver and the holy vessel of the Sangreal; and therewith the sick knight sat him upright, and held up both his hands, and said, "Fair, sweet Lord, which is here within the holy vessel, take heed to me, that I may be whole of this great malady." And therewith, upon his hands and upon his knees, he went so nigh that he touched the holy vessel and kissed it. And anon he was whole. Then the holy vessel went into the chapel again, with the candlestick and the light, so that Sir Launcelot wist not what became of it.

Then the sick knight rose up and kissed the cross; and anon his squire brought him his arms, and asked his lord how he did. "I thank God right heartily," said he, "for, through the holy vessel, I am healed. But I have great marvel of this sleeping knight, who hath had neither grace nor power to awake during the time that the holy vessel hath been here present." "I dare it right well say," said the squire, "that this same knight is stained with some manner of deadly sin, whereof he was never confessed." So they departed.

Then anon Sir Launcelot waked, and set himself upright, and bethought him of what he had seen, and whether it were dreams or not. And he was passing heavy, and wist not what to do. And he said: "My sin and my wretchedness hath brought me into great dishonor. For when I sought worldly adventures and worldly desires, I ever achieved them, and had the better in every place, and never was I discomfited in any quarrel, were it right or wrong. And now I take upon me the adventure of holy things, I see and understand that mine old sin hindereth me, so that I had no power to stir nor to speak when the holy blood appeared before me." So thus he sorrowed till it was day, and heard the fowls of the air sing. Then was he somewhat comforted.

Then he departed from the cross into the forest. And there he found a hermitage, and a hermit therein, who was going to mass. So when mass was done, Sir Launcelot called the hermit to him, and prayed him for charity to hear his confession. "With a good will," said the good man. And then he told that good man all his life, and how he had loved a queen unmeasurably many years. "And all my great deeds of arms that I have done, I did the most part for the queen's sake, and for her sake would I do battle, were it right or wrong, and never did I battle all only for God's sake, but for to win worship, and to cause me to be better beloved; and little or naught I thanked God for it. I pray you counsel me."

"I will counsel you," said the hermit, "if ye will insure me that ye will never come in that queen's fellowship as much as ye may forbear." And then Sir Launcelot promised the hermit, by his faith, that he would no more come in her company. "Look that your heart and your mouth accord," said the good man, "and I shall insure ye that ye shall have more worship than ever ye had."

Then the good man enjoined Sir Launcelot such penance as he might do, and he assoiled Sir Launcelot, and made him abide with him all that day And Sir Launcelot repented him greatly.

SIR PERCEVAL

Sir Perceval departed, and rode till the hour of noon; and he met in a valley about twenty men of arms. And when they saw Sir Perceval, they asked him whence he was; and he answered, "Of the court of King Arthur." Then they cried all at once, "Slay him." But Sir Perceval smote the first to the earth, and his horse upon him. Then seven of the knights smote upon his shield all at once, and the remnant slew his horse, so that he fell to the earth. So had they slain him or taken him, had not the good knight Sir Galahad, with the red cross, come there by adventure. And when he saw all the knights upon one, he cried out, "Save me that knight's life." Then he rode toward the twenty men of arms as fast as his horse might drive, with his spear in the rest, and smote the foremost horse and man to the earth. And when his spear was broken, he set his hand to his sword, and smote on the right hand and on the left, that it was marvel to see; and at every stroke he smote down one, or put him to rebuke, so that they would fight no more, but fled to a thick forest, and Sir Galahad followed them. And when Sir Perceval saw him chase them so, he made great sorrow that his horse was slain. And he wist well it was Sir Galahad. Then he cried aloud, "Ah, fair knight, abide, and suffer me to do thanks unto thee; for right well have ye done for me." But Sir Galahad rode so fast, that at last he passed out of his sight. When Sir Perceval saw that he would not turn, he said, "Now am I a very wretch, and most unhappy above all other knights." So in this sorrow he abode all that day till it was night; and then he was faint, and laid him down and slept till midnight; and then he awaked, and saw before him a woman, who said unto him, "Sir Perceval, what dost thou here?" He answered, "I do neither good, nor great ill." "If thou wilt promise me," said she, "that thou wilt fulfil my will when I summon thee, I will lend thee my own horse, which shall bear thee whither thou wilt." Sir Perceval was glad of her proffer, and insured her to fulfil all her desire. "Then abide me here, and I will go fetch you a horse." And so she soon came again, and brought a horse with her that was inky black. When

Perceval beheld that horse, he marvelled, it was so great and so well apparelled. And he leapt upon him, and took no heed of himself. And he thrust him with his spurs, and within an hour and less he bare him four days' journey thence, until he came to a rough water, which roared, and his horse would have bare him into it. And when Sir Perceval came nigh the brim, and saw the water so boisterous, he doubted to overpass it. And then he made the sign of the cross on his forehead. When the fiend felt him so charged, he shook off Sir Perceval, and went into the water crying and roaring; and it seemed unto him that the water burned. Then Sir Perceval perceived it was a fiend that would have brought him unto his perdition. Then he commended himself unto God, and prayed our Lord to keep him from all such temptations; and so he prayed all that night till it was day. Then he saw that he was in a wild place, that was closed with the sea nigh all about. And Sir Perceval looked forth over the sea, and saw a ship come sailing toward him; and it came and stood still under the rock. And when Sir Perceval saw this, he hied him thither, and found the ship covered with silk; and therein was a lady of great beauty, and clothed so richly that none might be better.

And when she saw Sir Perceval she saluted him, and Sir Perceval returned her salutation. Then he asked her of her country and her lineage. And she said, "I am a gentlewoman that am disinherited, and was once the richest woman of the world." "Damsel," said Sir Perceval, "who hath disinherited you? for I have great pity of you." "Sir," said she, "my enemy is a great and powerful lord, and aforetime he made much of me, so that of his favor and of my beauty I had a little pride more than I ought to have had. Also I said a word that pleased him not. So he drove me from his company and from mine heritage. Therefore I know no good knight nor good man but I get him on my side if I may. And, for that I know that thou art a good knight, I beseech thee to help me."

Then Sir Perceval promised her all the help that he might, and she thanked him.

And at that time the weather was hot and she called to her a gentlewoman, and bade her bring forth a pavilion. And she did so, and pitched it upon the gravel. "Sir," said she, "now may ye rest you in this heat of the day." Then he thanked her, and she put off his helm and his shield, and there he slept a great while. Then he awoke, and asked her if she had any meat, and she said yea, and so there was set upon the table all manner of meats that he could think on. Also he drank there the strongest wine that ever he drank, and therewith he was a little chafed more than he ought to be. With that he beheld the lady, and he thought she was the fairest creature that ever he saw. And then Sir Perceval proffered her love, and prayed her that she would be his. Then she refused him in a manner, for the cause he should be the more ardent on her, and ever he ceased not to pray her of love. And when she saw him well enchafed, then she said, "Sir Perceval, wit ye well I shall not give ye my love unless you swear from henceforth you will be my true servant, and do no thing but that I shall command you. Will you insure me this, as ye be a true knight?" "Yea," said he, "fair lady, by the faith of my body." And as he said this, by adventure and grace, he saw his sword lie on the ground naked, in whose pommel was a red cross, and the sign of the crucifix thereon. Then he made the sign of the cross upon his forehead, and therewith the pavilion shrivelled up, and changed into a smoke and a black cloud. And the damsel cried aloud, and hasted into the ship, and so she went with the wind roaring and yelling that it seemed all the water burned after her. Then Sir Perceval made great sorrow, and called himself a wretch, saying, "How nigh was I lost!" Then he took his arms, and departed thence.

CHAPTER XVI

THE END OF THE QUEST

SIR BOHORT

WHEN Sir Bohort departed from Camelot he met with a religious man, riding upon an ass; and Sir Bohort saluted him. "What are ye?" said the good man. "Sir," said Sir Bohort, "I am a knight that fain would be counselled in the quest of the Sangreal." So rode they both together till they came to a hermitage; and there he prayed Sir Bohort to dwell that night with him. So he alighted, and put away his armor, and prayed him that he might be confessed. And they went both into the chapel, and there he was clean confessed. And they ate bread and drank water together. "Now," said the good man, "I pray thee that thou eat none other till thou sit at the table where the Sangreal shall be." "Sir," said Sir Bohort, "but how know ye that I shall sit there?" "Yea," said the good man, "that I know well; but there shall be few of your fellows with you." Then said Sir Bohort, "I agree me thereto." And the good man, when he had heard his confession, found him in so pure a life and so stable that he marvelled thereof.

On the morrow, as soon as the day appeared, Sir Bohort departed thence, and rode into a forest unto the hour of midday. And there befell him a marvellous adventure. For he met, at the parting of two ways, two knights that led Sir Lionel, his brother, all naked, bound upon a strong hackney, and his hands bound before his breast; and each of them held in his hand thorns wherewith they went beating him, so that he was all bloody before and behind; but he said never a word, but, as he was great of heart, he suffered all that they did to him as though he had felt none anguish. Sir Bohort prepared to rescue his brother. But he looked on the other side of him, and saw a knight dragging along a fair gentlewoman, who cried out, "Saint Mary! succor your maid!" And when she saw Sir Bohort, she called to him and said, "By the faith that ye owe to knighthood, help me!" When Sir Bohort heard her say thus, he had such sorrow that he wist not what to do. "For if I let my brother be he must be slain, and that would I not for all the earth; and if I help not the maid I am shamed forever." Then lift he up his eyes and said, weeping, "Fair Lord, whose liegeman I am, keep Sir Lionel, my brother, that none of these knights slay him, and for pity of you, and our Lady's sake, I shall succor this maid."

Then he cried out to the knight, "Sir knight, lay your hand off that maid, or else ye be but dead." Then the knight set down the maid, and took his shield, and drew out his sword. And Sir Bohort smote him so hard that it went through his shield and habergeon, on the left shoulder, and he fell down to the earth. Then came Sir Bohort to the maid, "Ye be delivered of this knight this time." "Now," said she, "I pray you lead me there where this knight took me." "I shall gladly do it," said Sir Bohort. So he took the horse of the wounded knight and set the gentlewoman upon it, and brought her there where she desired to be. And there he found twelve knights seeking after her; and when she told them how Sir Bohort had delivered her, they made great joy, and besought him to come to her father, a great lord, and he should be right welcome. "Truly," said Sir Bohort, "that may not be; for I have a great adventure to do." So he commended them to God and departed.

Then Sir Bohort rode after Sir Lionel, his brother, by the trace of their horses. Thus he rode, seeking, a great while. Then he overtook a man clothed in a religious clothing, who said, "Sir knight, what seek ye?" "Sir," said Sir Bohort, "I seek my brother, that I saw within a little space beaten of two knights." "Ah, Sir Bohort, trouble not thyself to seek for him, for truly he is dead." Then he showed him a new-slain body, lying in a thick bush; and it seemed him that it was the body of Sir Lionel. And then he made such sorrow that he fell to the ground in a swoon, and lay there long. And when he came to himself again he said, "Fair brother, since the fellowship of you and me is sundered, shall I never have joy again; and now He that I have taken for my master He be my help!" And when he had said thus, he took up the body in his arms, and put it upon the horse. And then he said to the man, "Canst thou tell me the way to some chapel, where I may bury this body?" "Come on," said the man, "here is one fast by." And so they rode till they saw a fair tower, and beside it a chapel. Then they alighted both, and put the body into a tomb of marble.

Then Sir Bohort commended the good man unto God, and departed. And he rode all that day, and harbored with an old lady. And on the morrow he rode unto the castle in a valley, and there he met with a yeoman. "Tell me," said Sir Bohort, "knowest thou of any adventure?" "Sir," said he, "here shall be, under this castle, a great and marvellous tournament." Then Sir Bohort thought to be there, if he might meet with any of the fellowship that were in quest of the Sangreal; so he turned to a hermitage that was on the border of the forest. And when he was come thither, he found there Sir Lionel his brother, who sat all armed at the entry of the chapel door. And when Sir Bohort saw him, he had great joy, and he alighted off his horse, and said, "Fair brother, when came ye hither?" As soon as Sir Lionel saw him, he said, "Ah, Sir Bohort, make ye no false show, for, as for you, I might have been slain, for ye left me in peril of death to go succor a gentlewoman; and for that misdeed I now insure you but death, for ye have right well deserved it." When Sir Bohort perceived his brother's wrath, he kneeled down to the earth and cried him mercy, holding up both his hands, and prayed him to forgive him. "Nay," said Sir Lionel, "thou shalt have but death for it, if I have the upper hand; therefore leap upon thy horse and keep thyself; and if thou do not, I will run upon thee there, as thou standest on foot, and so the shame shall be mine, and the harm thine, but of that I reck not." When Sir Bohort saw that he must fight with his brother or else die, he wist not what to do. Then his heart counselled him not so to do, inasmuch as Sir Lionel was his elder brother, wherefore he ought to bear him reverence. Yet kneeled he down before Sir Lionel's horse's feet, and said, "Fair brother, have mercy upon me, and slay me not." But Sir Lionel cared not, for the fiend had brought him in such a will that he should slay him. When he saw that Sir Bohort would not rise to give him battle, he rushed over him, so that he smote him with his horse's feet to the earth, and hurt him sore, that he swooned of distress. When Sir Lionel saw this, he alighted from his horse for to have smitten off his head; and so he took him by the helm, and would have rent it from his head. But it happened that Sir Colgrevance, a knight of the Round Table, came at that time thither, as it was our Lord's will; and then he beheld how Sir Lionel would have slain his brother, and he knew Sir Bohort, whom he loved right well. Then leapt he down from his horse, and took Sir Lionel by the shoulders, and drew him strongly back from Sir Bohort, and said, "Sir Lionel, will ye slay your brother?" "Why," said Sir Lionel, "will ye slay me? If ye interfere in this, I will slay you, and him after." Then he ran upon Sir Bohort, and would have smitten him; but Sir Colgrevance ran between them, and said, "If ye persist to do so any more, we two shall meddle together." Then Sir Lionel defied him, and gave him a great stroke through the helm. Then he drew his sword, for he was a passing good knight, and defended himself right manfully. So long endured the battle, that Sir Bohort rose up all anguishly, and beheld Sir Colgrevance, the good knight, fight with his brother for his quarrel. Then was he full sorry and heavy, and thought that, if Sir Colgrevance slew him that was his brother, he should never have joy, and if his brother slew Sir Colgrevance, the shame should ever be his.

Then would he have risen for to have parted them, but he had not so much strength to stand on his feet; so he staid so long that Sir Colgrevance had the worse, for Sir Lionel was of great chivalry and right hardy. Then cried Sir Colgrevance, "Ah, Sir Bohort, why come ye not to bring me out of peril of death, wherein I have put me to succor you?" With that, Sir Lionel smote off his helm, and bore him to the earth. And when he had slain Sir Colgrevance, he ran upon his brother as a fiendly man, and gave him such a stroke that he made him stoop. And he that was full of humility prayed him, "For God's sake leave this battle, for if it befell, fair brother, that I slew you, or ye me, we should be dead of that sin." "Pray ye not me for mercy," said Sir Lionel. Then Sir Bohort, all weeping, drew his sword, and said, "Now God have mercy upon me, though I defend my life against my brother." With that Sir Bohort lifted up his sword, and would have stricken his brother. Then heard he a voice that said, "Flee, Sir Bohort, and touch him not." Right so alighted a cloud between them, in the likeness of a fire, and a marvellous flame, so that they both fell to the earth, and lay there a great while in a swoon. And when they came to themselves, Sir Bohort saw that his brother had no harm; and he was right glad, for he dread sore that God had taken vengeance upon him. Then Sir Lionel said to his brother, "Brother, forgive me, for God's sake, all that I have trespassed against you." And Sir Bohort answered, "God forgive it thee, and I do."

With that Sir Bohort heard a voice say, "Sir Bohort, take thy way anon, right to the sea, for Sir Perceval abideth thee there." So Sir Bohort departed, and rode the nearest way to the sea. And at last he came to an abbey that was nigh the sea. That night he rested him there, and in his sleep there came a voice unto him and bade him go to the sea-shore. He started up, and made the sign of the cross on his forehead, and armed himself, and made ready his horse and mounted him, and at a broken wall he rode out, and came to the sea-shore. And there he found a ship, covered all with white samite. And he entered into the ship; but it was anon so dark that he might see no man, and he laid him down and slept till it was day. Then he awaked, and saw in the middle of the ship a knight all armed, save his helm. And then he knew it was Sir Perceval de Galis, and each made of other right great joy. Then said Sir Perceval, "We lack nothing now but the good knight Sir Galahad."

Of Sir Launcelot Again

It befell upon a night Sir Launcelot arrived before a castle, which was rich and fair. And there was a postern that opened toward the sea, and was open without any keeping, save two lions kept the entry; and the moon shined clear. Anon Sir Launcelot heard a voice that said, "Launcelot, enter into the castle, where thou shalt see a great part of thy desire." So he went unto the gate, and saw the two lions; then he set hands to his sword, and drew it. Then there came suddenly as it were a stroke upon the arm, so sore that the sword fell out of his hand, and he heard a voice that said, "O man of evil faith, wherefore believest thou more in thy armor than in thy Maker?" Then said Sir Launcelot, "Fair Lord, I thank thee of thy great mercy, that thou reprovest me of my misdeed; now see I well that thou holdest me for thy servant." Then he made a cross on his forehead, and came to the lions; and they made semblance to do him harm, but he passed them without hurt, and entered into the castle, and he found no gate nor door but it was open. But at the last he found a chamber whereof the door was shut; and he set his hand thereto, to have opened it, but he might not. Then he listened, and heard a voice which sung so sweetly that it seemed none earthly thing; and the voice said, "Joy and honor be to the Father of heaven." Then Sir Launcelot kneeled down before the chamber, for well he wist that there was the Sangreal in that chamber. Then said he, "Fair sweet Lord, if ever I did anything that pleased thee for thy pity show me something of that which I seek." And with that he saw the chamber door open, and there came out a great clearness, that the house was as bright as though all the torches of the world had been there. So he came to the chamber door, and would have entered; and anon a voice said unto him, "Stay, Sir Launcelot, and enter not." And he withdrew him back, and was right heavy in his mind. Then looked he in the midst of the chamber, and saw a table of silver, and the holy vessel, covered with red samite, and many angels about it; whereof one held a candle of wax burning, and another held a cross, and the ornaments of the altar. Then, for very wonder and thankfulness, Sir Launcelot forgot himself, and he stepped forward and entered the chamber. And suddenly a breath that seemed intermixed with fire smote him so sore in the visage, that therewith he fell to the ground, and had no power to rise. Then felt he many hands about him, which took him up, and bare him out of the chamber, without any amending of his swoon, and left him there, seeming dead to all the people. So on the morrow, when it was fair daylight, and they within were arisen, they found Sir Launcelot lying before the chamber door. And they looked upon him and felt his pulse, to know if there were any life in him. And they found life in him, but he might neither stand nor stir any member that he had. So they took him and bare him into a chamber, and laid him upon a bed, far from all folk, and there he lay many days. Then the one said he was alive, and others said nay. But said an old man, "He is as full of life as the mightiest of you all, and therefore I counsel you that he be well kept till God bring him back again." And after twenty-four days he opened his eyes; and when he saw folk, he made great sorrow, and said, "Why have ye wakened me? for I was better at ease than I am now." "What have ye seen?" said they about him. "I have seen," said he, "great marvels that no tongue can tell, and more than any heart can think." Then they said, "Sir, the quest of the Sangreal is achieved right now in you, and never shall ye see more of it than ye have seen." "I thank God," said Sir Launcelot, "of His great mercy, for that I have seen, for it sufficeth me." Then he rose up and clothed himself; and when he was so arrayed, they marvelled all, for they knew it was Sir Launcelot, the good knight. And, after four days, he took his leave of the lord of the castle, and of all the fellowship that were there, and thanked them for their great labor and care of him. Then he departed, and turned to Camelot, where he found King Arthur and Queen Guenever; but many of the knights of the Round Table were slain and destroyed, more than half. Then all the court was passing glad of Sir Launcelot; and he told the king all his adventures that had befallen him since he departed.

SIR GALAHAD

Now. when Sir Galahad had rescued Perceval from the twenty knights, he rode into a vast forest, wherein he abode many days. Then he took his way to the sea, and it befell him that he was benighted in a hermitage. And the good man was glad when he saw he was a knight-errant. And when they were at rest, there came a gentlewoman knocking at the door; and the good man came to the door to wit what she would. Then she said, "I would speak with the knight which is with you." Then Galahad went to her, and asked her what she would. "Sir Galahad," said she, "I will that ye arm you, and mount upon your horse, and follow me; for I will show you the highest adventure that ever knight saw." Then Galahad armed himself and commended himself to God, and bade the damsel go before, and he would follow where she led.

So she rode as fast as her palfrey might bear her, till she came to the sea; and there they found the ship where Sir Bohort and Sir Perceval were, who cried from the ship, "Sir Galahad, you are welcome; we have awaited you long." And when he heard them, he asked the damsel who they were. "Sir," said she, "leave your horse here, and I shall leave mine, and we will join ourselves to their company." So they entered into the ship, and the two knights received them both with great joy. For they knew the damsel, that she was Sir Perceval's sister. Then the wind arose and drove them through the sea all that day and the next, till the ship arrived between two rocks, passing great and marvellous; but there they might not land, for there was a whirlpool; but there was another ship, and upon it they might go without danger. "Go we thither," said the gentlewoman, "and there shall we see adventures, for such is our Lord's will." Then Sir Galahad blessed him, and entered therein, and then next the gentlewoman, and then Sir Bohort and Sir Perceval. And when they came on board, they found there the table of silver, and the Sangreal, which was covered with red samite. And they made great reverence thereto, and Sir Galahad prayed a long time to our Lord, that at what time he should ask to pass out of this world, he should do so; and a voice said to him, "Galahad, thou shalt have thy request; and when thou askest the death of thy body thou shalt have it, and then shalt thou find the life of thy soul."

And anon the wind drove them across the sea, till they came to the city of Sarras. Then they took out of the ship the table

of silver, and he took it to Sir Perceval and Sir Bohort to go
before, and Sir Galahad came behind, and right so they came to
the city, and at the gate of the city they saw an old man, crooked.
Then Sir Galahad called him and bade him help bear this heavy
thing. "Truly," said the old man, "it is ten years ago that I might
not go save with crutches." "Care thou not," said Sir Galahad,
"but arise up and show thy good will." And so he assayed and
found himself as whole as ever he was. Then ran he to the table
and took one part against Sir Galahad. And anon arose there a
great noise in the city, that a cripple was made whole by knights
marvellous that entered into the city. Then anon after, the three
knights went to the water, and brought up into the palace Sir
Perceval's sister. And when the king of the city, which was cleped
Estorause, saw the fellowship, he asked them of whence they
were, and what thing it was they had brought upon the table
of silver. And they told him the truth of the Sangreal, and the
power which God had set there. Then the king was a tyrant, and
was come of the line of Paynims, and took them and put them in
prison in a deep hole.

But as soon as they were there, our Lord sent them the Sangreal,
through whose grace they were always filled while that they were
in prison. So at the year's end it befell that this king Estorause
lay sick, and felt that he should die. Then he sent for the three
knights, and they came afore him, and he cried them mercy of
that he had done to them, and they forgave it him goodly, and
he died anon. When the king was dead. all the city was dismayed,
and wist not who might be their king. Right so they were in council, there came a voice among them, and bade them choose the
youngest knight of them three to be their king, "for he shall well
maintain you and all yours." So they made Sir Galahad king by
all the assent of the whole city, and else they would have slain
him. And when he was come to behold the land, he had made about
the table of silver a chest of gold and of precious stones that
covered the holy vessel, and every day early the three fellows
would come afore it and make their prayers. Now at the year's
end, and the next day after Sir Galahad had borne the crown of
gold, he rose up early, and his fellows, and came to the palace,
and saw before them the holy vessel, and a man kneeling on his
knees, in likeness of a bishop, that had about him a great fellowship of angels, as it had been Jesus Christ himself. And then he
arose and began a mass of Our Lady. And when he came to the
sacrament of the mass, and had done, anon he called Sir Galahad,
and said to him, "Come forth, the servant of Jesus Christ, and

thou shalt see that thou hast much desired to see." And then he began to tremble right hard, when the deadly flesh began to behold the spiritual things. Then he held up his hands toward heaven, and said, "Lord, I thank thee, for now I see that that hath been my desire many a day. Now, blessed Lord, would I not longer live; if it might please thee, Lord." And therewith the good man took our Lord's body betwixt his hands, and proffered it to Sir Galahad, and he received it right gladly and meekly. "Now, wottest thou what I am?" said the good man. "Nay," said Sir Galahad. "I am Joseph of Arimathea, which our Lord hath sent here to bear thee fellowship. And wottest thou wherefore that he hath sent me more than any other? For thou hast resembled me in two things, in that thou hast seen the marvels of the Sangreal, and in that thou hast been a clean maiden as I have been and am." And when he had said these words Sir Galahad went to Sir Perceval and kissed him, and commended him to God. And so he went to Sir Bohort and kissed him, and commended him to God, and said, "Fair lord, salute me to my lord Sir Launcelot, my father, and as soon as ye see him bid him remember of this unstable world." And therewith he kneeled down before the table and made his prayers, and then suddenly his soul departed to Jesus Christ, and a great multitude of angels bare his soul up to heaven, that the two fellows might well behold it. Also the two fellows saw come from heaven a hand, but they saw not the body; and then it came right to the vessel, and took it and the spear, and so bare it up to heaven. Sithen there was never man so hardy to say that he had seen the Sangreal.

When Sir Perceval and Sir Bohort saw Sir Galahad dead they made as much sorrow as ever did two men; and if they had not been good men they might lightly have fallen into despair. And the people of the country and of the city were right heavy. And then he was buried. And as soon as he was buried Sir Perceval yielded him to an hermitage out of the city, and took a religious clothing; and Sir Bohort was always with him, but never changed he his secular clothing, for that he purposed to go again into the realm of Loegria. Thus a year and two months lived Sir Perceval in the hermitage a full holy life, and then he passed out of this world. And Sir Bohort let bury him by his sister and by Sir Galahad.

And when Sir Bohort saw that he was in so far countries as in the parts of Babylon, he departed from Sarras, and armed him, and came to the sea, and entered into a ship, and so it befell him in good adventure he came into the realm of Loegria. And he rode so fast till he came to Camelot, where the king was. And then was there great joy made of him in the court, for they wend all he had been dead, forasmuch as he had been so long out of the country. And when they had eaten, the king made great clerks to come afore him, that they should chronicle of the high adventures of the good knights. Then Sir Bohort told him of the adventures of the Sangreal, such as had befallen him and his three fellows, that was Sir Launcelot, Sir Perceval, and Sir Galahad. Then Sir Launcelot told the adventures of the Sangreal that he had seen. All this was made in great books, and put in almeries in Salisbury. And anon Sir Bohort said to Sir Launcelot, "Galahad, your own son, saluted you by me, and after you King Arthur, and all the court, and so did Sir Perceval; for I buried them with mine own hands in the city of Sarras. Also, Sir Launcelot, Galahad prayeth you to remember of this uncertain world, as ye behight him when ye were together more than half a year." "This is true," said Sir Launcelot; "now I trust to God his prayer shall avail me." Then Sir Launcelot took Sir Bohort in his arms, and said, "Gentle cousin, ye are right welcome to me, and all that ever I may do for you and for yours, ye shall find my poor body ready at all times whiles the spirit is in it, and that I promise you faithfully, and never to fail. And wit ye well, gentle cousin Sir Bohort, that ye and I will never part in sunder whilst our lives may last." "Sir," said he, "I will as ye will."

Thus endeth the history of the Sangreal, which is a story chronicled as one of the truest and holiest that is in this world.

Tennyson has among his shorter poems one on Sir Galahad, which we add as being the conception of this purest of knights held by the poet who has loved best of all English poets the old stories of the Knights of the Round Table:—

SIR GALAHAD

"My good blade carves the casques of men,
  My tough lance thrusteth sure,
My strength is as the strength of ten,
  Because my heart is pure.
The shattering trumpet shrilleth high,
  The hard brands shiver on the steel,
The splintered spear-shafts crack and fly,
  The horse and rider reel:
They reel, they roll in clanging lists,
  And when the tide of combat stands,
Perfume and flowers fall in showers,
  That lightly rain from ladies' hands

"How sweet are looks that ladies bend
    On whom their favors fall!
For them I battle to the end,
    To save from shame and thrall:
But all my heart is drawn above,
    My knees are bound in crypt and shrine:
I never felt the kiss of love,
    Nor maiden's hand in mine.
More bounteous aspects on me beam,
    Me mightier transports move and thrill;
So keep I fair thro' faith and prayer,
    A virgin heart in work and will.

"When down the stormy crescent goes,
    A light before me swims,
Between dark stems the forest glows,
    I hear a noise of hymns:
Then by some secret shrine I ride;
    I hear a voice, but none are there;
The stalls are void, the doors are wide,
    The tapers burning fair.
Fair gleams the snowy altar-cloth,
    The silver vessels sparkle clean,
The shrill bell rings, the censer swings,
    And solemn chants resound between.

"Sometimes on lonely mountain meres
    I find a magic bark;
I leap on board; no helmsman steers:
    I float till all is dark.
A gentle sound, an awful light!
    Three angels bear the holy Grail:
With folded feet, in stoles of white,
    On sleeping wings they sail.
Ah, blessed vision! blood of God!
    My spirit beats her mortal bars,
As down dark tides the glory slides
    And star-like mingles with the stars.

"When on my goodly charger borne
    Thro' dreaming towns I go,
The cock crows ere the Christmas morn,
    The streets are dumb with snow.
The tempest crackles on the leads,
    And, ringing, springs from brand and mail;
But o'er the dark a glory spreads
    And gilds the driving hail.
I leave the plain, I climb the height;
    No branchy thicket shelter yields;
But blessed forms in whisking storms
    Fly o'er waste fens and windy fields.

"A maiden knight—to me is given
    Such hope, I know not fear;
I yearn to breathe the airs of heaven
    That often meet me here.
I muse on joy that will not cease,
    Pure spaces clothed in living beams,

Pure lilies of eternal peace,
  Whose odors haunt my dreams;
And stricken by an angel's hand,
  This mortal armour that I wear,
This weight and rise, this heart and eyes,
  Are touched, are turned to finest air.

"The clouds are broken in the sky,
  And thro' the mountain-walls
A rolling organ-harmony
  Swells up, and shakes and falls.
Then move the trees, the copses nod,
  Wings flutter, voices hover clear:
O just and faithful knight of God!
  Ride on! the prize is near!
So pass I hostel, hall, and grange;
  By hedge and ford, by park and pale,
All armed I ride, whate'er betide,
  Until I find the holy Grail."

CHAPTER XVII

SIR AGRIVAIN'S TREASON

So after the quest of the Sangreal was fulfilled, and all the knights that were left alive were come again to the Table Round, there was great joy in the court, and in especial King Arthur and Queen Guenever made great joy of the remnant that were come home, and passing glad were the king and the queen of Sir Launcelot and of Sir Bohort, for they had been passing long away in the quest of the Sangreal.

Then Sir Launcelot began to resort unto Queen Guenever again, and forgot the promise that he made in the quest; so that many in the court spoke of it, and in especial Sir Agrivain, Sir Gawain's brother, for he was ever open-mouthed. So it happened Sir Gawain and all his brothers were in King Arthur's chamber, and then Sir Agrivain said thus openly, "I marvel that we all are not ashamed to see and to know so noble a knight as King Arthur so to be shamed by the conduct of Sir Launcelot and the queen." Then spoke Sir Gawain, and said, "Brother, Sir Agrivain, I pray you and charge you move not such matters any more before me, for be ye assured I will not be of your counsel." "Neither will we," said Sir Gaheris and Sir Gareth. "Then will I," said Sir Modred. "I doubt you not," said Sir Gawain, "for to all mischief ever were ye prone; yet I would that ye left all this, for I know what will come of it." "Fall of it what fall may," said Sir Agrivain, "I will disclose it to the king." With that came to them King Arthur. "Now, brothers, hold your peace," said Sir Gawain.

"We will not," said Sir Agrivain. Then said Sir Gawain, "I will not hear your tales, nor be of your counsel." "No more will I," said Sir Gareth and Sir Gaheris, and therewith they departed, making great sorrow.

Then Sir Agrivain told the king all that was said in the court of the conduct of Sir Launcelot and the queen, and it grieved the king very much. But he would not believe it to be true without proof. So Sir Agrivain laid a plot to entrap Sir Launcelot and the queen, intending to take them together unawares. Sir Agrivain and Sir Modred led a party for this purpose, but Sir Launcelot escaped from them, having slain Sir Agrivain and wounded Sir Modred. Then Sir Launcelot hastened to his friends, and told them what had happened, and withdrew with them to the forest; but he left spies to bring him tidings of whatever might be done.

So Sir Launcelot escaped, but the queen remained in the king's power, and Arthur could no longer doubt of her guilt. And the law was such in those days that they who committed such crimes, of what estate or condition soever they were, must be burned to death, and so it was ordained for Queen Guenever. Then said King Arthur to Sir Gawain, "I pray you make you ready, in your best armor, with your brethren, Sir Gaheris and Sir Gareth, to bring my queen to the fire, there to receive her death." "Nay, my most noble lord," said Sir Gawain, "that will I never do; for know thou well, my heart will never serve me to see her die, and it shall never be said that I was of your counsel in her death." Then the king commanded Sir Gaheris and Sir Gareth to be there, and they said, "We will be there, as ye command us, sire, but in peaceable wise, and bear no armor upon us."

So the queen was led forth, and her ghostly father was brought to her to shrive her, and there was weeping and wailing of many lords and ladies. And one went and told Sir Launcelot that the queen was led forth to her death. Then Sir Launcelot and the knights that were with him fell upon the troop that guarded the queen, and dispersed them, and slew all who withstood them. And in the confusion Sir Gareth and Sir Gaheris were slain, for they were unarmed and defenceless. And Sir Launcelot carried away the queen to his castle of La Joyeuse Garde.

Then there came one to Sir Gawain and told him how that Sir Launcelot had slain the knights and carried away the queen. "O Lord, defend my brethren!" said Sir Gawain. "Truly," said the man, "Sir Gareth and Sir Gaheris are slain." "Alas!" said Sir Gawain, "now is my joy gone." And then he fell down and swooned, and long he lay there as he had been dead.

When he arose out of his swoon Sir Gawain ran to the king,

crying, "O King Arthur, mine uncle, my brothers are slain." Then the king wept and he both. "My king, my lord, and mine uncle," said Sir Gawain, "bear witness now that I make you a promise that I shall hold by my knighthood, that from this day I will never fail Sir Launcelot until the one of us have slain the other. I will seek Sir Launcelot throughout seven kings' realms, but I shall slay him or he shall slay me." "Ye shall not need to seek him," said the king, "for, as I hear, Sir Launcelot will abide me and you in the Joyeuse Garde; and much people draweth unto him, as I hear say." "That may I believe," said Gawain, "but, my lord, summon your friends, and I will summon mine." "It shall be done," said the king. So then the king sent letters and writs throughout all England, both in the length and breadth, to summon all his knights. And unto Arthur drew many knights, dukes, and earls, so that he had a great host. Thereof heard Sir Launcelot, and collected all whom he could; and many good knights held with him, both for his sake and for the queen's sake. But King Arthur's host was too great for Sir Launcelot to abide him in the field; and he was full loath to do battle against the king. So Sir Launcelot drew him to his strong castle, with all manner of provisions. Then came King Arthur and Sir Gawain, and laid siege all about La Joyeuse Garde, both the town and the castle; but in no wise would Sir Launcelot ride out of his castle neither suffer any of his knights to issue out, until many weeks were past.

Then it befell upon a day in harvest-time Sir Launcelot looked over the wall, and spake aloud to King Arthur and Sir Gawain, "My lords both, all is vain that ye do at this siege, for here ye shall win no worship, but only dishonor; for if I list to come out, and my good knights, I shall soon make an end of this war." "Come forth," said Arthur, "if thou darest, and I promise thee I shall meet thee in the midst of the field." "God forbid me," said Sir Launcelot, "that I should encounter with the most noble king that made me knight." "Fie upon thy fair language," said the king, "for know thou well that I am thy mortal foe, and ever will be to my dying day." And Sir Gawain said, "What cause hadst thou to slay my brother, Sir Gaheris, who bore no arms against thee, and Sir Gareth, whom thou madest knight, and who loved thee more than all my kin? Therefore know thou well I shall make war to thee all the while that I may live."

When Sir Bohort, Sir Hector de Marys, and Sir Lionel heard this outcry they called to them Sir Palamedes, and Sir Saffire his brother, and Sir Lawayn, with many more, and all went to Sir Launcelot. And they said, "My lord, Sir Launcelot, we pray you, if you will have our service, keep us no longer within these walls, for know well all your fair speech and forbearance will not avail you." "Alas!" said Sir Launcelot, "to ride forth and to do battle I am full loath." Then he spake again unto the king and Sir Gawain, and willed them to keep out of the battle; but they depised his words. So then Sir Launcelot's fellowship came out of the castle in full good array. And always Sir Launcelot charged all his knights, in any wise, to save King Arthur and Sir Gawain.

Then came forth Sir Gawain from the king's host, and offered combat, and Sir Lionel encountered with him, and there Sir Gawain smote Sir Lionel through the body, that he fell to the earth as if dead. Then there began a great conflict, and much people were slain; but ever Sir Launcelot did what he might to save the people on King Arthur's party, and ever King Arthur followed Sir Launcelot to slay him; but Sir Launcelot suffered him, and would not strike again. Then Sir Bohort encountered with King Arthur, and smote him down; and he alighted and drew his sword, and said to Sir Launcelot, "Shall I make an end of this war?" for he meant to have slain King Arthur. "Not so," said Sir Launcelot, "touch him no more, for I will never see that most noble king that made me knight either slain or shamed;" and therewith Sir Launcelot alighted off his horse and took up the king, and horsed him again, and said thus: "My lord Arthur, for God's love, cease this strife." And King Arthur looked upon Sir Launcelot, and his tears burst from his eyes, thinking on the great courtesy that was in Sir Launcelot more than in any other man; and therewith the king rode his way. Then anon both parties withdrew to repose them, and buried the dead.

But the war continued, and it was noised abroad through all Christendom, and at last it was told afore the pope; and he, considering the great goodness of King Arthur, and of Sir Launcelot, called unto him a noble clerk, which was the Bishop of Rochester, who was then in his dominions, and sent him to King Arthur, charging him that he take his queen, dame Guenever, unto him again, and make peace with Sir Launcelot.

So, by means of this bishop, peace was made for the space of one year; and King Arthur received back the queen, and Sir Launcelot departed from the kingdom with all his knights, and went to his own country. So they shipped at Cardiff, and sailed unto Benwick, which some men call Bayonne. And all the people of those lands came to Sir Launcelot, and received him home right joyfully. And Sir Launcelot stablished and garnished all his towns and castles, and he greatly advanced all his noble knights, Sir Lionel and Sir Bohort, and Sir Hector de Marys, Sir Blamor, Sir Lawayne, and many others, and made them lords of lands and castles; till he left himself no more than any one of them.

But when the year was passed, King Arthur and Sir Gawain came with a great host, and landed upon Sir Launcelot's lands, and burnt and wasted all that they might overrun. Then spake Sir Bohort and said, "My lord, Sir Launcelot, give us leave to meet them in the field, and we shall make them rue the time that ever they came to this country." Then said Sir Launcelot, "I am full loath to ride out with my knights for shedding of Christian blood; so we will yet awhile keep our walls, and I will send a messenger unto my lord Arthur, to propose a treaty; for better is peace than always war." So Sir Launcelot sent forth a damsel, and a dwarf with her, requiring King Arthur to leave his warring upon his lands; and so she started on a palfrey, and the dwarf ran by her side. And when she came to the pavilion of King Arthur, she alighted, and there met her a gentle knight, Sir Lucan the butler, and said, "Fair damsel, come ye from Sir Launcelot du Lac?" "Yea, sir," she said, "I come hither to speak with the king." "Alas!" said Sir Lucan, "my lord Arthur would be reconciled to Sir Launcelot, but Sir Gawain will not suffer him." And with this Sir Lucan led the damsel to the king, where he sat with Sir Gawain, to hear what she would say. So when she had told her tale, the tears ran out of the king's eyes; and all the lords were forward to advise the king to be accorded with Sir Launcelot, save only Sir Gawain; and he said, "My lord, mine uncle, what will ye do? Will you now turn back, now you are so far advanced upon your journey? If ye do, all the world will speak shame of you." "Nay," said King Arthur, "I will do as ye advise me; but do thou give the damsel her answer, for I may not speak to her for pity."

Then said Sir Gawain, "Damsel, say ye to Sir Launcelot, that it is waste labor to sue to mine uncle for peace, and say that I, Sir Gawain, send him word that I promise him, by the faith I owe unto God and to knighthood, I shall never leave him till he have slain me or I him." So the damsel returned; and when Sir Launcelot had heard this answer, the tears ran down his cheeks.

Then it befell on a day Sir Gawain came before the gates, armed at all points, and cried with a loud voice, "Where art thou now, thou false traitor, Sir Launcelot? Why hidest thou thyself within holes and walls like a coward? Look out now, thou traitor knight, and I will avenge upon thy body the death of my three brethren." All this language heard Sir Launcelot, and the knights which were about him; and they said to him, "Sir Launcelot, now must ye defend you like a knight, or else be shamed for ever, for you have slept overlong and suffered overmuch." Then Sir Launcelot spoke on high unto King Arthur, and said, "My lord Arthur, now I have forborne long, and suffered you and Sir Gawain to do what ye would, and now must I needs defend myself, inasmuch as Sir Gawain hath appealed me of treason." Then Sir Launcelot armed him and mounted upon his horse, and the noble knights came out of the city, and the host without stood all apart; and so the covenant was made that no man should come near the two knights, nor deal with them, till one were dead or yielded.

Then Sir Gawain and Sir Launcelot departed a great way in sunder, and then they came together with all their horses' might as they might run, and either smote the other in the midst of their shields, but the knights were so strong, and their spears so big, that their horses might not endure their buffets, and so the horses fell to the earth. And then they avoided their horses, and dressed their shields afore them. Then they stood together, and gave many sad strokes on divers places of their bodies, that the blood burst out on many sides and places. Then had Sir Gawain such a grace and gift that an holy man had given to him, that every day in the year, from morning till high noon, his might increased those three hours, as much as thrice his strength, and that caused Sir Gawain to win great honor. And for his sake King Arthur made an ordinance that all manner of battles for any quarrels that should be done before King Arthur should begin at Underne,[1] and all was done for Sir Gawain's love, that by likelihood if that Sir Gawain were on the one part he should have the better in battle, whilst his strength endured three hours, but there were few knights that time living that knew this advantage that Sir Gawain had, but King Arthur only. Thus Sir Launcelot fought with Sir Gawain, and when Sir Launcelot felt his might evermore increase, Sir Launcelot wondered and dread him sore to be ashamed. For Sir Launcelot thought when he felt Sir Gawain double his strength, that he had been a fiend, and no earthly man; wherefore Sir Launcelot traced and traversed, and covered himself with his shield, and kept his might and his braid during three hours; and that while Sir Gawain gave him many sad brunts and many sad strokes, that all the knights that beheld Sir Launcelot marvelled how he might endure him, but full little understood they that travail that Sir Launcelot had for to endure him. And then when it was past noon Sir Gawain had no more but his own might. Then Sir Launcelot felt him so come down; then he stretched him up, and stood near Sir Gawain, and said thus: "My lord Sir Gawain, now I fear ye have done; now my lord Sir Gawain, I must do my part, for many great and grievous strokes I have endured you this day with great pain." Then Sir Launcelot

[1] Underne. The third hour in the day, nine o'clock.

doubled his strokes, and gave Sir Gawain such a buffet on the helmet that he fell down on his side, and Sir Launcelot withdrew from him. "Why turnest thou thee?" said Sir Gawain; "now turn again, false traitor knight, and slay me; for an thou leave me thus, when I am whole, I shall do battle with thee again." "I shall endure you, sir, by God's grace, but wit thou well, Sir Gawain, I will never smite a felled knight." And so Sir Launcelot went into the city, and Sir Gawain was borne into one of King Arthur's pavilions, and leeches were brought to him, and he was searched and salved with soft ointments. And then Sir Launcelot said, "Now have good day, my lord the king, for, wit you well, ye win no worship at these walls; and if I would my knights out bring, there should many a man die. Therefore, my lord Arthur, remember you of old kindness, and however I fare, Jesus be your guide in all places."

Thus the siege endured, and Sir Gawain lay helpless near a month; and when he was near recovered, came tidings unto King Arthur that made him return with all his host to England.

CHAPTER XVIII

MORTE D'ARTHUR

"And now the whole ROUND TABLE is dissolved,
Which was an image of the mighty world,
And I, the last, go forth companionless;
And the days darken round me, and the years
Among new men, strange faces, other minds."—TENNYSON.

SIR MODRED was left ruler of all England, and he caused letters to be written, as if from beyond sea, that King Arthur was slain in battle. So he called a Parliament, and made himself be crowned king; and he took the queen, Guenever, and said plainly that he would wed her, but she escaped from him, and took refuge in the Tower of London. And Sir Modred went and laid siege about the Tower of London, and made great assaults thereat, but all might not avail him. Then came word to Sir Modred that King Arthur had raised the siege of Sir Launcelot, and was coming home. Then Sir Modred summoned all the barony of the land; and much people drew unto Sir Modred, and said they would abide with him for better and for worse; and he drew a great host to Dover, for there he heard say that King Arthur would arrive.

And as Sir Modred was at Dover with his host, came King Arthur, with a great number of ships and galleys, and there was Sir Modred awaiting upon the landing. Then was there launching of great boats and small, full of noble men of arms, and there was much slaughter of gentle knights on both parts. But King Arthur was so courageous, there might no manner of knights prevent him to land, and his knights fiercely followed him; and so they landed, and put Sir Modred aback so that he fled, and all his people. And when the battle was done, King Arthur commanded to bury his people that were dead. And then was noble Sir Gawain found, in a great boat, lying more than half dead. And King Arthur went to him, and made sorrow out of measure. "Mine uncle," said Sir Gawain, "know thou well my death-day is come, and all is through mine own hastiness and wilfulness, for I am smitten upon the old wound which Sir Launcelot gave me, of the which I feel I must die. And had Sir Launcelot been with you as of old, this war had never begun, and of all this I am the cause." Then Sir Gawain prayed the king to send for Sir Launcelot, and to cherish him above all other knights. And so, at the hour of noon, Sir Gawain yielded up his spirit, and then the king bade inter him in a chapel within Dover Castle; and there all men may see the skull of him, and the same wound is seen that Sir Launcelot gave him in battle.

Then was it told the king that Sir Modred had pitched his camp upon Barrendown; and the king rode thither, and there was a great battle betwixt them, and King Arthur's party stood best, and Sir Modred and his party fled unto Canterbury.

And there was a day assigned betwixt King Arthur and Sir Modred that they should meet upon a down beside Salisbury, and not far from the seaside, to do battle yet again. And at night, as the king slept, he dreamed a wonderful dream. It seemed him verily that there came Sir Gawain unto him, with a number of fair ladies with him. And when King Arthur saw him, he said, "Welcome, my sister's son; I weened thou hadst been dead; and now I see thee alive, great is my joy. But, O fair nephew, what be these ladies that hither be come with you?" "Sir," said Sir Gawain, "all these be ladies for whom I have fought when I was a living man; and because I did battle for them in righteous quarrel, they have given me grace to bring me hither unto you, to warn you of your death, if ye fight to-morrow with Sir Modred. Therefore take ye treaty, and proffer you largely for a month's delay; for within a month shall come Sir Launcelot and all his noble knights, and rescue you worshipfully, and slay Sir Modred and all that hold with him." And then Sir Gawain and all the ladies vanished. And anon the king called to fetch his noble lords and wise bishops unto him. And when they were come, the king told them his vision, and what Sir Gawain had told him. Then the king sent Sir Lucan the butler, and Sir Bedivere, with two bishops, and charged them in any wise to take a treaty for a month and a day with Sir Modred. So they departed, and came to Sir Modred; and so, at the last, Sir Modred was agreed to have

Cornwall and Kent, during Arthur's life, and all England after his death.

Then was it agreed that King Arthur and Sir Modred should meet betwixt both their hosts, and each of them should bring fourteen persons, and then and there they should sign the treaty. And when King Arthur and his knights were prepared to go forth, he warned all his host, "If so be ye see any sword drawn, look ye come on fiercely, and slay whomsoever withstandeth, for I in no wise trust that traitor, Sir Modred." In likewise Sir Modred warned his host. So they met, and were agreed and accorded thoroughly. And wine was brought, and they drank. Right then came an adder out of a little heath-bush, and stung a knight on the foot. And when the knight felt him sting, he looked down and saw the adder, and then he drew his sword to slay the adder, and thought of no other harm. And when the host on both sides saw that sword drawn, they blew trumpets and horns, and shouted greatly. And King Arthur took his horse, and rode to his party, saying, "Alas, this unhappy day!" And Sir Modred did in like wise. And never was there a more doleful battle in Christian land. And ever King Arthur rode throughout the battle, and did full nobly, as a worthy king should, and Sir Modred that day did his devoir, and put himself in great peril. And thus they fought all the long day, till the most of all the noble knights lay dead upon the ground. Then the king looked about him, and saw of all his host were left alive but two knights, Sir Lucan the butler, and Sir Bedivere his brother, and they were full sore wounded.

Then King Arthur saw where Sir Modred leaned upon his sword among a great heap of dead men. "Now give me my spear," said Arthur unto Sir Lucan, "for yonder I espy the traitor that hath wrought all this woe." "Sir, let him be," said Sir Lucan; "for if ye pass this unhappy day ye shall be right well revenged upon him. Remember what the sprite of Sir Gawain told you, and leave off now, for ye have won the field; and if ye leave off now this evil day of destiny is past." "Betide me life, betide me death," said King Arthur, "he shall not now escape my hands." Then the king took his spear in both hands, and ran toward Sir Modred, crying, "Traitor, now is thy death-day come." And there King Arthur smote Sir Modred under the shield, with a thrust of his spear through the body. And when Sir Modred felt that he had his death-wound, with the might that he had he smote King Arthur, with his sword holden in both his hands, on the side of the head, that the sword pierced the helmet and the brain-pan; and then Sir Modred fell stark dead upon the earth. And the noble Arthur fell in a swoon to the earth. And Sir Lucan the butler and Sir Bedivere raised him up, and gently led him betwixt them both to a little chapel not far from the seaside.

And when the king was there he thought him well eased. Then heard they people cry in the field. And Sir Lucan went to see what that cry betokened; and he saw by the moonlight that pillers [1] and robbers were come to rob the dead. And he returned, and said to the king, "By my rede, it is best that we bring you to some town." "I would it were so," said the king. And when the king tried to go he fainted. Then Sir Lucan took up the king on the one part, and Sir Bedivere on the other part; and in the lifting Sir Lucan fell in a swoon to the earth, for he was grievously wounded. And then the noble knight's heart burst. And when the king awoke he beheld Sir Lucan, how he lay foaming at the mouth, and speechless. "Alas!" said the king, "this is to me a full heavy sight, to see this noble duke so die for my sake; for he would have holpen me that had more need of help than I, and he would not complain, his heart was so set to help me." Then Sir Bedivere wept for his brother. "Leave this mourning and weeping," said the king, "for wit thou well, if I might live myself, the death of Sir Lucan would grieve me evermore; but my time hieth fast. Therefore," said Arthur unto Sir Bedivere, "take thou Excalibar, my good sword, and go with it to yonder waterside; and when thou comest there I charge thee throw my sword in that water, and come again and tell me what thou there seest." "My lord," said Sir Bedivere, "your commandment shall be done." So Sir Bedivere departed, and by the way he beheld that noble sword, that the pommel and the haft were all of precious stones; and then he said to himself, "If I throw this rich sword into the water no good shall come thereof, but only harm and loss." And then Sir Bedivere hid Excalibar under a tree. And so, as soon as he might, he came again unto the king. "What sawest thou there?" said the king. "Sir," he said, "I saw nothing." "Alas! thou hast deceived me," said the king. "Go thou lightly again, and as thou love me, spare not to throw it in." Then Sir Bedivere went again, and took the sword in his hand to throw it; but again it beseemed him but sin and shame to throw away that noble sword, and he hid it away again, and returned, and told the king he had done his commandment. "What sawest thou there?" said the king. "Sir," he said, "I saw nothing but waters deep and waves wan." "Ah, traitor untrue!" said King Arthur, "now hast thou betrayed me twice. And yet thou art named a noble knight, and hast been lief and dear to me. But now go again, and do as I bid thee, for thy long tarrying putteth me in jeopardy of my life." Then Sir Bedivere went to the sword, and lightly took it up, and went to the waterside, and he bound the girdle about the hilt, and then he threw the sword as far into the water as he might. And there came an arm and

---

[1] Plunderers: the word is not now used.

a hand out of the water and met it, and caught it, and shook it thrice and brandished it, and then vanished away the hand with the sword in the water.

Then Sir Bedivere came again to the king, and told him what he saw. "Help me hence," said the king, "for I fear I have tarried too long." Then Sir Bedivere took the king on his back, and so went with him to that water-side; and when they came there, even fast by the bank there rode a little barge with many fair ladies in it, and among them was a queen; and all had black hoods, and they wept and shrieked when they saw King Arthur.

"Now put me in the barge," said the king. And there received him three queens with great mourning, and in one of their laps King Arthur laid his head. And the queen said, "Ah, dear brother, why have ye tarried so long? Alas! this wound on your head hath caught overmuch cold." And then they rowed from the land, and Sir Bedivere beheld them go from him. Then he cried: "Ah, my lord Arthur, will ye leave me here alone among mine enemies?" "Comfort thyself," said the king, "for in me is no further help; for I will to the Isle of Avalon, to heal me of my grievous wound." And as soon as Sir Bedivere had lost sight of the barge he wept and wailed; then he took the forest, and went all that night, and in the morning he was ware of a chapel and a hermitage.

Then went Sir Bedivere thither; and when he came into the chapel he saw where lay an hermit on the ground, near a tomb that was newly graven. "Sir," said Sir Bedivere, "what man is there buried that ye pray so near unto?" "Fair son," said the hermit, "I know not verily. But this night there came a number of ladies, and brought hither one dead, and prayed me to bury him." "Alas!" said Sir Bedivere, "that was my lord, King Arthur." Then Sir Bedivere swooned; and when he awoke he prayed the hermit he might abide with him, to live with fasting and prayers. "Ye are welcome," said the hermit. So there bode Sir Bedivere with the hermit; and he put on poor clothes, and served the hermit full lowly in fasting and in prayers.

Thus of Arthur I find never more written in books that he authorized, nor more of the very certainty of his death; but thus was he led away in a ship, wherein were three queens; the one was King Arthur's sister, Queen Morgane le Fay; the other was Viviane, the Lady of the Lake; and the third was the queen of North Galis. And this tale Sir Bedivere, knight of the Table Round, made to be written.

Yet some men say that King Arthur is not dead, but hid away into another place, and men say that he shall come again and reign over England. But many say that there is written on his tomb this verse:—

"Hic jacet Arthurus, Rex quondam, Rexque futurus."
Here Arthur lies, King once and King to be.

And when Queen Guenever understood that King Arthur was slain, and all the noble knights with him, she stole away, and five ladies with her; and so she went to Almesbury, and made herself a nun, and ware white clothes and black, and took great penance as ever did sinful lady, and lived in fasting, prayers, and alms-deeds. And there she was abbess and ruler of the nuns. Now turn we from her, and speak of Sir Launcelot of the Lake.

When Sir Launcelot heard in his country that Sir Modred was crowned king of England and made war against his own uncle, King Arthur, then was Sir Launcelot wroth out of measure, and said to his kinsmen: "Alas, that double traitor, Sir Modred! now it repenteth me that ever he escaped out of my hands." Then Sir Launcelot and his fellows made ready in all haste, with ships and galleys, to pass into England; and so he passed over till he came to Dover, and there he landed with a great army. Then Sir Launcelot was told that King Arthur was slain. "Alas!" said Sir Launcelot, "this is the heaviest tidings that ever came to me." Then he called the kings, dukes, barons, and knights, and said thus: "My fair lords, I thank you all for coming into this country with me, but we came too late, and that shall repent me while I live. But since it is so," said Sir Launcelot, "I will myself ride and seek my lady, Queen Guenever, for I have heard say she hath fled into the west; therefore ye shall abide me here fifteen days, and if I come not within that time, then take your ships and your host and depart into your country."

So Sir Launcelot departed and rode westerly, and there he sought many days; and at last he came to a nunnery, and was seen of Queen Guenever as he walked in the cloister; and when she saw him, she swooned away. And when she might speak, she bade him to be called to her. And when Sir Launcelot was brought to her, she said: "Sir Launcelot, I require thee and beseech thee, for all the love that ever was betwixt us, that thou never see me more, but return to thy kingdom and take thee a wife, and live with her with joy and bliss; and pray for me to my Lord, that I may get my soul's health." "Nay, madam," said Sir Launcelot, "wit you well that I shall never do; but the same destiny that ye have taken you to will I take me unto, for to please and serve God." And so they parted, with tears and much lamentation; and the ladies bare the queen to her chamber, and Sir Launcelot took his horse and rode away, weeping.

And at last Sir Launcelot was ware of a hermitage and a chapel, and then he heard a little bell ring to mass; and thither he rode and alighted, and tied his horse to the gate, and heard mass. And he that sang the mass was the hermit with whom Sir Bedivere had taken up his abode; and Sir Bedivere knew Sir Launcelot, and they spake together after mass. But when Sir Bedivere had told his tale, Sir Launcelot's heart almost burst for sorrow. Then he kneeled down, and prayed the hermit to shrive him, and besought that he might be his brother. Then the hermit said, "I will gladly"; and then he put a habit upon Sir Launcelot, and there he served God day and night, with prayers and fastings.

And the great host abode at Dover till the end of the fifteen days set by Sir Launcelot, and then Sir Bohort made them to go home again to their own country; and Sir Bohort, Sir Hector de Marys, Sir Blanor, and many others, took on them to ride through all England to seek Sir Launcelot. So Sir Bohort by fortune rode until he came to the same chapel where Sir Launcelot was; and when he saw Sir Launcelot in that manner of clothing, he prayed the hermit that he might be in that same. And so there was a habit put upon him, and there he lived in prayers and fasting. And within half a year came others of the knights, their fellows, and took such a habit as Sir Launcelot and Sir Bohort had. Thus they endured in great penance six years.

And upon a night there came a vision to Sir Launcelot, and charged him to haste him toward Almesbury, and "by the time thou come there, thou shalt find Queen Guenever dead." Then Sir Launcelot rose up early, and told the hermit thereof. Then said the hermit, "It were well that ye disobey not this vision." And Sir Launcelot took his seven companions with him, and on foot they went from Glastonbury to Almesbury, which is more than thirty miles. And when they were come to Almesbury, they found that Queen Guenever died but half an hour before. Then Sir Launcelot saw her visage, but he wept not greatly, but sighed. And so he did all the observance of the service himself, both the "dirige" at night, and at morn he sang mass. And there was prepared an horse-bier, and Sir Launcelot and his fellows followed the bier on foot from Almesbury until they came to Glastonbury; and she was wrapped in cered clothes, and laid in a coffin of marble. And when she was put in the earth, Sir Launcelot swooned, and lay long as one dead.

And Sir Launcelot never after ate but little meat, nor drank; but continually mourned. And within six weeks Sir Launcelot fell sick; and he sent for the hermit and all his true fellows, and said, "Sir hermit, I pray you give me all my rights that a Christian man ought to have." "It shall not need," said the hermit and all his fellows; "it is but heaviness of your blood, and to-morrow morn you shall be well." "My fair lords," said Sir Launcelot, "my careful body will into the earth; I have warning more than now I will say; therefore give me my rights." So when he was houseled and aneled, and had all that a Christian man ought to have, he prayed the hermit thal his fellows might bear his body to Joyous Garde. (Some men say it was Alnwick, and some say it was Bamborough.) "It repenteth me sore," said Sir Launcelot, "but I made a vow aforetime that in Joyous Garde I would be buried." Then there was weeping and wringing of hands among his fellows. And that night Sir Launcelot died; and when Sir Bohort and his fellows came to his bedside the next morning, they found him stark dead; and he lay as if he had smiled, and the sweetest savor all about him that ever they knew.

And they put Sir Launcelot into the same horse-bier that Queen Guenever was laid in, and the hermit and they all together went with the body till they came to Joyous Garde. And there they laid his corpse in the body of the quire, and sang and read many psalms and prayers over him. And ever his visage was laid open and naked, that all folks might behold him. And right thus, as they were at their service, there came Sir Hector de Marys, that had seven years sought Sir Launcelot his brother, through all England, Scotland and Wales. And when Sir Hector heard such sounds in the chapel of Joyous Garde, he alighted and came into the quire. And all they knew Sir Hector. Then went Sir Bohort, and told him how there lay Sir Launcelot his brother, dead. Then Sir Hector threw his shield, his sword, and helm from him. And when he beheld Sir Launcelot's visage, it were hard for any tongue to tell the doleful complaints he made for his brother. "Ah, Sir Launcelot!" he said, "there thou liest. And now I dare to say thou wert never matched of none earthly knight's hand. And thou wert the courteousest knight that ever bare shield; and thou wert the truest friend to thy lover that ever bestrode horse; and thou were the truest lover, of a sinful man, that ever loved woman; and thou wert the kindest man that ever struck with sword. And thou wert the goodliest person that ever came among press of knights. And thou wert the meekest man, and the gentlest, that ever ate in hall among ladies. And thou wert the sternest knight to thy mortal foe that ever put spear in the rest." Then there was weeping and dolor out of measure. Thus they kept Sir Launcelot's corpse fifteen days, and then they buried it with great devotion.

Then they went back with the hermit to his hermitage. And Sir Bedivere was there ever still hermit to his life's end. And Sir Bohort, Sir Hector, Sir Blanor and Sir Bleoberis went into the Holy Land. And these four knights did many battles upon the miscreants, the Turks; and there they died upon a Good Friday, as it pleased God.

Thus endeth this noble and joyous book, entitled La Morte d'Arthur; notwithstanding it treateth of the birth, life and acts of the said King Arthur, and of his noble Knights of the Round Table, their marvellous enquests and adventures, the achieving of the Sangreal, and in the end, la Morte d'Arthur, with the dolorous death and departing out of this world of them all. Which book was reduced into English by Sir Thomas Mallory, Knight, and divided into twenty-one books, chaptered and imprinted and finished in the Abbey Westmestre, the last day of July, the year of our Lord MCCCCLXXXV.

Caxton me fieri fecit.

PART II

THE MABINOGEON

THE MABINOGEON

CHAPTER XIX

THE BRITONS

THE earliest inhabitants of Britain are supposed to have been a branch of that great family known in history by the designation of Celts. Cambria, which is a frequent name for Wales, is thought to be derived from Cymri, the name which the Welsh traditions apply to an immigrant people who entered the island from the adjacent continent. This name is thought to be identical with those of Cimmerians and Cimbri, under which the Greek and Roman historians describe a barbarous people, who spread themselves from the north of the Euxine over the whole of Northwestern Europe.

The origin of the names *Wales* and *Welsh* has been much canvassed. Some writers make them a derivation from Gael or Gaul, which names are said to signify "woodlanders"; others observe that *Walsh*, in the Northern languages, signifies *a stranger*, and that the aboriginal Britons were so called by those who at a later era invaded the island and possessed the greater part of it, the Saxons and Angles.

The Romans held Britain from the invasion of Julius Cæsar till their voluntary withdrawal from the island, A.D. 420,—that is, about five hundred years. In that time there must have been a wide diffusion of their arts and institutions among the natives. The remains of roads, cities, and fortifications show that they did much to develop and improve the country, while those of their villas and castles prove that many of the settlers possessed wealth and taste for the ornamental arts. Yet the Roman sway was sustained chiefly by force, and never extended over the entire island. The northern portion, now Scotland, remained independent, and the western portion, constituting Wales and Cornwall, was only nominally subjected.

Neither did the later invading hordes succeed in subduing the remoter sections of the island. For ages after the arrival of the Saxons under Hengist and Horsa, A.D. 449, the whole western coast of Britain was possessed by the aboriginal inhabitants, engaged in constant warfare with the invaders.

It has, therefore, been a favorite boast of the people of Wales and Cornwall, that the original British stock flourishes in its unmixed purity only among them. We see this notion flashing out in poetry occasionally, as when Gray, in "The Bard," prophetically describing Queen Elizabeth, who was of the Tudor, a Welsh race, says:

> "Her eye proclaims her of the Briton line";

and, contrasting the princes of the Tudor with those of the Norman race, he exclaims:

> "All hail, ye genuine kings, Britannia's issue, hail!"

THE WELSH LANGUAGE AND LITERATURE

The Welsh language is one of the oldest in Europe. It possesses poems the origin of which is referred with probability to the sixth century. The language of some of these is so antiquated, that the best scholars differ about the interpretation of many passages; but, generally speaking, the body of poetry which the Welsh possess, from the year 1000 downwards, is intelligible to those who are acquainted with the modern language.

Till within the last half-century these compositions remained buried in the libraries of colleges or of individuals, and so difficult of access that no successful attempt was made to give them to the world. This reproach was removed, after ineffectual appeals to the patriotism of the gentry of Wales, by Owen Jones, a furrier of London, who at his own expense collected and published the chief productions of Welsh literature, under the title of the Myvyrian Archæology of Wales. In this task he was assisted by Dr. Owen and other Welsh scholars.

After the cessation of Jones's exertions, the old apathy returned, and continued till within a few years. Dr. Owen exerted himself to obtain support for the publication of the Mabinogeon, or Prose Tales of the Welsh, but died without accomplishing his purpose, which has since been carried into execution by Lady Charlotte Guest. The legends which fill the remainder of this volume are taken from this work, of which we have already spoken more fully in the introductory chapter to the First Part.

THE WELSH BARDS

The authors to whom the oldest Welsh poems are attributed are Aneurin, who is supposed to have lived A.D. 500 and 550, and Taliesin, Llywarch Hen (Llywarch the Aged), and Myrddin or Merlin, who were a few years later. The authenticity of the poems which bear their names has been assailed, and it is still an open question how many and which of them are authentic, though it is hardly to be doubted that some are so. The poem of Aneurin, entitled the "Gododin," bears very strong marks of authenticity. Aneurin was one of the Northern Britons of Strath-Clyde, who have left to that part of the district they inhabited the name of Cumberland, or Land of the Cymri. In this poem he laments the defeat of his countrymen by the Saxons at the battle of Cattraeth, in consequence of having partaken too freely of the mead before joining in combat. The bard himself and two of his fellow-warriors were all who escaped from the field. A portion of this poem has been translated by Gray, of which the following is an extract:—

> "To Cattraeth's vale, in glittering row,
> Twice two hundred warriors go;
> Every warrior's manly neck
> Chains of regal honor deck,
> Wreathed in many a golden link;
> From the golden cup they drink
> Nectar that the bees produce,
> Or the grape's exalted juice.
> Flushed with mirth and hope they burn,
> But none to Cattraeth's vale return,
> Save Aëron brave, and Conan strong,
> Bursting through the bloody throng,
> And I, the meanest of them all,
> That live to weep, and sing their fall."

The works of Taliesin are of much more questionable authenticity. There is a story of the adventures of Taliesin so strongly marked with mythical traits as to cast suspicion on the writings attributed to him. This story will be found in the subsequent pages.

THE TRIADS

The Triads are a peculiar species of poetical composition, of which the Welsh bards have left numerous examples. They are enumerations of a triad of persons, or events, or observations, strung together in one short sentence. This form of composition, originally invented, in all likelihood, to assist the memory, has been raised by the Welsh to a degree of elegance of which it hardly at first sight appears susceptible. The Triads are of all ages, some of them probably as old as anything in the language. Short as they are individually, the collection in the Myvyrian Archæology occupies more than one hundred and seventy pages of double columns. We will give some specimens, beginning with personal triads, and giving the first place to one of King Arthur's own composition:—

"I have three heroes in battle;
Mael the tall, and Llyr, with his army,
And Caradoc, the pillar of Wales."

"The three principal bards of the island of Britain:—
Merlin Ambrose
Merlin the son of Morfyn, called also Merlin the Wild,
And Taliesin, the chief of the bards."

"The three golden-tongued knights of the Court of Arthur:—
Gawain, son of Gwyar,
Drydvas, son of Tryphin,
And Eliwlod, son of Madag, ap Uther."

"The three honorable feasts of the island of Britain:—
The feast of Caswallaun, after repelling Julius Cæsar from this isle,
The feast of Aurelius Ambrosius, after he had conquered the Saxons;
And the feast of King Arthur, at Caerleon upon Usk."

"Guenever, the daughter of Laodegan the giant,
Bad when little, worse when great."

Next follow some moral triads:—

"Hast thou heard what Dremhidydd sung,
An ancient watchman on the castle walls?
A refusal is better than a promise unperformed."

"Hast thou heard what Llenleawg sung,
The noble chief wearing the golden torques?
The grave is better than a life of want."

"Hast thou heard what Garselit sung,
The Irishman whom it is safe to follow?
Sin is bad, if long pursued."

"Hast thou heard what Avaon sung,
The son of Taliesin, of the recording verse?
The cheek will not conceal the anguish of the heart."

"Didst thou hear what Llywarch sung,
The intrepid and brave old man?
Greet kindly, though there be no acquaintance."

CHAPTER XX

THE LADY OF THE FOUNTAIN

KYNON'S ADVENTURE

KING ARTHUR was at Caerleon upon Usk; and one day he sat in his chamber, and with him were Owain the son of Urien, and Kynon the son of Clydno, and Kay the son of Kyner, and Guenever and her handmaidens at needlework by the window. In the centre of the chamber King Arthur sat, upon a seat of green rushes [1] over which was spread a covering of flame-colored satin, and a cushion of red satin was under his elbow.

Then Arthur spoke. "If I thought you would not disparage me," said he, "I would sleep while I wait for my repast; and you can entertain one another with relating tales, and can obtain a flagon of mead and some meat from Kay." And the king went to sleep. And Kynon the son of Clydno asked Kay for that which Arthur had promised them. "I too will have the good tale which he promised me," said Kay. "Nay," answered Kynon; "fairer will it be for thee to fulfil Arthur's behest in the first place, and then we will tell thee the best tale that we know." So Kay went to the kitchen and to the mead-cellar, and returned, bearing a flagon of mead, and a golden goblet, and a handful of skewers, upon which were broiled collops of meat. Then they ate the collops, and began to drink the mead. "Now," said Kay, "it is time for you to give me my story." "Kynon," said Owain, "do thou pay to Kay the tale that is his due." "I will do so," answered Kynon.

"I was the only son of my mother and father, and I was exceedingly aspiring, and my daring was very great. I thought there was no enterprise in the world too mighty for me; and after I had achieved all the adventures that were in my own country, I equipped myself, and set forth to journey through deserts and distant regions. And at length it chanced that I came to the fairest valley in the world, wherein were trees all of equal growth; and a river ran through the valley, and a path was by the side of the river. And I followed the path until midday, and continued my journey along the remainder of the valley until the evening; and at the extremity of a plain I came to a large and lustrous castle, at the foot of which was a torrent. And I approached the castle, and there I beheld two youths with yellow curling hair, each with a frontlet of gold upon his head, and clad in a garment of yellow satin; and they had gold clasps upon their insteps. In the hand of each of them was an ivory bow, strung with the sinews of the stag, and their arrows and their shafts were of the bone of the whale, and were winged with peacocks' feathers. The shafts also had golden heads. And they had daggers with blades of gold, and with hilts of the bone of the whale. And they were shooting at a mark.

---

[1] The use of green rushes in apartments was by no means peculiar to the court of Caerleon upon Usk. Our ancestors had a great predilection for them, and they seem to have constituted an essential article, not only of comfort but of luxury. The custom of strewing the floor with rushes, it is well known, existed in England during the Middle Ages, and also in France.

"And a little way from them I saw a man in the prime of life, with his beard newly shorn, clad in a robe and mantle of yellow satin, and round the top of his mantle was a band of gold lace. On his feet were shoes of variegated leather,[1] fastened by two bosses of gold. When I saw him I went towards him and saluted him; and such was his courtesy, that he no sooner received my greeting than he returned it. And he went with me towards the castle. Now there were no dwellers in the castle, except those who were in one hall. And there I saw four and twenty damsels, embroidering satin at a window. And this I tell thee, Kay, that the least fair of them was fairer than the fairest maid thou didst ever behold in the island of Britain; and the least lovely of them was more lovely than Guenever, the wife of Arthur, when she appeared loveliest, at the feast of Easter. They rose up at my coming, and six of them took my horse, and divested me of my armor, and six others took my arms, and washed them in a vessel till they were perfectly bright. And the third six spread cloths upon the tables, and prepared meat. And the fourth six took off my soiled garments, and placed others upon me, namely, an under vest and a doublet of fine linen, and a robe and a surcoat, and a mantle of yellow satin, with a broad gold band upon the mantle. And they placed cushions both beneath and around me, with coverings of red linen. And I sat down. Now the six maidens who had taken my horse unharnessed him as well as if they had been the best squires in the island of Britain.

"Then behold they brought bowls of silver, wherein was water to wash, and towels of linen, some green and some white; and I washed. And in a little while the man sat down at the table. And I sat next to him, and below me sat all the maidens, except those who waited on us. And the table was of silver, and the cloths upon the table were of linen. And no vessel was served upon the table that was not either of gold or of silver or of buffalo-horn. And our meat was brought to us. And verily, Kay, I saw there every sort of meat and every sort of liquor that I ever saw elsewhere; but the meat and the liquor were better served there than I ever saw them in any other place.

"Until the repast was half over, neither the man nor any one of the damsels spoke a single word to me; but when the man perceived that it would be more agreeable for me to converse than

---

[1] *Cordwal* is the word in the original, and from the manner in which it is used it is evidently intended for the French Cordouan or Cordovan leather, which derived its name from Cordova, where it was manufactured. From this comes also our English word *cordwainer*.

to eat any more, he began to inquire of me who I was. Then I told the man who I was, and what was the cause of my journey, and said that I was seeking whether any one was superior to me, or whether I could gain the mastery over all. The man looked upon me, and he smiled and said, 'If I did not fear to do thee a mischief, I would show thee that which thou seekest.' Then I desired him to speak freely. And he said: 'Sleep here to-night, and in the morning arise early, and take the road upwards through the valley, until thou reachest the wood. A little way within the wood thou wilt come to a large sheltered glade, with a mound in the centre. And thou wilt see a black man of great stature on the top of the mound. He has but one foot, and one eye in the middle of his forehead. He is the wood-ward of that wood. And thou wilt see a thousand wild animals grazing around him. Inquire of him the way out of the glade, and he will reply to thee briefly, and will point out the road by which thou shalt find that which thou art in quest of.'

"And long seemed that night to me. And the next morning I arose and equipped myself, and mounted my horse, and proceeded straight through the valley to the wood, and at length I arrived at the glade. And the black man was there, sitting upon the top of the mound; and I was three times more astonished at the number of wild animals that I beheld, than the man had said I should be. Then I inquired of him the way, and he asked me roughly whither I would go. And when I had told him who I was, and what I sought, 'Take,' said he, 'that path that leads toward the head of the glade, and there thou wilt find an open space like to a large valley, and in the midst of it a tall tree. Under this tree is a fountain, and by the side of the fountain a marble slab, and on the marble slab a silver bowl, attached by a chain of silver, that it may not be carried away. Take the bowl, and throw a bowlful of water on the slab. And if thou dost not find trouble in that adventure, thou needest not seek it during the rest of thy life.'

"So I journeyed on until I reached the summit of the steep. And there I found everything as the black man had described it to me. And I went up to the tree, and beneath it I saw the fountain, and by its side the marble slab, and the silver bowl fastened by the chain. Then I took the bowl, and cast a bowlful of water upon the slab. And immediately I heard a mighty peal of thunder, so that heaven and earth seemed to tremble with its fury. And after the thunder came a shower; and of a truth I tell thee, Kay, that it was such a shower as neither man nor beast could endure and live. I turned my horse's flank toward the shower, and placed the beak of my shield over his head and neck, while I held the upper part of it over my own neck. And thus I withstood the shower. And presently the sky became clear, and with that, behold, the birds lighted upon the tree, and sang. And truly, Kay, I never heard any melody equal to that, either before or since. And when I was most charmed with listening to the birds, lo! a chiding voice was heard of one approaching me, and saying, 'O knight, what has brought thee hither? What evil have I done to thee, that thou shouidst act towards me and my possessions as thou hast this day? Dost thou not know that the shower to-day has left in my dominions neither man nor beast alive that was exposed to it?' And thereupon, behold, a knight on a black horse appeared, clothed in jet-black velvet, and with a tabard of black linen about him. And we charged each other, and, as the onset was furious, it was not long before I was overthrown. Then the knight passed the shaft of his lance through the bridle-rein of my horse, and rode off with the two horses, leaving me where I was. And he did not even bestow so much notice upon me as to imprison me, nor did he despoil me of my arms. So I returned along the road by which I had come. And when I reached the glade where the black man was, I confess to thee, Kay, it is a marvel that I did not melt down into a liquid pool, through the shame I felt at the black man's derision. And that night I came to the same castle where I had spent the night preceding. And I was more agreeably entertained that night than I had been the night before. And I conversed freely with the inmates of the castle; and none of them alluded to my expedition to the fountain, neither did I mention it to any. And I remained there that night. When I arose on the morrow I found ready saddled a dark bay palfrey, with nostrils as red as scarlet. And after putting on my armor, and leaving there my blessing, I returned to my own court. And that horse I still possess, and he is in the stable yonder. And I declare that I would not part with him for the best palfrey in the island of Britain.

"Now, of a truth, Kay, no man ever before confessed to an adventure so much to his own discredit; and verily it seems strange to me that neither before nor since have I heard of any person who knew of this adventure, and that the subject of it should exist within King Arthur's dominions without any other person lighting upon it."

CHAPTER XXI

THE LADY OF THE FOUNTAIN, CONTINUED

OWAIN'S ADVENTURE [1]

"Now," quoth Owain, "would it not be well to go and endeavor to discover that place?"

"By the hand of my friend," said Kay, "often dost thou utter that with thy tongue which thou wouldest not make good with thy deeds."

"In very truth," said Guenever, "it were better thou wert hanged, Kay, than to use such uncourteous speech towards a man like Owain."

"By the hand of my friend, good lady," said Kay; "thy praise of Owain is not greater than mine."

With that Arthur awoke, and asked if he had not been sleeping a little.

"Yes, lord," answered Owain, "thou hast slept awhile."

"Is it time for us to go to meat?"

"It is, lord," said Owain.

Then the horn for washing was sounded, and the king and all his household sat down to eat. And when the meal was ended, Owain withdrew to his lodging, and made ready his horse and his arms.

On the morrow with the dawn of day he put on his armor, and mounted his charger, and travelled through distant lands, and over desert mountains. And at length he arrived at the valley which Kynon had described to him, and he was certain that it was the same that he sought. And journeying along the valley, by the side of the river, he followed its course till he came to the plain, and within sight of the castle. When he approached the castle, he saw the youths shooting with their bows, in the place where Kynon had seen them, and the yellow man, to whom the castle

---

[1] Amongst all the characters of early British history none is more interesting, or occupies a more conspicuous place, than the hero of this tale. Urien, his father, was prince of Rheged, a district comprising the present Cumberland and part of the adjacent country. His valor and the consideration in which he was held are a frequent theme of Bardic song, and form the subject of several very spirited odes by Taliesin. Among the Triads there is one relating to him; it is thus translated: —

"Three Knights of Battle were in the court of Arthur: Cadwr the Earl of Cornwall, Launcelot du Lac, and Owain the son of Urien. And this was their characteristic,—that they would not retreat from battle, neither for spear, nor for arrow, nor for sword. And Arthur never had shame in battle the day he saw their faces there. And they were called the Knights of Battle."

belonged, standing hard by. And no sooner had Owain saluted the yellow man, than he was saluted by him in return.

And he went forward towards the castle, and there he saw the chamber; and when he had entered the chamber, he beheld the maidens working at satin embroidery, in chains of gold. And their beauty and their comeliness seemed to Owain far greater than Kynon had represented to him. And they arose to wait upon Owain, as they had done to Kynon. And the meal which they set before him gave even more satisfaction to Owain than it had done to Kynon.

About the middle of the repast the yellow man asked Owain the object of his journey. And Owain made it known to him, and said, "I am in quest of the knight who guards the fountain." Upon this the yellow man smiled, and said that he was as loath to point out that adventure to him as he had been to Kynon. However, he described the whole to Owain, and they retired to rest.

The next morning Owain found his horse made ready for him by the damsels, and he set forward and came to the glade where the black man was. And the stature of the black man seemed more wonderful to Owain than it had done to Kynon; and Owain asked of him his road, and he showed it to him. And Owain followed the road till he came to the green tree; and he beheld the fountain, and the slab beside the fountain, and the bowl upon it. And Owain took the bowl and threw a bowlful of water upon the slab. And, lo! the thunder was heard, and after the thunder came the shower, more violent than Kynon had described, and after the shower the sky became bright. And immediately the birds came and settled upon the tree and sang. And when their song was most pleasing to Owain, he beheld a knight coming towards him through the valley; and he prepared to receive him, and encountered him violently. Having broken both their lances, they drew their swords and fought blade to blade. Then Owain struck the knight a blow through his helmet, head-piece, and visor, and through the skin, and the flesh, and the bone, until it wounded the very brain. Then the black knight felt that he had received a mortal wound, upon which he turned his horse's head and fled. And Owain pursued him, and followed close upon him, although he was not near enough to strike him with his sword. Then Owain descried a vast and resplendent castle; and they came to the castle gate. And the black knight was allowed to enter, and the portcullis was let fall upon Owain; and it struck his horse behind the saddle, and cut him in two, and carried away the rowels of the spurs that were upon Owain's heels. And the portcullis descended to the floor. And the rowels of the spurs and part of the horse were without, and Owain with the other part of the horse remained between the two gates, and the inner gate was closed, so that Owain could not go thence; and Owain was in a perplexing situation. And while he was in this state, he could see through an aperture in the gate a street facing him, with a row of houses on each side. And he beheld a maiden, with yellow, curling hair, and a frontlet of gold upon her head; and she was clad in a dress of yellow satin, and on her feet were shoes of variegated leather. And she approached the gate, and desired that it should be opened. "Heaven knows, lady," said Owain, "it is no more possible for me to open to thee from hence, than it is for thee to set me free." And he told her his name, and who he was. "Truly," said the damsel, "it is very sad that thou canst not be released; and every woman ought to succor thee, for I know there is no one more faithful in the service of ladies than thou. Therefore," quoth she, "whatever is in my power to do for thy release, I will do it. Take this ring, and put it on thy finger, with the stone inside thy hand, and close thy hand upon the stone. And as long as thou concealest it, it will conceal thee. When they come forth to fetch thee, they will be much grieved that they cannot find thee. And I will await thee on the horseblock yonder, and thou wilt be able to see me, though I cannot see thee. Therefore come and place thy hand upon my shoulder, that I may know that thou art near me. And by the way that I go hence, do thou accompany me."

Then the maiden went away from Owain, and he did all that she had told him. And the people of the castle came to seek Owain to put him to death; and when they found nothing but the half of his horse, they were sorely grieved.

And Owain vanished from among them, and went to the maiden, and placed his hand upon her shoulder; whereupon she set off, and Owain followed her, until they came to the door of a large and beautiful chamber, and the maiden opened it, and they went in. And Owain looked around the chamber, and behold there was not a single nail in it that was not painted with gorgeous colors, and there was not a single panel that had not sundry images in gold portrayed upon it.

The maiden kindled a fire, and took water in a silver bowl, and gave Owain water to wash. Then she placed before him a silver table, inlaid with gold; upon which was a cloth of yellow linen, and she brought him food. And, of a truth, Owain never saw any kind of meat that was not there in abundance, but it was better cooked there than he had ever found it in any other place. And there was not one vessel from which he was served that was not of gold or of silver. And Owain ate and drank until late in the afternoon, when, lo! they heard a mighty clamor in the castle, and Owain asked the maiden what it was. "They are administering extreme unction," said she, "to the nobleman who owns the castle." And she prepared a couch for Owain which was meet for Arthur himself, and Owain went to sleep.

And a little after daybreak he heard an exceeding loud clamor and wailing, and asked the maiden what was the cause of it. "They are bearing to the church the body of the nobleman who owned the castle."

And Owain rose up, and clothed himself, and opened a window of the chamber, and looked towards the castle; and he could see neither the bounds nor the extent of the hosts that filled the streets. And they were fully armed; and a vast number of women were with them, both on horseback and on foot, and all the ecclesiastics in the city singing. In the midst of the throng he beheld the bier, over which was a veil of white linen; and wax tapers were burning beside and around it; and none that supported the bier was lower in rank than a powerful baron.

Never did Owain see an assemblage so gorgeous with silk [1] and satin. And, following the train, he beheld a lady with yellow hair falling over her shoulders, and stained with blood; and about her a dress of yellow satin, which was torn. Upon her feet were shoes of variegated leather. And it was a marvel that the ends of her fingers were not bruised from the violence with which she smote her hands together. Truly she would have been the fairest lady Owain ever saw had she been in her usual guise. And her cry was louder than the shout of the men or the clamor of the trumpets. No sooner had he beheld the lady than he became inflamed with her love, so that it took entire possession of him.

Then he inquired of the maiden who the lady was. "Heaven knows," replied the maiden, "she is the fairest, and the most chaste, and the most liberal, and the most noble of women. She is my mistress, and she is called the Countess of the Fountain, the wife of him whom thou didst slay yesterday." "Verily," said Owain,

---

[1] Before the sixth century all the silk used by Europeans had been brought to them by the Seres, the ancestors of the present Boukharians, whence it derived its Latin name of Serica. In 551 the silkworm was brought by two monks to Constantinople; but the manufacture of silk was confined to the Greek empire till the year 1130, when Roger, king of Sicily, returning from a crusade, collected some manufacturers from Athens and Corinth, and established them at Palermo, whence the trade was gradually disseminated over Italy. The varieties of silk stuffs known at this time were velvet, satin (which was called *samite*), and taffety (called *cendal* or *sendall*), all of which were occasionally stitched with gold and silver.

"she is the woman that I love best." "Verily," said the maiden, "she shall also love thee, not a little."

Then the maiden prepared a repast for Owain, and truly he thought he had never before so good a meal, nor was he ever so well served. Then she left him, and went towards the castle. When she came there she found nothing but mourning and sorrow; and the Countess in her chamber could not bear the sight of any one through grief. Luned, for that was the name of the maiden, saluted her, but the Countess answered her not. And the maiden bent down towards her, and said, "What aileth thee that thou answerest no one to-day?" "Luned," said the Countess, "what change hath befallen thee that thou hast not come to visit me in my grief? It was wrong in thee, and I so sorely afflicted." "Truly," said Luned, "I thought thy good sense was greater than I find it to be. Is it well for thee to mourn after that good man, or for anything else that thou canst not have?" "I declare to Heaven," said the Countess, "that in the whole world there is not a man equal to him." "Not so," said Luned, "for an ugly man would be as good as, or better than he." "I declare to Heaven," said the Countess, "that were it not repugnant to me to put to death one whom I have brought up I would have thee executed for making such comparison to me. As it is, I will banish thee." "I am glad," said Luned, "that thou hast no other cause to do so than that I would have been of service to thee, where thou didst not know what was to thine advantage. Henceforth evil betide whichever of us shall make the first advance towards reconciliation to the other, whether I should seek an invitation from thee, or thou of thine own accord shouldst send to invite me."

With that Luned went forth; and the Countess arose and followed her to the door of the chamber, and began coughing loudly. And when Luned looked back the Countess beckoned to her, and she returned to the Countess. "In truth," said the Countess, "evil is thy disposition; but if thou knowest what is to my advantage, declare it to me." "I will do so," said she.

"Thou knowest that, except by warfare and arms, it is impossible for thee to preserve thy possessions; delay not, therefore, to seek some one who can defend them." "And how can I do that?" said the Countess. "I will tell thee," said Luned; "unless thou canst defend the fountain thou canst not maintain thy dominions; and no one can defend the fountain except it be a knight of Arthur's household. I will go to Arthur's court, and ill betide me if I return not thence with a warrior who can guard the fountain, as well as, or even better, than he who defended it formerly."

"That will be hard to perform," said the Countess. "Go, however, and make proof of that which thou hast promised."

Luned set out under the pretence of going to Arthur's court; but she went back to the mansion where she had left Owain, and she tarried there as long as it might have taken her to travel to the court of King Arthur and back. And at the end of that time she apparelled herself, and went to visit the Countess. And the Countess was much rejoiced when she saw her, and inquired what news she brought from the court. "I bring thee the best of news," said Luned, "for I have compassed the object of my mission. When wilt thou that I should present to thee the chieftain who has come with me thither?" "Bring him here to visit me to-morrow," said the Countess, "and I will cause the town to be assembled by that time."

And Luned returned home. And the next day, at noon, Owain arrayed himself in a coat and a surcoat, and a mantle of yellow satin, upon which was a broad band of gold lace; and on his feet were high shoes of variegated leather, which were fastened by golden clasps, in the form of lions. And they proceeded to the chamber of the Countess.

Right glad was the Countess of their coming. And she gazed steadfastly upon Owain, and said, "Luned, this knight has not the look of a traveller." "What harm is there in that, lady?" said Luned. "I am certain," said the Countess, "that no other man than this chased the soul from the body of my lord." "So much the better for thee, lady," said Luned, "for had he not been stronger than thy lord, he could not have deprived him of life. There is no remedy for that which is past, be it as it may." "Go back to thine abode," said the Countess, "and I will take counsel."

The next day the Countess caused all her subjects to assemble, and showed them that her earldom was left defenceless, and that it could not be protected but with horse and arms, and military skill. "Therefore," said she, "this is what I offer for your choice: either let one of you take me, or give your consent for me to take a husband from elsewhere, to defend my dominions."

So they came to the determination that it was better that she should have permission to marry some one from elsewhere; and thereupon she sent for the bishops and archbishops, to celebrate her nuptials with Owain. And the men of the earldom did Owain homage.

And Owain defended the fountain with lance and sword. And this is the manner in which he defended it. Whensoever a knight came there, he overthrew him, and sold him for his full worth.

And what he thus gained he divided among his barons and his knights, and no man in the whole world could be more beloved than he was by his subjects. And it was thus for the space of three years.[1]

CHAPTER XXII

THE LADY OF THE FOUNTAIN, CONTINUED

GAWAIN'S ADVENTURE

IT befell that, as Gawain went forth one day with King Arthur, he perceived him to be very sad and sorrowful. And Gawain was much grieved to see Arthur in this state, and he questioned him, saying, "O my lord, what has befallen thee?" "In sooth, Gawain," said Arthur, "I am grieved concerning Owain, whom I have lost, these three years; and I shall certainly die if the fourth year pass without my seeing him. Now I am sure that it is through the tale which Kynon, the son of Clydno, related, that I have lost Owain." "There is no need for thee," said Gawain, "to summon to arms thy whole dominions on this account, for thou thyself, and the men of thy household, will be able to avenge Owain if he be slain, or to set him free if he be in prison; and, if alive, to bring him back with thee." And it was settled according to what Gawain had said.

Then Arthur and the men of his household prepared to go and seek Owain. And Kynon, the son of Clydno, acted as their guide. And Arthur came to the castle where Kynon had been before. And when he came there, the youths were shooting in the same place, and the yellow man was standing hard by. When the yellow man saw Arthur, he greeted him, and invited him to the castle. And Arthur accepted his invitation, and they entered the castle together. And great as was the number of his retinue, their presence was scarcely observed in the castle, so vast was its extent. And the maidens rose up to wait on them. And the service of the maidens appeared to them all to excel any attendance they had ever met with; and even the pages, who had charge of the horses,

[1] There exists an ancient poem, printed among those of Taliesin, called the Elegy of Owain ap Urien, and containing several very beautiful and spirited passages. It commences:

> "The soul of Owain ap Urien,
> May its Lord consider its exigencies!
> Reged's chief the green turf covers."

In the course of this Elegy, the bard, alluding to the incessant warfare with which this chieftain harassed his Saxon foes, exclaims:

> "Could England sleep with the light upon her eyes!"

were no worse served that night than Arthur himself would have been in his own palace.

The next morning Arthur set out thence, with Kynon for his guide, and came to the place where the black man was. And the stature of the black man was more surprising to Arthur than it had been represented to him. And they came to the top of the wooded steep, and traversed the valley, till they reached the green tree, where they saw the fountain and the bowl and the slab. And upon that Kay came to Arthur, and spoke to him. "My lord," said he, "I know the meaning of all this, and my request is that thou wilt permit me to throw the water on the slab, and to receive the first adventure that may befall." And Arthur gave him leave.

Then Kay threw a bowlful of water upon the slab, and immediately there came the thunder, and after the thunder the shower. And such a thunder-storm they had never known before. After the shower had ceased, the sky became clear, and on looking at the tree, they beheld it completely leafless. Then the birds descended upon the tree. And the song of the birds was far sweeter than any strain they had ever heard before. Then they beheld a knight, on a coal-black horse, clothed in black satin, coming rapidly towards them. And Kay met him and encountered him, and it was not long before Kay was overthrown. And the knight withdrew. And Arthur and his host encamped for the night.

And when they arose in the morning, they perceived the signal of combat upon the lance of the knight. Then, one by one, all the household of Arthur went forth to combat the knight, until there was not one that was not overthrown by him, except Arthur and Gawain. And Arthur armed himself to encounter the knight. "O my lord," said Gawain, "permit me to fight with him first." And Arthur permitted him. And he went forth to meet the knight, having over himself and his horse a satin robe of honor, which had been sent him by the daughter of the Earl of Rhangyr, and in this dress he was not known by any of the host. And they charged each other, and fought all that day until the evening. And neither of them was able to unhorse the other. And so it was the next day; they broke their lances in the shock, but neither of them could obtain the mastery.

And the third day they fought with exceeding strong lances. And they were incensed with rage, and fought furiously, even until noon. And they gave each other such a shock, that the girths of their horses were broken, so that they fell over their horses' cruppers to the ground. And they rose up speedily and drew their swords, and resumed the combat. And all they that witnessed their encounter felt assured that they had never before seen two men so valiant or so powerful. And had it been midnight, it would have been light, from the fire that flashed from their weapons. And the knight gave Gawain a blow that turned his helmet from off his face, so that the knight saw that it was Gawain. Then Owain said, "My lord Gawain, I did not know thee for my cousin, owing to the robe of honor that enveloped thee; take my sword and my arms." Said Gawain, "Thou, Owain, art the victor; take thou my sword." And with that Arthur saw that they were conversing, and advanced toward them. "My lord Arthur," said Gawain, "here is Owain who has vanquished me, and will not take my arms." "My lord," said Owain, "it is he that has vanquished me, and he will not take my sword." "Give me your swords," said Arthur, "and then neither of you has vanquished the other." Then Owain put his arms around Arthur's neck, and they embraced. And all the host hurried forward, to see Owain, and to embrace him. And there was nigh being a loss of life, so great was the press.

And they retired that night, and the next day Arthur prepared to depart. "My lord," said Owain, "this is not well of thee. For I have been absent from thee these three years, and during all that time, up to this very day, I have been preparing a banquet for thee, knowing that thou wouldst come to seek me. Tarry with me, therefore, until thou and thy attendants have recovered the fatigues of the journey, and have been anointed."

And they all proceeded to the castle of the Countess of the Fountain, and the banquet which had been three years preparing was consumed in three months. Never had they a more delicious or agreeable banquet. And Arthur prepared to depart. Then he sent an embassy to the Countess to beseech her to permit Owain to go with him for the space of three months, that he might show him to the nobles and the fair dames of the island of Britain. And the Countess gave her consent, although it was very painful to her. So Owain came with Arthur to the island of Britain. And when he was once more amongst his kindred and friends, he remained three years, instead of three months, with them.

THE ADVENTURE OF THE LION

And as Owain one day sat at meat, in the city of Caerleon upon Usk, behold a damsel entered the hall, upon a bay horse,[1]

---

[1] The custom of riding into a hall while the lord and his guests sat at meat might be illustrated by numerous passages of ancient romance and history But a quotation from Chaucer's beautiful and half-told tale of Cambuscan is sufficient:

with a curling name, and covered with foam; and the bridle, and as much as was seen of the saddle, were of gold. And the damsel was arrayed in a dress of yellow satin. And she came up to Owain, und took the ring from off his hand. "Thus," said she, "shall be treated the deceiver, the traitor, the faithless, the disgraced, and the beardless." And she turned her horse's head, and departed.

Then his adventure came to Owain's remembrance, and he was sorrowful. And having finished eating, he went to his own abode, and made preparations that night. And the next day he arose, but did not go to the court, nor did he return to the Countess of the Fountain, but wandered to the distant parts of the earth and to uncultivated mountains. And he remained there until all his apparel was worn out and his body was wasted away, and his hair was grown long. And he went about with the wild beasts, and fed with them, until they became familiar with him. But at length he became so weak that he could no longer bear them company. Then he descended from the mountains to the valley, and came to a park, that was the fairest in the world, and belonged to a charitable lady.

One day the lady and her attendants went forth to walk by a lake that was in the middle of the park. And they saw the form of a man lying as if dead. And they were terrified. Nevertheless they went near him, and touched him, and they saw that there was life in him. And the lady returned to the castle, and took a flask full of precious ointment and gave it to one of her maidens. "Go with this," said she, "and take with thee yonder horse, and clothing, and place them near the man we saw just now, and anoint him with this balsam near his heart; and if there is life in him he will revive, through the efficiency of this balsam. Then watch what he will do."

And the maiden departed from her, and went and poured of the balsam upon Owain, and left the horse and the garments hard by, and went a little way off and hid herself to watch him. In a

"And so befell that after the thridde cours,
While that this king sat thus in his nobley,
Herking his minstralles thir thinges play,
Beforne him at his bord deliciously,
In at the halle door all sodenly
Ther came a knight upon a stede of bras,
And in his hond a brod mirrour of glas,
Upon his thombe he had of gold a ring,
And by his side a naked sword hanging;
And up he rideth to the highe bord.
In all the halle ne was ther spoke a word,
For mervaille of this knight; him to behold
Full besily they waiten, young and old."

short time she saw him begin to move; and he rose up and looked at his person, and became ashamed of the unseemliness of his appearance. Then he perceived the horse and the garments that were near him. And he clothed himself, and with difficulty mounted the horse. Then the damsel discovered herself to him, and saluted him. And he and the maiden proceeded to the castle, and the maiden conducted him to a pleasant chamber, and kindled a fire, and left him.

And he stayed at the castle three months, till he was restored to his former guise, and became even more comely than he had ever been before. And Owain rendered signal service to the lady in a controversy with a powerful neighbor, so that he made ample requital to her for her hospitality; and he took his departure.

And as he journeyed he heard a loud yelling in a wood. And it was repeated a second and a third time. And Owain went towards the spot, and beheld a huge craggy mound, in the middle of the wood, on the side of which was a gray rock. And there was a cleft in the rock, and a serpent was within the cleft. And near the rock stood a black lion, and every time the lion sought to go thence the serpent darted towards him to attack him. And Owain unsheathed his sword, and drew near to the rock; and as the serpent sprung out he struck him with his sword and cut him in two. And he dried his sword, and went on his way as before. But behold the lion followed him, and played about him, as though it had been a greyhound that he had reared.

They proceeded thus throughout the day, until the evening. And when it was time for Owain to take his rest he dismounted, and turned his horse loose in a flat and wooded meadow. And he struck fire, and when the fire was kindled the lion brought him fuel enough to last for three nights. And the lion disappeared. And presently the lion returned, bearing a fine large roebuck. And he threw it down before Owain, who went towards the fire with it.

And Owain took the roebuck and skinned it, and placed collops of its flesh upon skewers round the fire. The rest of the buck he gave to the lion to devour. While he was so employed he heard a deep groan near him, and a second, and a third. And the place whence the groans proceeded was a cave in the rock; and Owain went near, and called out to know who it was that groaned so piteously. And a voice answered, "I am Luned, the handmaiden of the Countess of the Fountain." "And what dost thou here?" said he. "I am imprisoned," said she, "on account of the knight who came from Arthur's court and married the Countess. And he stayed a short time with her, but he afterwards departed for the court of Arthur, and has not returned since. And two of the Countess's pages traduced

him, and called him a deceiver. And because I said I would vouch
for it he would come before long and maintain his cause against
both of them they imprisoned me in this cave, and said that I should
be put to death unless he came to deliver me by a certain day; and
that is no further off than tomorrow, and I have no one to send
to seek him for me. His name is Owain, the son of Urien." "And art
thou certain that if that knight knew all this he would come to thy
rescue?" "I am most certain of it," said she.

When the collops were cooked, Owain divided them into two parts,
between himself and the maiden, and then Owain laid himself down
to sleep; and never did sentinel keep stricter watch over his lord
than the lion that night over Owain.

And the next day there came two pages with a great troop of
attendants to take Luned from her cell, and put her to death. And
Owain asked them what charge they had against her. And they told
him of the compact that was between them; as the maiden had done
the night before. "And," said they, "Owain has failed her, therefore
we are taking her to be burnt." "Truly," said Owain, "he is a good
knight, and if he knew that the maiden was in such peril, I marvel
that he came not to her rescue. But if you will accept me in his stead,
I will do battle with you." "We will," said the youths.

And they attacked Owain, and he was hard beset by them. And
with that, the lion came to Owain's assistance, and they two got
the better of the young men. And they said to him, "Chieftain, it
was not agreed that we should fight save with thyself alone, and it
is harder for us to contend with yonder animal than with thee."
And Owain put the lion in the place where Luned had been imprisoned, and blocked up the door with stones. And he went to fight
with the young men as before. But Owain had not his usual strength,
and the two youths pressed hard upon him. And the lion roared incessantly at seeing Owain in trouble. And he burst through the wall,
until he found his way out, and rushed upon the young men and
instantly slew them. So Luned was saved from being burned.

Then Owain returned with Luned to the castle of the Lady of the
Fountain. And when he went thence, he took the Countess with him
to Arthur's court, and she was his wife as long as she lived.

CHAPTER XXIII

GERAINT, THE SON OF ERBIN

ARTHUR was accustomed to hold his court at Caerleon upon Usk.
And there he held it seven Easters and five Christmases. And once
upon a time he held his court there at Whitsuntide. For Caerleon

was the place most easy of access in his dominions, both by sea
and by land. And there were assembled nine crowned kings, who
were his tributaries, and likewise earls and barons. For they were
his invited guests at all the high festivals, unless they were prevented by any great hinderance. And when he was at Caerleon holding his court, thirteen churches were set apart for mass. And thus
they were appointed: one church for Arthur and his kings, and his
guests; and the second for Guenever and her ladies; and the third
for the steward of the household and the suitors; and the fourth
for the Franks and the other officers; and the other nine churches
were for the nine masters of the household, and chiefly for Gawain,
for he, from the eminence of his warlike fame, and from the noble-
ness of his birth, was the most exalted of the nine. And there was
no other arrangement respecting the churches than that which we
have here mentioned.

And on Whit-Tuesday, as the king sat at the banquet, lo, there
entered a tall, fair-headed youth, clad in a coat and surcoat of satin,
and a golden-hilted sword about his neck, and low shoes of leather
upon his feet. And he came and stood before Arthur. "Hail to thee,
lord," said he. "Heaven prosper thee," he answered, "and be thou
welcome." "Dost thou bring any new tidings?" "I do, lord," he said.
"I am one of thy foresters, lord, in the forest of Dean, and my name
is Madoc, son of Turgadarn. In the forest I saw a stag, the like of
which beheld I never yet." "What is there about him," asked Arthur,
"that thou never yet didst see his like?" "He is of pure white, lord,
and he does not herd with any other animal, through stateliness
and pride, so royal is his bearing. And I come to seek thy counsel,
lord, and to know thy will concerning him. "It seems best to me,"
said Arthur, "to go and hunt him to-morrow at break of day, and
to cause general notice thereof to be given to-night, in all quarters
of the court." And Arryfuerys was Arthur's chief huntsman, and
Arelivri his chief page. And all received notice; and thus it was
arranged.

Then Guenever said to Arthur, "Wilt thou permit me, lord, to go
to-morrow to see and hear the hunt of the stag of which the young
man spoke?" "I will gladly," said Arthur. And Gawain said to
Arthur, "Lord, if it seem well to thee, permit that into whose hunt
soever the stag shall come, that one, be he a knight or one on foot,
may cut off his head, and give it to whom he pleases, whether to his
own lady-love, or to the lady of his friend." "I grant it gladly," said
Arthur, "and let the steward of the household be chastised, if all
things are not ready to-morrow for the chase."

And they passed the night with songs and diversions and discourse, and ample entertainment. And when it was time for them

all to go to sleep, they went. And when the next day came, they arose. And Arthur called the attendants who guarded his couch. And there were four pages whose names were Cadyrnerth, the son of Gandwy, and Ambreu, the son of Bedwor, and Amhar, the son of Arthur, and Goreu, the son of Custennin. And these men came to Arthur and saluted him, and arrayed him in his garments. And Arthur wondered that Guenever did not awake, and the attendants wished to awaken her. "Disturb her not," said Arthur, "for she had rather sleep than go to see the hunting."

Then Arthur went forth, and he heard two horns sounding, one from near the lodging of the chief huntsman, and the other from near that of the chief page. And the whole assembly of the multitudes came to Arthur, and they took the road to the forest.

And after Arthur had gone forth from the palace, Guenever awoke, and called to her maidens, and apparelled herself. "Maidens," said she, "I had leave last night to go and see the hunt. Go one of you to the stable, and order hither a horse such as a woman may ride." And one of them went, and she found but two horses in the stable; and Guenever and one of her maidens mounted them, and went through the Usk, and followed the track of the men and the horses. And as they rode thus, they heard a loud and rushing sound; and they looked behind them, and beheld a knight upon a hunter foal of mighty size. And the rider was a fair-haired youth, bare-legged, and of princely mien; and a golden-hilted sword was at his side, and a robe and a surcoat of satin were upon him, and two low shoes of leather were upon his feet; and around him was a scarf of blue purple, at each corner of which was a golden apple. And his horse stepped stately and swift and proud; and he overtook Guenever, and saluted her. "Heaven prosper thee, Geraint," said she; "and why didst thou not go with thy lord to hunt?" "Because I knew not when he went," said he. "I marvel too," said she, "how he could go, unknown to me. But thou, O young man, art the most agreeable companion I could have in the whole kingdom; and it may be I shall be more amused with the hunting than they; for we shall hear the horns when they sound, and we shall hear the dogs when they are let loose and begin to cry."

So they went to the edge of the forest, and there they stood. "From this place," said she, "we shall hear when the dogs are let loose." And thereupon they heard a loud noise; and they looked towards the spot whence it came, and they beheld a dwarf riding upon a horse, stately and foaming and prancing and strong and spirited. And in the hand of the dwarf was a whip. And near the dwarf they saw a lady upon a beautiful white horse, of steady and stately pace; and she was clothed in a garment of gold brocade.

And near her was a knight upon a war-horse of large size, with heavy and bright armor both upon himself and upon his horse. And truly they never before saw a knight, or a horse, or armor, of such remarkable size.

"Geraint," said Guenever, "knowest thou the name of that tall knight yonder?" "I know him not," said he, "and the strange armor that he wears prevents my either seeing his face or his features." "Go, maiden," said Guenever, "and ask the dwarf who that knight is." Then the maiden went up to the dwarf; and she inquired of the dwarf who the knight was. "I will not tell thee," he answered. "Since thou art so churlish," said she, "I will ask him, myself." "Thou shalt not ask him, by my faith," said he. "Wherefore not?" said she. "Because thou art not of honor sufficient to befit thee to speak to my lord." Then the maiden turned her horse's head towards the knight, upon which the dwarf struck her with the whip that was in his hand across the face and the eyes, so that the blood flowed forth. And the maiden returned to Guenever, complaining of the hurt she had received. "Very rudely has the dwarf treated thee," said Geraint, and he put his hand upon the hilt of his sword. But he took counsel with himself, and considered that it would be no vengeance for him to slay the dwarf, and to be attacked unarmed by the armed knight; so he refrained.

"Lady," said he, "I will follow him, with thy permission, and at last he will come to some inhabited place, where I may have arms, either as a loan or for a pledge, so that I may encounter the knight." "Go," said she, "and do not attack him until thou hast good arms; and I shall be very anxious concerning thee, until I hear tidings of thee." "If I am alive," said he, "thou shalt hear tidings of me by to-morrow afternoon;" and with that he departed.

And the road they took was below the palace of Caerleon, and across the ford of the Usk; and they went along a fair and even and lofty ridge of ground, until they came to a town, and at the extremity of the town they saw a fortress and a castle. And as the knight passed through the town, all the people arose and saluted him, and bade him welcome. And when Geraint came into the town, he looked at every house to see if he knew any of those whom he saw. But he knew none, and none knew him, to do him the kindness to let him have arms, either as a loan or for a pledge. And every house he saw was full of men and arms and horses. And they were polishing shields, and burnishing swords, and washing armor, and shoeing horses. And the knight and the lady and the dwarf rode up to the castle, that was in the town, and every one was glad in the castle. And from the battlements and the gates they risked their necks, through their eagerness to greet them, and to show their joy.

Geraint stood there to see whether the knight would remain in the castle; and when he was certain that he would do so, he looked around him. And at a little distance from the town he saw an old palace in ruins, wherein was a hall that was falling to decay. And as he knew not any one in the town, he went towards the old palace. And when he came near to the palace, he saw a hoary-headed man, standing by it, in tattered garments. And Geraint gazed steadfastly upon him. Then the hoary-headed man said to him, "Young man, wherefore art thou thoughtful?" "I am thoughtful," said he, "because I know not where to pass the night." "Wilt thou come forward this way, chieftain," said he, "and thou shalt have of the best that can be procured for thee." So Geraint went forward. And the hoary-headed man led the way into the hall. And in the hall he dismounted, and he left there his horse. Then he went on to the upper chamber with the hoary-headed man. And in the chamber he beheld an old woman, sitting on a cushion, with old, worn-out garments upon her; yet it seemed to him that she must have been comely when in the bloom of youth. And beside her was a maiden, upon whom were a vest and a veil, that were old, and beginning to be worn out. And truly he never saw a maiden more full of comeliness and grace and beauty than she. And the hoary-headed man said to the maiden, "There is no attendant for the horse of this youth but thyself." "I will render the best service I am able," said she, "both to him and to his horse." And the maiden disarrayed the youth, and then she furnished his horse with straw and with corn; and then she returned to the chamber. And the hoary-headed man said to the maiden, "Go to the town, and bring hither the best that thou canst find, both of food and of liquor." "I will gladly, lord," said she. And to the town went the maiden. And they conversed together while the maiden was at the town. And behold, the maiden came back, and a youth with her, bearing on his back a costrel full of good purchased mead, and a quarter of a young bullock. And in the hands of the maiden was a quantity of white bread, and she had some manchet bread in her veil, and she came into the chamber. "I could not obtain better than this," said she, "nor with better should I have been trusted." "It is good enough," said Geraint. And they caused the meat to be boiled; and when their food was ready, they sat down. And it was in this wise. Geraint sat between the hoary-headed man and his wife, and the maiden served them. And they ate and drank.

And when they had finished eating, Geraint talked with the hoary-headed man, and he asked him in the first place to whom belonged the palace that he was in. "Truly," said he, "it was I that built it, and to me also belonged the city and the castle which thou sawest." "Alas!" said Geraint, "how is it that thou hast lost them

now?" "I lost a great earldom as well as these," said he, "and this
is how I lost them. I had a nephew, the son of my brother, and I
took care of his possessions; but he was impatient to enter upon
them, so he made war upon me, and wrested from me not only his
own, but also my estates, except this castle." "Good sir," said
Geraint, "wilt thou tell me wherefore came the knight and the lady
and the dwarf just now into the town, and what is the preparation
which I saw, and the putting of arms in order?" "I will do so," said
he. "The preparations are for the game that is to be held to-morrow
by the young earl, which will be on this wise. In the midst of a
meadow which is here, two forks will be set up, and upon the two
forks a silver rod, and upon the silver rod a sparrow-hawk, and for
the sparrow-hawk there will be a tournament. And to the tournament
will go all the array thou didst see in the city, of men and of horses
and of arms. And with each man will go the lady he loves best; and
no man can joust for the sparrow-hawk, except the lady he loves
best be with him. And the knight that thou sawest has gained the
sparrow-hawk these two years; and if he gains it the third year, he
will be called the Knight of the Sparrow-hawk from that time forth."
"Sir," said Geraint, "what is thy counsel to me concerning this
knight, on account of the insult which the maiden of Guenever received from the dwarf?" And Geraint told the hoary-headed man
what the insult was that the maiden had received. "It is not easy
to counsel thee, inasmuch as thou hast neither dame nor maiden
belonging to thee, for whom thou canst joust. Yet I have arms here,
which thou couldst have, and there is my horse also, if he seem to
thee better than thine own." "Ah, sir," said he, "Heaven reward
thee! But my own horse, to which I am accustomed, together with
thine arms, will suffice me. And if, when the appointed time shall
come to-morrow, thou wilt permit me, sir, to challenge for yonder
maiden that is thy daughter, I will engage, if I escape from the
tournament, to love the maiden as long as I live." "Gladly will I
permit thee," said the hoary-headed man; "and since thou dost thus
resolve, it is necessary that thy horse and arms should be ready
to-morrow at break of day. For then the Knight of the Sparrow-
hawk will make proclamation, and ask the lady he loves best to
take the sparrow-hawk; and if any deny it to her, by force will he
defend her claim. And therefore," said the hoary-headed man, "it is
needful for thee to be there at daybreak, and we three will be with
thee." And thus was it settled.

And at night they went to sleep. And before the dawn they arose
and arrayed themselves; and by the time that it was day, they were
all four in the meadow. And there was the Knight of the Sparrow-
hawk making the proclamation and asking his lady-love to take the

sparrow-hawk. "Take it not," said Geraint, "for here is a maiden who is fairer, and more noble, and more comely, and who has a better claim to it than thou." Then said the knight, "If thou maintainest the sparrow-hawk to be due to her, come forward and do battle with me." And Geraint went forward to the top of the meadow, having upon himself and upon his horse armor which was heavy and rusty, and of uncouth shape. Then they encountered each other, and they broke a set of lances; and they broke a second set, and a third. And when the earl and his company saw the Knight of the Sparrow-hawk gaining the mastery, there was shouting and joy and mirth amongst them; and the hoary-headed man and his wife and his daughter were sorrowful. And the hoary-headed man served Geraint with lances as often as he broke them, and the dwarf served the Knight of the Sparrow-hawk. Then the hoary-headed man said to Geraint, "O chieftain, since no other will hold with thee, behold, here is the lance which was in my hand on the day when I received the honor of knighthood, and from that time to this I never broke it, and it has an excellent point." Then Geraint took the lance, thanking the hoary-headed man. And thereupon the dwarf also brought a lance to his lord. "Behold, here is a lance for thee, not less good than his," said the dwarf. "And bethink thee that no knight ever withstood thee so long as this one has done." "I declare to Heaven," said Geraint, "that unless death takes me quickly hence, he shall fare never the better for thy service." And Geraint pricked his horse towards him from afar, and, warning him, he rushed upon him, and gave him a blow so severe, and furious, and fierce, upon the face of his shield, that he cleft it in two, and broke his armor, and burst his girths, so that both he and his saddle were borne to the ground over the horse's crupper. And Geraint dismounted quickly. And he was wroth, and he drew his sword, and rushed fiercely upon him. Then the knight also arose, and drew his sword against Geraint. And they fought on foot with their swords until their arms struck sparks of fire like stars from one another; and thus they continued fighting until the blood and sweat obscured the light from their eyes. At length Geraint called to him all his strength, and struck the knight upon the crown of his head, so that he broke all his head-armour, and cut through all the flesh and the skin, even to the skull, until he wounded the bone.

Then the knight fell upon his knees, and cast his sword from his hand, and besought mercy from Geraint. "Of a truth," said he, "I relinquish my overdaring and my pride, and crave thy mercy; and unless I have time to commit myself to Heaven for my sins, and to talk with a priest, thy mercy will avail me little." "I will grant thee grace upon this condition," said Geraint; "that thou go to

Guenever, the wife of Arthur, to do her satisfaction for the insult which her maiden received from thy dwarf. Dismount not from the time thou goest hence until thou comest into the presence of Guenever, to make her what atonement shall be adjudged at the court of Arthur." "This will I do gladly; and who art thou?" "I am Geraint, the son of Erbin; and declare thou also who thou art." "I am Edeyrn, the son of Nudd." Then he threw himself upon his horse, and went forward to Arthur's court; and the lady he loved best went before him, and the dwarf, with much lamentation.

Then came the young earl and his hosts to Geraint, and saluted him, and bade him to his castle. "I may not go," said Geraint; "but where I was last night, there will I be to-night also." "Since thou wilt none of my inviting, thou shalt have abundance of all that I can command for thee; and I will order ointment for thee, to recover thee from thy fatigues, and from the weariness that is upon thee." "Heaven reward thee," said Geraint, "and I will go to my lodging." And thus went Geraint and Earl Ynywl, and his wife and his daughter. And when they reached the old mansion, the household servants and attendants of the young earl had arrived, and had arranged all the apartments, dressing them with straw and with fire; and in a short time the ointment was ready, and Geraint came there, and they washed his head. Then came the young earl, with forty honorable knights from among his attendants, and those who were bidden to the tournament. And Geraint came from the anointing. And the earl asked him to go to the hall to eat. "Where is the Earl Ynywl," said Geraint, "and his wife and his daughter?" "They are in the chamber yonder," said the earl's chamberlain, "arraying themselves in garments which the earl has caused to be brought for them." "Let not the damsel array herself," said he, "except in her vest and her veil, until she come to the court of Arthur, to be clad by Guenever in such garments as she may choose." So the maiden did not array herself.

Then they all entered the hall, and they washed, and sat down to meat. And thus were they seated. On one side of Geraint sat the young earl, and Earl Ynywl beyond him, and on the other side of Geraint was the maiden and her mother. And after these all sat according to their precedence in honor. And they ate. And they were served abundantly, and they received a profusion of divers kinds of gifts. Then they conversed together. And the young earl invited Geraint to visit him next day. "I will not, by Heaven," said Geraint. "To the court of Arthur will I go with this maiden to-morrow. And it is enough for me, as long as Earl Ynywl is in poverty and trouble; and I go chiefly to seek to add to his maintenance." "Ah, chieftain," said the young earl, "it is not by my fault that Earl Ynywl is without his possessions." "By my faith," said Geraint, "he shall not remain without them, unless death quickly takes me hence." "O chieftain," said he, "with regard to the disagreement between me and Ynywl, I will gladly abide by thy counsel, and agree to what thou mayest judge right between us." "I but ask thee," said Geraint, "to restore to him what is his, and what he should have received from the time he lost his possessions even until this day." "That will I do, gladly, for thee," answered he. "Then," said Geraint, "whosoever is here who owes homage to Ynywl, let him come forward, and perform it on the spot." And all the men did so; and by that treaty they abided. And his castle and his town, and all his possessions, were restored to Ynywl. And he received back all that he had lost, even to the smallest jewel.

Then spoke Earl Ynywl to Geraint. "Chieftain," said he, "behold the maiden for whom thou didst challenge at the tournament; I bestow her upon thee." "She shall go with me," said Geraint, "to the court of Arthur, and Arthur and Guenever, they shall dispose of her as they will." And the next day they proceeded to Arthur's court. So far concerning Geraint.

CHAPTER XXIV

GERAINT, THE SON OF ERBIN, CONTINUED

Now this is how Arthur hunted the stag. The men and the dogs were divided into hunting-parties, and the dogs were let loose upon the stag. And the last dog that was let loose was the favorite dog of Arthur, Cavall was his name. And he left all the other dogs behind him, and turned the stag. And at the second turn the stag came toward the hunting-party of Arthur. And Arthur set upon him, and before he could be slain by any other Arthur cut off his head. Then they sounded the death-horn for slaying, and they all gathered round.

Then came Kadyriath to Arthur, and spoke to him. "Lord," said he, "behold, yonder is Guenever, and none with her save only one maiden." "Command Gildas, the son of Caw, and all the scholars of the court," said Arthur, "to attend Guenever to the palace." And they did so.

Then they all set forth, holding converse together concerning the head of the stag, to whom it should be given. One wished that it should be given to the lady best beloved by him and another to the lady whom he loved best. And so they came to the palace. And when Arthur and Guenever heard them disputing about the head of the stag, Guenever said to Arthur, "My lord, this is my counsel concern-ing the stag's head; let it not be given away until Geraint, the son of Erbin, shall return from the errand he is upon." And Guenever told Arthur what that errand was. "Right gladly shall it be so," said Arthur. And Guenever caused a watch to be set upon the ramparts for Geraint's coming. And after midday they beheld an unshapely little man upon a horse, and after him a dame or a damsel, also on horseback, and after her a knight of large stature, bowed down, and hanging his head low and sorrowfully, and clad in broken and worth-less armor.

And before they came near to the gate one of the watch went to Guenever, and told her what kind of people they saw, and what aspect they bore. "I know not who they are," said he. "But *I* know," said Guenever; "this is the knight whom Geraint pursued, and me-thinks he comes not here by his own free will. But Geraint has over-taken him, and avenged the insult to the maiden to the uttermost." And thereupon, behold, a porter came to the spot where Guenever was. "Lady," said he, "at the gate there is a knight, and I saw never a man of so pitiful an aspect to look upon as he. Miserable and broken is the armor that he wears, and the hue of blood is more conspicuous upon it than its own color." "Knowest thou his name?" said she. "I do," said he; "he tells me that he is Edeyrn, the son of Nudd." Then she replied, "I know him not."

So Guenever went to the gate to meet him, and he entered. And Guenever was sorry when she saw the condition he was in, even though he was accompanied by the churlish dwarf. Then Edeyrn saluted Guenever. "Heaven protect thee," said she. "Lady," said he, "Geraint, the son of Erbin, thy best and most valiant servant, greets thee." "Did he meet with thee?" she asked. "Yes," said he, "and it was not to my advantage; and that was not his fault, but mine, lady. And Geraint greets thee well; and in greeting thee he com-pelled me to come hither to do thy pleasure for the insult which thy maiden received from the dwarf." "Now where did he overtake thee?" "At the place where we were jousting and contending for the sparrow-hawk, in the town which is now called Cardiff. And it was for the avouchment of the love of the maiden, the daughter of Earl Ynywl, that Geraint jousted at the tournament. And thereupon we encountered each other, and he left me, lady, as thou seest." "Sir," said she, "when thinkest thou that Geraint will be here?" "To-mor-row, lady, I think he will be here with the maiden."

Then Arthur came to them. And he saluted Arthur, and Arthur gazed a long time upon him, and was amazed to see him thus. And thinking that he knew him, he inquired of him, "Art thou Edeyrn, the son of Nudd?" "I am, lord," said he, "and I have met with much

trouble and received wounds insupportable." Then he told Arthur
all his adventure. "Well," said Arthur, "from what I hear it behooves
Guenever to be merciful towards thee." "The mercy which thou
desirest, lord," said she, "will I grant to him, since it is as insulting
to thee that an insult should be offered to me as to thyself." "Thus
will it be best to do," said Arthur; "let this man have medical care
until it be known whether he may live. And if he live he shall do such
satisfaction as shall be judged best by the men of the court. And if
he die too much will be the death of such a youth as Edeyrn for an
insult to a maiden." "This pleases me," said Guenever. And Arthur
caused Morgan Tud to be called to him. He was chief physician.
"Take with thee Edeyrn, the son of Nudd, and cause a chamber to
be prepared for him, and let him have the aid of medicine as thou
wouldst do unto myself if I were wounded; and let none into his
chamber to molest him, but thyself and thy disciples, to administer
to him remedies." "I will do so gladly, lord," said Morgan Tud.
Then said the steward of the household, "Whither is it right, lord,
to order the maiden?" "To Guenever and her handmaidens," said he.
And the steward of the household so ordered her.

The next day came Geraint towards the court; and there was a
watch set on the ramparts by Guenever, lest he should arrive unawares. And one of the watch came to Guenever. "Lady," said he,
"methinks that I see Geraint, and a maiden with him. He is on horseback, but he has his walking gear upon him, and the maiden appears
to be in white, seeming to be clad in a garment of linen." "Assemble
all the women," said Guenever, "and come to meet Geraint, to welcome him and wish him joy." And Guenever went to meet Geraint
and the maiden. And when Geraint came to the place where Guenever was he saluted her. "Heaven prosper thee," said she, "and welcome to thee." "Lady," said he, "I earnestly desired to obtain thee
satisfaction, according to thy will; and, behold here is the maiden
through whom thou hadst thy revenge." "Verily," said Guenever,
"the welcome of Heaven be unto her; and it is fitting that we should
receive her joyfully." Then they went in and dismounted. And
Geraint came to where Arthur was, and saluted him. "Heaven protect thee," said Arthur, "and the welcome of Heaven be unto thee.
And inasmuch as thou hast vanquished Edeyrn, the son of Nudd,
thou hast had a prosperous career." "Not upon me be the blame,"
said Geraint; "it was through the arrogance of Edeyrn, the son of
Nudd, himself, that we were not friends." "Now," said Arthur,
"where is the maiden for whom I heard thou didst give challenge?"
"She is gone with Guenever to her chamber." Then went Arthur to
see the maiden. And Arthur, and all his companions, and his whole
court, were glad concerning the maiden. And certain were they all

that, had her array been suitable to her beauty, they had never seen a maid fairer than she. And Arthur gave away the maiden to Geraint. And the usual bond made between two persons was made between Geraint and the maiden, and the choicest of all Guenever's apparel was given to the maiden; and thus arrayed, she appeared comely and graceful to all who beheld her. And that day and the night were spent in abundance of minstrelsy, and ample gifts of liquor, and a multitude of games. And when it was time for them to go to sleep they went. And in the chamber where the couch of Arthur and Guenever was the couch of Geraint and Enid was prepared. And from that time she became his wife. And the next day Arthur satisfied all the claimants upon Geraint with bountiful gifts. And the maiden took up her abode in the palace, and she had many companions both men and women, and there was no maiden more esteemed than she in the island of Britain.

Then spake Guenever. "Rightly did I judge," said she, "concerning the head of the stag, that it should not be given to any until Geraint's return; and behold, here is a fit occasion for bestowing it. Let it be given to Enid, the daughter of Ynywl, the most illustrious maiden. And I do not believe any will begrudge it her, for between her and every one there exists nothing but love and friendship." Much applauded was this by them all, and by Arthur also. And the head of the stag was given to Enid. And thereupon her fame increased, and her friends became more in number than before. And Geraint from that time forth loved the hunt, and the tournament, and hard encounters; and he came victorious from them all. And a year, and a second, and a third, he proceeded thus, until his fame had flown over the face of the kingdom.

And, once upon a time, Arthur was holding his court at Caerleon upon Usk; and behold, there came to him ambassadors, wise and prudent, full of knowledge and eloquent of speech, and they saluted Arthur. "Heaven prosper you!" said Arthur; "and whence do you come?" "We come, lord," said they, "from Cornwall, and we are ambassadors from Erbin, the son of Custennin, thy uncle, and our mission is unto thee. And he greets thee well, as an uncle should greet his nephew, and as a vassal should greet his lord. And he represents unto thee that he waxes heavy and feeble, and is advancing in years. And the neighboring chiefs, knowing this, grow insolent towards him, and covet his land and possessions. And he earnestly beseeches thee, lord, to permit Geraint his son to return to him, to protect his possessions, and to become acquainted with his boundaries. And unto him he represents that it were better for him to spend the flower of his youth and the prime of his age in preserving his own boundaries, than in tournaments which are productive of no profit, although he obtains glory in them."

"Well," said Arthur, "go and divest yourselves of your accoutrements, and take food, and refresh yourselves after your fatigues; and before you go from hence you shall have an answer." And they went to eat. And Arthur considered that it would go hard with him to let Geraint depart from him, and from his court; neither did he think it fair that his cousin should be restrained from going to protect his dominions and his boundaries, seeing that his father was unable to do so. No less was the grief and regret of Guenever, and all her women, and all her damsels, through fear that the maiden would leave them. And that day and that night was spent in abundance of feasting. And Arthur told Geraint the cause of the mission, and of the coming of the ambassadors to him out of Cornwall. "Truly," said Geraint, "be it to my advantage or disadvantage, lord, I will do according to thy will concerning this embassy." "Behold," said Arthur, "though it grieves me to part with thee, it is my counsel that thou go to dwell in thine own dominions, and to defend thy boundaries, and take with thee to accompany thee as many as thou wilt of those thou lovest best among my faithful ones, and among thy friends, and among thy companions in arms." "Heaven reward thee! and this will I do," said Geraint. "What discourse," said Guenever, "do I hear between you? Is it of those who are to conduct Geraint to his country?" "It is," said Arthur. "Then it is needful for me to consider," said she, "concerning companions and a provision for the lady that is with me." "Thou wilt do well," said Arthur.

And that night they went to sleep. And the next day the ambassadors were permitted to depart, and they were told that Geraint should follow them. And on the third day Geraint set forth, and many went with him,—Gawain, the son of Gwyar, and Riogoned, the son of the king of Ireland, and Ondyaw, the son of the Duke of Burgundy, Gwilim, the son of the ruler of the Franks, Howel, the son of the Earl of Brittany, Perceval, the son of Evrawk, Gwyr, a judge in the court of Arthur, Bedwyr, the son of Bedrawd, Kai, the son of Kyner, Odyar, the Frank, and Edeyrn, the son of Nudd. Said Geraint, "I think I shall have enough of knighthood with me." And they set forth. And never was there seen a fairer host journeying towards the Severn. And on the other side of the Severn were the nobles of Erbin, the son of Custennin, and his foster-father at their head, to welcome Geraint with gladness; and many of the women of the court, with his mother, came to receive Enid, the daughter of Ynywl, his wife. And there was great rejoicing and gladness throughout the whole court, and through all the country, concerning Geraint, because of the greatness of their love to him, and of the greatness of the fame which he had gained since he went from amongst them, and because he was come to take possession of his dominions, and to preserve his boundaries. And they came to the court. And in the court they had ample entertainment, and a multitude of gifts, and abundance of liquor, and a sufficiency of service, and a variety of games. And to do honor to Geraint, all the chief men of the country were invited that night to visit him. And they passed that day and that night in the utmost enjoyment. And at dawn next day Erbin arose, and summoned to him Geraint, and the noble persons who had borne him company. And he said to Geraint: "I am a feeble and an aged man, and whilst I was able to maintain the dominion for thee and for myself, I did so. But thou art young, and in the flower of thy vigor and of thy youth. Henceforth do thou preserve thy possessions." "Truly," said Geraint, "with my consent thou shalt not give the power over thy dominions at this time into my hands, thou shalt not take me from Arthur's court." "Into thy hands will I give them," said Erbin, "and this day shalt thou receive the homage of thy subjects."

Then said Gawain, "It were better for thee to satisfy those who have boons to ask, to-day, and to-morrow thou canst receive the homage of thy dominions." So all that had boons to ask were summoned into one place. And Kadyriath came to them to know what were the requests. And every one asked that which he desired. And the followers of Arthur began to make gifts, and immediately the men of Cornwall came, and gave also. And they were not long in giving, so eager was every one to bestow gifts. And of those who came to ask gifts, none departed unsatisfied. And that day and that night were spent in the utmost enjoyment.

And the next day at dawn Erbin desired Geraint to send messengers to the men to ask them whether it was displeasing to them that he should come to receive their homage, and whether they had anything to object to him. Then Geraint sent ambassadors to the men of Cornwall to ask them this. And they all said that it would be the fulness of joy and honor to them for Geraint to come and receive their homage. So he received the homage of such as were there. And the day after, the followers of Arthur intended to go away. "It is too soon for you to go away yet," said he; "stay with me until I have finished receiving the homage of my chief men, who have agreed to come to me." And they remained with him until he had done so. Then they set forth towards the court of Arthur. And Geraint went to bear them company, and Enid also, as far as Diganwy; there they parted. And Ondyaw, the son of the Duke of Burgundy, said to Geraint, "Go, now, and visit the uttermost parts of thy dominions, and see well to the boundaries of thy territories; and if thou hast any trouble respecting them, send unto thy companions." "Heaven reward thee!" said Geraint; "and this will I do." And Geraint journeyed to the uttermost parts of his dominions. And experienced guides, and the chief men of his country, went with him. And the furthermost point that they showed him he kept possession of.

CHAPTER XXV

GERAINT, THE SON OF ERBIN, CONTINUED

GERAINT, as he had been used to do when he was at Arthur's court, frequented tournaments. And he became acquainted with valiant and mighty men, until he had gained as much fame there as he had formerly done elsewhere. And he enriched his court, and his companions, and his nobles, with the best horses and the best arms, and with the best and most valuable jewels, and he ceased not until his fame had flown over the face of the whole kingdom. When he knew that it was thus, he began to love ease and pleasure, for there was no one who was worth his opposing. And he loved his wife, and liked to continue in the palace, with minstrelsy and diversions. So he began to shut himself up in the chamber of his wife, and he took no delight in anything besides, insomuch that he gave up the friendship of his nobles, together with his hunting and his amusements, and lost the hearts of all the host in his court. And there was murmuring and scoffing concerning him among the inhabitants of the palace, on account of his relinquishing so completely their companionship for the love of his wife. These tidings came to Erbin. And when Erbin had heard these things, he spoke unto Enid, and inquired of her whether it was she that had caused Geraint to act thus, and to forsake his people and his hosts. "Not I, by my confession unto heaven," said she; "there is nothing more hateful unto me than this." And she knew not what she should do, for, although it was hard for her to own this to Geraint, yet was it not more easy for her to listen to what she heard, without warning Geraint concerning it. And she was very sorrowful.

One morning in the summer-time they were upon their couch, and Geraint lay upon the edge of it. And Enid was without sleep in the apartment, which had windows of glass; [1] and the sun

[1] The terms of admiration in which the older writers invariably speak of *glass windows* would be sufficient proof, if other evidence were wanting, how rare an article of luxury they were in the houses of our ancestors. They were first introduced in ecclesiastical architecture, to which they were for a long time confined. Glass is said not to have been employed in domestic architecture before the fourteenth century.

shone upon the couch. And the clothes had slipped from off his arms and his breast, and he was asleep. Then she gazed upon the marvellous beauty of his appearance, and she said, "Alas! and am I the cause that these arms and this breast have lost their glory, and the warlike fame which they once so richly enjoyed?" As she said this the tears dropped from her eyes, and they fell upon his breast. And the tears she shed, and the words she had spoken, awoke him. And another thing contributed to awaken him, and that was the idea that it was not in thinking of him that she spoke thus, but that it was because she loved some other man more than him, and that she wished for other society. Thereupon Geraint was troubled in his mind, and he called his squire; and when he came to him, "Go quickly," said he, "and prepare my horse and my arms, and make them ready. And do thou arise," said he to Enid, "and apparel thyself; and cause thy horse to be accoutred, and clothe thee in the worst riding-dress that thou hast in thy possession. And evil betide me," said he, "if thou returnest here until thou knowest whether I have lost my strength so completely as thou didst say. And if it be so, it will then be easy for thee to seek the society thou didst wish for of him of whom thou wast thinking." So she arose, and clothed herself in her meanest garments. "I know nothing, lord," said she, "of thy meaning." "Neither wilt thou know at this time," said he.

Then Geraint went to see Erbin. "Sir," said he, "I am going upon a quest, and I am not certain when I may come back. Take heed, therefore, unto thy possessions until my return." "I will do so," said he; "but it is strange to me that thou shouldst go so suddenly. And who will proceed with thee, since thou art not strong enough to traverse the land of Loegyr alone?" "But one person only will go with me." "Heaven counsel thee, my son," said Erbin, "and may many attach themselves to thee in Loegyr." Then went Geraint to the place where his horse was, and it was equipped with foreign armor, heavy and shining. And he desired Enid to mount her horse, and to ride forward, and to keep a long way before him. "And whatever thou mayest see, and whatever thou mayest hear concerning me," said he, "do thou not turn back. And unless I speak unto thee, say not thou one word either." So they set forward. And he did not choose the pleasantest and most frequented road, but that which was the wildest and most beset by thieves and robbers and venomous animals.

And they came to a high-road, which they followed till they saw a vast forest; and they saw four armed horsemen come forth from the forest. When the armed men saw them, they said one to another, "Here is a good occasion for us to capture two horses and armor, and a lady likewise; for this we shall have no difficulty in doing against yonder single knight, who hangs his head so pensively and heavily." Enid heard this discourse, and she knew not what she should do through fear of Geraint, who had told her to be silent. "The vengeance of Heaven be upon me," said she, "if I would not rather receive my death from his hand than from the hand of any other; and though he should slay me, yet will I speak to him, lest I should have the misery to witness his death." So she waited for Geraint until he came near to her. "Lord," said she, "didst thou hear the words of those men concerning thee?" Then he lifted up his eyes, and looked at her angrily. "Thou hadst only," said he, "to hold thy peace, as I bade thee. I wish but for silence, and not for warning. And though thou shouldst desire to see my defeat and my death by the hands of those men, yet I do feel no dread." Then the foremost of them couched his lance, and rushed upon Geraint. And he received him, and that not feebly. But he let the thrust go by him, while he struck the horseman upon the centre of the shield, in such a manner that his shield was split, and his armor broken, so that a cubit's length of the shaft of Geraint's lance passed through his body, and sent him to the earth, the length of the lance over his horse's crupper. Then the second horseman attacked him furiously, being wroth at the death of his companion. But with one thrust Geraint overthrew him also, and killed him as he had done the other. Then the third set upon him, and he killed him in like manner. And thus also he slew the fourth. Sad and sorrowful was the maiden as she saw all this. Geraint dismounted his horse, and took the arms of the men he had slain, and placed them upon their saddles, and tied together the reins of their horses; and he mounted his horse again. "Behold what thou must do," said he; "take the four horses, and drive them before thee, and proceed forward as I bade thee just now. And say not one word unto me, unless I speak first unto thee. And I declare unto Heaven," said he, "if thou doest not thus, it will be to thy cost." "I will do as far as I can, lord," said she, "according to thy desire."

So the maiden went forward, keeping in advance of Geraint, as he had desired her; and it grieved him as much as his wrath would permit to see a maiden so illustrious as she having so much trouble with the care of the horses. Then they reached a wood, and it was both deep and vast, and in the wood night overtook them. "Ah, maiden," said he, "it is vain to attempt proceeding forward." "Well, lord," said she, "whatever thou wishest we will do." "It will be best for us," he answered, "to rest and wait for the day in order to pursue our journey." "That will we, gladly," said she. And they did so. Having dismounted himself, he took her down from her horse. "I cannot by any means refrain from sleep through weariness," said he; "do thou therefore watch the horses and sleep not." "I will, lord," said she. Then he went to sleep in his armor, and thus passed the night, which was not long at that season. And when she saw the dawn of day appear she looked around her to see if he were waking, and thereupon he awoke. Then he arose, and said unto her, "Take the horses and ride on, and keep straight on as thou didst yesterday." And they left the wood, and they came to an open country, with meadows on one hand, and mowers mowing the meadows. And there was a river before them, and the horses bent down and drank of the water. And they went up out of the river by a lofty steep; and there they met a slender stripling with a satchel about his neck, and they saw there was something in the satchel, but they knew not what it was. And he had a small blue pitcher in his hand, and a bowl on the mouth of the pitcher. And the youth saluted Geraint. "Heaven prosper thee!" said Geraint; "and whence dost thou come?" "I come," said he, "from the city that lies before thee. My lord," he added, "will it be displeasing to thee if I ask whence thou comest also?" "By no means; through yonder wood did I come." "Thou camest not through the wood to-day." "No," he replied; "we were in the wood last night." "I warrant," said the youth, "that thy condition there last night was not the most pleasant, and that thou hadst neither meat nor drink." "No, by my faith," said he. "Wilt thou follow my counsel," said the youth, "and take thy meal from me?" "What sort of meal?" he inquired. "The breakfast which is sent for yonder mowers, nothing less than bread and meat and wine; and if thou wilt, sir, they shall have none of it." "I will," said he, "and Heaven reward thee for it."

So Geraint alighted, and the youth took the maiden from off her horse. Then they washed, and took their repast. And the youth cut the bread in slices, and gave them drink, and served them withal. And when they had finished the youth arose and said to Geraint, "My lord, with thy permission, I will now go and fetch some food for the mowers." "Go first to the town," said Geraint, "and take a lodging for me in the best place thou knowest, and the most commodious one for the horses; and take thou whichever horse and arms thou choosest in payment for thy service and thy gift." "Heaven reward thee, lord!" said the youth; "and this would be ample to repay services much greater than those I have rendered unto thee." And to the town went the youth, and he took the best and most pleasant lodgings that he knew; and after that he went to the palace, having the horse and armor with him, and proceeded to the place where the earl was, and told him all his adventure. "I go now, lord," said he, "to meet the knight, and to conduct him to his lodging."

"Go, gladly," said the earl, "and right joyfully shall he be received here, if he so come." And the youth went to meet Geraint, and told him that he would be received gladly by the earl in his own palace; but he would go only to his lodgings. And he had a goodly chamber, in which was plenty of straw and drapery, and a spacious and commodious place he had for the horses; and the youth prepared for them plenty of provender. After they had disarrayed themselves, Geraint spoke thus to Enid: "Go," said he, "to the other side of the chamber, and come not to this side of the house; and thou mayst call to thee the woman of the house if thou wilt." "I will do, lord," said she, "as thou sayest." Thereupon the man of the house came to Geraint, and welcomed him. And after they had eaten and drank Geraint went to sleep, and so did Enid also.

In the evening, behold, the earl came to visit Geraint, and his twelve honorable knights with him. And Geraint rose up and welcomed him. Then they all sat down according to their precedence in honor. And the earl conversed with Geraint, and inquired of him the object of his journey. "I have none," he replied, "but to seek adventures and to follow my own inclination." Then the earl cast his eye upon Enid, and he looked at her steadfastly. And he thought he had never seen a maiden fairer or more comely than she. And he set all his thoughts and his affections upon her. Then he asked of Geraint, "Have I thy permission to go and converse with yonder maiden, for I see that she is apart from thee?" "Thou hast it gladly," said he. So the earl went to the place where the maiden was, and spake with her. "Ah! maiden," said he, "it cannot be pleasant to thee to journey with yonder man." "It is not unpleasant to me," said she. "Thou hast neither youths nor maidens to serve thee," said he. "Truly," she replied, "it is more pleasant for me to follow yonder man than to be served by youths and maidens." "I will give thee good counsel," said he; "all my earldom will I place in thy possession if thou wilt dwell with me." "That will I not, by Heaven," she said; "yonder man was the first to whom my faith was pledged, and shall I prove inconstant to him?" "Thou art in the wrong," said the earl; "if I slay the man yonder I can keep thee with me as long as I choose; and when thou no longer pleasest me I can turn thee away. But if thou goest with me by thy own goodwill, I protest that our union shall continue as long as I shall remain alive." Then she pondered those words of his, and she considered that it was advisable to encourage him in his request. "Behold then, chieftain, this is most expedient for thee to do to save me from all reproach; come here to-morrow and take me away as though I knew nothing thereof." "I will do so," said he. So he arose and took his leave, and went forth with his attendants. And she told not then to

Geraint any of the conversation which she had had with the earl
lest it should rouse his anger, and cause him uneasiness and care.

And at the usual hour they went to sleep. And at the beginning
of the night Enid slept a little; and at midnight she arose, and
placed all Geraint's armor together, so that it might be ready to put
on. And though fearful of her errand, she came to the side of
Geraint's bed; and she spoke to him softly and gently, saying, "My
lord, arise, and clothe thyself, for these were the words of the earl
to me, and his intention concerning me." So she told Geraint all that
had passed. And although he was wroth with her, he took warning,
and clothed himself. And she lighted a candle that he might have
light to do so. "Leave there the candle," said he, "and desire the
man of the house to come here." Then she went, and the man of
the house came to him. "Dost thou know how much I owe thee?"
asked Geraint. "I think thou owest but little." "Take the three
horses, and the three suits of armor." "Heaven reward thee, Lord,"
said he, "but I spent not the value of one suit of armor upon thee."
"For that reason," said he, "thou wilt be the richer. And now, wilt
thou come to guide me out of the town?" "I will, gladly," said he;
"and in which direction dost thou intend to go?" "I wish to leave
the town by a different way from that by which I entered it." So the
man of the lodgings accompanied him as far as he desired. Then
he bade the maiden to go on before him, and she did so, and went
straight forward, and his host returned home.

And Geraint and the maiden went forward along the high-road.
And as they journeyed thus, they heard an exceeding loud wailing
near to them. "Stay thou here," said he, "and I will go and see what
is the cause of this wailing." "I will," said she. Then he went forward
into an open glade that was near the road. And in the glade he saw
two horses, one having a man's saddle, and the other a woman's
saddle upon it. And behold there was a knight lying dead in his
armor, and a young damsel in a riding-dress standing over him
lamenting. "Ah, lady," said Geraint, "what hath befallen thee?"
"Behold," she answered, "I journeyed here with my beloved husband, when lo! three giants came upon us, and without any cause
in the world, they slew him." "Which way went they hence?" said
Geraint. "Yonder by the high-road," she replied. So he returned to
Enid. "Go," said he, "to the lady that is below yonder, and await
me there till I come." She was sad when he ordered her to do thus,
but nevertheless she went to the damsel, whom it was ruth to hear,
and she felt certain that Geraint would never return.

Meanwhile Geraint followed the giants, and overtook them. And
each of them was greater in stature than three other men, and a
huge club was on the shoulder of each. Then he rushed upon one

of them, and thrust his lance through his body. And having drawn it forth again, he pierced another of them through likewise. But the third turned upon him, and struck him with his club so that he split his shield and crushed his shoulder. But Geraint drew his sword, and gave the giant a blow on the crown of his head, so severe, and fierce, and violent, that his head and his neck were split down to his shoulders, and he fell dead. So Geraint left him thus, and returned to Enid. And when he reached the place where she was, he fell down lifeless from his horse. Piercing and loud and thrilling was the cry that Enid uttered. And she came and stood over him where he had fallen. And at the sound of her cries came the Earl of Limours, and they who journeyed with him, whom her lamentations brought out of their road. And the earl said to Enid, "Alas, lady, what hath befallen thee?" "Ah, good sir," said she, "the only man I have loved, or ever shall love, is slain." Then he said to the other, "And what is the cause of thy grief?" "They have slain my beloved husband also," said she. "And who was it that slew them?" "Some giants," she answered, "slew my best-beloved, and the other knight went in pursuit of them, and came back in the state thou seest." The earl caused the knight that was dead to be buried, but he thought that there still remained some life in Geraint; and to see if he yet would live, he had him carried with him in the hollow of his shield, and upon a bier. And the two damsels went to the court; and when they arrived there, Geraint was placed upon a little couch in front of the table that was in the hall. Then they all took off their travelling-gear, and the earl besought Enid to do the same, and to clothe herself in other garments. "I will not, by Heaven," said she. "Ah, lady," said he, "be not so sorrowful for this matter." "It were hard to persuade me to be otherwise," said she. "I will act towards thee in such wise that thou needest not be sorrowful, whether yonder knight live or die. Behold, a good earldom, together with myself, will I bestow upon thee; be therefore happy and joyful." "I declare to Heaven," said she, "that henceforth I shall never be joyful while I live." "Come," said he, "and eat." "No, by Heaven, I will not." "But by Heaven, thou shalt," said he. So he took her with him to the table against her will, and many times desired her to eat. "I call Heaven to witness," said she, "that I will not eat until the man that is upon yonder bier shall eat likewise." "Thou canst not fulfil that," said the earl; "yonder man is dead already." "I will prove that I can," said she. Then he offered her a goblet of liquor. "Drink this goblet," he said, "and it will cause thee to change thy mind." "Evil betide me," she answered, "if I drink aught until he drink also." "Truly," said the earl, "it is of no more avail for me to be gentle with thee than ungentle." And he gave

---

her a box in the ear. Thereupon she raised a loud and piercing shriek, and her lamentations were much greater than they had been before; for she considered in her mind that, had Geraint been alive, he durst not have struck her thus. But behold, at the sound of her cry, Geraint revived from his swoon, and he sat up on the bier; and finding his sword in the hollow of his shield, he rushed to the place where the earl was, and struck him a fiercely-wounding, severely-venomous, and sternly-smiting blow upon the crown of his head, so that he clove him in twain, until his sword was staid by the table. Then all left the board and fled away. And this was not so much through fear of the living, as through the dread they felt at seeing the dead man rise up to slay them. And Geraint looked upon Enid, and he was grieved for two causes; one was to see that Enid had lost her color and her wonted aspect; and the other, to know that she was in the right. "Lady," said he, "knowest thou where our horses are?" "I know, lord, where thy horse is," she replied, "but I know not where is the other. Thy horse is in the house yonder." So he went to the house, and brought forth his horse, and mounted him, and took up Enid, and placed her upon the horse with him. And he rode forward. And their road lay between two hedges; and the night was gaining on the day. And lo! they saw behind them the shafts of spears betwixt them and the sky, and they heard the tramping of horses, and the noise of a host approaching. "I hear something following us," said he, "and I will put thee on the other side of the hedge." And thus he did. And thereupon, behold, a knight pricked towards him, and couched his lance. When Enid saw this, she cried out, saying, "O chieftain, whoever thou art, what renown wilt thou gain by slaying a dead man?" "O Heaven!" said he, "is it Geraint?" "Yes, in truth," said she; "and who art thou?" "I am Gwiffert Petit," said he, "thy husband's ally, coming to thy assistance, for I heard that thou wast in trouble. Come with me to the court of a son-in-law of my sister, which is near here, and thou shalt have the best medical assistance in the kingdom." "I will do so gladly," said Geraint. And Enid was placed upon the horse of one of Gwiffert's squires, and they went forward to the baron's palace. And they were received there with gladness, and they met with hospitality and attention. The next morning they went to seek physicians; and it was not long before they came, and they attended Geraint until he was perfectly well. And while Geraint was under medical care, Gwiffert caused his armor to be repaired, until it was as good as it had ever been. And they remained there a month and a fortnight. Then they separated, and Geraint went towards his own dominions, and thenceforth he reigned prosperously, and his

warlike fame and splendor lasted with renown and honor both to
him and to Enid,[1] from that time forward.

CHAPTER XXVI

PWYLL, PRINCE OF DYVED

ONCE upon a time Pwyll was at Narberth, his chief palace, where
a feast had been prepared for him, and with him was a great host
of men. And after the first meal Pwyll arose to walk; and he went to
the top of a mound that was above the palace, and was called
Gorsedd Arberth. "Lord," said one of the court, "it is peculiar to
the mound that whosoever sits upon it cannot go thence without
either receiving wounds or blows, or else seeing a wonder." "I fear
not to receive wounds or blows," said Pwyll; "but as to the wonder,
gladly would I see it. I will therefore go and sit upon the mound."
And upon the mound he sat. And while he sat there, they saw a
lady, on a pure white horse of large size, with a garment of shining
gold around her, coming along the highway that led from the mound.
"My men," said Pwyll, "is there any among you who knows yonder
lady?" "There is not, lord," said they. "Go one of you and meet
her, that we may know who she is." And one of them arose, and as
he came upon the road to meet her, she passed by; and he followed
as fast as he could, being on foot, and the greater was his speed,
the further was she from him. And when he saw that it profited him
nothing to follow her, he returned to Pwyll, and said unto him,
"Lord, it is idle for any one in the world to follow her on foot."
"Verily," said Pwyll, "go unto the palace, and take the fleetest horse
that thou seest, and go after her."

And he took a horse and went forward. And he came to an open,
level plain, and put spurs to his horse; and the more he urged his
horse, the further was she from him. And he returned to the palace
where Pwyll was, and said, "Lord, it will avail nothing for any one
to follow yonder lady. I know of no horse in these realms swifter
than this, and it availed me not to pursue her." "Of a truth," said

---

[1] Throughout the broad and varied regions of romance, it would be difficult
to find a character of greater simplicity and truth than that of Enid, the
daughter of Earl Ynywl. Conspicuous for her beauty and noble bearing, we
are at a loss whether more to admire the patience with which she bore all the
hardships she was destined to undergo, or the constancy and affection which
finally achieved the triumph she so richly deserved.

The character of Enid is admirably sustained through the whole tale; and
as it is more natural, because less overstrained, so perhaps it is even more
touching, than that of Griselda, over which, however, Chaucer has thrown a
charm that leads us to forget the improbability of her story.

Pwyll, "there must be some illusion here; let us go towards the palace." So to the palace they went, and spent the day.

And the next day they amused themselves until it was time to go to meat. And when meat was ended, Pwyll said, "Where are the hosts that went yesterday to the top of the mound?" "Behold, lord, we are here," said they. "Let us go," said he, "to the mound, and sit there. And do thou," said he to the page who tended his horse, "saddle my horse well, and hasten with him to the road, and bring also my spurs with thee." And the youth did thus. And they went and sat upon the mound; and ere they had been there but a short time, they beheld the lady coming by the same road, and in the same manner, and at the same pace. "Young man," said Pwyll, "I see the lady coming; give me my horse." And before he had mounted his horse she passed him. And he turned after her and followed her. And he let his horse go bounding playfully, and thought that he should soon come up with her. But he came no nearer to her than at first. Then he urged his horse to his utmost speed, yet he found that it availed not. Then said Pwyll, "O maiden, for the sake of him whom thou best lovest, stay for me." "I will stay gladly," said she; "and it were better for thy horse hadst thou asked it long since." So the maiden stopped; and she threw back that part of her headdress which covered her face. Then he thought that the beauty of all the maidens and all the ladies that he had ever seen was as nothing compared to her beauty. "Lady," he said, "wilt thou tell me aught concerning thy purpose?" "I will tell thee," said she; "my chief quest was to see thee." "Truly," said Pwyll, "this is to me the most pleasing quest on which thou couldst have come; and wilt thou tell me who thou art?" "I will tell thee, lord," said she. "I am Rhiannon, the daughter of Heveydd, and they sought to give me to a husband against my will. But no husband would I have, and that because of my love for thee; neither will I yet have one, unless thou reject me; and hither have I come to hear thy answer." "By Heaven," said Pwyll, "behold this is my answer. If I might choose among all the ladies and damsels in the world, thee would I choose." "Verily," said she, "if thou art thus minded, make a pledge to meet me ere I am given to another." "The sooner I may do so, the more pleasing will it be to me," said Pwyll; "and wheresoever thou wilt, there will I meet with thee." "I will that thou meet me this day twelvemonth at the palace of Heveydd." "Gladly," said he, "will I keep this tryst." So they parted, and he went back to his hosts, and to them of his household. And whatsoever questions they asked him respecting the damsel, he always turned the discourse upon other matters.

And when a year from that time was gone, he caused a hundred knights to equip themselves, and to go with him to the palace of Heveydd. And he came to the palace, and there was great joy concerning him, with much concourse of people, and great rejoicing, and vast preparations for his coming. And the whole court was placed under his orders.

And the hall was garnished, and they went to meat, and thus did they sit: Heveydd was on one side of Pwyll, and Rhiannon on the other; and all the rest according to their rank. And they ate and feasted, and talked one with another. And at the beginning of the carousal after the meat, there entered a tall, auburn-haired youth, of royal bearing, clothed in a garment of satin. And when he came into the hall, he saluted Pwyll and his companions. "The greeting of Heaven be unto thee," said Pwyll; "come thou and sit down." "Nay," said he, "a suitor am I, and I will do my errand." "Do so, willingly," said Pwyll. "Lord," said he, "my errand is unto thee, and it is to crave a boon of thee that I come." "What boon soever thou mayest ask of me, so far as I am able, thou shalt have." "Ah!" said Rhiannon, "wherefore didst thou give that answer?" "Has he not given it before the presence of these nobles?" asked the youth. "My soul," said Pwyll, "what is the boon thou askest?" "The lady whom best I love is to be thy bride this night; I come to ask her of thee, with the feast and the banquet that are in this place." And Pwyll was silent, because of the promise which he had given. "Be silent as long as thou wilt," said Rhiannon, "never did man make worse use of his wits than thou hast done." "Lady," said he, "I knew not who he was." "Behold, this is the man to whom they would have given me against my will," said she; "and he is Gawl, the son of Clud, a man of great power and wealth, and because of the word thou hast spoken, bestow me upon him, lest shame befall thee." "Lady," said he, "I understand not thy answer; never can I do as thou sayest." "Bestow me upon him," said she, "and I will cause that I shall never be his." "By what means will that be?" asked Pwyll. Then she told him the thought that was in her mind. And they talked long together. Then Gawl said, "Lord, it is meet that I have an answer to my request." "As much of that thou hast asked as it is in my power to give, thou shalt have," replied Pwyll. "My soul," said Rhiannon unto Gawl, "as for the feast and the banquet that are here, I have bestowed them upon the men of Dyved, and the household and the warriors that are with us. These can I not suffer to be given to any. In a year from to-night, a banquet shall be prepared for thee in this palace, that I may become thy bride."

So Gawl went forth to his possessions, and Pwyll went also back to Dyved. And they both spent that year until it was the time for the feast at the palace of Heveydd. Then Gawl, the son of Clud, set out to the feast that was prepared for him; and he came to the palace, and was received there with rejoicing. Pwyll, also, the chief of Dyved, came to the orchard with a hundred knights, as Rhiannon had commanded him. And Pwyll was clad in coarse and ragged garments, and wore large, clumsy old shoes upon his feet. And when he knew that the carousal after the meat had begun, he went toward the hall; and when he came into the hall he saluted Gawl, the son of Clud, and his company, both men and women. "Heaven prosper thee," said Gawl, "and friendly greeting be unto thee!" "Lord," said he, "may Heaven reward thee! I have an errand unto thee." "Welcome be thine errand, and if thou ask of me that which is right, thou shalt have it gladly." "It is fitting," answered he; "I crave but from want, and the boon I ask is to have this small bag that thou seest filled with meat." "A request within reason is this," said he, "and gladly shalt thou have it. Bring him food." A great number of attendants arose and began to fill the bag; but for all they put into it, it was no fuller than at first. "My soul," said Gawl, "will thy bag ever be full?" "It will not, I declare to Heaven," said he, "for all that may be put into it, unless one possessed of lands, and domains, and treasure, shall arise and tread down with both his feet the food that is within the bag, and shall say, 'Enough has been put therein.'" Then said Rhiannon unto Gawl, the son of Clud, "Rise up quickly." "I will willingly arise," said he. So he rose up, and put his two feet into the bag. And Pwyll turned up the sides of the bag, so that Gawl was over his head in it. And he shut it up quickly, and slipped a knot upon the thongs, and blew his horn. And thereupon, behold, his knights came down upon the palace. And they seized all the host that had come with Gawl, and cast them into his own prison. And Pwyll threw off his rags, and his old shoes, and his tattered array. And as they came in every one of Pwyll's knights struck a blow upon the bag, and asked, "What is here?" "A badger," said they. And in this manner they played, each of them striking the bag, either with his foot or with a staff. And thus played they with the bag. And then was the game of Badger in the Bag first played.

"Lord," said the man in the bag, "if thou wouldst but hear me, I merit not to be slain in a bag." Said Heveydd, "Lord, he speaks truth; it were fitting that thou listen to him, for he deserves not this." "Verily," said Pwyll, "I will do thy counsel concerning him." "Behold, this is my counsel then," said Rhiannon. "Thou art now in a position in which it behooves thee to satisfy suitors and minstrels. Let him give unto them in thy stead, and take a pledge from him that he will never seek to revenge that which has been done to him. And this will be punishment enough." "I will do this gladly," said the man in the bag. "And gladly will I accept it," said Pwyll, "since it is the counsel of Heveydd and Rhiannon. Seek thyself sureties." "We will be for him," said Heveydd, "until his men be free to answer for him." And upon this he was let out of the bag, and his liegemen were liberated. "Verily, lord," said Gawl, "I am greatly hurt, and I have many bruises. With thy leave I will go forth. I will leave nobles in my stead to answer for me in all that thou shalt require." "Willingly," said Pwyll, "mayest thou do thus." So Gawl went to his own possessions.

And the hall was set in order for Pwyll and the men of his host, and for them also of the palace, and they went to the tables and sat down. And as they had sat at that time twelve-month, so sat they that night. And they ate and feasted, and spent the night in mirth and tranquillity. And the time came that they should sleep, and Pwyll and Rhiannon went to their chamber.

And next morning at break of day, "My lord," said Rhiannon, "arise and begin to give thy gifts unto the minstrels. Refuse no one to-day that may claim thy bounty." "Thus shall it be gladly," said Pwyll, "both to-day and every day while the feast shall last." So Pwyll arose, and he caused silence to be proclaimed, and desired all the suitors and minstrels to show and to point out what gifts they desired. And this being done, the feast went on, and he denied no one while it lasted. And when the feast was ended, Pwyll said unto Heveydd, "My lord, with thy permission, I will set out for Dyved to-morrow." "Certainly," said Heveydd; "may Heaven prosper thee! Fix also a time when Rhiannon shall follow thee." "By Heaven," said Pwyll, "we will go hence together." "Willest thou this, lord?" said Heveydd. "Yes, lord," answered Pwyll.

And the next day they set forward towards Dyved, and journeyed to the palace of Narberth, where a feast was made ready for them. And there came to them great numbers of the chief men and the most noble ladies of the land, and of these there were none to whom Rhiannon did not give some rich gift, either a bracelet, or a ring, or a precious stone. And they ruled the land prosperously that year and the next.

CHAPTER XXVII

BRANWEN, THE DAUGHTER OF LLYR

BENDIGEID VRAN, the son of Llyr, was the crowned king of this island, and he was exalted from the crown of London. And one afternoon he was at Harlech, in Ardudwy, at his court; and he sat upon the rock of Harlech, looking over the sea. And with him were his brother, Manawyddan, the son of Llyr, and his brothers by his mother's side, Nissyen and Evnissyen, and many nobles likewise, as was fitting to see around a king. His two brothers by the mother's side were sons of Euroswydd, and one of these youths was a good youth, and of gentle nature, and would make peace between his kindred, and cause his family to be friends when their wrath was at the highest, and this one was Nissyen; but the other would cause strife between his two brothers when they were most at peace. And as they sat thus they beheld thirteen ships coming from the south of Ireland, and making towards them; and they came with a swift motion, the wind being behind them; and they neared them rapidly. "I see ships afar," said the king, "coming swiftly towards the land. Command the men of the court that they equip themselves, and go and learn their intent." So the men equipped themselves, and went down towards them. And when they saw the ships near, certain were they that they had never seen ships better furnished. Beautiful flags of satin were upon them. And, behold, one of the ships out-stripped the others, and they saw a shield lifted up above the side of the ship, and the point of the shield was upwards, in token of peace. And the men drew near, that they might hold converse. Then they put out boats, and came toward the land. And they saluted the king. Now the king could hear them from the place where he was upon the rock above their heads. "Heaven prosper you," said he, "and be ye welcome! To whom do those ships belong, and who is the chief amongst you?" "Lord," said they, "Matholch, king of Ireland, is here, and these ships belong to him." "Wherefore comes he?" asked the king, "and will he come to the land?" "He is a suitor unto thee, lord," said they, "and he will not land unless he have his boon." "And what may that be?" inquired the king. "He desires to ally himself, lord, with thee," said they, "and he comes to ask Branwen, the daughter of Llyr, that, if it seem well to thee, the Island of the Mighty [1] may be leagued with Ireland, and both become more powerful." "Verily," said he, "let him come to land, and we will take counsel thereupon." And this answer was brought to Matholch. "I will go willingly," said he. So he landed, and they received him joyfully; and great was the throng in the palace that night between his hosts and those of the court; and next day they took counsel, and they resolved to bestow Branwen upon Matholch. Now she was one of the three chief ladies of this island, and she was the fairest damsel in the world.

And they fixed upon Aberfraw as the place where she should become his bride. And they went thence, and towards Aberfraw the

---

[1] The Island of the Mighty is one of the many names bestowed upon Britain by the Welsh.

hosts proceeded, Matholch and his host in their ships, Bendigeid
Vran and his host by land, until they came to Aberfraw. And at
Aberfraw they began the feast, and sat down. And thus sat they:
the king of the Island of the Mighty and Manawyddan, the son of
Llyr, on one side, and Matholch on the other side, and Branwen,
the daughter of Llyr, beside him. And they were not within a house,
but under tents. No house could ever contain Bendigeid Vran. And
they began the banquet, and caroused and discoursed. And when it
was more pleasing to them to sleep than to carouse, they went to
rest, and Branwen became Matholch's bride.

And the next day they arose, and all they of the court, and the
officers began to equip, and to range the horses and the attendants,
and they ranged them in order as far as the sea.

And, behold, one day Evnissyen, the quarrelsome man, of whom
it is spoken above, came by chance into the place where the horses
of Matholch were, and asked whose horses they might be. "They
are the horses of Matholch, king of Ireland, who is married to Branwen, thy sister; his horses are they." "And is it thus they have done
with a maiden such as she, and moreover my sister, bestowing her,
without my consent? They could have offered me no greater insult
than this," said he. And thereupon he rushed under the horses, and
cut off their lips at the teeth, and their ears close to their heads,
and their tails close to their backs; and he disfigured the horses,
and rendered them useless.

And they came with these tidings unto Matholch, saying that the
horses were disfigured and injured, so that not one of them could
ever be of any use again. "Verily, lord," said one, "it was an insult
unto thee, and as such was it meant." "Of a truth, it is a marvel to
me that, if they desire to insult me, they should have given me a
maiden of such high rank, and so much beloved by their kindred,
as they have done." "Lord," said another, "thou seest that thus it
is, and there is nothing for thee to do but to go to thy ships." And
thereupon towards his ships he set out.

And tidings came to Bendigeid Vran that Matholch was quitting
the court without asking leave, and messengers were sent to him
to inquire wherefore he did so. And the messengers that went were
Iddic, the son of Anarawd, and Heveyd Hir. And these overtook
him, and asked of him what he designed to do, and wherefore he
went forth. "Of a truth," said he "if I had known I had not come
hither. I have been altogether insulted; no one had ever worse treatment than I have had here." "Truly, lord, it was not the will of any
that are of the court," said they, "nor of any that are of the council,
that thou shouldst have received this insult; and as thou hast been
insulted the dishonor is greater unto Bendigeid Vran than unto

thee." "Verily," said he, "I think so. Nevertheless he cannot recall
the insult." These men returned with that answer to the place where
Bendigeid Vran was, and they told him what reply Matholch had
given them. "Truly," said he, "there are no means by which we may
prevent his going away at enmity with us that we will not take."
"Well, lord," said they, "send after him another embassy." "I will
do so," said he. "Arise, Manawyddan, son of Llyr, and Heveyd Hir,
and go after him, and tell him that he shall have a sound horse for
every one that has been injured. And besides that, as an atonement
for the insult, he shall have a staff of silver as large and as tall as
himself, and a plate of gold of the breadth of his face. And show
unto him who it was that did this, and that it was done against my
will; but that he who did it is my brother, and therefore it would
be hard for me to put him to death. And let him come and meet
me," said he, "and we will make peace in any way he may desire."

The embassy went after Matholch, and told him all these sayings
in a friendly manner; and he listened thereunto. "Men," said he,
"I will take counsel." So to the council he went. And in the council
they considered that, if they should refuse this, they were likely
to have more shame rather than to obtain so great an atonement.
They resolved, therefore, to accept it, and they returned to the court
in peace.

Then the pavilions and tents were set in order after the fashion
of a hall; and they went to meat, and as they had sat at the beginning of the feast so sat they there. And Matholch and Bendigeid
Vran began to discourse; and, behold, it seemed to Bendigeid Vran,
while they talked, that Matholch was not so cheerful as he had been
before. And he thought that the chieftain might be sad because of
the smallness of the atonement which he had for the wrong that
had been done him. "O man," said Bendigeid Vran, "thou dost not
discourse to-night so cheerfully as thou wast wont. And if it be
because of the smallness of the atonement thou shalt add thereunto
whatsoever thou mayest choose, and to-morrow I will pay thee for
the horses." "Lord," said he, "Heaven reward thee!" "And I will
enhance the atonement," said Bendigeid Vran, "for I will give thee
a caldron, the property of which is that if one of thy men be slain
to-day, and be cast therein, to-morrow he will be as well as ever
he was at the best, except that he will not regain his speech." And
thereupon he gave him great thanks, and very joyful was he for
that cause.

That night they continued to discourse as much as they would,
and had minstrelsy and carousing; and when it was more pleasant to
them to sleep than to sit longer, they went to rest. And thus was
the banquet carried on with joyousness; and when it was finished,

Matholch journeyed towards Ireland, and Branwen with him; and they went from Aber Menei with thirteen ships, and came to Ireland. And in Ireland was there great joy because of their coming. And not one great man nor noble lady visited Branwen unto whom she gave not either a clasp or a ring, or a royal jewel to keep, such as it was honorable to be seen departing with. And in these things she spent that year in much renown, and she passed her time pleasantly, enjoying honor and friendship. And in due time a son was born unto her, and the name that they gave him was Gwern, the son of Matholch, and they put the boy out to be nursed in a place where were the best men of Ireland.

And, behold, in the second year a great tumult arose in Ireland, on account of the insult which Matholch had received in Wales, and the payment made him for his horses. And his foster-brothers, and such as were nearest to him, blamed him openly for that matter. And he might have no peace by reason of the tumult, until they should revenge upon him this disgrace. And the vengeance which they took was to drive away Branwen from the same chamber with him, and to make her cook for the court; and they caused the butcher, after he had cut up the meat, to come to her and give her every day a blow on the ear; and such they made her punishment.

"Verily, lord," said his men to Matholch, "forbid now the ships and the ferry-boats, and the coracles, that they go not into Wales, and such as come over from Wales hither, imprison them, that they go not back for this thing to be known there." And he did so; and it was thus for no less than three years.

And Branwen reared a starling in the cover of the kneading-trough, and she taught it to speak, and she taught the bird what manner of man her brother was. And she wrote a letter of her woes, and the despite with which she was treated, and she bound the letter to the root of the bird's wing, and sent it toward Wales. And the bird came to that island; and one day it found Bendigeid Vran at Caer Seiont in Arvon, conferring there, and it alighted upon his shoulder, and ruffled its feathers, so that the letter was seen, and they knew that the bird had been reared in a domestic manner.

Then Bendigeid Vran took the letter and looked upon it. And when he had read the letter, he grieved exceedingly at the tidings of Branwen's woes. And immediately he began sending messengers to summon the island together. And he caused sevenscore and four of his chief men to come unto him, and he complained to them of the grief that his sister endured. So they took counsel. And in the council they resolved to go to Ireland, and to leave seven men as princes at home, and Caradoc,[1] the son of Bran, as the chief of them.

[1] Caractacus.

Bendigeid Vran, with the host of which we spoke, sailed towards Ireland; and it was not far across the sea, and he came to shoal water. Now the swineherds of Matholch were upon the seashore, and they came to Matholch. "Lord," said they, "greeting be unto thee." "Heaven protect you!" said he; "have you any news?" "Lord," said they, "we have marvellous news. A wood have we seen upon the sea, in a place where we never yet saw a single tree." "This is indeed a marvel," said he; "saw you aught else?" "We saw, lord," said they, "a vast mountain beside the wood, which moved, and there was a lofty ridge on the top of the mountain, and a lake on each side of the ridge. And the wood and the mountain, and all these things moved." "Verily," said he, "there is none who can know aught concerning this unless it be Branwen."

Messengers then went unto Branwen. "Lady," said they, "what thinkest thou that this is?" "The men of the Island of the Mighty, who have come hither on hearing of my ill-treatment and of my woes." "What is the forest that is seen upon the sea?" asked they. "The yards and the masts of ships," she answered. "Alas!" said they; "what is the mountain that is seen by the side of the ships?" "Bendigeid Vran, my brother," she replied, "coming to shoal water, and he is wading to the land." "What is the lofty ridge, with the lake on each side thereof?" "On looking towards this island he is wroth, and his two eyes on each side of his nose are the two lakes on each side of the ridge."

The warriors and chief men of Ireland were brought together in haste, and they took counsel. "Lord," said the neighbors unto Matholch, "there is no other counsel than this alone. Thou shalt give the kingdom to Gwern, the son of Branwen his sister, as a compensation for the wrong and despite that have been done unto Branwen. And he will make peace with thee." And in the council it was resolved that this message should be sent to Bendigeid Vran, lest the country should be destroyed. And this peace was made. And Matholch caused a great house to be built for Bendigeid Vran, and his host. Thereupon came the hosts into the house. The men of the island of Ireland entered the house on the one side, and the men of the Island of the Mighty on the other. And as soon as they had sat down, there was concord between them; and the sovereignty was conferred upon the boy. When the peace was concluded, Bendigeid Vran called the boy unto him, and from Bendigeid Vran the boy went unto Manawyddan, and he was beloved by all that beheld him. And from Manawyddan the boy was called by Nissyen, the son of Euroswydd, and the boy went unto him lovingly. "Wherefore," said Evnissyen, "comes not my nephew, the son of my sister, unto me? Though he were not king of Ireland, yet willingly would

I fondle the boy." "Cheerfully let him go to thee," said Bendigeid Vran; and the boy went unto him cheerfully. "By my confession to Heaven," said Evnissyen in his heart, "unthought of is the slaughter that I will this instant commit."

Then he arose and took up the boy, and before any one in the house could seize hold of him he thrust the boy headlong into the blazing fire. And when Branwen saw her son burning in the fire, she strove to leap into the fire also, from the place where she sat between her two brothers. But Bendigeid Vran grasped her with one hand, and his shield with the other. Then they all hurried about the house, and never was there made so great a tumult by any host in one house as was made by them, as each man armed himself. And while they all sought their arms Bendigeid Vran supported Branwen between his shield and his shoulder. And they fought.

Then the Irish kindled a fire under the caldron of renovation, and they cast the dead bodies into the caldron until it was full; and the next day they came forth fighting men, as good as before, except that they were not able to speak. Then when Evnissyen saw the dead bodies of the men of the Island of the Mighty nowhere resuscitated, he said in his heart, "Alas! woe is me, that I should have been the cause of bringing the men of the Island of the Mighty into so great a strait. Evil betide me if I find not a deliverance therefrom." And he cast himself among the dead bodies of the Irish; and two unshod Irishmen came to him, and taking him to be one of the Irish, flung him into the caldron. And he stretched himself out in the caldron, so that he rent the caldron into four pieces, and burst his own heart also.

In consequence of this the men of the Island of the Mighty obtained such success as they had; but they were not victorious, for only seven men of them all escaped, and Bendigeid Vran himself was wounded in the foot with a poisoned dart. Now the men that escaped were Pryderi, Manawyddan, Taliesin, and four others.

And Bendigeid Vran commanded them that they should cut off his head. "And take you my head," said he, "and bear it even unto the White Mount in London, and bury it there with the face towards France. And so long as it lies there, no enemy shall ever land on the island." So they cut off his head, and these seven went forward therewith. And Branwen was the eighth with them. And they came to land on Aber Alaw, and they sat down to rest. And Branwen looked towards Ireland, and towards the Island of the Mighty, to see if she could descry them. "Alas!" said she, "woe is me that I was ever born; two islands have been destroyed because of me." Then she uttered a groan, and there broke her heart. And they made her a four-sided grave, and buried her upon the banks of the Alaw.

Then the seven men journeyed forward, bearing the head with
them; and as they went, behold, there met them a multitude of men
and women. "Have you any tidings?" said Manawyddan. "We have
none," said they, "save that Caswallawn,[1] the son of Beli, has conquered the Island of the Mighty, and is crowned king in London."
"What has become," said they, "of Caradoc, the son of Bran, and
the seven men who were left with him in this island?" "Caswallawn
came upon them, and slew six of the men, and Caradoc's heart broke
for grief thereof." And the seven men journeyed on towards London, and they buried the head in the White Mount, as Bendigeid
Vran had directed them.[2]

CHAPTER XXVII

MANAWYDDAN

Pwyll and Rhiannon had a son, whom they named Pryderi.
And when he was grown up, Pwyll, his father, died. And Pryderi
married Kicva, the daughter of Gwynn Gloy.

Now Manawyddan returned from the war in Ireland, and he
found that his cousin had seized all his possessions, and much grief
and heaviness came upon him. "Alas! woe is me!" he exclaimed;
"there is none save myself without a home and a resting-place."
"Lord," said Pryderi, "be not so sorrowful. Thy cousin is king of
the Island of the Mighty, and though he has done thee wrong, thou
hast never been a claimant of land or possessions." "Yea," answered he, "but although this man is my cousin, it grieveth me to
see any one in the place of my brother, Bendigeid Vran; neither can
I be happy in the same dwelling with him." "Wilt thou follow the
counsel of another?" said Pryderi. "I stand in need of counsel," he
answered, "and what may that counsel be?" "Seven cantrevs belong
unto me," said Pryderi, "wherein Rhiannon, my mother, dwells. I
will bestow her upon thee, and the seven cantrevs with her; and
though thou hadst no possessions but those cantrevs only, thou
couldst not have any fairer than they. Do thou and Rhiannon enjoy
them; and if thou desire any possessions thou wilt not despise these."
"I do not, chieftain," said he. "Heaven reward thee for thy friendship! I will go with thee to seek Rhiannon, and to look at thy possessions." "Thou wilt do well," he answered; "and I believe thou
didst never hear a lady discourse better than she, and when she was

---

[1] Cassivellaunus.
[2] There is a Triad upon the story of the head buried under the White
Tower of London, as a charm against invasion. Arthur, it seems, proudly dis-
interred the head, preferring to hold the island by his own strength alone.

in her prime, none was ever fairer. Even now her aspect is not uncomely."

They set forth, and, however long the journey, they came at last to Dyved; and a feast was prepared for them by Rhiannon and Kicva. Then began Manawyddan and Rhiannon to sit and talk together; and his mind and his thoughts became warmed towards her, and he thought in his heart he had never beheld any lady more fulfilled of grace and beauty than she. "Pryderi," said he, "I will that it be as thou didst say." "What saying was that?" asked Rhiannon. "Lady," said Pryderi, "I did offer thee as a wife to Manawyddan, the son of Llyr." "By that will I gladly abide," said Rhiannon. "Right glad am I also," said Manawyddan; "may Heaven reward him who hath shown unto me friendship so perfect as this."

And before the feast was over she became his bride. Said Pryderi, "Tarry ye here the rest of the feast, and I will go into England to tender my homage unto Caswallawn, the son of Beli." "Lord," said Rhiannon, "Caswallawn is in Kent; thou mayest therefore tarry at the feast, and wait until he shall be nearer." "We will wait," he answered. So they finished the feast. And they began to make the circuit of Dyved, and to hunt, and to take their pleasure. And as they went through the country, they had never seen lands more pleasant to live in, nor better hunting-grounds, nor greater plenty of honey and fish. And such was the friendship between these four, that they would not be parted from each other by night nor by day.

And in the midst of all this he went to Caswallawn at Oxford, and tendered his homage; and honorable was his reception there, and highly was he praised for offering his homage.

And after his return Pryderi and Manawyddan feasted and took their ease and pleasure. And they began a feast at Narberth, for it was the chief palace. And when they had ended the first meal, while those who served them ate, they arose and went forth, and proceeded to the Gorsedd, that is, the Mound of Narberth, and their retinue with them. And as they sat thus, behold a peal of thunder, and with the violence of the thunder-storm, lo! there came a fall of mist, so thick that not one of them could see the other. And after the mist it became light all around. And when they looked towards the place where they were wont to see cattle and herds and dwellings, they saw nothing now, neither house, nor beast, nor smoke, nor fire, nor man, nor dwelling, but the buildings of the court empty, and desert, and uninhabited, without either man or beast within them. And truly all their companions were lost to them, without their knowing aught of what had befallen them, save those four only.

"In the name of Heaven," said Manawyddan, "where are they of the court, and all my host beside? Let us go and see."

So they came to the castle, and saw no man, and into the hall, and to the sleeping-place, and there was none; and in the mead-cellar and in the kitchen there was naught but desolation. Then they began to go through the land, and all the possessions that they had; and they visited the houses and dwellings, and found nothing but wild beasts. And when they had consumed their feast and all their provisions, they fed upon the prey they killed in hunting, and the honey of the wild swarms.

And one morning Pryderi and Manawyddan rose up to hunt, and they ranged their dogs and went forth. And some of the dogs ran before them, and came to a bush which was near at hand; but as soon as they were come to the bush, they hastily drew back, and returned to the men, their hair bristling up greatly. "Let us go near to the bush," said Pryderi, "and see what is in it." And as they came near, behold, a wild boar of a pure white color rose up from the bush. Then the dogs, being set on by the men, rushed towards him; but he left the bush, and fell back a little way from the men, and made a stand against the dogs, without retreating from them, until the men had come near. And when the men came up, he fell back a second time, and betook him to flight. Then they pursued the boar until they beheld a vast and lofty castle, all newly built, in a place where they had never before seen either stone or building. And the boar ran swiftly into the castle, and the dogs after him. Now when the boar and the dogs had gone into the castle, the men began to wonder at finding a castle in a place where they had never seen any building whatsoever. And from the top of the Gorsedd they looked and listened for the dogs. But so long as they were there, they heard not one of the dogs, nor aught concerning them.

"Lord," said Pryderi, "I will go into the castle to get tidings of the dogs." "Truly," he replied, "thou wouldst be unwise to go into this castle, which thou hast never seen till now. If thou wouldst follow my counsel, thou wouldst not enter therein. Whosoever has cast a spell over this land, has caused this castle to be here." "Of a truth," answered Pryderi, "I cannot thus give up my dogs." And for all the counsel that Manawyddan gave him, yet to the castle he went.

When he came within the castle neither man, nor beast, nor boar, nor dogs, nor house, nor dwelling, saw he within it. But in the centre of the castle floor he beheld a fountain with marble-work around it, and on the margin of the fountain a golden bowl upon a marble slab, and chains hanging from the air, to which he saw no end. And he was greatly pleased with the beauty of the gold, and with the rich workmanship of the bowl; and he went up to the bowl, and laid hold of it. And when he had taken hold of it his hands stuck to the bowl, and his feet to the slab on which the bowl was placed; and all his joyousness forsook him, so that he could not utter a word. And thus he stood.

And Manawyddan waited for him till near the close of the day. And late in the evening, being certain that he should have no tidings of Pryderi or the dogs, he went back to the palace. And as he entered Rhiannon looked at him. "Where," said she, "are thy companion and thy dogs?" "Behold," he answered, "the adventure that has befallen me." And he related it all unto her. "An evil companion hast thou been," said Rhiannon, "and a good companion hast thou lost." And with that word she went out, and proceeded towards the castle, according to the direction which he gave her. The gate of the castle she found open. She was nothing daunted, and she went in. And as she went in she perceived Pryderi laying hold of the bowl, and she went towards him. "O my lord," said she, "what dost thou here?" And she took hold of the bowl with him; and as she did so her hands also became fast to the bowl, and her feet to the slab, and she was not able to utter a word. And with that, as it became night, lo! there came thunder upon them, and a fall of mist; and thereupon the castle vanished, and they with it.

When Kicva, the daughter of Gwynn Gloy, saw that there was no one in the palace but herself and Manawyddan, she sorrowed so that she cared not whether she lived or died. And Manawyddan saw this. "Thou art in the wrong," said he, "if through fear of me thou grievest thus. I call Heaven to witness that thou hast never seen friendship more pure than that which I will bear thee, as long as Heaven will that thou shouldst be thus. I declare to thee that, were I in the dawn of youth, I would keep my faith unto Pryderi, and unto thee also will I keep it. Be there no fear upon thee, therefore." "Heaven reward thee!" she said; "and that is what I deemed of thee." And the damsel thereupon took courage, and was glad.

"Truly, lady," said Manawyddan, "it is not fitting for us to stay here; we have lost our dogs, and cannot get food. Let us go into England; it is easier for us to find support there." "Gladly, lord," said she, "we will do so." And they set forth together to England.

"Lord," said she, "what craft wilt thou follow? Take up one that is seemly." "None other will I take," answered he, "but that of making shoes." "Lord," said she, "such a craft becomes not a man so nobly born as thou." "By that however will I abide," said he. "I know nothing thereof," said Kicva. "But I know," answered Manawyddan, "and I will teach thee to stitch. We will not attempt to dress the leather, but we will buy it ready dressed, and will make the shoes from it."

So they went into England, and went as far as Hereford: and

they betook themselves to making shoes. And he began by buying the best cordwain that could be had in town, and none other would he buy. And he associated himself with the best goldsmith in the town, and caused him to make clasps for the shoes, and to gild the clasps; and he marked how it was done until he learned the method. And therefore is he called one of the three makers of gold shoes. And when they could be had from him not a shoe nor hose was bought from any of the cordwainers in the town. But when the cordwainers perceived that their gains were failing (for as Manawyddan shaped the work so Kicva stitched it), they came together and took counsel, and agreed that they would slay them. And he had warning thereof, and it was told him how the cordwainers had agreed to slay him.

"Lord," said Kicva, "wherefore should this be borne from these boors?" "Nay," said he, "we will go back unto Dyved." So towards Dyved they set forth.

Now Manawyddan, when he set out to return to Dyved, took with him a burden of wheat. And he proceeded towards Narberth, and there he dwelt. And never was he better pleased than when he saw Narberth again, and the lands where he had been wont to hunt with Pryderi and with Rhiannon. And he accustomed himself to fish and to hunt the deer in their covert. And then he began to prepare some ground, and he sowed a croft, and a second, and a third. And no wheat in the world ever sprang up better. And the three crofts prospered with perfect growth, and no man ever saw fairer wheat than it.

And thus passed the seasons of the year until the harvest came. And he went to look at one of his crofts, and, behold, it was ripe. "I will reap this to-morrow," said he. And that night he went back to Narberth, and on the morrow, in the gray dawn, he went to reap the croft; and when he came there he found nothing but the bare straw. Every one of the ears of the wheat was cut off from the stalk, and all the ears carried entirely away, and nothing but the straw left. And at this he marvelled greatly.

Then he went to look at another croft, and, behold, that also was ripe. "Verily," said he, "this will I reap to-morrow." And on the morrow he came with the intent to reap it; and when he came there he found nothing but the bare straw. "O gracious Heaven!" he exclaimed, "I know that whomsoever has begun my ruin is completing it, and has also destroyed the country with me."

Then he went to look at the third croft; and when he came there, finer wheat had there never been seen, and this also was ripe. "Evil betide me," said he, "if I watch not here to-night. Whoever carried off the other corn will come in like manner to take this, and I will know who it is." And he told Kicva all that had befallen. "Verily," said she, "what thinkest thou to do?" "I will watch the croft to-night," said he. And he went to watch the croft.

And at midnight he heard something stirring among the wheat; and he looked, and behold, the mightiest host of mice in the world, which could neither be numbered nor measured. And he knew not what it was until the mice had made their way into the croft, and each of them, climbing up the straw, and bending it down with its weight, had cut off one of the ears of wheat, and had carried it away, leaving there the stalk; and he saw not a single straw there that had not a mouse to it. And they all took their way, carrying the ears with them.

In wrath and anger did he rush upon the mice; but he could no more come up with them than if they had been gnats or birds of the air, except one only, which, though it was but sluggish, went so fast that a man on foot could scarce overtake it. And after this one he went, and he caught it, and put it in his glove, and tied up the opening of the glove with a string, and kept it with him, and returned to the palace. Then he came to the hall where Kicva was, and he lighted a fire, and hung the glove by the string upon a peg. "What hast thou there, lord?" said Kicva. "A thief," said he, "that I found robbing me." "What kind of a thief may it be, lord, that thou couldst put into thy glove?" said she. Then he told her how the mice came to the last of the fields in his sight. "And one of them was less nimble than the rest, and is now in my glove; to-morrow I will hang it." "My lord," said she, "this is marvellous; but yet it would be unseemly for a man of dignity like thee to be hanging such a reptile as this." "Woe betide me," said he "if I would not hang them all, could I catch them, and such as I have I will hang." "Verily, lord," said she, "there is no reason that I should succor this reptile, except to prevent discredit unto thee. Do therefore, lord, as thou wilt."

Then he went to the Mound of Narberth, taking the mouse with him. And he set up two forks on the highest part of the mound. And while he was doing this, behold, he saw a scholar coming towards him, in old and poor and tattered garments. And it was now seven years since he had seen in that place either man or beast, except those four persons who had remained together until two of them were lost.

"My lord," said the scholar, "good day to thee." "Heaven prosper thee, and my greeting be unto thee! And whence dost thou come, scholar?" asked he. "I come, lord, from singing in England; and wherefore dost thou inquire?" "Because for the last seven years," answered he, "I have seen no man here save four secluded persons, and thyself this moment." "Truly, lord," said he, "I go through this land unto mine own. And what work art thou upon, lord?" "I am hanging a thief that I caught robbing me," said he. "What manner of thief is that?" asked the scholar. "I see a creature in thy hand like unto a mouse, and ill does it become a man of rank equal to thine to touch a reptile such as this. Let it go forth free." "I will not let it go free, by Heaven," said he, "I caught it robbing me, and the doom of a thief will I inflict upon it, and I will hang it." "Lord," said he, "rather than see a man of rank equal to thine at such a work as this, I would give thee a pound, which I have received as alms, to let the reptile go forth free." "I will not let it go free," said he, "neither will I sell it." "As thou wilt, lord," he answered; "I care naught." And the scholar went his way.

And as he was placing the cross-beam upon the two forks, behold, a priest came towards him, upon a horse covered with trappings. "Good day to thee, lord," said he. "Heaven prosper thee!" said Manawyddan; "thy blessing." "The blessing of Heaven be upon thee! And what, lord, art thou doing?" "I am hanging a thief that I caught robbing me," said he. "What manner of thief, lord?" asked he. "A creature," he answered, "in form of a mouse. It has been robbing me, and I am inflicting upon it the doom of a thief." "Lord," said he, "rather than see thee touch this reptile, I would purchase its freedom." "By my confession to Heaven, neither will I sell it nor set it free." "It is true, lord, that it is worth nothing to buy; but rather than see thee defile thyself by touching such a reptile as this, I will give thee three pounds to let it go." "I will not, by Heaven," said he, "take any price for it. As it ought, so shall it be hanged." And the priest went his way.

Then he noosed the string around the mouse's neck, and as he was about to draw it up, behold, he saw a bishop's retinue, with his sumpter-horses and his attendants. And the bishop himself came towards him. And he stayed his work. "Lord Bishop," said he, "thy blessing." "Heaven's blessing be unto thee!" said he. "What work art thou upon?" "Hanging a thief that I caught robbing me," said he. "Is not that a mouse that I see in thy hand?" "Yes," answered he, "and she has robbed me." "Ah," said he, "since I have come at the doom of this reptile, I will ransom it of thee. I will give thee seven pounds for it, and that rather than see a man of rank equal to thine destroying so vile a reptile as this. Let it loose, and thou shalt have the money." "I declare to Heaven that I will not let it loose." "If thou wilt not loose it for this, I will give thee four and twenty pounds of ready money to set it free." "I will not set it free, by Heaven, for as much again," said he. "If thou wilt not set it free for this, I will give thee all the horses that thou seest in this plain, and the seven loads of baggage, and the seven horses that they are upon." "By Heaven, I will not," he replied. "Since for this thou wilt not set it free, do so at what price soever thou wilt." "I will that Rhiannon and Pryderi be free," said he. "That thou shalt have," he answered. "Not yet will I loose the mouse, by Heaven." "What then wouldst thou?" "That the charm and the illusion be removed from the seven cantrevs of Dyved." "This shalt thou have also; set therefore the mouse free." "I will not set it free, by Heaven," said he, "till I know who the mouse may be." "She is my wife." "Wherefore came she to me?" "To despoil thee," he answered. "I am Lloyd, the son of Kilwed, and I cast the charm over the seven cantrevs of Dyved. And it was to avenge Gawl, the son of Clud, from the friendship that I had towards him, that I cast the charm. And upon Pryderi did I avenge Gawl, the son of Clud, for the game of Badger in the Bag, that Pwyll, the son of Auwyn, played upon him. And when it was known that thou wast come to dwell in the land, my household came and besought me to transform them into mice, that they might destroy thy corn. And they went the first and the second night, and destroyed thy two crops. And the third night came unto me my wife and the ladies of the court, and besought me to transform them. And I transformed them. Now she is not in her usual health. And had she been in her usual health, thou wouldst not have been able to overtake her; but since this has taken place, and she has been caught, I will restore to thee Pryderi and Rhiannon, and I will take the charm and illusion from off Dyved. Set her therefore free." "I will not set her free yet." "What wilt thou more?" he asked. "I will that there be no more charm upon the seven cantrevs of Dyved, and that none shall be put upon it henceforth; moreover, that vengeance be never taken for this, either upon Pryderi or Rhiannon, or upon me." "All this shalt thou have. And truly thou hast done wisely in asking this. Upon thy head would have lit all this trouble." "Yea," said he, "for fear thereof was it that I required this." "Set now my wife at liberty." "I will not," said he, "until I see Pryderi and Rhiannon with me free." "Behold, here they come," he answered.

And thereupon behold Pryderi and Rhiannon. And he rose up to meet them, and greeted them, and sat down beside them. "Ah, chieftain, set now my wife at liberty," said the bishop. "Hast thou not received all thou didst ask?" "I will release her, gladly," said he. And thereupon he set her free.

Then he struck her with a magic wand, and she was changed back into a young woman, the fairest ever seen.

"Look round upon thy land," said he, "and thou wilt see it all tilled and peopled as it was in its best estate." And he rose up and looked forth. And when he looked he saw all the lands tilled, and full of herds and dwellings.

And thus ends this portion of the Mabinogi.

———

The following allusions to the preceding story are found in a letter of the poet Southey to John Rickman, Esq., dated June 6th, 1802:—

"You will read the Mabinogeon, concerning which I ought to have talked to you. In the last, that most odd and Arabian-like story of the mouse, mention is made of a begging scholar, that helps to the date; but where did the Cymri get the imagination that could pro-duce such a tale? That enchantment of the basin hanging by the chain from heaven is in the wildest spirit of the Arabian Nights. I am perfectly astonished that such fictions should exist in Welsh. They throw no light on the origin of romance, everything being utterly dissimilar to what we mean by that term, but they do open a new world of fiction; and if the date of their language be fixed about the twelfth or thirteenth century, I cannot but think the mythological substance is of far earlier date; very probably brought from the East by some of the first settlers or conquerors."

CHAPTER XXIX

KILWICH AND OLWEN

KILYDD, the son of Prince Kelyddon, desired a wife as a helpmate, and the wife that he chose was Goleudid, the daughter of Prince Anlawd. And after their union the people put up prayers that they might have an heir. And they had a son through the prayers of the people; and called his name Kilwich.

After this the boy's mother, Goleudid, the daughter of Prince Anlawd, fell sick. Then she called her husband to her, and said to him, "Of this sickness I shall die, and thou wilt take another wife. Now wives are the gift of the Lord, but it would be wrong for thee to harm thy son. Therefore I charge thee that thou take not a wife until thou see a briar with two blossoms upon my grave." And this he promised her. Then she besought him to dress her grave every year, that no weeds might grow thereon. So the queen died. Now the king sent an attendant every morning to see if anything were growing upon the grave. And at the end of the seventh year they neglected that which they had promised to the queen.

One day the king went to hunt; and he rode to the place of burial, to see the grave, and to know if it were time that he should take a wife; and the king saw the briar. And when he saw it, the king took counsel where he should find a wife. Said one of his counsellors, "I know a wife that will suit thee well; and she is the wife of King Doged." And they resolved to go to seek her; and they slew the king, and brought away his wife. And they conquered the king's lands. And he married the widow of King Doged, the sister of Yspadaden Penkawr.

And one day his stepmother said to Kilwich, "It were well for thee to have a wife." "I am not yet of an age to wed," answered the youth. Then said she unto him, "I declare to thee that it is thy destiny not to be suited with a wife until thou obtain Olwen, the daughter of Yspadaden Penkawr." And the youth blushed, and the love of the maiden diffused itself through all his frame, although he had never seen her. And his father inquired of him, "What has come over thee, my son, and what aileth thee?" "My stepmother has declared to me that I shall never have a wife until I obtain Olwen, the daughter of Yspadaden Penkawr." "That will be easy for thee," answered his father. "Arthur is thy cousin. Go, therefore, unto Arthur, to cut thy hair, and ask this of him as a boon."

And the youth pricked forth upon a steed with head dappled gray, four winters old, firm of limb, with shell-formed hoofs, having a bridle of linked gold on his head, and upon him a saddle of costly gold. And in the youth's hand were two spears of silver, sharp, well tempered, headed with steel, three ells in length, of an edge to wound the wind, and cause blood to flow, and swifter than the fall of the dew-drop from the blade of reed-grass, when the dew of June is at the heaviest. A gold-hilted sword was upon his thigh, the blade of which was gilded, bearing a cross of inlaid gold of the hue of the lightning of heaven. His war-horn was of ivory. Before him were two brindled, white-breasted greyhounds, having strong collars of rubies about their necks, reaching from the shoulder to the ear. And the one that was upon the left side bounded across to the right side, and the one on the right to the left, and, like two sea-swallows, sported around him. And his courser cast up four sods, with his four hoofs, like four swallows in the air, about his head, now above, now below. About him was a four-cornered cloth of purple, and an apple of gold was at each corner, and every one of the apples was of the value of an hundred kine. And there was precious gold of the value of three hundred kine upon his shoes, and upon his stirrups, from his knee to the tip of his toe. And the blade of grass bent not beneath him, so light was his courser's tread, as he journeyed toward the gate of Arthur's palace.

Spoke the youth: "Is there a porter?" "There is; and if thou holdest not thy peace, small will be thy welcome. I am Arthur's porter every first day of January." "Open the portal." "I will not open it." "Wherefore not?" "The knife is in the meat, and the drink is in the horn, and there is revelry in Arthur's hall; and none may enter therein but the son of a king of a privileged country, or a craftsman bringing his craft. But there will be refreshment for thy dogs and for thy horse; and for thee there will be collops cooked and peppered, and luscious wine, and mirthful songs; and food for fifty men shall be brought unto thee in the guest-chamber, where the stranger and the sons of other countries eat, who come not into the precincts of the palace of Arthur. Thou wilt fare no worse there than thou wouldst with Arthur in the court. A lady shall smooth thy couch, and shall lull thee with songs; and early to-morrow morning, when the gate is open for the multitude that come hither to-day, for thee shall it be opened first, and thou mayest sit in the place that thou shalt choose in Arthur's hall, from the upper end to the lower." Said the youth: "That will I not do. If thou openest the gate, it is well. If thou dost not open it, I will bring disgrace upon thy lord, and evil report upon thee. And I will set up three shouts at this very gate, than which none were ever heard more deadly." "What clamor soever thou mayest make," said Glewlwyd the porter, "against the laws of Arthur's palace, shalt thou not enter therein, until I first go and speak with Arthur."

Then Glewlwyd went into the hall. And Arthur said to him, "Hast thou news from the gate?" "Half of my life is passed," said Glewlwyd, "and half of thine. I was heretofore in Kaer Se and Asse, in Sach and Salach, in Lotor and Fotor, and I have been in India the Great and India the Lesser, and I have also been in Europe and Africa, and in the islands of Corsica, and I was present when thou didst conquer Greece in the East. Nine supreme sovereigns, handsome men, saw we there, but never did I behold a man of equal dignity with him who is now at the door of the portal." Then said Arthur, "If walking thou didst enter here, return thou running. It is unbecoming to keep such a man as thou sayest he is in the wind and the rain." Said Kay: "By the hand of my friend, if thou wouldst follow my counsel, thou wouldst not break through the laws of the court because of him." "Not so, blessed Kay," said Arthur; "it is an honor to us to be resorted to, and the greater our courtesy, the greater will be our renown and our fame and our glory."

And Glewlwyd came to the gate, and opened the gate before Kilwich; and although all dismounted upon the horse-block at the gate, yet did he not dismount, but he rode in upon his charger. Then said he, "Greeting be unto thee, sovereign ruler of this island, and be this greeting no less unto the lowest than unto the highest, and be it equally unto thy guests and thy warriors and thy chieftains; let all partake of it as completely as thyself. And complete be thy favor and thy fame and thy glory, throughout all this island." "Greeting unto thee also," said Arthur; "sit thou between two of my warriors, and thou shalt have minstrels before thee, and thou shalt enjoy the privileges of a king born to a throne, as long as thou remainest here. And when I dispense my presents to the visitors and strangers in this court, they shall be in thy hand at my commencing." Said the youth: "I came not here to consume meat and drink; but if I obtain the boon that I seek, I will requite it thee, and extol thee; but if I have it not I will bear forth thy dispraise to the four quarters of the world, as far as thy renown has extended." Then said Arthur, "Since thou wilt not remain here, chieftain, thou shalt receive the boon, whatsoever thy tongue may name, as far as the wind dries, and the rain moistens, and the sun revolves, and the sea encircles, and the earth extends; save only my ship Prydwen, and my mantle, and Caleburn, my sword, and Rhongomyant, my lance, and Guenever, my wife. By the truth of Heaven, thou shalt have it cheerfully, name what thou wilt." "I would that thou bless my hair," said he. "That shall be granted thee."

And Arthur took a golden comb, and scissors whereof the loops were of silver, and he combed his hair. And Arthur inquired of him who he was; "for my heart warms unto thee, and I know that thou art come of my blood. Tell me, therefore, who thou art." "I will tell thee," said the youth. "I am Kilwich, the son of Kilydd, the son of Prince Kelyddon, by Goleudid my mother, the daughter of Prince Anlawd." "That is true," said Arthur; "thou art my cousin. Whatsoever boon thou mayest ask, thou shalt receive, be it what it may that thy tongue shall name." "Pledge the truth of Heaven and the faith of thy kingdom thereof." "I pledge it thee gladly." "I crave of thee, then, that thou obtain for me Olwen, the daughter of Yspadaden Penkawr, to wife; and this boon I likewise seek at the hands of thy warriors. I seek it from Kay and from Bedwyr; and from Gwynn, the son of Nudd, and Gadwy, the son of Geraint, and Prince Flewddur Flam, and Iona, king of France, and Sel, the son of Selgi, and Taliesin, the chief of the bards, and Geraint, the son of Erbin, Garanwyn, the son of Kay, and Amren, the son of Bedwyr, Ol, the son of Olwyd, Bedwin, the bishop, Guenever, the chief lady, and Guenhywach, her hister, Morved, the daughter of Urien, and Gwenlian Deg, the majestic maiden, Creiddylad,[1] the daughter

---

[1] Creiddylad is no other than Shakespeare's Cordelia, whose father, King Lear, is by the Welsh authorities called indiscriminately Llyr or Llydd. All the old chroniclers give the story of her devotion to her aged parent, but none of them seems to have been aware that she is destined to remain with him till the day of doom, whilst Gwyn ap Nudd, the king of the fairies, and Gwythyr ap

of Lludd, the constant maiden, and Ewaedan, the daughter of Kynvelyn,[1] the half-man." All these did Kilwich, the son of Kilydd, adjure to obtain his boon.

Then said Arthur, "O chieftain, I have never heard of the maiden of whom thou speakest, nor of her kindred, but I will gladly send messengers in search of her. Give me time to seek her." And the youth said, "I will willingly grant from this night to that at the end of the year to do so." Then Arthur sent messengers to every land within his dominions to seek for the maiden, and at the end of the year Arthur's messengers returned without having gained any knowledge or intelligence concerning Olwen more than on the first day. Then said Kilwich, "Every one has received his boon, and I yet lack mine. I will depart, and bear away thine honor with me." Then said Kay, "Rash chieftain! dost thou reproach Arthur? Go with us, and we will not part until thou dost either confess that the maiden exists not in the world, or until we obtain her." Thereupon Kay rose up. And Arthur called Bedwyr, who never shrank from any enterprise upon which Kay was bound. None were equal to him in swiftness throughout this island except Arthur alone; and although he was one-handed, three warriors could not shed blood faster than he on the field of battle.

And Arthur called to Kyndelig, the guide, "Go thou upon this expedition with the chieftain." For as good a guide was he in a land which he had never seen as he was in his own.

He called Gurhyr Gwalstat, because he knew all tongues.

He called Gawain, the son of Gwyar, because he never returned home without achieving the adventure of which he went in quest.

And Arthur called Meneu, the son of Teirgwed, in order that, if they went into a savage country, he might cast a charm and an illusion over them, so that none might see them whilst they could see every one.

They journeyed until they came to a vast open plain, wherein they saw a great castle, which was the fairest of the castles of the world. And when they came before the castle they beheld a vast flock of sheep. And upon the top of a mound there was a herdsman

Greidiol, fight for her every first of May, and whichever of them may be fortunate enough to be the conqueror at that time will obtain her as his bride

[1] The Welsh have a fable on the subject of the half-man, taken to be illustrative of the force of habit. In this allegory Arthur is supposed to be met by a sprite, who appears at first in a small and indistinct form, but who, on approaching nearer, increases in size, and, assuming the semblance of half a man, endeavors to provoke the king to wrestle. Despising his weakness, and considering that he should gain no credit by the encounter, Arthur refuses to do so, and delays the contest until at length the half-man (Habit) becomes so strong that it requires his utmost efforts to overcome him.

keeping the sheep. And a rug made of skins was upon him, and by his side was a shaggy mastiff, larger than a steed nine winters old. Then said Kay, "Gurhyr Gwalstat, go thou and salute yonder man." "Kay," said he, "I engaged not to go further than thou thyself." "Let us go then together," answered Kay. Said Meneu, "Fear not to go thither, for I will cast a spell upon the dog so that he shall injure no one." And they went up to the mound whereon the herdsman was, and they said to him, "How dost thou fare, herdsman?" "Not less fair be it to you than to me." "Whose are the sheep that thou dost keep, and to whom does yonder castle belong?" "Stupid are ye, truly! not to know that this is the castle of Yspadaden Penkawr. And ye also, who are ye?" "We are an embassy from Arthur, come to seek Olwen, the daughter of Yspadaden Penkawr." "O men! the mercy of Heaven be upon you; do not that for all the world. None who ever came hither on this quest has returned alive." And the herdsman rose up. And as he rose Kilwich gave unto him a ring of gold. And he went home and gave the ring to his spouse to keep. And she took the ring when it was given her, and she said, "Whence came this ring, for thou art not wont to have good fortune?" "O wife, him to whom this ring belonged thou shalt see here this evening." "And who is he?" asked the woman. "Kilwich, the son of Kilydd, by Goleudid, the daughter of Prince Anlawd, who is come to seek Olwen as his wife." And when she heard that she had joy that her nephew, the son of her sister, was coming to her, and sorrow because she had never known any one depart alive who had come on that quest.

And the men went forward to the gate of the herdsman's dwelling. And when she heard their footsteps approaching she ran out with joy to meet them. And Kay snatched a billet out of the pile. And when she met them she sought to throw her arms about their necks. And Kay placed the log between her two hands, and she squeezed it so that it became a twisted coil. "O woman," said Kay, "if thou hadst squeezed me thus none could ever again set their affections on me. Evil love were this." They entered into the house and were served; and soon after they all went forth to amuse themselves. Then the woman opened a stone chest that was before the chimney-corner, and out of it rose a youth with yellow, curling hair. Said Gurhyr, "It is a pity to hide this youth. I know that it is not his own crime that is thus visited upon him." "This is but a remnant," said the woman. "Three and twenty of my sons has Yspadaden Penkawr slain, and I have no more hope of this one than of the others." Then said Kay, "Let him come and be a companion with me and he shall not be slain unless I also am slain with him." And they ate. And the woman asked them, "Upon what errand come ye here?" "We come to seek Olwen for this youth." Then said the woman, "In the name of Heaven, since no one from the castle hath yet seen you, return again whence you came." "Heaven is our witness that we will not return until we have seen the maiden. Does she ever come hither, so that she may be seen?" "She comes here every Saturday to wash her head, and in the vessel where she washes she leaves all her rings, and she never either comes herself or sends any messenger to fetch them." "Will she come here if she is sent to?" "Heaven knows that I will not destroy my soul, nor will I betray those that trust me; unless you will pledge me your faith that you will not harm her I will not send to her." "We pledge it," said they. So a message was sent, and she came.

The maiden was clothed in a robe of flame-colored silk, and about her neck was a collar of ruddy gold, on which were precious emeralds and rubies. More yellow was her head than the flower of the broom,[1] and her skin was whiter than the foam of the wave, and fairer were her hands and her fingers than the blossoms of the wood-anemone amidst the spray of the meadow fountain. The eye of the trained hawk was not brighter than hers. Her bosom was more snowy than the breast of the white swan, her cheek was redder than the reddest roses. Whoso beheld her was filled with her love. Four white trefoils sprung up wherever she trod. And therefore was she called Olwen.

She entered the house and sat beside Kilwich upon the foremost bench; and as soon as he saw her he knew her. And Kilwich said unto her, "Ah! maiden, thou art she whom I have loved; come away with me lest they speak evil of thee and of me. Many a day have I loved thee." "I cannot do this, for I have pledged my faith to my father not to go without his counsel, for his life will last only until the time of my espousals. Whatever is to be, must be. But I will give thee advice, if thou wilt take it. Go ask me of my father, and that which he shall require of thee, grant it, and thou wilt obtain me; but if thou deny him anything, thou wilt not obtain me, and it will be well for thee if thou escape with thy life." "I promise all this, if occasion offer," said he.

She returned to her chamber, and they all rose up, and followed her to the castle. And they slew the nine porters, that were at the nine gates, in silence. And they slew the nine watch-dogs without one of them barking. And they went forward to the hall.

"The greeting of Heaven and of man be unto thee, Yspadaden

---

[1] The romancers dwell with great complacency on the fair hair and delicate complexion of their heroines. This taste continued for a long time, and to render the hair light was an object of education. Even when wigs came into fashion they were all flaxen. Such was the color of the hair of the Gauls and of their German conquerors. It required some centuries to reconcile their eyes to the swarthy beauties of their Spanish and Italian neighbors.

Penkawr," said they. "And you, wherefore come you?" "We come to ask thy daughter Olwen for Kilwich, the son of Kilydd, the son of Prince Kelyddon." "Where are my pages and my servants? Raise up the forks beneath my two eyebrows, which have fallen over my eyes, that I may see the fashion of my son-in-law." And they did so. "Come hither to-morrow, and you shall have an answer."

They rose to go forth, and Yspadaden Penkawr seized one of the three poisoned darts that lay beside him, and threw it after them. And Bedwyr caught it, and flung it, and pierced Yspadaden Penkawr grievously with it through the knee. Then he said, "A cursed ungentle son-in-law, truly! I shall ever walk the worse for his rudeness, and shall ever be without a cure. This poisoned iron pains me like the bite of a gad-fly. Cursed be the smith who forged it, and the anvil on which it was wrought! So sharp is it!"

That night also they took up their abode in the house of the herdsman. The next day, with the dawn, they arrayed themselves and proceeded to the castle, and entered the hall; and they said, "Yspadaden Penkawr, give us thy daughter in consideration of her dower and her maiden fee, which we will pay to thee, and to her two kinswomen likewise." Then he said, "Her four great-grand-mothers, and her four great-grandsires are yet alive; it is needful that I take counsel of them." "Be it so," they answered; "we will go to meat." As they rose up, he took the second dart that was beside him, and cast it after them. And Meneu, the son of Gawedd, caught it, and flung it back at him, and wounded him in the centre of the breast. "A cursed ungentle son-in-law, truly!" said he; "the hard iron pains me like the bite of a horse-leech. Cursed be the hearth whereon it was heated, and the smith who formed it! So sharp is it! Henceforth, whenever I go up hill, I shall have a scant in my breath, and a pain in my chest, and I shall often loathe my food." And they went to meat.

And the third day they returned to the palace. And Yspadaden Penkawr said to them, "Shoot not at me again, unless you desire death. Where are my attendants? Lift up the forks of my eyebrows, which have fallen over my eyeballs, that I may see the fashion of my son-in-law." Then they arose, and, as they did so, Yspadaden Penkawr took the third poisoned dart and cast it at them. And Kilwich caught it, and threw it vigorously, and wounded him through the eyeball. "A cursed ungentle son-in-law, truly! As long as I remain alive, my eyesight will be the worse. Whenever I go against the wind, my eyes will water; and peradventure my head will burn, and I shall have a giddiness every new moon. Like the bite of a mad dog is the stroke of this poisoned iron. Cursed be the fire in which it was forged!" And they went to meat.

And the next day they came again to the palace, and they said, "Shoot not at us any more, unless thou desirest such hurt and harm and torture as thou now hast, and even more." Said Kilwich, "Give me thy daughter; and if thou wilt not give her, thou shalt receive thy death because of her." "Where is he that seeks my daughter? Come hither, where I may see thee." And they placed him a chair face to face with him.

Said Yspadaden Penkawr, "Is it thou that seekest my daughter?"

"It is I," answered Kilwich.

"I must have thy pledge that thou wilt not do toward me otherwise than is just; and when I have gotten that which I shall name, my daughter thou shalt have."

"I promise thee that, willingly," said Kilwich; "name what thou wilt."

"I will do so," said he. "Seest thou yonder red tilled ground?"

"I see it."

"When first I met the mother of this maiden, nine bushels of flax were sown therein, and none has yet sprung up, white or black. I require to have the flax to sow in the new land yonder, that when it grows up it may make a white wimple for my daughter's head on the day of thy wedding."

"It will be easy for me to compass this, although thou mayest think it will not be easy."

"Though thou get this, there is yet that which thou wilt not get,—the harp of Teirtu, to play to us that night. When a man desires that it should play, it does so of itself; and when he desires that it should cease, it ceases. And this he will not give of his own free will, and thou wilt not be able to compel him."

"It will be easy for me to compass this, although thou mayest think that it will not be easy."

"Though thou get this, there is yet that which thou wilt not get. I require thee to get me for my huntsman Mabon, the son of Modron. He was taken from his mother when three nights old, and it is not known where he now is, nor whether he is living or dead."

"It will be easy for me to compass this, although thou mayest think it will not be easy."

"Though thou get this, there is yet that which thou wilt not get,—the two cubs of the wolf Gast Rhymhi; no leash in the world will hold them, but a leash made from the beard of Dillus Varwawc, the robber. And the leash will be of no avail unless it be plucked from his beard while he is alive. While he lives, he will not suffer this to be done to him, and the leash will be of no use should he be dead, because it will be brittle."

"It will be easy for me to compass this, although thou mayest think it will not be easy."

"Though thou get this, there is yet that which thou wilt not get,—the sword of Gwernach the Giant; of his own free will he will not give it, and thou wilt never be able to compel him."

"It will be easy for me to compass this, although thou mayest think it will not be easy."

"Though thou get this, there is yet that which thou wilt not get. Difficulties shalt thou meet with, and nights without sleep, in seeking this, and if thou obtain it not, neither shalt thou obtain my daughter."

"Horses shall I have, and chivalry; and my lord and kinsman, Arthur, will obtain for me all these things. And I shall gain thy daughter, and thou shalt lose thy life."

"Go forward. And thou shalt not be chargeable for food or raiment for my daughter while thou art seeking these things; and when thou hast compassed all these marvels, thou shalt have my daughter for thy wife."

CHAPTER XXX

KILWICH AND OLWEN, CONTINUED

ALL that day they journeyed until the evening, and then they beheld a vast castle, which was the largest in the world. And lo! a black man, larger than three of the men of this world, came out from the castle. And they spoke unto him, and said, "O man, whose castle is that?" "Stupid are ye, truly, O men! There is no one in the world that does not know that this is the castle of Gwernach the Giant." "What treatment is there for guests and strangers that alight in that castle?" "O chieftain, Heaven protect thee! No guest ever returned thence alive, and no one may enter therein unless he brings with him his craft."

Then they proceeded towards the gate. Said Gurhyr Gwalstat, "Is there a porter!" "There is; wherefore dost thou call?" "Open the gate." "I will not open it." "Wherefore wilt thou not?" "The knife is in the meat, and the drink is in the horn, and there is revelry in the hall of Gwernach the Giant; and except for a craftsman who brings his craft, the gate will not be opened to-night." "Verily, porter," then said Kay, "my craft bring I with me." "What is thy craft?" "The best burnisher of swords am I in the world." "I will go and tell this unto Gwernach the Giant, and I will bring thee an answer."

So the porter went in, and Gwernach said to him, "Hast thou

news from the gate?" "I have. There is a party at the door of the gate who desire to come in." "Didst thou inquire of them if they possessed any art?" "I did inquire," said he, "and one told me that he was well skilled in the burnishing of swords." "We have need of him then. For some time have I sought for some one to polish my sword, and could find no one. Let this man enter, since he brings with him his craft."

The porter thereupon returned and opened the gate. And Kay went in by himself, and he saluted Gwernach the Giant. And a chair was placed for him opposite to Gwernach. And Gwernach said to him, "O man, is it true that is reported of thee, that thou knowest how to burnish swords?" "I know full well how to do so," answered Kay. Then was the sword of Gwernach brought to him. And Kay took a blue whet-stone from under his arm, and asked whether he would have it burnished white or blue. "Do with it as it seems good to thee, or as thou wouldst if it were thine own." Then Kay polished one half of the blade, and put it in his hand. "Will this please you?" asked he. "I would rather than all that is in my dominions that the whole of it were like this. It is a marvel to me that such a man as thou should be without a companion." "O noble sir, I have a companion, albeit he is not skilled in this art." "Who may he be?" "Let the porter go forth, and I will tell him whereby he may know him. The head of his lance will leave its shaft, and draw blood from the wind, and will descend upon its shaft again." Then the gate was opened, and Bedwyr entered. And Kay said, "Bedwyr is very skilful, though he knows not this art."

And there was much discourse among those who were without, because that Kay and Bedwyr had gone in. And a young man who was with them, the only son of the herdsman, got in also; and he contrived to admit all the rest, but they kept themselves concealed.

The sword was now polished, and Kay gave it unto the hand of Gwernach the Giant, to see if he were pleased with his work. And the Giant said, "The work is good; I am content therewith." Said Kay, "It is thy scabbard that hath rusted thy sword; give it to me, that I may take out the wooden sides of it, and put in new ones." And he took the scabbard from him, and the sword in the other hand. And he came and stood over against the giant, as if he would have put the sword into the scabbard; and with it he struck at the head of the giant, and cut off his head at one blow. Then they despoiled the castle, and took from it what goods and jewels they would. And they returned to Arthur's court, bearing with them the sword of Gwernach the Giant.

And when they told Arthur how they had sped, Arthur said, "It is a good beginning." Then they took counsel, and said, "Which of these marvels will it be best for us to seek next?" "It will be best," said one, "to seek Mabon, the son of Modron; and he will not be found unless we first find Eidoel, the son of Aer, his kinsman." Then Arthur rose up, and the warriors of the island of Britain with him, to seek for Eidoel; and they proceeded until they came to the castle of Glivi, where Eidoel was imprisoned. Glivi stood on the summit of his castle, and he said, "Arthur, what requirest thou of me, since nothing remains to me in this fortress, and I have neither joy nor pleasure in it, neither wheat nor oats? Seek not, therefore, to do me harm." Said Arthur, "Not to injure thee came I hither, but to seek for the prisoner that is with thee." "I will give thee my prisoner, though I had not thought to give him up to any one, and therewith shalt thou have my support and my aid."

His followers said unto Arthur, "Lord, go thou home; thou canst not proceed with thy host in quest of such small adventures as these." Then said Arthur, "It were well for thee, Gurhyr Gwalstat, to go upon this quest, for thou knowest all languages, and art familiar with those of the birds and the beasts. Thou, Eidoel, oughtest likewise to go with thy men in search of thy cousin. And as for you, Kay and Bedwyr, I have hope of whatever adventure ye are in quest of, that ye will achieve it. Achieve ye this adventure for me."

They went forward until they came to the Ousel of Cilgwri. And Gurhyr adjured her, saying, "Tell me if thou knowest aught of Mabon, the son of Modron, who was taken when three nights old from between his mother and the wall?" And the Ousel answered, "When I first came here, there was a smith's anvil in this place, and I was then a young bird; and from that time no work has been done upon it, save the pecking of my beak every evening; and now there is not so much as the size of a nut remaining thereof; yet during all that time I have never heard of the man for whom you inquire. Nevertheless, I will do that which is fitting that I should for an embassy from Arthur. There is a race of animals who were formed before me, and I will be your guide to them."

So they proceeded to the place where was the Stag of Redynvre. "Stag of Redynvre, behold, we are come to thee, an embassy from Arthur, for we have not heard of any animal older than thou. Say, knowest thou aught of Mabon, the son of Modron, who was taken from his mother when three nights old?" The Stag said, "When first I came hither there was a plain all around me, without any trees save one oak sapling,which grew up to be an oak with an hundred branches; and that oak has since perished, so that now nothing remains of it but the withered stump; and from that day to this I have been here, yet have I never heard of the man for whom you inquire. Nevertheless, being an embassy from Arthur, I will be your guide to the place where there is an animal which was formed before I was, and the oldest animal in the world, and the one that has travelled most, the Eagle of Gwern Abwy."

Gurhyr said, "Eagle of Gwern Abwy, we have come to thee, an embassy from Arthur, to ask thee if thou knowest aught of Mabon, the son of Modron, who was taken from his mother when he was three nights old?" The Eagle said, "I have been here for a great space of time, and when I first came hither there was a rock here from the top of which I pecked at the stars every evening; and it has crumbled away, and now it is not so much as a span high. All that time I have been here, and I have never heard of the man for whom you inquire, except once when I went in search of food as far as Llyn Llyw. And when I came there I struck my talons into a salmon, thinking he would serve me as food for a long time. But he drew me into the water, and I was scarcely able to escape from him. After that I made peace with him. And I drew fifty fish-spears out of his back, and relieved him. Unless he know something of him you seek I cannot tell who may. However, I will guide you to the place where he is."

So they went thither; and the Eagle said, "Salmon of Llyn Llyw, I have come to thee with an embassy from Arthur, to ask thee if thou knowest aught of Mabon, the son of Modron, who was taken away at three nights old from his mother." "As much as I know I will tell thee. With every tide I go along the river upward, until I come near to the walls of Gloucester, and there have I found such wrong as I never found elsewhere; and to the end that ye may give credence thereto, let one of you go thither upon each of my two shoulders." So Kay and Gurhyr Gwalstat went upon the two shoulders of the Salmon, and they proceeded until they came unto the wall of the prison; and they heard a great wailing and lamenting from the dungeon. Said Gurhyr, "Who is it that laments in this house of stone?" "Alas! it is Mabon, the son of Modron, who is here imprisoned; and no imprisonment was ever so grievous as mine." "Hast thou hope of being released for gold or for silver, or for any gifts of wealth, or through battle and fighting?" "By fighting will whatever I may gain be obtained."

Then they went thence, and returned to Arthur, and they told him where Mabon, the son of Modron, was imprisoned. And Arthur summoned the warriors of the island, and they journeyed as far as Gloucester, to the place where Mabon was in prison. Kay and Bedwyr went upon the shoulders of the fish, whilst the warriors of Arthur attacked the castle. And Kay broke through the wall into the dungeon, and brought away the prisoner upon his back, whilst the fight was going on between the warriors. And Arthur returned home, and Mabon with him at liberty.

On a certain day as Gurhyr Gwalstat was walking over a mountain he heard a wailing and a grievous cry. And when he heard it he sprung forward, and went towards it. And when he came there he saw a fire burning among the turf, and an ant-hill nearly surrounded with the fire. And he drew his sword, and smote off the ant-hill close to earth, so that it escaped being burned in the fire. And the ants said to him, "Receive from us the blessing of Heaven, and that which no man can give we will give thee." Then they fetched the nine bushels of flaxseed which Yspadaden Penkawr had required of Kilwich, and they brought the full measure, without lacking any, save one flaxseed, and that the lame pismire brought in before night.

Then said Arthur, "Which of the marvels will it be best for us to seek next?" "It will be best to seek for the two cubs of the wolf Gast Rhymhi."

"Is it known," said Arthur, "where she is?" "She is in Aber Cleddyf," said one. Then Arthur went to the house of Tringad, in Aber Cleddyf, and he inquired of him whether he had heard of her there. "She has often slain my herds, and she is there below in a cave of Aber Cleddyf."

Then Arthur went in his ship Prydwen by sea, and the others went by land to hunt her. And they surrounded her and her two cubs, and took them, and carried them away.

As Kay and Bedwyr sat on a beacon-cairn on the summit of Plinlimmon, in the highest wind that ever was, they looked around them and saw smoke afar off. Then said Kay, "By the hand of my friend, yonder is the fire of a robber." Then they hastened towards the smoke, and they came so near it that they could see Dillus Varwawc scorching a wild boar. "Behold, yonder is the greatest robber that ever fled from Arthur," said Bedwyr to Kay. "Dost thou know him?" "I do know him," answered Kay; "he is Dillus Varwawc, and no leash in the world will be able to hold the cubs of Gast Rhymhi save a leash made from the beard of him thou seest yonder. And even that will be useless unless his beard be plucked out alive, with wooden tweezers; for if dead it will be brittle." "What thinkest thou that we should do concerning this?" said Bedwyr. "Let us suffer him to eat as much as he will of the meat, and after that he will fall asleep." And during that time they employed themselves in making the wooden tweezers. And when Kay knew certainly that he was asleep, he made a pit under his feet, and he struck him a violent blow, and squeezed him into the pit. And there they twitched out his beard completely with the wooden tweezers, and after that they slew him altogether. And from thence they went, and took the leash made of Dillus Varwawc's beard, and they gave it into Arthur's hand.

Thus they got all the marvels that Yspadaden Penkawr had re- quired of Kilwich; and they set forward, and took the marvels to his court. And Kilwich said to Yspadaden Penkawr, "Is thy daughter mine now?" "She is thine," said he, "but therefore need- est thou not thank me, but Arthur, who hath accomplished this for thee." Then Goreu, the son of Custennin, the herdsman, whose brothers Yspadaden Penkawr had slain, seized him by the hair of his head, and dragged him after him to the keep, and cut off his head, and placed it on a stake in the citadel. Then they took possession of his castle, and of his treasures. And that night Olwen became Kilwich's bride, and she continued to be his wife as long as she lived.

CHAPTER XXXI

PEREDUR, THE SON OF EVRAWC

ARTHUR was in Caerleon upon the Usk; and he went to hunt, and Peredur [1] went with him. And Peredur let loose his dog upon a hart, and the dog killed the hart in a desert place. And a short space from him he saw signs of a dwelling, and towards the dwelling he went, and he beheld a hall, and at the door of the hall he found bold swarthy youths playing at chess. And when he entered he beheld three maidens sitting on a bench, and they were all clothed alike, as became persons of high rank. And he came and sat by them on the bench; and one of the maidens looked steadfastly at Peredur and wept. And Peredur asked her wherefore she was weeping. "Through grief that I shall see so fair a youth as thou art slain." "Who will slay me?" inquired Peredur. "If thou art so daring as to remain here to-night I will tell thee." "How great soever my danger may be from remaining here I will listen unto thee." "This palace is owned by him who is my father," said the maiden, "and he slays every one who comes hither without his leave." "What sort of a man is thy father that he is able to slay every one thus?" "A man who does violence and wrong unto his neighbors, and who ren- ders justice unto none." And hereupon he saw the youths arise

---

[1] Peredur, the son of Evrawc, is the Welsh for Perceval, a part of whose story in the preceding pages is taken from the Mabinogeon.

and clear the chessmen from the board. And he heard a great tumult; and after the tumult there came in a huge black one-eyed man, and the maidens arose to meet him. And they disarrayed him, and he went and sat down; and after he had rested and pondered awhile, he looked at Peredur, and asked who the knight was. "Lord," said one of the maidens, "he is the fairest and gentlest youth that ever thou didst see. And for the sake of Heaven, and thine own dignity, have patience with him." "For thy sake I will have patience, and I will grant him his life this night." Then Peredur came towards them to the fire, and partook of food and liquor, and entered into discourse with the ladies. And being elated with the liquor, he said to the black man, "It is a marvel to me, so mighty as thou sayest thou art, who could have put out thine eye?" "It is one of my habits," said the black man, "that whosoever puts to me the question which thou hast asked shall not escape with his life, either as a free gift, or for a price." "Lord," said the maiden, "whatsoever he may say to thee in jest, and through the excitement of liquor, make good that which thou saidest and didst promise me just now." "I will do so, gladly, for thy sake," said he. "Willingly will I grant him his life this night." And that night thus they remained.

And the next day the black man got up and put on his armor, and said to Peredur, "Arise, man, and suffer death." And Peredur said unto him, "Do one of two things, black man; if thou wilt fight with me, either throw off thy own armor, or give arms to me, that I may encounter thee." "Ha! man," said he, "couldst thou fight if thou hadst arms? Take then what arms thou dost choose." And thereupon the maiden came to Peredur with such arms as pleased him; and he fought with the black man and forced him to crave his mercy. "Black man, thou shalt have mercy, provided thou tell me who thou art, and who put out thine eye." "Lord, I will tell thee. I lost it in fighting with the Black Serpent of the Carn. There is a mound which is called the Mound of Mourning; and on the mound there is a carn, and in the carn there is a serpent, and on the tail of the serpent there is a stone, and the virtues of the stone are such that whosoever should hold it in one hand, in the other he will have as much gold as he may desire. And in fighting with this serpent was it that I lost my eye. And the Black Oppressor am I called. And for this reason I am called the Black Oppressor, that there is not a single man around me whom I have not oppressed, and justice have I done unto none." "Tell me," said Peredur, "how far is it hence?" "The same day that thou settest forth thou wilt come to the Palace of the Sons of the King of the Tortures." "Wherefore are they called thus?" "The Addanc [1] of the Lake slays them once every day. When thou goest

[1] The Addanc was a mighty aquatic monster.

thence thou wilt come to the Court of the Countess of Achievements." "What achievements are these?" said Peredur. "Three hundred men are there in her household, and unto every stranger that
comes to the Court the achievements of her household are related.
And this is the manner of it,—the three hundred men of the household sit next unto the Lady; and that not through disrespect unto
the guests, but that they may relate the achievements of the household. And the day that thou goest there thou wilt reach the Mound
of Mourning, and round about the mound there are the owners of
three hundred tents guarding the serpent." "Since thou hast indeed
been an oppressor so long," said Peredur, "I will cause that thou
continue so no longer." So he slew him.

Then the maiden spoke, and began to converse with him. "If thou
wast poor when thou camest here henceforth thou wilt be rich
through the treasure of the black man whom thou hast slain. Thou
seest the many lovely maidens that there are in this court, thou
shalt have her whom thou likest best for the lady of thy love."
"Lady, I came not hither from my country to woo; but match yourselves as it liketh you with the comely youths I see here; and none
of your goods do I desire, for I need them not." Then Peredur rode
forward, and he came to the Palace of the Sons of the King of the
Tortures; and when he entered the palace he saw none but women;
and they rose up and were joyful at his coming; and as they began
to discourse with him he beheld a charger arrive, with a saddle upon
it, and a corpse in the saddle. And one of the women arose, and
took the corpse from the saddle and anointed it in a vessel of warm
water, which was below the door, and placed precious balsam upon
it; and the man rose up alive, and came to the place where Peredur
was, and greeted him, and was joyful to see him. And two other
men came in upon their saddles, and the maiden treated these two
in the same manner as she had done the first. Then Peredur asked
the chieftain wherefore it was thus. And they told him there was an
Addanc in a cave, which slew them once every day. And thus they
remained one night.

And next morning the youths arose to sally forth, and Peredur
besought them, for the sake of the ladies of their love, to permit
him to go with them; but they refused him, saying, "If thou shouldst
be slain thou hast none to bring thee back to life again." And they
rode forward and Peredur followed after them; and after they had
disappeared out of his sight he came to a mound, whereon sat the
fairest lady he had ever beheld. "I know thy quest," said she; "thou
art going to encounter the Addanc, and he will slay thee, and that
not by courage but by craft. He has a cave, and at the entrance of
the cave there is a stone pillar, and he sees every one that enters,

and none sees him; and from behind the pillar he slays every one with a poisonous dart. And if thou wouldst pledge me thy faith, to love me above all women, I would give thee a stone, by which thou shouldst see him when thou goest in, and he should not see thee." "I will, by my faith," said Peredur, "for when first I beheld thee I loved thee; and where shall I seek thee?" "When thou seekest me seek towards India." And the maiden vanished after placing the stone in Peredur's hand.

And he came towards a valley, through which ran a river; and the borders of the valley were wooded, and on each side of the river were level meadows. And on one side of the river he saw a flock of white sheep, and on the other side a flock of black sheep. And whenever one of the white sheep bleated one of the black sheep would cross over and become white; and when one of the black sheep bleated one of the white sheep would cross over and become black. And he saw a tall tree by the side of the river, one-half of which was in flames from the root to the top, and the other half was green and in full leaf. And nigh thereto he saw a youth sitting upon a mound, and two greyhounds, white-breasted and spotted, in leashes, lying by his side. And certain was he that he had never seen a youth of so royal a bearing as he. And in the wood opposite he heard hounds raising a herd of deer. And Peredur saluted the youth, and the youth greeted him in return. And there were three roads leading from the mound; two of them were wide roads and the third was more narrow. And Peredur inquired where the three roads went. "One of them goes to my palace," said the youth. "And one of two things I counsel thee to do, either to proceed to my palace, which is before thee, and where thou wilt find my wife, or else to remain here to see the hounds chasing the roused deer from the wood to the plain. And thou shalt see the best greyhounds thou didst ever behold, and the boldest in the chase, kill them by the water beside us; and when it is time to go to meat my page will come with my horse to meet me, and thou shalt rest in my palace to-night." "Heaven reward thee; but I cannot tarry, and onward must I go." "The other road leads to the town, which is near here, wherein food and liquor may be bought; and the road which is narrower than the other goes towards the cave of the Addanc." "With thy permission, young man, I will go that way."

And Peredur went towards the cave. And he took the stone in his left hand, and his lance in his right. And as he went in he perceived the Addanc, and he pierced him through with his lance, and cut off his head. And as he came forth from the cave, behold the three companions were at the entrance; and they saluted Peredur, and told him that there was a prediction that he should slay the monster.

And Peredur gave the head to the young man, and they offered him in marriage which ever of the three sisters he might choose, and half their kingdom with her. "I came not hither to woo," said Peredur, "but if peradventure I took a wife, I should prefer your sister to all others." And Peredur rode forward, and he heard a noise behind him. And he looked back, and saw a man upon a red horse, and red armor upon him; and the man rode up by his side, and wished him the favor of Heaven and of man. And Peredur greeted the youth kindly. "Lord, I come to make a request unto thee." "What wouldst thou?" "That thou shouldst take me as thy attendant." "Who should I take as my attendant if I did so?" "I will not conceal from thee what kindred I am of. Etlym Gleddyv Coch am I called, an Earl from the East Country." "I marvel that thou shouldst offer to become attendant to a man whose possessions are no greater than thine own; for I have but an earldom like thyself. But now thou desirest to be my attendant, I will take thee joyfully."

And they went forward to the Court of the Countess, and all they of the Court were glad at their coming; and they were told it was not through disrespect they were placed below the household, but that such was the usage of the Court. For whoever should overthrow the three hundred men of her household would sit next the Countess, and she would love him above all other men. And Peredur, having overthrown the three hundred of her household, sat down beside her, and the Countess said, "I thank Heaven that I have a youth so fair and so radiant as thou, since I have not obtained the man whom best I love." "Whom is he whom best thou lovest? By my faith, Etlym Gleddyv Coch is the man whom I love best, and I have never seen him." "Of a truth, Etlym is my companion; and behold here he is, and for his sake did I come to joust with thy household. And he would have done so better than I had it pleased him." "Heaven reward thee, fair youth, and I will take the man whom I love above all others." And the Countess became Etlym's bride from that moment.

And the next day Peredur set forth toward the Mound of Mourning. "By thy hand, lord, but I will go with thee," said Etlym. Then they went forward till they came in sight of the mound and the forts. "Go unto yonder men," said Peredur to Etlym, "and desire them to come and do me homage." So Etlym went unto them, and said unto them thus: "Come and do homage to my lord." "Who is thy lord?" said they. "Peredur, with the long lance, is my lord," said Etlym. "Were it permitted to slay a messenger, thou shouldst not go back to thy lord alive, for making unto kings and earls and barons so arrogant a demand as to go and do him homage." On this

Peredur desired him to go back to them, and to give them their choice, either to do him homage or to do battle with him. And they chose rather to do battle. And that day Peredur overthrew the owners of a hundred tents. And the next day he overthrew the owners of a hundred more; and the third day the remaining third took counsel to do homage to Peredur. And Peredur inquired of them wherefore they were there. And they told him they were guarding the serpent until he should die. "For then should we fight for the stone among ourselves, and whoever should be conqueror among us would have the stone." "Wait here," said Peredur, "and I will go to encounter the serpent." "No, no, lord," said they; "we will go all together to encounter the serpent." "Verily," said Peredur, "that will I not permit; for if the serpent be slain, I shall derive no more fame therefrom than one of you." Then he went to the place where the serpent was, and slew it, and came back to them, and said, "Reckon up what you have spent since you have been here, and I will repay you to the full." And he paid to each what he said was his claim. And he required of them only that they should acknowledge themselves his vassals. And he said to Etlym, "Go back unto her whom thou lovest best, and I will go forwards, and I will reward thee for having been my attendant." And he gave Etlym the stone. "Heaven repay thee and prosper thee," said Etlym.

And Peredur rode thence, and he came to the fairest valley he had ever seen, through which ran a river; and there he beheld many tents of various colors. And he marvelled still more at the number of windmills and of water-mills that he saw. And there rode up with him a tall, auburn-haired man, in a workman's garb, and Peredur inquired of him who he was. "I am the chief miller," said he, "of all the mills yonder." "Wilt thou give me lodging?" said Peredur. "I will, gladly," he answered. And Peredur came to the miller's house, and the miller had a fair and pleasant dwelling. And Peredur asked money as a loan from the miller, that he might buy meat and liquor for himself, and for the household, and he promised him that he would pay him ere he went thence. And he inquired of the miller wherefore such a multitude were there assembled. Said the miller to Peredur, "One thing is certain: either thou art a man from afar, or thou art beside thyself. The Empress of Cristonobyl the Great is here; and she will have no one but the man who is most valiant; for riches she does not require. And it was impossible to bring food for so many thousands as are here, therefore were all these mills constructed." And that night they took their rest.

And the next day Peredur arose, and he equipped himself and his horse for the tournament. And among other tents he beheld one which was the fairest he had ever seen. And saw a beauteous maiden leaning her head out of a window of a tent, and he had never seen a maiden more lovely than she. And upon her was a garment of satin. And he gazed fixedly on the maiden and began to love her greatly. And he remained there, gazing upon the maiden from morning until midday, and from midday until evening; and then the tournament was ended; and he went to his lodging and drew off his armor. Then he asked money of the miller as a loan, and the miller's wife was wroth with Peredur; nevertheless the miller lent him the money. And the next day he did in like manner as he had done the day before. And at night he came to his lodging, and took money as a loan from the miller. And the third day, as he was in the same place, gazing upon the maiden, he felt a hard blow between the neck and the shoulder from the edge of an axe. And when he looked behind he saw that it was the miller; and the miller said unto him, "Do one of two things; either turn thy head from hence or go to the tournament." And Peredur smiled on the miller, and went to the tournament; and all that encountered him that day he overthrew. And as many as he vanquished he sent as a gift to the Empress, and their horses and arms he sent as a gift to the wife of the miller, in payment of the borrowed money. And the Empress sent to the Knight of the Mill, to ask him to come and visit her. And Peredur went not for the first nor for the second message. And the third time she sent one hundred knights to bring him against his will, and they went to him, and told him their mission from the Empress. And Peredur fought well with them, and caused them to be bound like stags, and thrown into the mill dyke. And the Empress sought advice of a wise man. "With thy permission, I will go to him myself." So he came to Peredur and besought him, for the sake of the lady of his love, to come and visit the Empress. And they went together with the miller. And Peredur went and sat down in the outer chamber of the tent, and she came and placed herself at his side. And there was but little discourse between them. And Peredur took his leave and went to his lodging.

And the next day he came to visit her, and when he came into the tent there was no one chamber less decorated than the others. And they knew not where he would sit. And Peredur went and sat beside the Empress, and discoursed with her courteously. And while they were there they beheld a black man enter with a goblet full of wine in his hand. And he dropped upon his knee before the Empress, and besought her to give it to no one who would not fight him for it. And she looked upon Peredur. "Lady," said he, "bestow upon me the goblet." And Peredur drank the wine, and gave the goblet to the miller's wife. And while they were thus, behold there entered a black man, of larger stature than the other, with a wild beast's claw in his hand, wrought into the form of a goblet, and filled with wine. And he presented it to the Empress, and besought her to give it to no one but the man who would fight with him. "Lady," said Peredur, "bestow it upon me." And she gave it to him. And Peredur drank the wine, and sent the goblet to the wife of the miller. And when they were thus, behold a rough-looking crisp-haired man, taller than either of the others, came in with a bowl in his hands full of wine; and he bent upon his knee, and gave it into the hands of the Empress, and he besought her to give it to none but him who would fight with him for it; and she gave it to Peredur, and he sent it to the miller's wife. And that night Peredur returned to his lodging; and the next day he accoutred himself and his horse, and went to the meadow, and slew the three men. Then Peredur proceeded to the tent, and the Empress said to him, "Goodly Peredur, remember the faith thou didst pledge me when I gave thee the stone, and thou didst kill the Addanc." "Lady," answered he, "thou sayest truth, I do remember it." For she was the maiden who had been sitting on the mound when Peredur had gone in search of the Addanc.

CHAPTER XXXII

TALIESIN

GWYDDNO GARANHIR was sovereign of Gwaelod, a territory bordering on the sea. And he possessed a weir upon the strand between Dyvi and Aberystwyth, near to his own castle, and the value of an hundred pounds was taken in that weir every May eve. And Gwyddno had an only son named Elphin, the most helpless of youths, and the most needy. And it grieved his father sore, for he thought he was born in an evil hour. By the advice of his council his father had granted him the drawing of the weir that year, to see if good luck would ever befall him, and to give him something wherewith to begin the world. And this was on the twenty-ninth of April.

The next day, when Elphin went to look, there was nothing in the weir but a leather bag upon a pole of the weir. Then said the weir-ward unto Elphin, "All thy ill-luck aforetime was nothing to this; and now thou hast destroyed the virtues of the weir, which always yielded the value of an hundred pounds every May eve; and to-night there is nothing but this leathern skin in it." "How now," said Elphin, "there may be therein the value of a hundred pounds." Well! they took up the leathern bag, and he who opened it saw the forehead of an infant, the fairest that was ever seen; and he said, "Behold a radiant brow!" (in the Welsh language, *taliesin*.)

"Taliesin be he called," said Elphin. And he lifted the bag in his arms, and, lamenting his bad luck, placed the boy sorrowfully behind him. And he made his horse amble gently, that before had been trotting, and he carried him as softly as if he had been sitting in the easiest chair in the world. And presently the boy made a Consolation and praise to Elphin; and the Consolation was as you may here see:—

> "Fair Elphin, cease to lament!
> Never in Gwyddno's weir
> Was there such good luck as this night.
> Being sad will not avail;
> Better to trust in God than to forebode ill;
> Weak and small as I am,
> On the foaming beach of the ocean,
> In the day of trouble I shall be
> Of more service to thee than three hundred salmon."

This was the first poem that Taliesin ever sung, being to console Elphin in his grief for that the produce of the weir was lost, and, what was worse, that all the world would consider that it was through his fault and ill-luck. Then Elphin asked him what he was, whether man or spirit. And he sung thus:—

> "I have been formed a comely person;
> Although I am but little, I am highly gifted;
> Into a dark leathern bag I was thrown,
> And on a boundless sea I was set adrift.
> From seas and from mountains
> God brings wealth to the fortunate man."

Then came Elphin to the house of Gwyddno, his father, and Taliesin with him. Gwyddno asked him if he had had a good haul at the weir, and he told him that he had got that which was better than fish. "What was that?" said Gwyddno. "A bard," said Elphin. Then said Gwyddno, "Alas! what will he profit thee?" And Taliesin himself replied and said, "He will profit him more than the weir ever profited thee." Asked Gwyddno, "Art thou able to speak, and thou so little?" And Taliesin answered him, "I am better able to speak than thou to question me." "Let me hear what thou canst say," quoth Gwyddno. Then Taliesin sang:—

> "Three times have I been born, I know by meditation;
> All the sciences of the world are collected in my breast,
> For I know what has been, and what hereafter will occur."

Elphin gave his haul to his wife, and she nursed him tenderly and lovingly. Thenceforward Elphin increased in riches more and more, day by day, and in love and favor with the king; and there abode Taliesin until he was thirteen years old, when Elphin, son of Gwyddno, went by a Christmas invitation to his uncle, Maelgan

Gwynedd, who held open court at Christmas-tide in the castle of Dyganwy, for all the number of lords of both degrees, both spiritual and temporal, with a vast and thronged host of knights and squires. And one arose and said, "Is there in the whole world a king so great as Maelgan, or one on whom Heaven has bestowed so many gifts as upon him,—form, and beauty, and meekness, and strength, besides all the powers of the soul?" And together with these they said that Heaven had given one gift that exceeded all the others, which was the beauty, and grace, and wisdom, and modesty of his queen, whose virtues surpassed those of all the ladies and noble maidens throughout the whole kingdom. And with this they put questions one to another, Who had braver men? Who had fairer or swifter horses or greyhounds? Who had more skilful or wiser bards than Maelgan?

When they had all made an end of their praising the king and his gifts, it befell that Elphin spoke on this wise: "Of a truth, none but a king may vie with a king; but were he not a king, I would say that my wife was as virtuous as any lady in the kingdom, and also that I have a bard who is more skilful than all the king's bards." In a short space some of his fellows told the king all the boastings of Elphin; and the king ordered him to be thrown into a strong prison until he might show the truth as to the virtues of his wife and the wisdom of his bard.

Now when Elphin had been put in a tower of the castle with a thick chain about his feet (it is said that it was a silver chain, as he was of royal blood), the king, as the story relates, sent his son Rhun to inquire into the demeanor of Elphin's wife. Now Rhun was the most graceless man in the world, and there was neither wife nor maiden with whom he held converse but was evil spoken of. While Rhun went in haste towards Elphin's dwelling, being fully minded to bring disgrace upon his wife, Taliesin told his mistress how that the king had placed his master in durance in prison, and how that Rhun was coming in haste to strive to bring disgrace upon her. Wherefore he caused his mistress to array one of the maids of the kitchen in her apparel; which the noble lady gladly did, and she loaded her hands with the best rings that she and her husband possessed.

In this guise Taliesin caused his mistress to put the maiden to sit at the board in her room at supper; and he made her to seem as her mistress, and the mistress to seem as the maid. And when they were in due time seated at their supper, in the manner that has been said, Rhun suddenly arrived at Elphin's dwelling, and was received with joy, for the servants knew him; and they brought him to the room of their mistress, in the semblance of whom the maid rose up from supper and welcomed him gladly. And afterwards she sat down to supper again, and Rhun with her. Then Rhun began jesting with the maid, who still kept the semblance of the mistress. And verily this story shows that the maiden became so intoxicated that she fell asleep; and the story relates that it was a powder that Rhun put into the drink that made her sleep so soundly that she never felt it when he cut off from her hand her little finger, whereon was the signet ring of Elphin, which he had sent to his wife as a token a short time before. And Rhun returned to the king with the finger and the ring as a proof, to show that he had cut it off from her hand without her awaking from her sleep of intemperance.

The king rejoiced greatly at these tidings, and he sent for his councillors, to whom he told the whole story from the beginning. And he caused Elphin to be brought out of prison, and he chided him because of his boast. And he spake on this wise: "Elphin, be it known to thee beyond a doubt, that it is but folly for a man to trust in the virtues of his wife further than he can see her; and that thou mayest be certain of thy wife's vileness, behold her finger, with thy signet ring upon it, which was cut from her hand last night, while she slept the sleep of intoxication." Then thus spake Elphin: "With thy leave, mighty king, I cannot deny my ring, for it is known of many; but verily I assert that the finger around which it is was never attached to the hand of my wife; for in truth and certainty there are three notable things pertaining to it, none of which ever belonged to any of my wife's fingers. The first of the three is, that it is certainly known to me that this ring would never remain upon her thumb, whereas you can plainly see that it is hard to draw it over the joint of the little finger of the hand whence this was cut. The second thing is, that my wife has never let pass one Saturday since I have known her, without paring her nails before going to bed, and you can see fully that the nail of this little finger has not been pared for a month. The third is, truly, that the hand whence this finger came was kneading rye dough within three days before the finger was cut therefrom, and I can assure your highness that my wife has never kneaded rye dough since my wife she has been."

The king was mightily wroth with Elphin for so stoutly withstanding him, respecting the goodness of his wife; wherefore he ordered him to his prison a second time, saying that he should not be loosed thence until he had proved the truth of his boast, as well concerning the wisdom of his bard as the virtues of his wife.

In the meantime his wife and Taliesin remained joyful at Elphin's dwelling. And Taliesin showed his mistress how that Elphin was in prison because of them; but he bade her be glad, for that he would go to Maelgan's court to free his master. So he took leave of his mistress, and came to the court of Maelgan, who was going to sit in his hall, and dine in his royal state, as it was the custom in those days for kings and princes to do at every chief feast. As soon as Taliesin entered the hall, he placed himself in a quiet corner, near the place where the bards and the minstrels were wont to come, in doing their service and duty to the king, as is the custom at the high festivals, when the bounty is proclaimed. So, when the bards and the heralds came to cry largess, and to proclaim the power of the king, and his strength, at the moment when they passed by the corner wherein he was crouching, Taliesin pouted out his lips after them, and played, "Blerwm, blerwm!" with his finger upon his lips. Neither took they much notice of him as they went by, but proceeded forward till they came before the king, unto whom they made their obeisance with their bodies, as they were wont, without speaking a single word, but pouting out their lips, and making mouths at the king, playing "Blerwm, blerwm!" upon their lips with their fingers, as they had seen the boy do. This sight caused the king to wonder, and to deem within himself that they were drunk with many liquors. Wherefore he commanded one of his lords, who served at the board, to go to them and desire them to collect their wits, and to consider where they stood, and what it was fitting for them to do. And this lord did so gladly. But they ceased not from their folly any more than before. Whereupon he sent to them a second time, and a third, desiring them to go forth from the hall. And the last the king ordered one of his squires to give a blow to the chief of them, named Heinin Vardd; and the squire took a broom and struck him on the head, so that he fell back in his seat. Then he arose, and went on his knees, and besought leave of the king's grace to show that this their fault was not through want of knowledge, neither through drunkenness, but by the influence of some spirit that was in the hall. And he spoke on this wise: "O honorable king, be it known to your grace that not from the strength of drink, or of too much liquor, are we dumb, but through the influence of a spirit that sits in the corner yonder, in the form of a child." Forthwith the king commanded the squire to fetch him; and he went to the nook where Taliesin sat, and brought him before the king, who asked him what he was, and whence he came. And he answered the king in verse:—

> "Primary chief bard am I to Elphin,
> And my native country is the region of the summer stars;
> I have been in Asia with Noah in the ark,
> I have seen the destruction of Sodom and Gomorrah,
> I was in India when Rome was built,
> I have now come here to the remnant of Troia."

When the king and his nobles had heard the song, they wondered much, for they had never heard the like from a boy so young as he. And when the king knew that he was the bard of Elphin, he bade Heinin, his first and wisest bard, to answer Taliesin, and to strive with him. But when he came, he could do no other than play "Blerwm!" on his lips; and when he sent for the others of the four and twenty bards, they all did likewise, and could do no other. And Maelgan asked the boy Taliesin what was his errand, and he answered him in song:—

> "Elphin, the son of Gwyddno,
> Is in the land of Artro,
> Secured by thirteen locks,
> For praising his instructor.
> Therefore I, Taliesin,
> Chief of the bards of the west,
> Will loosen Elphin
> Out of a golden fetter."

Then he sang to them a riddle:—

> "Discover thou what is
> The strong creature from before the flood,
> Without flesh, without bone,
> Without vein, without blood,
> Without head, without feet;
> It will neither be older nor younger
> Than at the beginning.
> Behold how the sea whitens
> When first it comes,
> When it comes from the south,
> When it strikes on coasts.
> It is in the field, it is in the wood,
> But the eye cannot perceive it.
> One Being has prepared it,
> By a tremendous blast,
> To wreak vengeance
> On Maelgan Gwynedd."

While he was thus singing his verse, there arose a mighty storm of wind, so that the king and all his nobles thought that the castle would fall upon their heads. And the king caused them to fetch Elphin in haste from his dungeon, and placed him before Taliesin. And it is said that immediately he sung a verse, so that the chains opened from about his feet.

After that Taliesin brought Elphin's wife before them, and showed that she had not one finger wanting. And in this manner did he set his master free from prison, and protect the innocence of his mistress, and silence the bards so that not one of them dared to say a word. Right glad was Elphin, right glad was Taliesin.

PART III

THE KNIGHTS OF ENGLISH HISTORY

THE KNIGHTS OF ENGLISH HISTORY

CHAPTER XXXIII

KING RICHARD AND THE THIRD CRUSADE

THE Crusades were the mightiest or rather the most ambitious undertaking of the chivalry of Europe. From the year 1096 for more than a century the knights of all countries looked to the Holy Land as a field for winning their spurs and obtaining pardon of their sins. And it is most natural that in giving a picture of English chivalry as it is shown in history that we should give a description of King Richard's exploits in Palestine.

In the last decade of the twelfth century Richard I. of England took the cross, which had come to him as a sort of legacy from his father, and sailed for Antioch, which was being besieged by the Christians, to assist in the war in the Holy Land. At the same time Philip Augustus of France and Frederick Barbarossa joined the Crusaders. Frederick was drowned in a river of Cilicia, and his force had so dwindled that when they reached Antioch hardly a tenth of the number were left that had started. Philip of France reached Antioch with his army, and there, as we shall learn later, he fought with the Turk and quarrelled with the Christian for a time, until he finally set sail for France without having accomplished the capture of the Holy City. As for Richard, he was not more successful, and although his deeds were so glorious as to cover him with honor, he was obliged to return home, leaving Jerusalem still in the hands of infidels.

THE EXPLOITS OF KING RICHARD

Now as the ships were proceeding, some being before others, two of the three first, driven by the violence of the winds, were broken on the rocks near the port of Cyprus; the third, which was English, more speedy than they, having turned back into the deep, escaped the peril. Almost all the men of both ships got away alive to land, many of whom the hostile Cypriotes slew, some they took captive, some, taking refuge in a certain church, were besieged. Whatever also in the ships was cast up by the sea fell a prey to the Cypriotes. The prince also of that island coming up, received for his share the gold and the arms; and he caused the shore to be guarded by all the armed force he could summon together, that he might not permit the fleet which followed to approach, lest the king should take again what had been thus stolen from him. Above the port was a strong city, and upon a natural rock, a high and fortified castle. The whole of that nation was warlike and accustomed to live by theft. They placed beams and planks at the entrance of the port, across the passage, the gates, and entrances; and the whole land with one mind prepared themselves for a conflict with the English. God so willed that the cursed people should receive the reward of their evil deeds by the hands of one who would not spare. The third English ship, in which were the women, having cast out their anchors, rode out at sea, and watched all things from opposite, to report the misfortunes to the king,[1] lest haply, being ignorant of the loss and disgrace, he should pass the place unavenged. The next line of the king's ships came up after the other, and they are stopped at the first. A full report reached the king, who, sending heralds to the lord of the island, and obtaining no satisfaction, commanded his entire army to arm, from the first even to the last, and to get out of the great ships into the galleys and boats, and follow him to the shore. What he commanded was immediately performed; they came in arms to the port. The king being armed, leaped first from the galley, and gave the first blow in the war; but before he was able to strike a second he had three thousand of his followers with him striking away at his side. All the timber that had been placed as a barricade in the port was cast down instantly, and the brave fellows went up into the city as ferocious as lionesses are wont to be when robbed of their young. The fight was carried on manfully against them, numbers fell wounded on both sides, and the swords of both parties were made drunk with blood. The Cypriotes are vanquished, the city is taken, with the castle besides; whatever the victors choose is ransacked; and the lord of the island is himself taken and brought to the king. He being taken, supplicates and obtains pardon; he offers homage to the king, and it is received; and he swears, though unasked, that henceforth he will hold the island of him as his liege lord, and will open all the castles of the land to him, and make satisfaction for the damage already done; and further bring presents of his own. On being dismissed after the oath, he is commanded to fulfil the conditions in the morning.

That night the king remained peaceably in the castle; and his newly-sworn vassal, flying, retired to another castle, and caused the

[1] Richard I. of England.

whole of the men of the land, who were able to bear arms, to be summoned to repair to him, and so they did. The king of Jerusalem, however, that same night landed in Cyprus, that he might assist the king and salute him, whose arrival he had desired above that of any other in the whole world. On the morrow the lord of Cyprus was sought for and found to have fled. The king seeing that he was abused, and having been informed where he was, directed the king of Jerusalem to follow the traitor by land with the best of the army, while he conducted the other part by water, intending to be in the way that he might not escape by sea. The divisions reassembled around the city in which he had taken refuge, and he, having sallied out against the king, fought with the English, and the battle was carried on sharply by both sides. The English would that day have been beaten had they not fought under the command of King Richard. They at length obtained a dear-bought victory, the Cypriote flies, and the castle is taken. The kings pursue him as before, the one by land and the other by water, and he is besieged in the third castle. Its walls are cast down by engines hurling huge stones; he, being overcome, promises to surrender, if only he might not be put in iron fetters. The king consents to the prayers of the supplicant, and caused silver shackles to be made for him. The prince of the pirates being thus taken, the king traversed the whole island, and took all its castles, and placed his constables in each, and constituted justiciaries and sheriffs, and the whole land was subjected to him in everything just like England. The gold, and the silks and the jewels from the treasuries that were broken open, he retained for himself; the silver and victuals he gave to the army. To the king of Jerusalem also he made a handsome present out of the booty.

The king proceeding thence, came to the siege of Acre, and was welcomed by the besiegers with as great a joy as if it had been Christ that had come again on earth to restore the kingdom of Israel. The king of the French had arrived at Acre first, and was very highly esteemed by the natives; but on Richard's arrival he became obscured and without consideration, just as the moon is wont to relinquish her lustre at the rising of the sun.

The king of the English, unused to delay, on the third day of his arrival at the siege, caused his wooden fortress, which he had called "Mate Grifun," when it was made in Sicily, to be built and set up, and before the dawn of the fourth day the machine stood erect by the walls of Acre, and from its height looked down upon the city lying beneath it; and there were thereon by sunrise archers casting missiles without intermission on the Turks and Thracians. Engines also for casting stones. placed in convenient positions, battered the walls with frequent volleys. More important than these, the sappers, making themselves a way beneath the ground, undermined the foundations of the walls; while soldiers, bearing shields, having planted ladders, sought an entrance over the ramparts. The king himself was running up and·down through the ranks, directing some, reproving some, and urging others, and thus was he everywhere present with every one of them, so that whatever they all did ought properly to be ascribed to him. The king of the French also did not lightly assail them, making as bold an assault as he could on the tower of the city which is called Cursed.

The renowned Carracois and Mestocus, after Saladin, the most powerful princes of the heathen, had at that time the charge of the besieged city, who, after a contest of many days, promised by their interpreters the surrender of the city, and a ransom for their heads; but the king of the English desired to subdue their obstinacy by force; and wished that the vanquished should pay their heads for the ransom of their bodies, but by the mediation of the king of the French their life and indemnity of limbs only was accorded, if, after the surrender of the city and yielding of everything they possessed, the Holy Cross should be given up.

All the heathen warriors in Acre were chosen men, and were in number nine thousand; many of whom, swallowing many gold coins, made a purse of their stomachs, because they foresaw that whatever they had of any value would be turned against them, even against themselves, if they should again oppose the cross, and would only fall a prey to the victors. So all of them came out before the kings entirely disarmed, and outside the city, without money, were given into custody; and the kings, with triumphal banners, having entered the city, divided the whole with all its stores into two parts between themselves and their soldiers; the pontiff's seat alone its bishop received by their united gift. The captives, being divided, Mestocus fell by lot to the portion of the king of the English, and Carracois, as a drop of cold water, fell into the mouth of the thirsty Philip, king of the French.

Messengers on the part of the captives having been sent to Saladin for their ransom, when the heathen could by no entreaty be moved to restore the Holy Cross, the king of the English beheaded all his, with the exception of Mestocus only, who on account of his nobility was spared, and declared openly, without any ceremony, that he would act in the same way toward Saladin himself.

The king of the English, then, having sent for the commanders of the French, proposed that in the first place they should conjointly attempt Jerusalem itself; but the dissuasion of the French discouraged the hearts of both parties, dispirited the troops, and restrained the king, thus destitute of men, from his intended march on that metropolis. The king, troubled at this, though not despairing, from that day forth separated his army from the French, and directing his arms to the storming of castles along the seashore, he took every fortress that came in his way from Tyre to Ascalon, though after hard fighting and deep wounds.[1]

On the Saturday, the eve of the Nativity of the blessed Virgin Mary, at earliest dawn, our men armed themselves with great care to receive the Turks, who were known to have preceded their march, and whose insolence nothing but a battle could check. The enemy had ranged themselves in order, drawing gradually nearer and nearer; and our men also took the utmost care to place themselves in as good order as possible. King Richard, who was most experienced in military affairs, arranged the army in squadrons, and directed who should march in front and who in the rear. He divided the army into twelve companies, and these again into five divisions, marshalled according as the men ranked in military discipline; and none could be found more warlike, if they had only had confidence in God, who is the giver of all good things. On that day the Templars formed the first rank, and after them came, in due order, the Bretons and men of Anjou; then followed King Guy, with the men of Pictou; and in the fourth line were the Normans and English, who had the care of the royal standard, and last of all marched the Hospitallers: this line was composed of chosen warriors, divided into companies. They kept together so closely that an apple, if thrown, would not have fallen to the ground without touching a man or a horse; and the army stretched from the army of Saracens to the seashore. There you might have seen their most appropriate distinctions,—standards, and ensigns of various forms, and hardy soldiers, fresh and full of spirits, and well fitted for war. Henry, Count of Champagne, kept guard on the mountain side, and maintained a constant lookout on the flank; the foot-soldiers, bowmen, and arbalesters were on the outside, and the rear of the army was closed by the post horses and wagons, which carried provisions and other things, and journeyed along between the army and the sea, to avoid an attack from the enemy.

This was the order of the army, as it advanced gradually, to prevent separation; for the less close the line of battle, the less effective was it for resistance. King Richard and the Duke of Burgundy, with a chosen retinue of warriors, rode up and down, narrowly watching the position and manner of the Turks, to correct anything in their

[1] The preceding narrative is taken from the Chronicle of Richard of Devizes. What follows is from the Chronicle of Geoffrey de Vinsauf.

own troops, if they saw occasion, for they had need, at that moment, of the utmost circumspection.

It was now nearly nine o'clock, when there appeared a large body of the Turks, ten thousand strong, coming down upon us at full charge, and throwing darts and arrows as far as they could, while they mingled their voices in one horrible yell. There followed after them an infernal race of men, of black color, and bearing a suitable appellation, expressive of their blackness. With them also were the Saracens, who live in the desert, called Bedouins; they are a savage race of men, blacker than soot; they fight on foot, and carry a bow, quiver, and round shield, and are a light and active race. These men dauntlessly attacked our army. Beyond these might be seen the well-arranged phalanxes of the Turks, with ensigns fixed to their lances, and standards and banners of separate distinctions. Their army was divided into troops, and the troops into companies, and their numbers seemed to exceed twenty thousand. They came on with irresistible charge, on horses swifter than eagles, and urged on like lightning to attack our men; and as they advanced they raised a cloud of dust, so that the air was darkened. In front came certain of their admirals, as it was their duty, with clarions and trumpets; some had horns, others had pipes and timbrels, gongs, cymbals, and other instruments, producing a horrible noise and clamor. The earth vibrated from the loud and discordant sounds, so that the crash of thunder could not be heard amidst the tumultuous noise of horns and trumpets. They did this to excite their spirit and courage, for the more violent their clamor became, the more bold were they for the fray. Thus the impious Turks threatened us, both on the side towards the sea and from the side of the land; and for the space of two miles not so much earth as could be taken up in one hand could be seen, on account of the hostile Turks who covered it. Oh, how obstinately they pressed on, and continued their stubborn attacks, so that our men suffered severe loss of their horses, which were killed by their darts and arrows. Oh, how useful to us on that day were our arbalesters and bowmen, who closed the extremities of the lines, and did their best to repel the obstinate Turks.

The enemy came rushing down, like a torrent, to the attack; and many of our arbalesters, unable to restrain the weight of their terrible and calamitous charge, threw away their arms, and, fearing lest they should be shut out, took refuge, in crowds, behind the dense lines of the army; yielding through fear of death to sufferings which they could not support. Those whom shame forbade to yield, or the hope of an immortal crown sustained, were animated with greater boldness and courage to persevere in the contest, and fought with indefatigable valor face to face against the Turks, whilst they at the same time receded step by step, and so reached their retreat. The whole of that day, on account of the Turks pressing them closely from behind, they faced around and went on skirmishing, rather than proceeding on their march.

Oh, how great was the strait they were in on that day! how great was their tribulation! when some were affected with fears, and no one had such confidence or spirit as not to wish, at that moment, he had finished his pilgrimage, and had returned home, instead of standing with trembling heart the chances of a doubtful battle. In truth our people, so few in number, were so hemmed in by the multitudes of the Saracens, that they had no means of escape, if they tried; neither did they seem to have valor sufficient to withstand so many foes,—nay, they were shut in like a flock of sheep in the jaws of wolves, with nothing but the sky above, and the enemy all around them. O Lord God! what feelings agitated that weak flock of Christ! straitened by such a perplexity, whom the enemy pressed with such unabating vigor, as if they would pass them through a sieve. What army was ever assailed by so mighty a force? There you might have seen our troopers, having lost their chargers, marching on foot with the footmen, or casting missiles from the arbalests, or arrows from bows, against the enemy, and repelling their attacks in the best manner they were able. The Turks, skilled in the bow, pressed unceasingly upon them; it rained darts; the air was filled with the shower of arrows, and the brightness of the sun was obscured by the multitude of missiles, as if it had been darkened by a fall of winter's hail or snow. Our horses were pierced by the darts and arrows, which were so numerous that the whole face of the earth around was covered with them, and if any one wished to gather them up, he might take twenty of them in his hand at a time.

The Turks pressed with such boldness that they nearly crushed the Hospitallers; on which the latter sent word to King Richard that they could not withstand the violence of the enemy's attack, unless he would allow their knights to advance at full charge against them. This the king dissuaded them from doing, but advised them to keep in a close body; they therefore persevered and kept together, though scarcely able to breathe for the pressure. By these means they were able to proceed on their way, though the heat happened to be very great on that day; so that they labored under two disadvantages,—the hot weather and the attacks of the enemy. These approved martyrs of Christ sweated in the contest; and he who could have seen them closed up in a narrow space, so patient under the heat and toil of the day and the attacks of the enemy, who exhorted each other to destroy the Christians, could not doubt in his mind that it augured ill to our success from their straitened and perilous position, hemmed in as they were by so large a multitude; for the enemy thundered at their backs as if with mallets, so that, having no room to use their bows, they fought hand to hand with swords, lances, and clubs, and the blows of the Turks, echoing from their metal armor, resounded as if they had been struck upon an anvil. They were now tormented with the heat, and no rest was allowed them. The battle fell heavy on the extreme line of the Hospitallers, the more so as they were unable to resist, but moved forward with patience under their wounds, returning not even a word for the blows which fell upon them, and advancing on their way because they were not able to bear the weight of the contest.

Then they pressed on for safety upon the centre of the army which was in front of them, to avoid the fury of the enemy who harassed them in the rear. Was it wonderful that no one could withstand so continuous an attack, when he could not even return a blow to the numbers who pressed on him? The strength of all Paganism had gathered together from Damascus and Persia, from the Mediterranean to the East; there was not left in the uttermost recesses of the earth one man of fame or power, one nation's valor, or one bold soldier, whom the sultan had not summoned to his aid, either by entreaty, by money, or by authority, to crush the Christian race; for he presumed to hope he could blot them from the face of the earth; but his hopes were vain, for their numbers were sufficient, through the assistance of God, to effect their purpose. The flower of the chosen youth and soldiers of Christendom had indeed assembled together, and were united in one body, like ears of corn on their stalks, from every region of the earth; and if they had been utterly destroyed, there is no doubt that there were some left to make resistance.

A cloud of dust obscured the air as our men marched on; and, in addition to the heat, they had an enemy pressing them in the rear, insolent, and rendered obstinate by the instigation of the devil. Still the Christians proved good men, and secure in their unconquerable spirit, kept constantly advancing, while the Turks threatened them without ceasing in the rear; but their blows fell harmless upon the defensive armor, and this caused the Turks to slacken in courage at the failure of their attempts, and they began to murmur in whispers of disappointment, crying out in their rage, "that our people were made of iron and would yield to no blow." Then the Turks, about twenty thousand strong, rushed again upon our men pell-mell, annoying them in every possible manner; when, as if overcome by their savage fury, brother Garnier de Napes, one of the Hospitallers, suddenly exclaimed with a loud voice, "O excellent St. George! will you leave us to be thus put to confusion? The whole of

Christendom is now on the point of perishing, because it fears to return a blow against this impious race."

Upon this the master of the Hospitallers went to the king, and said to him, "My lord the king, we are violently pressed by the enemy, and are in danger of eternal infamy, as if we did not dare to return their blows; we are each of us losing our horses one after another, and why should we bear with them any further?" To whom the king replied, "Good master, it is you who must sustain their attack; no one can be everywhere at once." On the master returning, the Turks again made a fierce attack on them from the rear, and there was not a prince or count amongst them but blushed with shame, and they said to each other, "Why do we not charge them at full gallop? Alas! alas! we shall forever deserve to be called cowards, a thing which never happened to us before, for never has such a disgrace befallen so great an army, even from unbelievers. Unless we defend ourselves by immediately charging the enemy we shall gain everlasting scandal, and so much the greater the longer we delay to fight." O, how blind is human fate! On what slippery points it stands! Alas, on how uncertain wheels doth it advance, and with what ambiguous success doth it unfold the course of human things! A countless multitude of the Turks would have perished if the aforesaid attempt had been orderly conducted; but to punish us for our sins, as it is believed, the potter's ware produces a paltry vessel instead of the grand design which he had conceived. For when they were treating on this point, and had come to the same decision about charging the enemy, two knights, who were impatient of delay, put everything in confusion. It had been resolved by common consent that the sounding of six trumpets in three different parts of the army should be a signal for a charge, viz., two in front, two in the rear, and two in the middle, to distinguish the sounds from those of the Saracens, and to mark the distance of each. If these orders had been attended to, the Turks would have been utterly discomfited; but from the too great haste of the aforesaid knights the success of the affair was marred.

They rushed at full gallop upon the Turks, and each of them prostrated his man by piercing him through with his lance. One of them was the marshal of the Hospitallers, the other was Baldwin de Carreo, a good and brave man, and the companion of King Richard, who had brought him in his retinue. When the other Christians observed these two rushing forward, and heard them calling with a clear voice on St. George for aid, they charged the Turks in a body with all their strength; then the Hospitallers, who had been distressed all day by their close array, following the two soldiers, charged the enemy in troops, so that the van of the army became the rear from their position in the attack, and the Hospitallers, who had been the last, were the first to charge.

The Count of Champagne also burst forward with his chosen company, and James d'Avennes with his kinsmen, and also Robert Count of Dreux, the bishop of Beauvais and his brother, as well as the Earl of Leicester, who made a fierce charge on the left towards the sea. Why need we name each? Those who were in the first line of the rear made a united and furious charge; after them the men of Poictou, the Bretons, and the men of Anjou, rushed swiftly onward, and then came the rest of the army in a body: each troop showed its valor, and boldly closed with the Turks, transfixing them with their lances, and casting them to the ground. The sky grew black with the dust that was raised in the confusion of that encounter. The Turks, who had purposely dismounted from their horses in order to take better aim at our men with their darts and arrows, were slain on all sides in that charge, for on being prostrated by the horse-soldiers they were beheaded by the foot-men. King Richard, on seeing his army in motion and in encounter with the Turks, flew rapidly on his horse at full speed through the Hospitallers, who had led the charge, and to whom he was bringing assistance with all his retinue, and broke into the Turkish infantry, who were astonished at his blows and those of his men, and gave way to the right and to the left.

Then might be seen numbers prostrated on the ground, horses without their riders in crowds, the wounded lamenting with groans their hard fate, and others drawing their last breath, weltering in their gore, and many lay headless, whilst their lifeless forms were trodden under foot both by friend and foe. Oh, how different are the speculations of those who meditate amidst the columns of the cloister from the fearful exercise of war! There the king, the fierce, the extraordinary king, cut down the Turks in every direction, and none could escape the force of his arm, for wherever he turned, brandishing his sword, he carved a wide path for himself; and as he advanced and gave repeated strokes with his sword, cutting them down like a reaper with his sickle, the rest, warned by the sight of the dying, gave him more ample space, for the corpses of the dead Turks which lay on the face of the earth extended over half a mile. In fine, the Turks were cut down, the saddles emptied of their riders, and the dust which was raised by the conflict of the combatants proved very hurtful to our men, for on becoming fatigued from slaying so many, when they were retiring to take fresh air, they could not recognize each other on account of the thick dust, and struck their blows indiscriminately to the right and to the left; so that unable to distinguish friend from foe they took their own men for enemies and cut them down without mercy. Then the Christians pressed hard on the Turks, the latter gave way before them: but for a long time the battle was doubtful; they still exchanged blows, and either party strove for the victory; on both sides were seen some retreating, covered with wounds, while others fell slain to the ground.

Oh, how many banners and standards of different forms, and pennons and many-colored ensigns, might there be seen torn and fallen on the earth; swords of proved steel, and lances made of cane with iron heads, Turkish bows, and maces bristling with sharp teeth, darts and arrows covering the ground, and missiles enough to load twenty wagons or more! There lay the headless trunks of the Turks who had perished, whilst others retained their courage for a time until our men increased in strength, when some of them concealed themselves in the copses, some climbed up trees, and, being shot with arrows, fell with a fearful groan to the earth; others, abandoning their horses, betook themselves by slippery footpaths to the seaside, and tumbled headlong into the waves from the precipitous cliffs that were five poles in height. The rest of the enemy were repulsed in so wonderful a manner that for the space of two miles nothing could be seen but fugitives, although they had before been so obstinate and fierce, and puffed up with pride; but by God's grace their pride was humbled, and they continued still to fly, for when our men ceased the pursuit fear alone added wings to their feet. Our army had been ranged in divisions when they attacked the Turks; the Normans and English also, who had the care of the standard, came up slowly towards the troops which were fighting with the Turks,—for it was very difficult to disperse the enemy's strength, and they stopped at a short distance therefrom, that all might have a rallying point. On the conclusion of the slaughter our men paused; but the fugitives, to the number of twenty thousand, when they saw this, immediately recovering their courage, and armed with maces, charged the hindmost of those who were retiring, and rescued some from our men who had just struck them down.

Oh, how dreadfully were our men then pressed! for the darts and arrows, thrown at them as they were falling back, broke the heads, arms, and other limbs of our horsemen, so that they bent, stunned, to their saddle-bows; but having quickly regained their spirits and resumed their strength, and thirsting for vengeance with greater eagerness, like a lioness when her whelps are stolen, they charged the enemy, and broke through them like a net. Then you might have seen the horses with their saddles displaced, and the Turks, who had but just now fled, returning, and pressing upon our people with the utmost fury; every cast of their darts would have told had our men kept marching and not stood still in a compact, immovable body. The commander of the Turks was an admiral, named Tekedmus, a kinsman of the sultan, having a banner with a remarkable device; namely, that of a pair of breeches carved thereon, a symbol well known to his men. He was a most cruel persecutor, and a persevering enemy of the Christians; and he had under his command seven hundred chosen Turks of great valor, of the household troops of Saladin, each of whose companies bore a yellow banner with pennons of a different color. These men, coming at full charge, with clamor and haughty bearing, attacked our men, who were turning off from them towards the standard, cutting at them, and piercing them severely, so that even the firmness of our chiefs wavered under the weight of the pressure; yet our men remained immovable, compelled to repel force by force. And the conflict grew thicker, the blows were redoubled, and the battle waxed fiercer than before: the one side labored to crush, the other to repel; both exerted their strength, and although our men were by far the fewest in numbers, they made havoc of great multitudes of the enemy; and that portion of the army which thus toiled in the battle could not return to the standard with ease, on account of the immense mass which pressed upon them so severely; for thus hemmed in they began to flag in courage, and but few dared to renew the attack of the enemy. In truth, the Turks were furious in the assault, and greatly distressed our men, whose blood poured forth in a stream beneath their blows. On perceiving them reel and give way, William de Barris, a renowned knight, breaking through the ranks, charged the Turks with his men; and such was the vigor of the onset that some fell by the edge of his sword, while others only saved themselves by rapid flight. For all that, the king, mounted on a bay Cyprian steed, which had not its match, bounded forward in the direction of the mountains, and scattered those he met on all sides; for the enemy fled from his sword and gave way, while helmets tottered beneath it, and sparks flew forth from its strokes. So great was the fury of his onset, and so many and deadly his blows that day, in his conflict with the Turks, that in a short space of time the enemy were all scattered, and allowed our army to proceed; and thus our men, having suffered somewhat, at last returned to the standard, and proceeded on their march as far as Arsur, and there they pitched their tents outside its walls.

While they were thus engaged a large body of the Turks made an attack on the extreme rear of our army. On hearing the noise of the assailants, King Richard, encouraging his men to battle, rushed at full speed, with only fifteen companions, against the Turks, crying out, with a loud voice, "Aid us, O God! and the Holy Sepulchre!" and this he exclaimed a second and a third time; and when our men heard it they made haste to follow him, and attacked, routed, and put them to flight; pursuing them as far as Arsur, whence they had first come out, cutting them down and subduing them. Many of the Turks fell there also. The king returned thence from the slaughter of the fugitives to his camp; and the men, overcome with the fatigue and exertions of the day, rested quietly that night.

Whoever was greedy of gain, and wished to plunder the booty, returned to the place of battle, and loaded himself to his heart's desire; and those who returned from thence reported that they had counted thirty-two Turkish chiefs who were found slain on that day, and whom they supposed to be men of great influence and power from the splendor of their armor and the costliness of their apparel. The Turks also made search for them to carry them away as being of the most importance; and besides these the Turks carried off seven thousand mangled bodies of those who were next in rank, besides of the wounded, who went off in straggling parties; and when their strength failed lay about the fields and died. But by the protection of God we did not lose a tenth, nor a hundredth part so many as fell in the Turkish army. Oh, the disasters of that day! Oh, the trials of the warriors! for the tribulations of the just are many. Oh, mournful calamity and bitter distress. How great must have been the blackness of our sins to require so fiery an ordeal to purify it, for if we had striven to overcome the urgent necessity by pious long-suffering, and without a murmur, the sense of our obligations would have been deeper.

And again the Christians were put in great peril, in the following manner. At the siege of Joppa a certain depraved set of men among the Saracens, called Menelones of Aleppo and Cordivi, an active race, met together to consult what should be done in the existing state of things. They spoke of the scandal which lay against them, that so small an army, without horses, had driven them out of Joppa, and they reproached themselves with cowardice and shameful baseness, and arrogantly made a compact among themselves that they would seize King Richard in his tent, and bring him before Saladin, from whom they would receive a most munificent reward.

So they prepared themselves in the middle of the night to surprise the king, and sallied forth armed, by the light of the moon, conversing with one another about the object they had in hand. Oh, hateful race of unbelievers! they are anxiously bent upon seizing Christ's steadfast soldier while he is asleep. They rush on in numbers to seize him, unarmed and apprehensive of no danger. They were not far from his tent, and were preparing to lay hands on him, when, lo! the God of mercy, who never neglects those who trust in Him, and acts in a wonderful manner even to those who know Him not, sent the spirit of discord among the aforesaid Cordivi and Menelones. The Cordivi said, "You shall go in on foot to take the king and his followers, whilst we will remain on horseback to prevent their escaping into the castle." But the Menelones replied, "Nay, it is your place to go in on foot, because our rank is higher than yours; but this service on foot belongs to you rather than us." Whilst thus the two parties were contending which of them were the greatest, their combined dispute caused much delay; and when at last they came to a decision how their nefarious attempt should be achieved, the dawn of the day appeared, viz., the Wednesday next following the feast of St. Peter *ad vincula*. But now by the providence of God, who had decreed that his holy champion should not be seized whilst asleep by the infidels, a certain Genoese was led by the divine impulse to go out early in the morning into the fields, where he was alarmed by the noise of men and horses advancing, and returned speedily, but just had time to see helmets reflecting back the light which now fell upon them. He immediately rushed with speed into the camp, calling out, "To arms! to arms!" The king was awakened by the noise, and leaping startled from his bed, put on his impenetrable coat of mail, and summoned his men to the rescue.

God of all mercies! lives there a man who would not be shaken by such a sudden alarm? The enemy rushed unawares, armed against unarmed, many against few, for our men had no time to arm or even to dress themselves. The king himself, therefore, and many others with him, on the urgency of the moment, proceeded without their cuishes to the fight, some even without their breeches, and they armed themselves in the best manner they could, though they were going to fight the whole day. Whilst our men were thus arming in haste, the Turks drew near, and the king mounted his horse, with only ten other knights with him. These alone had horses, and some even of them had base and impotent horses, unused to arms; the common men were drawn skilfully out in ranks and troops, with each a captain to command them. The knights were posted nearer to the sea, having the church of St. Nicholas on the left, because the Turks had directed their principal attack on that quarter, and the Pisans and Genoese were posted beyond the suburban gardens, having other troops mingled with them. Oh, who could fully relate the terrible attacks of the infidels? The Turks at first rushed on with horrid yells, hurling their javelins and shooting their arrows. Our men prepared themselves as they best could to receive their furious attack, each fixing his right knee in the ground, that so they might the better hold together and maintain their position; whilst there the thighs of their left legs were bent, and their left hands held their shields or bucklers; stretched out before them in their right hands they held their lances, of which the lower ends were fixed in the ground, and their iron heads pointed threateningly towards the enemy.

Between every two of the men who were thus covered with their shields, the king, versed in arms, placed an arbalester, and another behind him to stretch the arbalest as quickly as possible, so that the man in front might discharge his shot whilst the other was loading. This was found to be of much benefit to our men, and did much harm to the enemy. Thus everything was prepared as well as the shortness of the time allowed, and our little army was drawn up in order. The king ran along the ranks, and exhorted every man to be brave and not to flinch. "Courage, my brave men," said he; "and let not the attack of the enemy disturb you. Bear up against the powers of fortune, and you will rise above them. Everything may be borne by brave men; adversity sheds a light upon the virtues of mankind, as certainly as prosperity casts over them a shade; there is no room for flight, for the enemy surround us, and to attempt to flee is to provoke certain death. Be brave, therefore, and let the urgency of the case sharpen up your valor; brave men should either conquer nobly or gloriously die. Martyrdom is a boon which we should receive with willing mind; but before we die, let us, whilst still alive, do what we may to avenge our deaths, giving thanks to God that it has been our lot to die martyrs. This will be the end of our labors, the termination of our life and of our battles. These words were hardly spoken, when the hostile army rushed with ferocity upon them, in seven troops, each of which contained about a thousand horse. Our men received their attack with their right feet planted firm against the sand, and remained immovable. Their lances formed a wall against the enemy, who would have assuredly broken through, if our men had in the least given way.

The first line of the Turks, perceiving, as they advanced, that our men stood immovable, recoiled a little, when our men plied them with a shower of missiles, slaying large numbers of men and horses. Another line of Turks at once came on in like manner, and were again encountered and driven back. In this way the Turks came on like a whirlwind, again and again, making the appearance of an attack, that our men might be induced to give way, and when they were close up they turned their horses off in another direction. The king and his knights, who were on horseback, perceiving this, put spurs to their horses, and charged into the middle of the enemy, upsetting them right and left, and piercing a large number through the body with their lances; at last they pulled up their horses, because they found that they had penetrated entirely through the Turkish lines. The king, now looking about him, saw the noble earl of Leicester fallen from his horse, and fighting bravely on foot. No sooner did he see this, than he rushed to his rescue, snatched him out of the hands of the enemy, and replaced him on his horse. What a terrible combat was then waged! A multitude of Turks advanced, and used every exertion to destroy our small army; vexed at our success, they rushed toward the royal standard of the lion, for they would rather have slain the king than a thousand others. In the midst of the mêlée the king saw Ralph de Mauleon dragged off prisoner by the Turks, and spurring his horse to speed, in a moment released him from their hands, and restored him to the army; for the king was a very giant in the battle, and was everywhere in the field,—now here, now there, wherever the attacks of the Turks raged the hottest. So bravely did he fight, that there was no one, however gallant, that would not readily and deservedly yield to him the pre-eminence. On that day he performed the most gallant deeds on the furious army of the Turks, and slew numbers with his sword, which shone like lightning; some of them were cloven in two, from their helmet to their teeth, whilst others lost their heads, arms, and other members, which were lopped off at a single blow. While the king was thus laboring with incredible exertions in the fight, a Turk advanced towards him, mounted on a foaming steed. He had been sent by Saphadin of Archadia, brother to Saladin, a liberal and munificent man, if he had not rejected the Christian faith. This man now sent to the king, as a token of his well-known honorable character, two nobles horses, requesting him earnestly to accept them, and make use of them, and if he returned safe and sound out of that battle, to remember the gift and recompense it in any manner he pleased. The king readily received the present, and afterwards nobly recompensed the giver. Such is bravery, cognizable even in an enemy; since a Turk, who was our bitter foe, thus honored the king for his distinguished valor. The king, especially at such a moment of need, protested that he would have taken any number of horses equally good from any one even more a foe than Saphadin, so necessary were they to him at that moment. Fierce now raged the fight, when such numbers attacked so few; the whole earth was covered with the javelins and arrows of the unbelievers; they threw them, several at a time, at our men, of whom many were wounded. Thus the weight of battle fell heavier upon us than before, and the galley-men withdrew in the galleys which brought them; and so, in their anxiety to be safe, they sacrificed their character for bravery. Meanwhile a shout was raised by the Turks, as they strove who should first occupy the town, hoping to slay those of our men whom they should find within. The king, hearing the clamor, taking with him only two knights and two crossbow-men, met three Turks, nobly

caparisoned, in one of the principal streets. Rushing bravely upon
them, he slew the riders in his own royal fashion, and made booty of
two horses. The rest of the Turks who were found in the town were
put to the rout in spite of their resistance, and dispersing in different
directions, sought to make their escape, even where there was no
regular road. The king also commanded the parts of the walls which
were broken down to be made good, and placed sentinels to keep
watch lest the town should be again attacked.

These matters settled, the king went down to the shore, where
many of our men had taken refuge on board the galleys. These the
king exhorted by the most cogent arguments to return to the battle,
and share with the rest whatever might befall them. Leaving five
men as guards on board each galley, the king led back the rest to
assist his hard-pressed army; and he no sooner arrived than with all
his fury he fell upon the thickest ranks of the enemy, driving them
back and routing them, so that even those who were at a distance
and untouched by him were overwhelmed by the throng of the troops
as they retreated. Never was there such an attack made by an individual. He pierced into the middle of the hostile army, and performed
the deeds of a brave and distinguished warrior. The Turks at once
closed upon him, and tried to overwhelm him. In the meantime our
men, losing sight of the king, were fearful lest he should have been
slain, and when one of them proposed that they should advance to
find him, our lines could hardly contain themselves. But if by any
chance the disposition of our troops had been broken, without doubt
they would all have been destroyed. What, however, was to be
thought of the king, who was hemmed in by the enemy, a single man
opposed to so many thousands? The hand of the writer faints to see
it, and the mind of the reader to hear it. Who ever heard of such a
man? His bravery was ever of the highest order, no adverse storm
could sink it; his valor was ever becoming, and if we may from a
few instances judge of many, it was ever indefatigable in war. Why
then do we speak of the valor of Antæus, who regained his strength
every time he touched his mother earth, for Antæus perished when
he was lifted up from earth in the long wrestling match. The body
of Achilles also, who slew Hector, was invulnerable, because he was
dipped in the Stygian waves; yet Achilles was mortally wounded in
the very part by which he was held when they dipped him. Likewise
Alexander, the Macedonian, who was stimulated by ambition to
subjugate the whole world, undertook a most difficult enterprise, and
with a handful of choice soldiers fought many celebrated battles,
but the chief part of his valor consisted of the excellence of his
soldiers. In the same manner the brave Judas Maccabeus, of whom
all the world discoursed, performed many wonderful deeds worthy

forever to be remembered, but when he was abandoned by his soldiers in the midst of a battle, with thousands of enemies to oppose
him, he was slain, together with his brothers. But King Richard,
inured to battle from his tenderest years, and to whom even famous
Roland could not be considered equal, remained invincible, even in
the midst of the enemy; and his body, as if it were made of brass,
was impenetrable to any kind of weapon. In his right hand he
brandished his sword, which in its rapid descent broke the ranks
on either side of him. Such was his energy amid that host of Turks
that, fearing nothing, he destroyed all around him, mowing men
down with his scythe as reapers mow down the corn with their
sickles. Who could describe his deeds? Whoever felt one of his blows
had no need of a second. Such was the energy of his courage that it
seemed to rejoice at having found an occasion to display itself. The
sword wielded by his powerful hand cut down men and horses alike,
cleaving them to the middle. The more he was himself separated
from his men, and the more the enemy sought to overwhelm him,
the more did his valor shine conspicuous. Among other brave deeds
which he performed on that occasion he slew by one marvellous
stroke an admiral, who was conspicuous above the rest of the enemy
by his rich caparisons. This man by his gestures seemed to say that
he was going to do something wonderful, and whilst he reproached
the rest with cowardice he put spurs to his horse and charged full
against the king, who, waving his sword as he saw him coming,
smote off at a single blow not only his head, but his shoulder and
right arm. The Turks were terror-struck at the sight, and, giving
way on all sides, scarcely dared to shoot at him from a distance
with their arrows.

The king now returned safe and unhurt to his friends, and encouraged them more than ever with the hope of victory. How were
their minds raised from despair when they saw him coming safe out
of the enemy's ranks! They knew not what had happened to him,
but they knew that without him all the hopes of the Christian army
would be in vain. The king's person was stuck all over with javelins,
like a deer pierced by the hunters, and the trappings of his horse
were thickly covered with arrows. Thus, like a brave soldier, he returned from the contest, and a bitter contest it was, for it had lasted
from the morning sun to the setting sun. It may seem wonderful
and even incredible, that so small a body of men endured so long a
conflict; but by God's mercy we cannot doubt the truth of it, for
in that battle only one or two of our men were slain. But the number
of the Turkish horses that lay dead on the field is said to have
exceeded fifteen hundred; and of the Turks themselves more than
seven hundred were killed, and yet they did not carry back King

Richard, as they had boasted, as a present to Saladin; but, on the contrary, he and his horse performed so many deeds of valor in the sight of the Turks that the enemy shuddered to behold him.

In the meantime our men having by God's grace escaped destruction, the Turkish army returned to Saladin, who is said to have ridiculed them by asking where Melech Richard was, for they had promised to bring him a prisoner? "Which of you," continued he, "first seized him, and where is he? Why is he not produced?" To whom one of the Turks that came from the furthest countries of the earth replied, "In truth, my lord, Melech Richard, about whom you ask, is not here; we have never heard since the beginning of the world that there ever was such a knight, so brave and so experienced in arms. In every deed of arms he is ever the foremost; in deeds he is without a rival, the first to advance and the last to retreat; we did our best to seize him, but in vain, for no man can escape from his sword; his attack is dreadful; to engage with him is fatal, and his deeds are beyond human nature."

CHAPTER XXXIV

ROBIN HOOD OF SHERWOOD FOREST

In this our spacious isle I think there is not one,
But he of ROBIN HOOD hath heard and Little John;
And to the end of time the tales shall ne'er be done
Of Scarlock, George a Green, and Much the miller's son,
Of Tuck, the merry friar, which many a sermon made
In praise of ROBIN HOOD, his outlaws and their trade.
                                        DRAYTON.

EVERY reader of "Ivanhoe," at the mention of Richard the Crusader, will be reminded of Robin Hood, the noble outlaw of Sherwood Forest, and his band of merry bowmen. With these we next concern ourselves, and if the reader will pardon the dry outlines of the historian before proceeding to the more interesting and imaginative story of the ballad-singer, we will at first state what so careful an antiquary as Mr. Ritson considers to be truly trustworthy in Robin Hood's history.

Robin Hood was born at Locksley, in the county of Nottingham, in the reign of King Henry II, and about the year of Christ 1160. His extraction was noble, and his true name Robert Fitzooth, which vulgar pronunciation easily corrupted into Robin Hood. He is frequently styled, and commonly reputed to have been, Earl of Huntingdon; a title to which, in the latter part of his life at least, he actually appears to have had some sort of pretension. In his youth he is reported to have been of a wild and extravagant disposition, insomuch that, his inheritance being consumed or forfeited by his excesses, and his person outlawed for debt, either from necessity or choice he sought an asylum in the woods and forests, with which immense tracts, especially in the northern part of the kingdom, were at that time covered. Of these he chiefly affected Barnsdale, in Yorkshire; Sherwood in Nottinghamshire, and, according to some, Plompton Park in Cumberland. Here he either found or was afterwards joined by a number of persons in similar circumstances, who appear to have considered and obeyed him as their chief or leader. ... Having for a long series of years maintained a sort of independent sovereignty, and set kings, judges, and magistrates at defiance, a proclamation was published, offering a considerable reward for bringing him in either dead or alive; which, however, seems to have been productive of no greater success than former attempts for that purpose. At length the infirmities of old age increasing upon him, and desirous to be relieved, in a fit of sickness, by being let blood, he applied for that purpose to the prioress of Kirkley nunnery in Yorkshire, his relative (women, and particularly religious women, being in those times somewhat better skilled in surgery than the sex is at present), by whom he was treacherously suffered to bleed to death. This event happened on the 18th November, 1247, being the thirty-first year of King Henry III.; and if the date assigned to his birth be correct, about the eighty-seventh year of his age. He was interred under some trees at a short distance from the house; a stone being placed over his grave, with an inscription to his memory.

There are some who will have it that Robin Hood was not alive in the reign of Richard I., and who will have it that he preferred other forests to Sherwood. But the stories that we have chosen are of the Robin Hood of Sherwood Forest and of King Richard the Lion-hearted.

LITTLE JOHN

The lieutenant of Robin Hood's band was named Little John, not so much from his smallness in stature (for he was seven feet high and more), as for a reason which I shall tell later. And the manner in which Robin Hood, to whom he was very dear, met him was this.

Robin Hood on one occasion being hunting with his men and finding the sport to be poor, said: "We have had no sport now for some time. So I go abroad alone. And if I should fall into any peril whence I cannot escape I will blow my horn that ye may know of it and bear me aid." And with that he bade them adieu and departed alone, having with him his bow and the arrows in his quiver. And passing shortly over a brook by a long bridge he met at the middle a stranger. And neither of the two would give way to the other. And Robin Hood being angry fitted an arrow to his bow and made ready to fire. "Truly," said the stranger at this, "thou art a fine fellow that you must draw your long bow on me who have but a staff by me." "That is just truly," said Robin; "and so I will lay by my bow and get me a staff to try if your deeds be as good as your words." And with that he went into a thicket and chose him a small ground oak for a staff and returned to the stranger.

"Now," said he, "I am a match for you, so let us play upon this bridge, and if one should fall in the stream the other will have the victory." "With all my heart," said the stranger; "I shall not be the first to give out." And with that they began to make great play with their staves. And Robin Hood first struck the stranger such a blow as warmed all his blood, and from that they rattled their sticks as though they had been threshing corn. And finally the stranger gave Robin such a crack on his crown that he broke his head and the blood flowed. But this only urged him the more, so that he attacked the stranger with such vigor that he had like to have made an end of him. But he growing into a fury finally fetched him such a blow that he tumbled him from the bridge into the brook. Whereat the stranger laughed loudly and long, and cried out to him, "Where art thou now, I prythee, my good fellow?" And Robin replied, "Thou art truly a brave soul, and I will have no more to do with thee to-day; so our battle is at an end, and I must allow that thou hast won the day." And then wading to the bank he pulled out his horn and blew a blast on it so that the echoes flew throughout the valley. And at that came fifty bold bowmen out of the wood, all clad in green, and they made for Robin Hood, and said William Stukely, "What is the matter, my master? you are wet to the skin?" "Truly, nothing is the matter," said Robin, "but that the lad on the bridge has tumbled me into the stream." And on that the archers would have seized the stranger to duck him as well, but Robin Hood forbade them. "No one shall harm thee, friend," said he. "These are all my bowmen, threescore and nine, and if you will be one of us you shall straightway have my livery and accoutrements, fit for a man. What say you?" "With all my heart," said the stranger; "here is my hand on it. My name is John Little, and I will be a good man and true to you." "His name shall be changed," said William Stukely on this. "We will call him Little John, and I will be his godfather."

So they fetched a pair of fat does and some humming strong ale, and there they christened their babe Little John, for he was seven feet high and an ell round at his waist.

FRIAR TUCK

Now Robin Hood had instituted a day of mirth for himself and all his companions, and wagers were laid amongst them who should exceed at this exercise and who at that; some did contend who should jump farthest, some who should throw the bar, some who should be swiftest afoot in a race five miles in length; others there were with which Little John was most delighted, who did strive which of them should draw the strongest bow, and be the best marksman. "Let me see," said Little John, "which of you can kill a buck, and who can kill a doe, and who is he can kill a hart, being distant from it by the space of five hundred feet." With that, Robin Hood going before them, they went directly to the forest, where they found good store of game feeding before them. William Scarlock, that drew the strongest bow of them all, did kill a buck, and Little John made choice of a barren fat doe, and the well-directed arrow did enter in the very heart of it; and Midge, the miller's son, did kill a hart above five hundred feet distant from him. The hart falling, Robin Hood stroked him gently on the shoulder, and said unto him, "God's blessing on thy heart, I will ride five hundred miles to find a match for thee." William Scarlock, hearing him speak these words, smiled and said unto him, "Master, what needs that? Here is a Curtal Friar [1] not far off, that for a hundred pound will shoot at what distance yourself will propound, either with Midge or with yourself. An experienced man he is, and will draw a bow with great strength; he will shoot with yourself, and with all the men you have, one after another."

"Sayest thou so, Scarlock?" replied Robin Hood. "By the grace of God I will neither eat nor drink till I see this Friar thou dost speak of." And having prepared himself for his journey, he took Little John and fifty of his best archers with him, whom he bestowed in a convenient place, as he himself thought fitting. This being done, he ran down into the dale, where he found the Curtal Friar walking by the water side. He no sooner espied him, but presently he took unto him his broadsword and buckler, and put on his head a steel bonnet. The Friar, not knowing who he was, or for what intent he came, did presently arm himself to encounter with him. Robin Hood, coming near unto him, alighted from his horse, which he tied to a thorn that grew hard by, and looking wistfully on the Friar, said

[1] "The Curtal Friar," Dr. Stukely says, "is Cordelier, from the cord or rope which they wore round their waist, to whip themselves with. They were," adds he, "of the Franciscan order. Our Friar, however, is undoubtedly so called from his Curtal dogs, or curs, as we now say." *Thoms. Early Prose Romances:* in which, by the way, may be found many of the tales of Robin Hood printed here, and much more besides of interest.

unto him, "Carry me over the water, thou Curtal Friar, or else thy life lies at the stake." The Friar made no more ado, but took up Robin Hood and carried him on his back; deep water he did stride; he spake not so much as one word to him, but having carried him over, he gently laid him down on the side of the bank; which being done, the Friar said to Robin Hood, "It is now thy turn; therefore carry me over the water, thou bold fellow, or sure I shall make thee repent it." Robin Hood, to requite the courtesy, took the Friar on his back, and not speaking the least word to him, carried him over the water, and laid him gently down on the side of the bank; and turning to him, he spake unto him as at first, and bade him carry him over the water once more, or he should answer it with the forfeit of his life. The Friar in a smiling manner took him up, and spake not a word till he came in the midst of the stream, when, being up to the middle and higher, he did shake him from off his shoulders, and said unto him, "Now choose thee, bold fellow, whether thou wilt sink or swim."

Robin Hood, being soundly washed, got him up on his feet, and prostrating himself, did swim to a bush of broom on the other side of the bank; and the Friar swam to a willow tree which was not far from it. Then Robin Hood, taking his bow in his hand, and one of his best arrows, did shoot at the Friar, which the Friar received in his buckler of steel, and said unto him, "Shoot on, thou bold fellow; if thou shootest at me a whole summer's day I will stand your mark still." "That will I," said Robin Hood, and shot arrow after arrow at him, until he had not an arrow left in his quiver. He then laid down his bow, and drew out his sword, which but two days before had been the death of three men. Now hand to hand they went with sword and buckler; the steel buckler defends whatsoever blow is given; sometimes they make at the head, sometimes at the foot, sometimes at the side; sometimes they strike directly down, sometimes they falsify their blows, and come in foot and arm, with a free thrust at the body; and being ashamed that so long they exercise their unprofitable valor and cannot hurt one another, they multiply their blows, they hack, they hew, they slash, they foam. At last Robin Hood desired the Friar to hold his hand, and to give him leave to blow his horn.

"Thou wantest breath to sound it," said the Friar; "take thee a little respite, for we have been five hours at it by the Fountain Abbey clock." Robin Hood took his horn from his side, and having sounded it three times, behold where fifty lusty men, with their bended bows, came to his assistance. The Friar, wondering at it, "Whose men," said he, "be these?" "They are mine," said Robin Hood; "what is that to thee?" "False loon," said the Friar;

and making a little pause, he desired Robin Hood to show him the same courtesy which he gave him. "What is that?" said Robin Hood. "Thou soundest thy horn three times," said the Friar; "let me now but whistle three times." "Ay, with all my heart," said Robin Hood; "I were to blame if I should deny thee that courtesy." With that the Friar set his fist to his mouth, and whistled three times so shrilly that the place echoed again with it; and behold three and fifty fair ban-dogs (their hair rising on their back, betokening their rage), were almost on the backs of Robin Hood and his companions. "Here is for every one of thy men a dog," said the Friar, "and two for thee." "That is foul play," said Robin Hood. He had scarce spoken that word but two dogs came upon him at once, one before, another behind him, who, although they could not touch his flesh (his sword had made so swift a despatch of them), yet they tore his coat into two pieces. By this time the men had so laid about them that the dogs began to fly back, and their fury to languish into barking. Little John did so bestir himself, that the Curtal Friar, admiring at his courage and his nimbleness, did ask him who he was. He made him answer, "I will tell the truth, and not lie. I am he who is called Little John, and do belong to Robin Hood, who hath fought with thee this day, five hours together; and if thou wilt not submit unto him, this arrow shall make thee." The Friar, perceiving how much he was overpowered, and that it was impossible for him to deal with so many at once, did come to composition with Robin Hood. And the articles of agreement were these: That the Friar should abandon Fountain Dale and Fountain Abbey, and should live with Robin Hood, at his place not far from Nottingham, where for saying of mass, he should receive a noble for every Sunday throughout the year, and for saying mass on every holy day, a new change of garment. The Friar, contented with these conditions, did seal the agreement. And thus by the courage of Robin Hood and his yeomen, he was enforced at the last to submit, having for seven long years kept Fountain Dale, not all the power thereabouts being able to bring him on his knees.

But Friar Tuck was the only man of the clergy with whom Robin had friendly dealings. As a rule these churchmen fared as did the Bishop of Hereford in the following ballad, which we add for the sake of an example of the manner in which this True History of Robin Hood has come down to us from the year 1245:—

THE BISHOP OF HEREFORD'S ENTERTAINMENT BY ROBIN HOOD AND LITTLE JOHN AND THEIR COMPANY, IN MERRY BARNSDALE

SOME they will talk of bold Robin Hood,
    And some of barons bold;
But I'll tell you how he served the Bishop of Hereford,
    When he robbed him of his gold.

As it befell in merry Barnsdale,
    All under the greenwood tree,
The Bishop of Hereford was to come by,
    With all his company.

"Come, kill me a venison," said bold Robin Hood,
    "And dress it by the highway side,
And we will watch the bishop narrowly,
    Lest some other way he should ride."

Robin Hood dressed himself in shepherd's attire,
    With six of his men also;
And, when the Bishop of Hereford came by,
    They about the fire did go.

"O, what is the matter?" then said the bishop,
    "Or for whom do you make this ado?
Or why do you kill the king's ven'son,
    When your company is so few?"

"We are shepherds," said bold Robin Hood,
    "And we keep sheep all the year;
And we are disposed to be merry this day,
    And to kill of the king's fat deer."

"You are brave fellows," said the bishop,
    "And the king of your doings shall know;
Therefore make haste, and come along with me,
    For before the king you shall go."

"O pardon, O pardon," said bold Robin Hood,
    "O pardon, I thee pray;
For it becomes not your lordship's coat
    To take so many lives away."

"No pardon, no pardon," said the bishop,
    "No pardon I thee owe;
Therefore make haste, and come along with me,
    For before the king you shall go."

Then Robin he set his back against a tree,
    And his foot against a thorn,
And from underneath his shepherd's coat
    He pulled out a bugle horn.

He put the little end to his mouth,
    And a loud blast did he blow,
Till threescore and ten of bold Robin's men
    Came running all in a row:

All making obeisance to bold Robin Hood;
  'Twas a comely sight for to see.
"What is the matter, master," said Little John,
  "That you blow so lustily?"

"O here is the Bishop of Hereford,
  And no pardon we shall have."
"Cut off his head, master," said Little John,
  "And throw him into his grave."

"O pardon, O pardon," said the bishop,
  "O pardon, I thee pray;
For if I had known it had been you,
  I'd have gone some other way."

"No pardon, no pardon," said bold Robin Hood,
  "No pardon I thee owe;
Therefore make haste, and come along with me,
  For to merry Barnsdale you shall go."

Then Robin he took the bishop by the hand,
  And led him to merry Barnsdale;
He made him stay and sup with him that night,
  And to drink wine, beer, and ale.

"Call in a reckoning," said the bishop,
  "For methinks it grows wondrous high."
"Send me your purse, master," said Little John,
  "And I'll tell you bye and bye."

Then Little John took the bishop's cloak,
  And spread it upon the ground,
And out of the bishop's portmantua
  He told three hundred pound.

"Here's money enough, master," said Little John,
  "And a comely sight 'tis to see;
It makes me in charity with the bishop,
  Though he heartily loveth not me."

Robin Hood took the bishop by the hand,
  And he caused the music to play;
And he made the old bishop to dance in his boots,
  And glad to get so away

CHAPTER XXXV

ROBIN HOOD AND HIS ADVENTURES

··"They say he is already in the forest of Arden, and a many merry men wi.
him; and there they live like the old Robin Hood of England . . . and fleet the
time carelessly as they did in the golden world."—As You Like It.

As has been already said, some of the ballad makers have so
far erred from the truth as to represent Robin Hood as being
outlawed by Henry VIII., and several stories are told of Queen
Katherine's interceding with her husband for the pardon of the

bold outlaw.[1] However this may be, it is known that Robin Hood once shot a match on the queen's side against the king's archers, and here is the story:—

Robin Hood on one occasion sent a present to Queen Katherine with which she was so pleased that she swore she would be a friend to the noble outlaw as long as she might live. So one day the queen went to her chamber and called to her a page of her company and bade him make haste and prepare to ride to Nottinghamshire to find Robin Hood in Sherwood Forest; for the queen had made a match with the king, her archers against his archers, and the queen proposed to have Robin Hood and his band to shoot on her side against the king's archers.

Now as for the page, he started for Nottingham and posted all the way, and inquired on the road for Robin Hood, where he might be, but he could not find any one who could let him know exactly. So he took up his quarters at an inn at Nottingham. And in the room of the inn he sat him down and called for a bottle of Rhenish wine, and he drank the queen's health out of it. Now at his side was sitting a yeoman of the country, clad in Lincoln green, with a long bow in his hand. And he turned to the page and asked him, "What is thy business, my sweet boy, so far in the north country, for methinks you must come from

<hr />

[1] This seems to have been the opinion of the author from whom we draw the following account of our hero's life,—to show how the doctors will disagree even on a topic as important as Robin Hood:—

THE NOBLE BIRTH AND THE ACHIEVEMENTS OF ROBIN HOOD

"Robin Hood was descended from the noble family of the Earl of Huntingdon, and being outlawed by Henry VIII. for many extravagancies and outrages he had committed, he did draw together a company of such bold and licentious persons as himself, who lived for the most part on robberies committed in or near unto Sherwood Forest in Nottinghamshire. He had these always ready at his command, so that if need did require he at the winding of his horn would have fifty or more of them in readiness to assist him. He whom he most affected was called Little John by reason of his low stature, though not inferior to any of them in strength of body and stoutness of spirit. He would not entertain any into his service whom he had not first fought with himself and made sufficient trial of his courage and dexterity how to use his weapons, which was the reason that oftentimes he came home hurt and beaten as he was; which was nevertheless no occasion of the diminution of his love to the person whom he fought with, for ever afterwards he would be the more familiar with him, and better respect him for it. Many petitions were referred to the king for a pardon for him, which the king (understanding of the many mad pranks he and his associates played) would give no ear unto; but being attended with a considerable guard, did make a progress himself to find him out and bring him to condign punishment. At last, by the means and mediation of Queen Katherine the king's wrath was qualified, and his pardon sealed, and he spent his old age in peace, at a house of his own, not far from Nottingham, being generally beloved and respected by all."

London?" So then the page told him that it was his business to find Robin Hood the outlaw, and for that he asked every yeoman that he met. And he asked his friend if he knew anything which might help him. "Truly," said the yeoman, "that I do. And if you will get to horse early to-morrow morning I will show you Robin Hood and all his gay yeomen."

So the next morning they got them to horse and rode out into the forest, and the yeoman brought the page to where were Robin Hood and his yeomen. And the page fell down on his knee and said to Robin Hood, "Queen Katherine greets you well by me, and hath sent you this ring as a token. She bids you post up to London town, for that there shall be some sport there in which she has a mind you shall have a hand." And at this Robin took off his mantle of Lincoln green from his back and sent it by the page to Queen Katherine with a promise that he and his band would follow him as soon as they might.

So Robin Hood clothed all his men in Lincoln green and himself in scarlet, and each man wore a black hat with a white feather stuck therein. And thus Robin Hood and his band came up to London. And Robin fell down on his knees before the queen, and she bade him welcome with all his band. For the match between the queen's archers and the king's was to come off the next day in Finsbury fields.

Here first came the king's archers marching with bold bearing, and then came Robin Hood and his archers for the queen. And they laid out the marks there. And the king laid a wager with the queen on the shooting. Now the wager was three hundred tun of Rhenish, and three hundred tun of good English beer, and three hundred fat harts. So then the queen asked if there were any knights with the king who would take her side. But they were unwilling, for said they, "How shall we bet on these men whom we have never seen, when we know Clifton and the rest of the king's archers, and have seen them shoot?" Now this Clifton was one of the king's archers and a great boaster. And when he had reached the shooting field he had cried out, "Measure no marks for us, my lord the king, for we will shoot at the sun and moon." But for all that Robin Hood beat him at the shooting. And the queen asked the Bishop of Herefordshire to back her archers. But he swore by his mitre that he would not bet a single penny on the queen's archers for he knew them not. "What will you bet against them," asked Robin Hood at this, "since you think our shooting is the worse?" "Truly," said the bishop, "I will bet all the money that may be in my purse," and he pulled it up from where it hung at his side. "What is in your purse?" asked Robin Hood. And the bishop tossed it down on the ground, saying, "Fifteen rose-nobles, and that's an hundred pound." So Robin Hood tossed out a bag beside the bishop's purse on the green.

And with that they began shooting, and shot three bouts and they came out even; the king's and the queen's. "The next three shots," said the king, "shall pay for all." And so the king's archers shot, and then Robin Hood, and Little John and Midge the miller's son shot for the queen, and came every man of them nearer the prick in the willow wand than did any of the king's men. So the queen's archers having beaten, Queen Katherine asked a boon of the king, and he granted it. "Give me, I pray you," said the queen, "safe conduct for the archers of my party to come and to go home and to stay in London here some time to enjoy themselves." "I grant it," said the king. "Then you are welcome, Robin Hood," said the queen, "and so is Little John and Midge the miller's son and every one of you." "Is this Robin Hood?" asked the king, "for I had heard that he was killed in a quarrel in the north country." And the bishop too asked, "Is this Robin Hood? If I had known that I would not have bet a penny with him. He took me one Saturday evening and bound me fast to a tree, and there he made me sing a mass for him and his yeomanry about." "Well, if I did," said Robin Hood, "surely I needed all the masses that I might get for my soul." And with that he and his yeomanry departed, and when their safe conduct was expired they journeyed north again to Sherwood Forest.

ROBIN HOOD AND THE BEGGAR

But Robin Hood, once having supplied himself with good store of money, which he had gotten of the sheriff of Nottingham, bought him a stout gelding, and riding on him one day towards Nottingham, it was his fortune to meet with a poor beggar. Robin Hood was of a frolic spirit, and no accepter of persons; but observing the beggar to have several sorts of bags, which were fastened to his patched coat, he did ride up to him, and giving him the time of day, he demanded of him what countryman he was. "A Yorkshireman," said the beggar; "and I would desire of you to give me something." "Give thee!" said Robin Hood; "why, I have nothing to give thee. I am a poor ranger in the forest, and thou seemest to be a lusty knave; shall I give thee a good bastinado over thy shoulders?" "Content, content," said the beggar; "I durst lay all my bags to a threaden joust, thou wilt repent it." With that Robin Hood alighted, and the beggar, with his long quarterstaff, so well defended himself, that, let Robin Hood de what he could, he could not come within the beggar, to flash him to a remembrance of his overboldness; and nothing vexed him more than to find that the beggar's staff was as hard and as obdurate as iron itself; but not so Robin Hood's head, for the beggar with all his force did let his staff descend with such a side blow, that Robin Hood, for all his skill, could not defend it, but the blood came trickling down his face, which, turning Robin Hood's courage into revenge and fury, he let fly at him with his trusty sword, and doubled blow upon blow; but perceiving that the beggar did hold him so hard to it that one of his blows was but the forerunner of another, and every blow to be almost the Postilion of Death, he cried out to him to hold his hand. "That will I not do," said the beggar, "unless thou wilt resign unto me thy horse, and thy sword, and thy clothes, with all the money thou hast in thy pockets." "The change is uneven," said Robin Hood, "but for once I am content."

So, putting on the beggar's clothes, the beggar was the gentleman, and Robin Hood was the beggar, who, entering into Nottingham town with his patched coat and several wallets, understood that three brethren were that day to suffer at the gallows, being condemned for killing the king's deer, he made no more ado, but went directly to the sheriff's house, where a young gentleman, seeing him to stand at the door, demanded of him what he would have. Robin Hood returned answer that he came to crave neither meat nor drink, but the lives of these three brothers who were condemned to die. "That cannot be," said the young gentleman, "for they are all this day to suffer according to law, for stealing of the king's deer, and they are already conveyed out of the town to the place of execution." "I will be with them presently," said Robin Hood, and coming to the gallows he found many making great lamentation for them. Robin Hood did comfort them, and assured them they should not die; and blowing his horn, behold on a sudden a hundred brave archers came unto him, by whose help, having released the prisoners, and killed the hangman, and hurt many of the sheriff's officers, they took those who were condemned to die for killing the king's deer along with them, who, being very thankful for the preservation of their lives, became afterwards of the yeomanry of Robin Hood.

ROBIN HOOD AND KING RICHARD

Now King Richard, hearing of the deeds of Robin Hood and his men, wondered much at them, and desired greatly himself to see him, and his men as well. So he with a dozen of his lords rode to

Nottingham town and there took up his abode. And being at Nottingham, the king one day with his lords put on friars' gowns every one, and rode forth from Fountain Abbey down to Barnsdale. And as they were riding there they saw Robin Hood and all his band standing ready to assail them. The king, being taller than the rest, was thought by Robin to be the abbot. So he made up to him, and seized his horse by the head, and bade him stand. "For," said he, "it is against such knaves as you that I am bound to make war." "But," said the king himself, "we are messengers from the king, who is but a little away, waiting to speak with you." "God save the king," said Robin Hood, "and all his well-wishers. And accursed be every one who may deny his sovereignty." "You are cursing yourself," said the king, "for you are a traitor." "Now," said Robin Hood, "if you were not the king's messenger, I would make you rue that word of yours. I am as true a man to the king as lives. And I never yet injured any honest man and true, but only those who make their living by stealing from others. I have never in my life harmed either husbandman or huntsman. But my chief spite lies against the clergy, who have in these days great power. But I am right glad to have met you here. Come with me, and you shall taste our greenwood cheer." But the king and his lords marvelled, wondering what kind of cheer Robin might provide for them. And Robin took the king's horse by the head, and led him towards his tent. "It is because thou comest from the king," said he, "that I use you in this wise; and hadst thou as much gold as ever I had, it should be all of it safe for good King Richard's sake." And with that he took out his horn, and blew on it a loud blast. And thereat came marching forth from the wood five score and ten of Robin's followers, and each one bent the knee before Robin Hood. "Surely," thought the king, "it is a goodly sight to see; for they are more humble to their master than my servants are to me. Here may the court learn something from the greenwood." And here they laid a dinner for the king and his lords, and the king swore that he had never feasted better. Then Robin Hood, taking a can of ale, said, "Let us now begin, each man with his can. Here's a health to the king." And they all drank the health to the king, the king himself, as well as another.

And after the dinner they all took their bows, and showed the king such archery that the king said he had never seen such men as they in any foreign land. And then said the king to Robin Hood, "If I could get thee a pardon from King Richard, wouldst thou serve the king well in everything?" "Yes, with all my heart," said Robin. And so said all his men.

And with that the king declared himself to them, and said, "I am the king, your sovereign, that is now before you." And at this Robin and all his men fell down on their knees; but the king raised them up, saying to them that he pardoned each one of them, and that they should every one of them be in his service. So the king returned to Nottingham, and with him returned Robin Hood and his men, to the great joy of the townspeople, whom they had for a long time sorely vexed.

> "And they are gone to London court,
> Robin Hood and all his train;
> He once was there a noble peer,
> And now he's there again."

THE DEATH OF ROBIN HOOD

But Robin Hood returned to Sherwood Forest, and there met his death. For one day, being wounded in a fight, he fled out of the battle with Little John. And being at some distance, Robin Hood said to his lieutenant, "Now truly I cannot shoot even one shot more, for the arrows will not fly. For I am sore wounded. So I will go to my cousin, the abbess, who dwelleth near here in Kirkley Hall, and she shall bleed me, that I may be well again." So Robin Hood left Little John, and he went his way to Kirkley; and reaching the Hall, his strength nearly left him, yet he knocked heavily at the door. And his cousin came down first to let him in. And when she saw him she knew that it was her cousin Robin Hood, and she received him with a joyful face. Then said Robin, "You see me, my cousin, how weak I am. Therefore I pray you to bleed me, that I may be whole again." And his cousin took him by the hand, and led him into an upper room, and laid him on a bed, and she bled him. But the treacherous woman tied not up the vein again, but left him so that his life began to flow from him. And he, finding his strength leaving him, thought to escape; but he could not, for the door was locked, and the casement window was so high that he might not leap down from it. Then knowing that he must die, he reached forth his hand to his bugle horn, which lay by him on the bed. And setting the horn to his mouth, he blew weakly, though with all his strength, three blasts upon it. And Little John, as he sat under the tree in the greenwood, heard his blowing, and he said, "Now must Robin be near death, for his blast is very weak."

And he got up and ran to Kirkley Hall as fast as he might. And coming to the door, he found it locked; but he broke it down, and so came to Robin Hood. And coming to the bed, he fell upon his knees, and said, "Master, I beg a boon of thee,—that thou lettest me burn down Kirkley Hall and all the nunnery." "Nay," quoth Robin Hood; "nay, I cannot grant you your boon; for never in my life did I hurt woman, or man in woman's company, nor shall it be done when I die. But for me, give me my long bow, and I will let fly an arrow, and where you shall find the arrow, there bury me. And make my grave long and broad, that I may rest easily; and place my head upon a green sod, and place my bow at my side." And these words Little John readily promised him, so that Robin Hood was pleased. And they buried him as he had asked, an arrow-shot from Kirkley Hall.

CHAPTER XXXVI

CHEVY CHASE

"The Perse out of Northumberlande,
    And a vowe to God mayde he,
That he wold hunte in the mountayns
    Off Chyviat within days thre,
In the mauger of doughtè Dogles,
    And all that ever with him be."
PERCY: *Reliques of Ancient Poetry.*

SCARCELY less famous than Robin Hood as a subject for ballad makers was the battle of Chevy Chase. This battle was one of the many struggles rising out of the never-ending border quarrels between Scotland and England, of which poets are never tired of singing. Sometimes the Earl of Douglas, the great Scotch border-lord, would make an incursion into Northumberland, and then to revenge the insult Lord Percy would come riding over the Tweed into Scotland.

In the battle of Chevy Chase it would seem as if Earl Percy was the aggressor. As a matter of fact it mattered little which began the quarrel at any particular time. The feud was ever smouldering, and needed little to make it burst forth.

THE BALLAD OF CHEVY CHASE

God prosper long our noble king,
    Our lives and safetyes all;
A woefull hunting once there did
    In Chevy Chase befall.

To drive the deer with hound and horne,
    Erle Percy took his way,
The child may rue that is unborne
    The hunting of that day.

The stout Erle of Northumberland
A vow to God did make,
His pleasure in the Scottish woods
Three summer days to take;

The cheefest harts in Chevy Chase
To kill and bear away.
These tidings to Erle Douglas came,
In Scotland where he lay,

Who sent Erle Percy present word
He would prevent his sport.
The English Erle not fearing that,
Did to the woods resort,

With fifteen hundred bowmen bold;
All chosen men of might,
Who knew full well in time of neede
To ayme their shafts aright.

The gallant greyhounds swiftly ran
To chase the fallow deere:
On Monday they began to hunt
Ere daylight did appear;

And long before high noon they had
An hundred fat buckes slaine;
Then having dined the drovyers went
To rouse the deer again.

The bowmen mustered on the hill,
Well able to endure;
Their backsides all, with special care,
That day were guarded sure.

The hounds ran swiftly through the woods,
The nimble deere to take,
That with their cryes the hills and dales
An eccho shrill did make.

Lord Percy to the quarry went,
To view the slaughtered deer;
Quoth he, Erle Douglas promised
This day to meet me heere;

But if I thought he would not come,
Noe longer would I stay.
With that a brave young gentleman
Thus to the Erle did say:—

Loe, yonder doth Erle Douglas come,
His men in armour bright;
Full twenty hundred Scottish speres
All marching in our sight;

All men of pleasant Tivydale,
Fast by the river Tweede:
O cease your sports, Erle Percy said,
And take your bowes with speede.

And now with me, my countrymen,
  Your courage forth advance;
For there was never champion yett
  In Scotland or in France,

That ever did on horseback come,
  But if my hap it were,
I durst encounter man for man,
  With him to break a spere.

Erle Douglas on his milk-white steede,
  Most like a baron bold,
Rode foremost of his company,
  Whose armour shone like gold.

Show me, sayd he, whose men you be,
  That hunt so boldly heere,
That without my consent doe chase
  And kill my fallow deere.

The first man that did answer make
  Was noble Percy he;
Who sayd, We list not to declare,
  Nor show whose men we be.

Yet we will spend our deerest blood,
  Thy cheefest harts to slay.
The Douglas swore a solempne oathe,
  And thus in rage did say,

Ere thus I will outbraved be.
  One of us two shall dye:
I know thee well, an erle thou art;
  Lord Percy, soe am I.

But trust me, Percy, pittye it were
  And great offence to kill
Any of these our guiltless men,
  For they have done no ill.

Let thou and I the battell trye,
  And set our men aside.
Accurst be he, Erle Percy sayd,
  By whom this is denyed.

Then stept a gallant squier forth,
  Witherington was his name,
Who said, I wold not have it told
  To Henry our king for shame,

That ere my captaine fought on foot
  And I stood looking on.
You be two erles, sayd Witherington,
  And I a squier alone:

Ile doe the best that doe I may,
  While I have power to stand:
While I have power to wield my sword,
  Ile fight with hart and hand.

Our English archers bent their bowes
Their harts were good and trew;
At the first flight of arrowes sent,
Full fourscore Scots they slew.

Yet bides Erle Douglas on the bent,
As cheeftain stout and good,
As valiant captain, all unmoved,
The shock he firmly stood.

His host he parted had in three,
As leader ware and tryd,
And soon his spearmen on his foes
Bare down on every side.

To drive the deere with hound and horne,
Douglas bade on the bent:
Two captaines moved with mickle might
Their speares to shivers went.

Throughout the English archery
They dealt full many a wound;
But still our valiant Englishmen
All firmly kept their ground:

And throwing straight their bowes away,
They grasped their swords so bright:
And now sharp blows, a heavy shower,
On shields and helmets light.

They closed full fast on every side,
No slackness there was found;
And many a gallant gentleman
Lay gasping on the ground.

O Christ! it was a griefe to see,
And likewise for to heare,
The cries of men lying in their gore,
And scattered here and there.

At last these two stout erles did meet,
Like captaines of great might;
Like lyons wood, they layd on lode
And made a cruell fight:

They fought until they both did sweat,
With swords of tempered steele;
Until the blood, like drops of rain,
They trickling down did feele.

Yield thee, Lord Percy, Douglas sayd;
In faith I will thee bringe,
Where thou shalt high advanced be
By James our Scottish king:

Thy ransome I will freely give,
And this report of thee:
Thou art the most courageous knight
That ever I did see.

Noe, Douglas, quoth Erle Percy then,
  Thy proffer I do scorne;
I will not yield to any Scott,
  That ever yet was borne.

With that there came an arrow keene,
  Out of an English bow,
Which struck Erle Douglas to the heart,
  A deepe and deadly blow:

Who never spake more words than these,
  Fight on, my merry men all;
For why, my life is at an end;
  Lord Percy sees my fall.

Then leaving liffe, Erle Percy tooke
  The dead man by the hand;
And said, Erle Douglas, for thy life
  Wold I have lost my land.

O Christ, my very hart doth bleed
  With sorrow for thy sake;
For sure a more redoubted knight
  Mischance cold never take.

A knight among the Scotts there was
  Who saw Erle Douglas dye,
Who streight in wrath did vow revenge
  Upon the Lord Percy.

Sir Hugh Montgomery was he called,
  Who, with a spear most bright,
Well mounted on a gallant steed,
  Ran fiercely through the fight;

And past the English archers all,
  Without all dread and feare;
And through Earl Percy's body then
  He thrust his hatefull speare;

With such a vehement force and might
  He did his body gore,
The staff ran through the other side
  A large cloth-yard or more.

So thus did both these nobles dye,
  Whose courage none could staine:
An English archer then perceived
  The noble erle was slaine;

He had a bow bent in his hand,
  Made of a trusty tree;
An arrow of a cloth-yard long
  Up to the head drew he:

Against Sir Hugh Montgomery,
  So right the shaft he sett,
The grey goose-wing that was thereon,
  In his hart's blood was wett.

This fight did last from break of day
  Till setting of the sun;
For when they rang the evening-bell
  The battle scarce was done.

With stoute Erle Percy there was slaine
  Sir John of Egerton,
Sir Robert Ratcliff, and Sir John,
  Sir James that bold barron:

And with Sir George and stoute Sir James
  Both knights of good account,
Good Sir Ralph Raby there was slaine,
  Whose prowese did surmount.

For Witherington my hart is woe,
  That ever he slain should be;
For when his legs were hewn in two
  He knelt and fought on his knee.

And with Erle Douglas there was slaine
  Sir Hugh Montgomery,
Sir Charles Murray, that from the field
  One foot wold never flee.

Sir Charles Murray, of Ratcliff too,
  His sister's sonne was he;
Sir David Lamb, so well esteem'd,
  Yet savéd cold not be,

And the Lord Maxwell in like case
  Did with Erle Douglas dye:
Of twenty hundred Scottish speres
  Scarce fifty-five did flye.

Of fifteen hundred Englishmen,
  Went home but fifty-three;
The rest were slaine in Chevy Chase,
  Under the greene woode tree.

Next day did many widowes come,
  Their husbands to bewayle;
They washed their wounds in brinish teares,
  But all wold not prevayle.

Theyr bodyes, bathed in purple gore,
  They bore with them away;
They kist them dead a thousand times,
  Ere they were cladd in clay.

The newes was brought to Eddenborrow,
  Where Scotland's king did raigne,
That brave Erle Douglas suddenlye
  Was with an arrow slaine.

O heavy newes, King James did say,
  Scotland may witness be,
I have not any captain more
  Of such account as he.

Like tydings to King Henry came,
  Within as short a space,
That Percy of Northumberland
  Was slaine in Chevy Chase:

Now God be with him, said the king,
  Sith it will noe better be;
I trust I have within my realme,
  Five hundred as good as he.

Yet shall not Scotts nor Scotland say,
  But I will vengeance take;
Ile be revengéd on them all
  For brave Erle Percy's sake.

This vow full well the king performed
  After at Humbledowne;
In one day fifty knights were slaine,
  With lords of great renowne;

And of the rest of small account,
  Did many thousands dye:
Thus ended the hunting of Chevy Chase
  Made by the Erle Percy.

God save our king, and bless this land
  With plentye, joy, and peace;
And grant henceforth that foule debate
  'Twixt noblemen may cease.

CHAPTER XXXVII

THE BATTLE OF OTTERBOURNE

It fell about a Lamass-tide,
  When husbands wynn their hay,
The doughty Douglas bound him to ride
  In England to take a pray.

ANOTHER famous battle in the border-warfare between England and Scotland was fought at Otterbourne. This is a town in Northumberland, and here, as in Chevy Chase, the Douglas and the Percy matched their strength. Earl Douglas was killed in the fight, and Sir Henry Percy, called Hotspur, was taken prisoner. The story as it is told here is from the works of that most entertaining and long-winded historian of chivalry, Sir John Froissart.

We begin *in medias res* with a Scotch foray, in which the Douglas, with the earl of March and Dunbar and the earl of Moray, has penetrated as far into England as the city of Durham and is now returning to Scotland.

The three Scots lords, having completed the object of their expedition into Durham, lay before Newcastle three days, where there was an almost continual skirmish. The sons of the earl of

Northumberland, from their great courage, were always the first at the barriers, where many valiant deeds were done with lances hand to hand. The earl of Douglas had a long conflict with Sir Henry Percy, and in it, by gallantry of arms, won his pennon, to the great vexation of Sir Henry and the other English. The earl of Douglas said, "I will carry this token of your prowess with me to Scotland, and place it on the tower of my castle at Dalkeith, that it may be seen from afar." "By Heaven, Earl of Douglas," replied Sir Henry, "you shall not even bear it out of Northumberland: be assured you shall never have this pennon to brag of." "You must come then," answered Earl Douglas, "this night and seek for it. I will fix your pennon before my tent, and shall see if you will venture to take it away."

As it was now late the skirmish ended, and each party retired to their quarters to disarm and comfort themselves. They had plenty of everything, particularly flesh meat. The Scots kept up a very strict watch, concluding from the words of Sir Henry Percy they should have their quarters beaten up this night; they were disappointed, for Sir Henry Percy was advised to defer it.

On the morrow the Scots dislodged from before Newcastle; and, taking the road to their own country, they came to a town and castle called Ponclau, of which Sir Raymond de Laval, a very valiant knight of Northumberland, was the lord. They halted there about four o'clock in the morning, as they learned the knight to be within it, and made preparations for the assault. This was done with such courage that the place was won, and the knight made prisoner. After they had burnt the town and castle, they marched away for Otterbourne, which was eight English leagues from Newcastle, and there encamped themselves. This day they made no attack; but very early on the morrow their trumpets sounded, and they made ready for the assault, advancing towards the castle, which was tolerably strong, and situated among the marshes. They attacked it so long and so unsuccessfully that they were fatigued, and therefore sounded a retreat. When they had retired to their quarters, the chiefs held a council how to act; and the greater part were for decamping on the morrow, without attempting more against the castle, to join their countrymen in the neighborhood of Carlisle. But the earl of Douglas overruled this by saying, "In despite of Sir Henry Percy, who the day before yesterday declared he would take from me his pennon, that I conquered by fair deeds of arms before Newcastle, I will not return home for two or three days; and we will renew our attack on the castle, for it is to be taken: we shall thus gain double honor, and see if within that time he will come for his pennon; if he do it shall be well defended." Every one agreed to what Earl Douglas had said; for it was not only honorable, but he was the principal commander; and from affection to him they quietly returned to their quarters. They made huts of trees and branches, and strongly fortified themselves. They placed their baggage and servants at the entrance of the marsh on the road to Newcastle, and the cattle they drove into the marsh lands.

I will return to Sir Henry and Sir Ralph Percy, who were greatly mortified that the earl of Douglas should have conquered their pennon in the skirmish before Newcastle. They felt the more for this disgrace because Sir Henry had not kept his word; for he had told the earl that he should never carry his pennon out of England, and this he explained to the knights who were with him in Newcastle. The English imagined the army under the earl of Douglas to be only the van of the Scots, and that the main body was behind; for which reason those knights who had the most experience in arms, and were best acquainted with warlike affairs, strongly opposed the proposal of Sir Henry Percy to pursue them. They said, "Sir, many losses happen in war: if the earl of Douglas has won your pennon he has bought it dear enough; for he has come to the gates to seek it, and has been well fought with. Another time you will gain from him as much if not more. We say so, because you know as well as we do that the whole power of Scotland has taken the field. We are not sufficiently strong to offer them battle; and perhaps this skirmish may have been only a trick to draw us out of the town; and if they be, as reported, forty thousand strong, they will surround us, and have us at their mercy. It is much better to lose a pennon than two or three hundred knights and squires, and leave our country in a defenceless state." This speech checked the eagerness of the two brothers Percy, for they would not act contrary to the opinion of the council, when other news was brought them by some knights and squires who had followed and observed the Scots, their numbers, disposition, and where they had halted. This was all fully related by knights who had traversed the whole extent of country the Scots had passed through, that they might carry to their lords the most exact information. They thus spoke: "Sir Henry and Sir Ralph Percy, we come to tell you that we have followed the Scottish army, and observed all the country where they now are. They first halted at Ponclau, and took Sir Raymond de Laval in his castle; thence they went to Otterbourne, and took up their quarters for the night. We are ignorant of what they did on the morrow, but they seem to have taken measures for a long stay. We know for certain that their army does not consist of more than three thousand men, including all sorts." Sir Henry Percy on hearing this was greatly rejoiced, and cried out, "To horse! to horse! for by the faith I owe my God, and to my lord and father, I will seek to recover my pennon and to beat up their quarters this night." Such knights and squires in Newcastle as learned this were willing to be of the party, and made themselves ready.

The Bishop of Durham was expected daily at the town; for he had heard of the irruption of the Scots, and that they were before it, in which were the sons of the Earl of Northumberland preparing to offer them combat. The bishop had collected a number of men, and was hastening to their assistance, but Sir Henry Percy would not wait; for he was accompanied by six hundred spears, of knights and squires, and upwards of eight thousand infantry, which he said would be more than enough to fight the Scots, who were but three hundred lances and two thousand others. When they were all assembled they left Newcastle after dinner, and took the field in good array, following the road the Scots had taken, making for Otterbourne, which was eight short leagues distant; but they could not advance very fast, that their infantry might keep up with them.

As the Scots were supping,—some indeed had gone to sleep, for they had labored hard during the day at the attack of the castle, and intended renewing it in the cool of the morning,— the English arrived, and mistook, at their entrance, the huts of the servants for those of their masters. They forced their way into the camp, which was, however, tolerably strong, shouting out, "Percy! Percy!" In such cases you may suppose an alarm is soon given, and it was fortunate for the Scots that the English had made their first attack on the servants' quarters, which checked them some little. The Scots, expecting the English, had prepared accordingly; for while the lords were arming themselves they ordered a body of infantry to join their servants and keep up the skirmish. As their men were armed, they formed themselves under the pennons of the three principal barons, who each had his particular appointment. In the meantime the night advanced, but it was sufficiently light, for the moon shone, and it was the month of August, when the weather is temperate and serene.

When the Scots were quite ready, and properly arrayed, they left their camp in silence, but did not march to meet the English. They skirted the side of the mountain which was hard by; for during the preceding day they had well examined the country round, and said among themselves, "Should the English come to beat up our quarters we will do so and so," and thus settled their plans beforehand, which was the saving of them; for it is of the greatest advantage to men-at-arms when attacked in the night to have previously arranged their mode of defence, and well to have weighed the chance of victory or defeat. The English had soon overpowered their servants; but as they advanced into the camp they found fresh bodies ready to oppose them, and to continue the fight. The Scots, in the meantime, marched along the mountain side, and fell upon the enemy's flank quite unexpectedly, shouting their cries. This was a great surprise to the English, who however formed themselves in better order and reinforced that part of their army. The cries of Percy and Douglas resounded on either side.

The battle now raged: great was the pushing of lances, and very many of each party was struck down at the first onset. The English being more numerous, and anxious to defeat the enemy, kept in a compact body, and forced the Scots to retire, who were on the point of being discomfited. The earl of Douglas being young, and impatient to gain renown in arms, ordered his banner to advance, shouting, "Douglas! Douglas!" Sir Henry and Sir Ralph Percy, indignant for the affront the earl of Douglas had put on them, by conquering their pennon, and desirous of meeting him, hastened to the place from whence the sounds came, calling out, "Percy! Percy!" The two banners met, and many gallant deeds of arms ensued. The English were in superior strength, and fought so lustily that they drove back the Scots. Sir Patrick Hepburn and his son of the same name did honor to their knighthood and country by their gallantry, under the banner of Douglas, which would have been conquered but for the vigorous defence they made; and this circumstance not only contributed to their personal credit, but the memory of it is continued with honor to their descendants.

The knights and squires of either party were anxious to continue the combat with vigor as long as their spears might be capable of holding. Cowardice was there unknown, and the most splendid courage was everywhere exhibited by the gallant youths of England and Scotland; they were so closely intermixed that the archers' bows were useless, and they fought hand to hand, without either battalion giving way. The Scots behaved most valiantly, for the English were three to one. I do not mean to say the English did not acquit themselves well; for they would sooner be slain or made prisoners in battle than reproached with flight. As I before mentioned, the two banners of Douglas and Percy met, and the men-at-arms under each exerted themselves by every means to gain the victory; but the English, at this attack, were so much the stronger, that the Scots were driven back. The earl of Douglas, who was of a high spirit, seeing his men repulsed, seized a battle-axe with both his hands, like a gallant knight, and to rally his men dashed into the midst of his enemies, and gave such blows on all around him that no one could withstand them, but all made way for him on every side; for there was none so well armed with helmets and plates but that they suffered from his battle-axe. Thus he advanced, like another Hector, thinking to recover and conquer the field, from his own prowess, until he was met by three spears that were pointed at him. One struck him on the shoulder, another on the stomach, and the third entered his thigh. He could never disengage himself from these spears, but was borne to the ground, fighting desperately. From that time he never rose again. Some of his knights and squires had followed him, but not all; for, though the moon shone, it was rather dark. The three English lancers knew that they had struck down some person of considerable rank, but never thought it was Earl Douglas. Had they known it, they would have been so rejoiced that their courage would have been redoubled, and the fortune of the day had consequently been determined to their side. The Scots were ignorant also of their loss until the battle was over, otherwise they would certainly, from despair, have been discomfited.

I will relate what befell the earl afterward. As soon as he fell, his head was cleaved by a battle-axe, the spear thrust through his thigh, and the main body of the English marched over him, without paying any attention, not supposing him to be their principal enemy. In another part of the field, the earl of March and Dunbar combated valiantly; and the English gave the Scots full employment who had followed the earl of Douglas, and had engaged with the two Percies. The earl of Moray behaved so gallantly in pursuing the English, that they knew not how to resist him. Of all the battles that have been described in this history, great and small, this of which I am now speaking was the best fought and the most severe; for there was not a man, knight, or squire who did not acquit himself gallantly, hand to hand with the enemy. It resembled something that of Cocherel, which was as long and as hardily disputed. The sons of the earl of Northumberland, Sir Henry and Sir Ralph Percy, who were the leaders of this expedition, behaved themselves like good knights in the combat. Almost a similar accident befel Sir Ralph as that which happened to the earl of Douglas; for, having advanced too far, he was surrounded by the enemy and severely wounded, and, being out of breath, surrendered himself to a Scots knight, called Sir John Maxwell, who was under the command and of the household of the earl of Moray.

When made prisoner, the knight asked him who he was, for it

was dark, and he knew him not. Sir Ralph was so weakened by loss of blood, which was flowing from his wound, that he could scarcely avow himself to be Sir Ralph Percy. "Well," replied the knight, "Sir Ralph, rescued or not, you are my prisoner; my name is Maxwell." "I agree to it," said Sir Ralph. "But pay some attention to me; for I am so desperately wounded, that my drawers and greaves are full of blood." Upon this the Scots knight was very attentive to him; when suddenly hearing the cry of Moray hard by, and perceiving the earl's banner advancing to him, Sir John addressed himself to the earl of Moray, and said, "My lord, I present you with Sir Ralph Percy as a prisoner; but let good care be taken of him, for he is very badly wounded." The earl was much pleased at this, and replied, "Maxwell, thou hast well earned thy spurs this day." He then ordered his men to take every care of Sir Ralph, who bound up and staunched his wounds. The battle still continued to rage, and no one could say at that moment which side would be the conqueror, for there were very many captures and rescues that never came to my knowledge.

The young earl of Douglas had this night performed wonders in arms. When he was struck down there was a great crowd round him, and he could not raise himself; for the blow on his head was mortal. His men had followed him as closely as they were able, and there came to him his cousins, Sir James Lindsay, Sir John and Sir Walter Sinclair, with other knights and squires. They found by his side a gallant knight, that had constantly attended him, who was his chaplain, and had at this time exchanged his profession for that of a valiant man-at-arms. The whole night he had followed the earl, with his battle-axe in hand, and had by his exertions more than once repelled the English. This conduct gained the thanks of his countrymen, and turned out to his advantage, for in the same year he was promoted to the archdeaconry, and made canon of Aberdeen. His name was Sir William of North Berwick. To say the truth, he was well formed in all his limbs to shine in battle, and was severely wounded at this combat. When these knights came to the earl of Douglas they found him in a melancholy state, as well as one of his knights, Sir Robert Hart, who had fought by his side the whole of the night, and now lay beside him, covered with fifteen wounds from lances and other weapons.

Sir John Sinclair asked the earl, "Cousin, how fares it with you?" "But so so," replied he. "Thanks to God, there are but few of my ancestors who have died in chambers or in their beds. I bid you, therefore, revenge my death, for I have but little hope of living, as my heart becomes every minute more faint. Do you, Walter and Sir John Sinclair, raise up my banner, for certainly it is on the ground, from the death of David Campbell, that valiant squire who bore it, and who refused knighthood from my hands this day, though he was equal to the most eminent knights for courage and loyalty; and continue to shout 'Douglas!' but do not tell friend or foe whether I am in your company or not; for, should the enemy know the truth, they will be greatly rejoiced."

The two brothers Sinclair and Sir John Lindsay obeyed his orders. The banner was raised, and "Douglas!" shouted. Their men, who had remained behind, hearing the shouts of "Douglas!" so often repeated, ascended a small eminence, and pushed their lances with such courage that the English were repulsed, and many killed or struck to the ground. The Scots, by thus valiantly driving the enemy beyond the spot where the earl of Douglas lay dead,—for he had expired on giving his last orders,—arrived at his banner, which was borne by Sir John Sinclair. Numbers were continually increasing, from the repeated shouts of "Douglas!" and the greater part of the Scots knights and squires were now there. The earls of Moray and March, with their banners and men, came thither also. When they were all thus collected, perceiving the English retreat, they renewed the battle with greater vigor than before.

To say the truth, the English had harder work than the Scots, for they had come by a forced march that evening from Newcastle-on-Tyne, which was eight English leagues distant, to meet the Scots, by which means the greater part were exceedingly fatigued before the combat began. The Scots, on the contrary, had reposed themselves, which was to them of the utmost advantage, as was apparent from the event of the battle. In this last attack they so completely repulsed the English, that the latter could never rally again, and the former drove them far beyond where the earl of Douglas lay on the ground. Sir Henry Percy, during this attack, had the misfortune to fall into the hands of the Lord Montgomery, a very valiant knight of Scotland. They had long fought hand to hand with much valor, and without hindrance from any one; for there was neither knight nor squire of either party who did not find there his equal to fight with, and all were fully engaged. In the end, Sir Henry was made prisoner by the Lord Montgomery.

CHAPTER XXXVIII

EDWARD THE BLACK PRINCE

"ICH DIEN"

THE last hero of English chivalry with whom we have to do is Edward the Black Prince. And as the most characteristic part of the

knighthood of this most knightly of English princes, we have selected
the battles of Crecy and of Poitiers.

THE BATTLE OF CRECY

The English, who were drawn up in three divisions, and seated
on the ground, on seeing their enemies advance, rose undauntedly
up, and fell into their ranks. That of the prince [1] was the first to do
so, whose archers were formed in the manner of a portcullis or
harrow, and the men-at-arms in the rear. The earls of Northumberland and Arundel, who commanded the second division, had posted
themselves in good order on his wing, to assist and succor the prince
if necessary.

You must know that these kings, earls, barons, and lords of
France did not advance in any regular order, but one after the
other, or anyway most pleasing to themselves. As soon as the king
of France came in sight of the English, his blood began to boil,
and he cried out to his marshals, "Order the Genoese forward, and
begin the battle, in the name of God and St. Denis." There were
about fifteen thousand Genoese cross-bowmen, but they were quite
fatigued, having marched on foot that day six leagues, completely
armed and with their cross-bows. They told the constable they were
not in a fit condition to do any great things that day in battle. The
earl of Alençon, hearing this, said, "This is what one gets by employing such scoundrels, who fall off when there is any need of
them." During this time a heavy rain fell, accompanied by thunder
and a very terrible eclipse of the sun; and before this rain a great
flight of crows hovered in the air over all those battalions, making
a loud noise. Shortly afterwards it cleared up, and the sun shone
very bright, but the Frenchmen had it in their faces, and the Englishmen in their backs. When the Genoese were somewhat in order, and
approached the English, they set up a loud shout, in order to frighten
them; but they remained quite still, and did not seem to attend to
it. Then they set up a second shout, and advanced a little forward,
but the English never moved. They hooted a third time, advancing
with their crossbows presented, and began to shoot. The English
archers then advanced one step forward, and shot their arrows with
such force and quickness that it seemed as if it snowed. When
the Genoese felt these arrows, which pierced their arms, heads, and
through their armor, some of them cut the strings of their crossbows,
others flung them on the ground, and all turned about and retreated
quite discomfited. The French had a large body of men-at-arms on
horseback, richly dressed, to support the Genoese. The king of

[1] Edward the Black Prince; son of Edward III.

France, seeing them thus fall back, cried out, "Kill me those scoun-drels, for they stop up our road without any reason." You would then have seen the above-mentioned men-at-arms lay about them, killing all they could of these runaways.

The English continued shooting as vigorously and quickly as before; some of their arrows fell among the horsemen who were sumptuously equipped, and, killing and wounding many, made them caper and fall among the Genoese, so that they were in such con-fusion that they could never rally again. The valiant king of Bohemia was slain there. He was called Charles of Luxembourg, for he was the son of the gallant king and emperor, Henry of Luxem-bourg. Having heard the order of the battle, he inquired where his son, the lord Charles, was. His attendants answered that they did not know, but believed he was fighting. The king said to them, "Gentlemen, you are all my people, my friends and brethren at arms this day; therefore, as I am blind, I request of you to lead me so far into the engagement that I may strike one stroke with my sword." The knights replied they would directly lead him forward; and in order that they might not lose him in the crowd, they fastened all the reins of their horses together, and put the king at their head, that he might gratify his wish, and advanced towards the enemy. The lord Charles of Bohemia, who already signed his name as king of Germany, and bore the arms, had come in good order to the engagement; but when he perceived that it was likely to turn against the French, he departed, and I do not well know what road he took. The king, his father, had rode in among the enemy, and made good use of his sword, for he and his companions had fought most gallantly. They had advanced so far that they were all slain; and on the morrow they were found on the ground, with their horses all tied together.

The earl of Alençon advanced in regular order upon the English to fight with them, as did the earl of Flanders in another part. These two lords, with their detachments, coasting, as it were, the archers, came to the prince's battalion, where they fought valiantly for a length of time. The king of France was eager to march to the place where he saw their banners displayed, but there was a hedge of archers before him. He had that day made a present of a handsome black horse to Sir John of Hainault, who had mounted on it a knight of his that bore his banner, which horse ran off with him and forced his way through the English army, and, when about to return, stumbled and fell into a ditch and severely wounded him. He would have been dead if his page had not followed him round the bat-talions and found him unable to rise. He had not, however, any other hindrance than from his horse; for the English did not quit the ranks that day to make prisoners. The page alighted, and raised him up; but he did not return the way he came, as he would have found it difficult from the crowd.

This battle, which was fought on a Saturday between la Broyes and Crecy, was very murderous and cruel; and many gallant deeds of arms were performed that were never known. Towards evening, many knights and squires of the French had lost their masters. They wandered up and down the plain, attacking the English in small parties. They were soon destroyed, for the English had determined that day to give no quarter, or hear of ransom from any one.

Early in the day, some French, Germans, and Savoyards had broken through the archers of the prince's battalion and had engaged with the men-at-arms; upon which the second battalion came to his aid, and it was time, for otherwise he would have been hard pressed. The first division, seeing the danger they were in, sent a knight in great haste to the king of England, who was posted upon an eminence near a windmill. On the knight's arrival, he said, "Sir, the earl of Warwick, the lord Stafford, the lord Reginald Cobham, and the others who are about your son, are vigorously attacked by the French; and they entreat that you would come to their assistance with your battalion, for, if their numbers should increase, they fear he will have too much to do." The king replied, "Is my son dead, unhorsed, or so badly wounded that he cannot support himself?" "Nothing of the sort, thank God," rejoined the knight; "but he is in so hot an engagement that he has great need of your help." The king answered, "Now, Sir Thomas, return back to those that sent you, and tell them from me, not to send again for me this day, or expect that I shall come, let what will happen, as long as my son has life; and say that I command them to let the boy win his spurs; for I am determined, if it please God, that all the glory and honor of this day shall be given to him, and to those into whose care I have entrusted him." The knight returned to his lords, and related the king's answer, which mightily encouraged them, and made them repent they ever sent such a message.

Late after vespers the king of France had not more about him than sixty men, every one included. Sir John of Hainault, who was of the number, had once remounted the king; for his horse had been killed under him by an arrow. He said to the king, "Sir, retreat whilst you have an opportunity, and do not expose yourself so simply; if you have lost this battle, another time you will be the conqueror." After he had said this, he took the bridle of the king's horse and led him off by force, for he had before entreated him to retire. The king rode on until he came to the castle of la Broyes, where he found the gates shut, for it was very dark. The king ordered the governor of it to be summoned. He came upon the battlements, and asked who it was that called at such an hour. The king answered, "Open, open, governor; it is the fortune of France." The governor, hearing the king's voice, immediately descended, opened the gate, and let down the bridge. The king and his company entered the castle; but he had only with him five barons, Sir John of Hainault and four more. The king would not bury himself in such a place as that, but, having taken some refreshments, set out again with his attendants about midnight, and rode on, under the direction of guides who were well acquainted with the country, until, about daybreak, he came to Amiens, where he halted. This Saturday the English never quitted their ranks in pursuit of any one, but remained on the field, guarding their position, and defending themselves against all who attacked them. The battle was ended at the hour of vespers.

When on this Saturday night, the English heard no more hooting or shouting, nor any more crying out to particular lords or their banners, they looked upon the field as their own, and their enemies as beaten. They made great fires and lighted torches because of the obscurity of the night. King Edward then came down from his post, who all that day had not put on his helmet, and, with his whole battalion, advanced to the prince of Wales, whom he embraced in his arms and kissed, and said, "Sweet son, God give you good perseverance; you are my son, for most loyally have you acquitted yourself this day; you are worthy to be a sovereign." The prince bowed down very low and humbled himself, giving all honor to the king, his father. The English during the night made frequent thanksgiving to the Lord for the happy issue of the day, and without rioting; for the king had forbidden all riot or noise.

At Crecy the Black Prince won his spurs, but the great achievement of his life was his victory at Poitiers,—a battle fought by him alone with his army, when his father, Edward III., was absent from France in England. At the peace of Bretagne, agreed upon after the battle, several provinces were ceded by France to England, and these Edward added to his dominions in Guienne, and formed for himself a separate kingdom, which he ruled until his death. He never came to the throne of England; his son, Richard II., succeeded Edward III.

THE BATTLE OF POITIERS

On Sunday morning, the king of France, who was very impatient to combat the English, ordered a solemn mass to be sung in his pavilion, and he and his four sons received the communion. Mass being over, there came to him many barons of France, as well as other great lords who held fiefs in the neighborhood, according to a summons they had received for a council. They were a considerable time debating; at last it was ordered that the whole army should advance into the plain, and that each lord should display his banner, and push forward in the name of God and St. Denis. Upon this the trumpets of the army sounded, and every one got himself ready, mounted his horse, and made for that part of the plain where the king's banner was fluttering in the wind. There might be seen all the nobility of France, richly dressed out in brilliant armor, with banners and pennons gallantly displayed; for all the flower of the French nobility was there; no knight nor squire, for fear of dishonor, dared to remain at home. By the advice of the constable and the marshals, the army was divided into three battalions, each consisting of sixteen thousand men-at-arms, who had before shown themselves men of tried courage. The duke of Orleans commanded the first battalion, where there were thirty-six banners and twice as many pennons. The second was under command of the duke of Normandy, and his two brothers, the lord Lewis and lord John. The king of France commanded the third.

Whilst these battalions were forming, the king called to him the lord Eustace de Ribeaumont, the lord John de Landas, and the lord Guiscard de Beaujeu, and said to them, "Ride forward as near the English army as you can, and observe their countenance, taking notice of their numbers, and examine which will be the most advantageous manner to combat them, whether on horseback or on foot." The three knights left the king to obey his commands. The king was mounted on a white palfrey, and, riding to the head of his army, said aloud, "You men of Paris, Chartres, Rouen, and Orleans, have been used to threaten what you would do to the English if you could find them, and wished much to meet them in arms; now that wish shall be granted. I will lead you to them, and let us see how you will revenge yourselves for all the mischief and damage they have done you. Be assured we will not part without fighting." Those who heard him replied, "Sir, through God's assistance we will most cheerfully meet them."

At this instant the three knights returned, and pushing through the crowd, came to the king, who asked what news they had brought. Sir Eustace de Ribeaumont, whom his companions had requested to be their spokesman, answered, "Sir, we have observed accurately the English; they may amount, according to our estimate, to about two thousand men-at-arms, four thousand archers, and fifteen hundred footmen. They are in a very strong position; but we do not imagine they can make more than one battalion; nevertheless, they have posted themselves with great judgment, have fortified all the road along the hedge side, and lined the hedges with part of their archers; for, as that is the only road for an attack, one must pass through the midst of them. This lane has no other entry; for it is so narrow, that scarcely can four men ride abreast in it. At the end of this lane, amidst vines and thorns, where it is impossible to ride or march in any regular order, are posted the men-at-arms on foot; and they have drawn up before them their archers in the manner of a harrow, so that it will be no easy matter to defeat them." The king asked in what manner they would advise him to attack them. "Sir," replied Sir Eustace, "on foot; except three hundred of the most expert, to break, if possible, this body of archers; and then your battalions must advance quickly on foot, attack the men-at-arms hand to hand, and combat them valiantly. This is the best advice that I can give you, and if any one know a better, let him say it." The king replied, "Thus shall it be, then." And, in company with his two marshals, he rode from battalion to battalion, and selected, in conformity to their opinions, three hundred knights and squires of the greatest repute in his army, each well armed, and mounted on the best of horses. Soon after, the battalion of the Germans was formed, who were to remain on horseback, to assist the marshals; they were commanded by the earls of Salzburg, Neydo, and Nassau. King John was armed in royal armor, and nineteen others like him.

When the battalions of the king of France were drawn up, and each lord posted under his proper banner, and informed how they were to act, it was ordered that all those who were armed with lances should shorten them to the length of five feet, that they might be the more manageable, and that every one should take off his spurs. As the French were on the point of marching to their enemies, the cardinal of Perigord, who had left Poitiers that morning early, came full gallop to the king, making him a low reverence, and entreated him that he might be allowed to go to the prince of Wales, to endeavor to make peace between him and the king of France. The king answered, "It is very agreeable to us; but make haste back again."

So then the cardinal set off, and went in all speed to the prince; but though he spent all this Sunday in riding from one army to another, he could not make terms which were thought honorable alike by the king and by the prince of Wales. That same day, the French kept in their quarters, where they lived at their ease, having plenty of provisions; whilst the English, on the other hand, were but badly off, nor did they know whither to go for forage, as they were so straitly kept by the French they could not move without danger. This Sunday they made many mounds and ditches round where the archers were posted, the better to secure them.

On Monday morning the prince and his army were soon in readiness, and as well arranged as on the former day. The French were also drawn out by sunrise. The cardinal, returning again that morning, imagined that by his exhortations he could pacify both parties; but the French told him to return when he pleased, and not attempt bringing them any more treaties or pacifications, else worse might betide him. When the cardinal saw that he labored in vain, he took leave of the king of France, and set out towards the prince of Wales, to whom he said, "Fair son, exert yourself as much as possible, for there must be a battle; I cannot by any means pacify the king of France." The prince replied, "that such were the intentions of him and his army; and God defend the right." The cardinal then took leave of him, and returned to Poitiers.

The arrangement of the prince's army, in respect to the battalions, was exactly the same as what the three knights before named had related to the king of France, except that at this time he had ordered some valiant and intelligent knights to remain on horseback, similar to the battalion of the French marshals, and had also commanded three hundred men-at-arms, and as many archers on horseback, to post themselves on the right, on a small hill, that was not too steep nor too high, and, by passing over its summit, to get round the wings of the duke of Normandy's battalions, who was in person at the foot of it. These were all the alterations the prince had made in his order of battle; he himself was with the main body, in the midst of the vineyards, the whole completely armed, with their horses near, if there should be any occasion for them. They had fortified and inclosed the weaker parts with their wagons and baggage.

And when the prince of Wales saw, from the departure of the cardinal without being able to obtain any honorable terms, that a battle was inevitable, and that the king of France held both him and his army in great contempt, he thus addressed himself to them: "Now, my gallant fellows, what though we be a small body when compared to the army of our enemies; do not let us be cast down on that account, for victory does not always follow numbers, but where the Almighty God pleases to bestow it. If, through good fortune, the day shall be ours, we will gain the greatest honor and glory in this world; if the contrary should happen, and we be slain, I have a father and beloved brethren alive, and you all have some relations or good friends, who will be sure to revenge our deaths. I therefore entreat of you to exert yourselves, and combat manfully; for, if it please God and St. George, you shall see me this day act like a true knight." By such words and arguments as these the prince harangued his men, as did the marshals, by his orders, so that they were all in high spirits. Sir John Chandos placed himself near the prince, to guard and advise him; and never, during that day, would he, on any account, quit his post.

The lord James Audley remained also a considerable time near him; but, when he saw that they must certainly engage, he said to the prince: "Sir, I have ever served most loyally my lord your father, and yourself, and shall continue so to do as long as I have life. Dear sir, I must now acquaint you that formerly I made a vow, if ever I should be engaged in any battle where the king, your father, or any of his sons were, that I would be the foremost in the attack, and the best combatant on his side, or die in the attempt. I beg, therefore, most earnestly, as a reward for any services I may have done, that you would grant me permission honorably to quit you, that I may post myself in such wise to accomplish my vow." The prince granted this request, and, holding out his hand to him, said: "Sir James, God grant that this day you may shine in valor above all other knights." The knight then set off, and posted himself at the front of the battalion, with only four squires whom he had detained with him to guard his person. The lord James was a prudent and valiant knight; and by his advice the army had thus been drawn up in order of battle. The lord James began to advance, in order to fight with the battalion of the marshals. Sir Eustace d'Ambreticourt, being mounted, placed his lance in its rest, and, fixing his shield, struck spurs into his horse and galloped up to this battalion. A German knight, perceiving Sir Eustace quit his army, left his battalion that was under the command of earl John of Nassau, and made up to him. The shock of their meeting was so violent that they both fell to the ground. The German was wounded in the shoulder, so that he could not rise again so nimbly as Sir Eustace, who, when upon his legs, after he had taken breath, was hastening to the knight that lay on the ground; but five German men-at-arms came upon him, struck him down, and made him prisoner. They led him to those that were attached to the earl of Nassau, who did not pay much attention to him, nor do I know if they made him swear himself their prisoner; but they tied him to a car with some of their harness.

The engagement now began on both sides, and the battalion of the marshals was advancing before those who were intended to break the battalion of the archers, and had entered the lane where the hedges on both sides were lined by the archers, who, as soon as they saw them fairly entered, began shooting with their bows in such an excellent manner from each side of the hedge, that the horses, smarting under the pain of the wounds made by their bearded arrows, would not advance, but turned about, and, by their unruliness, threw their masters, who could not manage them; nor could those that had fallen get up again for the confusion, so that this battalion of the marshals could never approach that of the prince. However, there were some knights and squires so well mounted, that by the strength of their horses they passed through and broke the hedge, but, in spite of their efforts, could not get up to the battalion of the prince. The lord James Audley, attended by his four squires, had placed himself, sword in hand, in front of this battalion much before the rest, and was performing wonders. He had advanced through his eagerness so far that he engaged the lord Arnold d'Andreghen, marshal of France, under his banner when they fought a considerable time, and the lord Arnold was roughly enough treated. The battalion of the marshals was soon after put to the rout by the arrows of the archers and the assistance of the men-at-arms, who rushed among them as they were struck down and seized and slew them at their pleasure. The lord Arnold d'Andreghen was there made prisoner, but by others than the lord James Audley or his four squires, for that knight never stopped to make any one his prisoner that day, but was the whole time employed in fighting and following his enemies. In another part, the lord John Clermont fought under his banner as long as he was able, but being struck down, he could neither get up again nor procure his ransom; he was killed on the spot. In a short time this battalion of the marshals was totally discomfited; for they fell back so much on each other that the army could not advance, and those who were in the rear, not being able to get forward, fell back upon the battalion commanded by the duke of Normandy, which was broad and thick in the front, but it was soon thin enough in the rear; for when they learnt that the marshals had been defeated, they mounted their horses and set off. At this time a body of English came down from the hill, and, passing along the battalions on horseback, accompanied by a large body of archers, fell upon one of the wings of the duke of Normandy's division. To say the truth, the English archers were of infinite service to their army, for they shot so thickly and so well that the French did not know what way to turn themselves to avoid their arrows. By this means they kept advancing by little and little and gained ground. When the English men-at-arms perceived that the first battalion was beaten, and that the one under the duke of Normandy was in disorder and beginning to open, they hastened to mount their horses, which they had ready prepared close at hand. As soon as they were all mounted, they gave a shout of "St. George for Guienne!" and Sir John Chandos said to the prince, "Sir, sir, now push forward, for the day is ours. God will this day put it in your hand. Let us make for our adversary, the king of France; for where he is will lie the main stress of the business. I well know that his valor will not let him fly; and he will remain with us, if it please God and St. George; but he must be well fought with, and you have before said that you would show yourself this day a good knight." The prince replied: "John, get forward; you shall not see me turn my back this day, but I will always be among the foremost." He then said to Sir Walter Woodland, his banner-bearer, "Banner, advance, in the name of God and St. George." The knight obeyed the commands of the prince; and the prince upon this charged the division of the duke of Athens, and very sharp the encounter was, so that many were beaten down. The French, who fought in large bodies, cried out, "Montjoye St. Denis!" and the English answered them with "St. George for Guienne!" The prince next met the battalion of Germans under command of the earl of Salzburg, the earl of Nassau, and the earl of Neydo; but they were soon overthrown and put to flight. The English archers shot so well that none dared to come within reach of their arrows, and they put to death many who could not ransom themselves. Then the above-named earls were slain there, as well as many other knights and squires attached to them. In the confusion, Sir Eustace d'Ambreticourt was rescued by his own men, who remounted him. He afterwards performed many gallant deeds of arms, and made good captures that day.

When the battalion of the duke of Normandy saw the prince advancing so quick upon them, they bethought themselves how to escape. The sons of the king, the duke of Normandy, the earl of Poitiers, and the earl of Touraine, who were very young, too easily believed what those under whose management they were placed said to them. However, the lord Guiscard d'Angle and Sir John de Saintré, who were near the earl of Poitiers, would not fly, but rushed into the thickest of the combat. The three sons of the king, according to the advice given them, galloped away, with upwards of eighty lances who had never been near the enemy, and took the road to Chavigny.

Now the king's battalion advanced in good order to meet the English; many hard blows were given with swords, battleaxes, and other warlike weapons. The king of France, with the lord Philip, his youngest son, attacked the division of the marshals, the earls of Warwick and Suffolk, and in this combat were engaged many very noble lords on both sides.

The lord James Audley, with the assistance of his four squires, was always engaged in the heat of the battle. He was severely wounded in the body, head, and face; and, as long as his breath permitted him, he maintained the fight and advanced forward. He continued to do so until he was covered with blood. Then, toward the close of the engagement, his four squires, who were his body guard, took him, and led him out of the engagement, very weak and wounded, towards a hedge, that he might cool and take breath. They disarmed him as gently as they could, in order to examine his wounds, dress them, and sew up the most serious.

It often happens that fortune in war and love turns out more favorable and wonderful than could have been hoped for or expected. To say the truth, this battle, which was fought near Poitiers, in the plains of Beauvoir and Maupertuis, was very bloody and perilous. Many gallant deeds of arms were performed that were never known, and the combatants on either side suffered much. King John himself did wonders. He was armed with a battle-axe, with which he fought and defended himself; and if a fourth of his people had behaved as well the day would have been his own. The earl of Tancarville, in endeavoring to break through the crowd, was made prisoner close to him, as were also Sir James de Bourbon, earl of Ponthieu, and the lord John d'Artois, earl of Eu. The pursuit continued even to the gates of Poitiers, where there was much slaughter and overthrow of men and horses; for the inhabitants of Poitiers had shut their gates and would suffer none to enter; upon which account there was great butchery on the causeway before the gate, where such numbers were killed or wounded that several surrendered themselves the moment they spied an Englishman; and there were many English archers who had four, five, or six prisoners.

There was much pressing at this time through eagerness to take the king; and those who were nearest to him and knew him, cried out, "Surrender yourself, surrender yourself, or you are a dead man." In that part of the field was a young knight from St. Omer, who was engaged by a salary in the service of the king of England. His name was Denys de Morbeque, who for five years had attached himself to the English on account of having been banished in his younger days from France for a murder committed in an affray at St. Omer. It fortunately happened for this knight that he was at the time near to the king of France when he was so much pulled about. He by dint of force, for he was very strong and robust, pushed through the crowd, and said to the king in very good French, "Sire, sire, surrender yourself." The king, who found himself very disagreeably situated, turning to him, asked, "To whom shall I surrender myself; to whom? Where is my cousin, the prince of Wales? if I could see him I would speak to him." "Sire," replied Sir Denys, "he is not here; but surrender yourself to me and I will lead you to him." "Who are you?" said the king. "Sire, I am Denys de Morbeque, a knight from Artois, but I serve the king of England because I cannot belong to France, having forfeited all I possess there." The king then gave him his right-hand glove, and said, "I surrender myself to you." There was much crowding and pushing about, for every one was eager to cry out, "I have taken him." Neither the king nor his youngest son Philip were able to get forward, and free themselves from the throng.

The prince of Wales, who was as courageous as a lion, took great delight that day to combat his enemies. Sir John Chandos, who was near his person and had never quitted it during the whole of the day, nor stopped to take any prisoners, said to him toward the end of the battle, "Sir, it will be proper for you to halt here and plant your banner on the top of this bush, which will serve to rally your forces that seem very much scattered; for I do not see any banners or pennons of the French, nor any considerable bodies able to rally against us; and you must refresh yourself a little, as I perceive you are very much heated." Upon this, the banner of the prince was placed on a high bush; the minstrels began to play, and trumpets and clarions to do their duty. The prince took off his helmet, and the knights attendant on his person and belonging to his chamber were soon ready, and pitched a small pavilion of crimson color, which the prince entered. Liquor was then brought to him and the other knights who were with him. They increased every moment; for they were returning from the pursuit, and stopped there, surrounded by their prisoners.

As soon as the two marshals were come back, the prince asked them if they knew anything of the king of France. They replied, "No, sir, not for a certainty; but we believe he must be either killed or taken prisoner, since he has never quitted his battalion." The prince then, addressing the earl of Warwick and lord Cobham, said, "I beg of you to mount your horses and ride over the field, so that on your return you may bring me some certain intelligence of him." The two barons, immediately mounting their horses, left the prince and made for a small hillock, that they might look about them. From their stand they perceived a crowd of men-at-arms on foot, who were advancing very slowly. The king of France was in the midst of them, and in great danger; for the French and Gascons had taken him from Sir Denys de Morbeque and were disputing who should have him, the stoutest bawling out, "It is I who have got him." "No, no," replied the others, "we have him." The king to escape his peril, said, "Gentlemen, gentlemen, I pray you conduct me and my son in a courteous manner to my cousin the prince; and do not make such a riot over my capture, for I am so great a lord that I can make all sufficiently rich." These words, and others which fell from the king, appeased them a little, but the disputes were always beginning again, and they did not move a step without rioting. When the two barons saw this troop of people, they descended from the hillock, and, sticking spurs into their horses, made up to them. On their arrival, they asked what was the matter. They were answered that it was the king of France, who had been made prisoner, and that upwards of ten knights and squires challenged him at the same time as belonging to each of them. The two barons then pushed through the crowd by main force and ordered all to draw aside. They commanded, in the name of the prince and under pain of instant death, that every one should keep his distance, and not approach unless ordered or desired so to do. They all retreated behind the king; and the two barons, dismounting, advanced to the king with profound reverence, and conducted him in a peaceable manner to the prince of Wales.

Soon after the earl of Warwick and the lord Reginald Cobham had left the prince, as has been above related, he inquired from those knights around him of lord James Audley, and asked if any one knew what was become of him. "Yes, sir," replied some of the company, "he is very badly wounded, and is lying in a litter hard by." "By my troth," replied the prince, "I am sore vexed that he is so wounded. See, I beg of you, if he be able to bear being carried hither; otherwise I will come and visit him." Two knights directly left the prince, and, coming to lord James, told him how desirous the prince was of seeing him. "A thousand thanks to the prince," answered Lord James, "for condescending to remember so poor a knight as myself." He then called eight of his servants and had himself borne in his litter to where the prince was. When he was come into his presence, the prince bent down over him and embraced him, saying, "My lord James, I am bound to honor you very much, for by your valor this day you have acquired glory and renown above us all, and your prowess has proved you the bravest knight." Lord James replied, "My lord, you have a right to say whatever you please, but I wish it were as you have said. If I have this day been forward to serve you it has been to accomplish a vow that I had made, and ought not to be so much thought of." "Sir James," answered the prince, "I and all the rest of us deem you the bravest knight on our side in this battle; and to increase your renown and furnish you withal to pursue your career of glory in war, I retain you henceforward forever as my knight, with five hundred marcs of yearly revenue, which I will secure to you from my estates in England." "Sir," said lord James, "God make me deserving of the good fortune you bestow upon me." At these words he took leave of the prince, as he was very weak, and his servants carried him back to his tent. He could not have been at a great distance when the earl of Warwick and lord Reginald Cobham entered the pavilion of the prince and presented the king of France to him. The prince made a very low obeisance to the king and gave him as much comfort as he was able, which he well knew how to administer. He ordered wine and spices to be brought, which he presented to the king himself, as a mark of great affection.

Thus was this battle won, as you have heard related, in the plains of Maupertuis, two leagues from the city of Poitiers, on the 19th day of September, 1356. It commenced about nine o'clock and was ended by noon; but the English were not all returned from the pursuit, and it was to recall his people that the prince had placed his banner upon a high bush. They did not return till late after vespers from pursuing the enemy. It was reported that all the flower of French knighthood was slain, and that, with the king and his son the lord Philip, seventeen earls, without counting barons, knights, or squires, were made prisoners, and from five to six thousand of all sorts left dead in the field. When they were all collected, they found they had twice as many prisoners as themselves. They therefore consulted, if, considering the risk they might run, it would not be more advisable to ransom them on the spot. This was done, and the prisoners found the English and Gascons very civil; for there were many set at liberty that day on their promise of coming to Bordeaux before Christmas to pay their ransom.

When all were returned to their banners, they retired to their camp, which was adjoining to the field of battle. Some disarmed themselves and did the same to their prisoners, to whom they showed every kindness; for whoever made any prisoners they were solely at his disposal to ransom or not, as he pleased. It may be easily supposed that all those who accompanied the prince were very rich in glory and wealth, as well by the ransoms of his prisoners as by the quantities of gold and silver plate, rich jewels, and trunks stuffed full of belts that were weighty from their gold and silver ornaments and furred mantles. They set no value on armor, tents, or other things; for the French had come there as magnificently and richly dressed as if they had been sure of gaining the victory.

When the lord James Audley was brought back to his tent after having most respectfully thanked the prince for his gift, he did not remain long before he sent for his brother, Sir Peter Audley, and some more. They were all of his relations. He then sent for his four squires that had attended upon him that day, and, addressing himself to the knights, said: "Gentlemen, it has pleased my lord the prince to give me five hundred marcs as a yearly inheritance, for which gift I have done him very trifling bodily service. You see here these four squires who have always served me most loyally, and especially in this day's engagement. What glory I may have gained has been through their means and by their valor, on which account I wish to reward them. I therefore give and resign into their hands the gift of five hundred marcs which my lord the prince has been pleased to bestow on me, in the same form and manner that it has been presented to me. I disinherit myself of it and give it to them simply and without a possibility of revoking it." The knights looked on each other, and said, "It is becoming the noble mind of lord James to make such a gift;" and then unanimously added: "May the Lord God remember you for it! We will bear witness of this gift to them wheresoever and whensoever they may call upon us." They then took leave of him, when some went to the prince of Wales, who that night was to give a supper to the king of France from his own provisions; for the French had brought vast quantities with them, which were now fallen into the hands of the English, many of whom had not tasted bread for the last three days.

When evening was come, the prince of Wales gave a supper in his pavilion to the king of France and to the greater part of the princes and barons who were prisoners. The prince seated the king of France and his son the lord Philip at an elevated and well-covered table; and with them were some other French lords of high rank. The other knights and squires were placed at different tables. The prince himself served the king's table, as well as the others, with every mark of humility, and would not sit down at it, in spite of all his entreaties for him to do so, saying that he was not worthy of such an honor, nor did it appertain to him to seat himself at the table of so great a king or of so valiant a man as he had shown himself by his actions that day. He added also, with a noble air: "Dear sir, do not make a poor meal because the Almighty God has not gratified your wishes in the event of this day; for be assured that my lord and father will show you every honor and friendship in his power, and will arrange for your ransom so reasonably that you will henceforward always remain friends. In my opinion, you have cause to be glad that the success of this battle did not turn out as you desired; for you have this day acquired such high renown for prowess that you have surpassed all the best knights on your side. I do not, dear sir, say this to flatter you, for all those of our side who have seen and observed the actions of each party have unanimously allowed this to be your due, and decree you the prize and garland for it." At the end of this speech there were murmurs of praise heard from every one; and the French said the prince had spoken truly and nobly, and that he would be one of the most gallant princes in Christendom if God should grant him life to pursue his career of glory.

INDEX

THE AGE OF CHIVALRY

Addanc, the, 514.
Æneas, 314.
Agrivain, 347, 358, 421.
Albion, 314.
Alençon, Earl of, 575.
Alexander, 311.
Allemannus, 314.
Alyduke, 355.
Ambrosius, 324.
Argius, king of Ireland, 375.
Armor, 307.
Armorica, 322.
Arthur, 309, 312; historical evidences of, 322; story of, 325; slays the giant of St. Michael's Mount, 339; obtains Excalibur, 340, 398, 401, 403, 421; received by the three queens, 431; his epitaph, 432, 443; seeks Owain, 453, 459, 500, 510, 513.
Ascanius, 314.
Audley, Lord James, 582, 584, 587.
Audret, 377.
Avaon, quoted, 442.

Badger in the Bag, 483.
Bagdemagus, 352, 404.
Baldwin de Carreo, 537.
Ban, king, 326, 350.
Bedivere, 429, 434.
Bedwyr, 510.
Belinus, 319.
Bendigeid, Vran, 484, 491.
Bishop of Hereford and his entertainment by Robin Hood, 553.
Blaanor, 375.
Bladud, 317.
Bohort, 326, 350, 370; in quest of the Sangreal, 410; fights with his brother Lionel, 412, 416; at Joyeuse Garde, 423; seeks Sir Launcelot, 433.
Boiardo, quoted, 378.

Boy and the Mantle, the, 343.
Brademagus, 364.
Brandeles, 355, 358.
Branwen, 484.
Brengwain, 376, 386.
Brennus, 319.
Breuse sans Pitié, 384, 387.
Brice, Bishop, 326.
Britons, 439.
Britto, 314.
Brunne, Robert de, 311.
Brutus, 315.
Bryan, 355.

Cador, 342.
Caerleon, note on, 336.
Calidore, 397.
Camelot, note on, 336.
Caradoc, 342, 488, 491.
Carlisle, 325; note on, 336.
Carracois, 532.
Cassibellaunus, 321.
Charlemagne, 309, 312.
Chandos, Sir John, 583, 586.
Chaucer, quoted, 348.
Chevy Chase, 561.
Chivalry, 303.
Clerks, 306.
Clifton, 556.
Colgrevance, 413.
Constans, 324.
Cordelia, 318, 502.
Cordivi, 542.
Crecy, 575.
Crusade, the Third, 529.
Curtal Friar, 550.
Cymbeline, 321.
Cyprus, 529.

Daguenet, 387.
David, 312.
Denys de Morbeque, 585.

Diana, 315.
Dillus Varwawc, 507, 512.
Douglas, Earl, 562, 567; death of, 573.
Drayton, quoted, 327, 547.
Dremhidydd, quoted, 442.

Edeyrn, 465.
Edward the Black Prince, 574.
Elaine, 369, 403.
Eliaures, 342.
Elidure, 320.
Elphin, 520.
Enid and Geraint, 465, 468; receives
    the stag's head, 469; rides with Ge-
    raint, 473; her character, 476.
Erbin, 472.
Etlym Gleddyv Coch, 517.
Eustace de Ribeaumont, 579.
Evnissyen, 485.
Excalibur, 326.

Ferrex, 319.
Flollo, 335.
France, King of: at Crecy, 575; cap-
    tured at Poitiers, 585.
Francus, 314.
Frederick Barbarossa, 529.
Freeman, 306.
Friar Tuck, 550.
Froissart, 567.

Gaheris, 354, 385, 421.
Gaharet, 347.
Galahad, 403, 416; his death, 418.
Galleron, 390.
Galynde, 355.
Gareth, 347, 421.
Garsilet, quoted, 442.
Gast Rhymi, 507, 512.
Gawain, 329, 333; his parentage, 346;
    marriage, 347, 356, 362, 370, 385,
    391, 400, 402, 405, 421; his battle
    with Launcelot, 426; his adventure
    with the Lady of the Fountain,
    453; his death, 428.
Gawl, son of Clud, 482, 498.
Genoese archers, 575.
Geoffrey de Vinsauf, quoted, 533.
Geoffrey of Monmouth, 309.
Geraint, 458; and Enid, 465, 468, 472.
Glass windows, 472.
Godfrey of Boulogne, 312.

Goneril, 318.
Gouvernail, 372, 383.
Gray, quoted, 440, 441.
Guenever, 331, 358, 396, 421; con-
    demned to death, 422, 442; goes to
    see the hunt, 459.
Guest, Lady Charlotte, 313.
Gurhyr Gwalstat, 508, 510.
Guy, king of Jerusalem, 533.
Gwernach the Giant, 508, 509.

Hamo's Port, note on, 336.
Hector, 311.
Hector de Marys, 355, 356, 366, 370,
    382; at Joyeuse Garde, 423; seeks
    Launcelot, 433, 434.
Helen, 350.
Henry, Count of Champagne, 533.
Heveydd, 481.
Holy Cross, the, 532.
Holy Grail, the, 330, 392 (see San-
    greal).
Holy Land, the, 529.
Hospitallers, 533; Master of the, 536,
    537.

Igerne, 325.
Ironside, 359.
Isoude the Fair, 373, 387.
Isoude of the White Hands, 392.

James d'Avennes, 538.
Joppa, 541.
Joseph of Arimathea, 401, 403, 418.
Joshua, 312.
Judas Maccabæus, 312.
Julius Cæsar, 312.

Kadyriath, 466, 471.
Katherine, Queen, 554.
Kay, 326; note on, 335, 355, 358, 364,
    397, 400, 442, 501, 509, 510.
Kicva, 494.
Kilwich, 499.
King of North Wales, 353.
Kirkley Hall, 560.
Knight Errant, 303; education of,
    304.
Knight of the Sparrowhawk, 463.
Kynon, 453.

La Joyeuse Garde, 371, 422.
Lady of the Lake, 328, 340.
Ladynas of the Forest Savage, 359.
Laodegan, 331.
Launcelot, 333; parentage, 350; adventure of the cart, 358; and the Lady of Shalott, 365; saves Queen Guenever, 369, 385; in quest of the Sangreal, 406, 414; and Guenever, 421; battle with Gawain, 426; seeks Queen Guenever, 432; death of, 434.
Lear, 317, 502.
Lionel, 350, 355, 370, 411; fights with his brother Bohort, 412; at La Joyeuse Garde, 423.
Little John, 547, 548, 560; and the Bishop of Hereford, 553.
Llenleawg, quoted, 442.
Lloyd, 498.
Llywarch, quoted, 442.
Lucan, 428.
Lucius Tiberius, 338.
Lud, 320.
Luned, 451, 457.

Mabon, 510.
Madoc, 459.
Mador, 369.
Mallory, Sir Thomas, quoted, 435.
Manawyddan, 485, 490, 491.
March and Dunbar, Earl of, 567.
Mark, King of Cornwall, 372, 380.
Matholk, 485.
Meleagans, 359.
Meliadus, 372.
Menelones, 542.
Meneu, 503.
Merlin, 324; story of, 327, 331, 340.
Mestocus, 532.
Milton, quoted, 314, 316.
Modred, 323, 427; death of, 429.
Moines, 324.
Molmutius, 319.
Montgomery, Sir Hugh, 565.
Moraunt, 373, 386.
Moray, Earl of, 567.
Much the Miller's Son, 547, 557.

Neptune, 314.
Nissiyen, 485.
Nottinghamshire, 555.

Olwen, 499.
Otterbourne, 567; the battle of, 571.
Owain and Perceval, 395, 398, 442, 447; and the lion, 457.
Owen, quoted, 324.
Ozanna le Cure Hardy, 359.

Palamedes, 373, 376, 384, 389, 4 3.
Pecheur, King, 399, 402.
Pelenore, 396.
Pelleas, 359.
Pendragon, 328.
Perceval, youth of, 395; in quest of the Sangreal, 406, 408, 416; death of, 418 (see Peredur).
Percy, Earl, 561, 567.
Percy's Reliques, quoted, 346, 561.
Peredur, 513 (see Perceval).
Perigord, Cardinal, 580.
Perilous Seat, 386.
Perseant of Inde, 359.
Phelot, 357.
Philip Augustus, 529, 532.
Porrex, 319.
Pryderi, 490, 491.
Pwyll, 480, 491.

Queen Morgane le Fay, 352.
Queen of the Isles, 352.
Queen of Eastland, 352.
Queen of North Wales, 352.

Regan, 318.
Reginald Cobham, 577, 587.
Rhiannon, 482, 491.
Rhun, 523.
Richard of Devizes, quoted, 533.
Richard I. of England, 529; at Cyprus, 529; at the siege of Acre, 531; in battle with the Saracens, 533, 537; attacked by Saracens, 542.
Ritson, quoted, 547.
Robin Hood, 547, 553; and the beggar, 557; and King Richard, 558; death of, 560.
Round Table, 385.

Sagramore le Desirus, 356, 358.
Saffire, 423.
Saladin, 541, 547.

Sangreal, 400, 401, 407, 416.
Scarlock, 547.
Scott, Sir Walter, quoted, 375.
Shalott, Lady of, 365.
———, note on, 336.
Sherwood Forest, 547.
Silk in the Middle Ages, 450.
Southey, quoted, 499.
Spenser, quoted, 316, 322, 330, 394.
Stukely, quoted, 550.
Stukely, William, 549.

Taliesin, 440; quoted, 453, 520; his
    poems, 521, 525.
Templars, 533.
Tennyson, quoted, 324, 327, 331, 367,
    395, 401 (Sir Galahad), 419, 427.

Uther, 324, 328.
Uwaine, 356, 404.

Viviane, 328, 350, 380.
Vortigern, 324, 328.

Welsh, bards, 440.
——— language and literature, 440.
——— people, 439.
Wharton, quoted, 323.
Witherington, 563, 566.

Ynywl, Earl, 465.
Yspadaden Penkawr, 500.

LEGENDS OF CHARLEMAGNE

OR

ROMANCE OF THE MIDDLE AGES

"How Agrican with all his northern powers
Besieged Albracca, as romances tell;
The city of Galaphron, from thence to win
The fairest of her sex, Angelica,
His daughter, loved of many prowest knights,
Both paynim, and the peers of Charlemain."
Paradise Regained.

PREFACE

BESIDES the education which schools and colleges impart, there
is still another kind necessary to completeness. It is that which
has for its object a knowledge of polite literature. In the intercourse
of polished society a young person will more frequently need an
acquaintance with the creations of fancy than with the discoveries
of science or the speculations of philosophy.

In an age when intellectual darkness enveloped Western Europe,
a constellation of brilliant writers arose in Italy. Of these, Pulci
(born in 1431), Boiardo (1434), and Ariosto (1474) took for their
subjects the romantic fables which had for many ages been trans-
mitted in the lays of bards and the legends of monkish chroniclers.
These fables they arranged in order, adorned with the embellishments of fancy, amplified from their own invention, and stamped
with immortality. It may safely be asserted, that as long as civilization shall endure, these productions will retain their place among
the most cherished creations of human genius.

In the two preceding works, "The Age of Fable" and "The Age of
Chivalry," the author of this volume has endeavored to supply to
the modern reader such knowledge of the fables of classical and
mediæval literature as is needed to render intelligible the allusions
which occur in reading and conversation. This book is intended
to carry out the same design. Like its predecessors, it aspires to
a higher character than that of a work of mere amusement. It claims
to be useful, in acquainting its readers with the subjects of the
works of the great poets of Italy. Some knowledge of these is expected of every well-educated young person.

In reading these romances, we cannot fail to observe how the
primitive inventions have been used, again and again, by successive
generations of fabulists. The Siren of Ulysses is the prototype of the
Siren of Orlando, and the character of Circe reappears in Alcina.
The fountains of Love and Hatred may be traced to the story of
Cupid and Psyche; and similar effects produced by a magic draught
appear in the tale of Tristram and Isoude, and, substituting a flower
for the draught, in Shakespeare's "Midsummer Night's Dream."
There are many other instances of the same kind which the reader
will recognize without our assistance.

The sources whence we derive these stories are, first, the Italian poets named above; next, the "Romans de Chevalerie" of the Comte de Tressan; lastly, certain German collections of popular tales. Some chapters have been borrowed from Leigh Hunt's Translations from the Italian Poets. It seemed unnecessary to do over again what he had already done so well; yet, on the other hand, those stories could not be omitted from the series without leaving it incomplete.

CHAPTER I

INTRODUCTION

THOSE who have investigated the origin of the romantic fables relating to Charlemagne and his peers are of opinion that the deeds of Charles Martel, and perhaps of other Charleses, have been blended in popular tradition with those properly belonging to Charlemagne. It was indeed a most momentous era; and if our readers will have patience, before entering on the perusal of the fabulous annals which we are about to lay before them, to take a rapid survey of the real history of the times, they will find it hardly less romantic than the tales of the poets.

In the century beginning from the year 600, the countries bordering upon the native land of our Saviour, to the east and south, had not yet received his religion. Arabia was the seat of an idolatrous religion resembling that of the ancient Persians, who worshipped the sun, moon, and stars. In Mecca, in the year 571, Mahomet was born, and here, at the age of forty, he proclaimed himself the prophet of God, in dignity as superior to Christ as Christ had been to Moses. Having obtained by slow degrees a considerable number of disciples, he resorted to arms to diffuse his religion. The energy and zeal of his followers, aided by the weakness of the neighboring nations, enabled him and his successors to spread the sway of Arabia and the religion of Mahomet over the countries to the east as far as the Indus, northward over Persia and Asia Minor, westward over Egypt and the southern shores of the Mediterranean, and thence over the principal portion of Spain. All this was done within one hundred years from the Hegira, or flight of Mahomet from Mecca to Medina, which happened in the year 622, and is the era from which Mahometans reckon time, as we do from the birth of Christ.

From Spain the way was open for the Saracens (so the followers of Mahomet were called) into France, the conquest of which, if achieved, would have been followed very probably by that of all the rest of Europe, and would have resulted in the banishment of Christianity from the earth. For Christianity was not at that day universally professed, even by those nations which we now regard as foremost in civilization. Great part of Germany, Britain, Denmark, and Russia were still pagan or barbarous.

At that time there ruled in France, though without the title of king, the first of those illustrious Charleses of whom we have spoken, Charles Martel, the grandfather of Charlemagne. The Saracens of Spain had made incursions into France in 712 and 718, and had retired, carrying with them a vast booty. In 725, Anbessa, who was then the Saracen governor of Spain, crossed the Pyrenees with a numerous army, and took by storm the strong town of Carcassone. So great was the terror excited by this invasion, that the country for a wide extent submitted to the conqueror, and a Mahometan governor for the province was appointed and installed at Narbonne. Anbessa, however, received a fatal wound in one of his engagements, and the Saracens, being thus checked from further advance, retired to Narbonne.

In 732 the Saracens again invaded France under Abdalrahman. advanced rapidly to the banks of the Garonne, and laid siege to Bordeaux. The city was taken by assault and delivered up to the soldiery. The invaders still pressed forward, and spread over the territories of Orleans, Auxerre, and Sens. Their advanced parties were suddenly called in by their chief, who had received information of the rich abbey of St. Martin of Tours, and resolved to plunder and destroy it.

Charles during all this time had done nothing to oppose the Saracens, for the reason that the portion of France over which their incursions had been made was not at that time under his dominion, but constituted an independent kingdom, under the name of Aquitaine, of which Eude was king. But now Charles became convinced of the danger, and prepared to encounter it. Abdalrahman was advancing toward Tours, when intelligence of the approach of Charles, at the head of an army of Franks, compelled him to fall back upon Poitiers, in order to seize an advantageous field of battle.

Charles Martel had called together his warriors from every part of his dominions, and, at the head of such an army as had hardly ever been seen in France, crossed the Loire, probably at Orleans, and, being joined by the remains of the army of Aquitaine, came in sight of the Arabs in the month of October, 732. The Saracens seem to have been aware of the terrible enemy they were now to encounter, and for the first time these formidable conquerors hesitated. The two armies remained in presence during seven days before either ventured to begin the attack; but at length the signal for battle was given by Abdalrahman, and the immense mass of the Saracen army rushed with fury on the Franks. But the heavy line of the Northern warriors remained like a rock, and the Saracens, during nearly the whole day, expended their strength in vain attempts to make an impression upon them. At length, about four o'clock in the afternoon, when Abdalrahman was preparing for a new and desperate attempt to break the line of the Franks, a terrible clamor was heard in the rear of the Saracens. It was King Eude, who, with his Aquitanians, had attacked their camp, and a great part of the Saracen army rushed tumultuously from the field to protect their plunder. In this moment of confusion the line of the Franks advanced, and, sweeping the field before it, carried fearful slaughter amongst the enemy. Abdalrahman made desperate efforts to rally his troops, but when he himself, with the bravest of his officers, fell beneath the swords of the Christians, all order disappeared, and the remains of his army sought refuge in their immense camp, from which Eude and his Aquitanians had been repulsed. It was now late, and Charles, unwilling to risk an attack on the camp in the dark, withdrew his army, and passed the night in the plain, expecting to renew the battle in the morning.

Accordingly, when daylight came, the Franks drew up in order of battle, but no enemy appeared; and when at last they ventured to approach the Saracen camp, they found it empty. The invaders had taken advantage of the night to begin their retreat, and were already on their way back to Spain, leaving their immense plunder behind to fall into the hands of the Franks.

This was the celebrated battle of Tours, in which vast numbers of the Saracens were slain, and only fifteen hundred of the Franks. Charles received the surname of Martel (the Hammer) in consequence of this victory.

The Saracens, notwithstanding this severe blow, continued to hold their ground in the South of France; but Pepin, the son of Charles Martel, who succeeded to his father's power, and assumed the title of king, successively took from them the strong places they held; and in 759, by the capture of Narbonne, their capital, extinguished the remains of their power in France.

Charlemagne, or Charles the Great, succeeded his father, Pepin, on the throne in the year 768. This prince, though the hero of numerous romantic legends, appears greater in history than in fiction. Whether we regard him as a warrior or as a legislator, as a patron of learning or as the civilizer of a barbarous nation, he is entitled to our warmest admiration. Such he is in history; but the romancers represent him as often weak and passionate, the victim of treacherous counsellors, and at the mercy of turbulent barons, on whose prowess he depends for the maintenance of his throne. The historical representation is doubtless the true one, for it is handed down in trustworthy records, and is confirmed by the events of the age. At the height of his power, the French empire extended over what we now call France, Germany, Switzerland, Holland, Belgium, and a great part of Italy.

In the year 800, Charlemagne, being in Rome, whither he had gone with a numerous army to protect the Pope, was crowned by the Pontiff Emperor of the West. On Christmas day Charles entered the Church of St. Peter, as if merely to take his part in the celebration of the mass with the rest of the congregation. When he approached the altar and stooped in the act of prayer, the Pope stepped forward and placed a crown of gold upon his head; and immediately the Roman people shouted, "Life and victory to Charles the August, crowned by God the great and pacific Emperor of the Romans." The Pope then prostrated himself before him, and paid him reverence, according to the custom established in the times of the ancient Emperors, and concluded the ceremony by anointing him with consecrated oil.

Charlemagne's wars were chiefly against the pagan and barbarous people, who, under the name of Saxons, inhabited the countries now called Hanover and Holland. He also led expeditions against the Saracens of Spain; but his wars with the Saracens were not carried on, as the romances assert, in France, but on the soil of Spain. He entered Spain by the Eastern Pyrenees, and made an easy conquest of Barcelona and Pampeluna. But Saragossa refused to open her gates to him, and Charles ended by negotiating, and accepting a vast sum of gold as the price of his return over the Pyrenees.

On his way back, he marched with his whole army through the gorges of the mountains by way of the valleys of Engui, Eno, and Roncesvalles. The chief of this region had waited upon Charlemagne, on his advance, as a faithful vassal of the monarchy; but now, on the return of the Franks, he had called together all the wild mountaineers who acknowledged him as their chief, and they occupied the heights of the mountains under which the army had to pass. The main body of the troops met with no obstruction, and received no intimation of danger; but the rear-guard, which was considerably behind, and encumbered with its plunder, was overwhelmed by the mountaineers in the pass of Roncesvalles, and slain to a man. Some of the bravest of the Frankish chiefs perished on this occasion, among whom is mentioned Roland or Orlando, governor of the marches or frontier of Brittany. His name became famous in after times, and the disaster of Roncesvalles and death of Roland became eventually the most celebrated episode in the vast cycle of romance.

Though after this there were hostile encounters between the armies of Charlemagne and the Saracens, they were of small account, and generally on the soil of Spain. Thus the historical foundation for the stories of the romancers is but scanty, unless we suppose the events of an earlier and of a later age to be incorporated with those of Charlemagne's own time.

There is, however, a pretended history, which for a long time was admitted as authentic, and attributed to Turpin, Archbishop of Rheims, a real personage of the time of Charlemagne. Its title is "History of Charles the Great and Orlando." It is now unhesitatingly considered as a collection of popular traditions, produced by some credulous and unscrupulous monk, who thought to give dignity to his romance by ascribing its authorship to a well-known and eminent individual. It introduces its pretended author, Bishop Turpin, in this manner:—

"Turpin, Archbishop of Rheims, the friend and secretary of Charles the Great, excellently skilled in sacred and profane literature, of a genius equally adapted to prose and verse, the advocate of the poor, beloved of God in his life and conversation, who often fought the Saracens, hand to hand, by the Emperor's side, he relates the acts of Charles the Great in one book, and flourished under Charles and his son Louis, to the year of our Lord eight hundred and thirty."

The titles of some of Archbishop Turpin's chapters will show the nature of his history. They are these: "Of the Walls of Pampeluna, that fell of themselves." "Of the War of the holy Facundus, where the Spears grew." (Certain of the Christians fixed their spears, in the evening, erect in the ground, before the castle; and found them, in the morning, covered with bark and branches.) "How the Sun stood still for Three Days, and the Slaughter of Four Thousand Saracens."

Turpin's history has perhaps been the source of the marvellous adventures which succeeding poets and romancers have accumulated around the names of Charlemagne and his Paladins, or Peers. But Ariosto and the other Italian poets have drawn from different sources, and doubtless often from their own invention, numberless other stories which they attribute to the same heroes, not hesitating to quote as their authority "the good Turpin," though his history contains no trace of them;—and the more outrageous the improbability, or rather the impossibility, of their narrations, the more attentive are they to cite "the Archbishop," generally adding their testimonial to his unquestionable veracity.

The principal Italian poets who have sung the adventures of the peers of Charlemagne are Pulci, Boiardo, and Ariosto. The characters of Orlando, Rinaldo, Astolpho, Gano, and others, are the same in all, though the adventures attributed to them are different. Boiardo tells us of the loves of Orlando, Ariosto of his disappointment and consequent madness, Pulci of his death.

Ogier, the Dane, is a real personage. History agrees with romance in representing him as a powerful lord who, originally from Denmark and a Pagan, embraced Christianity, and took service under Charlemagne. He revolted from the Emperor, and was driven into exile. He afterwards led one of those bands of piratical Norsemen which ravaged France under the reigns of Charlemagne's degenerate successors. The description which an ancient chronicler gives of Charlemagne, as described by Ogier, is so picturesque, that we are tempted to transcribe it. Charlemagne was advancing to the siege of Pavia. Didier, King of the Lombards, was in the city with Ogier, to whom he had given refuge. When they learned that the king was approaching, they mounted a high tower, whence they could see far and wide over the country. "They first saw advancing the engines of war, fit for the armies of Darius or Julius Cæsar. 'There is Charlemagne,' said Didier. 'No,' said Ogier. The Lombard next saw a vast body of soldiers, who filled all the plain. 'Certainly Charles advances with that host,' said the king. 'Not yet,' replied Ogier. 'What hope for us,' resumed the king, 'if he brings with him a greater host than that?' At last Charles appeared, his head covered with an iron helmet, his hands with iron gloves, his breast and shoulders with a cuirass of iron, his left hand holding an iron lance, while his right hand grasped his sword. Those who went before the monarch, those who marched at his side, and those who followed him, all had similar arms. Iron covered the fields and the roads; iron points reflected the rays of the sun. This iron, so hard, was borne by a people whose hearts were harder still. The blaze of the weapons flashed terror into the streets of the city."

This picture of Charlemagne in his military aspect would be incomplete without a corresponding one of his "mood of peace." One of the greatest of modern historians, M. Guizot, has compared the glory of Charlemagne to a brilliant meteor, rising suddenly out of the darkness of barbarism to disappear no less suddenly in the darkness of feudalism. But the light of this meteor was not extinguished, and reviving civilization owed much that was permanently beneficial to the great Emperor of the Franks. His ruling hand is seen in the legislation of his time, as well as in the administration of the laws. He encouraged learning; he upheld the clergy, who were the only peaceful and intellectual class, against the encroaching and turbulent barons; he was an affectionate father, and watched carefully over the education of his children, both sons and daughters. Of his encouragement of learning, we will give some particulars.

He caused learned men to be brought from Italy and from other foreign countries, to revive the public schools of France, which had been prostrated by the disorders of preceding times. He recompensed these learned men liberally, and kept some of them near himself, honoring them with his friendship. Of these the most celebrated is Alcuin, an Englishman, whose writings still remain, and prove him to have been both a learned and a wise man. With the assistance of Alcuin, and others like him, he founded an academy or royal school, which should have the direction of the studies of all the schools of the kingdom. Charlemagne himself was a member of this academy on equal terms with the rest. He attended its meetings, and fulfilled all the duties of an academician. Each member took the name of some famous man of antiquity. Alcuin called himself Horace, another took the name of Augustin, a third of Pindar. Charlemagne, who knew the Psalms by heart, and who had an ambition to be, according to his conception, *a king after God's own heart,* received from his brother academicians the name of David.

Of the respect entertained for him by foreign nations an interesting proof is afforded in the embassy sent to him by the Caliph of the Arabians, the celebrated Haroun al Raschid, a prince in character and conduct not unlike to Charlemagne. The ambassadors brought with them, besides other rich presents, a clock, the first that was seen in Europe, which excited universal admiration. It had the form of a twelve-sided edifice with twelve doors. These doors formed niches, in each of which was a little statue representing one of the hours. At the striking of the hour the doors, one for each stroke, were seen to open, and from the doors to issue as many of the little statues, which, following one another, marched gravely round the tower. The motion of the clock was caused by water, and the striking was effected by balls of brass equal to the number of the hours, which fell upon a cymbal of the same metal, the number falling being determined by the discharge of the water, which, as it sunk in the vessel, allowed their escape.

Charlemagne was succeeded by his son Louis, a well-intentioned but feeble prince, in whose reign the fabric reared by Charles began rapidly to crumble. Louis was followed successively by two Charleses, incapable princes, whose weak and often tyrannical conduct is no doubt the source of incidents of that character ascribed in the romances to Charlemagne.

The lawless and disobedient deportment of Charles's paladins, instances of which are so frequent in the romantic legends, was also a trait of the declining empire, but not of that of Charlemagne.

CHAPTER II

THE PEERS, OR PALADINS

THE twelve most illustrious knights of Charlemagne were called
Peers, for the equality that reigned among them; while the name of
Paladins, also conferred on them, implies that they were inmates
of the palace and companions of the king. Their names are not always given alike by the romancers, yet we may enumerate the most
distinguished of them as follows: Orlando or Roland (the former the
Italian, the latter the French form of the name), favorite nephew of
Charlemagne; Rinaldo of Montalban, cousin of Orlando; Namo,
Duke of Bavaria; Salomon, King of Brittany; Turpin, the Archbishop; Astolpho, of England; Ogier, the Dane; Malagigi, the Enchanter; and Florismart, the friend of Orlando. There were others
who are sometimes named as paladins, and the number cannot be
strictly limited to twelve. Charlemagne himself must be counted one,
and Ganelon, or Gano, of Mayence, the treacherous enemy of all the
rest, was rated high on the list by his deluded sovereign, who was
completely the victim of his arts.

We shall introduce more particularly to our readers a few of the
principal peers, leaving the others to make their own introduction,
as they appear in the course of our narrative. We begin with Or-
ˀando.

ORLANDO

Milon, or Milone, a knight of great family, and distantly related
to Charlemagne, having secretly married Bertha, the Emperor's sister, was banished from France, and excommunicated by the Pope.
After a long and miserable wandering on foot as mendicants, Milon
and his wife arrived at Sutri, in Italy, where they took refuge in
a cave, and in that cave Orlando was born. There his mother continued, deriving a scanty support from the compassion of the neighboring peasants; while Milon, in quest of honor and fortune, went
into foreign lands. Orlando grew up among the children of the peasantry, surpassing them all in strength and manly graces. Among his
companions in age, though in station far more elevated, was Oliver,
son of the governor of the town. Between the two boys a feud arose,
that led to a fight, in which Orlando thrashed his rival; but this did
not prevent a friendship springing up between the two which lasted
through life.

Orlando was so poor that he was sometimes half naked. As he
was a favorite of the boys, one day four of them brought some cloth

to make him clothes. Two brought white and two red; and from this circumstance Orlando took his coat-of-arms, or *quarterings*.

When Charlemagne was on his way to Rome to receive the imperial crown, he dined in public in Sutri. Orlando and his mother that day had nothing to eat, and Orlando, coming suddenly upon the royal party, and seeing abundance of provisions, seized from the attendants as much as he could carry off, and made good his retreat in spite of their resistance. The Emperor, being told of this incident, was reminded of an intimation he had received in a dream, and ordered the boy to be followed. This was done by three of the knights, whom Orlando would have encountered with a cudgel on their entering the grotto, had not his mother restrained him. When they heard from her who she was, they threw themselves at her feet, and promised to obtain her pardon from the Emperor. This was easily effected. Orlando was received into favor by the Emperor, returned with him to France and so distinguished himself that he became the most powerful support of the throne and of Christianity.[1]

ROLAND AND FERRAGUS

Orlando, or Roland, particularly distinguished himself by his combat with Ferragus. Ferragus was a giant, and moreover, his skin was of such impenetrable stuff that no sword could make any impression upon it. The giant's mode of fighting was to seize his adversary in his arms and carry him off, in spite of all the struggles he could make. Roland's utmost skill only availed to keep him out of the giant's clutches, but all his efforts to wound him with the sword were useless. After long fighting, Ferragus was so weary that he proposed a truce, and when it was agreed upon, he lay down and immediately fell asleep. He slept in perfect security, for it was against all the laws of chivalry to take advantage of an adversary under such circumstances. But Ferragus lay so uncomfortably for the want of a pillow, that Orlando took pity upon him, and brought a smooth stone and placed it under his head. When the giant woke up, after a refreshing nap, and perceived what Orlando had done, he seemed quite grateful, became sociable, and talked freely in the usual boastful style of such characters. Among other things, he told Orlando that he need not attempt to kill him with a sword, for that every part of his body was invulnerable, except this; and as he spoke, he put his hand to the vital part, just in the middle of his breast. Aided by this information, Orlando succeeded, when the fight was renewed, in piercing the giant

[1] It is plain that Shakespeare borrowed from this source the similar incident in his "As you Like it." The names of characters in the play, Orlando, Oliver. Rowland, indicate the same thing.

in the very spot he had pointed out, and giving him a death-wound. Great was the rejoicing in the Christian camp, and many the praises showered upon the victorious paladin by the Emperor and all his host.

On another occasion, Orlando encountered a puissant Saracen warrior, and took from him, as the prize of victory, the sword Durindana. This famous weapon had once belonged to the illustrious prince Hector of Troy. It was of the finest workmanship, and of such strength and temper that no armor in the world could stand against it.

A ROLAND FOR AN OLIVER

Guerin de Montglave held the lordship of Vienne, subject to Charlemagne. He had quarrelled with his sovereign, and Charles laid siege to his city, having ravaged the neighboring country. Guerin was an aged warrior, but relied for his defence upon his four sons and two grandsons, who were among the bravest knights of the age. After the siege had continued two months, Charlemagne received tidings that Marsilius, king of Spain, had invaded France, and, finding himself unopposed, was advancing rapidly in the Southern provinces. At this intelligence, Charles listened to the counsel of his peers, and consented to put the quarrel with Guerin to the decision of Heaven, by single combat between two knights, one of each party, selected by lot. The proposal was acceptable to Guerin and his sons. The names of the four, together with Guerin's own, who would not be excused, and of the two grandsons, who claimed their lot, being put into a helmet, Oliver's was drawn forth, and to him, the youngest of the grandsons, was assigned the honor and the peril of the combat. He accepted the award with delight, exulting in being thought worthy to maintain the cause of his family. On Charlemagne's side Roland was the designated champion, and neither he nor Oliver knew who his antagonist was to be.

They met on an island in the Rhone, and the warriors of both camps were ranged on either shore, spectators of the battle. At the first encounter both lances were shivered, but both riders kept their seats, immovable. They dismounted, and drew their swords. Then ensued a combat which seemed so equal, that the spectators could not form an opinion as to the probable issue. Two hours and more the knights continued to strike and parry, to thrust and ward, neither showing any sign of weariness, nor ever being taken at unawares. At length Orlando struck furiously upon Oliver's shield, burying Durindana in its edge so deeply that he could not draw it back, and Oliver, almost at the same moment, thrust so vigorously upon Orlando's breastplate that his sword snapped off at the handle. Thus were the two warriors left weaponless. Scarcely pausing a moment, they rushed upon one another, each striving to throw his adversary to the ground, and failing in that, each snatched at the other's helmet to tear it away. Both succeeded, and at the same moment they stood bareheaded face to face, and Roland recognized Oliver, and Oliver recognized Roland. For a moment they stood still; and the next, with open arms, rushed into one another's embrace. "I am conquered," said Orlando. "I yield me," said Oliver.

The people on the shore knew not what to make of all this. Presently they saw the two late antagonists standing hand in hand, and it was evident the battle was at an end. The knights crowded round them, and with one voice hailed them as equals in glory. If there were any who felt disposed to murmur that the battle was left undecided, they were silenced by the voice of Ogier the Dane, who proclaimed aloud that all had been done that honor required, and declared that he would maintain that award against all gainsayers.

The quarrel with Guerin and his sons being left undecided, a truce was made for four days, and in that time, by the efforts of Duke Namo on the one side, and of Oliver on the other, a reconciliation was effected. Charlemagne, accompanied by Guerin and his valiant family, marched to meet Marsilius, who hastened to retreat across the frontier.

RINALDO

Rinaldo was one of the four sons of Aymon, who married Aya, the sister of Charlemagne. Thus Rinaldo was nephew to Charlemagne and cousin of Orlando.

When Rinaldo had grown old enough to assume arms, Orlando had won for himself an illustrious name by his exploits against the Saracens, whom Charlemagne and his brave knights had driven out of France. Orlando's fame excited a noble emulation in Rinaldo. Eager to go in pursuit of glory, he wandered in the country near Paris, and one day saw at the foot of a tree a superb horse, fully equipped and loaded with a complete suit of armor. Rinaldo clothed himself in the armor and mounted the horse, but took not the sword. On the day when, with his brothers, he had received the honor of knighthood from the Emperor, he had sworn never to bind a sword to his side till he had wrested one from some famous knight.

Rinaldo took his way to the forest of Arden, celebrated for so many adventures. Hardly had he entered it, when he met an old man, bending under the weight of years, and learned from him that the forest was infested with a wild horse, untamable, that broke and overturned everything that opposed his career. To attack him, he said, or even to meet him, was certain death. Rinaldo, far from being alarmed, showed the most eager desire to combat the animal. This was the horse Bayard, afterwards so famous. He had formerly belonged to Amadis of Gaul. After the death of that hero, he had been held under enchantment by the power of a magician, who predicted that, when the time came to break the spell, he should be subdued by a knight of the lineage of Amadis, and not less brave than he.

To win this wonderful horse, it was necessary to conquer him by force or skill; for from the moment when he should be thrown down, he would become docile and manageable. His habitual resort was a cave on the borders of the forest; but woe be to any one who should approach him, unless gifted with strength and courage more than mortal. Having told this, the old man departed. He was not, in fact, an old man, but Malagigi, the enchanter, cousin of Rinaldo, who, to favor the enterprises of the young knight, had procured for him the horse and armor which he so opportunely found, and now put him in the way to acquire a horse unequalled in the world.

Rinaldo plunged into the forest, and spent many days in seeking Bayard, but found no traces of him. One day he encountered a Saracen knight, with whom he made acquaintance, as often happened to knights, by first meeting him in combat. This knight, whose name was Isolier, was also in quest of Bayard. Rinaldo succeeded in the encounter, and so severe was the shock that Isolier was a long time insensible. When he revived, and was about to resume the contest, a peasant who passed by (it was Malagigi) interrupted them with the news that the terrible horse was near at hand, advising them to unite their powers to subdue him, for it would require all their ability.

Rinaldo and Isolier, now become friends, proceeded together to the attack of the horse. They found Bayard, and stood a long time, concealed by the wood, admiring his strength and beauty.

A bright bay in color (whence he was called Bayard), with a silver star in his forehead, and his hind feet white, his body slender, his head delicate, his ample chest filled out with swelling muscles, his shoulders broad and full, his legs straight and sinewy, his thick mane falling over his arching neck,—he came rushing through the forest, regardless of rocks, bushes, or trees, rending everything that opposed his way, and neighing defiance.

He first descried Isolier, and rushed upon him. The knight received him with lance in rest, but the fierce animal broke the spear, and his course was not delayed by it for an instant. The Spaniard adroitly stepped aside, and gave way to the rushing tempest. Bayard checked his career, and turned again upon the knight, who had

already drawn his sword. He drew his sword, for he had no hope
of taming the horse; that, he was satisfied, was impossible.

Bayard rushed upon him, fiercely rearing, now on this side, now
on that. The knight struck him with his sword, where the white
star adorned his forehead, but struck in vain, and felt ashamed,
thinking that he had struck feebly, for he did not know that the skin
of that horse was so tough that the keenest sword could make no
impression upon it.

Whistling fell the sword once more, and struck with greater force,
and the fierce horse felt it, and drooped his head under the blow, but
the next moment turned upon his foe with such a buffet that the
Pagan fell stunned and lifeless to the earth.

Rinaldo, who saw Isolier fall, and thought that his life was reft,
darted towards the horse, and, with his fist, gave him such a blow
on the jaws that the blood tinged his mouth with vermilion. Quicker
than an arrow leaves the bow the horse turned upon him, and tried
to seize his arm with his teeth.

The knight stepped back, and then, repeating his blow, struck him
on the forehead. Bayard turned, and kicked with both his feet with
a force that would have shattered a mountain. Rinaldo was on his
guard, and evaded his attacks, whether made with head or heels.
He kept at his side, avoiding both; but, making a false step, he at
last received a terrible blow from the horse's foot, and at the shock
almost fainted away. A second such blow would have killed him, but
the horse kicked at random, and a second blow did not reach Rinaldo,
who in a moment recovered himself. Thus the contest continued until
by chance Bayard's foot got caught between the branches of an oak.
Rinaldo seized it, and putting forth all his strength and address,
threw him on the ground.

No sooner had Bayard touched the ground, than all his rage subsided. No longer an object of terror, he became gentle and quiet,
yet with dignity in his mildness.

The paladin patted his neck, stroked his breast, and smoothed his
mane, while the animal neighed and showed delight to be caressed
by his master. Rinaldo, seeing him now completely subdued, took
the saddle and trappings from the other horse, and adorned Bayard
with the spoils.

Rinaldo became one of the most illustrious knights of Charlemagne's court,—indeed, the most illustrious, if we except Orlando.
Yet he was not always so obedient to the Emperor's commands as
he should have been, and every fault he committed was sure to be
aggravated by the malice of Gan, Duke of Maganza, the treacherous
enemy of Rinaldo and all his house.

At one time Rinaldo had incurred the severe displeasure of

Charlemagne, and been banished from court. Seeing no chance of being ever restored to favor, he went to Spain, and entered the service of the Saracen king, Ivo. His brothers, Alardo, Ricardo, and Ricciardetto, accompanied him, and all four served the king so faithfully that they rose to high favor with him. The king gave them land in the mountains on the frontiers of France and Spain, and subjected all the country round to Rinaldo's authority. There was plenty of marble in the mountains, the king furnished workmen, and they built a castle for Rinaldo, surrounded with high walls, so as to be almost impregnable. Built of white stone, and placed on the brow of a marble promontory, the castle shone like a star, and Rinaldo gave it the name of Montalban. Here he assembled his friends, many of whom were banished men like himself, and the country people furnished them with provisions in return for the protection the castle afforded. Yet some of Rinaldo's men were lawless, and sometimes the supplies were not furnished in sufficient abundance, so that Rinaldo and his garrison got a bad name for taking by force what they could not obtain by gift; and we sometimes find Montalban spoken of as a nest of freebooters, and its defenders called a beggarly garrison.

Charlemagne's displeasure did not last long, and, at the time our history commences, Rinaldo and his brothers were completely restored to the favor of the Emperor, and none of his cavaliers served him with greater zeal and fidelity than they, throughout all his wars with the Saracens and Pagans.

CHAPTER III

THE TOURNAMENT

It was the month of May and the feast of Pentecost. Charlemagne had ordered magnificent festivities, and summoned to them, besides his paladins and vassals of the crown, all strangers, Christian or Saracen, then sojourning at Paris. Among the guests were King Grandonio, from Spain; and Ferrau, the Saracen, with eyes like an eagle; Orlando and Rinaldo, the Emperor's nephews; Duke Namo; Astolpho, of England, the handsomest man living; Malagigi, the Enchanter; and Gano, of Maganza, that wily traitor, who had the art to make the Emperor think he loved him, while he plotted against him.

High sat Charlemagne at the head of his vassals and his paladins, rejoicing in the thought of their number and their might, while all were sitting and hearing music, and feasting, when suddenly there came into the hall four enormous giants, having between them a

lady of incomparable beauty, attended by a single knight. There
were many ladies present who had seemed beautiful till she made her
appearance, but after that they all seemed nothing. Every Christian
knight turned his eyes to her, and every Pagan crowded round her,
while she, with a sweetness that might have touched a heart of
stone, thus addressed the Emperor:—

"High-minded lord, the renown of your worthiness, and of the
valor of these your knights, which echoes from sea to sea, encour-
ages me to hope that two pilgrims, who have come from the ends
of the world to behold you, will not have encountered their fatigue
in vain. And, before I show the motive which has brought us hither,
learn that this knight is my brother Uberto, and that I am his sister
Angelica. Fame has told us of the jousting this day appointed, and
so the prince my brother has come to prove his valor, and to say
that, if any of the knights here assembled choose to meet him in the
joust, he will encounter them, one by one, at the stair of Merlin, by
the Fountain of the Pine. And his conditions are these: No knight
who chances to be thrown shall be allowed to renew the combat, but
shall remain prisoner to my brother, but if my brother be overthrown, he shall depart out of the country, leaving me as the prize
of the conqueror."

Now it must be stated that this Angelica and her brother who
called himself Uberto, but whose real name was Argalia, were the
children of Galafron, king of Cathay, who had sent them to be the
destruction of the Christian host; for Argalia was armed with an
enchanted lance, which unfailingly overthrew everything it touched,
and he was mounted on a horse, a creature of magic, whose swiftness
outstripped the wind. Angelica possessed also a ring which was a defence against all enchantments, and when put into the mouth rendered the bearer invisible. Thus Argalia was expected to subdue and
take prisoners whatever knights should dare to encounter him; and
the charms of Angelica were relied on to entice the paladins to make
the fatal venture, while her ring would afford her easy means of
escape.

When Angelica ceased speaking, she knelt before the king and
awaited his answer, and everybody gazed on her with admiration.
Orlando especially felt irresistibly drawn towards her, so that he
trembled and changed countenance. Every knight in the hall was in-
fected with the same feeling, not excepting old white-headed Duke
Namo and Charlemagne himself.

All stood for a while in silence, lost in the delight of looking at her.
The fiery youth Ferrau could hardly restrain himself from seizing
her from the giants and carrying her away; Rinaldo turned as red
as fire, while Malagigi, who had discovered by his art that the

stranger was not speaking the truth, muttered softly, as he looked at her, "Exquisite false creature! I will play thee such a trick for this, as will leave thee no cause to boast of thy visit."

Charlemagne, to detain her as long as possible before him, delayed his assent till he had asked her a number of questions, all of which she answered discreetly, and then the challenge was accepted.

As soon as she was gone, Malagigi consulted his book, and found out the whole plot of the vile, infidel king Galafron, as we have explained it, so he determined to seek the damsel and frustrate her designs. He hastened to the appointed spot, and there found the prince and his sister in a beautiful pavilion, where they lay asleep, while the four giants kept watch. Malagigi took his book and cast a spell out of it, and immediately the four giants fell into a deep sleep. Drawing his sword (for he was a belted knight), he softly approached the young lady, intending to despatch her at once; but, seeing her look so lovely, he paused for a moment, thinking there was no need of hurry, as he believed his spell was upon her, and she could not wake. But the ring which she wore secured her from the effect of the spell, and some slight noise, or whatever else it was, caused her at that moment to awake. She uttered a great cry, and flew to her brother, and waked him. By the help of her knowledge of enchantment, they took and bound fast the magician, and, seizing his book, turned his arts against himself. Then they summoned a crowd of demons, and bade them seize their prisoner and bear him to king Galafron, at his great city of Albracca, which they did, and, on his arrival, he was locked up in a rock under the sea.

While these things were going on, all was uproar at Paris, since Orlando insisted upon being the first to try the adventure at the stair of Merlin. This was resented by the other pretenders to Angelica, and all contested his right to the precedence. The tumult was stilled by the usual expedient of drawing lots, and the first prize was drawn by Astolpho. Ferrau, the Saracen, had the second, and Grandonio the third. Next came Berlinghieri, and Otho; then Charles himself, and, as his ill-fortune would have it, after thirty more, the indignant Orlando.

Astolpho, who drew the first lot, was handsome, brave, and rich. But, whether from heedlessness or want of skill, he was an unlucky jouster, and very apt to be thrown, an accident which he bore with perfect good-humor, always ready to mount again and try to mend his fortune, generally with no better success.

Astolpho went forth upon his adventure with great gayety of dress and manner, encountered Argalia, and was immediately tilted out of the saddle. He railed at fortune, to whom he laid all the fault; but his painful feelings were somewhat relieved by the kindness of Angelica, who, touched by his youth and good looks, granted him the liberty of the pavilion, and caused him to be treated with all kindness and respect.

The violent Ferrau had the next chance in the encounter, and was thrown no less speedily than Astolpho; but he did not so easily put up with his mischance. Crying out, "What are the Emperor's engagements to me?" he rushed with his sword against Argalia, who, being forced to defend himself, dismounted and drew his sword, but got so much the worse of the fight that he made a signal of surrender, and, after some words, listened to a proposal of marriage from Ferrau to his sister. The beauty, however, feeling no inclination to match with such a rough and savage-looking person, was so dismayed at the offer, that, hastily bidding her brother to meet her in the forest of Arden, she vanished from the sight of both by means of the enchanted ring. Argalia, seeing this, took to his horse of swiftness, and dashed away in the same direction. Ferrau pursued him, and Astolpho, thus left to himself, took possession of the enchanted lance in place of his own, which was broken, not knowing the treasure he possessed in it, and returned to the tournament. Charlemagne, finding the lady and her brother gone, ordered the jousting to proceed as at first intended, in which Astolpho, by aid of the enchanted lance, unhorsed all comers against him, equally to their astonishment and his own.

The paladin Rinaldo, on learning the issue of the combat of Ferrau and the stranger, galloped after the fair fugitive in an agony of love and impatience. Orlando, perceiving his disappearance, pushed forth in like manner; and, at length, all three are in the forest of Arden, hunting about for her who is invisible.

Now in this forest there were two fountains, the one constructed by the sage Merlin, who designed it for Tristram and the fair Isoude; [1] for such was the virtue of this fountain, that a draught of its waters produced an oblivion of the love which the drinker might feel, and even produced aversion for the object formerly beloved. The other fountain was endowed with exactly opposite qualities, and a draught of it inspired love for the first living object that was seen after tasting it. Rinaldo happened to come to the first-mentioned fountain, and, being flushed with heat, dismounted, and quenched in one draught both his thirst and his passion. So far from loving Angelica as before, he hated her from the bottom of his heart, became disgusted with the search he was upon, and, feeling fatigued with his ride, finding a sheltered and flowery nook, laid himself down and fell asleep.

Shortly after came Angelica, but, approaching in a different di-

[1] See their story in "The Age of Chivalry."

rection, she espied the other fountain, and there quenched her thirst. Then resuming her way, she came upon the sleeping Rinaldo. Love instantly seized her, and she stood rooted to the spot.

The meadow round was all full of lilies of the valley and wild roses. Angelica, not knowing what to do, at length plucked a handful of these, and dropped them, one by one, on the face of the sleeper. He woke up, and, seeing who it was, received her salutations with averted countenance, remounted his horse, and galloped away. In vain the beautiful creature followed and called after him, in vain asked him what she had done to be so despised. Rinaldo disappeared, leaving her in despair, and she returned in tears to the spot where she had found him sleeping. There, in her turn, she herself lay down, pressing the spot of earth on which he had lain, and, out of fatigue and sorrow, fell asleep.

As Angelica thus lay, fortune conducted Orlando to the same place. The attitude in which she was sleeping was so lovely, that it is not to be conceived, much less expressed. Orlando stood gazing like a man who had been transported to another sphere. "Am I on earth," he exclaimed, "or am I in Paradise? Surely it is I that sleep, and this is my dream."

But his dream was proved to be none in a manner which he little desired. Ferrau, who had slain Argalia, came up, raging with jealousy, and a combat ensued which awoke the sleeper.

Terrified at what she beheld, she rushed to her palfrey, and, while the fighters were occupied with one another, fled away through the forest. The champions continued their fight till they were interrupted by a messenger, who brought word to Ferrau that king Marsilius, his sovereign, was in pressing need of his assistance, and conjured him to return to Spain. Ferrau, upon this, proposed to suspend the combat to which Orlando, eager to pursue Angelica, agreed. Ferrau, on the other hand, departed with the messenger to Spain.

Orlando's quest for the fair fugitive was all in vain. Aided by the powers of magic, she made a speedy return to her own country.

But the thought of Rinaldo could not be banished from her mind, and she determined to set Malagigi at liberty, and to employ him to win Rinaldo, if possible, to make her a return of affection. She accordingly freed him from his dungeon, unlocking his fetters with her own hands, and restored him his book, promising him ample honors and rewards, on condition of his bringing Rinaldo to her feet.

Malagigi accordingly, with the aid of his book, called up a demon, mounted him, and departed. Arrived at his destination, he inveigled Rinaldo into an enchanted bark, which conveyed him, without any visible pilot, to an island where stood an edifice called Joyous Castle. The whole island was a garden. On the western side, close to the sea, was the palace, built of marble, so clear and polished that it reflected the landscape about it. Rinaldo leapt ashore, and soon met a lady, who invited him to enter. The house was as beautiful within as without, full of rooms adorned with azure and gold, and with noble paintings. The lady led the knight into an apartment painted with stories, and opening to the garden, through pillars of crystal, with golden capitals. Here he found a bevy of ladies, three of whom were singing in concert, while another played on an instrument of exquisite accord, and the rest danced round about them. When the ladies beheld him coming, they turned the dance into a circuit round him, and then one of them, in the sweetest manner, said, "Sir Knight, the tables are set, and the hour for the banquet is come"; and, with these words, still dancing, they drew him across the lawn, in front of the apartment, to a table that was spread with cloth of gold and fine linen, under a bower of damask roses by the side of a fountain.

Four ladies were already seated there, who rose, and placed Rinaldo at their head, in a chair set with pearls. And truly indeed was he astonished. A repast ensued, consisting of viands the most delicate, and wines as fragrant as they were fine, drunk out of jewelled cups; and, when it drew towards its conclusion, harps and lutes were heard in the distance, and one of the ladies said in the knight's ear: "This house and all that you see in it are yours; for you alone was it built, and the builder is a queen. Happy indeed must you think yourself, for she loves you, and she is the greatest beauty in the world. Her name is Angelica."

The moment Rinaldo heard the name he so detested, he started up, with a changed countenance, and, in spite of all that the lady could say, broke off across the garden, and never ceased hastening till he reached the place where he landed. The bark was still on the shore. He sprang into it, and pushed off, though he saw nobody in it but himself. It was in vain for him to try to control its movements, for it dashed on as if in fury, till it reached a distant shore covered with a gloomy forest. Here Rinaldo, surrounded by enchantments of a very different sort from those which he had lately resisted, was entrapped into a pit.

The pit belonged to a castle called Altaripa, which was hung with human heads, and painted red with blood. As the paladin was viewing the scene with amazement, a hideous old woman made her appearance at the edge of the pit, and told him that he was destined to be thrown to a monster, who was only kept from devastating the whole country by being supplied with living human flesh. Rinaldo said, "Be it so; let me but remain armed as I am, and I fear nothing." The old woman laughed in derision. Rinaldo remained in the pit all night, and the next morning was taken to the place where the monster had his den. It was a court surrounded by a high wall. Rinaldo was shut in with the beast, and a terrible combat ensued. Rinaldo was unable to make any impression on the scales of the monster, while he, on the contrary, with his dreadful claws, tore away plate and mail from the paladin. Rinaldo began to think his last hour was come, and cast his eyes around and above to see if there was any means of escape. He perceived a beam projecting from the wall at the height of some ten feet, and, taking a leap almost miraculous, he succeeded in reaching it, and in flinging himself up across it. Here he sat for hours, the hideous brute continually trying to reach him. All at once, he heard the sound of something coming through the air like a bird, and suddenly Angelica herself alighted on the end of the beam. She held something in her hand towards him, and spoke to him in a loving voice. But the moment Rinaldo saw her, he commanded her to go away, refused all her offers of assistance, and at length declared that, if she did not leave him, he would cast himself down to the monster and meet his fate.

Angelica, saying she would lose her life rather than displease him, departed; but first she threw to the monster a cake of wax she had prepared, and spread around him a rope knotted with nooses. The beast took the bait, and, finding his teeth glued together by the wax, vented his fury in bounds and leaps, and, soon getting entangled in the nooses, drew them tight by his struggles, so that he could scarcely move a limb.

Rinaldo, watching his chance, leapt down upon his back, seized him round the neck, and throttled him, not relaxing his grip till the beast fell dead.

Another difficulty remained to be overcome. The walls were of immense height, and the only opening in them was a grated window of such strength that he could not break the bars. In his distress Rinaldo found a file which Angelica had left on the ground, and, with the help of this, effected his deliverance.

What further adventures he met with will be told in another chapter.

CHAPTER IV

THE SIEGE OF ALBRACCA

AT the very time when Charlemagne was holding his plenary court and his great tournament, his kingdom was invaded by a mighty monarch, who was moreover so valiant and strong in battle that no one could stand against him. He was named Gradasso, and his kingdom was called Sericane. Now, as it often happens to the greatest and the richest to long for what they cannot have, and thus to lose what they already possess, this king could not rest content without Durindana, the sword of Orlando, and Bayard, the horse of Rinaldo. To obtain these he determined to war upon France, and for this purpose put in array a mighty army.

He took his way through Spain, and, after defeating Marsilius, the king of that country, in several battles, was rapidly advancing on France. Charlemagne, though Marsilius was a Saracen, and had been his enemy, yet felt it needful to succor him in this extremity from a consideration of common danger, and, with the consent of his peers, despatched Rinaldo with a strong body of soldiers against Gradasso.

There was much fighting, with doubtful results, and Gradasso was steadily advancing into France. But, impatient to achieve his objects, he challenged Rinaldo to single combat, to be fought on foot, and upon these conditions: If Rinaldo conquered, Gradasso agreed to give up all his prisoners and return to his own country; but if Gradasso won the day, he was to have Bayard.

The challenge was accepted, and would have been fought had it not been for the arts of Malagigi, who just then returned from Angelica's kingdom with set purpose to win Rinaldo to look with favor upon the fair princess who was dying for love of him. Malagigi drew Rinaldo away from the army, by putting on the semblance of Gradasso, and, after a short contest, pretending to fly before him, by which means Rinaldo was induced to follow him into a boat, in which he was borne away, and entangled in various adventures, as we have already related.

The army, left under the command of Ricciardetto, Rinaldo's brother, was soon joined by Charlemagne and all his peerage, but experienced a disastrous rout, and the Emperor and many of his paladins were taken prisoners. Gradasso, however, did not abuse his victory; he took Charles by the hand, seated him by his side, and told him he warred only for honor. He renounced all conquests, on condition that the Emperor should deliver to him Bayard and Durindana, both of them the property of his vassals, the former of which, as he maintained, was already forfeited to him by Rinaldo's failure to meet him as agreed. To these terms Charlemagne readily acceded.

Bayard, after the departure of his master, had been taken in charge by Ricciardetto, and sent back to Paris, where Astolpho was in command, in the absence of Charlemagne. Astolpho received with great indignation the message despatched for Bayard, and replied by a herald that "he would not surrender the horse of his kinsman Rinaldo, without a contest. If Gradasso wanted the steed, he might come and take him, and that he, Astolpho, was ready to meet him in the field."

Gradasso was only amused at this answer, for Astolpho's fame as a successful warrior was not high, and Gradasso willingly renewed with him the bargain which he had made with Rinaldo. On these conditions the battle was fought. The enchanted lance, in the hands of Astolpho, performed a new wonder; and Gradasso, the terrible Gradasso, was unhorsed.

He kept his word, set free his prisoners, and put his army on the march to return to his own country, renewing his oath, however, not to rest till he had taken from Rinaldo his horse, and from Orlando his sword, or lost his life in the attempt.

Charlemagne, full of gratitude to Astolpho, would have kept him near his person and loaded him with honors, but Astolpho preferred to seek Rinaldo, with the view of restoring to him his horse, and departed from Paris with that design.

Our story now returns to Orlando, whom we left fascinated with the sight of the sleeping beauty, who, however, escaped him while engaged in the combat with Ferrau. Having long sought her in vain through the recesses of the wood, he resolved to follow her to her father's court. Leaving, therefore, the camp of Charlemagne, he travelled long in the direction of the East, making inquiry everywhere, if, perchance, he might get tidings of the fugitive. After many adventures, he arrived one day at a place where many roads crossed, and, meeting there a courier, he asked him for news. The courier replied, that he had been despatched by Angelica to solicit the aid of Sacripant, king of Circassia, in favor of her father Galafron, who was besieged in his city, Albracca, by Agrican, king of Tartary. This Agrican had been an unsuccessful suitor to the damsel, whom he now pursued with arms. Orlando thus learned that he was within a day's journey of Albracca; and feeling now secure of Angelica, he proceeded with all speed to her city.

Thus journeying he arrived at a bridge, under which flowed a foaming river. Here a damsel met him with a goblet, and informed him that it was the usage of this bridge to present the traveller with a cup. Orlando accepted the offered cup and drank its contents. He had no sooner done so than his brain reeled, and he became unconscious of the object of his journey, and of everything else. Under the influence of this fascination he followed the damsel into a magnificent and marvellous palace. Here he found himself in company with many knights, unknown to him and to each

other, though if it had not been for the Cup of Oblivion of which
they all had partaken, they would have found themselves brothers
in arms.

———

Astolpho, proceeding on his way to seek Rinaldo, splendidly
dressed and equipped, as was his wont, arrived in Circassia, and
found there a great army encamped under the command of Sacripant, the king of that country, who was leading it to the defence
of Galafron, the father of Angelica. Sacripant, much struck by the
appearance of Astolpho and his horse, accosted him courteously,
and tried to enlist him in his service; but Astolpho, proud of his
late victories, scornfully declined his offers, and pursued his way.
King Sacripant was too much attracted by his appearance to
part with him so easily, and, having laid aside his kingly ornaments, set out in pursuit of him.

Astolpho next day encountered on his way a stranger knight,
named Sir Florismart, Lord of the Sylvan Tower, one of the bravest and best of knights, having as his guide a damsel, young, fair,
and virtuous, to whom he was tenderly attached, whose name was
Flordelis. Astolpho, as he approached, defied the knight, bidding
him yield the lady, or prepare to maintain his right by arms.
Florismart accepted the contest, and the knights encountered.
Florismart was unhorsed and his steed fell dead, while Bayard
sustained no injury by the shock.

Florismart was so overwhelmed with despair at his own disgrace and the sight of the damsel's distress, that he drew his sword,
and was about to plunge it into his own bosom. But Astolpho held
his hand, told him that he contended only for glory, and was contented to leave him the lady.

While Florismart and Flordelis were vowing eternal gratitude,
king Sacripant arrived, and coveting the damsel of the one champion as much as the horse and arms of the other, defied them to
the joust. Astolpho met the challenger, whom he instantly overthrew, and presented his courser to Florismart, leaving the king
to return to his army on foot.

The friends pursued their route, and erelong Flordelis discovered,
by signs which were known to her, that they were approaching
the waters of Oblivion, and advised them to turn back, or to change
their course. This the knights would not hear of, and, continuing
their march, they soon arrived at the bridge where Orlando had
been taken prisoner.

The damsel of the bridge appeared as before with the enchanted
cup, but Astolpho, forewarned, rejected it with scorn. She dashed

it to the ground, and a fire blazed up which rendered the bridge unapproachable. At the same moment the two knights were assailed by sundry warriors, known and unknown, who, having no recollection of anything, joined blindly in defence of their prison-house. Among these was Orlando, at sight of whom Astolpho, with all his confidence not daring to encounter him, turned and fled, owing his escape to the strength and fleetness of Bayard.

Florismart, meanwhile, overlaid by fearful odds, was compelled to yield to necessity, and comply with the usage of the fairy. He drank of the cup, and remained prisoner with the rest. Flordelis, deprived of her two friends, retired from the scene, and devoted herself to untiring efforts to effect her lover's deliverance. Astolpho pursued his way to Albracca, which Agrican was about to besiege. He was kindly welcomed by Angelica, and enrolled among her defenders. Impatient to distinguish himself, he one night sallied forth alone, arrived in Agrican's camp, and unhorsed his warriors right and left by means of the enchanted lance. But he was soon surrounded and overmatched, and made prisoner to Agrican.

Relief was, however, at hand; for as the citizens and soldiers were one day leaning over their walls, they descried a cloud of dust, from which horsemen were seen to prick forth, as it rolled on towards the camp of the besiegers. This turned out to be the army of Sacripant, which immediately attacked that of Agrican, with the view of cutting a passage through his camp to the besieged city. But Agrican, mounted upon Bayard, taken from Astolpho, but not armed with the lance of gold, the virtues of which were unknown to him, performed wonders, and rallied his scattered troops, which had given way to the sudden and unexpected assault. Sacripant, on the other hand, encouraged his men by the most desperate acts of valor, having as an additional incentive to his courage the sight of Angelica, who showed herself upon the city walls.

There she witnessed a single combat between the two leaders, Agrican and Sacripant. In this, at length, her defender appeared to be overmatched, when the Circassians broke the ring, and separated the combatants, who were borne asunder in the rush. Sacripant, severely wounded, profited by the confusion, and escaped into Albracca, where he was kindly received and carefully tended by Angelica.

The battle continuing, the Circassians were at last put to flight, and, being intercepted between the enemy's lines and the town, sought for refuge under the walls. Angelica ordered the drawbridge to be let down, and the gates thrown open to the fugitives. With these Agrican, not distinguished in the crowd, entered the place,

driving both Circassians and Cathayans before him, and the portcullis being dropped, he was shut in.

For a time the terror which he inspired put to flight all opposers,
but when at last it came to be known that few or none of his followers
had effected an entrance with him, the fugitives rallied and surrounded him on all sides. While he was thus apparently reduced to
the last extremities, he was saved by the very circumstance which
threatened him with destruction. The soldiers of Angelica, closing
upon him from all sides, deserted their defences; and his own besieging army entered the city in a part where the wall was broken
down.

In this way was Agrican rescued, the city taken, and the inhabitants put to the sword. Angelica, however, with some of the knights
who were her defenders, among whom was Sacripant, saved herself
in the citadel, which was planted upon a rock.

The fortress was impregnable, but it was scantily victualled, and
ill provided with other necessaries. Under these circumstances,
Angelica announced to those blockaded with her in the citadel her
intention to go in quest of assistance, and, having plighted her
promise of a speedy return, she set out, with the enchanted ring
upon her finger. Mounted upon her palfrey, the damsel passed
through the enemy's lines, and by sunrise was many miles clear of
their encampment.

It so happened that her road led her near the fatal bridge of
Oblivion, and, as she approached it, she met a damsel weeping bitterly. It was Flordelis, whose lover, Florismart, as we have related,
had met the fate of Orlando and many more, and fallen a victim to
the enchantress of the cup. She related her adventures to Angelica,
and conjured her to lend what aid she might to rescue her lord and
his companions. Angelica, accordingly, watching her opportunity and
aided by her ring, slipped into the castle unseen, when the door was
opened to admit a new victim. Here she speedily disenchanted
Orlando and the rest by a touch of her talisman. But Florismart was
not there. He had been given up to Falerina, a more powerful enchantress, and was still in durance. Angelica conjured the rescued
captives to assist her in the recovery of her kingdom, and all departed
together for Albracca.

The arrival of Orlando, with his companions, nine in all, and
among the bravest knights of France, changed at once the fortunes
of the war. Wherever the great paladin came, pennon and standard
fell before him. Agrican in vain attempted to rally his troops. Orlando kept constantly in his front, forcing him to attend to nobody
else. The Tartar king at length bethought him of a stratagem. He
turned his horse, and made a show of flying in despair. Orlando

dashed after him as he desired, and Agrican fled till he reached a green place in a wood, where there was a fountain.

The place was beautiful, and the Tartar dismounted to refresh himself at the fountain, but without taking off his helmet, or laying aside any of his armor. Orlando was quickly at his back, crying out, "So bold, and yet a fugitive! How could you fly from a single arm, and think to escape?"

The Tartar king had leaped on his saddle the moment he saw his enemy, and when the paladin had done speaking, he said, in a mild voice, "Without doubt you are the best knight I ever encountered, and fain would I leave you untouched for your own sake, if you would cease to hinder me from rallying my people. I pretended to fly, in order to bring you out of the field. If you insist upon fighting, I must needs fight and slay you, but I call the sun in the heavens to witness I would rather not. I should be very sorry for your death."

The Count Orlando felt pity for so much gallantry, and he said, "The nobler you show yourself, the more it grieves me to think that, in dying without a knowledge of the true faith, you will be lost in the other world. Let me advise you to save body and soul at once. Receptive baptism, and go your way in peace."

Agrican replied: "I suspect you to be the paladin Orlando. If you are, I would not lose this opportunity of fighting with you to be king of Paradise. Talk to me no more about your things of another world for you will preach in vain. Each of us for himself, and let the sword be umpire."

The Saracen drew his sword, boldly advancing upon Orlando, and a combat began, so obstinate and so long, each warrior being a miracle of prowess, that the story says it lasted from noon till night. Orlando then, seeing the stars come out, was the first to propose a respite.

"What are we to do," said he, "now that daylight has left us?"

Agrican answered readily enough, "Let us repose in this meadow, and renew the combat at dawn."

The repose was taken accordingly. Each tied up his horse, and reclined himself on the grass, not far from the other, just as if they had been friends, Orlando by the fountain, Agrican beneath a pine. It was a beautiful clear night, and, as they talked together before addressing themselves to sleep, the champion of Christendom, looking up at the firmament, said, "That is a fine piece of workmanship, that starry spectacle; God made it all, that moon of silver, and those stars of gold, and the light of day, and the sun,—all for the sake of human kind."

"You wish, I see, to talk of matters of faith," said the Tartar. "Now I may as well tell you at once, that I have no sort of skill in such matters, nor learning of any kind. I never could learn anything when I was a boy. I hated it so that I broke the man's head who was commissioned to teach me; and it produced such an effect on others, that nobody ever afterwards dared so much as show me a book. My boyhood was therefore passed, as it should be, in horsemanship and hunting, and learning to fight. What is the good of a gentle-man's poring all day over a book? Prowess to the knight, and preaching to the clergyman, that is my motto."

"I acknowledge," returned Orlando, "that arms are the first consideration of a gentleman; but not at all that he does himself dishonor by knowledge. On the contrary, knowledge is as great an embellishment of the rest of his attainments, as the flowers are to the meadow before us; and as to the knowledge of his Maker, the man that is without it is no better than a stock or a stone or a brute beast. Neither without study can he reach anything of a due sense of the depth and divineness of the contemplation."

"Learned or not learned," said Agrican, "you might show yourself better bred than by endeavoring to make me talk on a subject on which you have me at a disadvantage. If you choose to sleep, I wish you good night; but if you prefer talking, I recommend you to talk of fighting or of fair ladies. And, by the way, pray tell me, are you not that Orlando who makes such a noise in the world? And what is it, pray, that brings you into these parts? Were you ever in love? I suppose you must have been; for to be a knight, and never to have been in love, would be like being a man without a heart in his breast."

The Count replied: "Orlando I am, and in love I am. Love has made me abandon everything, and brought me into these distant regions, and, to tell you all in one word, my heart is in the hands of the daughter of King Galafron. You have come against him with fire and sword, to get possession of his castles and his dominions; and I have come to help him, for no object in the world but to please his daughter and win her beautiful hand. I care for nothing else in existence."

Now when the Tartar king, Agrican, heard his antagonist speak in this manner, and knew him to be indeed Orlando, and to be in love with Angelica, his face changed color for grief and jealousy, though it could not be seen for the darkness. His heart began beating with such violence that he felt as if he should have died. "Well," said he to Orlando, "we are to fight when it is daylight, and one or other is to be left here, dead on the ground. I have a proposal to make to you, —nay, an entreaty. My love is so excessive for the same lady, that I beg of you to leave her to me. I will owe you my thanks, and give up the siege and put an end to the war. I cannot bear that any one should love her, and that I should live to see it. Why, therefore, should either of us perish? Give her up. Not a soul shall know it."

"I never yet," answered Orlando, "made a promise which I did not keep, and nevertheless I own to you that, were I to make a promise like that, and even swear to keep it, I should not. You might as well ask me to tear away the limbs from my body, and the eyes out of my head. I could as well live without breath itself as cease loving Angelica."

Agrican had hardly patience to let him finish speaking, ere he leapt furiously on horseback, though it was midnight. "Quit her," said he, "or die!"

Orlando seeing the infidel getting up, and not being sure that he would not add treachery to fierceness, had been hardly less quick in mounting for the combat. "Never," exclaimed he; "I never could have quitted her if I would, and now I would not if I could. You must seek her by other means than these."

Fiercely dashed their horses together, in the night-time, on the green mead. Despiteful and terrible were the blows they gave and took by the moonlight. Agrican fought in a rage, Orlando was cooler. And now the struggle had lasted more than five hours, and day began to dawn, when the Tartar king, furious to find so much trouble given him, dealt his enemy a blow sharp and violent beyond conception. It cut the shield in two as if it had been made of wood, and, though blood could not be drawn from Orlando, because he was fated, it shook and bruised him as if it had started every joint in his body.

His *body* only, however, not a particle of his soul. So dreadful was the blow which the paladin gave in return, that not only shield, but every bit of mail on the body of Agrican was broken in pieces, and three of his ribs cut asunder.

The Tartar, roaring like a lion, raised his sword with still greater vehemence than before, and dealt a blow on the paladin's helmet, such as he had never yet received from mortal man. For a moment it took away his senses. His sight failed, his ears tinkled, his frightened horse turned about to fly; and he was falling from the saddle, when the very action of falling threw his head upwards, and thus recalled his recollection.

"What a shame is this!" thought he; "how shall I ever again dare to face Angelica! I have been fighting, hour after hour, with this man, and he is but one, and I call myself Orlando! If the combat last any longer, I will bury myself in a monastery, and never look on sword again."

Orlando muttered with his lips closed and his teeth ground together; and you might have thought that fire instead of breath came out of his nose and mouth. He raised his sword Durindana with both his hands, and sent it down so tremendously on Agrican's shoulder, that it cut through breastplate down to the very haunch, nay, crushed the saddle-bow, though it was made of bone and iron, and felled man and horse to the earth. Agrican turned as white as ashes, and felt death upon him. He called Orlando to come close to him, with a gentle voice, and said, as well as he could: "I believe on Him who died on the cross. Baptize me, I pray thee, with the fountain, before my senses are gone. I have lived an evil life, but need not be rebellious to God in death also. May He who came to save all the rest of the world, save me!" And he shed tears, that great king, though he had been so lofty and fierce.

Orlando dismounted quickly, with his own face in tears. He gathered the king tenderly in his arms, and took and laid him by the fountain, on a marble rim that it had, and then he wept in concert with him heartily, and asked his pardon, and so baptized him in the water of the fountain, and knelt and prayed to God for him with joined hands.

He then paused and looked at him; and when he perceived his countenance changed, and that his whole person was cold, he left him there on the marble rim of the fountain, all armed as he was, with the sword by his side, and the crown upon his head.

CHAPTER V

ADVENTURES OF RINALDO AND ORLANDO

WE left Rinaldo when, having overcome the monster, he quitted the castle of Altaripa, and pursued his way on foot. He soon met with a weeping damsel, who, being questioned as to the cause of her sorrow, told him she was in search of one to do battle to rescue her lover, who had been made prisoner by a vile enchantress, together with Orlando and many more. The damsel was Flordelis, the lady-love of Florismart, and Rinaldo promised his assistance, trusting to accomplish the adventure either by valor or skill. Flordelis insisted upon Rinaldo's taking her horse, which he consented to do, on condition of her mounting behind him.

As they rode on through a wood, they heard strange noises, and Rinaldo, reassuring the damsel, pressed forward towards the quarter from which they proceeded. He soon perceived a giant standing under a vaulted cavern, with a huge club in his hand, and of an appearance to strike the boldest spirit with dread. By the side of the cavern was chained a griffin, which, together with the giant, was stationed there to guard a wonderful horse, the same which was once Argalia's. This horse was a creature of enchantment, matchless in vigor, speed, and form, which disdained to share the diet of his fellow-steeds,—corn or grass,—and fed only on air. His name was Rabican.

This marvellous horse, after his master Argalia had been slain by Ferrau, finding himself at liberty, returned to his native cavern, and was here stabled under the protection of the giant and the griffin. As Rinaldo approached, the giant assailed him with his club. Rinaldo defended himself from the giant's blows, and gave him one in return, which, if his skin had not been of the toughest, would have finished the combat. But the giant, though wounded, escaped, and let loose the griffin. This monstrous bird towered in air, and thence pounced down upon Rinaldo, who, watching his opportunity, dealt her a desperate wound. She had, however, strength for another flight, and kept repeating her attacks, which Rinaldo parried as he could, while the damsel stood trembling by, witnessing the contest.

The battle continued, rendered more terrible by the approach of night, when Rinaldo determined upon a desperate expedient to bring it to a conclusion. He fell, as if fainting from his wounds, and, on the close approach of the griffin, dealt her a blow which sheared away one of her wings. The beast, though sinking, gripped him fast with her talons, digging through plate and mail; but Rinaldo plied his sword in utter desperation, and at last accomplished her destruction.

Rinaldo then entered the cavern, and found there the wonderful horse, all caparisoned. He was coal-black, except for a star of white on his forehead, and one white foot behind. For speed he was unrivalled, though in strength he yielded to Bayard. Rinaldo mounted upon Rabican, and issued from the cavern.

As he pursued his way, he met a fugitive from Agrican's army, who gave such an account of the prowess of a champion who fought on the side of Angelica, that Rinaldo was persuaded this must be Orlando, though at a loss to imagine how he could have been freed from captivity. He determined to repair to the scene of the contest to satisfy his curiosity, and Flordelis, hoping to find Florismart with Orlando, consented to accompany him.

While these things were doing, all was rout and dismay in the Tartarian army, from the death of Agrican. King Galafron, arriving at this juncture with an army for the relief of his capital, Albracca, assaulted the enemy's camp, and carried all before him. Rinaldo had now reached the scene of action, and was looking on as an unconcerned spectator, when he was espied by Galafron. The king instantly recognized the horse Rabican, which he had given to Argalia when he sent him forth on his ill-omened mission to Paris. Possessed with the idea that the rider of the horse was the murderer of Argalia, Galafron rode at Rinaldo, and smote him with all his force. Rinaldo was not slow to avenge the blow, and it would have gone hard with the king had not his followers instantly closed round him and separated the combatants.

Rinaldo thus found himself, almost without his own choice, enlisted on the side of the enemies of Angelica, which gave him no concern, so completely had his draught from the fountain of hate steeled his mind against her.

For several successive days the struggle continued, without any important results, Rinaldo meeting the bravest knights of Angelica's party, and defeating them one after the other. At length he encountered Orlando, and the two knights bitterly reproached one another for the cause they had each adopted, and engaged in a furious combat. Orlando was mounted upon Bayard, Rinaldo's horse, which Agrican had by chance become possessed of, and Orlando had taken from him as the prize of victory. Bayard would not fight against his master, and Orlando was getting the worse of the encounter, when suddenly Rinaldo, seeing Astolpho, who for love of him had arrayed himself on his side, hard beset by numbers, left Orlando, to rush to the defence of his friend. Night prevented the combat from being renewed; but a challenge was given and accepted for their next meeting.

But Angelica, sighing in her heart for Rinaldo, was not willing that he should be again exposed to so terrible a venture. She begged a boon of Orlando, promising she would be his, if he would do her bidding. On receiving his promise, she enjoined him to set out without delay to destroy the garden of the enchantress Falerina, in which many valiant knights had been entrapped, and were imprisoned.

Orlando departed, on his horse Brigliadoro, leaving Bayard in disgrace for his bad deportment the day before. Angelica, to conciliate Rinaldo, sent Bayard to him; but Rinaldo remained unmoved by this, as by all her former acts of kindness.

When Rinaldo learned Orlando's departure, he yielded to the entreaties of the lady of Florismart, and prepared to fulfil his promise, and rescue her lover from the power of the enchantress. Thus both Rinaldo and Orlando were bound upon the same adventure, but unknown to one another.

The castle of Falerina was protected by a river, which was crossed by a bridge, kept by a ruffian, who challenged all comers to the combat; and such was his strength that he had thus far prevailed in every encounter, as appeared by the arms of various knights which he had taken from them, and piled up as a trophy on the shore. Rinaldo attacked him, but with as bad success as the rest, for the bridge-ward struck him so violent a blow with an iron mace, that he fell to the ground. But when the villain approached to strip him of his armor, Rinaldo seized him, and the bridge-ward, being unable to free himself, leapt with Rinaldo into the lake, where they both disappeared.

Orlando meanwhile, in discharge of his promise to Angelica, pursued his way in quest of the same adventure. In passing through a wood he saw a cavalier armed at all points, and mounted, keeping guard over a lady who was bound to a tree, weeping bitterly. Orlando hastened to her relief, but was exhorted by the knight not to interfere, for she had deserved her fate by her wickedness. In proof of which he made certain charges against her. The lady denied them all, and Orlando believed her, defied the knight, overthrew him, and, releasing the lady, departed with her seated on his horse's croup.

While they rode, another damsel approached on a white palfrey, who warned Orlando of impending danger, and informed him that he was near the garden of the enchantress. Orlando was delighted with the intelligence, and entreated her to inform him how he was to procure access. She replied that the garden could only be entered at sunrise, and gave him such instructions as would enable him to gain admittance. She gave him also a book in which was painted the garden and all that it contained, together with the palace of the false enchantress, where she had secluded herself for the purpose of executing a magic work in which she was engaged. This was the manufacture of a sword capable of cutting even through enchanted substances. The object of this labor, the damsel told him, was the destruction of a knight of the west, by name Orlando, who, she had read in the book of Fate, was coming to demolish her garden. Having thus instructed him, the damsel departed.

Orlando, finding he must delay his enterprise till the next morning, now lay down and was soon asleep. Seeing this, the base woman whom he had rescued, and who was intent on making her escape to rejoin her paramour, mounted Brigliadoro, and rode off, carrying away Durindana.

When Orlando awoke, his indignation, as may be supposed, was great on the discovery of the theft; but, like a good knight and true, he was not to be diverted from his enterprise. He tore off a huge branch of an elm to supply the place of his sword; and, as the sun rose, took his way towards the gate of the garden, where a dragon was on his watch. This he slew by repeated blows, and entered the garden, the gate of which closed behind him, barring retreat. Looking around him, he saw a fair fountain, which overflowed into a river, and in the centre of the fountain a figure, over whose forehead was written,—

"The stream which waters violet and rose,
From hence to the enchanted palace goes."

Following the banks of this flowing stream, and rapt in the delights of the charming garden, Orlando arrived at the palace, and entering it, found the mistress, clad in white, with a crown of gold upon her head in the act of viewing herself in the surface of the magic sword. Orlando surprised her before she could escape, deprived her of the weapon, and holding her fast by her long hair, which floated behind, threatened her with immediate death if she did not yield up her prisoners, and afford him the means of egress. She, however, was firm of purpose, making no reply, and Orlando, unable to move her either by threats or entreaties, was under the necessity of binding her to a beech, and pursuing his quest as he best might.

He then bethought him of his book, and consulting it, found that there was an outlet to the south, but that to reach it, a lake was to be passed, inhabited by a siren, whose song was so entrancing as to be quite irresistible to whoever heard it; but his book instructed him how to protect himself against this danger. According to its directions, while pursuing his path, he gathered abundance of flowers, which sprung all around, and filled his helmet and his ears with them; then listened if he heard the birds sing. Finding that, though he saw the gaping beak, the swelling throat, and ruffled plumes, he could not catch a note, he felt satisfied with his defence, and advanced toward the lake. It was small but deep, and so clear and tranquil that the eye could penetrate to the bottom.

He had no sooner arrived upon the banks than the waters were seen to gurgle, and the siren, rising midway out of the pool, sung so sweetly that birds and beasts came trooping to the water-side, to listen. Of this Orlando heard nothing, but, feigning to yield to the charm, sank down upon the bank. The siren issued from the water with the intent to accomplish his destruction. Orlando seized her by the hair, and while she sang yet louder (song being her only defence) cut off her head. Then, following the directions of his book, he stained himself all over with her blood.

Guarded by this talisman, he met successively all the monsters set for defence of the enchantress and her garden, and at length found himself again at the spot where he had made captive the enchantress, who still continued fastened to the beech. But the scene was changed. The garden had disappeared, and Falerina, before so haughty, now begged for mercy; assuring him that many lives depended upon the preservation of hers. Orlando promised her life upon her pledging herself for the deliverance of her captives.

This, however, was no easy task. They were not in her possession, but in that of a much more powerful enchantress, Morgana, the Lady of the Lake, the very idea of opposing whom made Falerina turn pale with fear. Representing to him the hazards of the enterprise, she led him towards the dwelling of Morgana. To approach it he had to encounter the same uncourteous bridge-ward who had already defeated and made captive so many knights, and last of all, Rinaldo. He was a churl of the most ferocious character, named Arridano. Morgana had provided him with impenetrable armor, and endowed him in such a manner that his strength always increased in proportion to that of the adversary with whom he was matched. No one had ever yet escaped from the contest, since, such was his power of endurance, he could breathe freely under water. Hence, having grappled with a knight, and sunk with him to the bottom of the lake, he returned, bearing his enemy's arms in triumph to the surface.

While Falerina was repeating her cautions and her counsels, Orlando saw Rinaldo's arms erected in form of a trophy, among other spoils made by the villain, and, forgetting their late quarrel, determined upon revenging his friend. Arriving at the pass, the churl presuming to bar the way, a desperate contest ensued, during which Falerina escaped. The churl finding himself overmatched at a contest of arms, resorted to his peculiar art, grappled his antagonist, and plunged with him into the lake. When he reached the bottom Orlando found himself in another world, upon a dry meadow, with the lake overhead, through which shone the beams of our sun, while the water stood on all sides like a crystal wall. Here the battle was renewed, and Orlando had in his magic sword an advantage which none had hitherto possessed. It had been tempered by Falerina so that no spells could avail against it. Thus armed, and countervailing the strength of his adversary by his superior skill and activity, it was not long before he laid him dead upon the field.

Orlando then made all haste to return to the upper air, and, passing through the water, which opened a way before him, (such was the power of the magic sword,) he soon regained the shore, and found himself in a field, as thickly covered with precious stones as the sky is with stars.

Orlando crossed the field, not tempted to delay his enterprise by gathering any of the brilliant gems spread all around him. He next passed into a flowery meadow, planted with trees, covered with fruit and flowers, and full of all imaginable delights.

In the middle of this meadow was a fountain, and, fast by it lay Morgana asleep; a lady of a lovely aspect, dressed in white and vermilion garments, her forehead well furnished with hair, while she had scarcely any behind.

While Orlando stood in silence contemplating her beauty, he heard a voice exclaim, "Seize the fairy by the forelock, if thou hopest fair success." But his attention was arrested by another object, and he heeded not the warning. He saw on a sudden an array of towers, pinnacles and columns, palaces, with balconies and windows, extended alleys with trees, in short a scene of architectural magnificence surpassing all he had ever beheld. While he stood gazing in silent astonishment, the scene slowly melted away and disappeared.[1]

When he had recovered from his amazement, he looked again toward the fountain. The fairy had awaked and risen, and was dancing round its border with the lightness of a leaf, timing her footsteps to this song:—

> "Who in this world would wealth and treasure share,
> Honor, delight, and state, and what is best,
> Quick let him catch me by the lock of hair
> Which flutters from my forehead; and be blest.
>
> But let him not the proffered good forbear,
> Nor till he seize the fleeting blessing rest;
> For present loss is sought in vain to-morrow,
> And the deluded wretch is left in sorrow."

The fairy, having sung thus, bounded off, and fled from the flowery meadow over a high and inaccessible mountain. Orlando pursued her through thorns and rocks, while the sky gradually became overcast, and at last he was assailed by tempest, lightning, and hail.

While he thus pursued, a pale and meagre woman issued from a cave, armed with a whip, and, treading close upon his steps, scourged him with vigorous strokes. Her name was Repentance, and she told him it was her office to punish those who neglected to obey the voice of Prudence, and seize the fairy Fortune when he might.

Orlando, furious at this chastisement, turned upon his tormentor, but might as well have stricken the wind. Finding it useless to resist, he resumed his chase of the fairy, gained upon her, and made frequent snatches at her white and vermilion garments, which still eluded his grasp. At last, on her turning her head for an instant, he profited by the chance, and seized her by the forelock. In an instant the tempest ceased, the sky became serene, and Repentance retreated to her cave.

Orlando now demanded of Morgana the keys of her prison, and the fairy, feigning a complacent aspect, delivered up a key of silver, bidding him to be cautious in the use of it, since to break the lock would be to involve himself and all in inevitable destruc-

[1] This is a poetical description of a phenomenon which is said to be really exhibited in the strait of Messina, between Sicily and Calabria. It is called Fata Morgana, or Mirage.

tion; a caution which gave the Count room for long meditation, and led him to consider

> How few amid the suitors who importune
> The dame, know how to turn the keys of Fortune.

Keeping the fairy still fast by the forelock, Orlando proceeded toward the prison, turned the key, without occasioning the mischiefs apprehended, and delivered the prisoners.

Among these were Florismart, Rinaldo, and many others of the bravest knights of France. Morgana had disappeared, and the knights, under the guidance of Orlando, retraced the path by which he had come. They soon reached the field of treasure. Rinaldo, finding himself amidst this mass of wealth, remembered his needy garrison of Montalban, and could not resist the temptation of seizing part of the booty. In particular a golden chain, studded with diamonds, was too much for his self-denial, and he took it and was bearing it off, notwithstanding the remonstrances of Orlando, when a violent wind caught him and whirled him back, as he approached the gate. This happened a second and a third time, and Rinaldo at length yielded to necessity, rather than to the entreaties of his friends, and cast away his prize.

They soon reached the bridge and passed over without hinderance to the other side, where they found the trophy decorated with their arms. Here each knight resumed his own, and all, except the paladins and their friends, separated as their inclinations or duty prompted. Dudon, the Dane, one of the rescued knights, informed the cousins that he had been made prisoner by Morgana while in the discharge of an embassy to them from Charlemagne, who called upon them to return to the defence of Christendom. Orlando was too much fascinated by Angelica to obey this summons, and, followed by the faithful Florismart, who would not leave him, returned towards Albracca. Rinaldo, Dudon, Iroldo, Prasildo, and the others, took their way toward the west.

CHAPTER VI

THE INVASION OF FRANCE

AGRAMANT, King of Africa, convoked the kings, his vassals, to deliberate in council. He reminded them of the injuries he had sustained from France, that his father had fallen in battle with Charlemagne, and that his early years had hitherto not allowed him to wipe out the stain of former defeats. He now proposed to them to carry war into France.

Sobrino, his wisest councillor, opposed the project, representing the rashness of it; but Rodomont, the young and fiery king of Algiers, denounced Sobrino's counsel as base and cowardly, declaring himself impatient for the enterprise. The king of the Garamantes, venerable for his age and renowned for his prophetic lore, interposed, and assured the King that such an attempt would be sure to fail, unless he could first get on his side a youth marked out by destiny as the fitting compeer of the most puissant knights of France, the young Rogero, descended in direct line from Hector of Troy. This prince was now a dweller upon the mountain Carena, where Atlantes, his fosterfather, a powerful magician, kept him in retirement, having discovered by his art that his pupil would be lost to him if allowed to mingle with the world. To break the spells of Atlantes, and draw Rogero from his retirement, one only means was to be found. It was a ring possessed by Angelica, Princess of Cathay, which was a talisman against all enchantments. If this ring could be procured, all would go well; without it, the enterprise was desperate.

Rodomont treated this declaration of the old prophet with scorn, and it would probably have been held of little weight by the council, had not the aged king, oppressed by the weight of years, expired in the very act of reaffirming his prediction. This made so deep an impression on the council, that it was unanimously resolved to postpone the war until an effort should be made to win Rogero to the camp.

King Agramant thereupon proclaimed that the sovereignty of a kingdom should be the reward of whoever should succeed in obtaining the ring of Angelica. Brunello, the dwarf, the subtlest thief in all Africa, undertook to procure it.

In prosecution of this design, he made the best of his way to Angelica's kingdom, and arrived beneath the walls of Albracca while the besieging army was encamped before the fortress. While the attention of the garrison was absorbed by the battle that raged below, he scaled the walls, approached the Princess unnoticed, slipped the ring from her finger, and escaped unobserved. He hastened to the seaside, and, finding a vessel ready to sail, embarked, and arrived at Biserta, in Africa. Here he found Agramant, impatient for the talisman which was to foil the enchantments of Atlantes and to put Rogero into his hands. The dwarf, kneeling before the King, presented him with the ring, and Agramant, delighted at the success of his mission, crowned him in recompense King of Tingitana.

All were now anxious to go in quest of Rogero. The cavalcade accordingly departed, and in due time arrived at the mountain of Carena.

At the bottom of this was a fruitful and well-wooded plain, watered by a large river, and from this plain was descried a beautiful garden on the mountain-top, which contained the mansion of Atlantes; but the ring, which discovered what was before invisible, could not, though it revealed this paradise, enable Agramant or his followers to enter it. So steep and smooth was the rock by nature, that even Brunello failed in every attempt to scale it. He did not, for this, despair of accomplishing the object; but, having obtained Agramant's consent, caused the assembled courtiers and knights to celebrate a tournament upon the plain below. This was done with the view of seducing Rogero from his fastness, and the stratagem was attended with success.

Rogero joined the tourney, and was presented by Agramant with a splendid horse, Frontino, and a magnificent sword. Having learned from Agramant his intended invasion of France, he gladly consented to join the expedition.

Rodomont, meanwhile, was too impatient to wait for Agramant's arrangements, and embarked with all the forces he could raise, made good his landing on the coast of France, and routed the Christians in several encounters. Previously to this, however, Gano, or Ganelon (as he is sometimes called), the traitor, enemy of Orlando and the other nephews of Charlemagne, had entered into a traitorous correspondence with Marsilius, the Saracen king of Spain, whom he invited into France. Marsilius, thus encouraged, led an army across the frontiers, and joined Rodomont. This was the situation of things when Rinaldo and the other knights who had obeyed the summons of Dudon set forward on their return to France.

When they arrived at Buda in Hungary, they found the king of that country about despatching his son, Ottachiero, with an army to the succor of Charlemagne. Delighted with the arrival of Rinaldo, he placed his son and troops under his command. In due time the army arrived on the frontiers of France, and, united with the troops of Desiderius, king of Lombardy, poured down into Provence. The confederate armies had not marched many days through this gay tract, before they heard a crash of drums and trumpets behind the hills, which spoke the conflict between the paynims, led by Rodomont, and the Christian forces. Rinaldo, witnessing from a mountain the prowess of Rodomont, left his troops in charge of his friends, and galloped towards him with his lance in rest. The impulse was irresistible, and Rodomont was unhorsed. But Rinaldo, unwilling to avail himself of his advantage, galloped back to the hill, and, having secured Bayard among the baggage, returned to finish the combat on foot.

During this interval the battle had become general, the Hungarians were routed, and Rinaldo, on his return, had the mortification to find that Ottachiero was wounded, and Dudon taken prisoner. While he sought Rodomont in order to renew the combat, a new sound of drums and trumpets was heard, and Charlemagne, with the main body of his army, was descried advancing in battle array. Rodomont, seeing this, mounted the horse of Dudon, left Rinaldo, who was on foot, and galloped off to enounter this new enemy.

Agramant, accompanied by Rogero, had by this time made good his landing, and joined Rodomont with all his forces. Rogero eagerly embraced this first opportunity of distinguishing himself, and spread terror wherever he went, encountering in turn, and overthrowing many of the bravest knights of France. At length he found himself opposite to Rinaldo, who, being interrupted, as we have said, in his combat with Rodomont, and unable to follow him, being on foot, was shouting to his late foe to return and finish their combat. Rogero also was on foot, and seeing the Christian knight so eager for a contest, proffered himself to supply the place of his late antagonist. Rinaldo saw at a glance that the Moorish prince was a champion worthy of his arm, and gladly accepted the defiance. The combat was stoutly maintained for a time; but now fortune declared decisively in favor of the infidel army, and Charlemagne's forces gave way at all points in irreparable confusion. The two combatants were separated by the crowd of fugitives and pursuers, and Rinaldo hastened to recover possession of his horse. But Bayard, in the confusion, had got loose, and Rinaldo followed him into a thick wood, thus becoming effectually separated from Rogero.

Rogero, also seeking his horse in the medley, came where two warriors were engaged in mortal combat. Though he knew not who they were, he could distinguish that one was a paynim and the other a Christian; and, moved by the spirit of courtesy, he approached them, and exclaimed, "Let him of the two who worships Christ pause, and hear what I have to say. The army of Charles is routed and in flight, so that if he wishes to follow his leader he has no time for delay." The Christian knight, who was none other than Bradamante, a female warrior, in prowess equal to the best of knights, was thunderstruck with the tidings, and would gladly leave the contest undecided, and retire from the field; but Rodomont, her antagonist, would by no means consent. Rogero, indignant at his discourtesy, insisted upon her departure, while he took up her quarrel with Rodomont.

The combat, obstinately maintained on both sides, was interrupted by the return of Bradamante. Finding herself unable to overtake the fugitives, and reluctant to leave to another the burden and risk of a contest which belonged to herself, she had returned to reclaim the combat. She arrived, however, when her champion had dealt his enemy such a blow as obliged him to drop both his sword and bridle. Rogero, disdaining to profit by his adversary's defenceless situation, sat apart, upon his horse, while that of Rodomont bore his rider, stunned and stupefied, about the field.

Bradamante approached Rogero, conceiving a yet higher opinion of his valor on beholding such an instance of forbearance. She addressed him, excusing herself for leaving him exposed to an enemy from his interference in her cause; pleading her duty to her sovereign as the motive. While she spoke, Rodomont, recovered from his confusion, rode up to them. His bearing was, however, changed; and he disclaimed all thoughts of further contest with one who, he said, "had already conquered him by his courtesy." So saying, he quitted his antagonist, picked up his sword, and spurred out of sight.

Bradamante was now again desirous of retiring from the field, and Rogero insisted in accompanying her, though yet unaware of her sex.

As they pursued their way, she inquired the name and quality of her new associate; and Rogero informed her of his nation and family. He told her that Astyanax, the son of Hector of Troy, established the kingdom of Messina in Sicily. From him were derived two branches, which gave origin to two families of renown. From one sprang the royal race of Pepin and Charlemagne, and from the other, that of Reggio, in Italy. "From that of Reggio am I derived," he continued. "My mother, driven from her home by the chance of war, died in giving me life, and I was taken in charge by a sage enchanter, who trained me to feats of arms amidst the dangers of the desert and the chase."

Having thus ended his tale, Rogero entreated a similar return of courtesy from his companion, who replied, without disguise, that she was of the race of Clermont, and sister to Rinaldo, whose fame was perhaps known to him. Rogero, much moved by this intelligence, entreated her to take off her helmet, and, at the discovery of her face, remained transported with delight.

While absorbed in this contemplation, an unexpected danger assailed them. A party which was placed in a wood, in order to intercept the retreating Christians, broke from its ambush upon the pair, and Bradamante, who was uncasqued, was wounded in the head. Rogero was in fury at this attack; and Bradamante, replacing her helmet, joined him in taking speedy vengeance on their enemies. They cleared the field of them, but became separated in the pursuit; and Rogero, quitting the chase, wandered by hill and vale in search of her whom he had no sooner found than lost.

While pursuing this quest, he fell in with two knights, whom he joined, and engaged them to assist him in the search of his companion, describing her arms, but concealing, from a certain feeling of jealousy, her quality and sex.

It was evening when they joined company, and having ridden together through the night, the morning was beginning to break, when one of the strangers, fixing his eyes upon Rogero's shield, demanded of him by what right he bore the Trojan arms. Rogero declared his origin and race, and then, in his turn, interrogated the inquirer as to his pretensions to the cognizance of Hector, which he bore. The stranger replied, "My name is Mandricardo, son of Agrican, the Tartar king, whom Orlando treacherously slew. I say *treacherously,* for in fair fight he could not have done it. It is in search of him that I have come to France, to take vengeance for my father, and to wrest from him Durindana, that famous sword, which belongs to me, and not to him." When the knights demanded to know by what right he claimed Durindana, Mandricardo thus related his history:—

"I had been, before the death of my father, a wild and reckless youth. That event awakened my energies, and drove me forth to seek for vengeance. Determined to owe success to nothing but my own exertions, I departed without attendants or horse or arms. Travelling thus alone, and on foot, I espied one day a pavilion, pitched near a fountain, and entered it, intent on adventure. I found therein a damsel of gracious aspect, who replied to my inquiries, that the fountain was the work of a fairy, whose castle stood beyond a neighboring hill, where she kept watch over a treasure which many knights had tried to win, but fruitlessly, having lost their life or liberty in the attempt. This treasure was the armor of Hector, prince of Troy, whom Achilles treacherously slew. Nothing was wanting but his sword Durindana, and this had fallen into the possession of a queen named Penthesilea, from whom it passed through her descendants to Almontes, whom Orlando slew, and thus became possessed of the sword. The rest of Hector's arms were saved and carried off by Æneas, from whom this fairy received them in recompense of service rendered. 'If you have the courage to attempt their acquisition,' said the damsel, 'I will be your guide.' "

Mandricardo went on to say that he eagerly embraced the proposal, and being provided with horse and armor by the damsel, set forth on his enterprise, the lady accompanying him.

As they rode, she explained the dangers of the quest. The armor was defended by a champion, one of the numerous unsuccessful adventurers for the prize, all of whom had been made prisoners by the fairy and compelled to take their turn, day by day, in defending the arms against all comers. Thus speaking they arrived at the castle, which was of alabaster, overlaid with gold. Before it, on a lawn, sat an armed knight on horseback, who was none other than Gradasso, king of Sericane, who, in his return home from his unsuccessful inroad into France, had fallen into the power of the fairy, and was held to do her bidding. Mandricardo, upon seeing him, dropt his visor, and laid his lance in rest. The champion of the castle was equally ready, and each spurred towards his opponent. They met one another with equal force, splintered their spears, and, returning to the charge, encountered with their swords. The contest was long and doubtful, when Mandricardo, determined to bring it to an end, threw his arms about Gradasso, grappled with him, and both fell to the ground. Mandricardo, however, fell uppermost, and, preserving his advantage, compelled Gradasso to yield himself conquered. The damsel now interfered, congratulating the victor, and consoling the vanquished as well as she might.

Mandricardo and the damsel proceeded to the gate of the castle, which they found undefended. As they entered, they beheld a shield suspended from a pilaster of gold. The device was a white eagle on an azure field, in memory of the bird of Jove, which bore away Ganymede, the flower of the Phrygian race. Beneath was engraved the following couplet:—

> "Let none with hand profane my buckler wrong
> Unless he be himself as Hector strong."

The damsel, alighting from her palfrey, made obeisance to the arms, bending herself to the ground. The Tartar king bowed his head with equal reverence; then advancing towards the shield, touched it with his sword. Thereupon an earthquake shook the ground, and the way by which he had entered closed. Another and an opposite gate opened, and displayed a field bristling with stalks and grain of gold. The damsel, upon this, told him that he had no means of retreat but by cutting down the harvest which was before him, and by uprooting a tree which grew in the middle of the field. Mandricardo, without replying, began to mow the harvest with his sword, but had scarce smitten thrice when he perceived that every stalk that fell was instantly transformed into some poisonous or ravenous animal, which prepared to assail him. Instructed by the damsel, he snatched up a stone and cast it among the pack. A strange wonder followed; for no sooner had the stone fallen among the beasts, than they turned their rage against one another, and rent each other to pieces. Mandricardo did not stop to marvel at the miracle, but proceeded to fulfil his task, and uproot the tree. He clasped it round the trunk, and made vigorous efforts to tear it up by the roots. At each effort fell a shower of leaves, that were instantly changed into birds of prey, which attacked the knight, flapping their wings in his face, with horrid screeching. But undismayed by this new annoyance, he continued to tug at the trunk till it yielded to his efforts. A burst of wind and thunder followed, and the hawks and vultures flew screaming away.

But these only gave place to a new foe; for from the hole made by tearing up the tree issued a furious serpent, and, darting at Mandricardo, wound herself about his limbs with a strain that almost crushed him. Fortune, however, again stood his friend, for, writhing under the folds of the monster, he fell backwards into the hole, and his enemy was crushed beneath his weight.

Mandricardo, when he was somewhat recovered, and assured himself of the destruction of the serpent, began to contemplate the place into which he had fallen, and saw that he was in a vault, incrusted with costly metals, and illuminated by a live coal. In the middle was a sort of ivory bier, and upon this was extended what appeared to be a knight in armor, but was in truth an empty trophy, composed of the rich and precious arms once Hector's, to which nothing was wanting but the sword. While Mandricardo stood contemplating the prize, a door opened behind him, and a bevy of fair damsels entered, dancing, who, taking up the armor, piece by piece, led him away to the place where the shield was suspended; where he found the fairy of the castle seated in state. By her he was invested with the arms he had won, first pledging his solemn oath to wear no other blade but Durindana, which he was to wrest from Orlando, and thus complete the conquest of Hector's arms.

CHAPTER VII

THE INVASION OF FRANCE, CONTINUED

MANDRICARDO, having completed his story now turned to Rogero, and proposed that arms should decide which of the two was most worthy to bear the symbol of the Trojan knight.

Rogero felt no other objection to this proposal than the scruple which arose on observing that his antagonist was without a sword. Mandricardo insisted that this need be no impediment, since his oath prevented him from using a sword until he should have achieved the conquest of Durindana.

This was no sooner said than a new antagonist started up in Gradasso, who now accompanied Mandricardo. Gradasso vindicated his prior right to Durindana, to obtain which he had embarked (as was related in the beginning) in that bold inroad upon France. A quarrel was thus kindled between the kings of Tartary and Sericane. While the dispute was raging, a knight arrived upon the ground, accompanied by a damsel, to whom Rogero related the cause of the strife. The knight was Florismart, and his companion Flordelis. Florismart succeeded in bringing the two champions to accord, by informing them that he could bring them to the presence of Orlando, the master of Durindana.

Gradasso and Mandricardo readily made truce, in order to accompany Florismart, nor would Rogero be left behind.

As they proceeded on their quest, they were met by a dwarf, who entreated their assistance in behalf of his lady, who had been carried off by an enchanter, mounted on a winged horse. However unwilling to leave the question of the sword undecided, it was not possible for the knights to resist this appeal. Two of their number, Gradasso and Rogero, therefore accompanied the dwarf, Mandricardo persisted in his search for Orlando, and Florismart, with Flordelis, pursued their way to the camp of Charlemagne.

Atlantes, the enchanter, who had brought up Rogero, and cherished for him the warmest affection, knew by his art that his pupil was destined to be severed from him, and converted to the Christian faith through the influence of Bradamante, that royal maiden with whom chance had brought him acquainted. Thinking to thwart the will of Heaven in this respect, he now put forth all his arts to entrap Rogero into his power. By the aid of his subservient demons, he reared a castle on an inaccessible height, in the Pyrenean mountains, and, to make it a pleasant abode to his pupil, contrived to entrap and convey thither knights and damsels many a one, whom chance had brought into the vicinity of his castle. Here, in a sort of sensual paradise, they were but too willing to forget glory and duty, and to pass their time in indolent enjoyment.

It was by the enchanter that the dwarf had now been sent to tempt the knights into his power.

But we must now return to Rinaldo, whom we left interrupted in his combat with Rodomont. In search of his late antagonist, and intent on bringing their combat to a decision, he entered the forest of Arden, whither he suspected Rodomont had gone. While engaged on this quest, he was surprised by the vision of a beautiful child dancing naked, with three damsels as beautiful as himself. While he was lost in admiration at the sight, the child approached him, and, throwing at him handfuls of roses and lilies, struck him from his horse. He was no sooner down than he was seized by the dancers, by whom he was dragged about and scourged with flowers till he fell into a swoon. When he began to revive, one of the group approached him, and told him that his punishment was the consequence of his rebellion against that power before whom all things bend; that there was but one remedy to heal the wounds that had been inflicted, and that was to drink of the waters of Love. Then they left him.

Rinaldo, sore and faint, dragged himself toward a fountain which flowed near by, and, being parched with thirst, drank greedily and almost unconsciously of the water, which was sweet to the taste, but bitter at the heart. After repeated draughts he recovered his strength and recollection, and found himself in the same place where Angelica had formerly awakened him with a rain of flowers, and whence he had fled in contempt of her courtesy.

This remembrance of the scene was followed by the recognition of his crime; and, repenting bitterly his ingratitude, he leaped upon Bayard, with the intention of hastening to Angelica's country, and soliciting his pardon at her feet.

Let us now retrace our steps, and revert to the time when the paladins, having learned from Dudon the summons of Charlemagne to return to France to repel the invaders, had all obeyed the command with the exception of Orlando, whose passion for Angelica still held him in attendance on her. Orlando, arriving before Albracca, found it closely beleaguered. He, however, made his way into the citadel, and related his adventures to Angelica, from the time of his departure up to his separation from Rinaldo and the rest, when they departed to the assistance of Charlemagne. Angelica, in return, described the distresses of the garrison, and the force of the besiegers; and in conclusion prayed Orlando to favor her escape from the pressing danger, and escort her into France. Orlando, who did not suspect that love for Rinaldo was her secret motive, joyfully agreed to the proposal, and the sally was resolved upon.

Leaving lights burning in the fortress, they departed at nightfall, and passed in safety through the enemy's camp. After encountering numerous adventures, they reached the sea-side, and embarked on board a pinnace for France. The vessel arrived safely, and the travellers, disembarking in Provence, pursued their way by land. One day, heated and weary, they sought shelter from the sun in the forest of Arden, and chance directed Angelica to the fountain of Disdain, of whose waters she eagerly drank.

Issuing thence, the Count and damsel encountered a stranger

knight. It was no other than Rinaldo, who was just on the point of setting off on a pilgrimage in search of Angelica, to implore her pardon for his insensibility, and urge his new-found passion. Surprise and delight at first deprived him of utterance, but soon recovering himself, he joyfully saluted her, claiming her as his, and exhorting her to put herself under his protection. His presumption was repelled by Angelica with disdain, and Orlando, enraged at the invasion of his rights, challenged him to decide their claims by arms.

Terrified at the combat which ensued, Angelica fled amain through the forest, and came out upon a plain covered with tents. This was the camp of Charlemagne, who led the army of reserve destined to support the troops which had advanced to oppose Marsilius. Charles, having heard the damsel's tale, with difficulty separated the two cousins, and then consigned Angelica, as the cause of quarrel, to the care of Namo, Duke of Bavaria, promising that she should be his who should best deserve her in the impending battle.

But these plans and hopes were frustrated. The Christian army, beaten at all points, fled from the Saracens; and Angelica, indifferent to both her lovers, mounted a swift palfrey and plunged into the forest, rejoicing, in spite of her terror, at having regained her liberty. She stopped at last in a tufted grove, where a gentle zephyr blew, and whose young trees were watered by two clear runnels, which came and mingled their waters, making a pleasing murmur. Believing herself far from Rinaldo, and overcome by fatigue and the summer heat, she saw with delight a bank covered with flowers, so thick that they almost hid the green turf, inviting her to alight and rest. She dismounted from her palfrey, and turned him loose to recruit his strength with the tender grass which bordered the streamlets. Then, in a sheltered nook tapestried with moss and fenced in with roses and hawthorn-flowers, she yielded herself to grateful repose.

She had not slept long when she was awakened by the noise made by the approach of a horse. Starting up she saw an armed knight who had arrived at the bank of the stream. Not knowing whether he was to be feared or not, her heart beat with anxiety. She pressed aside the leaves to allow her to see who it was, but scarce dared to breathe for fear of betraying herself. Soon the knight threw himself on the flowery bank, and, leaning his head on his hand, fell into a profound reverie. Then arousing himself from his silence, he began to pour forth complaints, mingled with deep sighs. Rivers of tears flowed down his cheeks, and his breast seemed to labor with a hidden flame. "Ah, vain regrets!" he exclaimed; "cruel fortune! others triumph, while I endure hopeless misery! Better a thousand times to lose life, than wear a chain so disgraceful and so oppressive!"

Angelica by this time had recognized the stranger, and perceived that it was Sacripant, king of Circassia, one of the worthiest of her suitors. This prince had followed Angelica from his country, at the very gates of the day, to France, where he heard with dismay that she was under the guardianship of the Paladin Orlando, and that the Emperor had announced his decree to award her as the prize of valor to that one of his nephews who should best deserve her.

As Sacripant continued to lament, Angelica, who had always opposed the hardness of marble to his sighs, thought with herself that nothing forbade her employing his good offices in this unhappy crisis. Though firmly resolved never to accept him as a spouse, she yet felt the necessity of giving him a gleam of hope in reward for the service she required of him. All at once, like Diana, she stepped forth from the arbor. "May the gods preserve thee," she said, "and put far from thee all hard thoughts of me!" Then she told him all that had befallen her since she parted with him at her father's court, and how she had availed herself of Orlando's protection to escape from the beleaguered city. At that moment the noise of horse and armor was heard as of one approaching; and Sacripant, furious at the interruption, resumed his helmet, mounted his horse, and placed his lance in rest. He saw a knight advancing, with scarf and plume of snowy whiteness. Sacripant regarded him with angry eyes, and, while he was yet some distance off, defied him to the combat. The other, not moved by his angry tone to make reply, put himself on his defence. Their horses, struck at the same moment with the spur, rushed upon one another with the impetuosity of a tempest. Their shields were pierced each with the other's lance, and only the temper of their breastplates saved their lives. Both the horses recoiled with the violence of the shock; but the unknown knight's recovered itself at the touch of the spur; the Saracen king's fell dead, and bore down his master with him. The white knight, seeing his enemy in this condition, cared not to renew the combat, but, thinking he had done enough for glory, pursued his way through the forest and was a mile off before Sacripant had got free from his horse.

As a ploughman, stunned by a thunder-clap which has stricken dead the oxen at his plough, stands motionless, sadly contemplating his loss, so Sacripant stood confounded and overwhelmed with mortification at having Angelica a witness of his defeat. He groaned, he sighed, less from the pain of his bruises than for the shame of being reduced to such a state before her. The princess took pity on him, and consoled him as well as she could. "Banish your regrets, my lord," she said, "this accident has happened solely in consequence of the feebleness of your horse, which had more need of rest and food than of such an encounter as this. Nor can your adversary gain any credit by it, since he has hurried away, not venturing a second trial." While she thus consoled Sacripant they perceived a person approach, who seemed a courier, with bag and horn. As soon as he came up, he accosted Sacripant, and inquired if he had seen a knight pass that way, bearing a white shield and with a white plume to his helmet. "I have, indeed, seen too much of him," said Sacripant, "it is he who has brought me to the ground; but at least I hope to learn from you who that knight is." "That I can easily inform you," said the man; "know then that, if you have been overthrown, you owe your fate to the high prowess of a lady as beautiful as she is brave. It is the fair and illustrious Bradamante who has won from you the honors of victory."

At these words the courier rode on his way, leaving Sacripant more confounded and mortified than ever. In silence he mounted the horse of Angelica, taking the lady behind him on the croup, and rode away in search of a more secure asylum. Hardly had they ridden two miles when a new sound was heard in the forest, and they perceived a gallant and powerful horse, which, leaping the ravines and dashing aside the branches that opposed his passage, appeared before them, accoutred with a rich harness adorned with gold.

"If I may believe my eyes, which penetrate with difficulty the underwood," said Angelica, "that horse that dashes so stoutly through the bushes is Bayard, and I marvel how he seems to know the need we have of him, mounted as we are both on one feeble animal." Sacripant, dismounting from the palfrey, approached the fiery courser, and attempted to seize his bridle, but the disdainful animal, turning from him, launched at him a volley of kicks enough to have shattered a wall of marble. Bayard then approached Angelica with an air as gentle and loving as a faithful dog could his master, after a long separation. For he remembered how she had caressed him, and even fed him, in Albracca. She took his bridle in her left hand, while with her right she patted his neck. The beautiful animal, gifted with wonderful intelligence, seemed to submit entirely. Sacripant, seizing the moment to vault upon him, controlled his curvetings, and Angelica, quitting the croup of the palfrey, regained her seat.

But, turning his eyes toward a place where was heard a noise of arms, Sacripant beheld Rinaldo. That hero now loves Angelica more than his life, and she flies him as the timid crane the falcon.

The fountain of which Angelica had drunk produced such an effect on the beautiful queen, that, with distressed countenance and trembling voice, she conjured Sacripant not to wait the approach of Rinaldo, but to join her in flight.

"Am I, then," said Sacripant, "of so little esteem with you that you doubt my power to defend you? Do you forget the battle of Albracca, and how, in your defence, I fought single-handed against Agrican and all his knights?"

Angelica made no reply, uncertain what to do; but already Rinaldo was too near to be escaped. He advanced menacingly to the Circassian king, for he recognized his horse.

"Vile thief," he cried, "dismount from that horse, and prevent the punishment that is your due for daring to rob me of my property. Leave, also, the princess in my hands; for it would indeed be a sin to suffer so charming a lady and so gallant a charger to remain in such keeping."

The king of Circassia, furious at being thus insulted, cried out, "Thou liest, villain, in giving me the name of thief, which better belongs to thyself than to me. It is true, the beauty of this lady and the perfection of this horse are unequalled; come on, then, and let us try which of us is most worthy to possess them."

At these words the king of Circassia and Rinaldo attacked one another with all their force, one fighting on foot, the other on horseback. You need not, however, suppose that the Saracen king found any advantage in this; for a young page, unused to horsemanship, could not have failed more completely to manage Bayard than did this accomplished knight. The faithful animal loved his master too well to injure him, and refused his aid as well as his obedience to the hand of Sacripant, who could strike but ineffectual blows, the horse backing when he wished him to go forward, and dropping his head and arching his back, throwing out with his legs, so as almost to shake the knight out of the saddle. Sacripant, seeing that he could not manage him, watched his opportunity, rose on his saddle, and leapt lightly to the earth; then, relieved from the embarrassment of the horse, renewed the combat on more equal terms. Their skill to thrust and parry was equal; one rises, the other stoops; with one foot set firm, they turn and wind, to lay on strokes or to dodge them. At last Rinaldo, throwing himself on the Circassian, dealt him a blow so terrible that Fusberta, his good sword, cut in two the buckler of Sacripant, although it was made of bone, and covered with a thick plate of steel well tempered. The arm of the Saracen was deprived of its defence, and almost palsied with the stroke. Angelica, perceiving how victory was likely to incline, and shuddering at the thought of becoming the prize of Rinaldo, hesitated no longer. Turning her horse's head, she fled with the utmost speed; and, in spite of the round pebbles which covered a steep descent, she plunged into a deep valley, trembling with the fear that Rinaldo was in pursuit. At the bottom of this valley she encountered an aged hermit, whose white beard flowed to his middle, and whose venerable appearance seemed to assure his piety.

This hermit, who appeared shrunk by age and fasting, travelled slowly, mounted upon a wretched ass. The princess, overcome with fear, conjured him to save her life, and to conduct her to some port of the sea, whence she might embark and quit France, never more to hear the odious name of Rinaldo.

The old hermit was something of a wizard. He comforted Angelica, and promised to protect her from all peril. Then he opened his scrip, and took from thence a book, and had read but a single page when a goblin, obedient to his incantations, appeared, under the form of a laboring man, and demanded his orders. He received them, transported himself to the place where the knights still maintained their conflict, and boldly stepped between the two.

"Tell me, I pray you," he said, "what benefit will accrue to him who shall get the better in this contest? The object you are contending for is already disposed of; for the Paladin Orlando, without effort and without opposition, is now carrying away the princess Angelica to Paris. You had better pursue them promptly, for if they reach Paris, you will never see her again."

At these words you might have seen those rival warriors confounded, stupefied, silently agreeing that they were affording their rival a fair opportunity to triumph over them. Rinaldo, approaching Bayard, breathes a sigh of shame and rage, and swears a terrible oath that, if he overtakes Orlando, he will tear his heart out. Then mounting Bayard and pressing his flanks with his spurs, he leaves the king of Circassia on foot in the forest.

Let it not appear strange that Rinaldo found Bayard obedient at last, after having so long prevented any one from even touching his bridle; for that fine animal had an intelligence almost human; he had fled from his master only to draw him on the track of Angelica, and enable him to recover her. He saw when the princess fled from the battle, and Rinaldo being then engaged in a fight on foot, Bayard found himself free to follow the traces of Angelica. Thus he had drawn his master after him, not permitting him to approach, and had brought him to the sight of the princess. But Bayard now, deceived like his master with the false intelligence of the goblin, submits to be mounted and to serve his master as usual, and Rinaldo, animated with rage, makes him fly toward Paris, more slowly than his wishes, though the speed of Bayard outstripped the winds. Full of impatience to encounter Orlando, he gave but a few hours that night to sleep. Early the next day he saw before him the great city, under the walls of which the Em-

peror Charles had collected the scattered remains of his army.
Foreseeing that he would soon be attacked on all sides, the Emperor
had caused the ancient fortifications to be repaired, and new ones
to be built, surrounded by wide and deep ditches. The desire to
hold the field against the enemy made him seize every means of
procuring new allies. He hoped to receive from England aid sufficient to enable him to form a new camp, and as soon as Rinaldo
rejoined him, he selected him to go as his ambassador into England,
to plead for auxiliaries. Rinaldo was far from pleased with this
commission, but he obeyed the Emperor's commands, without giving himself time to devote a single day to the object nearest to his
heart. He hastened to Calais, and lost not a moment in embarking
for England, ardently desiring a hasty despatch of his commission,
and a speedy return to France.

CHAPTER VIII

BRADAMANTE AND ROGERO

BRADAMANTE, the knight of the white plume and shield, whose
sudden appearance and encounter with Sacripant we have already told, was in quest of Rogero, from whom chance had separated
her, almost at the beginning of their acquaintance. After her encounter with Sacripant, Bradamante pursued her way through the
forest, in hopes of rejoining Rogero, and arrived at last on the
brink of a fair fountain.

This fountain flowed through a broad meadow. Ancient trees
overshadowed it, and travellers, attracted by the sweet murmur of
its waters, stopped there to cool themselves. Bradamante, casting
her eyes on all sides to enjoy the beauties of the spot, perceived,
under the shade of a tree, a knight reclining, who seemed to be
oppressed with the deepest grief.

Bradamante accosted him, and asked to be informed of the cause
of his distress. "Alas! my lord," said he, "I lament a young and
charming friend, my affianced wife, who has been torn from me by
a villain,—let me rather call him a demon,—who, on a winged
horse, descended from the air, seized her, and bore her screaming to
his den. I have pursued them over rocks and through ravines till
my horse is no longer able to bear me, and I now wait only for
death." He added, that already a vain attempt on his behalf had
been made by two knights whom chance had brought to the spot.
Their names were Gradasso, king of Sericane, and Rogero, the
Moor. Both had been overcome by the wiles of the enchanter, and
were added to the number of the captives, whom he held in an

impregnable castle, situated on the height of the mountain. At the mention of Rogero's name, Bradamante started with delight, which was soon changed to an opposite sentiment when she heard that her lover was a prisoner in the toils of the enchanter. "Sir Knight," she said, "do not surrender yourself to despair; this day may be more happy for you than you think, if you will only lead me to the castle which enfolds her whom you deplore."

The knight responded, "After having lost all that made life dear to me, I have no motive to avoid the dangers of the enterprise, and I will do as you request; but I forewarn you of the perils you will have to encounter. If you fall, impute it not to me."

Having thus spoken, they took their way to the castle, but were overtaken by a messenger from the camp, who had been sent in quest of Bradamante to summon her back to the army, where her presence was needed to reassure her disheartened forces, and withstand the advance of the Moors.

The mournful knight, whose name was Pinabel, thus became aware that Bradamante was a scion of the house of Clermont, between which and his own of Mayence there existed an ancient feud. From this moment the traitor sought only how he might be rid of the company of Bradamante, from whom he feared no good would come to him, but rather mortal injury, if his name and lineage became known to her. For he judged her by his own base model, and, knowing his ill deserts, he feared to receive his due.

Bradamante, in spite of the summons to return to the army, could not resolve to leave her lover in captivity, and determined first to finish the adventure on which she was engaged. Pinabel leading the way, they at length arrived at a wood, in the centre of which rose a steep, rocky mountain. Pinabel, who now thought of nothing else but how he might escape from Bradamante, proposed to ascend the mountain to extend his view in order to discover a shelter for the night, if any there might be within sight. Under this pretence he left Bradamante, and advanced up the side of the mountain till he came to a cleft in the rock, down which he looked, and perceived that it widened below into a spacious cavern. Meanwhile Bradamante, fearful of losing her guide, had followed close on his footsteps, and rejoined him at the mouth of the cavern. Then the traitor, seeing the impossibility of escaping her, conceived another design. He told her that before her approach he had seen in the cavern a young and beautiful damsel, whose rich dress announced her high birth, who with tears and lamentations implored assistance; that before he could descend to relieve her, a ruffian had seized her, and hurried away into the recesses of the cavern.

Bradamante, full of truth and courage, readily believed this lie

of the Mayencian traitor. Eager to succor the damsel, she looked
round for the means of facilitating the descent, and seeing a large
elm with spreading branches, she lopped off with her sword one of
the largest, and thrust it into the opening. She told Pinabel to
hold fast to the larger end, while, grasping the branches with her
hands, she let herself down into the cavern.

The traitor smiled at seeing her thus suspended, and, asking her
in mockery, "Are you a good leaper?" he let go the branch with
perfidious glee, and saw Bradamante precipitated to the bottom
of the cave. "I wish your whole race were there with you," he
muttered, "that you might all perish together."

But Pinabel's atrocious design was not accomplished. The twigs
and foliage of the branch broke its descent, and Bradamante, not
seriously injured, though stunned with her fall, was reserved for
other adventures.

As soon as she recovered from the shock, Bradamante cast her
eyes around and perceived a door, through which she passed into
a second cavern, larger and loftier than the first. It had the appearance of a subterranean temple. Columns of the purest alabaster
adorned it, and supported the roof; a simple altar rose in the
middle; a lamp, whose radiance was reflected by the alabaster
walls, cast a mild light around.

Bradamante, inspired by a sense of religious awe, approached
the altar, and, falling on her knees, poured forth her prayers and
thanks to the Preserver of her life, invoking the protection of his
power. At that moment a small door opened, and a female issued
from it with naked feet, and flowing robe and hair, who called
her by her name, and thus addressed her. "Brave and generous
Bradamante, know that it is a power from above that has brought
you hither. The spirit of Merlin, whose last earthly abode was in
this place, has warned me of your arrival, and of the fate that
awaits you. This famous grotto," she continued, "was the work of
the enchanter Merlin; here his ashes repose. You have no doubt
heard how this sage and virtuous enchanter ceased to be. Victim
of the artful fairy of the lake, Merlin, by a fatal compliance with
her request, laid himself down living in his tomb, without power
to resist the spell laid upon him by that ingrate, who retained him
there as long as he lived. His spirit hovers about this spot, and will
not leave it, until the last trumpet shall summon the dead to
judgment. He answers the questions of those who approach his
tomb, where perhaps you may be privileged to hear his voice."

Bradamante, astonished at these words, and the objects which
met her view, knew not whether she was awake or asleep. Confused,
but modest, she cast down her eyes, and a blush overspread her

face. "Ah, what am I," said she, "that so great a prophet should deign to speak to me!" Still, with a secret satisfaction, she followed the priestess, who led her to the tomb of Merlin. This tomb was constructed of a species of stone hard and resplendent like fire. The rays which beamed from the stone sufficed to light up that terrible place, where the sun's rays never penetrated; but I know not whether that light was the effect of a certain phosphorescence of the stone itself, or of the many talismans and charms with which it was wrought over.

Bradamante had hardly passed the threshold of this sacred place, when the spirit of the enchanter saluted her with a voice firm and distinct. "May thy designs be prosperous, O chaste and noble maiden, the future mother of heroes, the glory of Italy, and destined to fill the whole world with their fame. Great captains, renowned knights, shall be numbered among your descendants, who shall defend the Church and restore their country to its ancient splendor. Princes, wise as Augustus and the sage Numa, shall bring back the age of gold.[1] To accomplish these grand destinies it is ordained that you shall wed the illustrious Rogero. Fly then to his deliverance, and lay prostrate in the dust the traitor who has snatched him from you, and now holds him in chains!"

Merlin ceased with these words, and left to Melissa, the priestess, the charge of more fully instructing the maiden in her future course. "To-morrow," said she, "I will conduct you to the castle on the rock where Rogero is held captive. I will not leave you till I have guided you through this wild wood, and I will direct you on your way so that you shall be in no danger of mistaking it."

The next morning Melissa conducted Bradamante, between rocks and precipices, crossing rapid torrents, and traversing intricate passes, employing the time in imparting to her such information as was necessary to enable her to bring her design to a successful issue.

"Not only would the castle, impenetrable by force, and that winged horse of his baffle your efforts, but know that he possesses also a buckler whence flashes a light so brilliant that the eyes of all who look upon it are blinded. Think not to avoid it by shutting your eyes, for how then will you be able to avoid his blows, and make him feel your own? But I will teach you the proper course to pursue.

"Agramant, the Moorish prince, possesses a ring stolen from a queen of India, which has power to render of no avail all enchantments. Agramant, knowing that Rogero is of more importance to

[1] This prophecy is introduced by Ariosto in this place to compliment the noble house of Este, the princess of his native state, the dukedom of Ferrara.

him than any one of his warriors, is desirous of rescuing him from
the power of the enchanter, and has sent for that purpose Brunello,
the most crafty and sagacious of his servants, provided with his
wonderful ring, and he is even now at hand, bent on this enterprise.
But, beautiful Bradamante, as I desire that no one but yourself
shall have the glory of delivering from thraldom your future spouse,
listen while I disclose the means of success. Following this path
which leads by the sea-shore, you will come erelong to a hostelry,
where the Saracen Brunello will arrive shortly after you. You will
readily know nim by his stature, under four feet, his great disproportioned head, his squint eyes, his livid hue, his thick eyebrows
joining his tufted beard. His dress, moreover, that of a courier,
will point him out to you.

"It will be easy for you to enter into conversation with him, announcing yourself as a knight seeking combat with the enchanter,
but let not the knave suspect that you know anything about the
ring. I doubt not that he will offer to be your guide to the castle
of the enchanter. Accept his offer, but take care to keep behind
him till you come in sight of the brilliant dome of the castle. Then
hesitate not to strike him dead, for the wretch deserves no pity,
and take from him the ring. But let him not suspect your intention,
for by putting the ring into his mouth he will instantly become invisible, and disappear from your eyes."

Saying thus, the sage Melissa and the fair Bradamante arrived
near the city of Bordeaux, where the rich and wide river Garonne
pours the tribute of its waves into the sea. They parted with tender
embraces. Bradamante, intent wholly on her purpose, hastened to
arrive at the hostelry, where Brunello had preceded her a few moments only. The young heroine knew him without difficulty. She
accosted him, and put to him some slight questions, to which he
replied with adroit falsehoods. Bradamante, on her part, concealed
from him her sex, her religion, her country, and the blood from
whence she sprung. While they talk together, sudden cries are
heard from all parts of the hostelry. "O queen of heaven!" exclaimed
Bradamante, "what can be the cause of this sudden alarm?" She
soon learned the cause. Host, children, domestics, all, with upturned
eyes, as if they saw a comet or a great eclipse, were gazing on a
prodigy which seemed to pass the bounds of possibility. She beheld
distinctly a winged horse, mounted with a cavalier in rich armor,
cleaving the air with rapid flight. The wings of this strange courser
were wide extended, and covered with feathers of various colors. The
polished armor of the knight made them shine with rainbow tints.
In a short time, the horse and rider disappeared behind the summits
of the mountains.

"It is an enchanter," said the host, "a magician who often is seen traversing the air in that way. Sometimes he flies aloft as if among the stars, and at others, skims along the land. He possesses a wonderful castle on the top of the Pyrenees. Many knights have shown their courage by going to attack him, but none have ever returned, from which it is to be feared they have lost either their life or their liberty."

Bradamante, addressing the host, said, "Could you furnish me a guide to conduct me to the castle of this enchanter?" "By my faith," said Brunello, interrupting, "that you shall not seek in vain; I have it all in writing, and I will myself conduct you." Bradamante, with thanks, accepted him for her guide.

The host had a tolerable horse to dispose of, which Bradamante bargained for, and the next day, at the first dawn of morning, she took her route by a narrow valley, taking care to have the Saracen Brunello lead the way.

They reached the summit of the Pyrenees, whence one may look down on France, Spain, and the two seas. From this height they descended again by a fatiguing road into a deep valley. From the middle of this valley an isolated mountain rose, composed of rough and perpendicular rock, on whose summit was the castle, surrounded with a wall of brass. Brunello said, "Yonder is the stronghold where the enchanter keeps his prisoners; one must have wings to mount thither; it is easy to see that the aid of a flying horse must be necessary for the master of this castle, which he uses for his prison and for his abode."

Bradamante, sufficiently instructed, saw that the time had now come to possess herself of the ring; but she could not resolve to slay a defenceless man. She seized Brunello before he was aware, bound him to a tree, and took from him the ring which he wore on one of his fingers. The cries and entreaties of the perfidious Saracen moved her not. She advanced to the foot of the rock whereon the castle stood, and, to draw the magician to the combat, sounded her horn, adding to it cries of defiance.

The enchanter delayed not to present himself, mounted on his winged horse. Bradamante was struck with surprise mixed with joy when she saw that this person, described as so formidable, bore no lance, nor club, nor any other deadly weapon. He had only on his arm a buckler, covered with a cloth, and in his hand an open book. As to the winged horse, there was no enchantment about him. He was a natural animal, of a species which exists in the Riphæan mountains. Like a griffin, he had the head of an eagle, claws armed with talons, and wings covered with feathers, the rest of his body being that of a horse. This strange animal is called a Hippogriff.

The heroine attacked the enchanter on his approach, striking on this side and on that, with all the energy of a violent combat, but wounding only the wind, and, after this pretended attack had lasted some time, dismounted from her horse, as if hoping to do battle more effectually on foot. The enchanter now prepares to employ his sole weapon, by uncovering the magic buckler which never failed to subdue an enemy by depriving him of his senses. Bradamante, confiding in her ring, observed all the motions of her adversary, and, at the unveiling of the shield, cast herself on the ground, pretending that the splendor of the shield had overcome her, but in reality to induce the enchanter to dismount and approach her.

It happened according to her wish. When the enchanter saw her prostrate, he made his horse alight on the ground, and, dismounting, fixed the shield on the pommel of his saddle, and approached in order to secure the fallen warrior. Bradamante, who watched him intently, as soon as she saw him near at hand, sprang up, seized him vigorously, threw him down, and, with the same chain which the enchanter had prepared for herself, bound him fast, without his being able to make any effectual resistance.

The enchanter, with the accents of despair, exclaimed, "Take my life, young man!" but Bradamante was far from complying with such a wish. Desirous of knowing the name of the enchanter, and for what purpose he had formed with so much art this impregnable fortress, she commanded him to inform her.

"Alas!" replied the magician, while tears flowed down his cheeks, "it is not to conceal booty, nor for any culpable design, that I have built this castle; it was only to guard the life of a young knight, the object of my tenderest affection, my art having taught me that he is destined to become a Christian, and to perish, shortly after, by the blackest of treasons.

"This youth, named Rogero, is the most beautiful and most accomplished of knights. It is I, the unhappy Atlantes, who have reared him from his childhood. The call of honor and the desire of glory led him from me to follow Agramant, his prince, in his invasion of France, and I, more devoted to Rogero than the tenderest of parents, have sought the means of bringing him back to this abode, in the hope of saving him from the cruel fate that menaces him.

"For this purpose I have got him in my possession by the same means as I attempted to employ against you; and by which I have succeeded in collecting a great many knights and ladies in my castle. My purpose was to render my beloved pupil's captivity light, by affording him society to amuse him, and keep his thoughts from running on subjects of war and glory. Alas! my cares have been in vain! Yet, take, I beseech you, whatever else I have, but spare me my beloved pupil. Take this shield, take this winged courser, deliver such of your friends as you may find among my prisoners, deliver them all if you will, but leave me my beloved Rogero; or if you will snatch him too from me, take also my life, which will cease then to be to me worth preserving."

Bradamante replied: "Old man, hope not to move me by your vain entreaties. It is precisely the liberty of Rogero that I require. You would keep him here in bondage and in slothful pleasure, to save him from a fate which you foresee. Vain old man! how can you foresee his fate when you could not foresee your own? You desire me to take your life. No, my arm and my soul refuse the request." This said, she required the magician to go before, and guide her to the castle. The prisoners were set at liberty, though some, in their secret hearts, regretted the voluptuous life which was thus brought to an end. Bradamante and Rogero met one another with transports of joy.

They descended from the mountain to the spot where the encounter had taken place. There they found the Hippogriff, with the magic buckler in its wrapper, hanging to his saddle-bow. Bradamante advanced to seize the bridle; the Hippogriff seemed to wait her approach, but before she reached him he spread his wings and flew away to a neighboring hill, and in the same manner, a second time, eluded her efforts. Rogero and the other liberated knights dispersed over the plain and hill-tops to secure him, and at last the animal allowed Rogero to seize his rein. The fearless Rogero hesitated not to vault upon his back, and let him feel his spurs, which so roused his mettle that, after galloping a short distance, he suddenly spread his wings, and soared into the air. Bradamante had the grief to see her lover snatched away from her at the very moment of reunion. Rogero, who knew not the art of directing the horse, was unable to control his flight. He found himself carried over the tops of the mountains, so far above them that he could hardly distinguish what was land and what water. The Hippogriff directed his flight to the west, and cleaved the air as swiftly as a new-rigged vessel cut the waves, impelled by the freshest and most favorable gales.

CHAPTER IX

ASTOLPHO AND THE ENCHANTRESS

In the long flight which Rogero took on the back of the Hippogriff, he was carried over land and sea, unknowing whither. As soon as he had gained some control over the animal, he made him alight on the nearest land. When he came near enough to earth, Rogero leapt lightly from his back, and tied the animal to a myrtle-tree. Near the spot flowed the pure waters of a fountain, surrounded by cedars and palm-trees. Rogero laid aside his shield, and, removing his helmet, breathed with delight the fresh air, and cooled his lips with the waters of the fountain. For we cannot wonder that he was excessively fatigued, considering the ride he had taken. He was preparing to taste the sweets of repose, when he perceived that the Hippogriff, which he had tied by the bridle to a myrtle-tree, frightened at something, was making violent efforts to disengage himself. His struggles shook the myrtle-tree so that many of its beautiful leaves were torn off, and strewed the ground.

A sound like that which issues from burning wood seemed to come from the myrtle-tree, at first faint and indistinct, but growing stronger by degrees, and at length was audible as a voice which spoke in this manner: "O knight, if the tenderness of your heart corresponds to the beauty of your person, relieve me, I pray you, from this tormenting animal. I suffer enough inwardly without having outward evils added to my lot."

Rogero, at the first accents of this voice, turned his eyes promptly on the myrtle, hastened to it, and stood fixed in astonishment when he perceived that the voice issued from the tree itself. He immediately untied his horse, and, flushed with surprise and regret, exclaimed, "Whoever thou art, whether mortal or the goddess of these woods, forgive me, I beseech you, my involuntary fault. Had I imagined that this hard bark covered a being possessed of feeling, could I have exposed such a beautiful myrtle to the insults of this steed? May the sweet influences of the sky and air speedily repair the injury I have done! For my part, I promise by the sovereign lady of my heart to do everything you wish in order to merit your forgiveness."

At these words the myrtle seemed to tremble from root to stem, and Rogero remarked that a moisture as of tears trickled down its bark, like that which exudes from a log placed on the fire. It then spoke:—

"The kindness which inspires your words compels me to disclose to you who I once was, and by what fatality I have been changed into this shape. My name was Astolpho, cousin of Orlando and Rinaldo, whose fame has filled the earth. I was myself reckoned among the bravest paladins of France, and was by birth entitled to reign over England, after Otho, my father. Returning from the distant East, with Rinaldo and many other brave knights, called home to aid with our arms the great Emperor of France, we reached a spot where the powerful enchantress Alcina possessed a castle on the borders of the sea. She had gone to the water-side to amuse herself with fishing, and we paused to see how, by her art, without hook or line, she drew from the water whatever she would.

"Not far from the shore an enormous whale showed a back so broad and motionless that it looked like an island. Alcina had fixed her eyes on me, and planned to get me into her power. Addressing us, she said: 'This is the hour when the prettiest mermaid in the sea comes regularly every day to the shore of yonder island. She sings so sweetly that the very waves flow smoother at the sound. If you wish to hear her, come with me to her resort.' So saying, Alcina pointed to the fish, which we all supposed to be an island. I, who was rash, did not hesitate to follow her; but swam my horse over, and mounted on the back of the fish. In vain Rinaldo and Dudon made signs to me to beware; Alcina, smiling, took me in charge, and led the way. No sooner were we mounted upon him than the whale moved off, spreading his great fins, and cleft rapidly the waters. I then saw my folly, but it was too late to repent. Alcina soothed my anger, and professed that what she had done was for love of me. Erelong we arrived at this island, where at first everything was done to reconcile me to my lot, and to make my days pass happily away. But soon Alcina, sated with her conquest, grew indifferent, then weary of me, and at last, to get rid of me, changed me into this form, as she had done to many lovers before me, making some of them olives, some palms, some cedars, changing others into fountains, rocks, or even into wild beasts. And thou, courteous knight, whom accident has brought to this enchanted isle, beware that she get not the power over thee, or thou shalt haply be made like us, a tree, a fountain, or a rock."

Rogero expressed his astonishment at this recital. Astolpho added, that the island was in great part subject to the sway of Alcina. By the aid of her sister Morgana, she had succeeded in dispossessing a third sister, Logestilla, of nearly the whole of her patrimony, for the whole isle was hers originally by her father's bequest. But Logestilla was temperate and sage, while the other sisters were false and voluptuous. Her empire was divided from theirs by a gulf and chain of mountains, which alone had thus far prevented her sisters from usurping it.

Astolpho here ended his tale, and Rogero who knew that he was the cousin of Bradamante, would gladly have devised some way for his relief; but, as that was out of his power, he consoled him as well as he could, and then begged to be told the way to the palace of Logestilla, and how to avoid that of Alcina. Astolpho directed him to take the road to the left, though rough and full of rocks. He warned him that this road would present serious obstacles; that troops of monsters would oppose his passage, employed by the art of Alcina to prevent her subjects from escaping from her dominion. Rogero thanked the myrtle, and prepared to set out on his way.

He at first thought he would mount the winged horse, and scale the mountain on his back; but he was too uncertain of his power to control him to wish to encounter the hazard of another flight through the air, besides that he was almost famished for the want of food. So he led the horse after him, and took the road on foot, which for some distance led equally to the dominions of both the sisters.

He had not advanced more than two miles when he saw before him the superb city of Alcina. It was surrounded with a wall of gold, which seemed to reach the skies. I know that some think that this wall was not of real gold, but only the work of alchemy; it matters not; I prefer to think it gold, for it certainly shone like gold.

A broad and level road led to the gates of the city, and from this another branched off, narrow and rough, which led to the mountain region. Rogero took without hesitation the narrow road; but he had no sooner entered upon it than he was assailed by a numerous troop which opposed his passage.

You never have seen anything so ridiculous, so extraordinary, as this host of hobgoblins were. Some of them bore the human form from the neck to the feet, but had the head of a monkey or a cat; others had the legs and the ears of a horse; old men and women, bald and hideous, ran hither and thither as if out of their senses, half clad in the shaggy skins of beasts; one rode full speed on a horse without a bridle, another jogged along mounted on an ass or a cow; others, full of agility, skipped about, and clung to the tails and manes of the animals which their companions rode. Some blew horns, others brandished drinking-cups; some were armed with spits, and some with pitchforks. One, who appeared to be the captain, had an enormous belly and a gross fat head; he was mounted on a tortoise, that waddled, now this way, now that, without keeping any one direction.

One of these monsters, who had something approaching the human form, though he had the neck, ears, and muzzle of a dog, set himself to bark furiously at Rogero, to make him turn off to the right, and re-enter upon the road to the gay city; but the brave chevalier exclaimed, "That will I not, so long as I can use this sword,"—and he thrust the point directly at his face. The monster tried to strike him with a lance, but Rogero was too quick for him, and thrust his sword through his body, so that it appeared a hand's breadth behind his back. The paladin, now giving full vent to his rage, laid about him vigorously among the rabble, cleaving one to the teeth, another to the girdle; but the troop was so numerous, and in spite of his blows pressed around him so close, that, to clear his way, he must have had as many arms as Briareus.

If Rogero had uncovered the shield of the enchanter which hung at his saddle-bow, he might easily have vanquished this monstrous rout; but perhaps he did not think of it, and perhaps he preferred to seek his defence nowhere but in his good sword. At that moment, when his perplexity was at its height, he saw issue from the city gate two young beauties, whose air and dress proclaimed their rank and gentle nurture. Each of them was mounted on a unicorn, whose whiteness surpassed that of ermine. They advanced to the meadow where Rogero was contending so valiantly against the hobgoblins, who all retired at their approach. They drew near, they extended their hands to the young warrior, whose cheeks glowed with the flush of exercise and modesty. Grateful for their assistance, he expressed his thanks, and, having no heart to refuse them, followed their guidance to the gate of the city.

This grand and beautiful entrance was adorned by a portico of four vast columns, all of diamond. Whether they were real diamond or artificial, I cannot say. What matter is it, so long as they appeared to the eye like diamond, and nothing could be more gay and splendid.

On the threshold, and between the columns, was seen a bevy of charming young women, who played and frolicked together. They all ran to receive Rogero, and conducted him into the palace, which appeared like a paradise.

We might well call by that name this abode, where the hours flew by, without account, in ever-new delights. The bare idea of satiety, want, and, above all, of age, never entered the minds of the inhabitants. They experienced no sensations except those of luxury and gayety; the cup of happiness seemed for them ever-flowing and exhaustless. The two young damsels to whom Rogero owed his deliverance from the hobgoblins, conducted him to the apartment of their mistress. The beautiful Alcina advanced, and greeted him with an air at once dignified and courteous. All her court surrounded the paladin, and rendered him the most flattering attentions. The castle was less admirable for its magnificence than for the charms of those who inhabited it. They were of either sex, well matched in beauty, youth, and grace; but among this charming group the brilliant Alcina shone, as the sun outshines the stars. The young warrior was fascinated. All that he had heard from the myrtle-tree appeared to him but a vile calumny. How could he suspect that falsehood and treason veiled themselves under smiles and the ingenuous air of truth? He doubted not that Astolpho had deserved his fate, and perhaps a punishment more severe; he regarded all his stories as dictated by a disappointed spirit, and a thirst for revenge. But we must not condemn Rogero too harshly, for he was the victim of magic power.

They seated themselves at table, and immediately harmonious lyres and harps waked the air with the most ravishing notes. The charms of poetry were added, in entertaining recitals; the magnificence of the feast would have done credit to a royal board. The traitress forgot nothing which might charm the paladin, and attach him to the spot, meaning, when she should grow tired of him, to metamorphose him as she had done others. In the same manner passed each succeeding day. Games of pleasant exercise, the chase, the dance, or rural sports, made the hours pass quickly; while they gave zest to the refreshment of the bath, or sleep.

Thus Rogero led a life of ease and luxury, while Charlemagne and Agramant were struggling for empire. But I cannot linger with him, while the amiable and courageous Bradamante is night and day directing her uncertain steps to every spot where the slightest chance invites her, in the hope of recovering Rogero.

I will therefore say, that, having sought him in vain in fields and in cities, she knew not whither next to direct her steps. She did not apprehend the death of Rogero. The fall of such a hero would have re-echoed from the Hydaspes to the farthest river of the West; but, not knowing whether he was on the earth or in the air, she concluded, as a last resource, to return to the cavern which contained the tomb of Merlin, to ask of him some sure direction to the object of her search.

While this thought occupied her mind, Melissa, the sage enchantress, suddenly appeared before her. This virtuous and beneficent magician had discovered by her spells that Rogero was passing his time in pleasure and idleness, forgetful of his honor and his sovereign. Not able to endure the thought that one who was born to be a hero should waste his years in base repose, and leave a sullied reputation in the memory of survivors, she saw that vigorous measures must be employed to draw him forth into the paths of virtue. Melissa was not blinded by her affection for the amiable paladin, like Atlantes, who, intent only on preserving Rogero's life, cared nothing for his fame. It was that old enchanter whose arts had guided the Hippogriff to the isle of the too charming Alcina, where he hoped his favorite would learn to forget honor, and lose the love of glory.

At the sight of Melissa, joy lighted up the countenance of Bradamante, and hope animated her breast. Melissa concealed nothing from her, but told her how Rogero was in the toils of Alcina. Bradamante was plunged in grief and terror; but the kind enchantress calmed her, dispelled her fears, and promised that before many days she would lead back the paladin to her feet.

"My daughter," she said, "give me the ring which you wear, and which possesses the power to overcome enchantments. By means of it, I doubt not but that I may enter the stronghold where the false Alcina holds Rogero in durance, and may succeed in vanquishing her, and liberating him." Bradamante unhesitatingly delivered her the ring, recommending Rogero to her best efforts. Melissa then summoned by her art a huge palfrey, black as jet, excepting one foot, which was bay. Mounted upon this animal, she rode with such speed that by the next morning she had reached the abode of Alcina.

She here transformed herself into the perfect resemblance of the old magician Atlantes, adding a palm-breadth to her height, and enlarging her whole figure. Her chin she covered with a long beard, and seamed her whole visage well with wrinkles. She assumed also his voice and manner, and watched her chance to find Rogero alone. At last she found him, dressed in a rich tunic of silk and gold, a collar of precious stones about his neck, and his arms, once so rough with exercise, decorated with bracelets. His air and his every motion indicated effeminacy, and he seemed to retain nothing of Rogero but the name; such power had the enchantress obtained over him.

Melissa, under the form of his old instructor, presented herself before him, wearing a stern and serious visage. "Is this, then," she said, "the fruit of all my labors? Is it for this that I fed you on the marrow of bears and lions, that I taught you to subdue dragons, and, like Hercules, strangle serpents in your youthful grasp, only to make you, by all my cares, a feeble Adonis? My nightly watchings of the stars, of the yet warm fibres of animals, the lots I have cast, the points of nativity that I have calculated, have they all falsely indicated that you were born for greatness? Who could have believed that you would become the slave of a base enchantress? O Rogero, learn to know this Alcina, learn to understand her arts and to countervail them. Take this ring, place it on your finger, return to her presence, and see for yourself what are her real charms."

At these words, Rogero, confused, abashed, cast his eyes upon the ground, and knew not what to answer. Melissa seized the moment, slipped the ring on his finger, and the paladin was himself again. What a thunder-clap to him! Overcome by shame, he dared not to encounter the looks of his instructor. When at last he raised his eyes, he beheld not that venerable form, but the priestess Melissa, who in virtue of the ring now appeared in her true person. She told him of the motives which had led her to come to his rescue, of the griefs and regrets of Bradamante, and of her unwearied search for him. "That charming Amazon," she said, "sends you this ring, which is a sovereign antidote to all enchantments. She would have sent you her heart in my hands, if it would have had greater power to serve you."

It was needless for Melissa to say more. Rogero's love for Alcina, being but the work of enchantment, vanished as soon as the enchantment was withdrawn, and he now hated her with an equal intensity, seeing no longer anything in her but her vices, and feeling only resentment for the shame that she had put upon him.

His surprise when he again beheld Alcina was no less than his indignation. Fortified by his ring from her enchantments, he saw her as she was, a monster of ugliness. All her charms were artificial, and, truly viewed, were rather deformities. She was, in fact, older than Hecuba or the Sibyl of Cumæ; but an art, which it is to be regretted our times have lost, enabled her to appear charming, and to clothe herself in all the attractions of youth. Rogero now saw all this, but, governed by the counsels of Melissa, he concealed his surprise, assumed under some pretext his armor, long neglected, and bound to his side Balisardo, his trusty sword, taking also the buckler of Atlantes, covered with its veil.

He then selected a horse from the stables of Alcina, without exciting her suspicions; but he left the Hippogriff, by the advice of Melissa, who promised to take him in charge, and train him to a more manageable state. The horse he took was Rabican, which belonged to Astolpho. He restored the ring to Melissa.

Rogero had not ridden far when he met one of the huntsmen of Alcina, bearing a falcon on his wrist, and followed by a dog. The huntsman was mounted on a powerful horse, and came boldly up to the paladin, demanding, in a somewhat imperious manner, whither he was going so rapidly. Rogero disdained to stop or to reply; whereupon the huntsman, not doubting that he was about making his escape, said, "What if I, with my falcon, stop your ride?" So saying, he threw off the bird, which even Rabican could not equal in speed. The huntsman then leapt from his horse, and the animal, open-mouthed, darted after Rogero with the swiftness of an arrow. The huntsman also ran as if the wind or fire bore him, and the dog was equal to Rabican in swiftness. Rogero, finding flight impossible, stopped and faced his pursuers; but his sword was useless against such foes. The insolent huntsman assailed him with words, and struck him with his whip, the only weapon he had; the dog bit his feet, and the horse drove at him with his hoofs. At the same time, the falcon flew over his head and over Rabican's, and attacked them with claws and wings, so that the horse in his fright began to be unmanageable. At that moment the sound of trumpets and cymbals was heard in the valley, and it was evident that Alcina had ordered out all her array to go in pursuit. Rogero felt that there was no time to be lost, and luckily remembered the shield of Atlantes, which he bore suspended from his neck. He unveiled it, and the charm worked wonderfully. The huntsman, the dog, the horse, fell flat; the trembling wings of the falcon could no longer sustain her, and she fell senseless to the ground. Rogero, rid of their annoyances, left them in their trance, and rode away.

Meanwhile Alcina, with all the force she could muster, sallied forth from her palace in pursuit. Melissa, left behind, took advantage of the opportunity to ransack all the rooms, protected by the ring. She undid one by one all the talismans and spells which she found, broke the seals, burned the images, and untied the hag-knots. Thence, hurrying through the fields, she disenchanted the victims changed into trees, fountains, stones, or brutes; all of whom recovered their liberty, and vowed eternal gratitude to their deliverer. They made their escape, with all possible despatch, to the realms of the good Logestilla, whence they departed to their several homes.

Astolpho was the first whom Melissa liberated, for Rogero had particularly recommended him to her care. She aided him to recover his arms, and particularly that precious golden-headed lance which once was Argalia's. The enchantress mounted with him upon the winged horse, and in a short time arrived through the air at the castle of Logestilla, where Rogero joined them soon after.

In this abode the friends passed a short period of delightful and improving intercourse with the sage Logestilla and her virtuous court; and then each departed, Rogero with the Hippogriff, ring, and buckler; Astolpho with his golden lance, and mounted on Rabican, the fleetest of steeds. To Rogero Logestilla gave a bit and bridle suited to govern the Hippogriff; and to Astolpho a horn of marvellous powers, to be sounded only when all other weapons were unavailing.

CHAPTER X

THE ORC

WE left the charming Angelica at the moment when, in her flight from her contending lovers, Sacripant and Rinaldo, she met an aged hermit. We have seen that her request to the hermit was to furnish her the means of gaining the sea-coast, eager to avoid Rinaldo, whom she hated, by leaving France and Europe itself. The pretended hermit, who was no other than a vile magician, knowing well that it would not be agreeable to his false gods to aid Angelica in this undertaking, feigned to comply with her desire. He supplied her a horse, into which he had by his arts caused a subtle devil to enter, and having mounted Angelica on the animal, directed her what course to take to reach the sea.

Angelica rode on her way without suspicion, but when arrived at the shore, the demon urged the animal headlong into the water. Angelica in vain attempted to turn him back to the land; he continued his course till, as night approached, he landed with his burden on a sandy headland.

Angelica, finding herself alone, abandoned in this frightful solitude, remained without movement, as if stupefied, with hands joined and eyes turned towards heaven, till at last, pouring forth a torrent of tears, she exclaimed: "Cruel fortune, have you not yet exhausted your rage against me! To what new miseries do you doom me? Alas! then, finish your work. Deliver me a prey to some ferocious beast, or by whatever fate you choose bring me to an end. I will be thankful to you for terminating my life and my misery." At last, exhausted by her sorrows, she fell asleep, and sunk prostrate on the sand.

Before recounting what next befell, we must declare what place it was upon which the unhappy lady was now thrown. In the sea that washes the coast of Ireland there is an island called Ebuda, whose inhabitants, once numerous, had been wasted by the anger of Proteus till there were now but few left. This deity was incensed by some neglect of the usual honors which he had in old times received from the inhabitants of the land, and, to execute his vengeance, had sent a horrid sea-monster, called an Orc, to devour them. Such were the terrors of his ravages, that the whole people of the isle had shut themselves up in the principal town, and relied on their walls alone to protect them. In this distress they applied to the Oracle for advice, and were directed to appease the wrath of the sea-monster by offering to him the fairest virgin that the country could produce.

Now it so happened that the very day when this dreadful oracle was announced, and when the fatal mandate had gone forth to seek among the fairest maidens of the land one to be offered to the monster, some sailors, landing on the beach where Angelica was, beheld that beauty as she lay asleep.

O blind Chance! whose power in human affairs is but too great, canst thou then abandon to the teeth of a horrible monster those charms which different sovereigns took arms against one another to possess? Alas, the lovely Angelica is destined to be the victim of those cruel islanders.

Still asleep, she was bound by the Ebudians, and it was not until she was carried on board the vessel that she came to a knowledge of her situation. The wind filled the sails and wafted the ship swiftly to the port, where all that beheld her agreed that she was unquestionably the victim selected by Proteus himself to be his prey. Who can tell the screams, the mortal anguish of this unhappy maiden, the reproaches she addressed even to the heavens themselves, when the dreadful information of her cruel fate was made known to her? I cannot; let me rather turn to a happier part of my story.

Rogero left the palace of Logestilla, careering on his flying courser far above the tops of the mountains, and borne westward by the Hippogriff, which he guided with ease, by means of the bridle that Melissa had given him. Anxious as he was to recover Bradamante, he could not fail to be delighted at the view his rapid flight presented of so many vast regions and populous countries as he passed over in his career. At last he approached the shores of England, and perceived an immense army in all the splendor of military pomp, as if about to go forth flushed with hopes of victory. He caused the Hippogriff to alight not far from the scene, and found himself immediately surrounded by admiring spectators, knights and soldiers, who could not enough indulge their curiosity and wonder. Rogero learned, in reply to his questions, that the fine array of troops before him was the army destined to go to the aid of the French Emperor, in compliance with the request presented by the illustrious Rinaldo, as ambassador of King Charles, his uncle.

By this time the curiosity of the English chevaliers was partly gratified in beholding the Hippogriff at rest, and Rogero, to renew their surprise and delight, remounted the animal, and, clapping spurs to his sides, made him launch into the air with the rapidity of a meteor, and directed his flight still westwardly, till he came within sight of the coasts of Ireland. Here he descried what seemed to be a fair damsel, alone, fast chained to a rock which projected into the sea. What was his astonishment when, drawing nigh, he beheld the beautiful princess Angelica. That day she had been led forth and bound to the rock, there to wait till the sea-monster should come to devour her. Rogero exclaimed as he came near, "What cruel hands, what barbarous soul, what fatal chance can have loaded thee with those chains?" Angelica replied by a torrent of tears, at first her only response; then, in a trembling voice, she disclosed to him the horrible destiny for which she was there exposed. While she spoke, a terrible roaring was heard far off on the sea. The huge monster soon came in sight, part of his body appearing above the

waves, and part concealed. Angelica, half dead with fear, abandoned
herself to despair.

Rogero, lance in rest, spurred his Hippogriff toward the Orc, and
gave him a thrust. The horrible monster was like nothing that nature
produces. It was but one mass of tossing and twisting body, with
nothing of the animal but head, eyes, and mouth, the last furnished
with tusks like those of the wild boar. Rogero's lance had struck
him between the eyes; but rock and iron are not more impenetrable
than were his scales. The knight, seeing the fruitlessness of the first
blow, prepared to give a second. The animal, beholding upon the
water the shadow of the great wings of the Hippogriff, abandoned
his prey, and turned to seize what seemed nearer. Rogero took the
opportunity, and dealt him furious blows on various parts of his
body, taking care to keep clear of his murderous teeth; but the
scales resisted every attack. The Orc beat the water with his tail
till he raised a foam which enveloped Rogero and his steed, so that
the knight hardly knew whether he was in the water or the air.
He began to fear that the wings of the Hippogriff would be so
drenched with water that they would cease to sustain him. At that
moment Rogero bethought him of the magic shield which hung
at his saddle-bow; but the fear that Angelica would also be blinded
by its glare, discouraged him from employing it. Then he remembered the ring which Melissa had given him, the power of which
he had so lately proved. He hastened to Angelica, and placed it on
her finger. Then, uncovering the buckler, he turned its bright disk
full in the face of the detestable Orc. The effect was instantaneous.
The monster, deprived of sense and motion, rolled over on the sea,
and lay floating on his back. Rogero would fain have tried the effect
of his lance on the now exposed parts, but Angelica implored him to
lose no time in delivering her from her chains, before the monster
should revive. Rogero, moved with her entreaties, hastened to do so,
and, having unbound her, made her mount behind him on the Hippogriff. The animal, spurning the earth, shot up into the air, and
rapidly sped his way through it. Rogero, to give time to the princess
to rest after her cruel agitations, soon sought the earth again, alighting on the shore of Brittany. Near the shore a thick wood presented
itself, which resounded with the songs of birds. In the midst, a
fountain of transparent water bathed the turf of a little meadow. A
gentle hill rose near by. Rogero, making the Hippogriff alight in
the meadow, dismounted, and took Angelica from the horse.

When the first tumults of emotion had subsided, Angelica, casting
her eyes downward, beheld the precious ring upon her finger, whose
virtues she was well acquainted with, for it was the very ring which
the Saracen Brunello had robbed her of. She drew it from her finger

and placed it in her mouth, and, quicker than we can tell it, disappeared from the sight of the paladin.

Rogero looked around him on all sides, like one frantic, but soon remembered the ring which he had so lately placed on her finger. Struck with the ingratitude which could thus recompense his services, he exclaimed: "Thankless beauty, is this then the reward you make me? Do you prefer to rob me of my ring rather than receive it as a gift? Willingly would I have given it to you, had you but asked it." Thus he said, searching on all sides, with arms extended, like a blind man, hoping to recover by the touch what was lost to sight; but he sought in vain. The cruel beauty was already far away.

Though sensible of her obligations to her deliverer, her first necessity was for clothing, food, and repose. She soon reached a shepherd's hut, where, entering unseen, she found what sufficed for her present relief. An old herdsman inhabited the hut, whose charge consisted of a drove of mares. When recruited by repose, Angelica selected one of the mares from the flock, and, mounting the animal, felt the desire revive in her mind of returning to her home in the East, and for that purpose would gladly have accepted the protection of Orlando or of Sacripant across those wide regions which divided her from her own country. In hopes of meeting with one or the other of them, she pursued her way.

Meanwhile, Rogero, despairing of seeing Angelica again, returned to the tree where he had left his winged horse, but had the mortification to find that the animal had broken his bridle and escaped. This loss, added to his previous disappointment, overwhelmed him with vexation. Sadly he gathered up his arms, threw his buckler over his shoulders, and, taking the first path that offered, soon found himself within the verge of a dense and wide-spread forest.

He had proceeded for some distance when he heard a noise on his right, and, listening attentively, distinguished the clash of arms. He made his way toward the place whence the sound proceeded, and found two warriors engaged in mortal combat. One of them was a knight of a noble and manly bearing, the other a fierce giant. The knight appeared to exert consummate address in defending himself against the massive club of the giant, evading his strokes, or parrying them with sword or shield. Rogero stood spectator of the combat, for he did not allow himself to interfere in it, though a secret sentiment inclined him strongly to take part with the knight. At length he saw with grief the massive club fall directly on the head of the knight, who yielded to the blow, and fell prostrate. The giant sprang forward to despatch him, and for that purpose unlaced his helmet, when Rogero, with dismay, recognized the face of Bradamante. He cried aloud, "Hold, miscreant!" and sprang forward with drawn sword. Whereupon the giant, as if he cared not to enter upon another combat, lifted Bradamante on his shoulders, and ran with her into the forest.

Rogero plunged after him, but the long legs of the giant carried him forward so fast that the paladin could hardly keep him in sight. At length they issued from the wood, and Rogero perceived before him a rich palace, built of marble, and adorned with sculptures executed by a master hand. Into this edifice, through a golden door, the giant passed, and Rogero followed; but, on looking round, saw nowhere either the giant or Bradamante. He ran from room to room, calling aloud on his cowardly foe to turn and meet him: but got no response, nor caught another glimpse of the giant or his prey. In his vain pursuit he met, without knowing them, Ferrau, Florismart, King Gradasso, Orlando, and many others, all of whom had been entrapped like himself into this enchanted castle. It was a new stratagem of the magician Atlantes to draw Rogero into his power, and to secure also those who might by any chance endanger his safety. What Rogero had taken for Bradamante was a mere phantom. That charming lady was far away, full of anxiety for her Rogero, whose coming she had long expected.

The Emperor had committed to her charge the city and garrison of Marseilles, and she held the post against the infidels with valor and discretion. One day Melissa suddenly presented herself before her. Anticipating her questions, she said, "Fear not for Rogero; he lives, and is as ever true to you; but he has lost his liberty. The fell enchanter has again succeeded in making him a prisoner. If you would deliver him, mount your horse and follow me." She told her in what manner Atlantes had deceived Rogero, in deluding his eyes with the phantom of herself in peril. "Such," she continued, "will be his arts in your own case, if you penetrate the forest and approach that castle. You will think you behold Rogero, when, in fact, you see only the enchanter himself. Be not deceived, plunge your sword into his body, and trust me when I tell you that, in slaying him, you will restore not only Rogero, but with him many of the bravest knights of France, whom the wizard's arts have withdrawn from the camp of their sovereign."

Bradamante promptly armed herself, and mounted her horse. Melissa led her by forced journeys, by field and forest, beguiling the way with conversation on the theme which interested her hearer most. When at last they reached the forest, she repeated once more her instructions, and then took her leave, for fear the enchanter might espy her, and be put on his guard.

Bradamante rode on about two miles when suddenly she beheld Rogero, as it appeared to her, hard pressed by two fierce giants.

While she hesitated, she heard his voice calling on her for help. At once the cautions of Melissa lost their weight. A sudden doubt of the faith and truth of her kind monitress flashed across her mind. "Shall I not believe my own eyes and ears?" she said, and rushed forward to his defence. Rogero fled, pursued by the giants, and Bradamante followed, passing with them through the castle gate. When there, Bradamante was undeceived, for neither giant nor knight was to be seen. She found herself a prisoner, but had not the consolation of knowing that she shared the imprisonment of her beloved. She saw various forms of men and women, but could recognize none of them; and their lot was the same with respect to her. Each viewed the others under some illusion of the fancy, wearing the semblance of giants, dwarfs, or even four-footed animals, so that there was no companionship or communication between them.

CHAPTER XI

ASTOLPHO'S ADVENTURES CONTINUED, AND ISABELLA'S BEGUN

WHEN Astolpho escaped from the cruel Alcina, after a short abode in the realm of the virtuous Logestilla, he desired to return to his native country. Logestilla lent him the best vessel of her fleet to convey him to the mainland. She gave him at parting a wonderful book, which taught the secret of overcoming all manner of enchantments, and begged him to carry it always with him, out of regard for her. She also gave him another gift, which surpassed everything of the kind that mortal workmanship can frame; yet it was nothing in appearance but a simple horn.

Astolpho, protected by these gifts, thanked the good fairy, took leave of her, and set out on his return to France. His voyage was prosperous, and on reaching the desired port he took leave of the faithful mariners, and continued his journey by land. As he proceeded over mountains and through valleys, he often met with bands of robbers, wild beasts, and venomous serpents, but he had only to sound his horn to put them all to flight.

Having landed in France, and traversed many provinces on his way to the army, he one day, in crossing a forest, arrived beside a fountain, and alighted to drink. While he stooped at the fountain, a young rustic sprang from the copse, mounted Rabican, and rode away. It was a new trick of the enchanter Atlantes. Astolpho, hearing the noise, turned his head just in time to see his loss; and, starting up, pursued the thief, who, on his part, did not press the horse to his full speed, but just kept in sight of his pursuer till they both issued from the forest; and then Rabican and his rider took shelter in a castle which stood near. Astolpho followed, and penetrated without difficulty within the court-yard of the castle, where he looked around for the rider and his horse, but could see no trace of either, nor any person of whom he could make inquiry. Suspecting that enchantment was employed to embarrass him, he bethought him of his book, and on consulting it discovered that his suspicions were well founded. He also learned what course to pursue. He was directed to raise the stone which served as a threshold, under which a spirit lay pent, who would willingly escape, and leave the castle free of access. Astolpho applied his strength to lift aside the stone. Thereupon the magician put his arts in force. The castle was full of prisoners, and the magician caused that to all of them Astolpho should appear in some false guise,—to some a wild beast, to others a giant, to others a bird of prey. Thus all assailed him, and would quickly have made an end of him, if he had not bethought him of his horn. No sooner had he blown a blast than, at the horrid alarm, fled the cavaliers and the necromancer with them, like a flock of pigeons at the sound of the fowler's gun. Astolpho then renewed his efforts on the stone, and turned it over. The under face was all inscribed with magical characters, which the knight defaced, as directed by his book; and no sooner had he done so, than the castle, with its walls and turrets, vanished into smoke.

The knights and ladies set at liberty were, besides Rogero and Bradamante, Orlando, Gradasso, Florismart, and many more. At the sound of the horn they fled, one and all, men and steeds, except Rabican, which Astolpho secured, in spite of his terror. As soon as the sound had ceased, Rogero recognized Bradamante, whom he had daily met during their imprisonment, but had been prevented from knowing by the enchanter's arts. No words can tell the delight with which they recognized each other, and recounted mutually all that had happened to each since they were parted. Rogero took advantage of the opportunity to press his suit, and found Bradamante as propitious as he could wish, were it not for a single obstacle, the difference of their faiths. "If he would obtain her in marriage," she said, "he must in due form demand her of her father, Duke Aymon, and must abandon his false prophet, and become a Christian." The latter step was one which Rogero had for some time intended taking, for reasons of his own. He therefore gladly accepted the terms, and proposed that they should at once repair to the abbey of Vallombrosa, whose towers were visible at no great distance. Thither they turned their horses' heads, and we will leave them to find their way without our company.

I know not if my readers recollect that, at the moment when Rogero had just delivered Angelica from the voracious Orc, that scornful beauty placed her ring in her mouth, and vanished out of sight. At the same time the Hippogriff shook off his bridle, soared away, and flew to rejoin his former master, very naturally returning to his accustomed stable. Here Astolpho found him, to his very great delight. He knew the animal's powers, having seen Rogero ride him, and he longed to fly abroad over all the earth, and see various nations and peoples from his airy course. He had heard Logestilla's directions how to guide the animal, and saw her fit a bridle to his head. He therefore was able, out of all the bridles he found in the stable, to select one suitable, and, placing Rabican's saddle on the Hippogriff's back, nothing seemed to prevent his immediate departure. Yet before he went, he bethought him of placing Rabican in hands where he would be safe, and whence he might recover him in time of need. While he stood deliberating where he should find a messenger, he saw Bradamante approach. That fair warrior had been parted from Rogero on their way to the abbey of Vallombrosa, by an inopportune adventure which had called the knight away. She was now returning to Montalban, having arranged with Rogero to join her there. To Bradamante, therefore, his fair cousin, Astolpho committed Rabican, and also the lance of gold, which would only be an encumbrance in his aerial excursion. Bradamante took charge of both; and Astolpho. bidding her farewell, soared in air.

Among those delivered by Astolpho from the magician's castle was Orlando. Following the guide of chance, the paladin found him-self at the close of day in a forest, and stopped at the foot of a mountain. Surprised to discern a light which came from a cleft in the rock, he approached, guided by the ray, and discovered a nar-row passage in the mountain-side, which led into a deep grotto.

Orlando fastened his horse, and then, putting aside the bushes that resisted his passage, stepped down from rock to rock till he reached a sort of cavern. Entering it, he perceived a lady, young and handsome, as well as he could discover through the signs of distress which agitated her countenance. Her only companion was an old woman, who seemed to be regarded by her young partner with terror and indignation. The courteous paladin saluted the women respectfully, and begged to know by whose barbarity they had been subjected to such imprisonment.

The younger lady replied, in a voice often broken with sobs:—

"Though I know well that my recital will subject me to worse treatment by the barbarous man who keeps me here, to whom this woman will not fail to report it. yet I will not hide from you the facts. Ah! why should I fear his rage? If he should take my life, I know not what better boon than death I can ask.

"My name is Isabella. I am the daughter of the king of Galicia, or rather I should say misfortune and grief are my parents. Young, rich, modest, and of tranquil temper, all things appeared to combine to render my lot happy. Alas! I see myself to-day poor, humbled, miserable, and destined perhaps to yet further afflictions. It is a year since, my father having given notice that he would open the lists for a tournament at Bayonne, a great number of chevaliers from all quarters came together at our court. Among these, Zerbino, son of the king of Scotland, victorious in all combats, eclipsed by his beauty and his valor all the rest. Before departing from the court of Galicia he testified the wish to espouse me, and I consented that he should demand my hand of the king, my father. But I was a Mahometan, and Zerbino a Christian, and my father refused his consent. The prince, called home by his father to take command of the forces destined to the assistance of the French Emperor, prevailed on me to be married to him secretly, and to follow him to Scotland. He caused a galley to be prepared to receive me, and placed in command of it the chevalier Oderic, a Biscayan, famous for his exploits both by land and sea. On the day appointed, Oderic brought his vessel to a sea-side resort of my father's, where I embarked. Some of my domestics accompanied me, and thus I departed from my native land.

"Sailing with a fair wind, after some hours we were assailed by a violent tempest. It was to no purpose that we took in all sail; we were driven before the wind directly upon the rocky shore. Seeing no other hopes of safety, Oderic placed me in a boat, followed himself with a few of his men, and made for land. We reached it through infinite peril, and I no sooner felt the firm land beneath my feet, than I knelt down and poured out heart-felt thanks to the Providence that had preserved me.

"The shore where we landed appeared to be uninhabited. We saw no dwelling to shelter us, no road to lead us to a more hospitable spot. A high mountain rose before us, whose base stretched into the sea. It was here the infamous Oderic, in spite of my tears and entreaties, sold me to a band of pirates, who fancied I might be an acceptable present to their prince, the Sultan of Morocco. This cavern is their den, and here they keep me under the guard of this woman, until it shall suit their convenience to carry me away."

Isabella had hardly finished her recital, when a troop of armed men began to enter the cavern. Seeing the prince Orlando, one said to the rest, "What bird is this we have caught, without even setting a snare for him?" Then addressing Orlando, "It was truly civil in you, friend, to come hither with that handsome coat of armor and vest, the very things I want." "You shall pay for them, then," said Orlando; and, seizing a half-burnt brand from the fire, he hurled it at him, striking his head, and stretching him lifeless on the floor.

There was a massy table in the middle of the cavern, used for the pirates' repasts. Orlando lifted it and hurled it at the robbers as they stood clustered in a group towards the entrance. Half the gang were laid prostrate. with broken heads and limbs; the rest got away as nimbly as they could.

Leaving the den and its inmates to their fate, Orlando, taking Isabella under his protection, pursued his way, for some days, without meeting with any adventure.

One day they saw a band of men advancing, who seemed to be guarding a prisoner, bound hand and foot, as if being carried to execution. The prisoner was a youthful cavalier, of a noble and ingenuous appearance. The band bore the ensigns of Count Anselm, head of the treacherous house of Maganza. Orlando desired Isabella to wait, while he rode forward to inquire the meaning of this array. Approaching, he demanded of the leader who his prisoner was, and of what crime he had been guilty. The man replied, that the prisoner was a murderer, by whose hand Pinabel, the son of Count Anselm, had been treacherously slain. At these words, the prisoner exclaimed, "I am no murderer, nor have I been in any way the cause of the young man's death." Orlando, knowing the cruel and ferocious character of the chiefs of the house of Maganza, needed no more to satisfy him that the youth was the victim of injustice. He commanded the leader of the troop to release his victim, and, receiving an insolent reply, dashed him to the earth with a stroke of his lance; then, by a few vigorous blows, dispersed the band, leaving deadly marks on those who were slowest to quit the field.

Orlando then hastened to unbind the prisoner, and to assist him to reclothe himself in his armor, which the false Magencian had dared to assume. He then led him to Isabella, who now approached the scene of action. How can we picture the joy, the astonishment, with which Isabella recognized in him Zerbino, her husband, and the prince discovered her whom he had believed overwhelmed in the waves! They embraced one another, and wept for joy. Orlando, sharing in their happiness, congratulated himself in having been the instrument of it. The princess recounted to Zerbino what the illustrious paladin had done for her, and the prince threw himself at Orlando's feet, and thanked him as having twice preserved his life.

While these exchanges of congratulation and thankfulness were going on, a sound in the underwood attracted their attention, and caused the two knights to brace their helmets and stand on their guard. What the cause of the interruption was, we shall record in another chapter.

CHAPTER XII

MEDORO

FRANCE was at this time the theatre of dreadful events. The Saracens and the Christians, in numerous encounters, slew one another. On one occasion Rinaldo led an attack on the infidel columns, broke and scattered them, till he found himself opposite to a knight whose armor (whether by accident or choice, it matters not) bore the blazon of Orlando. It was Dardinel, the young and brave prince of Zumara, and Rinaldo remarked him by the slaughter he spread all around. "Ah," said he to himself, "let us pluck up this dangerous plant before it has grown to its full height."

As Rinaldo advanced, the crowd opened before him, the Christians to let his sword have free course, the Pagans to escape its sweep. Dardinel and he stood face to face. Rinaldo exclaimed, fiercely, "Young man, whoever gave you that noble buckler to bear made you a dangerous gift; I should like to see how you are able to defend those quarterings, red and white. If you cannot defend them against me, how pray will you do so when Orlando chal- lenges them?" Dardinel replied: "Thou shalt learn that I can defend the arms I bear, and shed new glory upon them. No one shall rend them from me but with life." Saying these words, Dardinel rushed upon Rinaldo with sword uplifted.

The chill of mortal terror filled the souls of the Saracens when they beheld Rinaldo advance to attack the prince, like a lion against a young bull. The first blow came from the hand of Dardinel, and the weapon rebounded from Mambrino's helmet without effect. Rinaldo smiled, and said, "I will now show you my strokes are more effectual." At these words, he thrust the unfortunate Dardinel in the middle of his breast. The blow was so violent, that the cruel weapon pierced the body, and came out a palm-breadth behind his back. Through this wound the life of Dardinel issued with his blood, and his body fell helpless to the ground.

As a flower which the passing plough has uprooted languishes, and droops its head, so Dardinel, his visage covered with the pale- ness of death, expires, and the hopes of an illustrious race perish with him.

Like waters kept back by a dike, which, when the dike is broken, spread abroad through all the country, so the Moors, no longer kept in column by the example of Dardinel, fled in all directions.

Rinaldo despised too much such easy victories to pursue them; he wished for no combats but with brave men. At the same time, the other paladins made terrible slaughter of the Moors. Charles himself, Oliver, Guido, and Ogier the Dane, carried death into their ranks on all sides.

The infidels seemed doomed to perish to a man on that dreadful day; but the wise king, Marsilius, at last put some slight degree of method into the general rout. He collected the remnant of the troops, formed them into a battalion, and retreated in tolerable order to his camp. That camp was well fortified by intrenchments and a broad ditch. Thither the fugitives hastened, and by degrees all that remained of the Moorish army was brought together there.

The Emperor might perhaps that night have crushed his enemy entirely; but not thinking it prudent to expose his troops, fatigued as they were, to an attack upon a camp so well fortified, he contented himself with encompassing the enemy with his troops, prepared to make a regular siege. During the night, the Moors had time to see the extent of their loss. Their tents resounded with lamentations. This warrior had to mourn a brother, that a friend; many suffered with grievous wounds, all trembled at the fate in store for them.

There were two young Moors, both of humble rank, who gave proof at that time of attachment and fidelity rare in the history of man. Cloridan and Medoro had followed their prince, Dardinel, to the wars of France. Cloridan, a bold huntsman, combined strength with activity. Medoro was a mere youth, his cheeks yet fair and blooming. Of all the Saracens, no one united so much grace and beauty. His light hair was set off by his black and sparkling eyes. The two friends were together on guard at the rampart. About midnight they gazed on the scene in deep dejection. Medoro, with tears in his eyes, spoke of the good prince Dardinel, and could not endure the thought that his body should be cast out on the plain, deprived of funeral honors. "O my friend," said he, "must then the body of our prince be the prey of wolves and ravens? Alas! when I remember how he loved me, I feel that, if I should sacrifice my life to do him honor, I should not do more than my duty. I wish, dear friend, to seek out his body on the battlefield, and give it burial, and I hope to be able to pass through King Charles's camp without discovery, as they are probably all asleep. You, Cloridan, will be able to say for me, if I should die in the adventure, that gratitude and fidelity to my prince were my inducements."

Cloridan was both surprised and touched with this proof of the young man's devotion. He loved him tenderly, and tried for a long time every effort to dissuade him from his design; but he found

Medoro determined to accomplish his object or die in the endeavor.

Cloridan, unable to change his purpose, said, "I will go with you, Medoro, and help you in this generous enterprise. I value not life compared with honor, and if I did, do you suppose, dear friend, that I could live without you? I would rather fall by the arms of our enemies than die of grief for the loss of you."

When the two friends were relieved from their guard duty, they went without any followers into the camp of the Christians. All there was still; the fires were dying out; there was no fear of any attempt on the part of the Saracens, and the soldiers, overcome by fatigue or wine, slept secure, lying upon the ground in the midst of their arms and equipage. Cloridan stopped, and said, "Medoro, I am not going to quit this camp without taking vengeance for the death of our prince. Keep watch, be on your guard that no one shall surprise us; I mean to mark a road with my sword through the ranks of our enemies." So saying, he entered the tent where Alpheus slept, who a year before had joined the camp of Charles, and pretended to be a great physician and astrologer. But his science had deceived him, if it gave him hope of dying peacefully in his bed at a good old age; his lot was to die with little warning. Cloridan ran his sword through his heart. A Greek and a German followed, who had been playing late at dice: fortunate if they had continued their game a little longer; but they never reckoned a throw like this among their chances. Cloridan next came to the unlucky Grillon, whose head lay softly on his pillow. He dreamed probably of the feast from which he had but just retired; for when Cloridan cut off his head, wine flowed forth with the blood.

The two young Moors might have penetrated even to the tent of Charlemagne; but knowing that the paladins encamped around him, kept watch by turns, and judging that it was impossible they should all be asleep, they were afraid to go too near. They might also have obtained rich booty; but, intent only on their object, they crossed the camp, and arrived at length at the bloody field, where bucklers, lances, and swords lay scattered in the midst of corpses of poor and rich, common soldier and prince, horses and pools of blood. This terrible scene of carnage would have destroyed all hope of finding what they were in search of until dawn of day, were it not that the moon lent the aid of her uncertain rays.

Medoro raised his eyes to the planet, and exclaimed, "O holy goddess, whom our fathers have adored under three different forms,— thou who displayest thy power in heaven, on earth, and in the under-world,—thou who art seen foremost among the nymphs chasing the beasts of the forest,—cause me to see, I implore thee, the spot where my dear master lies, and make me all my life long follow the example which thou dost exhibit of works of charity and love."

Either by accident, or that the moon was sensible of the prayer of Medoro, the cloud broke away, and the moonlight burst forth as bright as day. The rays seemed especially to gild the spot where lay the body of Prince Dardinel; and Medoro, bathed in tears and with bleeding heart, recognized him by the quarterings of red and white on his shield.

With groans stifled by his tears, and lamentations in accents suppressed, not from any fear for himself, for he cared not for life, but lest any one should be roused to interrupt their pious duty while yet incomplete, he proposed to his companion that they should together bear Dardinel on their shoulders, sharing the burden of the beloved remains.

Marching with rapid strides under their precious load, they perceived that the stars began to grow pale, and that the shades of night would soon be dispersed by the dawn. Just then Zerbino, whose extreme valor had urged him far from the camp in pursuit of the fugitives, returning, entered the wood in which they were. Some knights in his train perceived at a distance the two brothers-in-arms. Cloridan saw the troop, and, observing that they dispersed themselves over the plain as if in search of booty, told Medoro to lay down the body, and let each save himself by flight. He dropped his part, thinking that Medoro would do the same; but the good youth loved his prince too well to abandon him, and continued to carry his load singly as well as he might, while Cloridan made his escape. Near by there was a part of the wood tufted as if nothing but wild animals had ever penetrated it. The unfortunate youth, loaded with the weight of his dead master, plunged into its recesses.

Cloridan, when he perceived that he had evaded his foes, discovered that Medoro was not with him. "Ah!" exclaimed he, "how could I, dear Medoro, so forget myself as to consult my own safety without heeding yours?" So saying, he retraced the tangled passes of the wood toward the place from whence he had fled. As he approached, he heard the noise of horses, and the menacing voices of armed men. Soon he perceived Medoro, on foot, with the cavaliers surrounding him. Zerbino, their commander, bade them seize him. The unhappy Medoro turned now this way, now that, trying to conceal himself behind an oak or a rock, still bearing the body, which he would by no means leave. Cloridan, not knowing how to help him, but resolved to perish with him, if he must perish, takes an arrow, fits it to his bow, discharges it, and pierces the breast of a Christian knight, who falls helpless from his horse. The others look this way and that, to discover whence the fatal bolt was sped. One, while demanding of his comrades in what direction the arrow came, received a second in his throat, which stopped his words, and soon closed his eyes to the scene.

Zerbino, furious at the death of his two comrades, ran upon Medoro, seized his golden hair, and dragged him forward to slay him. But the sight of so much youth and beauty commanded pity. He stayed his arm. The young man spoke in suppliant tones. "Ah! signor," said he, "I conjure you by the God whom you serve, deprive me not of life until I shall have buried the body of the prince, my master. Fear not that I will ask you any other favor; life is not dear to me; I desire death as soon as I shall have performed this sacred duty. Do with me then as you please. Give my limbs a prey to the birds and beasts; only let me first bury my prince." Medoro pronounced these words with an air so sweet and tender, that a heart of stone would have been moved by them. Zerbino was so to the bottom of his soul. He was on the point of uttering words of mercy, when a cruel subaltern, forgetting all respect to his commander, plunged his lance into the breast of the young Moor. Zerbino, enraged at this brutality, turned upon the wretch to take vengeance, but he saved himself by a precipitate flight.

Cloridan, who saw Medoro fall, could contain himself no longer. He rushed from his concealment, threw down his bow, and, sword in hand, seemed only desirous of vengeance for Medoro, and to die with him. In a moment, pierced through and through with many wounds, he exerts the last remnant of his strength in dragging himself to Medoro, to die embracing him. The cavaliers left them thus, to rejoin Zerbino, whose rage against the murderer of Medoro had drawn him away from the spot.

Cloridan died; and Medoro, bleeding copiously, was drawing near his end when help arrived.

A young maiden approached the fallen knights at this critical moment. Her dress was that of a peasant-girl, but her air was noble and her beauty celestial; sweetness and goodness reigned in her lovely countenance. It was no other than Angelica, the Princess of Cathay.

When she had recovered that precious ring, as we have before related, Angelica, knowing its value, felt proud in the power it conferred, travelled alone without fear, not without a secret shame that she had ever been obliged to seek protection in her wanderings of the Count Orlando and of Sacripant. She reproached herself too as with a weakness, that she had ever thought of marrying Rinaldo; in fine, her pride grew so high as to persuade her that no man living was worthy to aspire to her hand.

Moved with pity at the sight of the young man wounded, and melted to tears at hearing the cause, she quickly recalled to remembrance the knowledge she had acquired in India, where the virtues of plants and the art of healing formed part of the education even of princesses. The beautiful queen ran into the adjoining meadow to gather plants of virtue to stanch the flow of blood. Meeting on her way a countryman on horseback seeking a strayed heifer, she begged him to come to her assistance, and endeavor to remove the wounded man to a more secure asylum.

Angelica, having prepared the plants by bruising them between two stones, laid them with her fair hand on Medoro's wound. The remedy soon restored in some degree the strength of the wounded man, who, before he would quit the spot, made them cover with earth and turf the bodies of his friend and of the prince. Then surrendering himself to the pity of his deliverers, he allowed them to place him on the horse of the shepherd, and conduct him to his cottage. It was a pleasant farm-house on the borders of the wood, bearing marks of comfort and competency. There the shepherd lived with his wife and children. There Angelica tended Medoro, and there, by the devoted care of the beautiful queen, his sad wound closed over, and he recovered his perfect health.

O Count Rinaldo, O King Sacripant! what availed it you to possess so many virtues and such fame? What advantage have you derived from all your high deserts? O hapless king, great Agrican! if you could return to life, how would you endure to see yourself rejected by one who will bow to the yoke of Hymen in favor of a young soldier of humble birth? And thou, Ferrau, and ye numerous others who a hundred times have put your lives at hazard for this cruel beauty, how bitter will it be to you to see her sacrifice you all to the claims of the humble Medoro!

There, under the low roof of a shepherd, the flame of Hymen was lighted for this haughty queen. She takes the shepherd's wife to serve in place of mother, the shepherd and his children for witnesses, and marries the happy Medoro.

Angelica, after her marriage, wishing to endow Medoro with the sovereignty of the countries which yet remained to her, took with him the road to the East. She had preserved through all her adventures a bracelet of gold enriched with precious stones, the present of the Count Orlando. Having nothing else wherewith to reward the good shepherd and his wife, who had served her with so much care and fidelity, she took the bracelet from her arm and gave it to them, and then the newly-married couple directed their steps toward those mountains which separate France and Spain, intending to wait at Barcelona a vessel which should take them on their way to the East.

CHAPTER XIII

ORLANDO MAD

ORLANDO, on the loss of Angelica, laid aside his crest and arms, and arrayed himself in a suit of black armor, expressive of his despair. In this guise he carried such slaughter among the ranks of the infidels, that both armies were astonished at the achievements of the stranger knight. Mandricardo, who had been absent from the battle, heard the report of these achievements, and determined to test for himself the valor of the knight so extolled. He it was who broke in upon the conference of Zerbino and Isabella, and their benefactor Orlando, as they stood occupied in mutual felicitations, after the happy reunion of the lovers by the prowess of the paladin.

Mandricardo, after contemplating the group for a moment, addressed himself to Orlando in these words: "Thou must be the man I seek. For ten days and more I have been on thy track. The fame of thy exploits has brought me hither, that I may measure my strength with thine. Thy crest and shield prove thee the same who spread such slaughter among our troops. But these marks are superfluous, and if I saw thee among a hundred I should know thee by thy martial bearing to be the man I seek."

"I respect thy courage," said Orlando; "such a design could not have sprung up in any but a brave and generous mind. If the desire to see me has brought thee hither, I would, if it were possible, show thee my inmost soul. I will remove my visor, that you may satisfy your curiosity; but when you have done so, I hope that you will also try and see if my valor corresponds to my appearance."

"Come on," said the Saracen, "my first wish was to see and know thee; I will now gratify my second."

Orlando, observing Mandricardo, was surprised to see no sword at his side, nor mace at his saddle-bow. "And what weapon hast thou," said he, "if thy lance fail thee?"

"Do not concern yourself about that," said Mandricardo; "I have made many good knights give ground with no other weapon than you see. Know that I have sworn an oath never to bear a sword until I win back that famous Durindana that Orlando, the paladin, carries. That sword belongs to the suit of armor which I wear; that only is wanting. Without doubt it was stolen, but how it got into the hands of Orlando I know not. But I will make him pay dearly for it when I find him. I seek him the more anxiously that I may avenge with his blood the death of King Agrican, my father, whom he treacherously slew. I am sure he must have done it by treachery, for it was not in his power to subdue in fair fight such a warrior as my father."

"Thou liest," cried Orlando; "and all who say so lie. I am Orlando, whom you seek; yes, I am he who slew your father honorably. Hold, here is the sword: you shall have it if your courage avails to merit it. Though it belongs to me by right, I will not use it in this dispute. See, I hang it on this tree: you shall be master of it, if you bereave me of life; not else."

At these words, Orlando drew Durindana, and hung it on one of the branches of a tree near by.

Both knights, boiling with equal ardor, rode off in a semicircle; then rushed together with reins thrown loose, and struck one another with their lances. Both kept their seats, immovable. The splinters of their lances flew into the air, and no weapon remained for either but the fragment which he held in his hand. Then those two knights, covered with iron mail, were reduced to the necessity of fighting with staves, in the manner of two rustics, who dispute the boundary of a meadow, or the possession of a spring.

These clubs could not long keep whole in the hands of such sturdy smiters, who were soon reduced to fight with naked fists. Such warfare was more painful to him that gave than to him that received the blows. They next clasped, and strained each his adversary, as Hercules did Antæus. Mandricardo, more enraged than Orlando, made violent efforts to unseat the paladin, and dropped the rein of his horse. Orlando, more calm, perceived it. With one hand he resisted Mandricardo, with the other he twitched the horse's bridle over the ears of the animal. The Saracen dragged Orlando with all his might, but Orlando's thighs held the saddle like a vise. At last the efforts of the Saracen broke the girths of Orlando's horse; the saddle slipped; the knight, firm in his stirrups, slipped with it, and came to the ground hardly conscious of his fall. The noise of his armor in falling startled Mandricardo's horse, now without a bridle. He started off in full career, heeding neither trees nor rocks nor broken ground. Urged by fright, he ran with furious speed, carrying his master, who, almost distracted with rage, shouted and beat the animal with his fists, and thereby impelled his flight. After running thus three miles or more, a deep ditch opposed their progress. The horse and rider fell headlong into it, and did not find the bottom covered with feather-beds or roses. They got sadly bruised; but were lucky enough to escape without any broken limbs.

Mandricardo, as soon as he gained his feet, seized the horse by his mane with fury, but, having no bridle, could not hold him. He looked round in hopes of finding something that would do for a rein. Just then fortune, who seemed willing to help him at last, brought that way a peasant with a bridle in his hand, who was in search of his farm horse that had strayed away.

Orlando, having speedily repaired his horse's girths, remounted, and waited a good hour for the Saracen to return. Not seeing him, he concluded to go in search of him. He took an affectionate leave of Zerbino and Isabella, who would willingly have followed him; but this the brave paladin would by no means permit. He held it un-knightly to go in search of an enemy accompanied by a friend, who might act as a defender. Therefore, desiring them to say to Mandricardo, if they should meet him, that his purpose was to tarry in the neighborhood three days, and then repair to the camp of Charlemagne, he took down Durindana from the tree, and proceeded in the direction which the Saracen's horse had taken. But the animal, having no guide but its terror, had so doubled and confused its traces that Orlando, after two days spent in the search, gave up the attempt.

It was about the middle of the third day when the paladin arrived on the pleasant bank of a stream which wound through a meadow enamelled with flowers. High trees, whose tops met and formed an arbor, overshadowed the fountain; and the breeze which blew through their foliage tempered the heat. Hither the shepherds used to resort to quench their thirst, and to enjoy the shelter from the midday sun. The air, perfumed with the flowers, seemed to breathe fresh strength into their veins. Orlando felt the influence, though covered with his armor. He stopped in this delicious arbor, where everything seemed to invite to repose. But he could not have chosen a more fatal asylum. He there spent the most miserable moments of his life.

He looked around, and noted with pleasure all the charms of the spot. He saw that some of the trees were carved with inscriptions,—he drew near, and read them, and what was his surprise to find that they composed the name of Angelica. Farther on, he found the name of Medoro mixed with hers. The paladin thought he dreamed. He stood like one amazed,—like a bird that, rising to fly, finds its feet caught in a net.

Orlando followed the course of the stream, and came to one of its turns where the rocks of the mountain bent in such a way as to form a sort of grotto. The twisted stems of ivy and the wild vine draped the entrance of this recess, scooped by the hand of nature.

The unhappy paladin, on entering the grotto, saw letters which appeared to have been lately carved. They were verses which Medoro had written in honor of his happy nuptials with the beautiful queen. Orlando tried to persuade himself it must be some other Angelica whom those verses celebrated, and as for Medoro he had never heard his name. The sun was now declining, and Orlando remounted his horse, and went on his way. He soon saw the roof of a cottage whence the smoke ascended; he heard the barking of dogs and the lowing of cattle, and arrived at a humble dwelling which seemed to offer an asylum for the night. The inmates, as soon as they saw him, hastened to render him service. One took his horse, another his shield and cuirass, another his golden spurs. This cottage was the very same where Medoro had been carried, deeply wounded,—where Angelica had tended him, and afterwards married him. The shepherd who lived in it loved to tell everybody the story of this marriage, and soon related it, with all its details, to the miserable Orlando.

Having finished it, he went away, and returned with the precious bracelet which Angelica, grateful for his services, had given him as a memorial. It was the one which Orlando had himself given her.

This last touch was the finishing stroke to the excited paladin. Frantic, exasperated, he exclaimed against the ungrateful and cruel princess who had disdained him, the most renowned, the most indomitable of all the paladins of France,—him, who had rescued her from the most alarming perils,—him, who had fought the most terrible battles for her sake,—she to prefer to him a young Saracen! The pride of the noble Count was deeply wounded. Indignant, frantic, a victim to ungovernable rage, he rushed into the forest, uttering the most frightful shrieks.

"No, no!" cried he, "I am not the man they take me for! Orlando is dead! I am only the wandering ghost of that unhappy Count, who is now suffering the torments of hell!"

Orlando wandered all night, as chance directed, through the wood, and at sunrise his destiny led him to the fountain where Medoro had engraved the fatal inscription. The frantic paladin saw it a second time with fury, drew his sword, and hacked it from the rock.

Unlucky grotto! you shall no more attract by your shade and coolness, you shall no more shelter with your arch either shepherd or flock. And you, fresh and pure fountain, you may not escape the rage of the furious Orlando! He cast into the fountain branches, trunks of trees which he tore up, pieces of rocks which he broke off, plants uprooted, with the earth adhering, and turf and bushes, so as to choke the fountain, and destroy the purity of its waters. At length, exhausted by his violent exertions, bathed in sweat, breathless, Orlando sunk panting upon the earth, and lay there insensible three days and three nights.

The fourth day he started up and seized his arms. His helmet, his buckler, he cast far from him; his hauberk and his clothes he rent asunder; the fragments were scattered through the wood. In

fine, he became a furious madman. His insanity was such that he
cared not to retain even his sword. But he had no need of Durindana,
nor of other arms, to do wonderful things. His prodigious strength
sufficed. At the first wrench of his mighty arm, he tore up a pine-
tree by the roots. Oaks, beeches, maples, whatever he met in his
path, yielded in like manner. The ancient forest soon became as bare
as the borders of a morass, where the fowler has cleared away the
bushes to spread his nets. The shepherds, hearing the horrible crash-
ing in the forest, abandoned their flocks to run and see the cause
of this unwonted uproar. By their evil star, or for their sins, they
were led thither. When they saw the furious state the Count was
in, and his incredible force, they would fain have fled out of his
reach, but in their fears lost their presence of mind. The madman
pursued them, seized one and rent him limb from limb, as easily
as one would pull ripe apples from a tree. He took another by the
feet, and used him as a club to knock down a third. The shepherds
fled; but it would have been hard for any to escape, if he had not
at that moment left them to throw himself with the same fury
upon their flocks. The peasants, abandoning their ploughs and
harrows, mounted on the roofs of buildings and pinnacles of the
rocks, afraid to trust themselves even to the oaks and pines. From
such heights they looked on, trembling at the raging fury of the unhappy Orlando. His fists, his teeth, his nails, his feet, seize, break,
and tear cattle, sheep, and swine, the most swift in flight alone being
able to escape him.

When at last terror had scattered everything before him, he
entered a cottage which was abandoned by its inhabitants, and there
found that which served for food. His long fast had caused him to
feel the most ravenous hunger. Seizing whatever he found that was
eatable, whether roots, acorns, or bread, raw meat or cooked, he
gorged it indiscriminately.

Issuing thence again, the frantic Orlando gave chase to whatever
living thing he saw, whether men or animals. Sometimes he pursued
the deer and hind, sometimes he attacked bears and wolves, and with
his naked hands killed and tore them, and devoured their flesh.

Thus he wandered, from place to place, through France, imperil-
ling his life a thousand ways, yet always preserved by some mysterious providence from a fatal result. But here we leave Orlando
for a time, that we may record what befell Zerbino and Isabella
after their parting with him.

The prince and his fair bride waited, by Orlando's request, near
the scene of the battle for three days, that, if Mandricardo should
return, they might inform him where Orlando would give him
another meeting. At the end of that time, their anxiety to know the

issue led them to follow Orlando's traces, which led them at last
to the wood where the trees were inscribed with the names of Angelica and Medoro. They remarked how all these inscriptions were
defaced, and how the grotto was disordered, and the fountain clogged
with rubbish. But that which surprised them and distressed them
most of all was to find on the grass the cuirass of Orlando, and not far
from it his helmet, the same which the renowned Almontes once
wore.

Hearing a horse neigh in the forest, Zerbino turned his eyes in
that direction, and saw Brigliadoro, with the bridle yet hanging
at the saddle-bow. He looked round for Durindana, and found that
famous sword, without the scabbard, lying on the grass. He saw
also the fragments of Orlando's other arms and clothing scattered
on all sides over the plain.

Zerbino and Isabella stood in astonishment and grief, not knowing what to think, but little imagining the true cause. If they had
found any marks of blood on the arms or on the fragments of the
clothing, they would have supposed him slain, but there were none.
While they were in this painful uncertainty, they saw a young peasant approach. He, not yet recovered from the terror of the scene
which he had witnessed from the top of a rock, told them the whole
of the sad events.

Zerbino, with his eyes full of tears, carefully collected all the
scattered arms. Isabella also dismounted to aid him in the sad
duty. When they had collected all the pieces of that rich armor,
they hung them like a trophy on a pine; and to prevent their being
violated by any passers-by, Zerbino inscribed on the bark this
caution: "These are the arms of the Paladin Orlando."

Having finished this pious work, he remounted his horse, and just
then a knight rode up, and requested Zerbino to tell him the meaning of the trophy. The prince related the facts as they had happened; and Mandricardo, for it was that Saracen knight, full of
joy, rushed forward, and seized the sword, saying, "No one can
censure me for what I do; this sword is mine; I can take my own
wherever I find it. It is plain that Orlando, not daring to defend
it against me, has counterfeited madness to excuse him in surrendering it."

Zerbino vehemently exclaimed, "Touch not that sword. Think
not to possess it without a contest. If it be true that the arms you
wear are those of Hector, you must have got them by theft, and
not by prowess."

Immediately they attacked one another with the utmost fury.
The air resounded with thick-falling blows. Zerbino, skilful and
alert, evaded for a time with good success the strokes of Durindana;

but at length a terrible blow struck him on the neck. He fell from his horse, and the Tartar king, possessed of the spoils of his victory, rode away.

CHAPTER XIV

ZERBINO AND ISABELLA

ZERBINO's pain at seeing the Tartar prince go off with the sword surpassed the anguish of his wound; but now the loss of blood so reduced his strength, that he could not move from where he fell. Isabella, not knowing whither to resort for help, could only bemoan him, and chide her cruel fate. Zerbino said, "If I could but leave thee, my best beloved, in some secure abode, it would not distress me to die; but to abandon thee so, without protection, is sad indeed." She replied, "Think not to leave me, dearest; our souls shall not be parted; this sword will give me the means to follow thee." Zerbino's last words implored her to banish such a thought, but live, and be true to his memory. Isabella promised, with many tears, to be faithful to him so long as life should last.

When he ceased to breathe, Isabella's cries resounded through the forest, and reached the ears of a reverend hermit, who hastened to the spot. He soothed and calmed her, urging those consolations which the word of God supplies; and at last brought her to wish for nothing else but to devote herself for the rest of life wholly to religion.

As she could not bear the thoughts of leaving her dead lord abandoned, the body was, by the good hermit's aid, placed upon the horse, and taken to the nearest inhabited place, where a chest was made for it, suitable to be carried with them on their way. The hermit's plan was to escort his charge to a monastery, not many days' journey distant, where Isabella resolved to spend the remainder of her life. Thus they travelled day after day, choosing the most retired ways, for the country was full of armed men. One day a cavalier met them, and barred their way. It was no other than Rodomont, king of Algiers, who had just left the camp of Agramant, full of indignation for a fancied wrong received from that leader. At sight of the lovely lady and her reverend attendant, with their horse laden with a burden draped with black, he asked the meaning of their journey. Isabella told him her affliction, and her resolution to renounce the world and devote herself to religion, and to the memory of the friend she had lost. Rodomont laughed scornfully at this, and told her that her project was absurd; that charms like hers were meant to be enjoyed, not buried, and that he himself would more than make amends for her dead lover. The monk,

who promptly interposed to rebuke this impious talk, was commanded to hold his peace; and still persisting, was seized by the
knight and hurled over the edge of the cliff, where he fell into the
sea, and was drowned.

Rodomont, when he had got rid of the hermit, again applied to
the sad lady, heartless with affright, and, in the language used by
lovers, said, "she was his very heart, his life, his light." Having laid
aside all violence, he humbly sued that she would accompany him
to his retreat, near by. It was a ruined chapel from which the monks
had been driven by the disorders of the time, and which Rodomont
had taken possession of. Isabella, who had no choice but to obey,
followed him, meditating as she went what resource she could find
to escape out of his power, and keep her vow to her dead husband,
to be faithful to his memory as long as life should last. At length
she said, "If, my lord, you will let me go and fulfil my vow, and
my intention, as I have already declared it, I will bestow upon you
what will be to you of more value than a hundred women's hearts.
I know an herb, and I have seen it on our way, which, rightly prepared, affords a juice of such power, that the flesh, if laved with it,
becomes impenetrable to sword or fire. This liquor I can make, and
will, to-day, if you will accept my offer; and when you have seen
its virtue, you will value it more than if all Europe were made your
own."

Rodomont, at hearing this, readily promised all that was asked,
so eager was he to learn a secret that would make him as Achilles
was of yore. Isabella, having collected such herbs as she thought
proper, and boiled them, with certain mysterious signs and words,
at length declared her labor done, and, as a test, offered to try its
virtue on herself. She bathed her neck and bosom with the liquor,
and then called on Rodomont to smite with all his force, and see
whether his sword had power to harm. The pagan, who during the
preparations had taken frequent draughts of wine, and scarce knew
what he did, drew his sword at the word, and struck across her neck
with all his might, and the fair head leapt sundered from the snowy
neck and breast.

Rude and unfeeling as he was, the pagan knight lamented bitterly
this sad result. To honor her memory he resolved to do a work as
unparalleled as her devotion. From all parts round he caused laborers
to be brought, and had a tower built to enclose the chapel, within
which the remains of Zerbino and Isabella were entombed. Across
the stream which flowed near by he built a bridge, scarce two yards
wide, and added neither parapet nor rail. On the top of the tower
a sentry was placed, who, when any traveller approached the bridge,
gave notice to his master. Rodomont thereupon sallied out, and

defied the approaching knight to fight him upon the bridge, where any chance step a little aside would plunge the rider headlong in the stream. This bridge he vowed to keep until a thousand suits of armor should be won from conquered knights, wherewith to build a trophy to his victim and her lord.

Within ten days the bridge was built, and the tower was in progress. In a short time many knights, either seeking the shortest route, or tempted by a desire of adventure, had made the attempt to pass the bridge. All, without exception, had lost either arms or life, or both; some falling before Rodomont's lance, others precipitated into the river. One day, as Rodomont stood urging his workmen, it chanced that Orlando in furious mood came thither, and approached the bridge. Rodomont halloed to him, "Halt, churl; presume not to set foot upon that bridge; it was not made for such as you!" Orlando took no notice, but pressed on. Just then a gentle damsel rode up. It was Flordelis, who was seeking her Florismart. She saw Orlando, and, in spite of his strange appearance, recognized him. Rodomont, not used to have his commands disobeyed, laid hands on the madman, and would have thrown him into the river, but to his astonishment found himself in the grip of one not so easily disposed of. "How can a fool have such strength?" he growled between his teeth. Flordelis stopped to see the issue, where each of these two puissant warriors strove to throw the other from the bridge. Orlando at last had strength enough to lift his foe with all his armor, and fling him over the side, but had not wit to clear himself from him, so both fell together. High flashed the wave as they together smote its surface. Here Orlando had the advantage; he was naked, and could swim like a fish. He soon reached the bank, and, careless of praise or blame, stopped not to see what came of the adventure. Rodomont, entangled with his armor, escaped with difficulty to the bank. Meantime, Flordelis passed the bridge unchallenged.

After long wandering without success she returned to Paris, and there found the object of her search; for Florismart, after the fall of Albracca, had repaired thither. The joy of meeting was clouded to Florismart by the news which Flordelis brought of Orlando's wretched plight. The last she had seen of him was when he fell with Rodomont into the stream. Florismart, who loved Orlando like a brother, resolved to set out immediately, under guidance of the lady, to find him, and bring him where he might receive the treatment suited to his case. A few days brought them to the place where they found the Tartar king still guarding the bridge. The usual challenge and defiance was made, and the knights rode to encounter one another on the bridge. At the first encounter both horses were overthrown; and, having no space to regain their footing, fell with their riders into the water. Rodomont, who knew the soundings of the stream, soon recovered the land; but Florismart was carried downward by the current, and landed at last on a bank of mud where his horse could hardly find footing. Flordelis, who watched the battle from the bridge, seeing her lover in this piteous case, exclaimed aloud, "Ah! Rodomont, for love of her whom dead you honor, have pity on me, who love this knight, and slay him not. Let it suffice he yields his armor to the pile, and none more glorious will it bear than he." Her prayer, so well directed, touched the pagan's heart, though hard to move, and he lent his aid to help the knight to land. He kept him a prisoner, however, and added his armor to the pile. Flordelis, with a heavy heart, went her way.

———

We must now return to Rogero, who, when we parted with him, was engaged in an adventure which arrested his progress to the monastery whither he was bound with the intention of receiving baptism, and thus qualifying himself to demand Bradamante as his bride. On his way he met with Mandricardo, and the quarrel was revived respecting the right to wear the badge of Hector. After a warm discussion, both parties agreed to submit the question to King Agramant, and for that purpose took their way to the Saracen camp. Here they met Gradasso, who had his controversy also with Mandricardo. This warrior claimed the sword of Orlando, denying the right of Mandricardo to possess it in virtue of his having found it abandoned by its owner. King Agramant strove in vain to reconcile these quarrels, and was forced at last to consent that the points in dispute should be settled by one combat, in which Mandricardo should meet one of the other champions, to whom should be committed the cause of both. Rogero was chosen by lot to maintain Gradasso's cause and his own. Great preparations were made for this signal contest. On the appointed day it was fought in the presence of Agramant, and of the whole army. Rogero won it; and Mandricardo, the conqueror of Hector's arms, the challenger of Orlando, and the slayer of Zerbino, lost his life. Gradasso received Durindana as his prize, which lost half its value in his eyes, since it was won by another's prowess, not his own.

Rogero, though victorious, was severely wounded, and lay helpless many weeks in the camp of Agramant, while Bradamante, ignorant of the cause of his delay, expected him at Montalban. Thither he had promised to repair in fifteen days, or twenty at furthest, hoping to have obtained by that time an honorable discharge from his obligations to the Saracen commander. The twenty days were passed, and a month more, and still Rogero came not, nor did any tidings reach Bradamante accounting for his absence At the end of that time, a wandering knight brought news of the famous combat, and of Rogero's wound. He added, what alarmed Brada- mante still more, that Marphisa, a female warrior, young and fair, was in attendance on the wounded knight. He added, that the whole army expected that, as soon as Rogero's wounds were healed, the pair would be united in marriage.

Bradamante, distressed by this news, though she believed it but in part, resolved to go immediately and see for herself. She mounted Rabican, the horse of Astolpho, which he had committed to her care, and took with her the lance of gold, though unaware of its wonderful powers. Thus accoutred, she left the castle, and took the road toward Paris and the camp of the Saracens.

Marphisa, whose devotion to Rogero in his illness had so excited the jealousy of Bradamante, was the twin sister of Rogero. She, with him, had been taken in charge when an infant by Atlantes, the magician, but while yet a child she had been stolen away by an Arab tribe. Adopted by their chief, she had early learned horseman- ship and skill in arms, and at this time had come to the camp of Agramant with no other view than to see and test for herself the prowess of the warriors of either camp, whose fame rang through the world. Arriving at the very moment of the late encounter, the name of Rogero, and some few facts of his story which she learned, were enough to suggest the idea that it was her brother whom she saw victorious in the single combat. Inquiry satisfied the two of their near kindred, and from that moment Marphisa devoted herself to the care of her new-found and much-loved brother.

In those moments of seclusion Rogero informed his sister of what he had learned of their parentage from old Atlantes. Rogero, their father, a Christian knight, had won the heart of Galaciella, daughter of the Sultan of Africa, and sister of King Agramant, converted her to the Christian faith, and secretly married her. The Sultan, enraged at his daughter's marriage, drove her husband into exile, and caused her with her infant children, Rogero and Marphisa, to be placed in a boat and committed to the winds and waves, to perish; from which fate they were saved by Atlantes. On hearing this, Marphisa ex- claimed, "How can you, brother, leave our parents unavenged so long, and even submit to serve the son of the tyrant who so wronged them?" Rogero replied, that it was but lately he had learned the full truth; that when he learned it he was already embarked with Agramant, from whom he had received knighthood, and that he only waited for a suitable opportunity when he might with honor desert his standard, and at the same time return to the faith of his fathers.

Marphisa hailed this resolution with joy, and declared her intention to join with him in embracing the Christian faith.

———

We left Bradamante when, mounted on Rabican and armed with Astolpho's lance, she rode forth, determined to learn the cause of Rogero's long absence. One day, as she rode, she met a damsel, of visage and of manners fair, but overcome with grief. It was Flordelis, who was seeking far and near a champion capable of liberating and avenging her lord. Flordelis marked the approaching warrior, and, judging from appearances, thought she had found the champion she sought. "Are you, Sir Knight," she said, "so daring and so kind as to take up my cause against a fierce and cruel warrior who has made prisoner of my lord, and forced me thus to be a wanderer and a suppliant?" Then she related the events which had happened at the bridge. Bradamante, to whom noble enterprises were always welcome, readily embraced this, and the rather as in her gloomy forebodings she felt as if Rogero was forever lost to her.

Next day the two arrived at the bridge. The sentry descried them approaching, and gave notice to his lord, who thereupon donned his armor and went forth to meet them. Here, as usual, he called on the advancing warrior to yield his horse and arms an oblation to the tomb. Bradamante replied, asking by what right he called on the innocent to do penance for his crime. "Your life and your armor," she added, "are the fittest offering to her tomb, and I, a woman, the fittest champion to take them." With that she couched her spear, spurred her horse, and ran to the encounter. King Rodomont came on with speed. The trampling sounded on the bridge like thunder. It took but a moment to decide the contest. The golden lance did its office, and that fierce Moor, so renowned in tourney, lay extended on the bridge. "Who is the loser now?" said Bradamante: but Rodomont, amazed that a woman's hand should have laid him low, could not or would not answer. Silent and sad, he raised himself, unbound his helm and mail, and flung them against the tomb; then, sullen and on foot, left the ground; but first gave orders to one of his squires to release all his prisoners. They had been sent off to Africa. Besides Florismart, there were Sansonnet and Oliver, who had ridden that way in quest of Orlando, and had both in turn been overthrown in the encounter.

Bradamante after her victory resumed her route, and in due time reached the Christian camp, where she readily learned an explanation of the mystery which had caused her so much anxiety. Rogero and his fair and brave sister, Marphisa, were too illustrious by their station and exploits not to be the frequent topic of discourse even among their adversaries, and all that Bradamante was anxious to know reached her ear, almost without inquiry.

We now return to Gradasso, who by Rogero's victory had been made possessor of Durindana. There now only remained to him to seek the horse of Rinaldo; and the challenge, given and accepted, was yet to be fought with that warrior, for it had been interrupted by the arts of Malagigi. Gradasso now sought another meeting with Rinaldo, and met with no reluctance on his part. As the combat was for the possession of Bayard, the knights dismounted and fought on foot. Long time the battle lasted. Rinaldo, knowing well the deadly stroke of Durindana, used all his art to parry or avoid its blow. Gradasso struck with might and main, but wellnigh all his strokes were spent in air, or if they smote, they fell obliquely and did little harm.

Thus had they fought long, glancing at one another's eyes, and seeing naught else, when their attention was arrested perforce by a strange noise. They turned, and beheld the good Bayard attacked by a monstrous bird. Perhaps it was a bird, for such it seemed; but when or where such a bird was ever seen I have nowhere read, except in Turpin; and I am inclined to believe that it was not a bird, but a fiend, evoked from underground by Malagigi, and thither sent on purpose to interrupt the fight. Whether a fiend or a fowl, the monster flew right at Bayard, and clapped his wings in his face. Thereat the steed broke loose, and ran madly across the plain, pursued by the bird, till Bayard plunged into the wood, and was lost to sight.

Rinaldo and Gradasso, seeing Bayard's escape, agreed to suspend their battle till they could recover the horse, the object of contention. Gradasso mounted his steed, and followed the foot-marks of Bayard into the forest. Rinaldo, never more vexed in spirit, remained at the spot, Gradasso having promised to return thither with the horse, if he found him. He did find him, after long search, for he had the good fortune to hear him neigh. Thus he became possessed of both the objects for which he had led an army from his own country, and invaded France. He did not forget his promise to bring Bayard back to the place where he had left Rinaldo; but, only muttering, "Now I have got him, he little knows me who expects me to give him up; if Rinaldo wants the horse, let him seek him in India, as I have sought him in France,"—he made the best of his way to Arles, where his vessels lay; and in possession of the two objects of his ambition, the horse and the sword, sailed away to his own country.

CHAPTER XV

ASTOLPHO IN ABYSSINIA

When we last parted with the adventurous paladin Astolpho, he was just commencing that flight over the countries of the world from which he promised himself so much gratification. Our readers are aware that the eagle and the falcon have not so swift a flight as the Hippogriff on which Astolpho rode. It was not long, therefore, before the paladin, directing his course toward the southeast, arrived over that part of Africa where the great river Nile has its source. Here he alighted, and found himself in the neighborhood of the capital of Abyssinia, ruled by Senapus, whose riches and power were immense. His palace was of surpassing splendor; the bars of the gates, the hinges and locks, were all of pure gold; in fact this metal, in that country, is put to all those uses for which we employ iron. It is so common that they prefer for ornamental purposes rock crystal, of which all the columns were made. Precious stones of different kinds, rubies, emeralds, sapphires, and topazes were set in ornamental designs, and the walls and ceilings were adorned with pearls.

It is in this country those famous balms grow of which there are some few plants in that part of Judæa called Gilead. Musk, ambergris, and numerous gums, so precious in Europe, are here in their native climate. It is said the Sultan of Egypt pays a vast tribute to the monarch of this country to hire him not to cut off the source of the Nile, which he might easily do, and cause the river to flow in some other direction, thus depriving Egypt of the source of its fertility.

At the time of Astolpho's arrival in his dominions, this monarch was in great affliction. In spite of his riches and the precious productions of his country, he was in danger of dying of hunger. He was a prey to a flock of obscene birds called Harpies, which attacked him whenever he sat at meat, and with their claws snatched, tore, and scattered everything, overturning the vessels, devouring the food, and infecting what they left with their filthy touch. It was said this punishment was inflicted upon the king because when young, and filled with pride and presumption, he had attempted to invade with an army the terrestrial paradise, which is situated on the top of a mountain whence the Nile draws its source. Nor was this his only punishment. He was struck blind.

Astolpho, on arriving in the dominions of this monarch, hastened to pay him his respects. King Senapus received him graciously, and ordered a splendid repast to be prepared in honor of his arrival.

While the guests were seated at table, Astolpho filling the place of
dignity at the king's right hand, the horrid scream of the Harpies
was heard in the air, and soon they approached, hovering over the
tables, seizing the food from the dishes, and overturning everything
with the flapping of their broad wings. In vain the guests struck at
them with knives and any weapons which they had, and Astolpho
drew his sword and gave them repeated blows, which seemed to
have no more effect upon them than if their bodies had been made
of tow.

At last Astolpho thought of his horn. He first gave warning to
the king and his guests to stop their ears; then blew a blast. The
Harpies, terrified at the sound, flew away as fast as their wings
could carry them. The paladin mounted his Hippogriff, and pursued
them, blowing his horn as often as he came near them. They
stretched their flight towards the great mountain, at the foot of
which there is a cavern, which is thought to be the mouth of the
infernal abodes. Hither those horrid birds flew, as if to their home.
Having seen them all disappear in the recess, Astolpho cared not to
pursue them farther, but, alighting, rolled huge stones into the
mouth of the cave, and piled branches of trees therein, so that he
effectually barred their passage out, and we have no evidence of
their ever having been seen since in the outer air.

After this labor, Astolpho refreshed himself by bathing in a
fountain whose pure waters bubbled from a cleft of the rock.
Having rested awhile, an earnest desire seized him of ascending the
mountain which towered above him. The Hippogriff bore him swiftly
upwards, and landed him on the top of the mountain, which he
found to be an extensive plain.

A splendid palace rose in the middle of this plain, whose walls
shone with such brilliancy that mortal eyes could hardly bear the
sight. Astolpho guided the winged horse towards this edifice, and
made him poise himself in the air while he took a leisurely survey
of this favored spot and its environs. It seemed as if nature and
art had striven with one another to see which could do the most
for its embellishment.

Astolpho, on approaching the edifice, saw a venerable man advance to meet him. This personage was clothed in a long vesture as
white as snow, while a mantle of purple covered his shoulders, and
hung down to the ground. A white beard descended to his middle,
and his hair, of the same color, overshadowed his shoulders. His eyes
were so brilliant, that Astolpho felt persuaded that he was a blessed
inhabitant of the heavenly mansions.

The sage, smiling benignantly upon the paladin, who from respect had dismounted from his horse, said to him: "Noble chevalier,

know that it is by the Divine will you have been brought to the terrestrial paradise. Your mortal nature could not have borne to scale these heights and reach these seats of bliss if it were not the will of Heaven that you should be instructed in the means to succor Charles, and to sustain the glory of our holy faith. I am prepared to impart the needed counsels; but before I begin, let me welcome you to our sojourn. I doubt not your long fast and distant journey have given you a good appetite."

The aspect of the venerable man filled the prince with admiration; but his surprise ceased when he learned from him that he was that one of the Apostles of our Lord to whom he said, "I will that thou tarry till I come."

St. John, conducting Astolpho, rejoined his companions. These were the patriarch Enoch and the prophet Elijah; neither of whom had yet seen his dying day, but, taken from our lower world, were dwelling in a region of peace and joy, in a climate of eternal spring, till the last trumpet shall sound.

The three holy inhabitants of the terrestrial paradise received Astolpho with the greatest kindness, carried him to a pleasant apartment, and took great care of the Hippogriff, to whom they gave such food as suited him, while to the prince they presented fruits so delicious that he felt inclined to excuse our first parents for their sin in eating them without permission.

Astolpho, having recruited his strength, not only by these excellent fruits, but also by sweet sleep, roused himself at the first blush of dawn, and, as soon as he left his chamber, met the beloved Apostle coming to seek him. St. John took him by the hand, and told him many things relating to the past and the future. Among others, he said, "Son, let me tell you what is now going on in France. Orlando, the illustrious prince who received at his birth the endowment of strength and courage more than mortal, raised up as was Samson of old to be the champion of the true faith, has been guilty of the basest ingratitude in leaving the Christian camp when it most needed the support of his arm, to run after a Saracen princess, whom he would fain marry, though she scorns him. To punish him, his reason has been taken away, so that he runs naked through the land, over mountains and through valleys, without a ray of intelligence. The duration of his punishment has been fixed at three months, and that time having nearly expired, you have been brought hither to learn from us the means by which the reason of Orlando may be restored. True, you will be obliged to make a journey with me, and we must even leave the earth, and ascend to the moon, for it is in that planet we are to seek the remedy for the madness of the paladin. I propose to make our journey this evening, as soon as the moon appears over our head."

As soon as the sun sunk beneath the seas, and the moon presented its luminous disk, the holy man had the chariot brought out in which he was accustomed to make excursions among the stars, the same which was employed long ago to convey Elijah up from earth. The saint made Astolpho seat himself beside him, took the reins, and giving the word to the coursers, they bore them upward with astonishing celerity.

At length they reached the great continent of the Moon. Its surface appeared to be of polished steel, with here and there a spot which, like rust, obscured its brightness. The paladin was astonished to see that the earth, with all its seas and rivers, seemed but an insignificant spot in the distance.

The prince discovered in this region so new to him rivers, lakes, plains, hills, and valleys. Many beautiful cities and castles enriched the landscape. He saw also vast forests, and heard in them the sound of horns and the barking of dogs, which led him to conclude that the nymphs were following the chase.

The knight, filled with wonder at all he saw, was conducted by the saint to a valley, where he stood amazed at the riches strewed all around him. Well he might be so, for that valley was the receptacle of things lost on earth, either by men's fault, or by the effect of time and chance. Let no one suppose we speak here of kingdoms or of treasures; they are the toys of Fortune, which she dispenses in turning her wheel; we speak of things which she can neither give nor take away. Such are reputations, which appear at one time so brilliant, and a short time after are heard of no more. Here, also, are countless vows and prayers for unattainable objects, lovers' sighs and tears, time spent in gaming, dressing, and doing nothing, the leisure of the dull and the intentions of the lazy, baseless projects, intrigues and plots; these and such like things fill all the valley.

Astolpho had a great desire to understand all that he saw, and which appeared to him so extraordinary. Among the rest, he observed a great mountain of blown bladders, from which issued indistinct noises. The saint told him these were the dynasties of Assyrian and Persian kings, once the wonder of the earth, of which now scarce the name remains.

Astolpho could not help laughing when the saint said to him, "All these hooks of silver and gold that you see are the gifts of courtiers to princes, made in the hope of getting something better in return." He also showed him garlands of flowers in which snares were concealed; these were flatteries and adulations, meant to deceive. But nothing was so comical as the sight of numerous grass-hoppers which had burst their lungs with chirping. These, he told him, were sonnets, odes, and dedications, addressed by venal poets to great people.

The paladin beheld with wonder what seemed a lake of spilled milk. "It is," said the saint, "the charity done by frightened misers on their death-beds." It would take too long to tell all that the valley contained: meannesses, affectations, pretended virtues, and concealed vices were there in abundance.

Among the rest, Astolpho perceived many days of his own lost, and many imprudent sallies which he had made, and would have been glad not to have been reminded of. But he also saw among so many lost things a great abundance of one thing which men are apt to think they all possess, and do not think it necessary to pray for,—good sense. This commodity appeared under the form of a liquor, most light and apt to evaporate. It was therefore kept in vials, firmly sealed. One of these was labelled, "The sense of the Paladin Orlando."

All the bottles were ticketed, and the sage placed one in Astolpho's hand, which he found was his own. It was more than half full. He was surprised to find there many other vials which contained almost the whole of the wits of many persons who passed among men for wise. Ah, how easy it is to lose one's reason! Some lose theirs by yielding to the sway of the passions; some, in braving tempests and shoals in search of wealth; some, by trusting too much to the promises of the great; some, by setting their hearts on trifles. As might have been expected, the bottles which held the wits of astrologers, inventors, metaphysicians, and above all, of poets, were in general the best filled of all.

Astolpho took his bottle, put it to his nose, and inhaled it all; and Turpin assures us that he was for a long time afterwards as sage as one could wish; but the Archbishop adds, that there was reason to fear that some of the precious fluid afterwards found its way back into the bottle. The paladin took also the bottle which belonged to Orlando. It was a large one, and quite full.

Before quitting the planetary region, Astolpho was conducted to an edifice on the borders of a river. He was shown an immense hall full of bundles of silk, linen, cotton, and wool. A thousand different colors, brilliant or dull, some quite black, were among these skeins. In one part of the hall an old woman was busy winding off yarns from all these different bundles. When she had finished a skein, another ancient dame took it and placed it with others; a third selected from the fleeces spun, and mingled them in due proportions. The paladin inquired what all this might be. "These old women," said the saint, "are the Fates, who spin, measure, and terminate the lives of mortals. As long as the thread stretches in one of those skeins, so long does the mortal enjoy the light of day; but nature and death are on the alert to shut the eyes of those whose thread is spun."

Each one of the skeins had a label of gold, silver, or iron, bearing the name of the individual to whom it belonged. An old man, who, in spite of the burden of years, seemed brisk and active, ran without ceasing to fill his apron with these labels, and carried them away to throw them into the river, whose name was Lethe. When he reached the shore of the river, the old man shook out his apron, and the labels sunk to the bottom. A small number only floated for a time, hardly one in a thousand. Numberless birds, hawks, crows, and vultures hovered over the stream, with clamorous cries, and strove to snatch from the water some of these names; but they were too heavy for them, and after a while the birds were forced to let them drop into the river of oblivion. But two beautiful swans, of snowy whiteness, gathered some few of the names, and returned with them to the shore, where a lovely nymph received them from their beaks, and carried them to a temple placed upon a hill, and suspended them for all time upon a sacred column, on which stood the statue of Immortality.

Astolpho was amazed at all this, and asked his guide to explain it. He replied, "The old man is Time. All the names upon the tickets would be immortal if the old man did not plunge them into the river of oblivion. Those clamorous birds which make vain efforts to save certain of the names are flatterers, pensioners, venal rhymesters, who do their best to rescue from oblivion the unworthy names of their patrons; but all in vain; they may keep them from their fate a little while, but erelong the river of oblivion must swallow them all.

"The swans, that with harmonious strains carry certain names to the temple of Eternal Memory, are the great poets, who save from oblivion worse than death the names of those they judge worthy of immortality. Swans of this kind are rare. Let monarchs know the true breed, and fail not to nourish with care such as may chance to appear in their time."

CHAPTER XVI

THE WAR IN AFRICA

WHEN Astolpho had descended to the earth with the precious phial, St. John showed him a plant of marvellous virtues, with which he told him he had only to touch the eyes of the king of Abyssinia to restore him to sight. "That important service," said the saint.

"added to your having delivered him from the Harpies, will induce
him to give you an army wherewith to attack the Africans in their
rear, and force them to return from France to defend their own
country." The saint also instructed him how to lead his troops in
safety across the great deserts, where caravans are often overwhelmed with moving columns of sand. Astolpho, fortified with
ample instructions, remounted the Hippogriff, thanked the saint,
received his blessing, and took his flight down to the level country.

Keeping the course of the river Nile, he soon arrived at the capital
of Abyssinia, and rejoined Senapus. The joy of the king was great
when he heard again the voice of the hero who had delivered him
from the Harpies. Astolpho touched his eyes with the plant which
he had brought from the terrestrial paradise, and restored their sight.
The king's gratitude was unbounded. He begged him to name a
reward, promising to grant it, whatever it might be. Astolpho asked
an army to go to the assistance of Charlemagne, and the king not
only granted him a hundred thousand men, but offered to lead them
himself.

The night before the day appointed for the departure of the
troops, Astolpho mounted his winged horse, and directed his flight
towards a mountain, whence the fierce South-wind issues, whose
blast raises the sands of the Nubian desert, and whirls them onward
in overwhelming clouds. The paladin, by the advice of St. John,
had prepared himself with a leather bag, which he placed adroitly,
with its mouth open, over the vent whence issues this terrible wind.
At the first dawn of morning the wind rushed from its cavern to
resume its daily course, and was caught in the bag, and securely tied
up. Astolpho, delighted with his prize, returned to his army, placed
himself at their head, and commenced his march. The Abyssinians
traversed without danger or difficulty those vast fields of sand which
separate their country from the kingdoms of Northern Africa, for
the terrible South-wind, taken completely captive, had not force
enough left to blow out a candle.

Senapus was distressed that he could not furnish any cavalry,
for his country, rich in camels and elephants, was destitute of horses.
This difficulty the saint had foreseen, and had taught Astolpho the
means of remedying. He now put those means in operation. Having
reached a place whence he beheld a vast plain and the sea, he
chose from his troops those who appeared to be the best made and
the most intelligent. These he caused to be arranged in squadrons
at the foot of a lofty mountain which bordered the plain, and he
himself mounted to the summit to carry into effect his great design.
Here he found vast quantities of fragments of rock and pebbles.
These he set rolling down the mountain's side, and, wonderful to

relate, as they rolled they grew in size, made themselves bodies, legs, necks, and long faces. Next they began to neigh, to curvet, to scamper on all sides over the plain. Some were bay, some roan, some dapple, some chestnut. The troops at the foot of the mountain exerted themselves to catch these new-created horses, which they easily did, for the miracle had been so considerate as to provide all the horses with bridles and saddles. Astolpho thus suddenly found himself supplied with an excellent corps of cavalry, not fewer (as Archbishop Turpin asserts) than eighty thousand strong. With these troops Astolpho reduced all the country to subjection, and at last arrived before the walls of Agramant's capital city, Biserta, to which he laid siege.

We must now return to the camp of the Christians, which lay before Arles, to which city the Saracens had retired after being defeated in a night attack led on by Rinaldo. Agramant here received the tidings of the invasion of his country by a fresh enemy, the Abyssinians, and learned that Biserta was in danger of falling into their hands. He took counsel of his officers, and decided to send an embassy to Charles, proposing that the whole quarrel should be submitted to the combat of two warriors, one from each side, according to the issue of which it should be decided which party should pay tribute to the other, and the war should cease. Charlemagne, who had not heard of the favorable turn which affairs had taken in Africa, readily agreed to this proposal, and Rinaldo was selected on the part of the Christians to sustain the combat.

The Saracens selected Rogero for their champion. Rogero was still in the Saracen camp, kept there by honor alone, for his mind had been opened to the truth of the Christian faith by the arguments of Bradamante, and he had resolved to leave the party of the infidels on the first favorable opportunity, and to join the Christian side. But his honor forbade him to do this while his former friends were in distress; and thus he waited for what time might bring forth, when he was startled by the announcement that he had been selected to uphold the cause of the Saracens against the Christians, and that his foe was to be Rinaldo, the brother of Bradamante.

While Rogero was overwhelmed with this intelligence, Bradamante on her side felt the deepest distress at hearing of the proposed combat. If Rogero should fall, she felt that no other man living was worthy of her love; and if, on the other hand, Heaven should resolve to punish France by the death of her chosen champion, Bradamante would have to deplore her brother, so dear to her, and be no less completely severed from the object of her affections.

While the fair lady gave herself up to these sad thoughts, the sage enchantress, Melissa, suddenly appeared before her. "Fear not, my daughter," said she, "I shall find a way to interrupt this combat which so distresses you."

Meanwhile Rinaldo and Rogero prepared their weapons for the conflict. Rinaldo had the choice, and decided that it should be on foot, and with no weapons but the battle-axe and poniard. The place assigned was a plain between the camp of Charlemagne and the walls of Arles.

Hardly had the dawn announced the day appointed for this memorable combat, when heralds proceeded from both sides to mark the lists. Erelong the African troops were seen to advance from the city, Agramant at their head; his brilliant arms adorned in the Moorish fashion, his horse a bay, with a white star on his forehead. Rogero marched at his side, and some of the greatest warriors of the Saracen camp attended him, bearing the various parts of his armor and weapons. Charlemagne, on his part, proceeded from his intrenchments, ranged his troops in semicircle, and stood surrounded by his peers and paladins. Some of them bore portions of the armor of Rinaldo, the celebrated Ogier, the Dane, bearing the helmet which Rinaldo took from Mambrino. Duke Namo of Bavaria and Salomon of Bretagne bore two axes, of equal weight, prepared for the occasion.

The terms of the combat were then sworn to with the utmost solemnity by all parties. It was agreed that, if from either part any attempt was made to interrupt the battle, both combatants should turn their arms against the party which should be guilty of the interruption; and both monarchs assented to the condition, that in such case the champion of the offending party should be discharged from his allegiance, and at liberty to transfer his arms to the other side.

When all the preparations were concluded, the monarchs and their attendants retired each to his own side, and the champions were left alone. The two warriors advanced with measured steps towards each other, and met in the middle of the space. They attacked one another at the same moment, and the air resounded with the blows they gave. Sparks flew from their battle-axes, while the velocity with which they managed their weapons astonished the beholders. Rogero, always remembering that his antagonist was the brother of his betrothed, could not aim a deadly wound; he strove only to ward off those levelled against himself. Rinaldo, on the other hand, much as he esteemed Rogero, spared not his blows, for he eagerly desired victory for his own sake, and for the sake of his country and his faith.

The Saracens soon perceived that their champion fought feebly, and gave not to Rinaldo such blows as he received from him. His disadvantage was so marked, that anxiety and shame were manifest on the countenance of Agramant. Melissa, one of the most acute enchantresses that ever lived, seized this moment to disguise herself under the form of Rodomont, that rude and impetuous warrior, who had now for some time been absent from the Saracen camp. Approaching Agramant, she said, "How could you, my lord, have the imprudence of selecting a young man without experience to oppose the most redoubtable warrior of France? Surely you must have been regardless of the honor of your arms, and of the fate of your empire! But it is not too late. Break without delay the agreement which is sure to result in your ruin." So saying, she addressed the troops who stood near. "Friends," said she, "follow me; under my guidance every one of you will be a match for a score of those feeble Christians." Agramant, delighted at seeing Rodomont once more at his side, gave his consent, and the Saracens, at the instant, couched their lances, set spurs to their steeds, and swept down upon the French. Melissa, when she saw her work successful, disappeared.

Rinaldo and Rogero, seeing the truce broken, and the two armies engaged in general conflict, stopped their battle; their martial fury ceased at once, they joined hands, and resolved to act no more on either side until it should be clearly ascertained which party had failed to observe its oath. Both renewed their promise to abandon forever the party which had been thus false and perjured.

Meanwhile, the Christians, after the first moment of surprise, met the Saracens with courage redoubled by rage at the treachery of their foes. Guido the Wild, brother and rival of Rinaldo, Griffon and Aquilant, sons of Oliver, and numerous others whose names have already been celebrated in our recitals, beat back the assailants, and at last, after prodigious slaughter, forced them to take shelter within the walls of Arles.

———

We will now return to Orlando, whom we last heard of as furiously mad, and doing a thousand acts of violence in his senseless rage. One day he came to the borders of a stream which intercepted his course. He swam across it, for he could swim like an otter, and on the other side saw a peasant watering his horse. He seized the animal, in spite of the resistance of the peasant, and rode it with furious speed till he arrived at the sea-coast, where Spain is divided from Africa by only a narrow strait. At the moment of his arrival, a vessel had just put off to cross the strait. She was full of people who, with glass in hand, seemed to be taking a merry farewell of the land, wafted by a favorable breeze.

The frantic Orlando cried out to them to stop and take him in; but they, having no desire to admit a madman to their company, paid him no attention. The paladin thought this behavior very uncivil; and by force of blows made his horse carry him into the water in pursuit of the ship. The wretched animal soon had only his head above water; but as Orlando urged him forward, nothing was left for the poor beast but either to die or swim over to Africa.

Already Orlando had lost sight of the bark; distance and the swell of the sea completely hid it from his sight. He continued to press his horse forward, till at last it could struggle no more, and sunk beneath him. Orlando, nowise concerned, stretched out his nervous arms, puffing the salt water from before his mouth, and carried his head above the waves. Fortunately they were not rough, scarce a breath of wind agitated the surface; otherwise, the invincible Orlando would then have met his death. But fortune, which it is said favors fools, delivered him from this danger, and landed him safe on the shore of Ceuta. Here he rambled along the shore till he came to where the black army of Astolpho held its camp.

Now it happened, just before this time, that a vessel filled with prisoners which Rodomont had taken at the bridge had arrived, and, not knowing of the presence of the Abyssinian army, had sailed right into port, where of course the prisoners and their captors changed places, the former being set at liberty and received with all joy, the latter sent to serve in the galleys. Astolpho thus found himself surrounded with Christian knights, and he and his friends were exchanging greetings and felicitations, when a noise was heard in the camp, and seemed to increase every moment.

Astolpho and his friends seized their weapons, mounted their horses, and rode to the quarter whence the noise proceeded. Imagine their astonishment when they saw that the tumult was caused by a single man, perfectly naked, and browned with dirt and exposure, but of a force and fury so terrible that he overturned all that offered to lay hands on him.

Astolpho, Dudon, Oliver, and Florismart gazed at him with amazement. It was with difficulty they knew him. Astolpho, who had been warned of his condition by his holy monitor, was the first to recognize him. As the paladins closed round Orlando, the madman dealt one and another a blow of his fist, which, if they had not been in armor, or he had had any weapon, would probably have despatched them; as it was, Dudon and Astolpho measured their length on the sand. But Florismart seized him from behind, Sansonnet and another grasped his legs, and at last they succeeded in securing him with ropes. They took him to the water-side and washed him well, and then Astolpho, having first bandaged his mouth so that he could not breathe except through his nose, brought the precious phial, uncorked it, and placed it adroitly under his nostrils, when the good Orlando took it all up in one breath. O marvellous prodigy! The paladin recovered in an instant all his intelligence. He felt like one who had awakened from a painful dream, in which he had believed that monsters were about to tear him to pieces. He seemed prostrated, silent, and abashed. Florismart, Oliver, and Astolpho stood gazing upon him, while he turned his eyes around and on himself. He seemed surprised to find himself naked, bound, and stretched on the sea-shore. After a few moments he recognized his friends, and spoke to them in a tone so tender that they hastened to unbind him, and to supply him with garments. Then they exerted themselves to console him, to diminish the weight with which his spirits were oppressed, and to make him forget the wretched condition into which he had been sunk.

Orlando, in recovering his reason, found himself also delivered from his insane attachment to the queen of Cathay. His heart felt now no further influenced by the recollection of her than to be moved with an ardent desire to retrieve his fame by some distinguished exploit. Astolpho would gladly have yielded to him the chief command of the army, but Orlando would not take from the friend to whom he owed so much the glory of the campaign; but in everything the two paladins acted in concert, and united their counsels. They proposed to make a general assault on the city of Biserta, and were only waiting a favorable moment, when their plan was interrupted by new events.

Agramant, after the bloody battle which followed the infraction of the truce, found himself so weak that he saw it was in vain to attempt to remain in France. So, in concert with Sobrino, the bravest and most trusted of his chiefs, he embarked to return to his own country, having previously sent off his few remaining troops in the same direction. The vessel which carried Agramant and Sobrino approached the shore where the army of Astolpho lay encamped before Biserta, and, having discovered this fact before it was too late, the king commanded the pilot to steer eastward, with a view to seek protection of the king of Egypt. But the weather becoming rough, he consented to the advice of his companions, and sought harbor in an island which lies between Sicily and Africa. There he found Gradasso, the warlike king of Sericane, who had come to France to possess himself of the horse Bayard and the sword Durindana; and, having procured both these prizes, was returning to his own country.

The two kings, who had been companions in arms under the walls of Paris, embraced one another affectionately. Gradasso learned with regret the reverses of Agramant, and offered him his troops and his person. He strongly deprecated resorting to Egypt for aid. "Remember the great Pompey," said he, "and shun that fatal shore. My plan," he continued, "is this: I mean to challenge Orlando to single combat. Possessed of such a sword and steed as mine, if he were made of steel or bronze, he could not escape me. He being removed, there will be no difficulty in driving back the Abyssinians. We will rouse against them the Moslem nations from the other side of the Nile, the Arabians, Persians, and Chaldeans, who will soon make Senapus recall his army to defend his own territories."

Agramant approved this advice except in one particular. "It is for me," said he, "to combat Orlando; I cannot with honor devolve that duty on another."

"Let us adopt a third course," said the aged warrior Sobrino. "I would not willingly remain a simple spectator of such a contest. Let us send three squires to the shore of Africa to challenge Orlando and any two of his companions in arms to meet us three in this island of Lampedusa."

This counsel was adopted; the three squires sped on their way; and now presented themselves, and rehearsed their message to the Christian knights.

Orlando was delighted, and rewarded the squires with rich gifts. He had already resolved to seek Gradasso and compel him to restore Durindana, which he had learned was in his possession. For his two companions, the Count chose his faithful friend Florismart and his cousin Oliver.

The three warriors embarked, and sailing with a favorable wind, the second morning showed them, on their right, the island where this important battle was to be fought. Orlando and his two companions, having landed, pitched their tent. Agramant had placed his opposite.

Next morning, as soon as Aurora brightened the edges of the horizon, the warriors of both parties armed themselves and mounted their horses. They took their positions, face to face, lowered their lances, placed them in rest, clapped spurs to their horses, and flew to the charge. Orlando met the charge of Gradasso. The paladin was unmoved, but his horse could not sustain the terrible shock of Bayard. He recoiled, staggered, and fell some paces behind. Orlando tried to raise him, but, finding his efforts unavailing, seized his shield, and drew his famous Balisardo. Meanwhile Agramant and the brave Oliver gained no advantage, one or the other; but Florismart unhorsed the King Sobrino. Having brought his foe to the ground, he would not pursue his victory, but hastened to attack Gradasso, who had overthrown Orlando. Seeing him thus engaged,

Orlando would not interfere, but ran with sword upraised upon
Sobrino, and with one blow deprived him of sense and motion.
Believing him dead, he next turned to aid his beloved Florismart.
That brave paladin, neither in horse nor arms equal to his antagonist, could but parry and evade the blows of the terrible Durindana. Orlando, eager to succor him, was delayed for a moment in
securing and mounting the horse of the King Sobrino. It was but
an instant, and with sword upraised, he rushed upon Gradasso;
who, noways disconcerted at the onset of this second foe, shouted
his defiance, and thrust at him with his sword, but, having mis-
calculated the distance, scarcely reached him, and failed to pierce
his mail. Orlando, in return, dealt him a blow with Balisardo, which
wounded as it fell, face, breast, and thigh, and, if he had been a
little nearer, would have cleft him in twain. Sobrino, by this time
recovered from his swoon, though severely wounded, raised himself on his legs, and looked to see how he might aid his friends.
Observing Agramant hard pressed by Oliver, he thrust his sword
into the bowels of the latter's horse, which fell, and bore down
his master, entangling his leg as he fell, so that Oliver could not
extricate himself. Florismart saw the danger of his friend, and ran
upon Sobrino with his horse, overthrew him, and then turned to
defend himself from Agramant. They were not unequally matched,
for though Agramant, mounted on Brigliadoro, had an advantage
over Florismart, whose horse was but indifferent, yet Agramant had
received a serious wound in his encounter with Oliver.

Nothing could exceed the fury of the encounter between Orlando
and Gradasso. Durindana, in the hands of Gradasso, clove asunder
whatever it struck; but such was the skill of Orlando, who perfectly knew the danger to which he was exposed from a stroke
of that weapon, it had not yet struck him in such a way as to inflict
a wound. Meanwhile, Gradasso was bleeding from many wounds,
and his rage and incaution increased every moment. In his desperation, he lifted Durindana with both hands, and struck so terrible
a blow full on the helmet of Orlando, that for a moment it stunned
the paladin. He dropped the reins, and his frightened horse scoured
with him over the plain. Gradasso turned to pursue him, but at that
moment saw Florismart in the very act of striking a fatal blow
at Agramant, whom he had unhorsed. While Florismart was wholly
intent upon completing his victory, Gradasso plunged his sword
into his side. Florismart fell from his horse, and bathed the plain
with his blood.

Orlando recovered himself just in time to see the deed. Whether
rage or grief predominated in his breast, I cannot tell; but, seizing
Balisardo with fury, his first blow fell upon Agramant, who was

nearest to him, and smote his head from his shoulders. At this sight, Gradasso, for the first time, felt his courage sink, and a dark presentiment of death come over him. He hardly stood on his defence when Orlando cast himself upon him, and gave him a fatal thrust. The sword penetrated his ribs, and came out a palm's breadth on the other side of his body.

Thus fell beneath the sword of the most illustrious paladin of France the bravest warrior of the Saracen host. Orlando then, as if despising his victory, leaped lightly to the ground, and ran to his dear friend Florismart, embraced him, and bathed him with his tears. Florismart still breathed. He could even command his voice to utter a few parting words: "Dear friend, do not forget me,— give me your prayers,—and oh! be a brother to Flordelis." He died in uttering her name.

After a few moments given to grief, Orlando turned to look for his other companion and his late foes. Oliver lay oppressed with the weight of his horse, from which he had in vain struggled to liberate himself. Orlando extricated him with difficulty; he then raised Sobrino from the earth, and committed him to his squire, treating him as gently as if he had been his own brother. For this terrible warrior was the most generous of men to a fallen foe. He took Bayard and Brigliadoro, with the arms of the conquered knights; their bodies and their other spoils he remitted to their attendants.

But who can tell the grief of Flordelis when she saw the warriors return, and found not Florismart as usual after absence hasten to her side. She knew by the aspect of the others that her lord was slain. At the thought, and before the question could pass her lips, she fell senseless upon the ground. When life returned, and she learned the truth of her worst fears, she bitterly upbraided herself that she had let him depart without her. "I might have saved him by a single cry when his enemy dealt him that treacherous blow, or I might have thrown myself between, and given my worthless life for his. Or if no more, I might have heard his last words, I might have given him a last kiss." So she lamented, and could not be comforted.

CHAPTER XVII

ROGERO AND BRADAMANTE

AFTER the interruption of the combat with Rinaldo, as we have related, Rogero was perplexed with doubts what course to take. The terms of the treaty required him to abandon Agramant, who had broken it, and to transfer his allegiance to Charlemagne; and his love for Bradamante called him in the same direction; but unwillingness to desert his prince and leader in the hour of distress forbade this course. Embarking, therefore, for Africa, he took his way to rejoin the Saracen army; but was arrested midway by a storm which drove the vessel on a rock. The crew took to their boat, but that was quickly swamped in the waves, and Rogero with the rest were compelled to swim for their lives. Then while buffeting the waves Rogero bethought him of his sin in so long delaying his Christian profession, and vowed in his heart that, if he should live to reach the land, he would no longer delay to be baptized. His vows were heard and answered; he succeeded in reaching the shore, and was aided and relieved on landing by a pious hermit, whose cell overlooked the sea. From him he received baptism, having first passed some days with him, partaking his humble fare, and receiving instruction in the doctrines of the Christian faith.

While these things were going on, Rinaldo, who had set out on his way to seek Gradasso and recover Bayard from him, hearing on his way of the great things which were doing in Africa, repaired thither to bear his part in them. He arrived too late to do more than join his friends in lamenting the loss of Florismart, and to rejoice with them in their victory over the Pagan knights. On the death of their king, the Africans gave up the contest, Biserta submitted, and the Christian knights had only to dismiss their forces, and return home. Astolpho took leave of his Abyssinian army, and sent them back laden with spoil to their own country, not forgetting to entrust to them the bag which held the winds, by means of which they were enabled to cross the sandy desert again without danger, and did not untie it till they reached their own country.

Orlando now, with Oliver, who much needed the surgeon's care, and Sobrino, to whom equal attention was shown, sailed in a swift vessel to Sicily, bearing with him the body of Florismart, to be laid in Christian earth. Rinaldo accompanied them, as did Sansonnet and the other Christian leaders. Arrived at Sicily, the funeral was solemnized with all the rites of religion, and with the profound grief of those who had known Florismart, or had heard of his fame. Then they resumed their course, steering for Marseilles. But Oliver's wound grew worse instead of better, and his sufferings so distressed his friends that they conferred together, not knowing what to do. Then said the pilot, "We are not far from an isle, where a holy hermit dwells alone in the midst of the sea. It is said none seek his counsel or his aid in vain. He hath wrought marvellous cures, and if you resort to that holy man, without doubt he can heal the knight." Orlando bade him steer thither, and soon the bark was laid safely beside the lonely rock; the wounded man was lowered into their boat, and carried by the crew to the hermit's cell. It was the same hermit with whom Rogero had taken refuge after his shipwreck, by whom he had been baptized, and with whom he was now staying, absorbed in sacred studies and meditations.

The holy man received Orlando and the rest with kindness, and inquired their errand; and being told that they had come for help for one who, warring for the Christian faith, was brought to perilous pass by a sad wound, he straightway undertook the cure. His applications were simple, but they were seconded by his prayers. The paladin was soon relieved from pain, and in a few days his foot was perfectly restored to soundness. Sobrino, as soon as he perceived the holy monk perform that wonder, cast aside his false prophet, and with contrite heart owned the true God, and demanded baptism at his hands. The hermit granted his request, and also by his prayers restored him to health, while all the Christian knights rejoiced in his conversion almost as much as at the restoration of Oliver. More than all, Rogero felt joy and gratitude, and daily grew in grace and faith.

Rogero was known by fame to all the Christian knights, but not even Rinaldo knew him by sight, though he had proved his prowess in combat. Sobrino made him known to them, and great was the joy of all when they found one whose valor and courtesy were renowned through the world no longer an enemy and unbeliever, but a convert and champion of the true faith. All press about the knight; one grasps his hand, another locks him fast in his embrace; but more than all the rest, Rinaldo cherished him, for he more than any knew his worth.

It was not long before Rogero confided to his friend the hopes he entertained of a union with his sister, and Rinaldo frankly gave his sanction to the proposal. But causes unknown to the paladin were at that very time interposing obstacles to its success.

The fame of the beauty and worth of Bradamante had reached the ears of the Grecian Emperor Constantine, and he had sent to Charlemagne to demand the hand of his niece for Leo, his son, and the heir to his dominions. Duke Aymon, her father, had only reserved his consent until he should first have spoken with his son Rinaldo, now absent.

The warriors now prepared to resume their voyage. Rogero took a tender farewell of the good hermit who had taught him the true faith. Orlando restored to him the horse and arms which were rightly his, not even asserting his claim to Balisardo, that sword which he himself had won from the enchantress.

The hermit gave his blessing to the band, and they re-embarked.

The passage was speedy, and very soon they arrived in the harbor of Marseilles.

Astolpho, when he had dismissed his troops, mounted the Hippogriff, and at one flight shot over to Sardinia, thence to Corsica, thence, turning slightly to the left, hovered over Provence, and alighted in the neighborhood of Marseilles. There he did what he had been commanded to do by the holy saint; he unbridled the Hippogriff, and turned him loose to seek his own retreats, never more to be galled with saddle or bit. The horn had lost its marvellous power ever since the visit to the moon.

Astolpho reached Marseilles the very day when Orlando, Rinaldo, Oliver, Sobrino, and Rogero arrived there. Charles had already heard the news of the defeat of the Saracen kings, and all the accompanying events. On learning the approach of the gallant knights, he sent forward some of his most illustrious nobles to receive them, and himself, with the rest of his court, kings, dukes, and peers, the queen, and a fair and gorgeous band of ladies, set forward from Arles to meet them.

No sooner were the mutual greetings interchanged, than Orlando and his friends led forward Rogero, and presented him to the Emperor. They vouch him son of Rogero, Duke of Risa, one of the most renowned of Christian warriors, by adverse fortune stolen in his infancy, and brought up by Saracens in the false faith, now by a kind Providence converted, and restored to fill the place his father once held among the foremost champions of the throne and Church.

Rogero had alighted from his horse, and stood respectfully before the Emperor. Charlemagne bade him remount and ride beside him; and omitted nothing which might do him honor in sight of his martial train. With pomp triumphal and with festive cheer the troop returned to the city; the streets were decorated with garlands, the houses hung with rich tapestry, and flowers fell like rain upon the conquering host from the hands of fair dames and damsels, from every balcony and window. So welcomed, the mighty Emperor passed on till he reached the royal palace, where many days he feasted, high in hall, with his lords, amid tourney, revel, dance, and song.

When Rinaldo told his father, Duke Aymon, how he had promised his sister to Rogero, his father heard him with indignation, having set his heart on seeing her united to the Grecian Emperor's son. The Lady Beatrice, her mother, also appealed to Bradamante herself to reject a knight who had neither title nor lands, and give the preference to one who would make her Empress of the wide Levant. But Bradamante, though respect forbade her to refuse her mother's entreaty, would not promise to do what her heart repelled, and answered only with a sigh, until she was alone, and then gave a loose to tears.

Meanwhile Rogero, indignant that a stranger should presume to rob him of his bride, determined to seek the Prince of Greece, and defy him to mortal combat. With this design he donned his armor, but exchanged his crest and emblazonment, and bore instead a white unicorn upon a crimson field. He chose a trusty squire, and, commanding him not to address him as Rogero, rode on his quest. Having crossed the Rhine and the Austrian countries into Hungary, he followed the course of the Danube till he reached Belgrade. There he saw the imperial ensigns spread, and white pavilions, thronged with troops, before the town. For the Emperor Constantine was laying siege to the city to recover it from the Bulgarians, who had taken it from him not long before.

A river flowed between the camp of the Emperor and the Bulgarians, and at the moment when Rogero approached, a skirmish had begun between the parties from either camp, who had approached the stream for the purpose of watering. The Greeks in that affray were four to one, and drove back the Bulgarians in precipitate rout. Rogero, seeing this, and animated only by his hatred of the Grecian prince, dashed into the middle of the flying mass, calling aloud on the fugitives to turn. He encountered first a leader of the Grecian host in splendid armor, a nephew of the Emperor, as dear to him as a son. Rogero's lance pierced shield and armor, and stretched the warrior breathless on the plain. Another and another fell before him, and astonishment and terror arrested the advance of the Greeks, while the Bulgarians, catching courage from the cavalier, rally, change front, and chase the Grecian troops, who fly in their turn. Leo, the prince, was at a distance when this sudden skirmish rose, but not so far but that he could see distinctly, from an elevated position which he held, how the changed battle was all the work of one man, and could not choose but admire the bravery and prowess with which it was done. He knew by the blazonry displayed that the champion was not of the Bulgarian army, though he furnished aid to them. Although he suffered by his valor, the prince could not wish him ill, for his admiration surpassed his resentment. By this time the Greeks had regained the river, and, crossing it by fording or swimming, some made their escape, leaving many more prisoners in the hands of the Bulgarians. Rogero, learning from some of the captives that Leo was at a point some distance down the river, rode thither with a view to meet him, but arrived not before the Greek prince had retired beyond the stream, and broken up the bridge. Day was spent, and Rogero,

wearied, looked round for a shelter for the night. He found it in a
cottage, where he soon yielded himself to repose. It so happened,
a knight who had narrowly escaped Rogero's sword in the late
battle also found shelter in the same cottage, and, recognizing the
armor of the unknown knight, easily found means of securing him
as he slept, and next morning carried him in chains, and delivered
him to the Emperor. By him he was in turn delivered to his sister
Theodora, mother of the young knight, the first victim of Rogero's
spear. By her he was cast into a dungeon, till her ingenuity could
devise a death sufficiently painful to satiate her revenge.

Bradamante, meanwhile, to escape her father's and mother's
importunity, had begged a boon of Charlemagne, which the monarch
pledged his royal word to grant; it was that she should not be
compelled to marry any one unless he should first vanquish her in
single combat. The Emperor, therefore, proclaimed a tournament
in these words: "He that would wed Duke Aymon's daughter must
contend with the sword against that dame, from the sun's rise to
his setting; and if, in that time, he is not overcome, the lady shall
be his."

Duke Aymon and the Lady Beatrice, though much incensed at
the course things had taken, brought their daughter to court, to
await the day appointed for the tournament. Bradamante, not finding there him whom her heart required, distressed herself with
doubts what could be the cause of his absence. Of all fancies, the
most painful one was that he had gone away to learn to forget her,
knowing her father's and her mother's opposition to their union,
and despairing to contend against them. But O how much worse
would be the maiden's woe, if it were known to her what her betrothed was then enduring!

He was plunged in a dungeon where no ray of daylight ever penetrated, loaded with chains, and scantily supplied with the coarsest
food. No wonder despair took possession of his heart, and he longed
for death as a relief, when one night (or one day, for both were
equally dark to him) he was roused with the glare of a torch, and
saw two men enter his cell. It was the Prince Leo, with an attendant,
who had come as soon as he had learned the wretched fate of the
brave knight whose valor he had seen and admired on the field of
battle. "Cavalier," said he, "I am one whom thy valor hath so bound
to thee, that I willingly peril my own safety to lend thee aid."
"Infinite thanks I owe you," replied Rogero, "and the life you give
me I promise faithfully to render back upon your call, and promptly
to stake it at all times for your service." The prince then told Rogero
his name and rank, at hearing which a tide of contending emotions

almost overwhelmed Rogero. He was set at liberty, and had his horse and arms restored to him.

Meanwhile, tidings arrived of King Charles's decree that whoever aspired to the hand of Bradamante must first encounter her with sword and lance. This news made the Grecian prince turn pale, for he knew he was no match for her in fight. Communing with himself, he sees how he may make his wit supply the place of valor, and employ the French knight, whose name was still unknown to him, to fight the battle for him. Rogero heard the proposal with extreme distress; yet it seemed worse than death to deny the first request of one to whom he owed his life. Hastily he gave his assent "to do in all things that which Leo should command." Afterward, bitter repentance came over him; yet, rather than confess his change of mind, death itself would be welcome. Death seems his only remedy; but how to die? Sometimes he thinks to make none but a feigned resistance, and allow her sword a ready access, for never can death come more happily than if her hand guide the weapon. Yet this will not avail, for, unless he wins the maid for the Greek prince, his debt remains unpaid. He had promised to maintain a real, not a feigned encounter. He will then keep his word, and banish every thought from his bosom except that which moved him to maintain his truth.

The young prince, richly attended, set out, and with him Rogero. They arrived at Paris, but Leo preferred not to enter the city, and pitched his tents without the walls, making known his arrival to Charlemagne by an embassy. The monarch was pleased, and testified his courtesy by visits and gifts. The prince set forth the purpose of his coming, and prayed the Emperor to dispatch his suit,—"to send for the damsel who refused ever to take in wedlock any lord inferior to herself in fight; for she should be his bride, or he would perish beneath her sword."

Rogero passed the night before the day assigned for the battle like that which the felon spends, condemned to pay the forfeit of his life on the ensuing day. He chose to fight with sword only, and on foot, for he would not let her see Frontino, knowing that she would recognize the steed. Nor would he use Balisardo, for against that enchanted blade all armor would be of no avail, and the sword that he did take he hammered well upon the edge to abate its sharpness. He wore the surcoat of Prince Leo, and his shield, emblazoned with a golden, double-headed eagle. The prince took care to let himself be seen by none.

Bradamante, meanwhile, prepared herself for the combat far differently. Instead of blunting the edge of her falchion, she whets the steel, and would fain infuse into it her own acerbity. As the moment approached, she seemed to have fire within her veins, and waited impatiently for the trumpet's sound. At the signal, she drew her sword, and fell with fury upon her Rogero. But as a well-built wall or aged rock stands unmoved by the fury of the storm, so Rogero, clad in those arms which Trojan Hector once wore, withstood the strokes which stormed about his head and breast and flank. Sparks flew from his shield, his helm, his cuirass; from direct and back strokes, aimed now high, now low, falling thick and fast, like hailstones on a cottage roof; but Rogero, with skilful ward, turns them aside, or receives them where his armor is a sure protection, careful only to protect himself, and with no thought of striking in return. Thus the hours passed away, and, as the sun approached the west, the damsel began to despair. But so much the more her anger increases, and she redoubles her efforts, like the craftsman who sees his work unfinished while the day is wellnigh spent. O miserable damsel! didst thou know whom thou wouldst kill,—if, in that cavalier matched against thee thou didst but know Rogero, on whom thy very life-threads hang, rather than kill him thou wouldst kill thyself, for he is dearer to thee than life.

King Charles and the peers, who thought the cavalier to be the Grecian prince, viewing such force and skill exhibited, and how without assaulting her the knight defended himself, were filled with admiration, and declared the champions well matched, and worthy of each other.

When the sun was set, Charlemagne gave the signal for terminating the contest, and Bradamante was awarded to Prince Leo as a bride. Rogero, in deep distress, returned to his tent. There Leo unlaced his helmet, and kissed him on both cheeks. "Henceforth," said he, "do with me as you please, for you cannot exhaust my gratitude." Rogero replied little, laid aside the ensigns he had worn, and resumed the unicorn, then hasted to withdraw himself from all eyes. When it was midnight he rose, saddled Frontino, and sallied from his tent, taking that direction which pleased his steed. All night he rode absorbed in bitter woe, and called on Death as alone capable of relieving his sufferings. At last he entered a forest, and penetrated into its deepest recesses. There he unharnessed Frontino, and suffered him to wander where he would. Then he threw himself down on the ground, and poured forth such bitter wailings that the birds and beasts, for none else heard him, were moved to pity with his cries.

Not less was the distress of the lady Bradamante, who, rather than wed any one but Rogero, resolved to break her word, and defy kindred, court, and Charlemagne himself; and, if nothing else would do, to die. But relief came from an unexpected quarter. Marphisa,

sister of Rogero, was a heroine of warlike prowess equal to Bradamante. She had been the confidante of their loves, and felt hardly
less distress than themselves at seeing the perils which threatened
their union. "They are already united by mutual vows," she said,
"and in the sight of Heaven what more is necessary?" Full of this
thought she presented herself before Charlemagne, and declared
that she herself was witness that the maiden had spoken to Rogero
those words which they who marry swear; and that the compact
was so sealed between the pair that they were no longer free, nor
could forsake, the one the other, to take another spouse. This her
assertion she offered to prove, in single combat, against Prince Leo,
or any one else.

Charlemagne, sadly perplexed at this, commanded Bradamante
to be called, and told her what the bold Marphisa had declared.
Bradamante neither denied nor confirmed the statement, but hung
her head, and kept silence. Duke Aymon was enraged, and would
fain have set aside the pretended contract on the ground that, if
made at all, it must have been made before Rogero was baptized,
and therefore void. But not so thought Rinaldo, nor the good
Orlando, and Charlemagne knew not which way to decide, when
Marphisa spoke thus:—

"Since no one else can marry the maiden while my brother lives,
let the prince meet Rogero in mortal combat, and let him who
survives take her for his bride."

This saying pleased the Emperor, and was accepted by the prince,
for he thought that, by the aid of his unknown champion, he should
surely triumph in the fight. Proclamation was therefore made for
Rogero to appear and defend his suit; and Leo, on his part, caused
search to be made on all sides for the knight of the Unicorn.

Meanwhile Rogero, overwhelmed with despair, lay stretched on
the ground in the forest night and day without food, courting death.
Here he was discovered by one of Leo's people, who, finding him
resist all attempts to remove him, hastened to his master, who was
not far off, and brought him to the spot. As he approached, he heard
words which convinced him that love was the cause of the knight's
despair; but no clew was given to guide him to the object of that
love. Stooping down, the prince embraced the weeping warrior, and,
in the tenderest accents, said: "Spare not, I entreat you, to disclose
the cause of your distress, for few such desperate evils betide mankind as are wholly past cure. It grieves me much that you would
hide your grief from me, for I am bound to you by ties that nothing
can undo. Tell me, then, your grief, and leave me to try if wealth,
art, cunning, force, or persuasion cannot relieve you. If not, it will
be time enough, after all has been tried in vain, to die."

He spoke in such moving accents, that Rogero could not choose but yield. It was some time before he could command utterance; at last he said, "My lord, when you shall know me for what I am, I doubt not you, like myself, will be content that I should die. Know, then, I am that Rogero whom you have so much cause to hate, and who so hated you that, intent on putting you to death, he went to seek you at your father's court. This I did because I could not submit to see my promised bride borne off by you. But, as man proposes and God disposes, your great courtesy, well tried in time of sore need, so moved my fixed resolve, that I not only laid aside the hate I bore, but purposed to be your friend forever. You then asked of me to win for you the lady Bradamante, which was all one as to demand of me my heart and soul. You know whether I served you faithfully or not. Yours is the lady; possess her in peace; but ask me not to live to see it. Be content rather that I die; for vows have passed between myself and her which forbid that while I live she can lawfully wive with another."

So filled was gentle Leo with astonishment at these words, that for a while he stood silent, with lips unmoved, and steadfast gaze, like a statue. And the discovery that the stranger was Rogero not only abated not the good-will he bore him, but increased it, so that his distress for what Rogero suffered seemed equal to his own. For this, and because he would appear deservedly an Emperor's son, and, though in other things outdone, would not be surpassed in courtesy, he says: "Rogero, had I known, that day when your matchless valor routed my troops, that you were Rogero, your virtue would have made me your own, as then it made me while I knew not my foe, and I should have no less gladly rescued you from Theodora's dungeon. And if I would willingly have done so then, how much more gladly will I now restore the gift of which you would rob yourself to confer it upon me. The damsel is more due to you than to me, and though I know her worth, I would forego not only her, but life itself, rather than distress a knight like you."

This and much more he said to the same intent; till at last Rogero replied, "I yield, and am content to live, and thus a second time owe my life to you."

But several days elapsed before Rogero was so far restored as to return to the royal residence, where an embassy had arrived from the Bulgarian princes to seek the knight of the Unicorn, and tender to him the crown of that country, in place of their king, fallen in battle.

Thus were things situated when Prince Leo, leading by the hand Rogero, clad in the battered armor in which he had sustained the conflict with Bradamante, presented himself before the king. "Be-

hold," he said, "the champion who maintained from dawn to setting
sun the arduous contest; he comes to claim the guerdon of the
fight." King Charlemagne, with all his peerage, stood amazed; for
all believed that the Grecian prince himself had fought with Bradamante. Then stepped forth Marphisa, and said, "Since Rogero is not
here to assert his rights, I, his sister, undertake his cause, and will
maintain it against whoever shall dare dispute his claim." She said
this with so much anger and disdain, that the prince deemed it no
longer wise to feign, and withdrew Rogero's helmet from his brow,
saying, "Behold him here!" Who can describe the astonishment and
joy of Marphisa! She ran and threw her arms about her brother's
neck, nor would give way to let Charlemagne and Rinaldo, Orlando,
Dudon, and the rest who crowded round, embrace him, and press
friendly kisses on his brow. The joyful tidings flew fast by many a
messenger to Bradamante, who in her secret chamber lay lamenting.
The blood that stagnated about her heart flowed at that notice so
fast, that she had wellnigh died for joy. Duke Aymon and the Lady
Beatrice no longer withheld their consent, and pledged their daughter to the brave Rogero before all that gallant company.

Now came the Bulgarian ambassadors, and, kneeling at the feet
of Rogero, besought him to return with them to their country, where,
in Adrianople, the crown and sceptre were awaiting his acceptance.
Prince Leo united his persuasions to theirs, and promised, in his
royal father's name, that peace should be restored on their part.
Rogero gave his consent, and it was surmised that none of the
virtues which shone so conspicuously in him so availed to recommend
Rogero to the Lady Beatrice, as the hearing her future son-in-law
saluted as a sovereign prince.

CHAPTER XVIII

THE BATTLE OF RONCESVALLES

AFTER the expulsion of the Saracens from France, Charlemagne
led his army into Spain, to punish Marsilius, the king of that country, for having sided with the African Saracens in the late war.
Charlemagne succeeded in all his attempts, and compelled Marsilius
to submit, and pay tribute to France. Our readers will remember
Gano, otherwise called Gan, or Ganelon, whom we mentioned in
one of our early chapters as an old courtier of Charlemagne, and a
deadly enemy of Orlando, Rinaldo, and all their friends. He had
great influence over Charles, from equality of age and long in-
timacy; and he was not without good qualities: he was brave and
sagacious, but envious, false, and treacherous. Gan prevailed on

Charles to send him as ambassador to Marsilius, to arrange the tribute. He embraced Orlando over and over again at taking leave, using such pains to seem loving and sincere, that his hypocrisy was manifest to every one but the old monarch. He fastened with equal tenderness on Oliver, who smiled contemptuously in his face, and thought to himself, "You may make as many fair speeches as you choose, but you lie." All the other paladins who were present thought the same, and they said as much to the Emperor, adding, that Gan should on no account be sent ambassador to the Spaniards. But Charles was infatuated.

Gan was received with great honor by Marsilius. The king, attended by his lords, came fifteen miles out of Saragossa to meet him, and then conducted him into the city with acclamations. There was nothing for several days but balls, games, and exhibitions of chivalry, the ladies throwing flowers on the heads of the French knights, and the people shouting, "France! Mountjoy and St. Denis!"

After the ceremonies of the first reception, the king and the ambassador began to understand one another. One day they sat together in a garden on the border of a fountain. The water was so clear and smooth it reflected every object around, and the spot was encircled with fruit-trees which quivered with the fresh air. As they sat and talked, as if without restraint, Gan, without looking the king in the face, was enabled to see the expression of his countenance in the water, and governed his speech accordingly. Marsilius was equally adroit, and watched the face of Gan while he addressed him. Marsilius began by lamenting, not as to the ambassador, but as to the friend, the injuries which Charles had done him by invading his dominions, charging him with wishing to take his kingdom from him, and give it to Orlando; till at length he plainly uttered his belief that, if that ambitious paladin were but dead, good men would get their rights.

Gan heaved a sigh, as if he was unwillingly compelled to allow the force of what the king said; but, unable to contain himself long, he lifted up his face, radiant with triumphant wickedness, and exclaimed: "Every word you utter is truth; die he must, and die also must Oliver, who struck me that foul blow at court. Is it treachery to punish affronts like these? I have planned everything,—I have settled everything already with their besotted master. Orlando will come to your borders,—to Roncesvalles,—for the purpose of receiving the tribute. Charles will await him at the foot of the mountains. Orlando will bring but a small band with him: you, when you meet him, will have secretly your whole army at your back. You surround him, and who receives tribute then?"

The new Judas had scarcely uttered these words when his exultation was interrupted by a change in the face of nature. The sky was suddenly overcast, there was thunder and lightning, a laurel was split in two from head to foot, and the Carob-tree under which Gan was sitting, which is said to be the species of tree on which Judas Iscariot hung himself, dropped one of its pods on his head.

Marsilius, as well as Gan, was appalled at this omen; but on assembling his soothsayers they came to the conclusion that the laurel-tree turned the omen against the Emperor, the successor of the Cæsars, though one of them renewed the consternation of Gan by saying that he did not understand the meaning of the tree of Judas, and intimating that perhaps the ambassador could explain it. Gan relieved his vexation by anger; the habit of wickedness pre-vailed over all other considerations; and the king prepared to march to Roncesvalles at the head of all his forces.

Gan wrote to Charlemagne to say how humbly and submissively Marsilius was coming to pay the tribute into the hands of Orlando, and how handsome it would be of the Emperor to meet him half-way, and so be ready to receive him after the payment at his camp. He added a brilliant account of the tribute, and the accompanying presents. The good Emperor wrote in turn to say how pleased he was with the ambassador's diligence, and that matters were ar-ranged precisely as he wished. His court, however, had its suspicions still, though they little thought Gan's object in bringing Charles into the neighborhood of Roncesvalles was to deliver him into the hands of Marsilius, after Orlando should have been destroyed by him.

Orlando, however, did as his lord and sovereign desired. He went to Roncesvalles, accompanied by a moderate train of warriors, not dreaming of the atrocity that awaited him. Gan, meanwhile, had hastened back to France, in order to show himself free and easy in the presence of Charles, and secure the success of his plot; while Marsilius, to make assurance doubly sure, brought into the passes of Roncesvalles no less than three armies, which were successively to fall on the paladin in case of the worst, and so extinguish him with numbers. He had also, by Gan's advice, brought heaps of wine and good cheer to be set before his victims in the first in-stance; "for that," said the traitor, "will render the onset the more effective, the feasters being unarmed. One thing, however, I must not forget," added he; "my son Baldwin is sure to be with Orlando; you must take care of his life for my sake."

"I give him this vesture off my own body," said the king; "let him wear it in the battle, and have no fear. My soldiers shall be directed not to touch him."

Gan went away rejoicing to France. He embraced the sovereign and the court all round with the air of a man who had brought them nothing but blessings, and the old king wept for very tenderness and delight.

"Something is going on wrong, and looks very black," thought Malagigi, the good wizard; "Rinaldo is not here, and it is indispensably necessary that he should be. I must find out where he is, and Ricciardetto too, and send for them with all speed."

Malagigi called up by his art a wise, terrible, and cruel spirit, named Ashtaroth. "Tell me, and tell me truly, of Rinaldo," said Malagigi to the spirit. The demon looked hard at the paladin, and said nothing. His aspect was clouded and violent.

The enchanter, with an aspect still cloudier, bade Ashtaroth lay down that look; and made signs as if he would resort to angrier compulsion; and the devil, alarmed, loosened his tongue, and said, "You have not told me what you desire to know of Rinaldo."

"I desire to know what he has been doing, and where he is."

"He has been conquering and baptizing the world, east and west," said the demon, "and is now in Egypt with Ricciardetto."

"And what has Gan been plotting with Marsilius?" inquired Malagigi; "and what is to come of it?"

"I know not," said the devil. "I was not attending to Gan at the time, and we fallen spirits know not the future. All I discern is that by the signs and comets in the heavens something dreadful is about to happen,—something very strange, treacherous, and bloody;—and that Gan has a seat ready prepared for him in hell."

"Within three days," cried the enchanter, loudly, "bring Rinaldo and Ricciardetto into the pass of Roncesvalles. Do it, and I hereby undertake to summon thee no more."

"Suppose they will not trust themselves with me?" said the spirit.

"Enter Rinaldo's horse, and bring him, whether he trust thee or not."

"It shall be done," returned the demon.

There was an earthquake, and Ashtaroth disappeared.

———

Marsilius now made his first movement towards the destruction of Orlando, by sending before him his vassal, King Blanchardin, with his presents of wines and other luxuries. The temperate but courteous hero took them in good part, and distributed them as the traitor wished; and then Blanchardin, on pretence of going forward to salute Charlemagne, returned, and put himself at the head of the second army, which was the post assigned him by his liege-lord. King Falseron, whose son Orlando had slain in battle, headed the first army, and King Balugante the third. Marsilius made a speech to them, in which he let them into his design, and concluded by recommending to their good-will the son of his friend Gan, whom they would know by the vest he had sent him, and who was the only soul amongst the Christians they were to spare.

This son of Gan, meanwhile, and several of the paladins, who distrusted the misbelievers, and were anxious at all events to be with Orlando, had joined the hero in the fated valley; so that the little Christian host, considering the tremendous valor of their lord and his friends, were not to be sold for nothing. Rinaldo, alas! the second thunderbolt of Christendom, was destined not to be there in time to meet the issue. The paladins in vain begged Orlando to be on his guard against treachery, and sent for a more numerous body of men. The great heart of the Champion of the Faith was unwilling to harbor suspicion as long as he could help it. He refused to summon aid which might be superfluous; neither would he do anything but what his liege-lord had directed. And yet he could not wholly repress a misgiving. A shadow had fallen on his heart, great and cheerful as it was. The anticipations of his friends disturbed him, in spite of the face with which he met them. Perhaps by a certain foresight he felt his death approaching; but he felt bound not to encourage the impression. Besides, time pressed; the moment of the looked-for tribute was at hand, and little combinations of circumstances determine often the greatest events.

King Marsilius was to arrive early next day with the tribute, and Oliver, with the morning sun, rode forth to reconnoitre, and see if he could discover the peaceful pomp of the Spanish court in the distance. He rode up the nearest height, and from the top of it beheld the first army of Marsilius already forming in the passes. "O devil Gan," he exclaimed, "this then is the consummation of thy labors!" Oliver put spurs to his horse, and galloped back down the mountain to Orlando.

"Well," cried the hero, "what news?"

"Bad news," said his cousin, "such as you would not hear of yesterday. Marsilius is here in arms, and all the world is with him."

The paladins pressed round Orlando, and entreated him to sound his horn, in token that he needed help. His only answer was to mount his horse, and ride up the mountain with Sansonetto.

As soon, however, as he cast forth his eyes, and beheld what was round about him, he turned in sorrow, and looked down into Roncesvalles, and said, "O miserable valley! the blood shed in thee this day will color thy name forever."

Orlando's little camp were furious against the Saracens. They armed themselves with the greatest impatience. There was nothing but lacing of helmets and mounting of horses, while good Archbishop Turpin went from rank to rank exhorting and encouraging the warriors of Christ. Orlando and his captains withdrew for a moment to consultation. He fairly groaned for sorrow, and at first had not a word to say; so wretched he felt at having brought his people to die in Roncesvalles. Then he said: "If it had entered into my heart to conceive the king of Spain to be such a villain, never would you have seen this day. He has exchanged with me a thousand courtesies and good words; and I thought that the worse enemies we had been before, the better friends we had become now. I fancied every human being capable of this kind of virtue on a good opportunity, saving, indeed, such base-hearted wretches as can never forgive their very forgivers; and of these I did not suppose him to be one. Let us die, if die we must, like honest and gallant men, so that it shall be said of us, it was only our bodies that died. The reason why I did not sound the horn was partly because I thought it did not become us, and partly because our liege-lord could hardly save us, even if he heard it." And with these words Orlando sprang to his horse, crying, "Away, against the Saracens!" But he had no sooner turned his face, than he wept bitterly, and said, "O Holy Virgin, think not of me, the sinner Orlando, but have pity on these thy servants!"

And now, with a mighty dust, and an infinite sound of horns and tambours which came filling the valley, the first army of the infidels made its appearance, horses neighing, and a thousand pennons flying in the air. King Falseron led them on, saying to his officers: "Let nobody dare to lay a finger on Orlando. He belongs to myself. The revenge of my son's death is mine. I will cut the man down that comes between us."

"Now, friends," said Orlando, "every man for himself, and St. Michael for us all! There is not one here that is not a perfect knight." And he might well say it, for the flower of all France was there, except Rinaldo and Ricciardetto,—every man a picked man, all friends and constant companions of Orlando.

So the captains of the little troop and of the great army sat looking at one another, and singling one another out as the latter came on, and then the knights put spear in rest, and ran for a while two and two in succession, one against the other.

Astolpho was the first to move. He ran against Arlotto of Soria, and thrust his antagonist's body out of the saddle, and his soul into the other world. Oliver encountered Malprimo, and, though he received a thrust which hurt him, sent his lance right through the heart of Malprimo.

Faiseron was daunted at this blow. "Truly," thought he, "this is a marvel." Oliver did not press on among the Saracens, his wound was too painful; but Orlando now put himself and his whole band in motion, and you may guess what an uproar ensued. The sound of the rattling of blows and helmets was as if the forge of Vulcan had been thrown open. Falseron beheld Orlando coming so furiously, that he thought him a Lucifer who had burst his chain, and was quite of another mind than when he purposed to have him all to himself. On the contrary, he recommended himself to his gods, and turned away, meaning to wait for a more auspicious season of revenge. But Orlando hailed him, with a terrible voice, saying, "O thou traitor! was this the end to which old quarrels were made up?" Then he dashed at Falseron with a fury so swift, and at the same time with a mastery of his lance so marvellous, that, though he plunged it in the man's body so as instantly to kill him, and then withdrew it, the body did not move in the saddle. The hero himself, as he rushed onwards, was fain to see the end of a stroke so perfect, and turning his horse back, touched the carcass with his sword, and it fell on the instant!

When the infidels beheld their leader dead, such fear fell upon them that they were for leaving the field to the paladins, but they were unable. Marsilius had drawn the rest of his forces round the valley like a net, so that their shoulders were turned in vain. Orlando rode into the thick of them, and wherever he went thunderbolts fell upon helmets. Oliver was again in the fray, with Walter and Baldwin, Avino and Avolio, while Archbishop Turpin had changed his crosier for a lance, and chased a new flock before him to the mountains.

Yet what could be done against foes without number? Marsilius constantly pours them in. The paladins are as units to thousands. Why tarry the horses of Rinaldo and Ricciardetto?

The horses did not tarry, but fate had been quicker than enchantment. Ashtaroth had presented himself to Rinaldo in Egypt, and, after telling his errand, he and Foul-mouth, his servant, entered the horses of Rinaldo and Ricciardetto, which began to neigh, and snort, and leap with the fiends within them, till off they flew through the air over the pyramids and across the desert, and reached Spain and the scene of action just as Marsilius brought up his third army. The two paladins on their horses dropped right into the midst of the Saracens, and began making such havoc among them that Marsilius, who overlooked the fight from a mountain, thought his soldiers had turned against one another. Orlando beheld it, and guessed it could be no other but his cousins, and pressed to meet them. Oliver coming up at the same moment, the rapture of the whole party is not to be expressed. After a few hasty words of explanation they were forced to turn again upon the enemy, whose numbers seemed perfectly without limit.

Orlando, making a bloody passage towards Marsilius, struck a youth on the head, whose helmet was so strong as to resist the blow, but at the same time flew off. Orlando prepared to strike a second blow, when the youth exclaimed, "Hold! you loved my father; I am Bujaforte!" The paladin had never seen Bujaforte, but he saw the likeness to the good old man, his father, and he dropped his sword. "O Bujaforte," said he, "I loved him indeed; but what does his son do here fighting against his friends?"

Bujaforte could not at once speak for weeping. At length he said: "I am forced to be here by my lord and master, Marsilius; and I have made a show of fighting, but have not hurt a single Christian. Treachery is on every side of you. Baldwin himself has a vest given him by Marsilius, that everybody may know the son of his friend Gan, and do him no harm."

"Put your helmet on again," said Orlando, "and behave just as you have done. Never will your father's friend be an enemy to the son."

The hero then turned in fury to look for Baldwin, who was hastening towards him, at that moment, with friendliness in his looks.

" 'Tis strange," said Baldwin, "I have done my duty as well as I could, yet nobody will come against me. I have slain right and left, and cannot comprehend what it is that makes the stoutest infidels avoid me."

"Take off your vest," said Orlando, contemptuously, "and you will soon discover the secret, if you wish to know it. Your father has sold us to Marsilius, all but his honorable son."

"If my father," said Baldwin, impetuously tearing off the vest, "has been such a villain, and I escape dying, I will plunge this sword through his heart. But I am no traitor, Orlando, and you do me wrong to say it. Think not I can live with dishonor."

Baldwin spurred off into the fight, not waiting to hear another word from Orlando, who was very sorry for what he had said, for he perceived that the youth was in despair.

And now the fight raged beyond all it had done before; twenty pagans went down for one paladin, but still the paladins fell. Sansonetto was beaten to earth by the club of Grandonio, Walter d'Amulion had his shoulder broken, Berlinghieri and Ottone were slain, and at last Astolpho fell, in revenge of whose death Orlando turned the spot where he died into a lake of Saracen blood. The luckless Bujaforte met Rinaldo, and, before he could explain how he seemed to be fighting on the Saracen side, received such a blow

upon the head that he fell, unable to utter a word. Orlando, cutting
his way to a spot where there was a great struggle and uproar, found
the poor youth Baldwin, the son of Gan, with two spears in his
breast. "I am no traitor now," said Baldwin, and those were the
last words he said. Orlando was bitterly sorry to have been the
cause of his death, and tears streamed from his eyes. At length
down went Oliver himself. He had become blinded with his own
blood, and smitten Orlando without knowing him. "How now,
cousin," cried Orlando, "have you too gone over to the enemy?"
"O my lord and master," cried the other, "I ask your pardon. I
can see nothing; I am dying. Some traitor has stabbed me in the
back. If you love me, lead my horse into the thick of them, so that
I may not die unavenged."

"I shall die myself before long," said Orlando, "out of very toil
and grief; so we will go together."

Orlando led his cousin's horse where the press was thickest, and
dreadful was the strength of the dying man and his tired companion. They made a street through which they passed out of the
battle, and Orlando led his cousin away to his tent, and said, "Wait
a little till I return, for I will go and sound the horn on the hill
yonder."

" 'Tis of no use," said Oliver, "my spirit is fast going, and desires to be with its Lord and Saviour."

He would have said more, but his words came from him imperfectly, like those of a man in a dream, and so he expired.

When Orlando saw him dead, he felt as if he was alone on the
earth, and he was quite willing to leave it; only he wished that
King Charles, at the foot of the mountains, should know how the
case stood before he went. So he took up the horn and blew it three
times, with such force that the blood burst out of his nose and
mouth. Turpin says that at the third blast the horn broke in two.

In spite of all the noise of the battle, the sound of the horn broke
over it like a voice out of the other world. They say that birds fell
dead at it, and that the whole Saracen army drew back in terror.
Charlemagne was sitting in the midst of his court when the sound
reached him; and Gan was there. The Emperor was the first to
hear it.

"Do you hear that?" said he to his nobles. "Did you hear the
horn as I heard it?"

Upon this they all listened, and Gan felt his heart misgive him.
The horn sounded a second time.

"What is the meaning of this?" said Charles.

"Orlando is hunting," observed Gan, "and the stag is killed."

But when the horn sounded yet a third time, and the blast was one of so dreadful a vehemence, everybody looked at the other, and then they all looked at Gan in fury. Charles rose from his seat.

"This is no hunting of the stag," said he. "The sound goes to my very heart. O Gan! O Gan! Not for thee do I blush, but for myself. O foul and monstrous villain! Take him, gentlemen, and keep him in close prison. Would to God I had not lived to see this day!"

But it was no time for words. They put the traitor in prison, and then Charles with all his court took his way to Roncesvalles, grieving and praying.

It was afternoon when the horn sounded, and half an hour after it when the Emperor set out; and meantime Orlando had returned to the fight that he might do his duty, however hopeless, as long as he could sit his horse. At length he found his end approaching, for toil and fever, and rode all alone to a fountain where he had before quenched his thirst. His horse was wearier than he, and no sooner had his master alighted than the beast, kneeling down as if to take leave, and to say, "I have brought you to a place of rest," fell dead at his feet. Orlando cast water on him from the fountain, not wishing to believe him dead; but when he found it to no purpose, he grieved for him as if he had been a human being, and addressed him by name with tears, and asked forgiveness if he had ever done him wrong. They say that the horse, at these words, opened his eyes a little, and looked kindly at his master, and then stirred never more. They say also that Orlando then, summoning all his strength, smote a rock near him with his beautiful sword Durindana, thinking to shiver the steel in pieces, and so prevent its falling into the hands of the enemy; but though the rock split like a slate, and a great cleft remained ever after to astonish the eyes of pilgrims, the sword remained uninjured.

And now Rinaldo and Ricciardetto came up, with Turpin, having driven back the Saracens, and told Orlando that the battle was won. Then Orlando knelt before Turpin, and begged remission of his sins, and Turpin gave him absolution. Orlando fixed his eyes on the hilt of his sword as on a crucifix, and embraced it, and he raised his eyes and appeared like a creature seraphical and transfigured, and, bowing his head, he breathed out his pure soul.

And now King Charles and his nobles came up. The Emperor, at sight of the dead Orlando, threw himself, as if he had been a reckless youth, from his horse, and embraced and kissed the body, and said: "I bless thee, Orlando; I bless thy whole life, and all that thou wast, and all that thou ever didst, and the father that begat thee; and I ask pardon of thee for believing those who brought thee to thine end. They shall have their reward, O thou beloved one!

But indeed it is thou that livest, and I who am worse than dead."

Horrible to the Emperor's eyes was the sight of the field of Roncesvalles. The Saracens indeed had fled, conquered; but all his paladins but two were left on it dead, and the whole valley looked like a great slaughter-house, trampled into blood and dirt, and reeking to the heat. Charles trembled to his heart's core for wonder and agony. After gazing dumbly on the place, he cursed it with a solemn curse, and wished that never grass might grow in it again, nor seed of any kind, neither within it nor on any of its mountains around, but the anger of Heaven abide over it forever.

Charles and his warriors went after the Saracens into Spain. They took and fired Saragossa, and Marsilius was hung to the carob-tree under which he had planned his villainy with Gan; and Gan was hung and drawn and quartered in Roncesvalles, amidst the execrations of the country.

CHAPTER XIX

RINALDO AND BAYARD

CHARLEMAGNE was overwhelmed with grief at the loss of so many of his bravest warriors at the disaster of Roncesvalles, and bitterly reproached himself for his credulity in resigning himself so completely to the counsels of the treacherous Count Gan. Yet he soon fell into a similar snare when he suffered his unworthy son Charlot to acquire such an influence over him, that he constantly led him into acts of cruelty and injustice that in his right mind he would have scorned to commit. Rinaldo and his brothers, for some slight offence to the imperious young prince, were forced to fly from Paris, and to take shelter in their castle of Montalban; for Charles had publicly said, if he could take them, he would hang them all. He sent numbers of his bravest knights to arrest them, but all without success. Either Rinaldo foiled their efforts and sent them back, stripped of their armor and of their glory, or, after meeting and conferring with him, they came back and told the king they could not be his instruments for such a work.

At last Charles himself raised a great army, and went in person to compel the paladin to submit. He ravaged all the country round about Montalban, so that supplies of food should be cut off, and he threatened death to any who should attempt to issue forth, hoping to compel the garrison to submit for want of food.

Rinaldo's resources had been brought so low that it seemed useless to contend any longer. His brothers had been taken prisoners in a skirmish, and his only hope of saving their lives was in making terms with the king.

So he sent a messenger, offering to yield himself and his castle if the king would spare his and his brothers' lives. While the messenger was gone, Rinaldo, impatient to learn what tidings he might bring, rode out to meet him. When he had ridden as far as he thought prudent he stopped in a wood, and, alighting, tied Bayard to a tree. Then he sat down, and, as he waited, he fell asleep. Bayard meanwhile got loose, and strayed away where the grass tempted him. Just then came along some country people, who said to one another, "Look, is not that the great horse Bayard that Rinaldo rides? Let us take him, and carry him to King Charles, who will pay us well for our trouble." They did so, and the king was delighted with his prize, and gave them a present that made them rich to their dying day.

When Rinaldo woke he looked round for his horse, and, finding him not, he groaned, and said, "O unlucky hour that I was born! how fortune persecutes me!" So desperate was he, that he took off his armor and his spurs, saying, "What need have I of these, since Bayard is lost?" While he stood thus lamenting, a man came from the thicket, seemingly bent with age. He had a long beard hanging over his breast, and eyebrows that almost covered his eyes. He bade Rinaldo good day. Rinaldo thanked him, and said, "A good day I have hardly had since I was born." Then said the old man, "Signor Rinaldo, you must not despair, for God will make all things turn to the best." Rinaldo answered, "My trouble is too heavy for me to hope relief. The king has taken my brothers, and means to put them to death. I thought to rescue them by means of my horse Bayard, but while I slept some thief has stolen him." The old man replied, "I will remember you and your brothers in my prayers. I am a poor man, have you not something to give me?" Rinaldo said, "I have nothing to give," but then he recollected his spurs. He gave them to the beggar, and said, "Here, take my spurs. They are the first present my mother gave me when my father, Count Aymon, dubbed me knight. They ought to bring you ten pounds."

The old man took the spurs, and put them into his sack, and said, "Noble sir, have you nothing else you can give me?" Rinaldo replied, "Are you making sport of me? I tell you truly if it were not for shame to beat one so helpless, I would teach you better manners." The old man said, "Of a truth, sir, if you did so, you would do a great sin. If all had beaten me of whom I have begged, I should have been killed long ago, for I ask alms in churches and convents, and wherever I can." "You say true," replied Rinaldo, "if you did not ask, none would relieve you." The old man said, "True, noble sir, therefore I pray if you have anything more to spare, give it me." Rinaldo gave him his mantle, and said, "Take it, pilgrim. I give it you for the love of Christ, that God would save my brothers from a shameful death, and help me to escape out of King Charles's power."

The pilgrim took the mantle, folded it up, and put it into his bag. Then a third time he said to Rinaldo, "Sir, have you nothing left to give me that I may remember you in my prayers?" "Wretch!" exclaimed Rinaldo, "do you make me your sport?" and he drew his sword, and struck at him; but the old man warded off the blow with his staff, and said, "Rinaldo, would you slay your cousin, Malagigi?" When Rinaldo heard that he stayed his hand, and gazed doubtingly on the old man, who now threw aside his disguise, and appeared to be indeed Malagigi. "Dear cousin," said Rinaldo, "pray forgive me. I did not know you. Next to God, my trust is in you. Help my brothers to escape out of prison, I entreat you. I have lost my horse, and therefore cannot render them any assistance." Malagigi answered, "Cousin Rinaldo, I will enable you to recover your horse. Meanwhile, you must do as I say."

Then Malagigi took from his sack a gown, and gave it to Rinaldo to put on over his armor, and a hat that was full of holes, and an old pair of shoes to put on. They looked like two pilgrims, very old and poor. Then they went forth from the wood, and, after a little while, saw four monks riding along the road. Malagigi said to Rinaldo, "I will go meet the monks, and see what news I can learn."

Malagigi learned from the monks that on the approaching festival there would be a great crowd of people at court, for the prince was going to show the ladies the famous horse Bayard that used to belong to Rinaldo. "What!" said the pilgrim; "is Bayard there?" "Yes," answered the monks; "the king has given him to Charlot, and, after the prince has ridden him, the king means to pass sentence on the brothers of Rinaldo, and have them hanged." Then Malagigi asked alms of the monks, but they would give him none, till he threw aside his pilgrim garb, and let them see his armor, when, partly for charity and partly for terror, they gave him a golden cup, adorned with precious stones that sparkled in the sunshine.

Malagigi then hastened back to Rinaldo, and told him what he had learned.

The morning of the feast-day Rinaldo and Malagigi came to the place where the sports were to be held. Malagigi gave Rinaldo his spurs back again, and said, "Cousin, put on your spurs, for you will need them." "How shall I need them," said Rinaldo, "since I have lost my horse?" Yet he did as Malagigi directed him.

When the two had taken their stand on the border of the field among the crowd, the princes and ladies of the court began to assemble. When they were all assembled, the king came also, and Charlot with him, near whom the horse Bayard was led, in the charge of grooms, who were expressly enjoined to guard him safely. The king, looking round on the circle of spectators, saw Malagigi and Rinaldo, and observed the splendid cup that they had, and said to Charlot, "See, my son, what a brilliant cup those two pilgrims have got. It seems to be worth a hundred ducats." "That is true," said Charlot; "let us go and ask where they got it." So they rode to the place where the pilgrims stood, and Charlot stopped Bayard close to them.

The horse snuffed at the pilgrims, knew Rinaldo, and caressed his master. The king said to Malagigi, "Friend, where did you get that beautiful cup?" Malagigi replied, "Honorable sir, I paid for it all the money I have saved from eleven years' begging in churches and convents. The Pope himself has blessed it, and given it the power that whosoever eats or drinks out of it shall be pardoned of all his sins." Then said the king to Charlot, "My son, these are right holy men; see how the dumb beast worships them."

Then the king said to Malagigi, "Give me a morsel from your cup, that I may be cleared of my sins." Malagigi answered, "Illustrious lord, I dare not do it, unless you will forgive all who have at any time offended you. You know that Christ forgave all those who had betrayed and crucified him." The king replied, "Friend, that is true; but Rinaldo has so grievously offended me, that I cannot forgive him, nor that other man, Malagigi, the magician. These two shall never live in my kingdom again. If I catch them, I will certainly have them hanged. But tell me, pilgrim, who is that man who stands beside you?" "He is deaf, dumb, and blind," said Malagigi. Then the king said again, "Give me to drink of your cup, to take away my sins." Malagigi answered, "My lord king, here is my poor brother, who for fifty days has not heard, spoken, nor seen. This misfortune befell him in a house where we found shelter, and the day before yesterday we met with a wise woman, who told him the only hope of a cure for him was to come to some place where Bayard was to be ridden, and to mount and ride him; that would do him more good than anything else." Then said the king, "Friend, you have come to the right place, for Bayard is to be ridden here to-day. Give me a draught from your cup, and your companion shall ride upon Bayard." Malagigi, hearing these words, said, "Be it so." Then the king, with great devotion, took a spoon, and dipped a portion from the pilgrim's cup, believing that his sins should be thereby forgiven.

When this was done, the king said to Charlot, "Son, I request that you will let this sick pilgrim sit on your horse, and ride if he can, for by so doing he will be healed of all his infirmities." Charlot replied, "That will I gladly do." So saying, he dismounted, and the servants took the pilgrim in their arms, and helped him on the horse.

When Rinaldo was mounted, he put his feet in the stirrups, and said, "I would like to ride a little." Malagigi, hearing him speak, seemed delighted, and asked him whether he could see and hear also. "Yes," said Rinaldo, "I am healed of all my infirmities." When the king heard it, he said to Bishop Turpin, "My lord bishop, we must celebrate this with a procession, with crosses and banners, for it is a great miracle."

When Rinaldo remarked that he was not carefully watched, he spoke to the horse, and touched him with the spurs. Bayard knew that his master was upon him, and he started off upon a rapid pace, and in a few moments was a good way off. Malagigi pretended to be in great alarm. "O noble king and master," he cried, "my poor companion is run away with; he will fall and break his neck." The king ordered his knights to ride after the pilgrim, and bring him back, or help him if need were. They did so, but it was in vain. Rinaldo left them all behind him, and kept on his way till he reached Montalban. Malagigi was suffered to depart, unsuspected, and he went his way, making sad lamentation for the fate of his comrade, who he pretended to think must surely be dashed to pieces.

Malagigi did not go far, but, having changed his disguise, returned to where the king was, and employed his best art in getting the brothers of Rinaldo out of prison. He succeeded; and all three got safely to Montalban, where Rinaldo's joy at the rescue of his brothers and the recovery of Bayard was more than tongue can tell.

CHAPTER XX

DEATH OF RINALDO

THE distress in Rinaldo's castle for want of food grew more severe every day, under the pressure of the siege. The garrison were forced to kill their horses, both to save the provision they would consume, and to make food of their flesh. At last, all the horses were killed except Bayard, and Rinaldo said to his brothers, "Bayard must die, for we have nothing else to eat." So they went to the stable and brought out Bayard to kill him. But Alardo said, "Brother, let Bayard live a little longer; who knows what God may do for us."

Bayard heard these words, and understood them as if he was a man, and fell on his knees, as if he would beg for mercy. When

Rinaldo saw the distress of his horse his heart failed him, and he let him live.

Just at this time, Aya, Rinaldo's mother, who was the sister of the Emperor, came to the camp, attended by knights and ladies, to intercede for her sons. She fell on her knees before the king, and besought him that he would pardon Rinaldo and his brothers; and all the peers and knights took her side, and entreated the king to grant her prayer. Then said the king, "Dear sister, you act the part of a good mother, and I respect your tender heart, and yield to your entreaties. I will spare your sons their lives, if they submit implicitly to my will."

When Charlot heard this, he approached the king and whispered in his ear. And the king turned to his sister and said, "Charlot must have Bayard, because I have given the horse to him. Now go, my sister, and tell Rinaldo what I have said."

When the Lady Aya heard these words, she was delighted, thanked God in her heart, and said, "Worthy king and brother, I will do as you bid me." So she went into the castle, where her sons received her most joyfully and affectionately, and she told them the king's offer. Then Alardo said, "Brother, I would rather have the king's enmity than give Bayard to Charlot, for I believe he will kill him." Likewise said all the brothers. When Rinaldo heard them, he said, "Dear brothers, if we may win our forgiveness by giving up the horse, so be it. Let us make our peace, for we cannot stand against the king's power." Then he went to his mother, and told her they would give the horse to Charlot, and more, too, if the king would pardon them, and forgive all that they had done against his crown and dignity. The lady returned to Charles and told him the answer of her sons.

When the peace was thus made between the king and the sons of Aymon, the brothers came forth from the castle, bringing Bayard with them, and, falling at the king's feet, begged his forgiveness. The king bade them rise, and received them into favor in the sight of all his noble knights and counsellors, to the great joy of all, especially of the Lady Aya, their mother. Then Rinaldo took the horse Bayard, gave him to Charlot, and said, "My lord and prince, this horse I give to you; do with him as to you seems good." Charlot took him, as had been agreed on. Then he made the servants take him to the bridge, and throw him into the water. Bayard sank to the bottom, but soon came to the surface again and swam, saw Rinaldo looking at him, came to land, ran to his old master, and stood by him as proudly as if he had understanding, and would say, "Why did you treat me so?" When the prince saw that, he said, "Rinaldo, give me the horse again, for he must die." Rinaldo replied,

"My lord and prince, he is yours without dispute," and gave him to him. The prince then had a millstone tied to each foot, and two to his neck, and made them throw him again into the water. Bayard struggled in the water, looked up to his master, threw off the stones, and came back to Rinaldo.

When Alardo saw that, he said, "Now must thou be disgraced forever, brother, if thou give up the horse again." But Rinaldo answered, "Brother, be still. Shall I for the horse's life provoke the anger of the king again?" Then Alardo said, "Ah, Bayard! what a return do we make for all thy true love and service!" Rinaldo gave the horse to the prince again, and said, "My lord, if the horse comes out again, I cannot return him to you any more, for it wrings my heart too much." Then Charlot had Bayard loaded with the stones as before, and thrown into the water; and commanded Rinaldo that he should not stand where the horse would see him. When Bayard rose to the surface he stretched his neck out of the water and looked round for his master, but saw him not. Then he sunk to the bottom.

Rinaldo was so distressed for the loss of Bayard, that he made a vow to ride no horse again all his life long, nor to bind a sword to his side, but to become a hermit. He resolved to betake himself to some wild wood, but first to return to his castle, to see his children, and to appoint to each his share of his estate.

So he took leave of the king and of his brothers, and returned to Montalban, and his brothers remained with the king. Rinaldo called his children to him, and he made his eldest born, Aymeric, a knight, and made him lord of his castle and of his land. He gave to the rest what other goods he had, and kissed and embraced them all, commended them to God, and then departed from them with a heavy heart.

He had not travelled far when he entered a wood, and there met with a hermit, who had long been retired from the world. Rinaldo greeted him, and the hermit replied courteously, and asked him who he was and what was his purpose. Rinaldo replied, "Sir, I have led a sinful life; many deeds of violence have I done, and many men have I slain, not always in a good cause, but often under the impulse of my own headstrong passions. I have also been the cause of the death of many of my friends, who took my part, not because they thought me in the right, but only for love of me. And now I come to make confession of all my sins, and to do penance for the rest of my life, if perhaps the mercy of God will forgive me." The hermit said, "Friend, I perceive you have fallen into great sins, and have broken the commandments of God, but His mercy is greater than your sins; and if you repent from your heart, and lead a new life, there is yet hope for you that He will forgive you what is past." So Rinaldo was comforted, and said, "Master, I will stay with you, and what you bid me I will do." The hermit replied, "Roots and vegetables will be your food; shirt or shoes you may not wear; your lot must be poverty and want, if you stay with me." Rinaldo replied, "I will cheerfully bear all this, and more." So he remained three whole years with the hermit, and after that his strength failed, and it seemed as if he was like to die.

One night the hermit had a dream, and heard a voice from heaven, which commanded him to say to his companion that he must without delay go to the Holy Land, and fight against the heathen. The hermit, when he heard that voice, was glad, and, calling Rinaldo, he said, "Friend, God's angel has commanded me to say to you that you must without delay go to Jerusalem, and help our fellow-Christians in their struggle with the Infidels." Then said Rinaldo, "Ah! master, how can I do that? It is over three years since I made a vow no more to ride a horse, nor take a sword or spear in my hand." The hermit answered, "Dear friend, obey God, and do what the angel commanded." "I will do so," said Rinaldo, "and pray for me, my master, that God may guide me right." Then he departed, and went to the seaside, and took ship and came to Tripoli in Syria.

And as he went on his way his strength returned to him, till it was equal to what it was in his best days. And though he never mounted a horse, nor took a sword in his hand, yet with his pilgrim's staff he did good service in the armies of the Christians; and it pleased God that he escaped unhurt, though he was present in many battles, and his courage inspired the men with the same. At last a truce was made with the Saracens, and Rinaldo, now old and infirm, wishing to see his native land again before he died, took ship and sailed for France. When he arrived, he shunned to go to the resorts of the great, and preferred to live among the humble folk, where he was unknown. He did country work and lived on milk and bread, drank water, and was therewith content. While he so lived, he heard that the city of Cologne was the holiest and best of cities, on account of the relics and bodies of saints who had there poured out their blood for the faith. This induced him to betake himself thither. When the pious hero arrived at Cologne, he went to the monastery of St. Peter, and lived a holy life, occupied night and day in devotion. It so happened that at that time, in the next town to Cologne, there raged a dreadful pestilence. Many people came to Rinaldo, to beg him to pray for them, that the plague might be stayed. The holy man prayed fervently, and besought the Lord to take away the plague from the people, and his prayer was heard. The stroke of the pestilence was arrested, and all the people thanked the holy man and praised God.

Now there was at this time at Cologne a Bishop, called Agilolphus, who was a wise and understanding man, who led a pure and secluded life, and set a good example to others. This Bishop undertook to build the Church of St. Peter, and gave notice to all stone-masons and other workmen round about to come to Cologne, where they should find work and wages. Among others came Rinaldo; and he worked among the laborers and did more than four or five common workmen. When they went to dinner, he brought stone and mortar so that they had enough for the whole day. When the others went to bed, he stretched himself out on the stones. He ate bread only, and drank nothing but water; and had for his wages but a penny a day. The head-workman asked him his name, and where he belonged. He would not tell, but said nothing and pursued his work. They called him St. Peter's workman, because he was so devoted to his work.

When the overseer saw the diligence of this holy man, he chid the laziness of the other workmen, and said, "You receive more pay than this good man, but do not do half as much work." For this reason the other workmen hated Rinaldo, and made a secret agreement to kill him. They knew that he made it a practice to go every night to a certain church to pray and give alms. So they agreed to lay wait for him with the purpose to kill him. When he came to the spot, they seized him, and beat him over the head till he was dead. Then they put his body into a sack, and stones with it, and cast it into the Rhine, in the hope the sack would sink to the bottom, and be there concealed. But God willed not that it should be so, but caused the sack to float on the surface, and be thrown upon the bank. And the soul of the holy martyr was carried by angels, with songs of praise, up to the heavens.

Now at that time the people of Dortmund had become converted to the Christian faith; and they sent to the Bishop of Cologne, and desired him to give them some of the holy relics that are in such abundance in that city. So the Bishop called together his clergy to deliberate what answer they should give to this request. And it was determined to give to the people of Dortmund the body of the holy man who had just suffered martyrdom.

When now the body with the coffin was put on the cart, the cart began to move toward Dortmund without horses or help of men, and stopped not till it reached the place where the church of St. Rinaldo now stands. The Bishop and his clergy followed the holy man to do him honor, with singing of hymns, for a space of three miles. And St. Rinaldo has ever since been the patron of that place, and many wonderful works has God done through him, as may be seen in the legends.

CHAPTER XXI

HUON OF BORDEAUX

WHEN Charlemagne grew old he felt the burden of government become heavier year by year, till at last he called together his high barons and peers to propose to abdicate the empire and the throne of France in favor of his sons, Charlot and Lewis.

The Emperor was unreasonably partial to his eldest son; he would have been glad to have had the barons and peers demand Charlot for their only sovereign; but that prince was so infamous, for his falsehood and cruelty, that the council strenuously opposed the Emperor's proposal of abdicating, and implored him to continue to hold a sceptre which he wielded with so much glory.

Amaury of Hauteville, cousin of Ganelon, and now head of the wicked branch of the house of Maganza, was the secret partisan of Charlot, whom he resembled in his loose morals and bad dispositions. Amaury nourished the most bitter resentment against the house of Guienne, of which the former Duke, Sevinus, had often rebuked his misdeeds. He took advantage of this occasion to do an injury to the two young children whom the Duke Sevinus had left under the charge of the Duchess Alice, their mother; and, at the same time, to advance his interest with Charlot by increasing his wealth and power. With this view, he suggested to the prince a new idea.

He pretended to agree with the opinion of the barons; he said that it would be best to try Charlot's capacity for government, by giving him some rich provinces, before placing him upon the throne; and that the Emperor, without depriving himself of any part of his realm, might give Charlot the investiture of Guienne. For although seven years had passed since the death of Sevinus, the young Duke, his son, had not yet repaired to the court of Charlemagne to render the homage due to his lawful sovereign.

We have often had occasion to admire the justice and wisdom of the advice which on all occasions the Duke Namo of Bavaria gave to Charlemagne, and he now discountenanced, with indignation, the selfish advice of Amaury. He represented to the Emperor the early age of the children of Sevinus, and the useful and glorious service of their late father, and proposed to Charlemagne to send two knights to the Duchess, at Bordeaux, to summon her two sons to the court of the Emperor, to pay their respects and render homage.

Charlemagne approved this advice, and sent two chevaliers to demand the two young princes of their mother. No sooner had the Duchess learned the approach of the two knights, than she sent distinguished persons to receive them; and as soon as they entered the palace she presented herself before them, with her elder and younger sons, Huon and Girard.

The deputies, delighted with the honors and caresses they received, accompanied with rich presents, left Bordeaux with regret, and, on their return, represented to Charlemagne that the young Duke Huon seemed born to tread in the footsteps of his brave father, informing him that in three months the young princes of Guienne would present themselves at his court.

The Duchess employed the short interval in giving her sons her last instructions. Huon received them in his heart, and Girard gave as much heed to them as could be expected from one so young.

The preparations for their departure having been made, the Duchess embraced them tenderly, commending them to the care of Heaven, and charged them to call, on their way, at the celebrated monastery of Cluny, to visit the Abbot, the brother of their father. This Abbot, worthy of his high dignity, had never lost an opportunity of doing good, setting an example of every excellence, and making virtue attractive by his example.

He received his nephews with the greatest magnificence; and, aware how useful his presence might be to them with Charlemagne, whose valued counsellor he was, he took with them the road to Paris.

When Amaury learned what reception the two deputies of Charlemagne had received at Bordeaux, and the arrangements made for the visit of the young princes to the Emperor's court, he suggested to Charlot to give him a troop of his guards, with which he proposed to lay wait for the young men in the wood of Montlery, put them to death, and thereby give the prince Charlot possession of the duchy of Guienne.

A plan of treachery and violence agreed but too well with Charlot's disposition. He not only adopted the suggestion of Amaury, but insisted upon taking a part in it. They went out secretly, by night, followed by a great number of attendants, all armed in black, to lie in ambuscade in the wood where the brothers were to pass.

Girard, the younger of the two, having amused himself as he rode by flying his hawk at such game as presented itself, had ridden in advance of his brother and the Abbot of Cluny. Charlot, who saw him coming, alone and unarmed, went forth to meet him, sought a quarrel with him, and threw him from his horse with a stroke of his lance. Girard uttered a cry as he fell; Huon heard it, and flew to his defence, with no other weapon than his sword. He came up with him, and saw the blood flowing from his wound. "What has this child done to you, wretch?" he exclaimed to Charlot. "How cowardly to attack him when unprepared to defend himself!" "By my faith," said Charlot, "I mean to do the same by you. Know that I am the son of Duke Thierry of Ardennes, from whom your father, Sevinus, took three castles; I have sworn to avenge him, and I defy you." "Coward," answered Huon, "I know well the baseness that dwells in your race; worthy son of Thierry, use the advantage that your armor gives you; but know that I fear you not." At these words Charlot had the wickedness to put his lance in rest, and to run upon Huon, who had barely time to wrap his arm in his mantle. With this feeble buckler he received the thrust of the lance. It penetrated the mantle, but missed his body. Then, rising upon his stirrups, Sir Huon struck Charlot so terrible a blow with his sword that the helmet was cleft asunder, and his head too. The dastardly prince fell dead upon the ground.

Huon now perceived that the wood was full of armed men. He called the men of his suite, and they hastily put themselves in order, but nobody issued from the wood to attack him. Amaury, who saw Charlot's fall, had no desire to compromit himself; and, feeling sure that Charlemagne would avenge the death of his son, he saw no occasion for his doing anything more at present. He left Huon and the Abbot of Cluny to bind up the wound of Girard, and, having seen them depart and resume their way to Paris, he took up the body of Charlot, and, placing it across a horse, had it carried to Paris, where he arrived four hours after Huon.

The Abbot of Cluny presented his nephew to Charlemagne, but Huon refrained from paying his obeisance, complaining grievously of the ambush which had been set for him, which he said could not have been without the Emperor's permission. Charlemagne, surprised at a charge which his magnanimous soul was incapable of meriting, asked eagerly of the Abbot what were the grounds of the complaints of his nephew. The Abbot told him faithfully all that had happened, informing him that a coward knight, who called himself the son of Thierry of Ardennes, had wounded Girard, and run upon Huon, who was unarmed; but by his force and valor he had overcome the traitor, and left him dead upon the plain.

Charlemagne indignantly disavowed any connection with the action of the infamous Thierry, congratulated the young Duke upon his victory, himself conducted the two brothers to a rich apartment, stayed to see the first dressing applied to the wound of Girard, and left the brothers in charge of Duke Namo of Bavaria, who, having been a companion in arms of the Duke Sevinus, regarded the young men almost as if they were his own sons.

Charlemagne had hardly quitted them when, returning to his chamber, he heard cries, and saw through the window a party of armed men just arrived. He recognized Amaury, who bore a dead knight stretched across a horse; and the name of Charlot was heard among the exclamations of the people assembled in the court-yard.

Charles's partiality for this unworthy son was one of his weaknesses. He descended in trepidation to the court-yard, ran to Amaury, and uttered a cry of grief on recognizing Charlot. "It is Huon of Bordeaux," said the traitor Amaury, "who has massacred your son before it was in my power to defend him." Charlemagne, furious at these words, seized a sword, and flew to the apartment of the two brothers to plunge it into the heart of the murderer of his son. Duke Namo stopped his hand for an instant, while Charles told him the crime of which Huon was accused. "He is a peer of the realm," said Namo, "and if he is guilty, is he not here in your power, and are not we peers the proper judges to condemn him to death? Let not your hand be stained with his blood." The Emperor, calmed by the wisdom of Duke Namo, summoned Amaury to his presence. The peers assembled to hear his testimony, and the traitor accused Huon of Bordeaux of having struck the fatal blow, without allowing Charlot an opportunity to defend himself, and though he knew that his opponent was the Emperor's eldest son.

The Abbot of Cluny, indignant at the false accusation of Amaury, advanced, and said, "By Saint Benedict, sire, the traitor lies in his throat. If my nephew has slain Charlot, it was in his own defence, and after having seen his brother wounded by him, and also in ignorance that his adversary was the prince. Though I am a son of the Church," added the good Abbot, "I forget not that I am a knight by birth. I offer to prove with my body the lie upon Amaury, if he dares sustain it, and I shall feel that I am doing a better work to punish a disloyal traitor, than to sing lauds and matins."

Huon to this time had kept silent, amazed at the black calumny of Amaury; but now he stepped forth, and, addressing Amaury, said: "Traitor! darest thou maintain in arms the lie thou hast uttered?" Amaury, a knight of great prowess, despising the youth and slight figure of Huon, hesitated not to offer his glove, which Huon seized; then, turning again to the peers, he said: "I pray you let the combat be allowed me, for never was there a more legitimate cause." The Duke Namo and the rest, deciding that the question should be remitted to the judgment of Heaven, the combat was ordained, to which Charlemagne unwillingly consented. The young Duke was restored to the charge of Duke Namo, who the next morning invested him with the honors of knighthood, and gave him armor of proof, with a white shield. The Abbot of Cluny, delighted to find in his nephew sentiments worthy of his birth, embraced him, gave him his blessing, and hastened to the church of St. Germains to pray for him, while the officers of the king prepared the lists for the combat.

The battle was long and obstinate. The address and agility of Huon enabled him to avoid the terrible blows which the ferocious Amaury aimed at him. But Huon had more than once drawn blood from his antagonist. The effect began to be perceived in the failing strength of the traitor; at last he threw himself from his horse, and, kneeling, begged for mercy. "Spare me," he said, "and I will confess all. Aid me to rise and lead me to Charlemagne." The brave and loyal Huon, at these words, put his sword under his left arm, and stretched out his right to raise the prostrate man, who seized the opportunity to give him a thrust in the side. The hauberk of Huon resisted the blow, and he was wounded but slightly. Transported with rage at this act of baseness, he forgot how necessary for his complete acquittal the confession of Amaury was, and without delay dealt him the fatal blow.

Duke Namo and the other peers approached, had the body of Amaury dragged forth from the lists, and conducted Huon to Charlemagne. The Emperor, however, listening to nothing but his resentment and grief for the death of his son, refused to be satisfied; and under the plea that Huon had not succeeded in making his accuser retract his charge, seemed resolved to confiscate his estates and to banish him forever from France. It was not till after long entreaties on the part of Duke Namo and the rest, that he consented to grant Huon his pardon, under conditions which he should impose.

Huon approached, and knelt before the Emperor, rendered him homage, and cried him mercy for the involuntary killing of his son. Charlemagne would not receive the hands of Huon in his own, but touched him with his sceptre, saying, "I receive thy homage, and pardon thee the death of my son, but only on one condition. You shall go immediately to the court of the Sultan Gaudisso; you shall present yourself before him as he sits at meat; you shall cut off the head of the most illustrious guest whom you shall find sitting nearest to him; you shall kiss three times on the mouth the fair princess his daughter, and you shall demand of the sultan, as token of tribute to me, a handful of the white hair of his beard, and four grinders from his mouth."

These conditions caused a murmur from all the assembly. "What!" said the Abbot of Cluny; "slaughter a Saracen prince without first offering him baptism?" "The second condition is not so hard," said the young peers, "but the demand that Huon is bound to make of the old Sultan is very uncivil, and will be hard to obtain."

The Emperor's obstinacy when he had once resolved upon a thing is well known. To the courage of Huon nothing seemed impossible. "I accept the conditions," said he, silencing the intercessions of the old Duke of Bavaria; "my liege, I accept my pardon at this price. I go to execute your commands, as your vassal and a peer of France."

The Duke Namo and the Abbot of Cluny, being unable to obtain any relaxation of the sentence passed by Charlemagne, led forth the young Duke, who determined to set out at once on his expedition. All that the good Abbot could obtain of him was, that he should prepare for this perilous undertaking by going first to Rome, to pay his homage to the Pope, who was the brother of the Duchess Alice, Huon's mother, and from him demand absolution and his blessing. Huon promised it, and forthwith set out on his way to Rome.

CHAPTER XXII

HUON OF BORDEAUX, CONTINUED

Huon, having traversed the Apennines and Italy, arrived at the environs of Rome, where, laying aside his armor, he assumed the dress of a pilgrim. In this attire he presented himself before the Pope, and not till after he had made a full confession of his sins did he announce himself as his nephew. "Ah! my dear nephew," exclaimed the Holy Father, "what harder penance could I impose than the Emperor has already done? Go in peace, my son," he added, absolving him, "I go to intercede for you with the Most High." Then he led his nephew into his palace, and introduced him to all the Cardinals and Princes of Rome as the Duke of Guienne, son of the Duchess Alice, his sister.

Huon, at setting out, had made a vow not to stop more than three days in a place. The Holy Father took advantage of this time to inspire him with zeal for the glory of Christianity, and with confidence in the protection of the Most High. He advised him to embark for Palestine, to visit the Holy Sepulchre, and to depart thence for the interior of Asia.

Loaded with the blessings of the Holy Father, Huon, obeying his counsels, embarked for Palestine, arrived, and visited with the greatest reverence the holy places. He then departed, and took his way toward the east. But, ignorant of the country and of the language, he lost himself in a forest, and remained three days without seeing a human creature, living on honey and wild fruits which he found on the trees. The third day, seeking a passage through a rocky defile, he beheld a man in tattered clothing, whose beard and hair covered his breast and shoulders. This man stopped on seeing him, observed him, and recognized the arms and bearing of a French knight. He immediately approached, and exclaimed, in the language of the South of France, "God be praised! Do I indeed behold a chevalier of my own country, after fifteen years passed in this desert without seeing the face of a fellow-countryman?"

Huon, to gratify him still more, unlaced his helmet, and came towards him with a smiling countenance. The other regarded him with more surprise than at first. "Good Heaven!" he exclaimed, "was there ever such a resemblance! Ah, noble sir," he added, "tell me, I beseech you, of what country and race you come?" "I require," replied Huon, "before telling you mine, that you first reveal your own; let it suffice you at present to know that I am a Christian, and that in Guienne I was born." "Ah! Heaven grant that my eyes and my heart do not deceive me," exclaimed the unknown; "my name is Sherasmin; I am brother to Guire, the Mayor of Bordeaux. I was taken prisoner in the battle where my dear and illustrious master, Sevinus, lost his life. For three years I endured the miseries of slavery; at length I broke my chains and escaped to this desert, where I have sustained myself in solitude ever since. Your features recall to me my beloved sovereign, in whose service I was from my infancy till his death." Huon made no reply but by embracing the old man, with tears in his eyes. Then Sherasmin learned that his arms enfolded the son of the Duke Sevinus. He led him to his cabin, and spread before him the dry fruits and honey which formed his only aliment.

Huon recounted his adventures to Sherasmin, who was moved to tears at the recital. He then consulted him on the means of conducting his enterprise. Sherasmin hesitated not to confess that success seemed impossible; nevertheless, he swore a solemn oath never to abandon him. The Saracen language, which he was master of, would be serviceable to them when they should leave the desert, and mingle with men.

They took the route of the Red Sea, and entered Arabia. Their way lay through a region which Sherasmin described as full of terrors. It was inhabited by Oberon, King of the Fairies, who made captive such knights as were rash enough to penetrate into it, and transformed them into Hobgoblins. It was possible to avoid this district at the expense of somewhat lengthening their route; but no dangers could deter Huon of Bordeaux; and the brave Sherasmin, who had now resumed the armor of a knight, reluctantly consented to share with him the dangers of the shorter route.

They entered a wood, and arrived at a spot whence alleys branched off in various directions. One of them seemed to be terminated by a superb palace, whose gilded roofs were adorned with brilliant weathercocks covered with diamonds. A superb chariot issued from the gate of the palace, and drove toward Huon and his companion, as if to meet them half-way. The prince saw no one in the chariot but a child apparently about five years old, very beautiful, and clad in a robe which glittered with precious stones. At the sight of him, Sherasmin's terror was extreme. He seized the reins of Huon's horse, and turned him about, hurrying the prince away, and assuring him that they were lost if they stopped to parley with the mischievous dwarf, who, though he appeared a child, was full of years and of treachery. Huon was sorry to lose sight of the beautiful dwarf, whose aspect had nothing in it to alarm; yet he followed his friend, who urged on his horse with all possible speed. Presently a storm began to roar through the forest, the daylight grew dim, and they found their way with difficulty. From time to time they seemed to hear an infantine voice, which said, "Stop, Duke Huon; listen to me: it is in vain you fly me!"

Sherasmin only fled the faster, and stopped not until he had reached the gate of a monastery of monks and nuns, the two communities of which were assembled at that time in a religious procession. Sherasmin, feeling safe from the malice of the dwarf in the presence of so many holy persons and the sacred banners, stopped to ask an asylum, and made Huon dismount also. But at that moment they were joined by the dwarf, who blew a blast upon an ivory horn which hung from his neck. Immediately the good Sherasmin, in spite of himself, began to dance like a young collegian, and seizing the hand of an aged nun, who felt as if it would be her death, they footed it briskly over the grass, and were imitated by all the other monks and nuns, mingled together, forming the strangest dancing-party ever beheld. Huon alone felt no disposition to dance; but he came near dying of laughter at seeing the ridiculous postures and leaps of the others.

The dwarf, approaching Huon, said, in a sweet voice, and in Huon's own language, "Duke of Guienne, why do you shun me? I conjure you, in Heaven's name, speak to me." Huon, hearing himself addressed in this serious manner, and knowing that no evil spirit would dare to use the holy name in aid of his schemes, replied, "Sir, whoever you are, I am ready to hear and answer you." "Huon, my friend," continued the dwarf, "I always loved your race, and you have been dear to me ever since your birth. The gracious state of conscience in which you were when you entered my wood has protected you from all enchantments, even if I had intended to practise any upon you. If these monks, these nuns, and even your friend Sherasmin, had had a conscience as pure as yours, my horn would not have set them dancing, but where is the monk or the nun who can always be deaf to the voice of the tempter, and Sherasmin in the desert has often doubted the power of Providence."

At these words Huon saw the dancers overcome with exertion. He begged mercy for them, the dwarf granted it, and the effect of the horn ceased at once; the nuns got rid of their partners, smoothed their dresses, and hastened to resume their places in the procession. Sherasmin, overcome with heat, panting, and unable to stand on his legs, threw himself upon the grass, and began, "Did not I tell you—" He was going on in an angry tone, but the dwarf, approaching, said, "Sherasmin, why have you murmured against Providence? why have you thought evil of me? You deserved this light punishment; but I know you to be good and loyal; I mean to show myself your friend, as you shall soon see." At these words, he presented him a rich goblet. "Make the sign of the cross on this cup," said he, "and then believe that I hold my power from the God you adore, whose faithful servant I am, as well as you." Sherasmin obeyed, and on the instant the cup was filled with delicious wine, a draught of which restored vigor to his limbs, and made him feel young again. Overcome with gratitude, he threw himself on his knees, but the dwarf raised him, and bade him sit beside him, and thus commenced his history:—

"Julius Cæsar, going by sea to join his army, was driven by a storm to take shelter in the island of Celea, where dwelt the fairy Glorianda. From this renowned pair I draw my birth. I am the inheritor of that which was most admirable in each of my parents: my father's heroic qualities, and my mother's beauty and magic art. But a malicious sister of my mother's, in revenge for some slight offence, touched me with her wand when I was only five years old, and forbade me to grow any bigger; and my mother, with all her power, was unable to annul the sentence. I have thus continued infantile in appearance, though full of years and experience. The power which I derive from my mother I use sometimes for my own diversion, but always to promote justice and to reward virtue. I am able and willing to assist you, Duke of Guienne, for I know the errand on which you come hither. I presage for you, if you follow my counsels, complete success; and the beautiful Clarimunda for a wife."

When he had thus spoken, he presented to Huon the precious and useful cup, which had the faculty of filling itself when a good man took it in his hand. He gave him also his beautiful horn of ivory, saying to him, "Huon, when you sound this gently, you will make the hearers dance, as you have seen; but if you sound it forcibly, fear not that I shall hear it, though at a hundred leagues' distance, and will fly to your relief; but be careful not to sound it in that way, unless upon the most urgent occasion."

Oberon directed Huon what course he should take to reach the country of the Sultan Gaudisso. "You will encounter great perils," said he, "before arriving there, and I fear me," he added, with tears in his eyes, "that you will not in everything obey my directions, and in that case you will suffer much calamity." Then he embraced Huon and Sherasmin, and left them.

Huon and his follower travelled many days through the desert before they reached any inhabited place, and all this while the wonderful cup sustained them, furnishing them not only wine, but food also. At last they came to a great city. As day was declining, they entered its suburbs, and Sherasmin, who spoke the Saracen language perfectly, inquired for an inn where they could pass the night. A person who appeared to be one of the principal inhabitants, seeing two strangers of respectable appearance making this inquiry, stepped forward and begged them to accept the shelter of his mansion. They entered, and their host did the honors of his abode with a politeness which they were astonished to see in a Saracen. He had them served with coffee and sherbet, and all was conducted with great decorum, till one of the servants awkwardly overturned a cup of hot coffee on the host's legs, when he started up, exclaiming in very good Gascon, "Blood and thunder! you blockhead, you deserve to be thrown over the mosque!"

Huon could not help laughing to see the vivacity and the language of his country thus break out unawares. The host, who had no idea that his guests understood his words, was astonished when Huon addressed him in the dialect of his country. Immediately confidence was established between them; especially when the domestics had retired. The host, seeing that he was discovered, and that the two pretended Saracens were from the borders of the Garonne, embraced them, and disclosed that he was a Christian. Huon, who had learned prudence from the advice of Oberon, to test his host's sincerity, drew from his robe the cup which the Fairy-king had given him, and presented it empty to the host. "A fair cup," said he, "but I should like it better if it was full." Immediately it was so. The host, astonished, dared not put it to his lips. "Drink boldly, my dear fellow-countryman," said Huon; "your truth is proved by this cup, which only fills itself in the hands of an honest man." The host did not hesitate longer; the cup passed freely from hand to hand; their mutual cordiality increased as it passed, and each recounted his adventures. Those of Huon redoubled his host's respect; for he recognized in him his legitimate sovereign; while the host's narrative was in these words:—

"My name is Floriac; this great and strong city, you will hear with surprise and grief, is governed by a brother of Duke Sevinus, and your uncle. You have no doubt heard that a young brother of the Duke of Guienne was stolen away from the sea-shore, with his companions, by some corsairs. I was then his page, and we were carried by those corsairs to Barbary, where we were sold for slaves. The Barbary prince sent us as part of the tribute which he yearly paid to his sovereign, the Sultan Gaudisso. Your uncle, who had been somewhat puffed up by the flattery of his attendants, thought to increase his importance with his new master by telling him his rank. The Sultan, who, like a true Mussulman, detested all Christian princes, exerted himself from that moment to bring him over to the Saracen faith. He succeeded but too well. Your uncle, seduced by the arts of the Santons, and by the pleasures and indulgences which the Sultan allowed him, committed the horrid crime of apostasy; he renounced his baptism, and embraced Mahometanism. Gaudisso then loaded him with honors, made him espouse one of his nieces, and sent him to reign over this city and adjoining country. Your uncle preserved for me the same friendship which he had had when a boy; but all his caresses and efforts could not make me renounce my faith. Perhaps he respected me in his heart for my resistance to his persuasions, perhaps he had hopes of inducing me in time to imitate him. He made me accompany him to this city, of which he was master, he gave me his confidence, and permits me to keep in my service some Christians, whom I protect for the sake of their faith."

"Ah!" exclaimed Huon, "take me to this guilty uncle. A prince of the house of Guienne, must he not blush at the cowardly abandonment of the faith of his fathers?"

"Alas!" replied Floriac, "I fear he will neither be sensible of shame at your reproaches, nor of pleasure at the sight of a nephew so worthy of his lineage. Brutified by sensuality, jealous of his power, which he often exercises with cruelty, he will more probably restrain you by force or put you to death."

"Be it so," said the brave and fervent Huon; "I could not die in a better cause; and I demand of you to conduct me to him to-morrow, after having told him of my arrival, and my birth." Floriac still objected, but Huon would take no denial, and he promised obedience.

Next morning Floriac waited upon the Governor, and told him of the arrival of his nephew, Huon of Bordeaux; and of the intention of the prince to present himself at his court that very day

The Governor, surprised, did not immediately answer; though he at once made up his mind what to do. He knew that Floriac loved Christians and the princes of his native land too well to aid in any treason to one of them; he therefore feigned great pleasure at hearing of the arrival of the eldest born of his family at his court. He immediately sent Floriac to find him; he caused his palace to be put in festal array, his divan to be assembled, and, after giving some secret orders, went himself to meet his nephew, whom he introduced under his proper name and title to all the great officers of his court.

Huon burned with indignation at seeing his uncle with forehead encircled with a rich turban, surmounted with a crescent of precious stones. His natural candor made him receive with pain the embraces which the treacherous Governor lavished upon him. Meanwhile the hope of finding a suitable moment to reproach him for his apostasy made him submit to those honors which his uncle caused to be rendered to him. The Governor evaded with address the chance of being alone with Huon, and spent all the morning in taking him through his gardens and palace. At last, when the hour of dinner approached, and the Governor took him by the hand to lead him into the dining-hall, Huon seized the opportunity, and said to him in a low voice, "O my uncle! O Prince, brother of the Duke Sevinus! in what condition have I the grief and shame of seeing you!" The Governor pretended to be moved, pressed his hand, and whispered in his ear, "Silence! my dear nephew; to-morrow morning I will hear you fully."

Huon, comforted a little by these words, took his seat at the table by the side of the Governor. The Mufti, some Cadis, Agas, and Santons, filled the other places. Sherasmin sat down with them; but Floriac, who could not lose sight of his guests, remained standing, and passed in and out to observe what was going on within the palace. He soon perceived a number of armed men gliding through the passages and antechambers connected with the dining-hall. He was about to enter to give his guests notice of what he had seen, when he heard a violent noise and commotion in the hall. The cause was this.

Huon and Sherasmin were well enough suited with the first course, and ate with good appetite; but the people of their country not being accustomed to drink only water at their meals, Huon and Sherasmin looked at one another, not very well pleased at such a regimen. Huon laughed outright at the impatience of Sherasmin, but soon, experiencing the same want himself, he drew forth Oberon's cup, and made the sign of the cross. The cup filled, and he drank it off, and handed it to Sherasmin, who followed his example. The Governor and his officers, seeing this abhorred sign, contracted their brows, and sat in silent consternation. Huon pretended not to observe it, and having filled the cup again, handed it to his uncle, saying, "Pray join us, dear uncle; it is excellent Bordeaux wine, the drink that will be to you like mother's milk." The Governor, who often drank in secret with his favorite Sultanas the wines of Greece and Shiraz, never in public drank anything but water. He had not for a long time tasted the excellent wines of his native land; he was sorely tempted to drink what was now handed to him, it looked so bright in the cup, outshining the gold itself. He stretched forth his hand, took the brimming goblet and raised it to his lips, when immediately it dried up and disappeared. Huon and Sherasmin, like Gascons as they were, laughed at his astonishment. "Christian dogs!" he exclaimed, "do you dare to insult me at my own table? But I will soon be revenged." At these words he threw the cup at the head of his nephew, who caught it with his left hand, while with the other he snatched the turban, with its crescent, from the Governor's head, and threw it on the floor. All the Saracens started up from table, with loud outcries, and prepared to avenge the insult. Huon and Sherasmin put themselves on their defence, and met with their swords the scimitars directed against them. At this moment the doors of the hall opened, and a crowd of soldiers and armed eunuchs rushed in, who joined in the attack upon Huon and Sherasmin. The Prince and his followers took refuge on a broad shelf or sideboard, where they kept at bay the crowd of assailants, making the most forward of them smart for their audacity. But more troops came pressing in, and the brave Huon, inspired by the wine of Bordeaux, and not angry enough to lose his relish for a joke, blew a gentle note on his horn, and no sooner was it heard than it quelled the rage of the combatants and set them to dancing. Huon and Sherasmin, no longer attacked, looked down from their elevated position on a scene the most singular and amusing. Very soon the Sultanas, hearing the sound of the dance, and finding their guards withdrawn, came into the hall and mixed with the dancers. The favorite Sultana seized upon a young Santon, who performed jumps two feet high; but soon the long dresses of this couple got intermingled and threw them down. The Santon's beard was caught in the Sultana's necklace, and they could not disentangle them. The Governor by no means approved this familiarity, and took two steps forward to get at the Santon, but he stumbled over a prostrate Dervise and measured his length on the floor. The dancing continued till the strength of the performers was exhausted, and they fell, one after the other, and lay helpless. The Governor at length made signs to

Huon that he would yield everything, if he would but allow him to rest. The bargain was ratified; the Governor allowed Huon and Sherasmin to depart on their way, and even gave them a ring which would procure them safe passage through his country and access to the Sultan Gaudisso. The two friends hastened to avail themselves of this favorable turn, and, taking leave of Floriac, pursued their journey.

CHAPTER XXIII

HUON OF BORDEAUX, CONTINUED

HUON had seen many beauties at his mother's court, but his heart had never been touched with love. Honor had been his mistress, and in pursuit of that he had never found time to give a thought to softer cares. Strange that a heart so insensible should first be touched by something so unsubstantial as a dream; but so it was.

The day after the adventure with his uncle, night overtook the travellers as they passed through a forest. A grotto offered them shelter from the night dews. The magic cup supplied their evening meal; for such was its virtue that it afforded not only wine, but more solid fare when desired. Fatigue soon threw them into profound repose. Lulled by the murmur of the foliage, and breathing the fragrance of the flowers, Huon dreamed that a lady more beautiful than he had ever before seen hung over him, and imprinted a kiss upon his lips. As he stretched out his arms to embrace her, a sudden gust of wind swept her away.

Huon awoke in an agony of regret. A few moments sufficed to afford some consolation in showing him that what had passed was but a dream; but his perplexity and sadness could not escape the notice of Sherasmin. Huon hesitated not to inform his faithful follower of the reason of his pensiveness; and got nothing in return but his rallyings for allowing himself to be disturbed by such a cause. He recommended a draught from the fairy goblet, and Huon tried it with good effect.

At early dawn they resumed their way. They travelled till high noon, but said little to one another. Huon was musing on his dream, and Sherasmin's thoughts flew back to his early days on the banks of the flowery Garonne.

On a sudden they were startled by the cry of distress, and, turning an angle of the wood, came where a knight hard pressed was fighting with a furious lion. The knight's horse lay dead, and it seemed as if another moment would end the combat, for terror and fatigue had quite disabled the knight for further resistance. He fell, and the lion's paw was raised over him, when a blow from Huon's sword turned the monster's rage upon a new enemy. His roar shook the forest, and he crouched in act to spring, when, with the rapidity of lightning, Huon plunged his sword into his side. He rolled over on the plain in the agonies of death.

They raised the knight from the ground, and Sherasmin hastened to offer him a draught from the fairy cup. The wine sparkled to the brim, and the warrior put forth his lips to quaff it, but it shrunk away, and did not even wet his lips. He dashed the goblet angrily on the ground, with an exclamation of resentment. This incident did not tend to make either party more acceptable to the other; and what followed was worse. For when Huon said, "Sir knight, thank God for your deliverance,"—"Thank Mahomet, rather, yourself," said he, "for he has led you this day to render service to no less a personage than the Prince of Hyrcania."

At the sound of this blasphemy Huon drew his sword and turned upon the miscreant, who, little disposed to encounter the prowess of which he had so lately seen proof, betook himself to flight. He ran to Huon's horse, and, lightly vaulting on his back, clapped spurs to his side, and galloped out of sight.

The adventure was vexatious, yet there was no remedy. The prince and Sherasmin continued their journey with the aid of the remaining horse as they best might. At length, as evening set in, they descried the pinnacles and towers of a great city full before them, which they knew to be the famous city of Bagdad.

They were wellnigh exhausted with fatigue when they arrived at its precincts, and in the darkness, not knowing what course to take, were glad to meet an aged woman, who, in reply to their inquiries, offered them such accommodations as her cottage could supply. They thankfully accepted the offer, and entered the low door. The good dame busily prepared the best fare her stores supplied,—milk, figs, and peaches,—deeply regretting that the bleak winds had nipped her almond-trees.

Sir Huon thought he had never in his life tasted any fare so good. The old lady talked while her guests ate. She doubted not, she said, they had come to be present at the great feast in honor of the marriage of the Sultan's daughter, which was to take place on the morrow. They asked who the bridegroom was to be, and the old lady answered, "The Prince of Hyrcania," but added, "Our princess hates him, and would rather wed a dragon than him." "How know you that?" asked Huon; and the dame informed him that she had it from the princess herself, who was her foster-child. Huon inquired the reason of the princess's aversion; and the woman, pleased to find her chat excite so much interest, replied that it was all in consequence of a dream. "A dream!" exclaimed Huon. "Yes!

a dream. She dreamed that she was a hind, and that the Prince, as a hunter, was pursuing her, and had almost overtaken her, when a beautiful dwarf appeared in view, drawn in a golden car, having by his side a young man of yellow hair and fair complexion, like one from a foreign land. She dreamed that the car stopped where she stood, and that, having resumed her own form, she was about to ascend it, when suddenly it faded from her view, and with it the dwarf and the fair-haired youth. But from her heart that vision did not fade, and from that time her affianced bridegroom, the Hyrcanian prince, had become odious to her sight. Yet the Sultan, her father, by no means regarding such a cause as sufficient to prevent the marriage, had named the morrow as the time when it should be solemnized, in presence of his court and many princes of the neighboring countries, whom the fame of the princess's beauty and the bridegroom's splendor had brought to the scene."

We may suppose this conversation woke a tumult of thoughts in the breast of Huon. Was it not clear that Providence led him on, and cleared the way for his happy success? Sleep did not early visit the eyes of Huon that night; but, with the sanguine temper of youth, he indulged his fancy in imagining the sequel of his strange experience.

The next day, which he could not but regard as the decisive day of his fate, he prepared to deliver the message of Charlemagne. Clad in his armor, fortified with his ivory horn and his ring, he reached the palace of Gaudisso when the guests were assembled at the banquet. As he approached the gate, a voice called on all true believers to enter; and Huon, the brave and faithful Huon, in his impatience passed in under that false pretension. He had no sooner passed the barrier than he felt ashamed of his baseness, and was overwhelmed with regret. To make amends for his fault he ran forward to the second gate, and cried to the porter, "Dog of a misbeliever, I command you in the name of Him who died on the cross, open to me!" The points of a hundred weapons immediately opposed his passage. Huon then remembered for the first time the ring he had received from his uncle, the Governor. He produced it, and demanded to be led to the Sultan's presence. The officer of the guard recognized the ring, made a respectful obeisance, and allowed him free entrance. In the same way he passed the other doors to the rich saloon where the great Sultan was at dinner with his tributary princes. At sight of the ring the chief attendant led Huon to the head of the hall, and introduced him to the Sultan and his princes as the ambassador of Charlemagne. A seat was provided for him near the royal party.

The Prince of Hyrcania, the same whom Huon had rescued from

the lion, and who was the destined bridegroom of the beautiful
Clarimunda, sat on the Sultan's right hand, and the princess herself on his left. It chanced that Huon found himself near the seat
of the princess, and hardly were the ceremonies of reception over,
before he made haste to fulfil the commands of Charlemagne by
imprinting a kiss upon her rosy lips, and after that a second, not
by command, but by good-will. The Prince of Hyrcania cried out,
"Audacious infidel! take the reward of thy insolence!" and aimed
a blow at Huon, which, if it had reached him, would have brought
his embassy to a speedy termination. But the ingrate failed of his
aim, and Huon punished his blasphemy and ingratitude at once by
a blow which severed his head from his body.

So suddenly had all this happened, that no hand had been raised
to arrest it; but now Gaudisso cried out, "Seize the murderer!"
Huon was hemmed in on all sides, but his redoubtable sword kept
the crowd of courtiers at bay. But he saw new combatants enter,
and could not hope to maintain his ground against so many. He
recollected his horn, and, raising it to his lips, blew a blast almost
as loud as that of Roland at Roncesvalles. It was in vain. Oberon
heard it; but the sin of which Huon had been guilty in bearing,
though but for a moment, the character of a believer in the false
prophet, had put it out of Oberon's power to help him. Huon, finding himself deserted, and conscious of the cause, lost his strength
and energy, was seized, loaded with chains, and plunged into a
dungeon.

His life was spared for the time, merely that he might be reserved
for a more painful death. The Sultan meant that, after being made
to feel all the torments of hunger and despair, he should be flayed
alive.

But an enchanter more ancient and more powerful than Oberon
himself interested himself for the brave Huon. That enchanter was
Love. The Princess Clarimunda learned with horror the fate to
which the young prince was destined. By the aid of her governante
she gained over the keeper of the prison, and went herself to lighten
the chains of her beloved. It was her hand that removed his fetters,
from her he received supplies of food to sustain a life which he
devoted from thenceforth wholly to her. After the most tender ex-
planations the princess departed, promising to repeat her visit on
the morrow.

The next day she came according to promise, and again brought
supplies of food. These visits were continued during a whole month.
Huon was too good a son of the Church to forget that the amiable
princess was a Saracen, and he availed himself of these interviews
to instruct her in the true faith. How easy it is to believe the truth

when uttered by the lips of those we love! Clarimunda erelong professed her entire belief in the Christian doctrines, and desired to be baptized.

Meanwhile the Sultan had repeatedly inquired of the jailer how his prisoner bore the pains of famine, and learned to his surprise that he was not yet much reduced thereby. On his repeating the inquiry, after a short interval, the keeper replied that the prisoner had died suddenly, and had been buried in the cavern. The Sultan could only regret that he had not sooner ordered the execution of the sentence.

While these things were going on, the faithful Sherasmin, who had not accompanied Huon in his last adventure, but had learned by common rumor the result of it, came to the court in hopes of doing something for the rescue of his master. He presented himself to the Sultan as Solario, his nephew. Gaudisso received him with kindness, and all the courtiers loaded him with attentions. He soon found means to inform himself how the Princess regarded the brave but unfortunate Huon, and, having made himself known to her, confidence was soon established between them. Clarimunda readily consented to assist in the escape of Huon, and to quit with him her father's court to repair to that of Charlemagne. Their united efforts had nearly perfected their arrangement, a vessel was secretly prepared, and all things in forwardness for the flight, when an unlooked-for obstacle presented itself. Huon himself positively refused to go, leaving the orders of Charlemagne unexecuted.

Sherasmin was in despair. Bitterly he complained of the fickleness and cruelty of Oberon in withdrawing his aid at the very crisis when it was most necessary. Earnestly he urged every argument to satisfy the prince that he had done enough for honor, and could not be held bound to achieve impossibilities. But all was of no avail, and he knew not which way to turn, when one of those events occurred which are so frequent under Turkish despotism. A courier arrived at the court of the Sultan, bearing the ring of his sovereign, the mighty Agrapard, Caliph of Arabia, and bringing the bowstring for the neck of Gaudisso. No reason was assigned; none but the pleasure of the Caliph is ever required in such cases; but it was suspected that the bearer of the bow-string had persuaded the Caliph that Gaudisso, whose rapacity was well known, had accumulated immense treasures, which he had not duly shared with his sovereign, and thus had obtained an order to supersede him in his Emirship.

The body of Gaudisso would have been cast out a prey to dogs and vultures, had not Sherasmin, under the character of nephew of the deceased, been permitted to receive it, and give it decent burial, which he did, but not till he had taken possession of the beard and grinders, agreeably to the orders of Charlemagne.

No obstacle now stood in the way of the lovers and their faithful follower in returning to France. They sailed, taking Rome in their way, where the Holy Father himself blessed the union of his nephew, Duke Huon of Bordeaux, with the Princess Clarimunda.

Soon afterward they arrived in France, where Huon laid his trophies at the feet of Charlemagne, and, being restored to the favor of the Emperor, hastened to present himself and his bride to the Duchess, his mother, and to the faithful liegemen of his province of Guienne and his city of Bordeaux, where the pair were received with transports of joy.

CHAPTER XXIV

OGIER, THE DANE

OGIER, the Dane, was the son of Geoffroy, who wrested Denmark from the Pagans, and reigned the first Christian king of that country. When Ogier was born, and before he was baptized, six ladies of ravishing beauty appeared all at once in the chamber of the infant. They encircled him, and she who appeared the eldest took him in her arms, kissed him, and laid her hand upon his heart. "I give you," said she, "to be the bravest warrior of your times." She delivered the infant to her sister, who said, "I give you abundant opportunities to display your valor." "Sister," said the third lady, "you have given him a dangerous boon; I give him that he shall never be vanquished." The fourth sister added, as she laid her hand upon his eyes and his mouth, "I give you the gift of pleasing." The fifth said, "Lest all these gifts serve only to betray, I give you sensibility to return the love you inspire." Then spoke Morgana, the youngest and handsomest of the group, "Charming creature, I claim you for my own; and I give you not to die till you shall have come to pay me a visit in my isle of Avalon." Then she kissed the child and departed with her sisters.

After this the king had the child carried to the font and baptized with the name of Ogier.

In his education nothing was neglected to elevate him to the standard of a perfect knight, and render him accomplished in all the arts necessary to make him a hero.

He had hardly reached the age of sixteen years, when Charlemagne, whose power was established over all the sovereigns of his time, recollected that Geoffroy, Ogier's father, had omitted to render the homage due to him as Emperor, and sovereign lord of Denmark, one of the grand fiefs of the empire. He accordingly sent an embassy to demand of the king of Denmark this homage, and on receiving a refusal, couched in haughty terms, sent an army to enforce the demand. Geoffroy, after an unsuccessful resistance, was forced to comply, and as a pledge of his sincerity delivered Ogier, his eldest son, a hostage to Charles, to be brought up at his court. He was placed in charge of the Duke Namo of Bavaria, the friend of his father, who treated him like his own son.

Ogier grew up more and more handsome and amiable every day. He surpassed in form, strength, and address all the noble youths his companions; he failed not to be present at all tourneys; he was attentive to the elder knights, and burned with impatience to imitate them. Yet his heart rose sometimes in secret against his condition as a hostage, and as one apparently forgotten by his father.

The king of Denmark, in fact, was at this time occupied with new loves. Ogier's mother having died, he had married a second wife, and had a son named Guyon. The new queen had absolute power over her husband, and fearing that, if he should see Ogier again, he would give him the preference over Guyon, she had adroitly persuaded him to delay rendering his homage to Charlemagne, till now four years had passed away since the last renewal of that ceremony. Charlemagne, irritated at this delinquency, drew closer the bonds of Ogier's captivity until he should receive a response from the king of Denmark to a fresh summons which he caused to be sent to him.

The answer of Geoffroy was insulting and defiant, and the rage of Charlemagne was roused in the highest degree. He was at first disposed to wreak his vengeance upon Ogier, his hostage; but at the entreaties of Duke Namo, who felt towards his pupil like a father, consented to spare his life, if Ogier would swear fidelity to him as his liege-lord, and promise not to quit his court without his permission. Ogier accepted these terms, and was allowed to retain all the freedom he had before enjoyed.

The Emperor would have immediately taken arms to reduce his disobedient vassal, if he had not been called off in another direction by a message from Pope Leo, imploring his assistance. The Saracens had landed in the neighborhood of Rome, occupied Mount Janiculum, and prepared to pass the Tiber and carry fire and sword to the capital of the Christian world. Charlemagne hesitated not to yield to the entreaties of the Pope. He speedily assembled an army, crossed the Alps, traversed Italy, and arrived at Spoleto, a strong place to which the Pope had retired. Leo, at the head of his Cardinals. advanced to meet him, and rendered him homage, as to the son of Pepin, the illustrious protector of the Holy See, coming, as his father had done, to defend it in the hour of need.

Charlemagne stopped but two days at Spoleto, and learning that the Infidels, having rendered themselves masters of Rome, were besieging the Capitol, which could not long hold out against them, marched promptly to attack them.

The advance posts of the army were commanded by Duke Namo, on whom Ogier waited as his squire. He did not yet bear arms, not having received the order of knighthood. The Oriflamme, the royal standard, was borne by a knight named Alory, who showed himself unworthy of the honor.

Duke Namo, seeing a strong body of the Infidels advancing to attack him, gave the word to charge them. Ogier remained in the rear, with the other youths, grieving much that he was not permitted to fight. Very soon he saw Alory lower the Oriflamme, and turn his horse in flight. Ogier pointed him out to the young men, and, seizing a club, rushed upon Alory and struck him from his horse. Then, with his companions, he disarmed him, clothed himself in his armor, raised the Oriflamme, and, mounting the horse of the unworthy knight, flew to the front rank, where he joined Duke Namo, drove back the Infidels, and carried the Oriflamme quite through their broken ranks. The Duke, thinking it was Alory, whom he had not held in high esteem, was astonished at his strength and valor. Ogier's young companions imitated him, supplying themselves with armor from the bodies of the slain; they followed Ogier and carried death into the ranks of the Saracens, who fell back in confusion upon their main body.

Duke Namo now ordered a retreat, and Ogier obeyed with reluctance, when they perceived Charlemagne advancing to their assistance. The combat now became general, and was more terrible than ever. Charlemagne had overthrown Corsuble, the commander of the Saracens, and had drawn his famous sword, Joyeuse, to cut off his head, when two Saracen knights set upon him at once, one of whom slew his horse, and the other overthrew the Emperor on the sand. Perceiving by the eagle on his casque who he was, they dismounted in haste to give him his death-blow. Never was the life of the Emperor in such peril. But Ogier, who saw him fall, flew to his rescue. Though embarrassed with the Oriflamme, he pushed his horse against one of the Saracens and knocked him down; and with his sword dealt the other so vigorous a blow that he fell stunned to the earth. Then helping the Emperor to rise, he remounted him on the horse of one of the fallen knights. "Brave and generous Alory!" Charles exclaimed, "I owe to you my honor and my life!" Ogier made no answer; but, leaving Charlemagne surrounded by a great many of the knights who had flown to his succor, he plunged into the thickest ranks of the enemy, and carried the Oriflamme, followed by a gallant train of youthful warriors, till the standard of Mahomet turned in retreat and the Infidels sought safety in their intrenchments.

Then the good Archbishop Turpin laid aside his helmet and his bloody sword, (for he always felt that he was clearly in the line of his duty while slaying infidels,) took his mitre and his crosier, and intoned Te Deum.

At this moment, Ogier, covered with blood and dust, came to lay the Oriflamme at the feet of the Emperor. He was followed by a train of warriors of short stature, who walked ill at ease loaded with armor too heavy for them. Ogier knelt at the feet of Charlemagne, who embraced him, calling him Alory, while Turpin, from the height of the altar, blessed him with all his might. Then young Orlando, son of the Count Milone and nephew of Charlemagne, no longer able to endure this misapprehension, threw down his helmet, and ran to unlace Ogier's, while the other young men laid aside theirs. Our author says he cannot express the surprise, the admiration, and the tenderness of the Emperor and his peers. Charles folded Ogier in his arms, and the happy fathers of those brave youths embraced them with tears of joy. The good Duke Namo stepped forward, and Charlemagne yielded Ogier to his embrace. "How much do I owe you," he said, "good and wise friend, for having restrained my anger! My dear Ogier! I owe you my life! My sword leaps to touch your shoulder, yours, and those of your brave young friends." At these words he drew that famous sword, Joyeuse, and, while Ogier and the rest knelt before him, gave them the accolade conferring on them the order of knighthood. The young Orlando and his cousin Oliver could not refrain, even in the presence of the Emperor, from falling upon Ogier's neck, and pledging with him that brotherhood in arms, so dear and so sacred to the knights of old time; but Charlot, the Emperor's son, at the sight of the glory with which Ogier had covered himself, conceived the blackest jealousy and hate.

The rest of the day and the next were spent in the rejoicings of the army. Turpin in a solemn service implored the favor of Heaven upon the youthful knights, and blessed the white armor which was prepared for them. Duke Namo presented them with golden spurs, Charles himself girded on their swords. But what was his astonishment when he examined that intended for Ogier! The loving Fairy, Morgana, had had the art to change it, and to substitute one of her own procuring, and when Charles drew it out of the scabbard, these words appeared written on the steel: "My name is Cortana, of the same steel and temper as Joyeuse and Durindana." Charles saw that a superior power watched over the destinies of Ogier; he vowed to love him as a father would, and Ogier promised him the devotion of a son. Happy had it been for both if they had always continued mindful of their promises.

The Saracen army had hardly recovered from its dismay when Carahue, King of Mauritania, who was one of the knights over-thrown by Ogier at the time of the rescue of Charlemagne, deter-mined to challenge him to single combat. With that view, he assumed the dress of a herald, resolved to carry his own message. The French knights admired his air, and said to one another that he seemed more fit to be a knight than a bearer of messages.

Carahue began by passing the warmest eulogium upon the knight who bore the Oriflamme on the day of the battle, and concluded by saying that Carahue, King of Mauritania, respected that knight so much that he challenged him to the combat.

Ogier had risen to reply, when he was interrupted by Charlot, who said that the gage of the King of Mauritania could not fitly be received by a vassal, living in captivity; by which he meant Ogier, who was at that time serving as hostage for his father. Fire flashed from the eyes of Ogier, but the presence of the Emperor restrained his speech, and he was calmed by the kind looks of Charlemagne, who said, with an angry voice, "Silence, Charlot! By the life of Bertha, my queen, he who has saved my life is as dear to me as yourself. Ogier," he continued, "you are no longer a hostage. Herald! report my answer to your master, that never does knight of my court refuse a challenge on equal terms. Ogier, the Dane, accepts of his, and I myself am his security."

Carahue, profoundly bowing, replied, "My lord, I was sure that the sentiments of so great a sovereign as yourself would be worthy of your high and brilliant fame; I shall report your answer to my master, who I know admires you, and unwillingly takes arms against you." Then, turning to Charlot, whom he did not know as the son of the Emperor, he continued, "As for you, Sir Knight, if the desire of battle inflames you, I have it in charge from Sadon, cousin of the King of Mauritania, to give the like defiance to any French knights who will grant him the honor of the combat."

Charlot, inflamed with rage and vexation at the public reproof which he had just received, hesitated not to deliver his gage. Carahue received it with Ogier's, and it was agreed that the combat should be on the next day, in a meadow environed by woods and equally distant from both armies.

The perfidious Charlot meditated the blackest treason. During the night he collected some knights unworthy of the name, and like himself in their ferocious manners; he made them swear to avenge his injuries, armed them in black armor, and sent them to lie in ambush in the wood, with orders to make a pretended attack upon the whole party, but in fact to lay heavy hands upon Ogier and the two Saracens.

At the dawn of day Sadon and Carahue, attended only by two pages to carry their spears, took their way to the appointed meadow; and Charlot and Ogier repaired thither also, but by different paths. Ogier advanced with a calm air, saluted courteously the two Saracen knights, and joined them in arranging the terms of combat.

While this was going on, the perfidious Charlot remained behind and gave his men the signal to advance. That cowardly troop issued from the wood and encompassed the three knights. All three were equally surprised at the attack, but neither of them suspected the other to have any hand in the treason. Seeing the attack made equally upon them all, they united their efforts to resist it, and made the most forward of the assailants bite the dust. Cortana fell on no one without inflicting a mortal wound, but the sword of Carahue was not of equal temper and broke in his hands. At the same instant his horse was slain, and Carahue fell, without a weapon and entangled with his prostrate horse. Ogier, who saw it, ran to his defence, and, leaping to the ground, covered the prince with his shield, supplied him with the sword of one of the fallen ruffians, and would have had him mount his own horse. At that moment Charlot, inflamed with rage, pushed his horse upon Ogier, knocked him down, and would have run him through with his lance if Sadon, who saw the treason, had not sprung upon him and thrust him back. Carahue leapt lightly upon the horse which Ogier presented him, and had time only to exclaim, "Brave Ogier, I am no longer your enemy, I pledge to you an eternal friendship," when numerous Saracen knights were seen approaching, having discovered the treachery, and Charlot with his followers took refuge in the wood.

The troop which advanced was commanded by Dannemont, the exiled king of Denmark, whom Geoffroy, Ogier's father, had driven from his throne and compelled to take refuge with the Saracens. Learning who Ogier was he instantly declared him his prisoner, in spite of the urgent remonstrances and even threats of Carahue and Sadon, and carried him, under a strong guard, to the Saracen camp. Here he was at first subjected to the most rigorous captivity, but Carahue and Sadon insisted so vehemently on his release, threatening to turn their arms against their own party if it was not granted, while Dannemont as eagerly opposed the measure, that Corsuble, the Saracen commander, consented to a middle course, and allowed Ogier the freedom of his camp, upon his promise not to leave it without permission.

Carahue was not satisfied with this partial concession. He left the city next morning, proceeded to the camp of Charlemagne, and demanded to be led to the Emperor. When he reached his presence he dismounted from his horse, took off his helmet, drew his sword, and, holding it by the blade, presented it to Charlemagne as he knelt before him.

"Illustrious prince," he said, "behold before you the herald who brought the challenge to your knights from the King of Mauritania. The cowardly old King Dannemont has made the brave Ogier prisoner, and has prevailed on our general to refuse to give him up. I come to make amends for this ungenerous conduct by yielding myself, Carahue, King of Mauritania, your prisoner."

Charlemagne, with all his peers, admired the magnanimity of Carahue; he raised him, embraced him, and restored to him his sword. "Prince," said he, "your presence and the bright example you afford my knights consoles me for the loss of Ogier. Would to God you might receive our holy faith, and be wholly united with us." All the lords of the court, led by Duke Namo, paid their respects to the King of Mauritania. Charlot only failed to appear, fearing to be recognized as a traitor; but the heart of Carahue was too noble to pierce that of Charlemagne by telling him the treachery of his son.

Meanwhile the Saracen army was rent by discord. The troops of Carahue clamored against the commander-in-chief because their king was left in captivity. They even threatened to desert the cause, and turn their arms against their allies. Charlemagne pressed the siege vigorously, till at length the Saracen leaders found themselves compelled to abandon the city and betake themselves to their ships. A truce was made; Ogier was exchanged for Carahue, and the two friends embraced one another with vows of perpetual brotherhood. The Pope was reestablished in his dominions, and Italy being tranquil, Charlemagne returned, with his peers and their followers, to France.

CHAPTER XXV

OGIER, THE DANE, CONTINUED

CHARLEMAGNE had not forgotten the offence of Geoffroy, the King of Denmark, in withholding homage, and now prepared to enforce submission. But at this crisis he was waited upon by an embassy from Geoffroy, acknowledging his fault, and craving assistance against an army of invaders who had attacked his states with a force which he was unable to repel. The soul of Charlemagne was too great to be implacable, and he took this opportunity to test that of Ogier, who had felt acutely the unkindness of his father, in leaving him, without regard or notice, fifteen years in captivity. Charles asked Ogier whether, in spite of his father's neglect, he was disposed to lead an army to his assistance. He replied, "A son can never be excused from helping his father by any cause short of death." Charlemagne placed an army of a thousand knights under the command of Ogier, and great numbers more volunteered to march undei so distinguished a leader. He flew to the succor of his father, repelled the invaders, and drove them in confusion to their vessels. Ogier then hastened to the capital, but as he drew near the city he heard all the bells sounding a knell. He soon learned the cause; it was the obsequies of Geoffroy, the King. Ogier felt keenly the grief of not having been permitted to embrace his father once more, and to learn his latest commands; but he found that his father had declared him heir to his throne. He hastened to the church where the body lay; he knelt and bathed the lifeless form with his tears. At that moment a celestial light beamed all around, and a voice as of an angel said, "Ogier, leave thy crown to Guyon, thy brother, and bear no other title than that of 'The Dane.' Thy destiny is glorious; and other kingdoms are reserved for thee." Ogier obeyed the divine behest. He saluted his stepmother respectfully, and, embracing his brother, told him that he was content with his lot in being reckoned among the paladins of Charlemagne, and resigned all claims to the crown of Denmark.

Ogier returned covered with glory to the court of Charlemagne, and the Emperor, touched with this proof of his attachment, loaded him with caresses, and treated him almost as an equal.

We pass in silence the adventures of Ogier for several ensuing years, in which the fairy-gifts of his infancy showed their force in making him successful in all enterprises, both of love and war. He married the charming Belicene, and became the father ot young Baldwin, a youth who seemed to inherit in full measure the strength and courage of his father and the beauty of his mother. When the lad was old enough to be separated from his mother, Ogier took him to court and presented him to Charlemagne, who embraced him, and took him into his service. It seemed to Duke Namo, and all the elder knights, as if they saw in him Ogier himself, as he was when a youth; and this resemblance won for the lad their kind regards. Even Charlot at first seemed to be fond of him, though after a while the resemblance to Ogier which he noticed had the effect to excite his hatred.

Baldwin was attentive to Charlot, and lost no occasion to be serviceable. The Prince loved to play chess, and Baldwin, who played well, often made a party with him.

One day Charlot was nettled at losing two pieces in succession; he thought he could, by taking a piece from Baldwin, get some amends for his loss; but Baldwin, seeing him fall into a trap which he had set for him, could not help a slight laugh, as he said, "Checkmate." Charlot rose in a fury, seized the rich and heavy chess-board, and dashed it with all his strength on the head of Baldwin, who fell, and died where he fell.

Frightened at his own crime, and fearing the vengeance of the terrible Ogier, Charlot concealed himself in the interior of the palace. A young companion of Baldwin hastened and informed Ogier of the event. He ran to the chamber, and beheld the body of his child bathed in blood, and it could not be concealed from him that Charlot gave the blow. Transported with rage, Ogier sought Charlot through the palace, and Charlot, feeling safe nowhere else, took refuge in the hall of Charlemagne, where he seated himself at table with Duke Namo and Salomon, Duke of Brittany. Ogier, with sword drawn, followed him to the very table of the Emperor. When a cupbearer attempted to bar his way, he struck the cup from his hand and dashed the contents in the Emperor's face. Charles rose in a passion, seized a knife, and would have plunged it into his breast, had not Salomon and another baron thrown themselves between, while Namo, who retained his ancient influence over Ogier, drew him out of the room. Foreseeing the consequences of this violence, pitying Ogier, and in his heart excusing him, Namo hurried him away before the guards of the palace could arrest him, made him mount his horse, and leave Paris.

Charlemagne called together his peers, and made them take an oath to do all in their power to arrest Ogier, and bring him to condign punishment. Ogier on his part sent messages to the Emperor, offering to give himself up on condition that Charlot should be punished for his atrocious crime. The Emperor would listen to no conditions, and went in pursuit of Ogier at the head of a large body of soldiers. Ogier, on the other hand, was warmly supported by many knights, who pledged themselves in his defence. The contest raged long, with no decisive results. Ogier more than once had the Emperor in his power, but declined to avail himself of his advantage, and released him without conditions. He even implored pardon for himself, but demanded at the same time the punishment of Charlot. But Charlemagne was too blindly fond of his unworthy son to subject him to punishment for the sake of conciliating one who had been so deeply injured.

At length, distressed at the blood which his friends had lost in his cause, Ogier dismissed his little army, and, slipping away from those who wished to attend him, took his course to rejoin the Duke Guyon, his brother. On his way, having reached the forest of Ardennes, weary with long travel, the freshness of a retired valley tempted him to lie down to take some repose. He unsaddled Beiffror, relieved himself of his helmet, lay down on the turf, rested his head on his shield, and slept.

It so happened that Turpin, who occasionally recalled to mind that he was Archbishop of Rheims, was at that time in the vicinity, making a pastoral visit to the churches under his jurisdiction. But his dignity of peer of France, and his martial spirit, which caused him to be reckoned among the "preux chevaliers" of his time, forbade him to travel without as large a retinue of knights as he had of clergymen. One of these was thirsty, and knowing the fountain on the borders of which Ogier was reposing, he rode to it, and was struck by the sight of a knight stretched on the ground. He hastened back, and let the Archbishop know, who approached the fountain, and recognized Ogier.

The first impulse of the good and generous Turpin was to save his friend, for whom he felt the warmest attachment; but his archdeacons and knights, who also recognized Ogier, reminded the Archbishop of the oath which the Emperor had exacted of them all. Turpin could not be false to his oath; but it was not without a groan that he permitted his followers to bind the sleeping knight. The Archbishop's attendants secured the horse and arms of Ogier, and conducted their prisoner to the Emperor at Soissons.

The Emperor had become so much embittered by Ogier's obstinate resistance, added to his original fault, that he was disposed to order him to instant death. But Turpin, seconded by the good Dukes Namo and Salomon, prayed so hard for him, that Charlemagne consented to remit a violent death, but sentenced him to close imprisonment, under the charge of the Archbishop, strictly limiting his food to one quarter of a loaf of bread per day, with one piece of meat, and a quarter of a cup of wine. In this way he hoped quickly to put an end to his life without bringing on himself the hostility of the King of Denmark, and other powerful friends of Ogier. He exacted a new oath of Turpin to obey his orders strictly.

The good Archbishop loved Ogier too well not to cast about for some means of saving his life, which he foresaw he would soon lose if subjected to such scanty fare, for Ogier was seven feet tall, and had an appetite in proportion. Turpin remembered, moreover, that Ogier was a true son of the Church, always zealous to propagate the faith and subdue unbelievers; so he felt justified in practising on this occasion what in later times has been entitled "mental reservation," without swerving from the letter of the oath which he had taken. This is the method he hit upon.

Every morning he had his prisoner supplied with a quarter of a loaf of bread, made of two bushels of flour; to this he added a quarter of a sheep or a fat calf, and he had a cup made which held forty pints of wine, and allowed Ogier a quarter of it daily.

Ogier's imprisonment lasted long. Charlemagne was astonished to hear, from time to time, that he still held out; and when he inquired more particularly of Turpin, the good Archbishop, relying on his own understanding of the words, did not hesitate to affirm positively that he allowed his prisoner no more than the permitted ration.

We forgot to say that, when Ogier was led prisoner to Soissons, the Abbot of Saint Faron, observing the fine horse Beiffror, and not having at the time any other favor to ask of Charlemagne, begged the Emperor to give him the horse, and had him taken to his abbey. He was impatient to try his new acquisition, and, when he had arrived in his litter at the foot of the mountain where the horse had been brought to meet him, mounted him and rode onward. The horse, accustomed to bear the enormous weight of Ogier in his armor, when he perceived nothing on his back but the light weight of the Abbot, whose long robes fluttered against his sides, ran away, making prodigious leaps over the steep acclivities of the mountain, till he reached the convent of Jouaire, where, in sight of the Abbess and her nuns, he threw the Abbot, already half dead with fright, to the ground. The Abbot, bruised and mortified, revenged himself on poor Beiffror, whom he condemned, in his wrath, to be given to the workmen to drag stones for a chapel that was building near the abbey. Thus, ill-fed, hard-worked, and often beaten, the noble horse Beiffror passed the time while his master's imprisonment lasted.

That imprisonment would have been as long as his life if it had not been for some important events which forced the Emperor to set Ogier at liberty.

The Emperor learned at the same time, that Carahue, King of Mauritania, was assembling an army to come and demand the liberation of Ogier; that Guyon, King of Denmark, was prepared to second the enterprise with all his forces; and, worse than all, that the Saracens, under Bruhier, Sultan of Arabia, had landed in Gascony, taken Bordeaux, and were marching with all speed for Paris.

Charlemagne now felt how necessary the aid of Ogier was to him. But, in spite of the representations of Turpin, Namo, and Salomon, he could not bring himself to consent to surrender Charlot to such punishment as Ogier should see fit to impose. Besides, he believed

that Ogier was without strength and vigor, weakened by imprisonment and long abstinence.

At this crisis he received a message from Bruhier, proposing to
put the issue upon the result of a combat between himself and the
Emperor or his champion; promising, if defeated, to withdraw his
army. Charlemagne would willingly have accepted the challenge;
but his counsellors all opposed it. The herald was therefore told
that the Emperor would take time to consider his proposition, and
give his answer the next day.

It was during this interval that the three Dukes succeeded in
prevailing upon Charlemagne to pardon Ogier, and to send for him
to combat the puissant enemy who now defied him; but it was no
easy task to persuade Ogier. The idea of his long imprisonment and
the recollection of his son, bleeding and dying in his arms by the
blow of the ferocious Charlot, made him long resist the urgency of
his friends. Though glory called him to encounter Bruhier, and the
safety of Christendom demanded the destruction of this proud
enemy of the faith, Ogier only yielded at last on condition that
Charlot should be delivered into his hands to be dealt with as he
should see fit.

The terms were hard, but the danger was pressing, and Charlemagne, with a returning sense of justice, and a strong confidence in
the generous though passionate soul of Ogier, at last consented to
them.

Ogier was led into the presence of Charlemagne by the three
peers. The Emperor, faithful to his word, had caused Charlot to
be brought into the hall where the high barons were assembled, his
hands tied, and his head uncovered. When the Emperor saw Ogier
approach, he took Charlot by the arm, led him towards Ogier, and
said these words: "I surrender the criminal; do with him as you
think fit." Ogier, without replying, seized Charlot by the hair, forced
him on his knees, and lifted with the other hand his irresistible
sword. Charlemagne, who expected to see the head of his son rolling
at his feet, shut his eyes and uttered a cry of horror.

Ogier had done enough. The next moment he raised Charlot, cut
his bonds, kissed him on the mouth, and hastened to throw himself
at the feet of the Emperor.

Nothing can exceed the surprise and joy of Charlemagne at seeing
his son unharmed and Ogier kneeling at his feet. He folded him in
his arms, bathed him with tears, and exclaimed to his barons, "I
feel at this moment that Ogier is greater than I." As for Charlot,
his base soul felt nothing but the joy of having escaped death; he
remained such as he had been, and it was not till some years after-

wards he received the punishment he deserved, from the hands of
Huon of Bordeaux, as we have seen in a former chapter.

CHAPTER XXVI

OGIER, THE DANE, CONTINUED

WHEN Charlemagne had somewhat recovered his composure, he
was surprised to observe that Ogier appeared in good case, and had
a healthy color in his cheeks. He turned to the Archbishop, who
could not help blushing as he met his eye. "By the head of Bertha,
my queen," said Charlemagne, "Ogier has had good quarters in your
castle, my Lord Archbishop; but so much the more am I indebted
to you." All the barons laughed, and jested with Turpin, who only
said, "Laugh as much as you please, my lords; but for my part I am
not sorry to see the arm in full vigor that is to avenge us on the
proud Saracen."

Charlemagne immediately despatched his herald, accepting the
challenge, and appointing the next day but one for the encounter.
The proud and crafty Bruhier laughed scornfully when he heard the
reply accepting his challenge, for he had a reliance on certain resources besides his natural strength and skill. However, he swore by
Mahomet to observe the conditions as proposed and agreed upon.

Ogier now demanded his armor, and it was brought to him in
excellent condition, for the good Turpin had kept it faithfully; but
it was not easy to provide a horse for the occasion. Charlemagne had
the best horses of his stables brought out, except Blanchard, his own
charger; but all in vain, the weight of Ogier bent their backs to the
ground. In this embarrassment the Archbishop remembered that the
Emperor had given Beiffror to the Abbot of St. Faron, and sent off
a courier in haste to re-demand him.

Monks are hard masters, and the one who directed the laborers
at the abbey had but too faithfully obeyed the orders of the Abbot.
Poor Beiffror was brought back lean, spiritless, and chafed with the
harness of the vile cart that he had had to draw so long. He carried
his head down, and trod heavily before Charlemagne; but when
he heard the voice of Ogier he raised his head, he neighed, his eyes
flashed, his former ardor showed itself by the force with which he
pawed the ground. Ogier caressed him, and the good steed seemed
to return his caresses; Ogier mounted him, and Beiffror, proud of
carrying his master again, leapt and curvetted with all his youthful
vigor.

Nothing being now wanted, Charlemagne, at the head of his army,
marched forth from the city of Paris, and occupied the hill of Mont-

martre, whence the view extended over the plain of St. Denis, where the battle was to be fought.

When the appointed day came, the Dukes Namo and Salomon, as seconds of Ogier, accompanied him to the place marked out for the lists, and Bruhier, with two distinguished Emirs, presented himself on the other side.

Bruhier was in high spirits, and jested with his friends, as he advanced, upon the appearance of Beiffror. "Is that the horse they presume to match with Marchevallée, the best steed that ever fed in the vales of Mount Atlas?" But now the combatants, having met and saluted each other, ride apart, to come together in full career. Beiffror flew over the plain, and met the adversary more than half-way. The lances of the two combatants were shivered at the shock, and Bruhier was astonished to see almost at the same instant the sword of Ogier gleaming above his head. He parried it with his buckler, and gave Ogier a blow on his helmet, who returned it with another, better aimed or better seconded by the temper of his blade, for it cut away part of Bruhier's helmet, and with it his ear and part of his cheek. Ogier, seeing the blood, did not immediately repeat his blow, and Bruhier seized the moment to gallop off on one side. As he rode he took a vase of gold which hung at the saddle-bow, and bathed with its contents the wounded part. The blood instantly ceased to flow, the ear and the flesh were restored quite whole, and the Dane was astonished to see his antagonist return to the ground as sound as ever.

Bruhier laughed at his amazement. "Know," said he, "that I possess the precious balm that Joseph of Arimathea used upon the body of the Crucified One. Whom you worship. If I should lose an arm, I could restore it with a few drops of this. It is useless for you to contend with me. Yield yourself, and, as you appear to be a strong fellow, I will make you first oarsman in one of my galleys."

Ogier, though boiling with rage, forgot not to implore the assistance of Heaven. "O Lord," he exclaimed, "suffer not the enemy of Thy name to profit by the powerful help of that which owes all its virtue to Thy divine blood." At these words he attacked Bruhier again with more vigor than ever; both struck terrible blows, and made grievous wounds; but the blood flowed from those of Ogier, while Bruhier stanched his by the application of his balm. Ogier, desperate at the unequal contest, grasped Cortana with both hands, and struck his enemy such a blow that it cleft his buckler, and cut off his arm with it; but Bruhier at the same time launched one at Ogier, which, missing him, struck the head of Beiffror, and the good horse fell, and drew down his master in his fall.

Bruhier had time to leap to the ground, to pick up his arm and apply his balsam; then, before Ogier had recovered his footing, he rushed forward with sword uplifted to complete his destruction.

Charlemagne, from the height of Montmartre, seeing the brave Ogier in this situation, groaned, and was ready to murmur against Providence; but the good Turpin, raising his arms, with a faith like that of Moses, drew down upon the Christian warrior the favor of Heaven.

Ogier, promptly disengaging himself, pressed Bruhier with so much impetuosity that he drove him to a distance from his horse, to whose saddle-bow the precious balm was suspended; and very soon Charlemagne saw Ogier, now completely in the advantage, bring his enemy to his knees, tear off his helmet, and, with a sweep of his sword, strike his head from his body.

After the victory, Ogier seized Marchevallée, leaped upon his back, and became possessed of the precious flask, a few drops from which closed his wounds and restored his strength. The French knights who had been Bruhier's captives, now released, pressed round Ogier to thank him for their deliverance.

Charlemagne and his nobles, as soon as their attention was relieved from the single combat, perceived from their elevated position an unusual agitation in the enemy's camp. They attributed it at first to the death of their general, but soon the noise of arms, the cries of combatants, and new standards which advanced, disclosed to them the fact that Bruhier's army was attacked by a new enemy.

The Emperor was right; it was the brave Carahue of Mauritania, who, with an army, had arrived in France, resolved to attempt the liberation of Ogier, his brother in arms. Learning on his arrival the changed aspect of affairs, he hesitated not to render a signal service to the Emperor, by attacking the army of Bruhier in the midst of the consternation occasioned by the loss of its commander.

Ogier recognized the standard of his friend, and, leaping upon Marchevallée, flew to aid his attack. Charlemagne followed with his army; and the Saracen host, after an obstinate conflict, was forced to surrender unconditionally.

The interview of Ogier and Carahue was such as might be anticipated of two such attached friends and accomplished knights. Charlemagne went to meet them, embraced them, and putting the King of Mauritania on his right and Ogier on his left, returned in triumph to Paris. There the Empress Bertha and the ladies of her court crowned them with laurels, and the sage and gallant Eginhard, chamberlain and secretary of the Emperor, wrote all these great events in his history.

A few days after, Guyon, King of Denmark, arrived in France

with a chosen band of knights, and sent an ambassador to Charlemagne, to say that he came, not as an enemy, but to render homage
to him as the best knight of the time and the head of the Christian
world. Charlemagne gave the ambassador a cordial reception, and,
mounting his horse, rode forward to meet the King of Denmark.

These great princes, being assembled at the court of Charles,
held council together, and the ancient and sage barons were called
to join it.

It was decided that the united Danish and Mauritanian armies
should cross the sea and carry the war to the country of the Saracens,
and that a thousand French knights should range themselves under
the banner of Ogier, the Dane, who, though not a king, should have
equal rank with the two others.

We have not space to record all the illustrious actions performed
by Ogier and his allies in this war. Suffice it to say, they subdued
the Saracens of Ptolemais and Judæa, and, erecting those regions
into a kingdom, placed the crown upon the head of Ogier. Guyon
and Carahue then left him, to return to their respective dominions.
Ogier adopted Walter, the son of Guyon of Denmark, to be his
successor in his kingdom. He superintended his education, and
saw the young prince grow up worthy of his cares. But Ogier, in
spite of all the honors of his rank, often regretted the court of
Charlemagne, the Duke of Namo, and Salomon of Brittany, for
whom he had the respect and attachment of a son. At last, finding
Walter old enough to sustain the weight of government, Ogier caused
a vessel to be prepared secretly, and, attended only by one squire,
left his palace by night, and embarked to return to France.

The vessel, driven by a fair wind, cut the sea with the swiftness
of a bird; but on a sudden it deviated from its course, no longer
obeyed the helm, and sped fast towards a black promontory which
stretched into the sea. This was a mountain of loadstone, and, its
attractive power increasing as the distance diminished, the vessel
at last flew with the swiftness of an arrow towards it, and was dashed
to pieces on its rocky base. Ogier alone saved himself, and reached
the shore on a fragment of the wreck.

Ogier advanced into the country, looking for some marks of in-
habitancy, but found none. On a sudden he encountered two monstrous animals, covered with glittering scales, accompanied by a
horse breathing fire. Ogier drew his sword and prepared to defend
himself; but the monsters, terrific as they appeared, made no attempt
to assail him, and the horse, Papillon, knelt down, and appeared to
court Ogier to mount upon his back. Ogier hesitated not to see the
adventure through; he mounted Papillon, who ran with speed, and
soon cleared the rocks and precipices which hemmed in and con-

cealed a beautiful landscape. He continued his course till he reached a magnificent palace, and, without allowing Ogier time to admire it, crossed a grand court-yard adorned with colonnades, and entered a garden, where, making his way through alleys of myrtle, he checked his course, and knelt down on the enamelled turf of a fountain.

Ogier dismounted and took some steps along the margin of the stream, but was soon stopped by meeting a young beauty, such as they paint the Graces, and almost as lightly attired as they. At the same moment, to his amazement, his armor fell off of its own accord. The young beauty advanced with a tender air, and placed upon his head a crown of flowers. At that instant the Danish hero lost his memory; his combats, his glory, Charlemagne and his court, all vanished from his mind; he saw only Morgana, he desired nothing but to sigh forever at her feet.

We abridge the narrative of all the delights which Ogier enjoyed for more than a hundred years. Time flew by, leaving no impression of its flight. Morgana's youthful charms did not decay, and Ogier had none of those warnings of increasing years which less-favored mortals never fail to receive. There is no knowing how long this blissful state might have lasted, if it had not been for an accident, by which Morgana one day, in a sportive moment, snatched the crown from his head. That moment Ogier regained his memory, and lost his contentment. The recollection of Charlemagne, and of his own relatives and friends, saddened the hours which he passed with Morgana. The fairy saw with grief the changed looks of her lover. At last she drew from him the acknowledgment that he wished to go, at least for a time, to revisit Charles's court. She consented with reluctance, and with her own hands helped to reinvest him with his armor. Papillon was led forth, Ogier mounted him, and, taking a tender adieu of the tearful Morgana, crossed at rapid speed the rocky belt which separated Morgana's palace from the borders of the sea.

The sea-goblins which had received him at his coming awaited him on the shore. One of them took Ogier on his back, and the other placing himself under Papillon, they spread their broad fins, and in a short time traversed the wide space that separates the isle of Avalon from France. They landed Ogier on the coast of Languedoc, and then plunged into the sea and disappeared.

Ogier remounted on Papillon, who carried him across the kingdom almost as fast as he had passed the sea. He arrived under the walls of Paris, which he would scarcely have recognized if the high towers of St. Genevieve had not caught his eye. He went straight to the palace of Charlemagne, which seemed to him to have been entirely rebuilt. His surprise was extreme. and increased still more on finding that he understood with difficulty the language of the guards and attendants in replying to his questions; and seeing them smile as they tried to explain to one another the language in which he addressed them. Presently the attention of some of the barons who were going to court was attracted to the scene, and Ogier, who recognized the badges of their rank, addressed them, and inquired if the Dukes Namo and Salomon were still residing at the Emperor's court. At this question the barons looked at one another in amazement; and one of the eldest said to the rest, "How much this knight resembles the portrait of my grand-uncle, Ogier the Dane." "Ah! my dear nephew, I am Ogier the Dane," said he; and he remembered that Morgana had told him that he was little aware of the flight of time during his abode with her.

The barons, more astonished than ever, concluded to conduct him to the monarch who then reigned, the great Hugh Capet.

The brave Ogier entered the palace without hesitation; but when, on reaching the royal hall, the barons directed him to make his obeisance to the King of France, he was astonished to see a man of short stature and large head, whose air, nevertheless, was noble and martial, seated upon the throne on which he had so often seen Charlemagne, the tallest and handsomest sovereign of his time.

Ogier recounted his adventures with simplicity and unaffectedness. Hugh Capet was slow to believe him; but Ogier recalled so many proofs and circumstances, that at last he was forced to recognize the aged warrior to be the famous Ogier the Dane.

The king informed Ogier of the events which had taken place during his long absence; that the line of Charlemagne was extinct; that a new dynasty had commenced; that the old enemies of the kingdom, the Saracens, were still troublesome; and that at that very time an army of those miscreants was besieging the city of Chartres, to which he was about to repair in a few days to its relief. Ogier, always inflamed with the love of glory, offered the service of his arm, which the illustrious monarch accepted graciously, and conducted him to the queen. The astonishment of Ogier was redoubled when he saw the new ornaments and head-dresses of the ladies; still, the beautiful hair which they built up on their foreheads, and the feathers interwoven, which waved with so much grace, gave them a noble air that delighted him. His admiration increased when, instead of the old Empress Bertha, he saw a young queen who combined a majestic mien with the graces of her time of life, and manners candid and charming, suited to attach all hearts. Ogier saluted the youthful queen with a respect so profound that many of the courtiers took him for a foreigner, or at least for some nobleman brought up at a distance from Paris, who retained the manners of what they called the *old court*.

When the queen was informed by her husband that it was the celebrated Ogier the Dane whom he presented to her, whose memorable exploits she had often read in the chronicles of antiquity, her surprise was extreme, which was increased when she remarked the dignity of his address, the animation and even the youthfulness of his countenance. This queen had too much intelligence to believe hastily; proof alone could compel her assent; and she asked him many questions about the old court of Charlemagne, and received such instructive and appropriate answers as removed every doubt. It is to the corrections which Ogier was at that time enabled to make to the popular narratives of his exploits, that we are indebted for the perfect accuracy and trustworthiness of all the details of our own history.

King Hugh Capet, having received that same evening couriers from the inhabitants of Chartres, informing him that they were hard pressed by the besiegers, resolved to hasten with Ogier to their relief.

Ogier terminated this affair as expeditiously as he had so often done others. The Saracens having dared to offer battle, he bore the Oriflamme through the thickest of their ranks; Papillon, breathing fire from his nostrils, threw them into disorder, and Cortana, wielded by his invincible arm, soon finished their overthrow.

The king, victorious over the Saracens, led back the Danish hero to Paris, where the deliverer of France received the honors due to his valor. Ogier continued some time at the court, detained by the favor of the king and queen; but erelong he had the pain to witness the death of the king. Then it was that, impressed with all the perfections which he had discerned in the queen, he could not withhold the tender homage of the offer of his hand. The queen would perhaps have accepted it, she had even called a meeting of her great barons to deliberate on the proposition, when, the day before the meeting was to be held, at the moment when Ogier was kneeling at her feet, she perceived a crown of gold which an invisible hand had placed on his brow, and in an instant a cloud enveloped Ogier, and he disappeared forever from her sight. It was Morgana, the fairy, whose jealousy was awakened at what she beheld, who now resumed her power, and took him away to dwell with her in the island of Avalon. There, in company with the great King Arthur of Britain, he still lives, and when his illustrious friend shall return to resume his ancient reign, he will doubtless return with him, and share his triumph.

INDEX

LEGENDS OF CHARLEMAGNE

Abdalrahman, 600.
Achilles, 639, 688.
Adonis, 662.
Agilolphus, Bishop, 736.
Agramant, King, 634, 635, 652, 655, 687, 690, 701, 702, 705, 708.
Agrapard, Caliph of Arabia, 754.
Agrican, King, 595, 620, 622, 639, 647, 680, 681.
Alardo, 612, 732.
Albracca, 595, 614, 620, 628, 634, 635, 643, 646, 689.
Alcina, 597, 657, 670
Alcuin, 605.
Alice, Duchess, 737, 742.
Almontes, 639, 686.
Alory, 757.
Alpheus, 677.
Altaripa, 617, 627.
Amadis of Gaul, 610.
Amaury of Hauteville, 737, 740.
Amulin, Walter d', 725.
Anbessa, 600.
Angelica, 595, 605, 613, 614, 615, 619, 620, 635, 643, 664, 666, 671, 679.
Anselm, Count, 674.
Antæus, 682.
Aquilant, 703.
Arden, forest of, 609, 615, 642.
Argalia, 613, 614, 627, 664.
Ariosto, 597, 603, 652.
Arlotto of Soria, 723.
Arridano, 632.
Arthur, King, 773
Ashtaroth, 721, 724.
"As You Like It," 607.
Astolpho, 603, 606, 614, 619, 657, 663, 670, 691, 694, 699, 711, 723, 725.
Astyanax, 638.
Atlantes, 635, 642, 655, 661, 664, 669, 670, 691.
Augustin, 605.
Augustus, 652.
Aurora, 706.

Avino, 724.
Avalon, 771, 773.
Avolia, 724.
Aya, Lady, 733.
Ayman, Duke, 671, 710, 713, 716, 718, 729, 733.
Aymeric, 734.

Baldwin, 720, 724, 725, 762.
Balisardo, 663, 707, 714.
Balugante, 722.
Bayard, 610, 619, 622, 628, 637, 642, 646, 693, 705, 709, 728, 732.
Beatrice, Lady, 711, 713, 718.
Beiffrar, 764, 767, 768.
Belicene, 762.
Berlinghieri, 614, 725.
Bertha, Orlando's mother, 606.
Bertha, Queen, 759, 767, 769, 772.
Biserta, 635, 701, 705.
Blanchard, 767.
Blanchardin, 721.
Boiardo, 597, 603.
Bradamante, 637, 642, 646, 649, 658, 666, 668, 671, 690, 701, 708.
Briareus, 660.
Brigliadoro, 629, 630, 686, 707.
Bruhier, Sultan, 765, 766, 768, 769.
Brunello, the thief, 635, 653, 667.
Bujaforte, 725.

Cæsar, Julius, 604, 745.
Capet, Hugh, 772, 773.
Carahue, King, 759, 765, 769, 770.
Carena, 636.
Ceuta, 704.
Charlemagne (King Charles), 595, 599; Pontiff Emperor of the West, 602, 607; at siege of Vienne, 608; and the feast of Pentecost, 61.; siege of Albracca, 618; battle with Hungarians, 637; builds fortifica

Charlemagne—(*Contd.*)
  tions of Paris, 649; struggle with
  Agramant, 661; tent of, 677; camp
  of, 683; St. John on, 696; embassy
  to, 701; at Arles, 702; allegiance of
  Rogero, 708; honors Rogero, 711;
  and Bradamante, 713; defied by
  Bradamante, 715; Gan's influence
  over, 718; hears sound of horn,
  726; at Roncesvalles, 727; his
  grief, 728; at Montalban, 728;
  proposes to abdicate, 737; greets
  Huron and Girard, 738; demands
  homage of Geoffroy, 755; at
  Spoleto, 757; confers accolade
  upon Ogier, 758; and Carahue,
  761; gives Ogier command of
  army, 762; orders Ogier's arrest,
  763; praises Ogier, 766; at Mont-
  martre, 769.
Charlot, 728, 730, 733, 737, 738, 758,
  759, 761, 762, 766.
Circe, 597.
Clarimunda, 745, 753.
Clermont, 638.
Cloridan, 676.
Cluny, Abbot of, 738.
Constantine, Emperor, 710, 712.
Corsuble, 757, 760.
Cortana, 758, 760, 768, 773.
Cupid, 597.

Dannemont, King, 760.
Dardinel, 675.
Darius, 604.
David, 605.
Desiderius, 636.
Diana, 645.
Didier, King, 604.
Dudon, the Dane, 634, 636, 658, 704,
  717.
Durindana, 608, 619, 626, 630, 639,
  641, 681, 690, 693, 705, 759.

Ebuda, 665.
Eginhard, 769.
Elijah, 696.
Enoch, 696.
Este, 652.
Eude, King, 601.

Facundus, 603.
Falerina, 623, 629, 631.

Falseron, 721, 723.
Ferragus, 607.
Ferrara, 652.
Ferrau, 612, 613, 614, 620, 628, 669,
  680.
Flordelis, 621, 627, 642, 689, 692, 708.
Floriac, 747.
Florismart, Sir, 606, 621, 627, 642,
  669, 671, 689, 692, 704, 706, 709.
Frontino, 636, 714.
Fusberta, 647.

Galaciella, 691.
Galafron, King, 595, 613, 614, 620,
  625, 628.
Gano, (Gan, Ganelon), Duke of
  Maganza, 603, 606, 611, 612, 636,
  718, 726, 728, 737.
Ganymede, 640.
Gaudisso, Sultan, 741, 746, 750, 752.
Geoffroy, 755, 760, 761.
Girard, 738.
Glorianda, 745.
Gradasso, King, 618, 640, 649, 669,
  671, 690, 693, 705, 709.
Grandonio, King, 612, 614, 725.
Griffon, 703.
Grillon, 677.
Guido, 676, 703.
Guire, Mayor of Bordeaux, 743.
Guyon, 756, 764, 765, 769, 770.
Guizot, M., 604.

Haroun al Raschid, 605.
Harpies, the, 694, 700.
Hector, 608, 635, 638, 639, 640, 641,
  690, 715.
Hecuba, 663.
Hercules, 662, 682.
Hippogriff, the, 654, 656, 661, 663,
  666, 672, 694, 700, 711.
"History of Charles the Great and
  Orlando," 603.
Horace, 605.
Huon of Bordeaux, 737, 767.
Hydaspes, 661.
Hymen, 680.
Hyrcania, 758.

Iroldo, 634.
Isabella, 670, 673, 681, **687**.
Isolier, 610.

Isoude, 597.
Ivo, King, 612.

Joseph of Arimathea, 768.
Joyeuse, 757, 759.

Leo, Pope, 756.
Lethe, 699.
Logestilla, 658, 666, 670.
Louis (Leo, Lewis), 603, 605, 710, 712, 713, 714, 716, 737.
Lucifer, 724.

Mahomet, 599, 751, 758.
Malagigi, the Enchanter, 606, 610, 612, 613, 616, 619, 693, 721, 730.
Malprimo, 723.
Mambrino, 675, 702.
Mandricardo, 639, 681, 690.
Marchevallée, 768, 769.
Marphisa, 691, 716.
Marsilius, King, 609, 616, 619, 636, 644, 676, 718.
Martel, Charles (the Hammer), 599.
Medoro, 675, 683.
Melissa, 652, 661, 666, 669, 702.
Merlin, 614, 651, 661.
"Midsummer Night's Dream," 597.
Milon, Orlando's father, (Milone), 606, 758.
Milton, 595.
Montalban, 634, 672, 690, 728, 732, 734.
Montglave, Guerin de, 608.
Morgana, Fata, 633.
Morgana, the Lady of the Lake, 631, 634, 658, 755, 758, 771, 772, 773.

Namo, Duke of Bavaria, 606, 609, 612, 613, 644, 702, 737, 740, 756, 758, 761, 763, 765, 768, 770, 772.
Numa, 652.

Oberon, 743, 754.
Oblivion, Cup of, 621.
Oderic, Chevalier, 673.
Ogier the Dane, 604, 606, 609, 676, 702, 755.
Oliver, 606, 607, 608, 676, 692, 703, 706, 709, 718, 722, 723, 726.

Orc, the, 664, 671.
Oriflamme, the, 757, 759.
Orlando, 597, 602, 603, 606, 607, 608, 612, 614, 616, 619, 622, 627, 639, 643, 657, 669, 671, 675, 681, 696, 703, 709, 717, 718.
Otho, 614, 657.
Ottachiero, 636.
Ottone, 725.

Papillon, 770, 771, 773.
Pavia, siege of, 604.
Penthesilea, 639.
Pepin, father of Charlemagne, 601, 638, 757.
Pinabel, 650.
Pindar, 605.
Pompey, 706.
Prasildo, 634.
Proteus, 665.
Psyche, 597.
Pulci, 597, 603.

Rabican, 628, 663, 670, 691.
Ricardo, 612.
Ricciardetto, 612, 619, 721, 723, 727.
Rinaldo of Montalban, 606, 609, 612, 615, 619, 627, 634, 636, 638, 642, 657, 664, 675, 679, 693, 701, 708, 717, 718, 723, 725, 728, 732.
Riphæan mountains, 654.
Risa, Duke of, 711.
Rodomont, King, 635, 636, 642, 687, 692, 703.
Rogero, 635, 638, 641, 649, 656, 666, 671, 690, 701, 708.
Roland, see Orlando.
"Romans de Chevalerie," 598.
Roncesvalles, Battle of, 602, 718, 728.

Sacripant, King, 620, 622, 644, 649, 664, 668, 679.
Sadon, 759, 760.
Salomon, King of Brittany, 606, 702, 763, 765, 768, 770, 772.
Sansonnet, 692, 722.
Senapus, King, 694, 700, 706.
Sevinus, 737, 739, 743.
Sherasmin, 743.

Sibyl of Cumæ, 663.
Sobrino, 635, 705, 710.
Solario, 754.
St. Benedict, 740.
St. Denis, 768.
St. Faron, Abbot of, 765, 767.
St. Genevieve, 771.
St. John, 696, 699.
St. Michael, 723.
St. Peter, 735.
St. Rinaldo, church of, 736.
Sultan of Morocco, 673.

Theodora, 713, 717.
Thierry, Duke, 739.
Tristram, 597, 615.
Tressan, Comte de, 598.

Turpin, Archbishop of Rheims, 603,
    606, 693, 701, 723, 724, 726, 727,
    732, 758, 764, 765, 769.

Uberto, 613.
Ulysses, 597.
Unicorn, Knight of the, 716, 717.

Vallombrosa, abbey of, 671.
Vulcan, 724.

Walter, 724, 770.

Zerbino, 673, 678, 681, 687, 690.

MODERN LIBRARY GIANTS

A series of sturdily bound and handsomely printed, full-sized library editions of books formerly available only in expensive sets. These volumes contain from 600 to 1,400 pages each.

THE MODERN LIBRARY GIANTS REPRESENT A
SELECTION OF THE WORLD'S GREATEST BOOKS

G76 ANDERSEN & GRIMM: *Tales*
G74 AUGUSTINE, ST.: *The City of God*
G58 AUSTEN, JANE: *Complete Novels*
G70 BLAKE, WILLIAM & DONNE, JOHN: *Complete Poetry*
G2   BOSWELL, JAMES: *Life of Samuel Johnson*
G17 BROWNING, ROBERT: *Poems and Plays*
G14 BULFINCH: *Mythology* (ILLUSTRATED)
G35 BURY, J. B.: *A History of Greece*
G13 CARLYLE, THOMAS: *The French Revolution*
G28 CARROLL, LEWIS: *Complete Works*
G15 CERVANTES: *Don Quixote*
G33 COLLINS, WILKIE: *The Moonstone* and *The Woman in White*
G27 DARWIN, CHARLES: *Origin of Species* and *The Descent of Man*
G43 DEWEY, JOHN: *Intelligence in the Modern World: John Dewey's Philosophy*
G70 DONNE, JOHN & BLAKE, WILLIAM: *Complete Poetry*
G36 DOSTOYEVSKY, FYODOR: *The Brothers Karamazov*
G60 DOSTOYEVSKY, FYODOR: *The Idiot*
G51 ELIOT, GEORGE: *Best-Known Novels*
G41 FARRELL, JAMES T.: *Studs Lonigan*
G82 FAULKNER, WILLIAM: *The Faulkner Reader*
G39 FREUD, SIGMUND: *The Basic Writings*
G6
G7   GIBBON, EDWARD: *The Decline and Fall of the Roman Empire* (COMPLETE IN THREE VOLUMES)
G8
G25 GILBERT & SULLIVAN: *Complete Plays*
G76 GRIMM & ANDERSEN: *Tales*
G37 HAWTHORNE, NATHANIEL: *Compl. Novels & Selected Tales*
G78 HOLMES, OLIVER WENDELL: *The Mind and Faith of Justice Holmes*
G19 HOMER: *Complete Works*
G3   HUGO, VICTOR: *Les Miserables*
G18 IBSEN, HENRIK: *Eleven Plays*
G11 JAMES, HENRY: *Short Stories*
G52 JOYCE, JAMES: *Ulysses*
G4   KEATS & SHELLEY: *Complete Poems*
G24 LAMB, CHARLES: *The Complete Works and Letters*
G20 LINCOLN, ABRAHAM: *The Life and Writings of Abraham Lincoln*
G84 MANN, THOMAS: *Stories of Three Decades*
G26 MARX, KARL: *Capital*
G57 MELVILLE, HERMAN: *Selected Writings*
G38 MURASAKA, LADY: *The Tale of Genji*
G30 MYERS, GUSTAVUS: *History of the Great American Fortunes*
G34 NIETZSCHE, FRIEDRICH: *The Philosophy of Nietzsche*
G88 O'HARA, JOHN: *49 Stories*

G55   O'NEILL, EUGENE: *Nine Plays*
G68   PAINE, TOM: *Selected Work*
G86   PASTERNAK, BORIS: *Doctor Zhivago*
G5   PLUTARCH: *Lives* (The Dryden Translation)
G40   POE, EDGAR ALLAN: *Complete Tales and Poems*
G29   PRESCOTT, WILLIAM H.: *The Conquest of Mexico* and *The Conquest of Peru*
G62   PUSHKIN: *Poems, Prose and Plays*
G65   RABELAIS: *Complete Works*
G12   SCOTT, SIR WALTER: *The Most Popular Novels* (Quentin Durward, Ivanhoe & Kenilworth)
G4   SHELLEY & KEATS: *Complete Poems*
G32   SMITH, ADAM: *The Wealth of Nations*
G61   SPAETH, SIGMUND: *A Guide to Great Orchestral Music*
G92   SPENGLER, OSWALD: *The Decline of the West* (one volume)
G91   SPENSER, EDMUND: *Selected Poetry*
G75   STEVENSON, ROBERT LOUIS: *Selected Writings*
G53   SUE, EUGENE: *The Wandering Jew*
G42   TENNYSON: *The Poems and Plays*
G23   TOLSTOY, LEO: *Anna Karenina*—tr. revised
G1   TOLSTOY, LEO: *War and Peace*
G49   TWAIN, MARK: *Tom Sawyer* and *Huckleberry Finn*
G50   WHITMAN, WALT: *Leaves of Grass*
G83   WILSON, EDMUND: *The Shock of Recognition*

MISCELLANEOUS

G77   *An Anthology of Famous American Stories*
G54   *An Anthology of Famous British Stories*
G67   *Anthology of Famous English and American Poetry*
G81   *An Encyclopedia of Modern American Humor*
G47   *The English Philosophers from Bacon to Mill*
G16   *The European Philosophers from Descartes to Nietzsche*
G31   *Famous Science-Fiction Stories*
G85   *Great Ages and Ideas of the Jewish People*
G89   *Great Classical Myths*
G72   *Great Tales of Terror and the Supernatural*
G9   *Great Voices of the Reformation*
G87   *Medieval Epics*
G48   *The Metropolitan Opera Guide*
G46   *A New Anthology of Modern Poetry*
G69   *One Hundred and One Years' Entertainment*
G93   *Parodies: An Anthology from Chaucer to Beerbohm and After*
G90   *Philosophies of Art and Beauty: Readings in Aesthetics from Plato to Heidegger*
G21   *Sixteen Famous American Plays*
G63   *Sixteen Famous British Plays*
G71   *Sixteen Famous European Plays*
G45   *Stoic and Epicurean Philosophers*
G22   *Thirty Famous One-Act Plays*
G66   *Three Famous Murder Novels, Before the Fact*, FRANCIS ILES, *Trent's Last Case*, E. C. BENTLEY, *The House of the Arrow*, A. E. W. MASON
G10   *Twelve Famous Plays of the Restoration and Eighteenth Century* (1660–1820): Dryden, Congreve, Wycherley, Gay, etc.
G56   *The Wisdom of Catholicism*
G59   *The Wisdom of China and India*
G79   *The Wisdom of Israel*

291
B93
1934

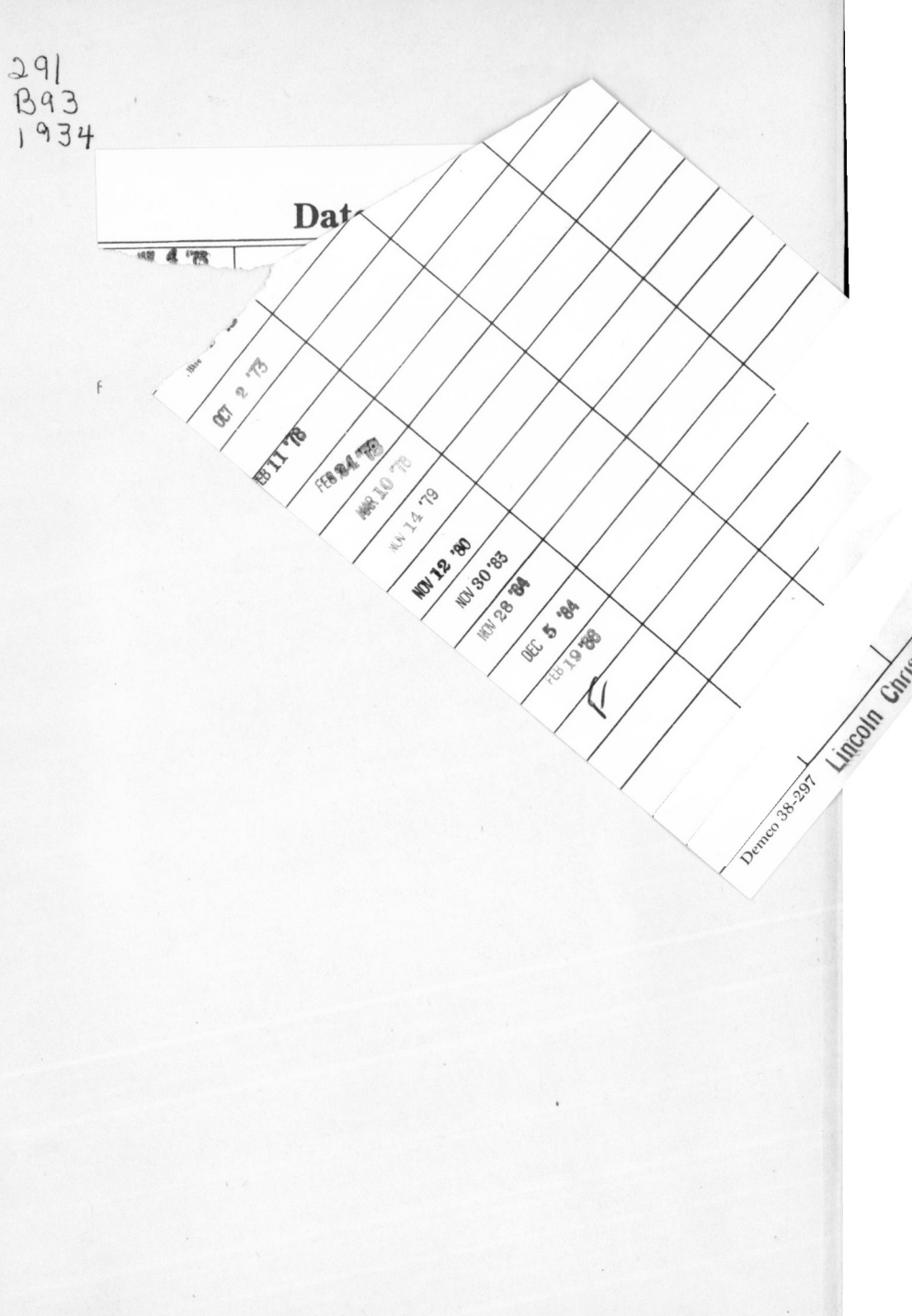

Date